c. 500 B.C. Rise of Athe-
nian civilization. c. 400
B.C. Democritus: atomic
theory. Hippocrates:
medicine. Plato: philos-
ophy.

c. 350 B.C. Aristotle classifies animals, writes
first textbook of physics. Reign of Alexander the
Great.

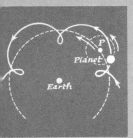

200-1200 A.D. Decline and fall of the Roman
Empire. Rise of Christianity. Middle ages. Beginning of town life.

Omar Khayyam (11th
Cent.) Persian poet,
mathematician. Al
Hazen: optics (Arabia).

c. 1502 Leonardo da
Vinci develops mechan-
ics, optics, chemistry,
astronomy and geology.
1504 Michelangelo com-
pletes his "David".

1527 Paracelsus found modern science of medicine by applying his knowledge of chemistry.
1543 Copernicus' "De Revolutionibus Orbis Ter-
rarum".
1546 Agricola founds mineralogy.

1619 Harvey reveals circulation of the blood.
1621 Snell discovers law of refraction of light.
1632 Galileo's "Systems of the World" con-
demned by the Inquisition. 1638 Galileo reports
on dynamics of falling bodies.

1643 Torricelli invents
the barometer. 1650
Guericke of Magdeburg
invents the air pump.

1700-1750 Theological
skepticism, political lib-
eratism: Voltaire, Mon-
tesquieu. Mathematical
development of mechan-
ics, materialism in phys-
ical theories.

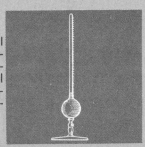

1720 Fahrenheit: thermometers. 1736 Euler
founds analytical mechanics. 1738 Bernoulli as-
serts gases are composed of molecules in rapid
motion. 1745 Leyden jar (capacitor.)

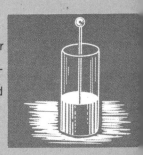

1774 Priestley discovers oxygen. 1775 Kant's
Anthropology anticipates idea of evolution. 1786
Lagrange's "Mechanique Analytique" deduces
all mechanics from law of virtual work. 1789
Lavoisier founds modern chemistry.

1798 The Philosophical
Magazine founded. 1798
Benjamin Thompson,
Count Rumford, estab-
lishes the mechanical
theory of heat.

Physics for Science and Engineering

Physics for Science and Engineering

First Edition, Revised

ROBERT L. WEBER

MARSH W. WHITE

KENNETH V. MANNING

The Pennsylvania State University

McGRAW-HILL BOOK COMPANY, INC.

1959 · New York · Toronto · London

PHYSICS FOR SCIENCE AND ENGINEERING

For the photographs used on the part-title pages, credit is given as follows: Electricity and Magnetism—background (lightning) based on a photograph by Hobart, Monkmeyer Press Photo Service; Light—background (detail, lighthouse prism) photographed by permission at Bon Portage Light, Nova Scotia; Modern Physics—background (cosmic rays) courtesy of Brookhaven National Laboratory, Upton, New York; Geiger counter tubes lent for photogram by The Atomic Center for Instruments and Equipment, Inc., New York City.

II
68810

Preface

The objective of *Physics for Science and Engineering* is to introduce the basic concepts and principles of general physics at the university level. The treatment is designed particularly for students of science and engineering. The aim of the authors has been to assist technical students in acquiring a precise understanding of the important physical principles that are the foundations of all advanced work in science and technology. It is hoped that the rigorous treatment of this book will give serious students a better appreciation of the power of these fundamental concepts by providing insight into the complex physical phenomena that are basic to progress in modern scientific and engineering work. When students are well grounded in these fundamentals, they can rapidly acquire facility in the solution of physical problems.

The scope of this book is designed to meet the needs of one-year courses that usually begin with the second semester of the freshman year or the first semester of the sophomore year. Careful attention has been given to the recommendations of the American Institute of Physics Committee on Physics in Engineering Education. Particular stress is placed on the *understanding* of the fundamental ideas, principles, and methodology of physics, rather than on mere facts and formulas. This treatment helps develop the reasoning powers of the student instead of mere memorization. The user of the book is encouraged to test his grasp of the principles by several specific techniques, such as the derivation of special equations from general principles, the answering of many skillfully designed questions that involve logical reasoning, and the solution of a large number of carefully graded problems that begin with the simple substitutional variety and continue through those of intermediate multistep difficulty to some items that challenge the intellectual abilities of the better students.

Much effort has been expended by the authors in a careful selection of material to ensure inclusion of topics of really fundamental significance and the omission of items that are of lesser importance and that are covered in other related courses. This has resulted in a book that is somewhat shorter than many physics textbooks.

It is expected that the student will have a working knowledge of trigonometry and algebra and that he will be taking an introductory course in calculus concurrently with his work in physics. Consequently, calculus notation is introduced when it is especially advantageous in the development of the physical ideas. Derivations of important equations are made when useful by the use of calculus methods, in addition to the statement of these equations without calculus derivations. Hence an experienced teacher can place more or less emphasis upon the use of calculus in accordance with his personal preferences. A limited number of items in the problem lists require the use of calculus solutions.

Recent developments in physics are integrated into the general treatment at appropriate places. For example relativity considerations, quantum theory, and solid-state concepts are presented with topics where these developments are significant. The concluding chapters on modern atomic physics and nuclear physics cover important ideas in quantum and particle physics appropriate to a well-oriented general physics course. These chapters also furnish an introduction to more advanced and specialized courses in "modern physics."

A careful effort has been made to minimize the number of systems of units that must be considered by the student. In the chapters on mechanics, the more familiar British engineering units are mostly used; the metric absolute systems are introduced where required as the basis for units commonly used in scientific work. In the chapters on electricity, rationalized mks units are used. Magnetic concepts and units are developed in the spirit of the mks system rather than by reference to fictitious isolated magnetic poles. The British absolute and the metric gravitational systems are not used in this book. In the Appendix various systems of units are tabulated and conversion tables are given.

A feature of this book is the liberal use of solved numerical examples that are designed to clarify each important principle. In these examples conversion factors and the appropriate units are carefully included with numerical values and treated as algebraic quantities in the equations. This leads the student to a realization of the dimensional character and the balancing of symbolic equations.

In this book there is strict adherence to the proper use of significant figures in *all* numerical data, both in the text and in the problem lists. Thus the reader is encouraged to utilize the fact that physical data can be manipulated only with the precision of the experimentally known values.

In the chapter summaries, definitions, defining equations, units, laws, and principles are concisely restated and arranged in the order of topics in the text. This encourages students to use the summaries for efficient and systematic review.

An unusually large number of discussion questions are given in lists at the end of each chapter. They are designed to develop the reasoning ability of the student and not merely his memory alone. Most of these questions can be answered by a thoughtful student if he has really mastered the material of the chapter. Some of them may be answered in various ways that often lead to spirited discussion in the class. Teachers who have made extensive use of these unique lists of questions are gratified to see the increase in the learning process as students acquire familiarity with reasoning techniques.

The problems are listed in the order of topics in the chapter. Successive problems on each topic are arranged in the order of increasing difficulty. Although some of the earlier problems involve mainly simple substitution in basic equations, with perhaps some complexity as to units, most of the problems require the student to do a reasonable amount of logical analysis based upon the concepts that the problem is designed to illustrate. Derivations of special equations, calculus proofs, and symbolic solutions are included in some of the problems lists. Answers are given to the even-numbered problems.

In the Appendix is given a systematic plan for the solution of physics problems. The authors have statistical evidence that by following such a plan the student can increase significantly the facility with which he solves physical problems.

Material to illustrate the principles studied is in general selected from the everyday experiences of the usual student. "Engineering applications" are avoided so that the time available can be utilized for mastering the fundamentals of physics.

The present book has evolved from the authors' *College Technical Physics* and its successor *College Physics*. We have gladly received and considered suggestions and recommendations from colleagues, teachers, and students who have used these books in some one hundred colleges and universities. Further comments from users of this book will be gratefully received.

In *College Physics* we acknowledged the help of a number of physicists and instrument companies in the preparation of copy for that book. Some of those contributions have been carried into the present book and we repeat our expression of thanks for this assistance.

ROBERT L. WEBER
MARSH W. WHITE
KENNETH V. MANNING

Contents

Preface v

MECHANICS

1. The Fields and Uses of Physics; Measurement 3
2. Vectors; Forces at a Point 11
3. Velocity and Acceleration 25
4. Force and Motion 35
5. Projectile Motion 48
6. Friction 55
7. Work and Power 64
8. Energy 74
9. Torque 82
10. Rotation of Rigid Bodies 92
11. Momentum 104
12. Uniform Circular Motion 115
13. Elastic Properties of Solids 124
14. Vibratory Motion 133
15. Liquids at Rest 145
16. Fluids in Motion 156
17. Properties of Gases 166
18. Molecular Theory of Matter 175

HEAT

19. Temperature Measurement; Thermal Expansion 189
20. Heat Quantities 205
21. Heat Transfer 218
22. Thermodynamics 228

SOUND

23. Wave Motion 243
24. Sound Waves 253
25. Acoustics 265

ELECTRICITY AND MAGNETISM

26. Electric Charges and Fields 281
27. Electric Potential 292
28. The Electric Current 303
29. Electric Circuits 316
30. Electrical Measurements 332
31. Magnetic Effects of Electric Current . . 344

32. Electric Instruments 360
33. Magnetic Properties; The Magnetic Circuit 372
34. Electric Energy and Power 384
35. Induced Emf's 397
36. Electromagnetic Induction 404
37. Capacitance 420
38. Alternating-current Series Circuits . . 431
39. Conduction in Gases; Electronics . . . 445

LIGHT

40. Light and Illumination 461
41. Reflection of Light 476
42. Refraction of Light 490
43. Thin Lenses 501
44. The Eye and Optical Instruments . . . 514
45. Dispersion; Spectra 529
46. Color 538
47. Interference and Diffraction 550
48. Polarized Light 563

MODERN PHYSICS

49. Relativity and Quantum Theory . . . 577
50. Atomic Physics 588
51. Solid State Electronics 597
52. Nuclear Physics 602

APPENDIX

1. Solution of Physical Problems 621
2. Significant Figures in Measurements and Computations 621
3. Metric Systems of Electric Units . . . 623
   Table 1. Permittivity and Permeability for Free Space 624
   Table 2. Electric and Magnetic Quantities in Different Metric Systems 624
4. Greek Alphabet 625
5. Tables 626
   1. Values of Important Physical Constants 626
   2. Natural Sines and Cosines 627
   3. Natural Tangents and Cotangents . . 629

Index 631

MECHANICS

1. The Fields and Uses of Physics; Measurement

This is a scientific age. Our material prosperity, the conveniences of life, and often life itself rest upon the development of our science. Although the practical fruits of science are not to be despised, its true significance is more subtle. The study of science has profoundly influenced the way men think. Science has created gadgets, but it has also given man confidence in his intellectual supremacy over nature and has provided the method of approach to all problems requiring a conclusion from observed facts. The science of physics, which provides the tools for the chemist, geologist, engineer, and astronomer, has also originated the scientific method.

A science is a body of organized knowledge. The steps in the origin and development of a science are *observation, recording, analysis, prediction,* and *verification*. Accurate observation under controlled conditions is the first step in understanding nature. Records provide for the transmission of knowledge and aid its continued growth. Analysis proceeds from conjecture of the causes or relationships of certain observations, and, when the hypotheses have been tested, erects a theory that relates a large number of phenomena. The theory usually predicts certain as yet unsuspected phenomena or relationships. Verification of these predictions by experiment supports the theory and may lead to formulation of a law or principle. Failure to obtain experimental verification of predictions may not overthrow a theory, but causes its modification and often enriches it. The principal aspects of the scientific method are selective analysis, accurate measurement, and mathematical treatment. These techniques originated and received their fullest development in the field of physics. Other fields of knowledge, by common consent, are considered scientific to just the extent that their ideas are subject to analysis, measurement, and mathematical treatment.

To understand one's environment today and to be able to adapt oneself to it demand some appreciation of the scientific attitude. As consumers of the products of a scientific age, we want to understand the foundations of our industrial science, to keep informed of current discoveries, to be able profitably to use new developments, to recognize reliable information and true scientific progress, and to avoid quackery.

An understanding of the essential character of scientific investigation is best acquired from the study of a representative particular science. It seems desirable to choose the science which is most responsible for the attitude and viewpoint of the scientific age and which is today influencing scientific thought most profoundly, namely, physics.

Occasional discoveries of important phenomena were made by primitive man. The Babylonians and Egyptians possessed surprisingly refined methods of measuring time, distance, and weight. But these observations and inventions did not lead to statements of general principles. The observations were largely isolated and unrelated. Science, in contrast, is systematic and cumulative. Much of our science has its roots in Greek thought. But the Greeks were preoccupied with the question of *why* things moved and behaved in a certain manner and their answers were based on speculation, not experimentation. The modern approach to nature is to ask the more modest question, *how* things move, and to seek the answer in experiment. Not until the sixteenth century did man adopt the scientific method of studying his environment. Great progress was made then and in the succeeding centuries technological development has become increasingly rapid.

The rise of all the natural sciences has been almost simultaneous. Until as recently as about a hundred and fifty years ago the content of all the physical sciences including physics, astronomy, chemistry, and engineering, resided in a study called *natural philosophy*. This entire body of knowledge was so small that it was possible for a capable man to be an authority in all these fields and to contribute to the progress in each.

In the nineteenth century an avalanche in the development of natural philosophy led to specialization. James Watt's invention, which made the steam engine practical (1769), gave importance to the field of applied physics or engineering. This field received further impetus with the applications of the electrical discoveries of Faraday and Ampère and the invention of the internal combustion engine. With the atomic theory of matter placed on an experimental basis by John Dalton (1808),

chemistry developed as a separate science. Astronomy, using the tools and ideas of physics, became a specialized field.

Physics is often defined as the *science of matter and energy*. Physics is concerned chiefly with the laws and properties of the material universe. These are studied in the closely related sciences of mechanics, heat, sound, electricity, light, and atomic and nuclear structure. The principles studied in these fields have been applied in numerous combinations to build our mechanical age. Such recent terms as *chemical physics* and *biophysics* are indicative of the widening application of the principles of physics, even in the study of living organisms.

Mechanics is the oldest and basic branch of physics. This portion of the subject deals with such ideas as inertia, motion, force, and energy. Of especial interest are the laws dealing with the effects of forces upon the form and motion of objects, since these principles apply to all devices and structures such as machines, buildings, and bridges. Mechanics includes the properties and laws of both solids and fluids.

The subject of *heat* includes the principles of temperature measurement, the effects of temperature on the properties of materials, heat flow, and thermodynamics—the study of transformations involving heat and work. These studies have led to increased efficiency of power production, the development of high-temperature alloys and ceramics, the production of temperatures near absolute zero, and to important theories about the behavior of matter and radiation.

The study of *sound* is of importance not only in music and speech but also in communications and industry. The acoustical and communications engineer is concerned with the generation, transmission, and absorption of sound. An understanding of scientific principles in sound is of importance to the radio engineer. The industrial engineer is greatly concerned with the effects of sound in producing fatigue in production personnel.

Electricity and *magnetism* are fields of physics which are of peculiar importance in the rapid development of technology in power distribution, lighting, communications, and the many electronic devices which provide conveniences, entertainment, and tools for investigation in other fields. An understanding of the sources, effects, measurements, and uses of electricity and magnetism is valuable to the worker in that it enables him to use more effectively the manifold electrical devices now so vital to our efficiency and comfort.

Optics is the portion of physics that includes the study of the nature and propagation of light, the laws of reflection, and the bending or refraction that occurs in the transmission of light through prisms and lenses. Of importance also are the separation of white light into its constituent colors, the nature and types of spectra, interference, diffraction, and polarization phenomena. Photometry involves the measurement of luminous intensities of light sources and of the illumination of surfaces.

A fascinating portion of physics is known as *modern physics*. This includes electronics, atomic and nuclear phenomena, photoelectricity, x rays, radioactivity, the transmutations of matter and energy, relativity, and the phenomena associated with electron tubes and the electric waves of modern radio. The breaking up of atoms now provides a practical source of energy. Many of the devices that are commonplace today are applications of one or more of these branches of modern physics. Radio, long-distance telephony, sound amplification, and television are a few of the many developments made possible by the use of electron tubes. Photoelectricity makes possible television, transmission of pictures by wire or radio, sound motion pictures, and many devices for the control of machinery. Examination of welds and castings by x rays to locate hidden flaws is standard procedure in many industries. The practical application of the developments of physics continues at an ever increasing rate.

Practical applications of physics are not all made by those labeled as physicists, for the majority of those who apply the principles of physics are called *engineers*. In fact most of the branches of engineering are closely allied with one or more sections of physics: civil engineering applies the principles of mechanics; mechanical engineering utilizes the laws of mechanics and heat; electrical engineering is based on the fundamentals of electricity; acoustical engineering and optical engineering are the industrial applications of the physics of sound and light. The alliance between engineering and physics is so close that a thorough knowledge and understanding of physical principles is essential for progress in engineering.

One of the tools common to physics and engineering is mathematics. Principles are expressed quantitatively, concisely, and most usefully in the language of mathematics. In development and application, careful measurement is essential. If we are to make effective use of the principles and measurements of physical science, we must have a workable knowledge of mathematics. Physics and mathematics are thus basic to all science and engineering.

MEASUREMENT

Engineering design, manufacture, and commerce today no longer rest on guesswork. Cut-and-try methods have given way to measurement, so that the stone cut in the quarry slips neatly into its prepared place in a building under construction hundreds of miles away. A new spark plug or a piston ring can be purchased in Philadelphia to fit a car made in Detroit. Cooperative planning and the manufacture of interchangeable parts became possible only when people quit guessing and learned to measure.

1-1. The Measuring Process. Measuring anything means comparing it with some standard to see how many times as big it is. The process is simplified by using as few standards as possible. These few must be carefully devised and kept. The standard with which other things are compared is called a *unit*. So also are its multiples and submultiples, which may be of more convenient size. The numerical ratio of the thing measured to the unit with which it is compared is called the *numerical measure*, or *magnitude*, of the thing measured.

Some measurements are *direct*, that is, they are made by comparing the quantity to be measured directly with the unit of that kind, as when we find the length of a table by placing a yard or meter scale beside it. But most measurements are *indirect*. For example, to measure the speed of a plane we measure the distance it travels and the time required, and, by calculation, we find the number of units that represents its speed.

1-2. Fundamental Quantities. Surprising as it may seem, only three kinds of fundamental quantities are necessary in mechanics. All other quantities can be derived from these. The choice of these three fundamental quantities is arbitrary. The three customarily chosen for use in physics are *length, mass*, and *time*. An alternative choice is commonly made, namely, *length, force*, and *time*.

1-3. Fundamental and Derived Units. For each of the three fundamental quantities we must arbitrarily select a suitable unit. The choice of these *fundamental units* is dictated by convenience and ease of duplication. Many other units are based on these three. For example, a unit of length multiplied by itself serves as a unit of area. A unit area multiplied by unit length becomes a unit of volume. A unit of length divided by a unit of time represents a unit of speed. Any unit formed by multiplying or dividing a fundamental unit by another fundamental unit (or a numeric) is called a *derived unit*.

1-4. Length. To specify a distance, we must use some unit of length. The unit commonly employed for scientific use and accepted as an international standard is the *meter*. The meter is defined as the distance between two lines on a certain bar of platinum-

iridium when the temperature of the bar is that of melting ice (0°C). The prototype meter is kept at the International Bureau of Weights and Measures at Sèvres, France. In order that it could be reproduced if destroyed,

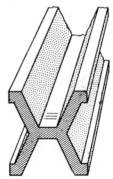

Fig. 1. A section of the standard meter bar showing the markings at one end.

it was intended by the designers that this length should be one ten-millionth of the distance from a pole of the earth to the equator, measured along a great circle, but this ideal was not quite realized.

One one-hundredth of the meter is called the *centimeter* (0.01 m), a unit of length that we shall often employ. Other decimal fractions of the meter are the *decimeter* (0.1 m) and the *millimeter* (0.001 m). For large distances the *kilometer* (1000 m) is employed.

Units of length popularly used in English-speaking countries are the *yard* and its multiples and submultiples. The British or Imperial yard has its legal definition as the distance between two lines on a bronze bar, kept at the office of the Exchequer in London, when its temperature is 62°F. Other common units of length are the mile (1760 yd), the foot ($\frac{1}{3}$ yd), and the inch ($\frac{1}{36}$ yd).

In the United States the yard is legally defined in terms of the meter:

$$1 \text{ yd} = \frac{3600}{3937} \text{ m}$$

This leads to the simple approximate relation 1 in. = 2.54 cm.

1-5. Mass. The mass of an object is a measure of the amount of material in it as evidenced by its inertia. Inertia is the measure of resistance to change of motion.

The fundamental unit of mass is the *kilogram*, the mass of the kilogram prototype—a block made of the same platinum-iridium

FIG. 2. The national standard of mass. Kilogram No. 20, a cylinder 39 mm in diameter and 39 mm high, with slightly rounded edges, made of an alloy containing 90 per cent platinum and 10 per cent iridium. It was furnished by the International Bureau of Weights and Measures in pursuance of the metric treaty of 1875.

alloy as the meter prototype and also kept at Sèvres. The unit of mass often employed in physics is the gram, which is defined as one one-thousandth of the mass of the kilogram prototype. These units were originally chosen with the object of making the gram equal to the mass of 1 cm³ of water at 4°C, but this equality was not realized exactly. Fractions and multiples of the gram in common use are named as follows: milligram (0.001 gm), centigram (0.01 gm), decigram (0.1 gm), kilogram (1000 gm), and the metric ton (1000 kg or 1,000,000 gm).

In the United States the pound, as a unit of mass, is legally defined in terms of the kilo-gram: 1 kg = 2.2046 lb, so that 1 lb equals approximately 454 gm.

1-6. Weight. Sir Isaac Newton (1642–1727) pointed out that besides having inertia all material objects have the ability to attract all other objects. As a result of this *universal gravitation* everything on or near the surface of the earth is attracted toward the earth with a force we call *weight*.

The force with which the earth pulls on a mass of 1 lb under standard conditions is called the *weight* of 1 lb or the pound of force. This force is one of the basic units in common usage.

1-7. Time. The fundamental unit of time is the mean solar *second*. This is defined as 1/86,400 (NOTE: 86,400 = 24 × 60 × 60) of the mean solar day, which is the average, throughout a year, of the time between successive transits of the sun across the meridian at any place. Thus, the time it takes for the earth to turn once on its axis, with respect to the sun, serves as the basis for the unit of time. A properly regulated watch or clock, a pendulum of suitable length, or an oscillating quartz crystal may be the working standard for measuring time.

1-8. Systems of Units. A complete set of units, both fundamental and derived, for all kinds of quantities is called a *system* of units. Several such systems have been devised and are commonly used. Each is named in terms of the *three fundamental* units upon which it is based.

The system most widely used in the United States is based upon the foot as a unit of length, the pound as a unit of force, and the second as a unit of time. From the initials of these three units this system is called the *fps* system. Except in the field of electricity, this system is largely used in engineering practice.

A system largely used in scientific work throughout the world is based upon the centimeter as a unit of length, the gram as a unit of mass, and the second as a unit of time. From the initials it is called the *cgs* system. Because of the decimal nature of this system conversions within the system are relatively simple as compared with the fps system. Unfortunately, many of the derived units in the cgs system are inconveniently small.

A third system, adopted by the International Committee on Weights and Measures in 1935, is based upon the meter as a unit of length, the kilogram as a unit of mass, and the second as a unit of time. This system is called the *mks* system. It has the advantage that some of the derived units are of convenient size.

Conversion between systems of units can be made by use of a very few conversion factors. Ideally only three such factors are necessary, one for each of the fundamental quantities. Some conversion factors are given in Table 1.

TABLE 1. EQUIVALENTS OF CERTAIN UNITS

1 meter	= 39.37 inches (exactly)
1 liter	= 1.057 liquid quarts
1 kilogram	= 2.205 pounds, avoirdupois
1 kilogram weighs 2.205 pounds, avoirdupois
453.6 grams weigh 1 pound, avoirdupois

Example: Change 115 in. to centimeters.

115 in. = 115 in. (2.54 cm/in.) = 292 cm

If all units are inserted into an equation, they can be handled as algebraic quantities and, when they are handled in this manner, the correct final unit is obtained. This method has an added advantage in that it frequently calls attention to a factor that has been forgotten.

Example: Convert 165 lb to kilograms.

$$165 \text{ lb} = \frac{165 \text{ lb}}{2.205 \text{ lb/kg}} = 74.8 \text{ kg}$$

Example: Express 50 mi/hr in feet per second.

$$50 \text{ mi/hr} = \frac{50 \frac{\text{mi}}{\text{hr}} \times 5280 \frac{\text{ft}}{\text{mi}}}{3600 \frac{\text{sec}}{\text{hr}}} = 73 \frac{\text{ft}}{\text{sec}}$$

1-9. Significant Figures. In physics we deal almost exclusively with measured quanti-

ties. The accuracy of any measurement is always limited and hence the number that expresses the magnitude should be written with the number of digits that properly expresses the accuracy of the measurement. These figures and only these are *significant*. When computations are made with numbers obtained experimentally, the number of digits retained in the result is determined by the number of significant figures in the original data. Approximate rules for determining the number of significant figures are given in Appendix 2. In examples we shall not retain more digits than are significant in the result. When there is doubt as to the number of significant figures, we shall overscore the *last significant digit:* thus 38,$\overline{4}$00 ft. Here there are three significant digits 3, 8, and 4. The zeros are present merely to locate the decimal point.

SUMMARY

Physics is the science of matter and energy. Physics deals with mechanics, heat, sound, electricity, light, and atomic and nuclear structure.

Measurement means comparing a thing with a standard to see how many times as big it is.

Three *fundamental quantities* are necessary in mechanics. These are commonly chosen as *length*, *mass*, and *time* or as *length*, *force*, and *time*.

For each fundamental quantity there is an arbitrarily chosen *fundamental unit*. Other units based on the fundamental units are called *derived units*.

In the United States our units are defined in terms of the metric standards.

A complete set of units both fundamental and derived is called a *system* of units. Systems of units are named from the fundamental units used as basic for the system as fps, cgs, or mks. Only a few conversion factors are needed to convert all derived units from one system to another.

In measured and computed quantities *significant* figures only should be retained.

QUESTIONS   **1.** By what steps is a science developed?

2. What is meant by the scientific method?

3. What value may the study of physics have in character formation? in the attitude toward all problems of life?

4. What is meant when a procedure is criticized as being not scientific?

5. Do all sciences make use of experimentation?

6. Give several informative definitions of physics. What tendency is observed as to the branching of this science?

7. What have mathematics, astronomy, physics, and chemistry in common that leads to their being called *sciences?*

8. Comment on the statement attributed to Lord Kelvin (1883):

"I often say that when you can measure what you are speaking about, and express it in numbers, you know something about it; but when you cannot measure it, when you cannot express it in numbers, your knowledge is of a meagre and unsatisfactory kind; it may be the beginning of knowledge, but you have scarcely, in your thoughts, advanced to the stage of science, whatever the matter may be."

9. What do you consider the most important characteristics of a standard unit?

10. Give examples of things that can be measured and some that cannot.

11. Why is it necessary to specify the temperature at which comparisons with the standard meter bar are to be made?

12. Suggest several ways in which primary standards of length and mass might be defined in order that, if destroyed, they could be reproduced without loss of accuracy.

13. Show that it is possible to shift from British to metric units on a screw-cutting lathe by the introduction of a gear ratio of 127 to 50 teeth.

PROBLEMS   **1.** Express your height in meters and your mass in kilograms.

2. A shaft is to be turned to a diameter of $\frac{5}{8}$ in. Express this in decimal form in inches and in centimeters.   *Ans.* 0.625 in.; 1.59 cm

3. The Washington National Monument is stated by the Monument Society to be 555 ft, $5\frac{1}{8}$ in. in height. Comment on the significant figures in this measurement. Express this height in meters.

4. In short-distance running the 440-yd dash is used. How many meters is this?   *Ans.* 402 m

5. Convert 18 oz to grams; 2.94 m to feet and inches; one week to seconds.

6. If an industrial process uses 500 tons of iron ore each hour, how many pounds are used per day? per minute?   *Ans.* 24,$\overline{0}$00,000 lb/day; 16,$\overline{7}$00 lb/min

7. Express 30 mi/hr in feet per second.

8. A thin circular sheet of iron has a diameter of 14 cm. Find its area. If a square meter of the material has a mass of 0.30 kg, find the mass of the sheet.   *Ans.* 1$\overline{5}$0 cm²; 4.5 gm

9. Express properly to three significant figures the volume in cubic meters of 1.00 lb of water.

10. A replica meter bar is guaranteed to be accurate within 0.0025%. Express this uncertainty (*a*) in millimeters and (*b*) in inches.   *Ans.* 0.025 mm; 9.8 × 10⁻⁴ in.

11. Calculate the volumetric displacement of an 8-cylinder car which has cylinders of bore 7.50 cm and a stroke of 10.4 cm.

12. A cubic centimeter of water has a mass of approximately one gram. How many kilograms of water would fill a cylindrical cistern 25.4 in. in diameter and 30.0 in. high?   *Ans.* 249 kg

13. The mass of a hydrogen atom is 1.673×10^{-24} gm. Calculate the number of atoms in (*a*) 1.00 gm of hydrogen and (*b*) in 1.00 oz.

14. The mass of an electron is 9.11×10^{-28} gm. How many electrons would be required to make (*a*) 1.00 gm and (*b*) 1.00 ton?   *Ans.* 1.10×10^{27}; 1.00×10^{33}

15. Density in cgs units is expressed in grams per cubic centimeter and in mks units in kilograms per cubic meter. Convert a density of 7.85 gm/cm³ to mks units.

16. Convert a speed of 27 mi/hr to (*a*) feet per second, (*b*) kilometers per minute, and (*c*) centimeters per second.

Ans. 40 ft/sec; 0.72 km/min; 1.2×10^3 cm/sec

17. The Empire State Building is 1245 ft high. What is its height in (*a*) meters, (*b*) miles, (*c*) inches, and (*d*) millimeters?

18. Calculate the decimal equivalent of a distance of 1.00 km expressed in miles.   *Ans.* 0.622 mi/km

19. (*a*) How many seconds are there in a year? (*b*) How many months in 3.5×10^{12} sec?

20. How many cubic centimeters are there in 1.000 ft³?   *Ans.* 28,3$\bar{2}$0 cm³/ft³

21. Calculate the number of milliliters in a fluid ounce, if 16 fluid ounces are equivalent to a pint.

22. Calculate the number of quarts in a liter.   *Ans.* 1.057

23. The average weight of a baby at birth is 7.25 lb. Express this in kilograms.

24. What volume of copper will have a mass of 4.0 kg, if the density of copper is 8.9 gm/cm³?   *Ans.* 4$\bar{5}$0 cm³

25. The density of aluminum is 2.7 gm/cm³. Express this density in pounds per cubic foot.

26. The speed *v* of radio waves is equal to the product of the wavelength λ and the frequency *f*. If $v = 3.00 \times 10^8$ m/sec, find the wavelength of a radio wave from a transmitter broadcasting on a frequency of 760 kilocycles/sec. Express the wavelength (*a*) in meters and (*b*) in feet.   *Ans.* 395 m; 12$\bar{9}$0 ft

27. What is the distance from Philadelphia to New York, 90 mi, expressed in kilometers?

28. A contestant ran a 100-m dash in 10.6 sec. What was his speed (*a*) in feet per second and (*b*) in miles per hour?   *Ans.* 31 ft/sec; 21 mi/hr

29. (*a*) Express 30° in radians. (*b*) Express 0.60 radian in degrees and minutes. An angle of 2π radians is equivalent to 360°.

30. The Cleveland Terminal Tower Building, 708 ft tall, is observed by a man 1.5 mi away. What is the angle between the ground and his line of sight to the top of the building?   *Ans.* 5.12°

31. A ship receives radio signals from two radio transmitters *A* and *B*, 160 mi apart, *A* being located due north of *B*. The direction finder shows that transmitter *A* is 30°N of W, while transmitter *B* is due west. How far is the ship from each transmitter?

2. *Vectors; Forces at a Point*

The most elementary kind of measurement is simple counting, the result of which is expressed by a number: 3, 10, etc. In most measurements it is necessary to specify the unit in terms of which the comparison is made: 3 ft, 10 sec, etc. The units are a significant part of the statement of a physical measurement. Generally only quantities expressed in similar units can be compared. While 10,001 is nearly equal to 10,000, it would be meaningless to compare 10,001 dollars with 10,000 doughnuts.

A number and a unit are sufficient to specify many physical quantities. Such quantities add by ordinary arithmetic:

$$3 \text{ sec} + 5 \text{ sec} = 8 \text{ sec}$$

For the complete specification of certain other quantities, it is necessary that a *direction* also be stated. Such quantities add geometrically by a process that is more involved than arithmetic addition, but is not difficult.

2-1. Scalar and Vector Quantities. Some quantities encountered in physics, such as distance, volume, and mass, can be completely specified by a number and the appropriate unit: 3 ft, 7 in., 2 kg. Other quantities, such as velocity and displacement, require that the *direction* also be specified: 30 mi/hr north, 15 ft NE. The quantities that are completely specified by a number and its unit are called *scalar quantities*. Those quantities that

have both magnitude and direction are designated *vector quantities*.

Let an object initially at O (Fig. 1) be moved 4 ft east to A, and then 3 ft north to B. The final position of the object is distant OB

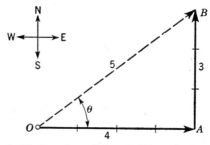

Fig. 1. Motion along OA and AB results in a displacement OB.

from the starting point O, even though it did not travel the path OB. The *displacement* of the body is its direction and distance from the origin O. Displacement is a vector quantity.

2-2. Vectors. A vector quantity is conveniently represented by a *vector;* this is an arrow-tipped line segment. The length of the vector indicates to scale the *magnitude* of the vector quantity. The direction of the vector specifies the *direction* of the vector quantity. The *sense* of the vector is indicated by an arrowhead on the end of the line segment. In Fig. 1, the eastward displacement of the body is represented by vector OA, its northward displacement by AB. The *resultant* displacement from the starting point is represented by vector OB.

The displacement OB is equivalent to the displacement OA plus the displacement AB. Thus it is apparent that vectors follow a special law of geometrical addition. For while it is not true that $4 + 3 = 5$, it is true that $\overrightarrow{OA} + \overrightarrow{AB} = \overrightarrow{OB}$, where the arrows signify the vector nature of the quantities in the addition.

A vector combines with another vector by *geometrical* addition to form a resultant vector which represents the combined effect of the quantities represented by the original vectors.

In Fig. 1, the vector AB is at right angles to the vector OA. The resultant of these two vectors is the vector OB drawn from the origin O to B the head of the second vector, closing the right triangle OAB. From the Pythagorean theorem, $(OA)^2 + (AB)^2 = (OB)^2$ or

$$4^2 + 3^2 = (OB)^2$$

and $OB = 5$ units. The direction of the resultant vector OB may be specified by the angle θ which it makes with OA. Since $\sin \theta = AB/OB = 0.60$, $\theta = 37°$. The resultant OB therefore represents a displacement of 5 ft from O in the direction 37°N of E.

A vector quantity multiplied by a scalar quantity is a vector quantity in the same direction as the original vector.

When two or more vectors are given, their sum or resultant may be found in a variety of ways. We shall describe three useful methods: the parallelogram method, the polygon method, and the method of components.

2-3. The Parallelogram Method. In the parallelogram method of addition, the vectors M and N are brought to a common origin O in a parallelogram constructed as in Fig. 2. The resultant is the diagonal drawn from the common origin of M and N.

With a ruler we can measure the resultant R in the units chosen for M and N, and the angle ϕ can be measured with a protractor. This graphic solution is always possible but its accuracy is limited by the accuracy with which the drawing can be made and measured.

An analytical method for determining the resultant R of any two vector quantities M and N makes use of the law of cosines and the

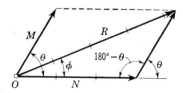

Fig. 2. Parallelogram method of adding vectors.

law of sines from trigonometry. To compute the magnitude of the resultant, we use the law of cosines, which when applied to Fig. 2 gives

$$R^2 = M^2 + N^2 + 2MN \cos \theta \qquad (1)$$

The direction of R can be determined by use of the law of sines. Applying the law of sines to Fig. 2 gives

$$\frac{\sin \phi}{M} = \frac{\sin (180° - \theta)}{R} \qquad (2)$$

from which we can determine the angle ϕ.

The resultant of two forces may be greater or less in magnitude than either of them, depending on the angle between them. In Fig. 3a, two vectors M and N of 2 and 3 units, respectively, are shown separately. In *b* where the vectors are in the same direction their resultant is merely their arithmetic sum. As the angle between the vectors increases, the resultant becomes less, as shown in *c*, *d*, and *e*. At *f* the resultant is (numerically) the difference between the vectors.

Example: Add vectors of 8.0 units and 5.0 units making an angle of 60° with each other.

Using a convenient scale, draw vectors A and B (Fig. 4a), making an angle of 60° with each other from a common origin O. Complete the parallelogram with A and B as sides and draw the diagonal from O, placing an arrowhead at the end of R. On the scale selected, R represents a resultant of 11 units at an angle of 20° with A, the 8-unit vector.

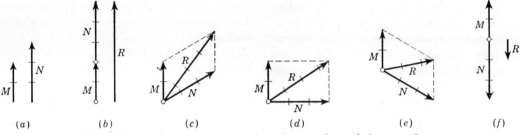

Fig. 3. The resultant of two vectors depends upon the angle between them.

The resultant may be determined analytically from the cosine law

$$R^2 = A^2 + B^2 + 2AB \cos 60°$$
$$= 64 + 25 + 2(8.0)(5.0)(0.50) = 1\overline{3}0$$
$$R = 11 \text{ units}$$

The angle ϕ may be determined from the sine law

$$\frac{R}{\sin 120°} = \frac{C}{\sin \phi}$$
$$\sin \phi = \frac{C}{R} \sin 120° = \frac{5.0}{11} \times 0.87 = 0.38$$

hence   Angle $\phi = 22°$

2-4. Polygon Method. The parallelogram method just described can be used to find the resultant of any set of vectors, but it becomes cumbersome when there are more

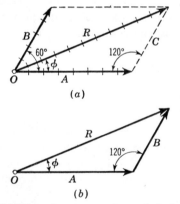

(a)

(b)

Fig. 4. Addition of two vectors by analytical method.

than two. Another graphic method called the *polygon method* is more useful for several vectors. In Fig. 4a, we found the resultant by completing the parallelogram, but we can get the same result by moving vector B parallel to itself until it coincides with C (Fig. 4b). We then have the tail of vector B placed at the

head of vector A. The vector sum or resultant is the vector R that closes the triangle, drawn from the origin O to the head of vector B.

This process may be extended to the addition of more than two vectors. The addition of vectors A, B, C, and D to give the resultant R should be clear from Fig. 5. Notice that the vectors to be added follow one another head to tail, like arrows indicating a trail. The only place where we may have two arrow points touching is where the head of the resultant arrow R joins the head of the last vector that was added, D. The vectors can be drawn in any order without changing the result.

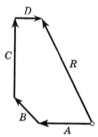

Fig. 5. Polygon method of vector addition. $A = 6$ mi, west; $B = 4$ mi, northwest; $C = 8$ mi, north; $D = 3$ mi, east.

2-5. Components of a Vector. In Fig. 1, the two vectors OA and AB taken together are equivalent to the single vector OB, called their *resultant*. Given the single vector OB, we may replace it by the two equivalent vectors OA and AB. This process is called the *resolution* of a vector into its components. The *components* of a vector are those vectors which when added together give the original vector.

A given vector may have any number of components. In Fig. 6a, R has been resolved into five components. In Fig. 6b, vector R has been resolved into two components. The most useful choice of components is usually that in which the components, X and Y of Fig. 6c, are at right angles to each other. If θ is the angle between vectors X and R, then

$$X = R \cos \theta \qquad (3)$$
$$Y = R \sin \theta \qquad (4)$$

Consider the vector AB, which makes an angle of 45° with the horizontal, as is shown in Fig. 7. In order to obtain a set of rectangular components of AB, one of which shall be horizontal, draw a horizontal line through the tail of the vector AB. Now from the head of AB draw CB perpendicular to the horizontal line. We see that the vector

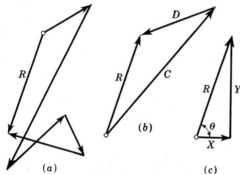

Fig. 6. Components of a vector.

AB can be considered as the resultant of the vectors AC and CB. The values of the horizontal and vertical components are $AB \cos 45°$ and $AB \sin 45°$. The directions of the arrowheads are important, for we are now considering that AC has been added to CB to give the resultant AB; therefore the arrows must follow head to tail along AC and CB, so that AB can properly be considered as a resultant drawn from the tail of the first arrow AC to the head of the last arrow CB. This resolution into components now allows us to discard the vector AB in our problem and keep only the two components AC and CB. These two taken together are in every way equivalent to the single vector AB.

What is the advantage of having two vec-

tors to deal with where there was one before? The advantage lies in the fact that several vectors making various odd angles with each other can be replaced by two sets of vectors making angles of either 90 or 0° with one

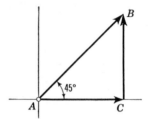

Fig. 7. Vertical and horizontal components of a vector.

another. Each of these two groups of vectors can then be summed up algebraically, thus reducing the problem to one of two vectors at right angles.

2-6. Component Method of Adding Vectors. To add a number of vectors A, B, C, and D (Fig. 8) by the method of components, we proceed as follows. Place the vectors at the origin on a set of rectangular coordinates (Fig. 8b). Next resolve each vector into x and y components by drawing a perpendicular from the vector head to the proper axis.

Add all the components along the x axis (A_x, B_x, C_x, etc.), the sum being called ΣX. Similarly add the components along the y axis to obtain ΣY.

$$\Sigma X = A_x + B_x + C_x + D_x$$
$$\Sigma Y = A_y + B_y + C_y + D_y$$

Some of the components are negative (for example, D_x and A_y) since each points along its axis in the direction that is conventionally called negative.

The resultant R (Fig. 8c) is obtained by the Pythagorean theorem

$$R^2 = (\Sigma X)^2 + (\Sigma Y)^2$$

while the angle θ which R makes with the x axis, measured counterclockwise, is given by

$$\tan \theta = \frac{\Sigma Y}{\Sigma X} \qquad \text{or} \qquad \sin \theta = \frac{\Sigma Y}{R}$$

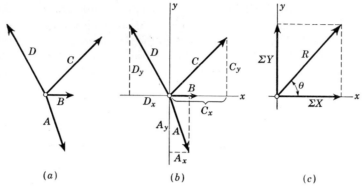

Fig. 8. Addition of vectors by the method of components.

Example: Find the sum of the following vectors: 3.00 units directed east, 12.00 units directed 40°N of E and 7.00 units directed 60°S of W (Fig. 9).

$$\alpha = 40° \qquad \text{and} \qquad \beta = 240°$$
$$\sin \alpha = 0.643 \qquad \cos \alpha = 0.766$$
$$\sin \beta = -0.866 \qquad \cos \beta = -0.500$$
$$\Sigma X = 3.00 + 12.0(0.766) + 7.00(-0.500)$$
$$= 8.70$$
$$\Sigma Y = 0 + 12.0(0.643) + 7.00(-0.866)$$
$$= 1.65$$
$$R^2 = 8.70^2 + 1.65^2 = 78.4$$
$$R = 8.86$$
$$\tan \theta = \frac{1.65}{8.70} \qquad \theta = 10°45'$$

It should be noted that a vector has zero component at right angles to itself. For instance, in the example just above, the 3-unit vector has zero y component. This example also illustrates the fact that the algebraic sign

of a component may be determined either by the sign of a trigonometric function or by inspection of the vector diagram.

2-7. Equilibrium. Forces are familiar examples of concepts that may be represented by vectors. Many of the problems of the design engineer involve various forces acting upon or within a structure or machine but in which these forces do not produce change in

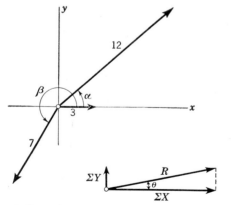

Fig. 9. Example of component method of addition.

Fig. 10. An example of equilibrium.

motion. His problem resolves itself into the determination of the forces necessary to produce equilibrium in the device.

The state in which there is no *change* in the motion of a body is called *equilibrium*. A body

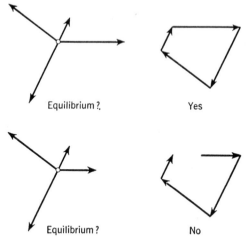

FIG. 11. Concurrent forces may or may not be in equilibrium.

to be in equilibrium may be at rest but does not necessarily have to be at rest; it may be moving with uniform speed in a straight line or rotating uniformly around a fixed axis.

In this chapter the discussion will be restricted to the action of forces that are in equilibrium and also that have lines of action which pass through the same point. Forces whose lines of action intersect at a common point are said to be *concurrent*.

2-8. First Condition for Equilibrium. In so far as linear motion is concerned, a body

is in equilibrium if the vector sum of the forces acting upon it is zero. This statement is known as the *first condition for equilibrium*.

Forces acting in the same direction can be added arithmetically to find the value of their resultant, which is the single force whose effect is equivalent to their combined action. In order to determine the resultant of two forces that do not act in the same straight line, it is necessary to make use of vector addition.

The several forces may be added by the use of any of the methods previously described. When the vectors are added by the polygon method, the vector sum is zero if the length of the arrow representing the resultant is zero. But this can occur only if the head of the last vector to be added comes back to touch the tail of the first vector as in the first part of Fig. 11. The vector sum is zero *if the vector diagram is a closed polygon.* The polygon method is especially useful when there are three concurrent forces.

Example: An object weighing 100 lb and suspended by a rope A, Fig. 12a, is pulled aside by the horizontal rope B and held so that rope A makes an angle of 30° with the vertical. Find the tensions in ropes A and B.

Consider the junction O as the point in equilibrium. It is acted upon by the three forces W (known), F_1 and F_2 (unknown). These forces are represented in Fig. 12b, with W scaled to represent the known weight, but only the directions and not the magnitudes of F_1 and F_2 known. Since the junction O is in equilibrium under the action of

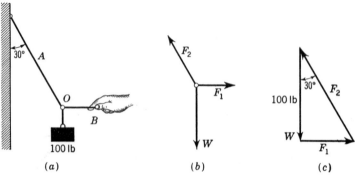

FIG. 12. Finding an unknown force by the polygon method.

these three forces, their resultant must be zero. Therefore, the vectors representing W, F_1, and F_2 can be redrawn as in Fig. 12c so that they combine to form a closed triangle. Note the fact that each vector is drawn parallel to the force that it represents. It is also important to draw the vector diagram so that the forces considered are those which act *upon* the point that is in equilibrium.

In order to solve the vector triangle of Fig. 12c, it may be observed that

$$\frac{F_1}{100} = \tan 30° = 0.58$$

so that $F_1 = (100\ \text{lb})(0.58) = 58\ \text{lb}$.
To get F_2, we can put

$$\frac{100\ \text{lb}}{F_2} = \cos 30° = 0.866$$

Therefore

$$F_2 = \frac{100\ \text{lb}}{0.866} = 116\ \text{lb}$$

That is, in order to hold the system in the position of Fig. 12a, one must pull on the horizontal rope with a force of 58 lb. The tension in rope A is then 116 lb. The tension in the segment of rope directly supporting the weight is, of course, just 100 lb.

In order to solve problems involving a body in equilibrium the following steps are recommended: (1) draw a sketch to picture the apparatus, as in Fig. 12a. Include on the sketch the known data. Indicate by a suitable symbol, such as O, the point which is to be considered in equilibrium under the action of the several forces; (2) make a figure, like Fig. 12b, to show the *directions* of all the forces acting about the point that is in equilibrium, as well as both the magnitudes and directions of the known forces; (3) draw a closed vector polygon, such as Fig. 12c, scaled to show both the magnitude and direction of each of the forces; (4) finally solve the vector polygon by suitable mathematical methods.

If the resultant of several forces is not zero, the body acted upon is not in equilibrium but it can be placed in a condition of equilibrium by adding a single force equal in magnitude to the resultant but opposite in direction.

This force is called the *equilibrant*. In Fig. 5, if the vectors were drawn to represent forces, the equilibrant of the four forces, A, B, C, and D, is a force equal in magnitude to R but opposite in direction. If this force were combined with the original four forces, the polygon would be closed.

Example: By the method of components find the resultant and the equilibrant of a 7.0-lb horizontal force and a 12-lb force making an angle of 60° with the horizontal (Fig. 13).

The horizontal and vertical components of the 12-lb force are, respectively, $12\ \text{lb} \times \cos 60° = 6.0\ \text{lb}$ and $12\ \text{lb} \times \sin 60° = 10.4\ \text{lb}$. The horizontal component of the 7.0-lb force is 7.0 lb,

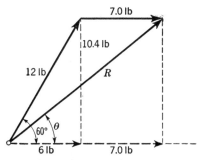

FIG. 13. Resultant of forces by the component method.

and its vertical component is zero. Thus we replace the original two forces by three forces: one vertical and two horizontal. Since the two horizontal forces are in the same direction, they may be added as ordinary numbers, giving a total horizontal force of $6.0\ \text{lb} + 7.0\ \text{lb} = 13.0\ \text{lb}$. The problem is now reduced to the simple one of adding two forces at right angles, giving the resultant

$$R = (\sqrt{10.4^2 + 13.0^2})\ \text{lb} = 16.6\ \text{lb}$$

The angle θ, which R makes with the horizontal, is given by $\tan \theta = 10.4/13.0 = 0.80$, so that $\theta = 38.7°$.

The equilibrant is equal in magnitude but opposite in direction to R. Hence it is a force of 16.6 lb at an angle of 218.7°.

When the component method of adding vectors is used, the condition that the vector sum of the forces shall be zero is satisfied if each set of components adds to zero separately. That is,

$$\Sigma F_x = 0 \qquad (5)$$

and

$$\Sigma F_y = 0 \qquad (6)$$

These equations can be used for any set of forces, but the method is particularly useful when there are more than three forces.

Example: An object weighing 100 lb and suspended by a rope A (Fig. 12) is pulled aside by the horizontal rope B and held so that rope A makes an angle of 30° with the vertical. Find the tensions in ropes A and B.

We have previously solved this problem by the straightforward method of adding the vectors to form a closed figure. That method is quite appropriate to such simple cases but, for the sake of illustration, let us now solve the problem again by the more general method of components. In Fig. 14

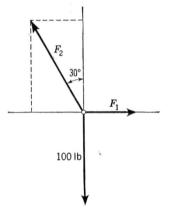

FIG. 14. Component method of solving the problem of Fig. 12.

are shown the same forces, separated for greater convenience of resolution. The horizontal and vertical components of the 100-lb force are, respectively, 0 and 100 lb down. The horizontal and vertical components of F_1 are, respectively, F_1 (to the right) and 0. Although we do not yet know the numerical value of F_2, whatever it is, the horizontal and vertical components will certainly be $F_2 \sin 30°$ to the left and $F_2 \cos 30°$ up. We now have four forces, two vertical and two horizontal, whose vector sum must be zero to ensure equilibrium. In order that the resultant may be zero, the sum of the horizontal components and the sum of the vertical

components must each be equal to zero. Therefore,

$$F_1 - F_2 \sin 30° = 0 \qquad \text{(horizontal)}$$
$$F_2 \cos 30° - 100 \text{ lb} = 0 \qquad \text{(vertical)}$$

If we solve the second equation, we find that $F_2 = 116$ lb, as in the previous solution. By substituting this value in the first equation, we obtain $F_1 = 58$ lb, as before.

Example: A load of 100 lb is hung from the middle of a rope, which is stretched between two walls 30.0 ft apart (Fig. 15). Under the load the rope sags 4.0 ft in the middle. Find the tensions in sections A and B.

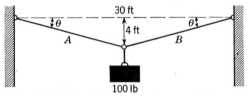

FIG. 15. Finding the tension of a stretched rope.

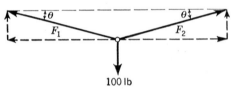

FIG. 16. Horizontal and vertical components of the forces in a stretched rope.

The mid-point of the rope is in equilibrium under the action of the three forces exerted on it by sections A and B of the rope and the 100-lb weight. A vector diagram of the forces appears in Fig. 16. The horizontal and vertical components of the 100-lb force are, respectively, 0 and 100 lb downward. The horizontal and vertical components of F_1 are, respectively, $F_1 \cos \theta$ to the left, and $F_1 \sin \theta$ upward. Similarly, the horizontal and vertical components of F_2 are, respectively, $F_2 \cos \theta$ to the right, and $F_2 \sin \theta$ upward. In order that the resultant shall be zero, the sum of the horizontal components and the sum of the vertical components must each be equal to zero. Therefore,

$$F_2 \cos \theta - F_1 \cos \theta = 0$$
$$\text{(horizontal)} \qquad (a)$$
$$F_1 \sin \theta + F_2 \sin \theta - 100 \text{ lb} = 0$$
$$\text{(vertical)} \qquad (b)$$

Since these two equations involve three unknown

quantities F_1, F_2, and θ, we cannot solve them completely without more information.

The value of $\sin \theta$ can be determined from the dimensions shown in Fig. 15

$$\sin \theta = \frac{4.0 \text{ ft}}{A}$$

$$A = \sqrt{15.0^2 + 4.0^2} \text{ ft} = \sqrt{241} \text{ ft} = 15.5 \text{ ft}$$

and

$$\sin \theta = \frac{4.0 \text{ ft}}{15.5 \text{ ft}} = 0.26$$

From Eq. (a), $F_1 = F_2$. Substituting in Eq. (b),

$$F_1 \sin \theta + F_1 \sin \theta - 100 \text{ lb} = 0$$
$$2F_1 \sin \theta = 100 \text{ lb}$$
$$2F_1(0.26) = 100 \text{ lb}$$
$$F_1 = \frac{100 \text{ lb}}{2(0.26)} = 1\overline{9}0 \text{ lb}$$

and

$$F_2 = 1\overline{9}0 \text{ lb}$$

Two things should be noticed about the problem just solved: (1) that the value of a function of an angle in the vector diagram was needed in order to carry out the solution; (2) that the value of that function was determined from the geometry of the original problem.

Example: Calculate the force needed to hold a 1000-lb car on an inclined plane that makes an angle of 30° with the horizontal, if the force is to be parallel to the incline.

The forces on the car include (see Fig. 17) its weight W vertically downward, the force B parallel

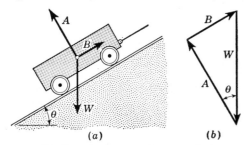

FIG. 17. Finding the forces acting on a body on an incline.

to the incline, and the force A exerted on the car by the inclined plane itself. The last force mentioned is perpendicular to the plane if there is no friction.

Since the car is in equilibrium under the action of the three forces A, B, and W, a closed triangle

can be formed with vectors representing them, as in Fig. 17b. In the vector diagram, $B = W \sin \theta$. Since θ is 30° and $W = 1000$ lb,

$$B = (1000 \text{ lb}) \sin 30° = (1000 \text{ lb})(0.500) = 500 \text{ lb}$$

The value of A, the perpendicular force exerted by the plane, can be found by observing that

$$A = W \cos 30° = (1000 \text{ lb})(0.866) = 866 \text{ lb}$$

It should be noticed that W can be resolved into two components that are, respectively, parallel and perpendicular to the incline. These components are equal in magnitude and opposite in direction to B and A, respectively.

SUMMARY

Quantities whose measurement is specified by *magnitude* and *direction* are called *vector quantities*. Those which have only magnitude are called *scalar quantities*.

A vector quantity may be represented graphically by a directed line segment, called a vector. A *vector* is the line whose length indicates to scale the magnitude of the vector quantity and whose direction indicates the direction of the quantity.

The *resultant* of two or more vector quantities is that single quantity that would produce the same result.

In the parallelogram method for the addition of two vectors the resultant R is conveniently found from the law of cosines and the law of sines

$$R^2 = M^2 + N^2 + 2MN \cos \theta$$
$$\frac{\sin \phi}{M} = \frac{\sin (180° - \theta)}{R}$$

Vectors are conveniently added graphically by placing them "head to tail" and drawing the resultant from the origin to the head of the last vector, closing the polygon. This is known as the *polygon* method.

The *rectangular components* of a vector are its projections on a set of right-angle axes, for example, the horizontal and vertical axes.

$$X = R \cos \theta$$
$$Y = R \sin \theta$$

The *component* method of adding vectors is

to resolve each into its rectangular components, which are then added algebraically and the resultant found.

$$R^2 = (\Sigma X)^2 + (\Sigma Y)^2$$

A body is in *equilibrium* when there is no change in its motion.

When a body is in equilibrium, the vector sum of all the forces acting on it is zero. This is known as the *first condition for equilibrium*. When a body is in equilibrium, the vector diagram is a closed polygon, or the sums of the rectangular components of all the forces must each equal zero: $\Sigma F_x = 0$ and $\Sigma F_y = 0$.

QUESTIONS

1. What items must be stated to specify a vector quantity completely?

2. Give several examples of scalar quantities; of vector quantities.

3. Are vectors necessary, or is the concept of a vector merely a convenience in expressing physical quantities?

4. Two forces of 50 lb and 80 lb act upon a body. What are the maximum and minimum possible values of the resultant forces?

5. What are the handicaps which one has in solving complicated vector problems by the parallelogram method?

6. Show by a series of vector polygons that it is immaterial which order is used in laying off the vectors end to end and that the resultant is always the same.

7. Show how the parallelogram method of solving vector problems can be simplified by the use of the polygon method.

8. An automobile is acted upon by the following forces: a horizontal force due to air resistance; the weight of the car; a force almost vertically upward on the front wheels; the force of the ground on the rear wheels. Draw a vector polygon to show these forces in equilibrium. What does this imply with respect to the velocity of the car?

9. Make a three-dimensional sketch to show how one could portray the resultant of a force upward, one toward the east and one toward the north.

10. Why does an airplane pilot prefer to take off and land into the wind? Explain by the use of a vector diagram.

11. In moving a sled over the snow is it better to pull the sled with a rope or to push on the sled with a pole? Explain by the use of vectors.

12. Explain how an iceboat can be made to sail faster than 20 mi/hr in a 20 mi/hr wind. What limits the speed attainable with the iceboat?

13. Give several examples of moving bodies which are in equilibrium.

14. Which of the following groups of forces could be in equilibrium: (*a*) 20, 30, and 40 lb; (*b*) 15, 30, and 50 lb; (*c*) 25, 25, and 25 lb; (*d*) 100, 50, and 25 lb?

15. A picture is hung from a wall by two wires. Show by diagrams the configuration which the wires must have in order to be under a minimum of tension.

16. Describe an experiment that demonstrates the physical meaning of the terms component, resultant, and equilibrant.

17. When telephone wires are covered with ice, is there more danger of their breaking when they are taut or when they sag?

18. Show that if a body is in equilibrium any one of the forces acting upon it must be equal in magnitude and opposite in direction to the resultant of all the other forces.

PROBLEMS

In all these problems carefully drawn figures should be made to accompany the analytical solution. The solutions can be checked to a rough approximation if the vector diagrams are drawn to scale.

1. Forces of 12 lb and 15 lb act at right angles. What is their resultant?

2. After a trip it is found that a car has traveled 25 mi east and 50 mi north. How far and in what direction is the car from its starting point?

Ans. 56 mi; 63° N of E

3. A boat sails 20 mi due east and then sails 12 mi southeast. How far is it from its starting point, and in what direction is it from that point?

4. A boat travels 10.0 mi/hr in still water. If it is headed 60°S of W in a current that moves at 12.0 mi/hr due east, what is the resultant velocity of the boat?

Ans. 11.1 mi/hr at 51°S of E

5. An airplane is flying at 150 mi/hr on a north-to-south course according to the compass. A cross wind of 30 mi/hr is blowing south 47°W and carries the airplane west of its course. What is the speed and course of the airplane?

6. Two forces of 24 tons and 11 tons, respectively, are applied to an object at a common point and have an included angle of 60°. Calculate the magnitude of their resultant and the angle it makes with the 24-ton force. *Ans.* 31 tons; 18°

7. A pencil is moving with a speed of 3.0 ft/sec along the diagonal of a square that is itself moving in the direction of one of its edges at the rate of 4.0 ft/sec. Find the resultant speed of the pencil.

8. What is the angle between two equal forces whose resultant is equal to one-half of one of the forces? *Ans.* 151°

9. A boy weighing 80 lb sits in a swing, which is pulled to one side by a horizontal force of 60 lb. What is the tension in the swing rope?

10. As a flag is hoisted up the mast at 15 ft/sec, a ship goes south at 22 ft/sec, and the tide moves east at 4.0 ft/sec. What is the speed of the flag relative to the earth? *Ans.* 27 ft/sec

11. Along a certain mountain road the grade is such that the road rises 10.0 ft in every 100 ft of horizontal distance. How much force, neglecting friction, would be required to pull a load of 2000 lb up this grade, the force being applied parallel to the road and the load being moved with constant speed?

12. The iron sphere in Fig. 18 weighs 100 lb and rests in a smooth V-shaped trough whose sides form an angle of 60°. What is the normal force exerted by the sphere on each side of the trough? *Ans.* 100 lb

Fig. 18.

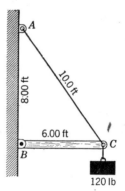

Fig. 19.

13. A 120-lb box is supported by a cord attached to a hook in a vertical wall at point *A*, Fig. 19. The cord is displaced by the length of the horizontal strut *BC*, 6.00 ft long. Assuming cord and strut to have negligible weights, (*a*) draw a vector diagram representing the forces acting at *C*. (*b*) What is the horizontal force exerted by the wall on the strut at *B*? (*c*) What is the force exerted on the hook in the direction *AC*?

14. The beam of a wall crane 7.5 ft long is held at right angles to the wall by a tie that is attached to the wall 6.0 ft above the foot of the beam. If the load lifted is 3.0 tons, find the tension in the tie and the compressional force in the beam. Neglect the weight of the beam.   *Ans.* 4.8 tons; 3.8 tons

15. A load of 50 lb is suspended from the ceiling by a cord 8.0 ft long. A second cord is tied to the first 2.0 ft above the load, and a pull is exerted by this attached cord always making an angle of 30° above the horizontal. When the tension in the second cord becomes 20 lb, it is tied fast. (*a*) Find the tension in the first cord, above and below the knot. (*b*) What angle does the first cord make with the horizontal?

16. A ship is sailing 20°N of E at the rate of 14 mi/hr. How fast is it going northward and how fast eastward?   *Ans.* 4.8 mi/hr; 13 mi/hr

17. If a ship is sailing 21°E of N at the rate of 15.0 mi/hr, what are its component speeds, northward and eastward?

18. If a wind is blowing 17.5 ft/sec and crosses the direction of artillery fire at an angle of 38°, what are its component speeds along, and directly across, the direction of fire?   *Ans.* 13.8 ft/sec; 10.8 ft/sec

19. A boy is pulling his sled along level ground, his pull on the rope being 12.0 lb. What are the vertical and horizontal components of the force if the rope makes an angle of 21° with the ground?

20. A person who is 35 ft east of you runs north at 16 ft/sec. At what angle north of east would you throw a ball at 60 ft/sec ground speed in order to hit him?   *Ans.* 15.4°

21. The angle between the rafters of a roof is 120°. What thrust is produced along the rafters when a 1200-lb object is hung from the peak?

22. Add the following displacements by the component method: 10 ft directed northeast, 15 ft directed south, and 25 ft directed 30°W of S.
                    Ans. 30 ft; 10.4°W of S

23. A safe is suspended by two wires, each inclined 22° with the horizontal. If the greatest straight pull which either wire could sustain is 450 lb, how heavy a safe could the two support as specified?

24. A rope 100 ft long is stretched between a tree and a car. A man pulls with a force of 100 lb at right angles to and at the middle point of the rope, and moves this point 5.0 ft. Assuming no stretching of the rope, what is the tension in the rope at the final position?   *Ans.* 500 lb

25. Four boxes each weighing 100 lb are suspended from a beam (Fig. 20). What is the tension in each of the wires?

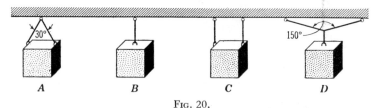

A   B   C   D

Fig. 20.

26. A 20-lb picture is suspended from the wall by a single cord attached at two corners of the frame and hung over a pin. What is the tension in the cord if the angle between the two halves of the cord is 60°? What is the tension if the angle is increased to 90°?   *Ans.* 12 lb; 14 lb

27. An acrobat weighing 150 lb performs on a horizontal wire 15.0 ft long capable of withstanding 3000 lb. How far below the level of the supports must the wire be allowed to sag at the middle if the performer at the center is to be supported with a factor of safety of 3?

28. A motorboat that has a speed of 12 mi/hr in still water crosses from the east to the west bank of a river 1.0 mi wide. The river flows from north to south, the speed of the current being 4.0 mi/hr. The boat crosses with its keel pointing due east. (*a*) What is the speed of the boat with reference to its starting point? (*b*) How long does it take for the boat to reach the west bank? (*c*) How far south of its starting point will it land?   *Ans.* 13 mi/hr; 5.0 min; 0.33 mi

29. A man travels 15 mi southeast, then 8.0 mi north, then 10 mi northwest. In what direction and how far will he have to travel before he reaches the starting point?

30. A man walks westward on a boat with a speed of 4.0 mi/hr; the ship's propeller drives it 15 mi/hr northwest; tide and wind drive the ship 5.0 mi/hr south. What is the actual speed of the man relative to the earth? What is the direction of his velocity?   *Ans.* 16 mi/hr at 21°N of W

31. Three forces of 4.00, 6.00, and 8.00 lb are in equilibrium. Find the angles between the forces.

32. A string 7.0 ft long has its ends attached to the ceiling at points 5.0 ft apart. When a load is hung on the string 3.0 ft from one end, there is a force of 8.0 lb in the shorter length and 6.0 lb in the greater. Find the weight of the suspended load.   *Ans.* 10 lb

33. Two stones, one weighing 9.00 lb and the other weighing 12.0 lb, are attached to the ends of a string which passes over two fixed, frictionless pulleys. At a point on the string between the pulleys a third stone weighing 15.0 lb is hung. What is the configuration of the string for which the system will be in equilibrium?

34. Find the force in a cable necessary just to keep in equilibrium a 1000-lb car on a 30° incline (*a*) when the cable is parallel to the incline and (*b*) when the cable makes an angle of 60° above the horizontal.   *Ans.* 500 lb; 577 lb

35. A 4000-lb wagon is to be drawn with uniform speed up a grade rising 40.0 ft in a distance of 200 ft measured along the grade. Calculate the force which would be necessary if it were applied (*a*) parallel to the grade, (*b*) horizontally?

36. A bridge span is in the shape of an inverted V. The apex is 5.00 m above the roadway and the distance between piers is 20.0 m. Find the vertical and horizontal forces which the span exerts upon each pier per ton of load at the apex of the span. Calculate also the thrust which the span exerts on each pier.

Ans. $100\overline{0}$ lb; $200\overline{0}$ lb; $224\overline{0}$ lb

37. A load of 250 lb is suspended from a crane of right-angle design, similar to the one shown in Fig. 19. The tie rope is 18.0 ft long and the boom is 15.0 ft long. Neglecting the weight of the bar, find the force in the tie rope and the force which the boom exerts on the wall.

38. An object weighing 40.0 lb is suspended from the end of a horizontal bar 50.0 in. long, the other end of the bar resting against a vertical wall. At a point 40.0 in. vertically above the point where the bar meets the wall, a string is attached, the other end of the string being tied to the bar at the end where the load is hung. Determine the tensional force in the string and the compressional force in the beam. Neglect the weight of the bar.   *Ans.* 63.7 lb; 50.0 lb

39. Three forces of 12, 15, and 20 lb are in equilibrium. If the 12-lb force is directed horizontally toward the right, what must the directions of the other two forces be?

40. A derrick boom is attached to a vertical mast at its lower end so that it makes an angle of 30° with the mast. Its upper end is held in position by a rope which makes an angle of 90° with the boom. Neglecting the weight of the boom, calculate the tension in the rope and the thrust of the boom when a load of 900 lb is carried by the upper end of the boom.   *Ans.* 450 lb; 779 lb

41. A group of four men pull on ropes attached to a common knot. The forces exerted by the men are as follows: $A = 40$ lb at 0° (with respect to the horizontal x axis); $B = 50$ lb at 105°; $C = 30$ lb at 210°; $D = 60$ lb at 270°. Calculate the magnitude and direction of the resultant force.

42. Compute the equilibrant of the following four forces: $A = 800$ lb at 20°; $B = 600$ lb at 130°; $C = 1000$ lb at 295°; and $D = 300$ lb at 210°.

Ans. 620 lb at 329°

3. *Velocity and Acceleration*

As we observe objects around us, one of the most noticeable properties is their motion. Some motions appear to be very simple; others very complicated. Motion can be dangerous if it is erratic and uncontrolled as we observe it in a flooded river, a hurricane, or a runaway automobile, but controlled motion is an exceedingly useful tool.

A study of the motions of objects is necessary if we are to understand their behavior and learn to control them. Since most motions are very complex, it is necessary to begin with the simplest of cases. It is surprising what complicated motions can be analyzed and represented in terms of a few elementary types, when these simple types of motion are thoroughly understood.

3-1. Speed and Velocity. The simplest kind of motion that an object can have is a uniform motion in a straight line. In every second the body moves the same distance in the same direction as it did in each other second. Every part of the body moves in exactly the same way. An object moving in this manner is moving with constant *velocity*. Constant velocity implies not only *constant speed* but *unchanging direction* as well.

The *speed* of a moving body is the distance it moves per unit of time. If the speed is uniform the object moves equal distances in each successive unit of time. Whether or not the speed is constant, the *average speed* is the dis-

tance the body moves divided by the time required for the motion.

$$\text{Average speed} = \frac{\text{distance traveled}}{\text{time elapsed}}$$

$$\bar{v} = \frac{s}{t} \qquad (1a)$$

where s is the distance traversed, $\bar{v}$ the average speed, and t the time. The mks unit of speed is the meter per second (m/sec); the fps unit is the foot per second (ft/sec); many other units are common, such as the mile per hour (mi/hr), centimeter per second (cm/sec), knot, etc. Equation (1a) may be put in the form

$$s = \bar{v}t \qquad (1)$$

If the speed is constant, its value is, of course, identical with the average speed. If, for example, an automobile travels 200 mi in 4 hr, its average speed is 50 mi/hr. In 6 hr it would travel 300 mi.

The concept of speed does not involve the idea of direction. A body moving with constant speed may move in a straight line or in a circle or in any one of an infinite variety of paths so long as the distance moved in any unit of time is the same as that moved in any other equal unit of time.

The concept of *velocity* includes the idea of direction as well as magnitude. Hence we must consider the *displacement* of a body and not merely the *distance* traveled. The definition of *average velocity* is given by

$$\text{Average velocity} = \frac{\text{displacement}}{\text{time elapsed}}$$

The defining equation for average velocity is identical with Eq. (1*a*), except that it must be understood that both $\bar{v}$ and the displacement s are vector quantities. Sometimes the symbol $\vec{s}$ is used to emphasize this fact.

Constant *velocity* is a particular case of constant speed. Not only does the distance traveled in unit time remain the same but the *direction* as well does not change. An automobile that travels for 1 hr at a constant velocity of 20 mi/hr *north*, reaches a place 20 mi north of its first position. If, on the other hand, it travels around a race track for 1 hr at a constant *speed* of 20 mi/hr, it may traverse the same distance without getting anywhere. At one instant its velocity may be 20 mi/hr east; at another, 20 mi/hr south.

The statement, "An automobile is moving with a *velocity* of 20 mi/hr," is incorrect by virtue of incompleteness, since the direction of motion must be stated in order to specify a velocity. For this reason one should always use the word *speed* when he does not wish to specify the direction of the motion, or when the direction is changing.

Example: An automobile traveled by a circuitous path for a time of 3.0 hr and covered a total distance of 180 mi. (*a*) What was the average speed in feet per second? (*b*) If at the end of the trip the car was exactly 60 mi north of its starting point what was the average velocity?

(*a*) The average speed was

$$\bar{v} = \frac{s}{t} = \frac{180 \text{ mi}}{3.0 \text{ hr}} = \frac{180 \text{ mi}}{3.0 \text{ hr}} \times \frac{5280 \text{ ft}}{1 \text{ mi}} \times \frac{1 \text{ hr}}{60 \text{ min}}$$
$$\times \frac{1 \text{ min}}{60 \text{ sec}} = 88 \frac{\text{ft}}{\text{sec}}$$

(*b*) The average velocity was

$$\bar{v} = \frac{\vec{s}}{t} = \frac{60 \text{ mi N}}{3.0 \text{ hr}} = 20 \frac{\text{mi}}{\text{hr}} \text{ north}$$

3-2. Instantaneous Velocity. We are frequently interested in knowing the speed and velocity of a body at a particular instant and not merely the average value over a considerable time interval. For this purpose it is convenient to consider the ratio $\Delta s/\Delta t$, where Δs

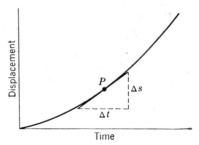

FIG. 1. Displacement-time curve.

is the increment of displacement which the body has during the small time interval Δt. If Δt is made smaller and smaller, approaching zero as a limit, Δs becomes equally infinitesimal and the *instantaneous velocity* is the limit of this ratio

$$v = \lim_{\Delta t \to 0} \frac{\Delta s}{\Delta t} = \frac{ds}{dt} \qquad (1b)$$

Thus instantaneous velocity is the time rate of change of displacement. In the language of the calculus the ratio ds/dt is called the derivative of s with respect to t. Unless otherwise stated, the single term speed, or velocity, is meant to refer to the instantaneous value.

Suppose we consider the case of a body which is traveling in a straight line with a uniformly increasing speed. A curve of displacement against time for such a body is shown in Fig. 1. From the definition of instantaneous speed it may be seen that the speed of the body at the point P is equal to the slope of the line drawn tangent to the curve at P. If the speed were constant, the slope would be the same at every point and the curve would be a straight line. From the shape of the curve in Fig. 1 it is evident that the speed of the body in question is not constant, since the slope is steadily increasing.

3-3. Accelerated Motion. Objects seldom move with constant velocity. In almost all cases the velocity of an object is continually changing in magnitude or in direction or in both. Motion in which the velocity is changing is called *accelerated motion*, and the rate at which the *velocity* changes is called the *acceleration*.

The velocity of a body may be changed by changing the speed or by changing the direction or by changing both speed and direction. If the direction of the acceleration is parallel to the direction of motion, only the speed changes, while, if the acceleration is at right angles to the direction of motion, only the direction changes. Acceleration in any other direction produces changes in both speed and direction.

For the present we shall confine our attention to the simplest type of accelerated motion, called *uniformly accelerated motion*, in which the direction is always the same and parallel to the direction of the original motion and the speed changes at a constant rate. The acceleration in this case is equal to the rate of change of speed, since there is no change in direction. The acceleration is called *positive* if the speed is increased, *negative* if the speed is decreased. Negative acceleration is sometimes called deceleration.

3-4. Average and Instantaneous Acceleration. The acceleration of a body is defined as its time rate of change of velocity. Using algebraic symbols to represent average acceleration $\bar{a}$, initial velocity v_1, final velocity v_2, and time t, the defining equation for average acceleration is written

$$\text{Average acceleration} = \frac{\text{change in velocity}}{\text{elapsed time}}$$

$$\bar{a} = \frac{v_2 - v_1}{t} \qquad (2a)$$

Since units of acceleration are obtained by dividing a unit of velocity by a unit of time it may be seen that the fps unit of acceleration is the foot per second per second (ft/sec²), the mks unit is the meter per second per second (m/sec²), and the cgs unit is the centimeter per second per second (cm/sec²).

We are frequently concerned with the acceleration of a body at a particular instant. This is defined in a manner similar to that used for the definition of instantaneous velocity, namely

$$a = \lim_{\Delta t \to 0} \frac{\Delta v}{\Delta t} = \frac{dv}{dt} \qquad (2b)$$

or instantaneous acceleration is the derivative of velocity with respect to time. If a curve of velocity against time is drawn, the acceleration at any point is given by the slope of the curve at that point.

Example: An automobile accelerates at a constant rate from 15 mi/hr to 45 mi/hr in 10 sec while traveling in a straight line. What is the acceleration?

The acceleration, or the rate of change of speed in this case, is the change in speed divided by the time in which it took place, or

$$\bar{a} = \frac{45 \text{ mi/hr} - 15 \text{ mi/hr}}{10 \text{ sec}} = \frac{30 \text{ mi/hr}}{10 \text{ sec}}$$
$$= 3.0 \text{ (mi/hr) per sec}$$

indicating that the speed increases 3.0 mi/hr during each second.

Since

$$30 \text{ mi/hr} = 30 \frac{\text{mi}}{\text{hr}} \times \frac{5280 \text{ ft/mi}}{3600 \text{ sec/hr}} = 44 \text{ ft/sec}$$

the acceleration can be written also as

$$a = \frac{44 \text{ ft/sec}}{10 \text{ sec}} = 4.4 \text{ ft/sec}^2$$

This statement means simply that the speed increases 4.4 ft/sec during each second, or 4.4 ft/sec².

3-5. Equations of Uniformly Accelerated Linear Motion. It is convenient to list and remember the equations which apply to a body moving with *constant* acceleration in a straight line, a special case but one often encountered. If both sides of Eq. (2a) are multiplied by t, we obtain

$$v_2 - v_1 = at \qquad (2)$$

which expresses the fact that the *change in speed* is equal to the rate of change in speed multiplied by the time during which it is changing.

The distance traveled during any time is given by the equation

$$s = \bar{v}t$$

but the average speed $\bar{v}$ must be obtained from the initial and final speeds, v_1 and v_2. Since the speed changes at a uniform rate, the average speed $\bar{v}$ is equal to the average of the initial and final speeds, or

$$\bar{v} = \frac{v_1 + v_2}{2} \qquad (3)$$

Example: How far does the automobile of the previous example move while its speed increases from 15 to 45 mi/hr?

$\bar{v} = \frac{1}{2}(15 + 45)$ mi/hr = 30 mi/hr = 44 ft/sec
and $s = 44$ ft/sec $\times$ 10 sec = $4\overline{4}0$ ft

Three equations for uniformly accelerated motion have been considered:

$$s = \bar{v}t \qquad (1)$$
$$v_2 - v_1 = at \qquad (2)$$
$$\bar{v} = \frac{v_1 + v_2}{2} \qquad (3)$$

By combining these, two other useful equations can be obtained. Eliminating v_2 and $\bar{v}$, we obtain

$$s = v_1t + \tfrac{1}{2}at^2 \qquad (4)$$

If we eliminate $\bar{v}$ and t from Eqs. (1) to (3), we obtain

$$2as = v_2{}^2 - v_1{}^2 \qquad (5)$$

Of these five equations, Eq. (1) is true for all types of motion; the remaining four equations hold only for *uniformly accelerated linear motion*. In the solution of a given problem that equation should be used in which the quantity to be determined is the only one not known.

Example: A truck starting from rest acquires a speed of 30 mi/hr in 20 sec. What is the acceleration? How far does the truck travel?

$$v_2 = 30 \text{ mi/hr} = \frac{30 \text{ mi/hr} \times 5280 \text{ ft/mi}}{3600 \text{ sec/hr}}$$
$$= 44 \text{ ft/sec}$$

From Eq. (2)

$$a = \frac{v_2 - v_1}{t} = \frac{44 \text{ ft/sec} - 0}{20 \text{ sec}} = 2.2 \text{ ft/sec}^2$$

From Eq. (4)

$$s = v_1t + \tfrac{1}{2}at^2 = 0 + \tfrac{1}{2}(2.2 \text{ ft/sec}^2)(20 \text{ sec})^2$$
$$= 4\overline{4}0 \text{ ft}$$

or from Eq. (1)

$$s = \bar{v}t = \frac{v_1 + v_2}{2}t$$
$$= \frac{0 + 44 \text{ ft/sec}}{2} \times 20 \text{ sec} = 4\overline{4}0 \text{ ft}$$

Example: A train traveling with a speed of 60 mi/hr is brought to an emergency stop in 2000 ft. What is the acceleration and the time required to stop?

$$v_1 = 60 \text{ mi/hr} = 88 \text{ ft/sec}$$

From Eq. (5)

$$2as = v_2{}^2 - v_1{}^2$$
$$2a(2000 \text{ ft}) = 0 - (88 \text{ ft/sec})^2$$
$$a = \frac{-(88 \text{ ft/sec})^2}{2(2000 \text{ ft})} = -1.9 \text{ ft/sec}^2$$

From Eq. (2)

$$t = \frac{v_2 - v_1}{a} = \frac{0 - 88 \text{ ft/sec}}{-1.9 \text{ ft/sec}^2} = 46 \text{ sec}$$

3-6. Freely Falling Bodies; Acceleration Due to Gravity. The most common example of uniformly accelerated motion is the motion of a body falling freely, that is, a body which is falling under the action of its weight alone. If a stone is dropped, it falls to the earth. If air resistance is negligible, the stone is uniformly accelerated.

The acceleration of freely falling bodies is so important and so frequently used that it is customary to represent it by the special symbol g. At sea level and 45° latitude, g has a value of 32.17 ft/sec², or 980.6 cm/sec², or

9.806 m/sec². For our purposes it is sufficiently accurate to use $g = 32$ ft/sec² or 980 cm/sec², or 9.80 m/sec².

The value of g is not quite the same at all places on the earth. Since the weight of a body depends upon its distance from the center of the earth, the acceleration of a freely falling body also depends upon this distance. At a given latitude the value is greater at sea level than at higher altitude. At sea level, the value is greater near the poles than at the equator. Locally there may be small variations because of irregularities in the layers of rock beneath the surface. Such local variations are the basis of one type of prospecting for oil.

Since a freely falling body is uniformly accelerated, the five equations already developed for that type of motion may be applied when air resistance is neglected.

Example: A body starting from rest falls freely. What is its speed at the end of 1.0 sec?

From Eq. (2)

$$v_2 = v_1 + at = 0 + (32 \text{ ft/sec}^2)(1.0 \text{ sec})$$
$$= 32 \text{ ft/sec}$$

Example: When starting from rest, how far does a body fall during the first second?

From Eq. (4)

$$s = v_1t + \tfrac{1}{2}at^2 = 0 + \tfrac{1}{2}(32 \text{ ft/sec}^2)(1.0 \text{ sec})^2$$
$$= 16 \text{ ft}$$

Table 1 and Fig. 2 show the speed at the end of time t and the distance fallen during time t for a body that starts from rest.

TABLE 1

Time t, sec	Speed, ft/sec, at end of time t	Distance, ft, fallen in time t
1	32	16
2	64	64
3	96	144
4	128	256

When, instead of falling from rest, an object is thrown with initial speed v_1, the first term of Eq. (4) is no longer zero. If it is thrown downward, both v_1 and a have the same direction and hence are given the same algebraic sign. If, however, the object is thrown upward, v_1 is directed upward while a is directed downward, and thus the latter must be considered as negative.

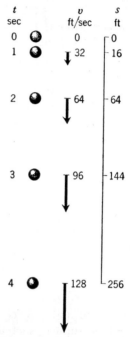

Fig. 2. Position and speed of a body falling freely from rest after successive intervals of time.

Example: A body is thrown upward with an initial speed of 40 ft/sec. Find the distance traveled during the first second, the speed at the end of the first second, and the greatest elevation reached by the object.

$$v_1 = 40 \text{ ft/sec}$$
$$a = -32 \text{ ft/sec}^2$$

From Eq. (4)

$$s = v_1t + \tfrac{1}{2}at^2 = (40 \text{ ft/sec}) \times (1.0 \text{ sec})$$
$$+ \tfrac{1}{2}(-32 \text{ ft/sec}^2) \times (1.0 \text{ sec})^2 = 24 \text{ ft}$$

From Eq. (2)

$$v_2 = v_1 + at = 40 \text{ ft/sec} + (-32 \text{ ft/sec}^2)$$
$$\times (1.0 \text{ sec}) = 8.0 \text{ ft/sec}$$

At the highest point the object stops and hence $v_2 = 0$.

From Eq. (5)

$$2as = v_2{}^2 - v_1{}^2$$
$$2(-32 \text{ ft/sec}^2)s = 0 - (40 \text{ ft/sec})^2$$
$$s = \frac{-(40 \text{ ft/sec})^2}{2(-32 \text{ ft/sec}^2)} = 25 \text{ ft}$$

This is the greatest elevation reached by the object.

3-7. Terminal Speed. In the preceding discussion we have assumed that there is no air resistance. In the actual motion of every falling body this is far from true. The frictional resistance of the air depends upon the speed of the moving object. The resistance is quite small for the first one or two seconds but as the speed of fall increases the resistance becomes large enough to reduce appreciably the net downward force on the body and the acceleration decreases. After some time of uninterrupted fall, the body is moving so rapidly that the drag of the air is as great as the weight of the body, so that there is no acceleration. The body has then reached its *terminal speed*, a speed that it cannot exceed in falling from rest.

Very small objects, such as dust particles and water droplets, and objects of very low density and large surface, such as feathers, have very low terminal speeds; hence they fall only small distances before losing most of their acceleration. The effect of the air can be shown by an experiment in which a coin and a feather are enclosed in a long tube. When the tube filled with air is inverted, the coin falls much faster than the feather. If the air is pumped out and the tube again inverted, the coin and feather fall together.

A man jumping from a plane reaches a terminal speed of about 120 mi/hr if he delays opening his parachute. When the parachute is opened, the terminal speed is reduced because of the increased air resistance to about 14 mi/hr, which is about equal to the speed gained in jumping from a height of 7 ft. A large parachute encounters more air resistance than a small one and hence causes slower descent. A plane in a vertical dive without the use of its motor can attain a speed of about 400 mi/hr.

SUMMARY

Speed is distance per unit time and *velocity* is displacement per unit time. Their *average* values are defined by the equation

$$\bar{v} = \frac{s}{t}$$

Instantaneous velocity is the derivative of displacement with respect to time

$$v = \frac{ds}{dt}$$

A statement of *velocity* must specify the direction as well as the speed, for example, 25 mi/hr east, 30 ft/sec southwest.

Acceleration is the rate of change of velocity. Average acceleration is defined by

$$\bar{a} = \frac{v_2 - v_1}{t}$$

Instantaneous acceleration is the derivative of the velocity with respect to time

$$a = \frac{dv}{dt}$$

The equations of uniformly accelerated motion for the particular case in which the direction of motion remains fixed and the speed changes uniformly are

$$s = \bar{v}t \tag{1}$$
$$v_2 - v_1 = at \tag{2}$$
$$\bar{v} = \frac{v_1 + v_2}{2} \tag{3}$$
$$s = v_1t + \tfrac{1}{2}at^2 \tag{4}$$
$$2as = v_2{}^2 - v_1{}^2 \tag{5}$$

A freely falling body is one that is acted on by no forces of appreciable magnitude other than its weight.

The acceleration of a freely falling body at sea level and 45° latitude is approximately 32 ft/sec², or 980 cm/sec², or 9.8 m/sec².

The *terminal speed* of a falling object is the vertical speed at which the force of air resistance is just sufficient to balance its weight.

QUESTIONS   1. Show by the use of graphs why the average speed of an object is $\frac{1}{2}(v_1 + v_2)$ only for the case of uniform acceleration and is not true for variable acceleration.

2. A man on a moving flatcar throws a ball toward his companion on the other end of the car. Describe the velocity of the ball (a) relative to the companion and (b) relative to the earth, when the car is moving (1) forward and (2) backward.

3. An airplane travels in a straight line with constant speed at a fixed elevation above the ocean. Show why the velocity is not constant. What is the direction of the acceleration?

4. Sketch rough curves to illustrate the velocity as a function of time for the following cases: (a) baseball thrown vertically upward, beginning with the start of the motion from the pitcher's hand; (b) an elevator starting upward from rest in a high building; (c) a train approaching a station. (Consider upward velocities as positive and downward velocities as negative.)

5. Show by a vector diagram how much the smokestack on a moving train caboose would have to be inclined in order for a vertically falling raindrop to pass through the stack without hitting the sides.

6. Cite some examples of (a) uniform motion, (b) uniformly accelerated motion, and (c) nonuniformly accelerated motion.

7. Can a body have a velocity without an acceleration? Can it have an acceleration with zero velocity? Give examples.

8. Cite an example to show that it is possible for an object to have an acceleration without its speed changing.

9. Identify a motion that occurs in nature in which (a) an object has a velocity (not zero) but has zero acceleration, (b) the acceleration is nearly constant, (c) the acceleration varies from point to point in the motion.

10. An iron ball and a ball of putty fall from a distance and strike a concrete pavement. Describe the acceleration of these objects after they hit the pavement.

11. A marble rolls with negligible friction down an inclined plane. Show by means of a vector polygon how the acceleration parallel to the plane may be expressed in terms of the geometrical dimensions of the plane. Galileo referred to this experiment as "diluting gravity." Show why this is an appropriate designation.

12. If we call the upward direction positive, what sign should be given to the velocity and acceleration of a ball (a) just after it is thrown vertically upward? (b) at the highest point of its path? (c) when it is falling?

13. A body is thrown vertically downward with an initial velocity and falls freely thereafter. Sketch rough curves to show the following relations: acceleration vs. distance; speed vs. time; distance fallen vs. time; speed vs. distance fallen.

14. State two reasons why the value of g is different at various places on the earth. What would one expect about this value on the moon? on the sun?

15. A light object is dropped from a stationary balloon. Taking air resistance into account, show by a rough graph how the speed of the object varies with time.

16. If a body falls from a great height, can its speed reach a maximum value and thereafter decrease? Explain.

17. A body is thrown vertically upward. If air resistance is considered, is the time during which the body rises longer or is it shorter than the time during which it falls?

1. A racing automobile travels around a half-mile track in 26.54 sec. What is its average speed in miles per hour? in feet per second?

2. A runner A can run the mile race in 4.25 min. Another runner B requires 4.55 min to run this distance. If they start out together and maintain their normal speeds, how far apart will they be as A crosses the finish line?

Ans. 348 ft

3. When a batter struck a ball, its velocity changed from 150 ft/sec west to 150 ft/sec east. What was (*a*) the change in speed? (*b*) the change in velocity?

4. A steamboat travels in still water with a speed of 15.5 mi/hr. How long will it take to travel 50.0 mi? If there is a river current of 2.25 mi/hr, what time is required to travel this distance when the travel is (*a*) upstream? (*b*) downstream? *Ans.* 3.22 hr; 3.79 hr; 2.82 hr

5. An airplane normally cruises at 200 mi/hr. There is a southwest wind blowing at 50 mi/hr. The pilot wishes to reach a place 500 mi north of his starting point. What course must he set and how long will it take him to arrive?

6. A car travels with a constant velocity of 30 mi/hr north for 15 min. It then quickly speeds up to 50 mi/hr and maintains this velocity for 30 min. What is the average velocity for the whole period? *Ans.* 43 mi/hr north

7. A speedboat can normally travel at 25.0 mi/hr. The boat heads away from a pier at an angle of 70° with the shore line. A tide of 3.65 mi/hr is running toward the shore. How far will the boat travel in 15.0 min? Where will it be with respect to its starting point?

8. A train starts from rest and at the end of 90 sec has a speed of 45 mi/hr. What is its acceleration? *Ans.* 0.73 ft/sec²

9. A car changes its speed from 20.0 mi/hr to 30.0 mi/hr in 5.00 sec. Express the acceleration in miles per hour per second, feet per minute per second, and feet per second per second.

10. The initial speed of a car having excellent brakes was 30 mi/hr (44 ft/sec). When the brakes were applied, it stopped in 2.0 sec. Find the acceleration.

Ans. −22 ft/sec²

11. An automobile starts from rest and accelerates 2.0 m/sec². How far will it travel during the third second?

12. An automobile has a speed of 60 mi/hr. When the brakes are applied, it slows to 15 mi/hr in 4.0 sec. What is the acceleration? How far does it travel during the fourth second? *Ans.* −16 ft/sec²; 32 ft

13. A train has a speed of 60 ft/sec at a given instant and 12.0 sec later its speed is 42 ft/sec. What is its acceleration, assuming it to be constant? After how long a time will the train come to rest? How far will it travel after the first instant mentioned?

14. A body slides down a frictionless incline 10.0 m long. If the incline makes an angle of 30.0° with the horizontal, calculate (*a*) the time of descent, (*b*) the speed with which it reaches the bottom, and (*c*) the distance traversed during the second second after it starts from rest.

Ans. (*a*) 2.02 sec; (*b*) 990 cm/sec; (*c*) 735 cm

15. An object slides down a frictionless plane inclined at an angle of 60° to the horizontal. (*a*) If the plane is 30.0 ft long, how long will it take for the object to reach the foot of the plane? (*b*) How far will it travel along the horizontal frictionless surface at the foot of the plane in 3.00 sec?

16. A train has a speed of 30 mi/hr. The brakes are applied, and a uniform retardation of 4.0 ft/sec² is obtained. Find (*a*) how long it will be before the train comes to rest, (b) the distance traversed in coming to rest, and (c) the distance traversed during the fifth second after the brakes are applied.

Ans. 11 sec; 242 ft; 26 ft

17. A body slides down a frictionless inclined plane and during the third second after starting from rest it travels **19.4** m. What is the inclination of the plane?

18. How high will a body rise that is projected vertically upward with a speed of 100 ft/sec? How long will it take for the body to reach its maximum height?

Ans. 156 ft; 3.1 sec

19. A stone is thrown vertically upward with an initial speed of 96 ft/sec. (a) How long does it continue to rise? (b) How high does it rise?

20. How high will a body rise if it is projected vertically upward with a speed of 15.4 m/sec? How long will it rise? *Ans.* 12.1 m; 1.58 sec

21. What vertical speed will cause a ball to rise 16 ft? 64 ft?

22. A baseball is thrown vertically downward from the top of a cliff 500 ft high with an initial speed of 100 ft/sec. (a) What will be the speed after 3.00 sec? (b) After how long a time will the ball reach the ground?

Ans. 196 ft/sec; 3.26 sec

23. A stone is thrown vertically downward from the top of a tower 100 m high with an initial speed of 30 m/sec. What is its speed at the end of 2.0 sec? How long a time is required to reach the ground? With what speed does it strike the ground?

24. A stone is thrown vertically upward with a speed of 160 ft/sec. How high will it rise and when will it return to the ground? *Ans.* 4̄00 ft; 10 sec

25. A stone is thrown from the ground to the top of a flagpole. It returns to the ground after 5.0 sec. How high is the pole?

26. A balloon which is ascending at the rate 12 m/sec is 80 m above the ground when a stone is dropped. How long a time is required for the stone to reach the ground? *Ans.* 5.4 sec

27. From a balloon, which is ascending at the rate of 32 ft/sec, a stone is dropped and reaches the ground in 16.0 sec. How high was the balloon when the stone was dropped?

28. A stone is dropped from a high altitude, and 3.00 sec later another is projected vertically downward with a speed of 150 ft/sec. When and where will the second overtake the first? *Ans.* 5.67 sec; 514 ft

29. A bullet is shot vertically upward with a speed of 320 ft/sec and 10.0 sec later a second bullet is shot upward with a speed of 190 ft/sec. Will they ever pass? If so, where?

30. An elevator is ascending with an acceleration of 4.0 ft/sec². At the instant its upward speed is 8.0 ft/sec a bolt drops from the top of the cage 9.0 ft from the floor. Find the time until the bolt strikes the floor and the distance it has fallen.

Ans. 0.71 sec; 2.3 ft

31. An automobile moves with constant speed v along a line which we may designate as an x axis. If the auto is at a place x_0 at time $t = 0$, at any other time its position is given by $x = x_0 + vt$. Show by differentiation that this equation correctly leads to an expression for the instantaneous velocity.

32. Calculate the speed with which a bomb will hit a battleship 300 ft below if the bomb is projected from a stationary balloon (a) with an initial velocity of 25.0 ft/sec vertically upward and (b) with an initial velocity of 25.0 ft/sec vertically downward. *Ans.* 140 ft/sec; 140 ft/sec

33. An elevator moves upward with a uniform acceleration for a short time. The distance which it travels is represented by the equation $s = 15t + 2t^2$. Plot a curve to show the instantaneous speeds at time 0, 1, 2, 3, 4 sec.

34. A particle moves with an acceleration that is *not* constant. Its displacement at any instant is given by $s = s_0 + At^2 + Bt^3$, where A and B are constants. By taking derivatives derive expressions for the speed and acceleration at any time.   *Ans.* $v = 2At + 3Bt^2$; $a = 2A + 6Bt$

35. Show that the definition of average speed $\bar{v} = s/t$ is identical with the *time average* of the instantaneous speeds. HINT: Use $v = ds/dt$ and take the time integral of $v\, dt$, namely,

$$\frac{1}{t_2 - t_1} \int_{t_1}^{t_2} v\, dt.$$

36. A cork is thrown vertically downward from a cliff which is 1500 ft high. The initial speed of the cork is 170 ft/sec. Air friction produces a uniform negative acceleration of -13.33 ft/sec^2, until the cork reaches a terminal speed of 10 ft/sec. How long will it take for the cork to reach the bottom of the cliff?

Ans. 54 sec

37. A raindrop has its terminal speed of 50.0 ft/sec just as it reaches the surface of the earth. A certain drop enters a well which is 300 ft deep. If sound travels at 1125 ft/sec, how long will it take after the drop enters the well for an observer to hear the drop strike the water at the bottom of the well?

4. Force and Motion

In our studies of statics (Chap. 2) we examined that branch of mechanics that deals with the balance or equilibrium of forces on objects that remain at rest or that are moving with constant velocity, that is, bodies that are not accelerated. In Chap. 3 we studied the motion of bodies that are moving with uniform acceleration. We shall now seek, in the study of classical dynamics, to analyze the relationship between resultant forces and the accelerations they produce.

When a body is at rest, we know from experience that it will remain at rest unless something is done to change that state. We walk without fear in front of a standing locomotive because we know that it will not suddenly move. A heavy box on the floor will stay in place unless it is pushed or pulled. We must exert a force upon it to change its motion, that is, to give it an acceleration.

We readily accept the fact that no body can be set in motion without having a force act upon it. It may not be as easy to accept the equally true fact that a body in motion cannot change its motion unless a resultant force acts on it. We seldom if ever observe a body that has no force acting on it.

A box resting on the floor has more than one force acting on it, but they do not produce a change in motion. A rather large horizontal force must be exerted to start the box moving, and it stops quickly when the force is removed. If the box is mounted on wheels, a smaller force is required to start it, and it continues to move longer. If more care is taken to reduce the resistance (friction) of the floor to the motion, it becomes easier to start the box, and it continues to move more readily. We are finally led to the conclusion that if the resistance of the floor could be entirely removed *any* horizontal force could start the box moving and once started it would continue to move indefinitely unless a force were exerted to stop it. The property of a body by virtue of which a net force is required to change its motion is called *inertia*.

4-1. The Law of Inertia: Newton's First Law. The conclusion which has been reached regarding the need of a force to change the motion of a body was stated by Sir Isaac Newton (1642–1727). *There is no change in the motion of a body unless a resultant force is acting upon it.* If the body is at rest, it will continue at rest. If it is in motion, it will continue in motion with constant speed in a straight line unless there is a net force acting. This law of inertia is usually called *Newton's first law of motion.* It is the purely negative statement that no acceleration will occur without a net force to cause that change.

4-2. Mass. By the mass of a body is meant the numerical measure of its inertia, in terms of an arbitrary standard mass, for example, the standard kilogram (Chap. 1).

In principle, the mass of a body could be determined by measuring its interaction with the standard body when both were very far away from all other bodies in the universe. The masses would be in the inverse ratio of the accelerations produced by the mutual gravitational attraction of the two bodies.

More practically, we can compare the test body and the standard kilogram on an equal-arm balance when both are attracted by the earth. The force of gravity acts on all bodies in proportion to their masses. The operation of weighing in the balance determines the mass of the test body. The mass is independent of the location of the body. The mass of a body is constant unless we add matter or remove it. In contrast, the weight of the body, the earth-pull on it, depends on the location of the body on the earth and of course would be quite different on another planet.

4-3. Force and Acceleration: Newton's Second Law. *Whenever a net (unbalanced) force acts on a body, it produces an acceleration in the direction of the net force, an acceleration that is directly proportional to the net force and inversely proportional to the mass of the body.*

If successively greater resultant forces are applied to a given body, correspondingly greater accelerations are produced. A given force applied in turn to several different bodies will produce accelerations inversely proportional to the masses of the bodies.

According to the second law, the following proportions may be written

$$a \propto F$$

and
$$a \propto \frac{1}{m}$$

These proportions may be combined as

$$a \propto \frac{F}{m}$$

and written as an equation

$$F = kma \tag{1}$$

In Eq. (1) any unit of force, any unit of mass, and any unit of acceleration can be used, provided the proper value is assigned to the constant k. In general, a different value of k would have to be assigned for each combination chosen. For simplicity, it is customary to use a system of units for which k has a value of *one*.

4-4. Systems of Units. In Chap. 1 we observed that three fundamental quantities are required to set up a system of units in mechanics. The choice of these fundamental quantities is rather arbitrary, and the kind of units set up depends upon the choice. Commonly, the fundamental quantities are length, mass, and time. Another system of fundamental quantities utilizes length, force, and time.

Mass is independent of the place at which observation is made, and hence a system of units based on length, mass, and time is called an *absolute* system. In the alternative choice, length, force, and time, the force commonly chosen is a gravitational force, or weight, and hence the system of units is called a *gravitational* system.

4-5. Absolute Systems of Units. In an absolute system of units a fundamental unit is arbitrarily assigned to each of the fundamental quantities length, mass, and time, as described in Chap. 1. Three such systems are commonly set up: two metric, *cgs* and *mks*, and one British.

In the *cgs* system, the centimeter, gram, and second are the fundamental units. From these units we have derived a unit of acceleration, the centimeter per second per second. By the use of Eq. (1) we can derive a unit of force, conveniently one of such size that the constant k has a value of unity. If m is 1 gm and a is 1 cm/sec², then k will be 1 if there is unit force. To this unit force we give the name dyne. The *dyne* is the net force that will give to a mass of 1 gm an acceleration of 1 cm/sec².

When a set of units, such as the *cgs*, in which one unit is defined in such a way as to make k unity, is used, Eq. (1) becomes

$$F = ma \tag{2}$$

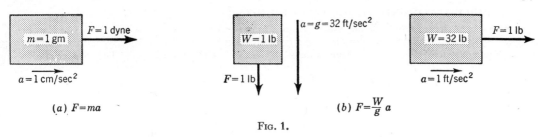

(a) $F=ma$

(b) $F=\dfrac{W}{g}\,a$

FIG. 1.

Equation (2) is not a general equation since it can be used only *when a consistent set of units is employed*.

When the fundamental units are selected as the meter, kilogram, and second, a new system of units, the *mks*, results. In this system the unit of acceleration is the meter per second per second. As before, we can derive a unit of force that makes k of Eq. (1) unity. The *newton* is the force that will give to a mass of 1 kg an acceleration of 1 m/sec². From the method of defining the unit of force we see that this set of units can also be used in Eq. (2). The mks system of units was adopted by an international conference in 1940 to supplant the cgs system. The principal advantage of the mks system is that it leads directly to the electrical units in common use.

A British absolute system is based upon the foot, pound, and second. In it the pound is used as a unit of mass, and as before a unit of force is defined to make k of Eq. (1) unity. The *poundal* is the force that will give to a mass of 1 pd an acceleration of 1 ft/sec².

4-6. Gravitational Systems of Units. In a gravitational system of units the fundamental unit of force is defined in terms of the pull of the earth upon an arbitrarily chosen body. In a metric gravitational system the gram is used as a unit of force. The *gram-force* is defined as one-thousandth the pull of the earth upon a standard kilogram at a place where g has a value of 980.665 cm/sec². In this gravitational system the unit of mass is derived from Eq. (1) in such a manner as to make k unity. No name has been assigned to this gravitational unit of mass. This nameless unit is the mass to which a gram-force would give an acceleration of 1 cm/sec².

In the British gravitational system the fundamental unit of force, the pound (lb), is 1/2.2046 the force with which the earth pulls on a standard kilogram at a place where g is 32.17398 ft/sec². In this system we define a unit of mass, the slug, from Eq. (1). The *slug* is the mass to which a force of 1 lb will give an acceleration of 1 ft/sec².

4-7. Choice of Units to Be Used. We have outlined five systems of units each of which is consistent, logical, and suitable for use in Eq. (2). It is unfortunate that in the different sets of units the same word is used to designate a unit of mass in one set, but a unit of force in another. Therefore throughout the mechanics section of this book we shall omit completely reference to the British absolute system and to the cgs gravitational system. Whenever the term *gram* or *kilogram* is used, it will refer to *mass*. Whenever the term *pound* is used, it will refer to *force*.

4-8. Relation between Mass and Weight. When a body falls freely, the only force acting on it is its weight. This net force produces the acceleration g observed in freely falling bodies. Thus, from Eq. (1), we obtain

$$W = kmg$$

If we use units that are consistent with Eq. (2), the value of k is unity and

$$W = mg \qquad (3)$$

or

$$m = \frac{W}{g} \qquad (4)$$

Since weight is a force, we use Eq. (3) to find

TABLE 1. CONSISTENT SYSTEMS OF UNITS FOR NEWTON'S SECOND LAW

In each set the starred unit is the one usually defined from the second law so as to make $k = 1$ in $F = kma$

Name of system	Unit of mass	Unit of force	Unit of acceleration
Mks (absolute)............	kilogram	newton *	meter/second²
Cgs absolute..............	gram	dyne *	centimeter/second²
Cgs gravitational.........	No name assigned $m = W/g$	gram	centimeter/second²
British absolute...........	pound	poundal *	foot/second²
British gravitational.......	slug *	pound	foot/second²
Any system...............	W/g	Same unit as that used for W	Same unit as that used for g

weights in *dynes* or in *newtons* when we use the absolute cgs or mks units, respectively. In the British gravitational system we commonly compute the mass in slugs from Eq. (4). In any case, where we use units that are consistent with Eq. (2) we can always substitute W/g for m and mg for W.

Table 1 lists consistent sets of mechanical units.

4-9. Procedure in the Solution of Problems. In applying the second law of motion to the solution of a problem, much difficulty can be avoided by following a definite procedure. The most common source of difficulty is the failure to recognize that the F of the second law always refers to the *resultant* force acting on a body and the m refers to the mass of that same body. In solving any problem involving force and motion, the following steps are recommended:

1. Make a sketch showing the conditions of the problem. Indicate on it dimensions or other data given in the problem.

2. Select for consideration the *one body whose motion is to be studied*. Construct a force vector diagram. On this vector diagram, represent by vectors *all* the forces acting *on* the body that has been selected. If any forces are unknown, represent them also by vectors and label them as unknown quantities.

3. From the vector diagram, find the *resultant* force acting on the body. This resultant is the F of Eq. (2).

4. Find the unknown quantity (a, F, or m) from the relation $F = ma$. If the weight of the body is given, compute m from $m = W/g$. If the problem asks for a distance, velocity, or time, apply the equations of accelerated motion (Chap. 3) as required.

Example: A 100-lb block rests at the top of a smooth plane whose length is 200 in. and whose height is 50 in. How long will it take for the block to slide to the bottom of the plane when released?

As indicated in Fig. 2, the forces acting on the block are the weight W downward, and the force

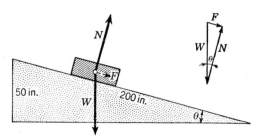

FIG. 2. Inclined plane.

N of the plane against the block. This force is perpendicular to the plane. The resultant (unbalanced) force F is parallel to the plane. The force triangle and the space triangle are similar and the angle θ is common to the two triangles. From the force triangle

$$F = W \sin \theta$$

From the space triangle

$$\sin \theta = \frac{50 \text{ in.}}{200 \text{ in.}} = 0.25$$
$$F = W \sin \theta = 100 \text{ lb} \times 0.25 = 25 \text{ lb}$$
$$m = \frac{W}{g} = \frac{100 \text{ lb}}{32 \text{ ft/sec}^2} = 3.1 \text{ slugs}$$

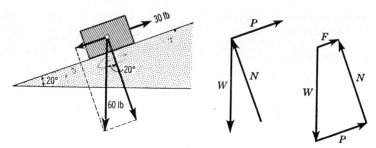

Fig. 3. Determination of unbalanced force acting on block.

From Eq. (2)

$$a = \frac{F}{m} = \frac{25 \text{ lb}}{3.1 \text{ slugs}} = 8.0 \text{ ft/sec}^2$$

The time of descent is determined from $s = \frac{1}{2}at^2$ since the block starts from rest.

$$t = \sqrt{\frac{2s}{a}} = \sqrt{\frac{2 \times 200 \text{ in.}}{(12 \text{ in./ft})(8.0 \text{ ft/sec}^2)}} = 2.0 \text{ sec}$$

Example: A 60.0-lb block rests on a smooth plane inclined at an angle of 20° with the horizontal (Fig. 3). The block is pulled up the plane with a force of 30.0 lb parallel to the plane. What is its acceleration?

Here three forces are acting on the block. Its weight W is 60 lb downward. The force of the plane on the block is a thrust N normal to the plane. There is a pull P parallel to the plane. Addition of these vectors by the polygon rule shows an unbalanced force F acting on the block parallel to the plane.

The weight of the block may be resolved into components of 60.0 lb × cos 20° normal to the plane and 60.0 lb × sin 20° parallel to the plane. The normal component is balanced by the force N. Hence the unbalanced force F parallel to the plane and directed up the plane is

$$F = 30.0 \text{ lb} - 60.0 \text{ lb} \times \sin 20° =$$
$$30.0 \text{ lb} - (60.0 \times 0.342) \text{ lb} = 9.5 \text{ lb}$$

$$m = \frac{W}{g} = \frac{60.0 \text{ lb}}{32 \text{ ft/sec}^2} = 1.87 \text{ slugs}$$

From Eq. (2)

$$a = \frac{F}{m} = \frac{9.5 \text{ lb}}{1.87 \text{ slugs}} = 5.1 \text{ ft/sec}^2$$

Note that if the angle were 30°, the component of the weight down the plane would be equal to the force up the plane and there would be no unbalanced force acting on the block. Hence it would not be accelerated. If the angle were greater than 30°, the block would be accelerated down the plane.

Example: A 2.0-ton elevator is supported by a cable that can safely support $6\overline{4}00$ lb. What is the shortest distance in which the elevator can be brought to a stop when it is descending with a speed of 4.0 ft/sec?

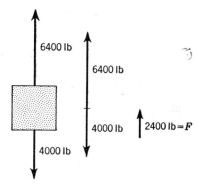

Fig. 4. Finding unbalanced force from vector addition of forces.

The maximum net force acting on the elevator (Fig. 4) is

$$6\overline{4}00 \text{ lb} - 4\overline{0}00 \text{ lb} = 2\overline{4}00 \text{ lb} \qquad (\text{upward})$$

The mass being accelerated is

$$m = \frac{W}{g} = \frac{4\overline{0}00 \text{ lb}}{32 \text{ ft/sec}^2} = 125 \text{ slugs}$$

From Eq. (2)

$$a = \frac{F}{m} = \frac{2\overline{4}00 \text{ lb}}{125 \text{ slugs}} = 19 \text{ ft/sec}^2 \qquad (\text{upward})$$

Since the initial velocity is downward the upward acceleration will be considered negative.

The time required to stop the elevator is

$$t = \frac{v_2 - v_1}{a} = \frac{0 - 4.0 \text{ ft/sec}}{-19 \text{ ft/sec}^2} = 0.21 \text{ sec}$$

In this time the elevator will have covered a distance

$$s = \bar{v}t = \left(\frac{4.0 \text{ ft/sec} + 0}{2}\right)(0.21 \text{ sec}) = 0.42 \text{ ft}$$

Example: A 5.0-kg block is placed on a smooth horizontal surface (Fig. 5). A horizontal cord attached to the block passes over a light frictionless

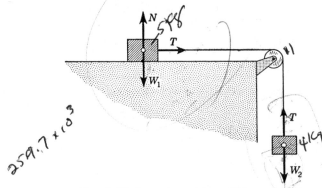

FIG. 5. Block accelerated by a falling mass.

pulley and is attached to a 4.0-kg body. Find the acceleration and the tension in the cord when the system is released.

Consider first the 5.0-kg block. The forces acting on this body are: its weight W_1 downward, the reaction N of the plane upward, and the tension T of the cord to the right. Since there is no vertical acceleration, $N = W_1$ and the resultant force is T. Thus, from Eq. (2),

$$T = m_1 a$$

The forces on the 4.0-kg body are its weight W_2 downward and the tension T upward. The net downward force is $W_2 - T$ and

$$W_2 - T = m_2 a$$

Since the two bodies move together, the accelerations are equal in magnitude although the directions are not the same. If we divide the first equation by the second, we obtain

$$\frac{T}{W_2 - T} = \frac{m_1 a}{m_2 a} = \frac{m_1}{m_2} = \frac{5.0 \text{ kg}}{4.0 \text{ kg}}$$

$$W_2 = m_2 g = 4.0 \text{ kg} \times 9.8 \text{ m/sec}^2 = 39 \text{ newtons}$$

$$4.0 \text{ kg} \times T = 5.0 \text{ kg} \times (39 \text{ newtons} - T)$$

$$T = 22 \text{ newtons}$$

$$a = \frac{T}{m_1} = \frac{22 \text{ newtons}}{5.0 \text{ kg}} = 4.4 \text{ m/sec}^2$$

Example: Two bodies having masses $m_1 = 30$ gm and $m_2 = 40$ gm are attached to the ends of a string of negligible mass and suspended from a

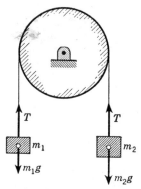

FIG. 6. Unequal masses suspended from a pulley.

pulley as shown in Fig. 6. Find the accelerations of the bodies and the tension in the string.

Consider the body of mass m_1. Two external forces act on it, the weight $m_1 g$ downward and the upward pull T of the string. The resultant force on this body is $T - m_1 g$ upward. From Eq. (2) we may write

$$T - m_1 g = m_1 a$$

where a is the upward acceleration of this body.

Now consider the body of mass m_2. The forces acting on this body are its weight $m_2 g$ downward and the tension T upward. The resultant force is $m_2 g - T$ downward and from Eq. (2)

$$m_2 g - T = m_2 a$$

where a is the downward acceleration of this body. Since the two bodies move together, the accelerations are equal in magnitude but they are opposite in direction.

$$T - 30 \text{ gm} \times 980 \text{ cm/sec}^2 = 30 \text{ gm} \times a$$

and

$$40 \text{ gm} \times 980 \text{ cm/sec}^2 - T = 40 \text{ gm} \times a$$

When the two equations are added we obtain

$$10 \text{ gm} \times 980 \text{ cm/sec}^2 = 70 \text{ gm} \times a$$
$$a = \frac{100}{70} \times 980 \text{ cm/sec}^2 = 140 \text{ cm/sec}^2$$
$$T = m_1 g + m_1 a = m_1(g + a)$$
$$= 30 \text{ gm} \times (980 + 140) \text{ cm/sec}^2$$
$$= 35,000 \text{ dynes}$$

4-10. Variable Acceleration. In our discussion thus far we have assumed that the forces considered have been constant in magnitude and in direction. In general, forces may vary in any manner. If there is any such variation, Newton's second law applies at each instant and the instantaneous value of the acceleration is proportional to the net force at that instant and in the direction of that force. We may rewrite Eq. (2) as

$$F = ma = m\frac{dv}{dt} \qquad (5)$$

The change in velocity over any period of time may be found from Eq. (5) if the manner of variation of F is known.

Example: A 160-lb body starts from rest under the action of a net force that varies linearly with time according to the relationship

$$F = 25 \text{ lb} - 0.50t$$

What is the initial acceleration? the acceleration at the end of 10 sec? What is the speed of the body at the end of 10 sec?

$$m = \frac{160 \text{ lb}}{32 \text{ ft/sec}^2} = 5.0 \text{ slugs}$$
$$a_0 = \frac{F_0}{m} = \frac{25 \text{ lb} - 0}{5.0 \text{ slugs}} = 5.0 \text{ ft/sec}^2$$
$$a_f = \frac{F_f}{m} = \frac{(25 - 0.50 \times 10) \text{ lb}}{5.0 \text{ slugs}} = 4.0 \text{ ft/sec}^2$$

From Eq. (5)

$$\frac{dv}{dt} = \frac{F}{m}$$

or

$$dv = \frac{F}{m}\,dt$$

By integration

$$\int_0^v dv = \int_{t=0}^{t=10} \frac{F}{m}\,dt$$
$$\int_0^v dv = \frac{1}{5.0 \text{ slugs}} \int_0^{10} (25 - 0.50t)\,dt$$

$$v - 0 = \frac{1}{5.0 \text{ slugs}} \left[25t - \tfrac{1}{2} \times 0.50t^2 \right]_0^{10}$$
$$v = \frac{1}{5.0 \text{ slugs}} (25 \times 10 - \tfrac{1}{2} \times 0.50 \times 10^2)$$
$$\text{lb-sec}$$
$$v = \frac{1}{5.0 \text{ slugs}} (250 - 25) \text{ lb-sec} = 45 \text{ ft/sec}$$

The mass of a body does not necessarily remain constant during its motion. As a rocket consumes fuel and expels the exhaust gas to achieve the thrust, the mass continually decreases. Other bodies may pick up material as they move. A small particle whose speed approaches the speed of light is found to have an increase in mass because of its speed (Chap. 49).

4-11. Reacting Forces: Newton's Third Law. *For every force that acts on one body there is a second force equal in magnitude but opposite in direction that acts upon another body.* These forces are often referred to as *acting* and *reacting* forces. Here the term *acting force* means the force that one body exerts on a second body, while *reacting force* means the force that the second body exerts on the first. There can be no force unless two bodies are involved. It should be remembered that acting and reacting forces though equal in magnitude and opposite in direction, can never neutralize each other for they always act on *different* objects. In order for two forces to neutralize each other, they must act on the *same* object.

When a baseball bat strikes a ball, it exerts a force on the ball while the two are in contact. During the same time the ball exerts a force of the same magnitude but opposite in direction on the bat. A freely falling body is accelerated by the net force with which the earth attracts the body. The earth in turn is accelerated by the opposite reacting force the body exerts on the earth. Because of the great mass of the earth this acceleration is too small to be observed. In throwing a light object, one has the feeling that he cannot put much effort into the throw, for he cannot exert any more force on the object thrown than that object exerts in reaction against his hand. This reacting force is proportional to the mass of the object $(F \propto m)$ and to the acceleration $(F \propto a)$. The thrower's arm must be accelerated along with the object thrown; hence the larger part of the effort exerted in throwing a light object is expended in "throwing" one's arm.

When one steps from a small boat to the shore, he observes that the boat is pushed away as he steps. The force he exerts on the boat is responsible for its motion; while the force of reaction, exerted by the boat on him, is responsible for his motion toward the shore. The two forces are equal in magnitude and opposite in direction, while the accelerations which they produce (in boat and passenger, respectively) are inversely proportional to the masses of the objects on which they act. Thus a large boat will experience only a small acceleration when one steps from it to shore.

A book lying on a table is attracted by the earth. At the same time it attracts the earth, so that they would be accelerated toward each other if the table were not between them. Hence, each exerts a force on the table, and, in reaction, the table exerts an outward force on each of them keeping them apart. It is interesting to note that the table exerts outward forces on the book and the earth by virtue of being slightly compressed by the pair of inward forces, which they exert on it.

Example: A 0.96-lb ball A and a 1.28-lb ball B are connected by a stretched spring of negligible mass as shown in Fig. 7. When the two balls are released simultaneously, the initial acceleration of B is 5.0 ft/sec² westward. What is the initial acceleration of A?

$$m_A = \frac{W_A}{g} = \frac{0.96 \text{ lb}}{32 \text{ ft/sec}^2} = 0.030 \text{ slug}$$

$$m_B = \frac{W_B}{g} = \frac{1.28 \text{ lb}}{32 \text{ ft/sec}^2} = 0.040 \text{ slug}$$

$$m_A a_A = m_B(-a_B)$$

$$a_A = (-a_B)\frac{m_B}{m_A} = -5.0 \frac{\text{ft}}{\text{sec}^2} \times \frac{0.040 \text{ slug}}{0.030 \text{ slug}}$$

$$= -6.7 \text{ ft/sec}^2$$

The acceleration is eastward.

4-12. Universal Gravitation. In addition to the three laws of motion, Newton formulated a law of great importance in mechanics, the law of *universal gravitation*. *Every particle in the universe attracts every other*

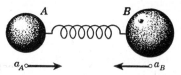

Fig. 7. Acceleration inversely proportional to mass.

particle with a force that is directly proportional to the product of the masses of the two particles and inversely proportional to the square of the distance between them. This relation may be expressed symbolically by the equation

$$F = \frac{Gm_1m_2}{s^2} \tag{6}$$

where F is the force of attraction, m_1 and m_2 are the respective masses of the two particles, s is the distance between them, and G is a constant called the *gravitational constant*. The value of G depends upon the system of units used in Eq. (6). If force is expressed in dynes, mass in grams, and distance in centimeters, G has the value 6.670×10^{-8} cm³/gm-sec².

Newton checked his law of gravitation by calculation upon the orbit of the moon. With the approximate data at his disposal he still found reasonable agreement between his computations and observations. Careful measurement of the force of attraction between small bodies has established the validity of the law of universal gravitation and led to the determination of the value of G given above.

Example: Two lead balls whose masses are 5200 gm and 250 gm are placed with their centers 50.0 cm apart. With what force do they attract each other?

From Eq. (6)

$$F = G\frac{m_1m_2}{s^2}$$

$$F = \left(\frac{6.670 \times 10^{-8} \text{ cm}^3}{\text{gm-sec}^2}\right)\left(\frac{5200 \text{ gm} \times 250 \text{ gm}}{(50.0 \text{ cm})^2}\right)$$

$$= 3.47 \times 10^{-5} \text{ dyne}$$

SUMMARY

The relation between forces and the motions produced by them was described by Newton in three laws of motion. They are:

1. A body at rest remains at rest and a body in motion continues to move at constant speed in a straight line unless acted upon by an external, unbalanced force.

2. An unbalanced force acting on a body produces an acceleration in the direction of the net force, an acceleration that is directly proportional to the force and inversely proportional to the mass of the body.

3. For every force that acts on one body there is a force equal in magnitude but opposite in direction that reacts upon a second body.

The relation expressed in Newton's second law may be written in equation form as

$$F = kma$$

where F, m, and a can be in any units, provided that the proper value is assigned to k, or

$$F = ma$$

where one can use *only* those consistent sets of units in which one of the units is defined in such a manner as to make $k = 1$.

The *dyne* is defined as the force that will impart to a 1-gm mass an acceleration of 1 cm/sec².

A *newton* is defined as the force that will impart to a 1-kg mass an acceleration of 1 m/sec².

The *slug* is the mass to which a force of 1 lb will give an acceleration of 1 ft/sec².

If either the force or the mass varies during a motion, Newton's second law is still valid for the instantaneous acceleration in the motion.

The law of *universal gravitation* expresses the fact that every particle attracts every other particle with a force directly proportional to the product of their masses and inversely proportional to the square of the distance between them. In equation form

$$F = G\,\frac{m_1 m_2}{s^2}$$

QUESTIONS   1. Why does a loaded coal truck start more slowly than an empty truck?

2. Consider an object on a horizontal frictionless plane, acted upon by a single horizontal force.

(a) If the mass is 1 gm and the force 1 dyne, the acceleration is _____.

(b) If the mass is 1 gm and the force 5 dynes, the acceleration is _____.

(c) If the mass is 5 gm and the force 10 dynes, the acceleration is _____.

(d) If the weight is 32 lb and the force 1 lb, the acceleration is _____.

(e) If the weight is 320 lb and the force 20 lb, the acceleration is _____.

(f) If the weight is 500 lb and the force 10 lb, the acceleration is _____.

(g) If the mass is 10.0 gm and the force 9800 dynes, the acceleration is _____.

(h) If the mass is 6.0 kg and the force is 2.0 newtons, the acceleration is _____.

(i) If the mass is 1.0 kg and the force is 9.8 newtons, the acceleration is _____.

3. An automobile, starting from rest, increases its speed uniformly until it reaches a speed of 40 mi/hr. After a time the machine is brought to rest again. Is the force required to stop the car necessarily equal to the force that brought it up to the stated speed? Explain.

4. Which is greater, the attraction of the earth for a pound of lead, or the attraction of the pound of lead for the earth?

5. Why is one less likely to be injured when jumping from an elevation if he lands in sand rather than upon a stone pavement?

6. If an elevator supported by a cable is stopped quickly, it may oscillate up and down. Explain.

7. Does the seat on a roller coaster always support exactly the weight of the passenger? Explain.

8. Suppose an aviator is in his plane, the plane being at rest on the ground. Point out how one or more of Newton's laws of motion are illustrated by (or can be applied to) the man.

9. Apply Newton's laws of motion to an aviator in steady flight. Apply them when he is falling from his plane both before and after his parachute opens.

10. What experiences are responsible for our first ideas about the nature of force? Are they adequate as a means of defining force?

11. State some commonly recognized effects of force on material bodies, giving an example of each.

12. By what different effects may the magnitudes of forces be compared? Of these, which is the only one suitable in defining an absolute standard of force? Why?

13. If acting and reacting forces are "equal and opposite," why can they never balance or cancel?

14. In view of Newton's third law of motion, what is an unbalanced force?

15. What is the fallacy in the following argument? "A horse pulls on a cart. By Newton's third law, the cart pulls back on the horse with a force equal to that exerted by the horse on the cart. Hence the sum of the forces is zero, from which it follows that it is not possible for the horse to accelerate the cart."

16. As a body is taken from the equator toward the north pole, what will be the effect on its weight? on its mass?

17. The distance of sea level from the center of the earth is 3963.34 mi at the equator and decreases to 3949.99 mi at the poles. Suggest an experiment by which this information about the shape of the earth might be obtained. In view of it, what is meant by *vertical?* by *horizontal?* What basis is there for the statement sometimes made that the Mississippi River flows uphill?

18. How would the weight of a body en route from the earth to the moon vary? How would its weight vary while being carried to the center of the earth? Would its mass change?

PROBLEMS

1. (*a*) Express a force of 25 newtons in pounds. (*b*) Express a force of 5.0×10^6 dynes in pounds.

2. What unbalanced force is needed to give a mass of 10 kg an acceleration of 5.0 m/sec²? *Ans.* 50 newtons

3. With what steady force must a 3.0-ton boat be pulled toward the dock in order to move the boat through the water 10 ft in 5.0 sec, starting from rest, if friction is neglected?

4. A rifle bullet (mass 10 gm) acquires a speed of 750 m/sec in a rifle barrel 50 cm long. What is the average force exerted on the bullet?

Ans. 56×10^7 dynes

5. In towing a 5.00-ton trailer along a level road, what horizontal force must be exerted on it to produce an acceleration of 4.00 ft/sec², if friction exerts a backward drag of 450 lb on the trailer?

6. A 3200-lb automobile is being towed along a level road by a rope that will withstand a pull of 1000 lb. If the towrope is parallel to the roadbed, what is the greatest acceleration that can be imparted to the car, assuming that it requires a force of 200 lb to overcome frictional resistance? *Ans.* 8.0 ft/sec²

7. Two forces of 30.0 and 40.0 lb act on an object of 100-lb weight at angles of 30° and 75°, respectively. What is the horizontal component of the acceleration which they impart to the body?

8. A force of 4900 dynes acts on a 20-gm mass for 8.0 sec. (*a*) What acceleration is caused? (*b*) How far does the mass move from rest in the 8.0 sec? (*c*) How fast is it going at the end of 8.0 sec? *Ans.* $2\overline{4}0$ cm/sec²; $7\overline{7}00$ cm; $2\overline{0}00$ cm/sec

9. A 160-lb object is subjected to a constant force of 50 lb. How much time will be required for it to acquire a speed of 80 ft/sec?

10. What force will impart a speed of 40 ft/sec to a 640-lb body in 5.0 sec?
Ans. $1\overline{6}0$ lb

11. A 10.0-lb hammer moving with a speed of 18.0 ft/sec strikes a nail and drives it 0.50 in. into a block of wood. Assume that the hammer is decelerated at a constant rate. Compute (*a*) the time required for the hammer to stop after it comes into contact with the nail and (*b*) the force exerted on the nail.

12. A train traveling at 50 mi/hr is brought uniformly to a stop in 22.8 sec. During this deceleration, (*a*) at what angle with the vertical does a plumb bob hang in one of the coaches, and (*b*) if the tender is half full of water, and is 11 times as long as it is deep, will water spill over, and if so, from which end?
Ans. 5°43′; yes, forward end

13. The normal motorist has a reaction time of 0.7 sec. Assume that, by means of the brakes, a retarding force equal to two-thirds of the weight of the car can be applied to the car. If a 2800-lb car is traveling at 45 mi/hr, find (*a*) the acceleration when the brakes are applied and (*b*) the distance in which the car can be stopped. (*c*) How does this distance compare with the stopping distance for a heavier car?

14. A 1.50-ton automobile crashed into a wall at a speed of 10.0 mi/hr. The car moved 5.00 in. before being brought to rest. What was the average force exerted on the wall by the car? *Ans.* $24,\overline{3}00$ lb

15. A 160-lb object is subjected to a constant force of 30 lb. How much time will be required for it to acquire a speed of 48 ft/sec?

16. A 100-ton car is moving at a speed of 40 mi/hr. A force of 1.0 ton opposes the motion. Find the time required to bring the car to rest and the distance it will travel in stopping. *Ans.* 3.0 min; 1.0 mi

17. On an ordinary road surface the frictional force on a 3000-lb car when the brakes are applied may be as high as 1500 lb. What time will be required to stop the car with this force from a speed of 30 mi/hr (44 ft/sec)?

18. A sled, which with its load weighs 160 lb, is started into motion by a boy who exerts a constant horizontal force of 28.2 lb for a period of 3.00 sec. The friction on the horizontal surface causes a retarding force of 3.2 lb. Find the distance the sled travels after the boy stops pushing. *Ans.* $1\overline{8}0$ ft

19. What pull must a locomotive exert on a 5000-ton train in order to attain a speed of 20 mi/hr in 6.0 min? Assume uniform acceleration and consider 25 per cent of the force applied is used in overcoming friction.

20. A 1000-gm block on a smooth table is connected to a 500-gm piece of lead by a light cord that passes over a small pulley at the end of the table. (*a*) What is the acceleration of the system? (*b*) What is the tension in the cord?
Ans. 3.27 m/sec²; 3.27 newtons

21. What force, applied parallel to the plane, is necessary to move a 100-gm object up a frictionless plane with a uniform acceleration of 20 cm/sec², if the plane makes an angle of 30° with the horizontal?

22. What force, applied parallel to the plane, is necessary so that a 100-lb object will slide down the frictionless plane with an acceleration of 8.0 ft/sec², if the plane makes an angle of 30° with the horizontal? *Ans.* 25 lb, up the plane

23. Two identical blocks of mass m are connected by a string of length $3h$ on a double plane with the dimensions shown in Fig. 8. How fast will block A be moving when block B hits the ground if B starts from the top of the incline? The surfaces are frictionless.

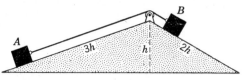

FIG. 8.

24. A 100-lb box slides down a frictionless skid inclined at an angle of 60° with the horizontal. Find (*a*) the accelerating force, (*b*) the time required to travel the first 20 ft and (*c*) the time required to travel the next 20 ft.

Ans. 87 lb; 1.2 sec; 0.49 sec

25. A 2.00-kg body rests on a plane which makes an angle of 20° with the horizontal. An object of mass 500 gm is attached to the body by a cord which passes over a pulley at the upper end of the plane. Find the acceleration of the system. Neglect friction.

26. In Fig. 9, the masses of C and D are 200 gm and 300 gm, respectively. Find the accelerations of masses C and D, the tension in the cord, and the force on the lower hook.   *Ans.* 4.20, 1.40 m/sec²; 1.12, 3.35 newtons

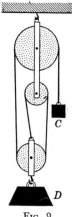

FIG. 9.

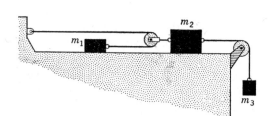

FIG. 10.

27. In the arrangement shown in Fig. 10, $m_1 = 100$ gm, $m_2 = 400$ gm, and $m_3 = 200$ gm, the pulleys are massless and the surfaces are frictionless. What is the acceleration of the block of mass m_2?

28. A 200-lb man stands in an elevator. What force does the floor exert on him when the elevator is (*a*) stationary, (*b*) accelerating upward 16.0 ft/sec², (*c*) moving upward at constant speed, and (*d*) moving upward but decelerating at 12.0 ft/sec²?   *Ans.* 200 lb; 300 lb; 200 lb; 125 lb

29. A spring balance fastened to the roof of a moving elevator car indicates 75 lb as the weight of a 100-lb body. (*a*) What is the acceleration of the elevator? (Give direction as well as magnitude.) (*b*) Can one determine from these data the direction in which the elevator is moving?

30. An elevator, which with its load weighs 8.0 tons, is descending with a speed of 900 ft/min. If the load on the cables must not exceed 14 tons, what is the shortest distance in which the elevator can be stopped?   *Ans.* 4.7 ft

31. An Atwood machine (Fig. 6) consists of two 1000-gm masses hung by a string over a massless, frictionless pulley. To determine g, a 20.0-gm rider is added to one side; it is found that at the end of 2.00 sec the system has moved 19.2 cm, starting from rest. Find (*a*) the acceleration of the system and (*b*) g.

32. Two objects of mass 500 gm each are fastened together by a cord and suspended over a frictionless pulley at the top of a double-inclined plane. One side of the plane makes an angle of 45° with the horizontal, and the other side makes an angle of 30°, so that there is an angle of 105° at the top of the plane where the pulley is attached. Calculate the acceleration of the system and the force in the cord.   *Ans.* 102 cm/sec²; 2.96 × 10⁵ dynes

33. Two blocks are suspended by a string which passes over a light pulley. The blocks weigh 94.0 and 98.0 lb, and are initially each 12.0 ft above the floor. (*a*) What time is required for one of the blocks to reach the floor? (*b*) What is the force in the string?

34. A spring and four masses m_1, m_2, m_3, and m_4 are used in an experiment similar to that represented by Fig. 7. With m_1 at A and the spring extended 10 cm, accelerations of 15 cm/sec², 3.5 cm/sec², and 40 cm/sec² are imparted, respectively, to m_2, m_3, and m_4 placed in turn at B, while m_1 has an acceleration of 20 cm/sec². Compute the masses m_2, m_3, and m_4 in terms of m_1 as the standard mass.   *Ans.* $1.33m_1$; $5.71m_1$; $0.50m_1$

35. Find the acceleration of the masses and the tensions in the rope for the arrangement shown in Fig. 11. The rope ends are tied at point P.

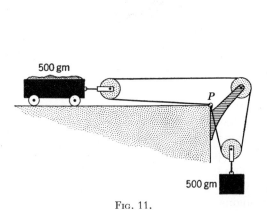

500 gm

P

500 gm

Fɪɢ. 11.

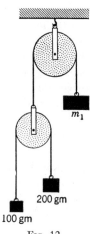

m_1

200 gm

100 gm

Fɪɢ. 12.

36. In the system shown in Fig. 12, (*a*) what should be the value of m_1 such that the 100-gm mass does not move? (*b*) If m_1 has this value, what is its acceleration?   *Ans.* 160 gm; ¼ g

37. Find the mass of the earth from the following experimental data: $g =$ 9.80 m/sec², and $G = 6.67 \times 10^{-11}$ newton-m²/kg. The radius of the earth is 6.37×10^6 m.

38. What is the acceleration due to gravity on the surface of the moon if its mass is 0.0127 the mass of the earth and its radius 0.25 that of the earth?   *Ans.* 6.5 ft/sec²

5. *Projectile Motion*

The science of the motion of projectiles is called *ballistics*. In the study of ballistics we consider the paths followed by the flying objects, the forces required to start them on their flight, and the forces set up when they strike their targets. In designing guns, either large or small, these factors must be considered. The problem of aiming a small rifle is simple and can be solved by adjustment of the sights, but the task of directing the fire of long-range artillery involves extensive calculation considering many factors. We shall consider some of the simpler aspects of the motion of projectiles.

5-1. Projectile Motion. The simplest type of motion of a projectile is that in which it is given an initial velocity and then allowed to move under the influence of gravity alone. The motion is one of constant acceleration but differs from that discussed in Chap. 3 in that the direction of the acceleration is seldom the same as the direction of the initial velocity. Hence the velocity is continually changing in both magnitude and direction.

It is convenient in studying such projectile motion to consider it as made up of two components, one vertical and the other horizontal. Since the gravitational force is vertically downward, it produces an acceleration only in that direction, leaving the horizontal component of the velocity unchanged if air resistance is neglected. The complex motion of the projectile reduces to two simple motions, constant horizontal velocity and uniformly accelerated vertical motion.

Suppose we ask ourselves how a stone will move if it is thrown horizontally at a speed of

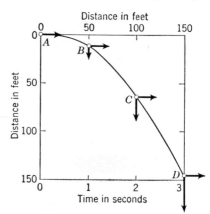

Fig. 1. Path of a stone thrown horizontally with a speed of 50 ft/sec.

50 ft/sec. Neglecting air resistance, the stone will travel with a constant horizontal speed of 50 ft/sec until it strikes something. At the same time it will execute the uniformly accelerated motion of an object falling freely from rest; that is, beginning with a vertical speed of zero, it will acquire downward speed at the rate of 32 ft/sec in each second. It will fall 16 ft during the first second, 48 ft during the next, 80 ft during the third, and so on, just as if it had no horizontal motion. Its

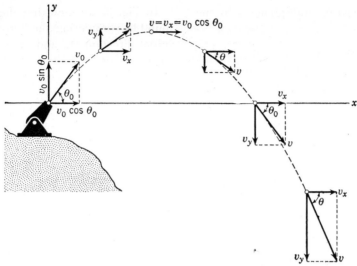

Fig. 2. Components of velocity in projectile motion.

progress during the first three seconds is illustrated in Fig. 1. At A the stone has no vertical speed; at B (after 1 sec) its vertical speed is 32 ft/sec; at C, 64 ft/sec; and at D, 96 ft/sec. The curved line $ABCD$ in Fig. 1 is the path that the stone follows, and the arrows at A, B, C, and D represent the velocities at those places. Note that the horizontal arrows are all the same length, indicating the constant horizontal speed, while the vertical arrows increase in length to indicate the increasing vertical speed. The vertical arrow at C is twice as long as that at B while that at D is three times as long. The resultant velocity of the projectile is at each point tangent to the curve $ABCD$. It is constantly changing both in magnitude and direction.

No matter what may be the initial direction of motion of the projectile, its motion can be resolved into horizontal and vertical parts that are independent of each other. Suppose a projectile is fired with a speed and direction such as represented by vector v_0 in Fig. 2. Consider the components of velocity v_0 along the x (horizontal) and y (vertical) axes. An object that had the *simultaneous* horizontal and vertical speeds represented by $v_0 \cos \theta_0$ and $v_0 \sin \theta_0$ would follow exactly the same path, in the initial direction of v_0. In discussing the

motion of the projectile, one may use either the whole speed in the direction of v, or the horizontal and vertical parts may be used. The latter viewpoint simplifies the problem.

The horizontal acceleration a_x is zero, if air resistance be negligible. Hence the horizontal component of the velocity v_x remains constant, and at any time t

$$v_x = v_0 \cos \theta_0 \qquad (1)$$

The vertical acceleration of the projectile is in the negative (downward) direction along the y axis; thus the vertical velocity at any time t is

$$v_y = v_0 \sin \theta_0 - gt \qquad (2)$$

The magnitude of the velocity at any instant is $v = \sqrt{v_x{}^2 + v_y{}^2}$ and the angle this resultant velocity makes with the horizontal can be found from

$$\tan \theta = \frac{v_y}{v_x} \qquad (3)$$

In projectile motion one frequently wishes to determine the height to which the projectile rises, the time of flight, and the horizontal range. The first two may be obtained by the use of Eqs. (5) and (2) of Chap. 3 while the range is determined by multiplying v_x by the time of flight.

Example: A projectile is thrown with a speed of 100 ft/sec in a direction 30° above the horizontal. Find the height to which it rises, the time of flight, and the horizontal range.

$$v_y = v \sin \theta = (100 \text{ ft/sec})(\sin 30°) = 50.0 \text{ ft/sec}$$
$$v_x = v \cos \theta = (100 \text{ ft/sec})(\cos 30°) = 86.6 \text{ ft/sec}$$

Using Eq. (5), Chap. 3, as applied to the vertical motion

$$v_2{}^2 - v_1{}^2 = 2as$$
$$0 - (50 \text{ ft/sec})^2 = 2 (-32 \text{ ft/sec}^2)s$$
$$s = \frac{2500 \text{ ft}^2/\text{sec}^2}{64 \text{ ft/sec}^2} = 39 \text{ ft}$$

The time required to reach the highest point is, from Eq. (2), Chap. 3,

$$v_2 - v_1 = at$$
$$0 - 50 \text{ ft/sec} = (-32 \text{ ft/sec}^2)t$$
$$t = \frac{50 \text{ ft/sec}}{32 \text{ ft/sec}^2} = 1.6 \text{ sec}$$

Assuming that the surface above which the projectile moves is horizontal, an equal time will be required for the projectile to return to the surface. Hence the time t' elapsed before the projectile strikes the surface is

$$t' = 2t = 2 \times 1.6 \text{ sec} = 3.2 \text{ sec}$$

During all this time the projectile travels horizontally with a uniform speed of 86.6 ft/sec. The horizontal range R is therefore

$$R = v_x t' = (86.6 \text{ ft/sec})(3.2 \text{ sec}) = 2\overline{8}0 \text{ ft}$$

If the surface above which the projectile moves is not level, the time of flight will be increased or decreased depending upon whether the striking point is below or above the firing point. The range is correspondingly increased or decreased.

The motion of any projectile, neglecting air resistance may be treated in this same manner no matter what may be the initial speed and angle of projection. The initial velocity is resolved into vertical and horizontal components and the two are considered separately.

In Fig. 3, we note that the path may be found by considering a uniform motion in the initial direction OC and finding the distance the projectile has fallen from this path at each instant. In 1 sec under the action of gravity, the projectile falls 16 ft; hence at the end of 1 sec it is 16 ft below A; in 2 sec it falls 64 ft, and hence is 64 ft below B, and so on.

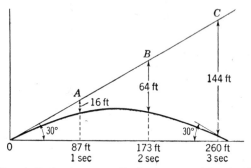

FIG. 3. Path of a projectile fired at an angle of 30° above the horizontal with an initial speed of 100 ft/sec. Air resistance is neglected. The projectile strikes with a speed equal to the initial speed and at an angle of 30° above the horizontal.

5-2. Range and Angle of Elevation. The range of a projectile depends upon the angle at which it is fired as well as upon the initial speed. If the angle is small, the horizontal velocity is relatively high but the time of flight is so short that the range is small. On the other hand if the angle of projection is very large, the time of flight is long but the horizontal velocity is small. In the absence of air resistance the maximum horizontal range is attained when the angle of elevation is 45°.

In aiming a gun, allowance must always be made for the distance that the projectile falls while it is in flight. If a gun were aimed by sighting through the barrel, the bullet would always hit below the point at which it was directed. The allowance is made by means of the sights. At short ranges the amount of fall is slight for a high-speed bullet, and no change in adjustment is ordinarily made. Long-range rifles have adjustable sights so constructed that the marksman can make allowance for the greater fall in the longer distances by so changing the rear sight that the muzzle of the gun is properly elevated.

5-3. Air Resistance. So far in the discussion of the motion of projectiles the resistance of the air has been neglected. However, for high-speed projectiles this resistance is no small factor. It introduces a force which opposes the motion, a force which varies both in

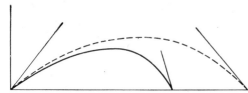

FIG. 4. Path of a projectile. The dotted curve represents the path that would be followed if there were no air resistance, while the solid line is an actual path. The maximum height, range, and striking speed are decreased, while the striking angle is increased.

magnitude and in direction and hence produces variable acceleration in addition to the constant acceleration we have assumed previously. This resistance reduces the height of flight, the range of the projectile, and the speed of the projectile when it strikes its target. An example of such influence is shown in Fig. 4. The dotted curve is the path that the projectile would follow if there were no air resistance, while the solid line shows an actual path.

Complete analysis of the motion of a projectile subject to air resistance is beyond the scope of this discussion, but some of the factors to be considered may be mentioned. The retarding force depends upon the speed of the projectile. For low speeds, air resistance is quite small, but as the speed becomes greater the resistance increases very rapidly. The air resistance also depends upon the height to which the projectile rises, for at high elevations where the air is less dense the resistance is small. Long-range guns shoot the projectile at such an angle that a considerable part of the path is in the high atmosphere where air resistance is small. Thus the angle at which the gun must be fired to attain maximum

range may be considerably greater than the 45° necessary when air resistance is negligible. The optimum angle depends upon the size, shape, and speed of the projectile.

During the First World War a gun was developed by the German Army with a range of 75 mi. The initial speed of the projectile was almost 1 mi/sec at an angle of 50° with the horizontal. The shell reached a maximum height of about 27 mi and more than two-thirds of the path was above 13 mi. At such altitude the air resistance is so small that the path is essentially the same as that for no friction. The striking speed of the shell was less than half the initial speed.

In determining the direction and angle of fire of a large gun many factors must be considered if the firing is to be accurate. Among these factors are wind, barometric pressure, temperature, rotation of the earth, shape of the shell, and the number of times the gun has been fired.

5-4. Self-propelled Projectiles. A true projectile is an object that is given an initial velocity and then allowed to proceed under the action of gravity and air resistance. However, other objects, such as rockets, move in much the same manner as projectiles except that they do not depend upon an initial impulse alone but rather upon the force provided by a fuel carried along with them. As the fuel burns, the expanding gas is forced out at the rear of the projectile. As a result, there is a force of reaction on the projectile itself, which produces an acceleration. The initial speed of the rocket may be quite low since it is continually accelerated along its path. Eventually the speed of the rocket may be greater than that of the free projectile in the corresponding part of its path.

If the fuel of the rocket is such as to supply its own oxygen, there is no dependence upon the air for combustion or propulsion. Such rockets operate effectively at extremely high altitudes where there is very little air. With a suitable fuel supply and proper controls a rocket could navigate beyond the atmosphere.

For such flights, of course, wings and rudders would be entirely useless since there would be no air to exert forces on them.

A spectacular example of the true rocket is the German V-2 weapon of the Second World War. This remarkable missile had a length of 46 ft; a diameter of 5 ft, 5 in.; and a total weight loaded of 27,300 lb. As a propulsive fuel, it used 1220 gal of liquid oxygen and an equal amount of alcohol. The warhead consisted of 1800 lb of TNT. Five thousand such rockets were produced.

In flight these rockets had an average range of 215 mi. The range was controlled by shutting off the fuel supply at a prearranged proper moment in the trajectory. The whole flight required 380 sec with the fuel active only 70 sec. The missile reached an altitude of 70 mi, had a top speed of 3600 mi/hr (1 mi/sec) and a terminal speed of 1800 mi/hr. In recent firings, rockets have reached altitudes of more than 200 mi.

Air friction is a very important factor in such high-speed bodies. The heating produced was sometimes sufficient to cause the missile to explode. For this cause and others 60 per cent of the early rockets and 30 per cent of the later ones exploded in the air. When they reached the ground and exploded, a crater 36 ft across and 10 ft deep was produced.

Jet propulsion differs from rocket propulsion in that air is necessary to supply oxygen for combustion. Such engines therefore can operate only in the atmosphere. The propulsive force, as with the rocket, is the reaction set up when the hot gases are expelled from the engine.

SUMMARY

Ballistics is the science of the motion of projectiles.

A *projectile* is an object which is given an initial velocity and which is then allowed to move under the action of gravity.

In projectile motion the vertical and horizontal motions may be treated separately. If air resistance is neglected, the horizontal motion is uniform while the vertical motion is uniformly accelerated. Under these conditions the path is parabolic.

The *range* of a projectile depends upon its initial speed and the angle of projection. If air resistance is negligible, maximum range is attained with an angle of 45°.

Air resistance decreases the speed, the maximum height, and the range of a projectile.

Self-propelled projectiles depend upon fuel carried within the projectiles rather than upon an initial impulse. Their initial speeds are usually small, but they may reach much higher final speeds than ordinary projectiles.

QUESTIONS   1. Why are the rear sights of a long-range rifle adjustable?

2. Show clearly how the concepts expressed in Newton's laws of motion, apply to the motion of a projectile.

3. How does air friction affect the path of a projectile?

4. Describe the effect that an increase in the angle of elevation has on the range of a projectile for various angles of elevation.

5. If air resistance is neglected, a projectile follows a parabolic path. How is the path of the center of mass affected if the projectile explodes in mid-air?

6. Derive an expression for the speed of a projectile at time t after it is fired with velocity v at an angle of elevation θ.

7. A dart in a blowgun is aimed directly at a monkey in a tree. Just as the dart leaves the gun the monkey falls from the tree. Will a hit be made? Why?

8. A man stands in the center of a flatcar moving with a uniform speed of 40 mi/hr. He throws a baseball into the air with a speed of 40 mi/hr. Compare the path of the ball as viewed by the man with that as viewed by an observer on the ground for the following cases: (*a*) ball thrown vertically upward, (*b*) ball thrown forward horizontally, and (*c*) ball thrown backward horizontally.

9. Justify the statement that the speeds of a projectile at any two points at the same elevation are the same.

10. Discuss the factors that would affect the acceleration of the V-2 rocket as it rises during the 70 sec that the fuel burns.

PROBLEMS   *Neglect air resistance unless otherwise stated.*

1. A rifle is fired in a direction 40° above the horizontal. The speed of the bullet is 1200 ft/sec. What are the horizontal and vertical components of the velocity?

2. A ball is thrown from the roof of a building with a speed of 20 ft/sec at an angle of 15° below the horizontal. Find the vertical and horizontal components of the velocity.   *Ans.* 5.2 ft/sec; 19 ft/sec

3. A projectile is fired with a speed of 600 m/sec at an angle of 20° below the horizontal. Find the vertical and horizontal components of the velocity.

4. A body is projected with a speed of 800 ft/sec in a direction 40° above the horizontal. Find the horizontal and vertical components of the velocity.
          Ans. 612 ft/sec; 514 ft/sec

5. A ball is thrown horizontally from the roof of a tall building with a speed of 19.6 m/sec. Find the position and velocity of the ball after 4.0 sec.

6. A stone is thrown horizontally from the top of a tower with a speed of 50.0 ft/sec. Find the velocity and position at the end of 3.00 sec.
Ans. 108 ft/sec, 62° below horizontal; 144 ft below, 150 ft horizontally from starting point

7. A projectile is fired horizontally from the top of a building 225 ft above horizontal ground with a speed of 550 ft/sec. What is the time of flight? What horizontal distance does it travel?

8. A ball is thrown horizontally from the top of the Washington Monument, 555 ft high. What is the time of fall? If the initial speed is 50 ft/sec, how far from the base does it fall, assuming the ground to be level?   *Ans.* 5.9 sec; 290 ft

9. A stone is thrown horizontally from the top of a high river bank and falls into the water 100 ft below. It strikes the water 150 ft from the bank. Find the time of flight and the initial speed of the stone.

10. A bomb is dropped from an airplane traveling horizontally with a speed of 300 mi/hr. If the airplane is 10,000 ft above the ground, how far from the target must the bomb be released? Neglect air friction.   *Ans.* 2.1 mi

11. A bomb is dropped from an airplane 5000 ft above the ground when the plane is moving horizontally at the rate of 100 mi/hr. Where should the plane be with respect to the target when the bomb is dropped if a hit is to be made?

12. A bomb is dropped from an airplane traveling horizontally with a speed of 210 mi/hr. (*a*) If the airplane is 2000 ft above the ground, what will be the horizontal distance traversed by the bomb (neglecting air friction)? (*b*) Where will the airplane be when the bomb reaches the ground, if its course is not changed?   *Ans.* 3450 ft; directly above bomb

13. A girl standing on a diving board throws a ball with a horizontal velocity of 50 ft/sec to a man in the water. In doing so, she loses her balance, falls off the board, and strikes the water in 2.0 sec. (*a*) How far from the man is the diving board? (*b*) How high is the diving board above the water? (*c*) What is the final velocity of the ball?

14. A batted baseball leaves the bat at an angle of 37.0° above the horizontal and with a velocity of 120 ft/sec. The ball is caught by a spectator in the outfield bleachers at a horizontal distance of 384 ft from home plate. How far above the level at which the ball was struck was it caught?   *Ans.* 32 ft

15. A ball is thrown at an angle of 60.0° above the horizontal with a speed of $320/\sqrt{3}$ ft/sec. (a) How high will it rise? (b) What is the range? (c) Where will the ball be at the end of 6.0 sec?

16. A mortar shell is projected with a speed of 200 ft/sec at an angle of 45° above the horizontal. (a) What is its initial vertical velocity? (b) What is its vertical velocity after 2.0 sec? (c) What is its horizontal velocity after 2.0 sec? (d) When the shell is descending, it strikes a building at a point 64 ft above the level ground. What is the vertical component of the velocity at the instant the shell strikes?   *Ans.* $1\overline{4}0$ ft/sec; 77 ft/sec; $1\overline{4}0$ ft/sec; -124 ft/sec

17. A bomb is projected at an angle of 30° below the horizontal from an airplane 5000 ft above the ground. If the initial speed of the bomb is 60.0 mi/hr, how long will it take to reach the ground and how far will it travel horizontally?

18. A projectile was fired at an angle of 30° above the horizontal from the top of a cliff 600 ft high. The initial speed of the projectile was 2000 ft/sec. How far did the projectile move horizontally before it hit the level ground at the base of the cliff?   *Ans.* $10\overline{9},000$ ft

19. Find the horizontal range of a shell fired from a cannon with a muzzle velocity of $1\overline{2}00$ ft/sec at an angle of 30° above the horizontal.

20. Find the horizontal range of a shell fired from a cannon with a muzzle velocity of $2\overline{4}00$ ft/sec at an angle of 40° above the horizontal   *Ans.* $1\overline{8}0,000$ ft

21. A trench mortar throws a shell with a muzzle speed of 180 ft/sec. When the elevation is 40°, the range is 295 yd. How much is the range diminished by air resistance?

22. A gun throws a shell with a muzzle speed of 300 ft/sec. When the elevation is 45°, the range is 840 yd. How much is the range decreased by air resistance?   *Ans.* 96 yd

23. A boy on the top of a vertical wall throws a ball with a velocity that has a horizontal component of 48 ft/sec and a vertical component of 32 ft/sec, upward. At the instant of release the ball is 48 ft above the level ground. (a) How many seconds elapse between the instant the ball is thrown and the instant it reaches the ground? (b) What is the horizontal range? (c) What is the approximate velocity with which the ball strikes the ground?

24. A ball is thrown from the top of a 60-ft tower. It starts with a speed of 64 ft/sec in a direction 30° above the horizontal. Neglecting air resistance, find (a) the height above the ground to which it will rise, (b) the time of flight, and (c) the distance from the foot of the tower to the point at which it strikes the level surface.   *Ans.* 76 ft; 3.2 sec; $1\overline{8}0$ ft

25. A projectile is fired at an elevation of 45° and reaches the highest point in its path in 22 sec. Neglecting air resistance, calculate (a) the muzzle speed, (b) the maximum height reached, and (c) the distance from gun to target if they are on the same level.

26. The initial speed of a shell is $1\overline{2}00$ ft/sec. At what angle must the gun be fired if the projectile is to strike a target at the same level as the gun and distant 6000 yards? Neglect air resistance.   *Ans.* 12°

27. The initial speed of a shell is $1\overline{5}00$ ft/sec. At what angle must the gun be fired if the projectile is to strike a target at the same level as the gun and distant $12,\overline{0}00$ yd? Neglect air resistance.

28. A ball thrown by a boy in the street is caught 2.00 sec later by another boy on the porch of a house 48.0 ft away and 16.0 ft above the street level. What was the speed of the ball and the angle above the horizontal at which it was thrown?   *Ans.* 46.6 ft/sec; 59.2°

6. *Friction*

Whenever an object moves while in contact with another object, frictional forces oppose the relative motion. These forces are caused by the adhesion of one surface to the other and by the interlocking of the irregularities of the rubbing surfaces. The force of frictional resistance depends upon the properties of the surfaces and upon the force keeping the surfaces in contact.

The effects of friction are often undesirable. Friction increases the work necessary to operate machinery, it causes wear, and it generates heat, which often does additional damage. To reduce this waste of energy, friction is minimized by the use of wheels, bearings, rollers, and lubricants. Automobiles and airplanes are streamlined in order to decrease air friction, which is large at high speeds.

On the other hand, friction is desirable in many cases. Nails and screws hold boards together by means of friction. Power may be transmitted from a motor to a machine by means of a clutch or a friction belt. In walking, driving a car, striking a match, tying our shoes, or sewing fabric together we find friction a useful force. Sand is placed on rails in front of the drive wheels of locomotives, cinders are scattered on icy streets, chains are attached to the wheels of automobiles, and special materials are developed for use in brakes—all for the purpose of increasing friction where it is desirable.

6-1. Sliding Friction. When we slide a box across a floor, we find that we must continue to apply a steady horizontal force to cause the box to slide uniformly over the horizontal surface. We conclude that there is a force, parallel to the surfaces in contact, opposing the motion. This opposing force is called *friction*. The frictional force is the result of the roughness of the two surfaces in contact, which causes interlocking between them, giving rise to a force that resists motion. If the applied force is just equal to the frictional force, the body will continue to move uniformly; if the applied force is greater than the frictional force, the body will be accelerated.

The observations regarding sliding friction are these: (1) the frictional force is parallel to the surfaces sliding over one another; (2) the frictional force is proportional to the force which is normal (perpendicular) to the surfaces and which presses them together; (3) the frictional force is roughly independent of the area of the surface of contact; (4) the frictional force is roughly independent of the speed of sliding, provided that the resulting heat does not alter the condition of the surfaces; and (5) the frictional force depends upon the nature of the substances in contact and the condition of the surface (that is, on polish, roughness, grain, and wetness). Sliding friction is sometimes called *kinetic* friction.

These facts may be illustrated by simple

experiments. By the use of a spring balance to pull a brick uniformly on a table top (Fig. 1), the frictional force may be found to be 1 lb, whereas a force of 2 lb is required to maintain the motion if a second brick is

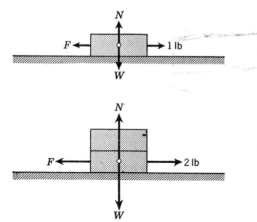

FIG. 1. The frictional force is directly proportional to the normal force pressing the two surfaces together.

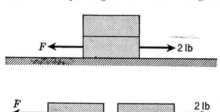

FIG. 2. The frictional force is independent of the area of the surface of contact.

placed on top of the first to increase the normal force. If the second brick is tied behind the first (Fig. 2), the frictional force is still 2 lb showing its independence of area of contact. If the bricks are placed on glass or metal surfaces, one finds that friction depends upon the nature of the surfaces in contact.

6-2. Coefficient of Kinetic Friction. When one body is in uniform motion on another body, the ratio of the frictional force to the perpendicular force pressing the two surfaces together is called the *coefficient of kinetic friction.*

$$\mu_k = \frac{F}{N} \qquad (1)$$

where μ (mu) is the coefficient of friction, F the frictional force, and N the normal or perpendicular force.

Example: A 65-lb horizontal force is sufficient to draw a 1200-lb sled on level well-packed snow. What is the value of the coefficient of friction?

$$\mu_k = \frac{F}{N} = \frac{65 \text{ lb}}{1200 \text{ lb}} = 0.054$$

The frictional force is proportional to the normal force, which must include all normal components of forces pressing the surfaces together. Only in very special cases is the normal force the weight of the body.

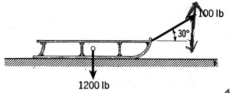

FIG. 3. Forces acting on a sled.

Example: A 1200-lb sled is pulled along a horizontal surface at uniform speed by means of a rope that makes an angle of 30° above the horizontal (Fig. 3). If the tension in the rope is 100 lb, what is the coefficient of friction?

The frictional force (parallel to the surface) is

$$F = 100 \text{ lb} \times \cos 30° = 100 \text{ lb} \times 0.866 = 86.6 \text{ lb}$$

The normal force N is the weight of the sled downward minus the vertical component of the tension upward.

$$N = 1200 \text{ lb} - 100 \text{ lb} \times \sin 30° = 1150 \text{ lb}$$

$$\mu_k = \frac{F}{N} = \frac{86.6 \text{ lb}}{1150 \text{ lb}} = 0.0753$$

Example: A 50-kg box is placed on an inclined plane making an angle of 30° with the horizontal (Fig. 4). If the coefficient of kinetic friction is 0.30, find the resultant force on the box.

The weight of the box is a force acting vertically downward. This force may be separated into components parallel ($W \sin 30°$) and perpendicular ($W \cos 30°$) to the plane. A frictional force (parallel to the plane) acts up the plane.

$$N = W \cos 30° = 50 \text{ kg} \times 9.8 \text{ m/sec}^2 \times 0.87 = 430 \text{ newtons}$$

The frictional force is given by

$$F = \mu_k N = 0.30 \times 430 \text{ newtons} = 130 \text{ newtons}$$

The resultant force is

$$R = W \sin 30° - F$$
$$= 50 \text{ kg} \times 9.8 \text{ m/sec}^2 \times 0.50 - 130 \text{ newtons}$$
$$= 120 \text{ newtons down the plane}$$

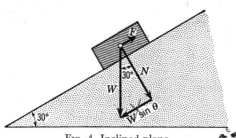

FIG. 4. Inclined plane.

When two surfaces are lubricated, friction is reduced by the substitution of the internal friction of the lubricant for the friction between the original surfaces. The ratio F/N is then not a simple constant but depends upon the properties of the lubricant and the area and relative speed of the moving surfaces.

6-3. Static Friction. When a body at rest on a horizontal surface is pushed gently sideward, it does not move because there is a frictional force just equal to the sideward push. If the push is increased, the frictional force increases until a *limiting friction* is reached. If the side push exceeds the limiting friction, the body is accelerated. When there is no relative motion between the two surfaces in contact, the friction is called *static friction*, and the frictional force can have any value from zero up to the limiting value.

For limiting friction (but not for all static friction) the same laws apply as for sliding friction except, of course, that referring to the speed of sliding. The *coefficient of static (limiting) friction* is the ratio of the limiting frictional force to the normal force.

$$\mu_s = \frac{F_{max}}{N} \qquad (2)$$

For any two surfaces the coefficient of static

friction μ_s is somewhat greater than the coefficient of sliding or kinetic friction μ_k.

TABLE 1. COEFFICIENTS OF FRICTION

Material	μ_s	μ_k
Steel on steel.....................	0.15	0.09
Metal on metal, lubricated.........	0.03	0.03
Leather on oak....................	0.4	0.3
Rubber tire on dry concrete road....	1.0	0.7
Rubber tire on wet concrete road ...	0.7	0.5

6-4. Limiting Angle; Angle of Repose. The coefficient of static friction may be found without measurement of forces by the following simple and convenient method. Let the plane AC (Fig. 5) be tilted upward (gradually) until the body B just begins to slide down

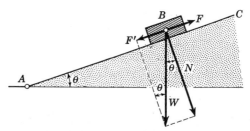

FIG. 5. Limiting angle for friction.

the incline. Consider the weight W of the body to be resolved into components N and F', respectively perpendicular and parallel to the incline. The component N presses the two surfaces together, the component F' is directed down the plane, and the frictional force F is directed up the plane. Just before sliding occurs, there is no acceleration, and F' is balanced by the friction F. From the figure

$$\frac{F'}{N} = \frac{F}{N} = \tan \theta$$

And hence the coefficient of friction is given by

$$\mu_s = \tan \theta$$

6-5. Rolling Friction. Rolling friction is the resistance to motion caused chiefly by the deformation produced where a wheel or cylinder pushes against the surface on which it rolls. The deformation of an automobile tire in contact with the pavement is readily visible. Even in the case of a steel wheel rolling on a steel rail there is some deformation of the two surfaces. A force F (Fig. 6) is required to roll

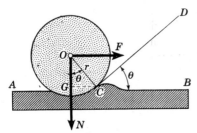

Fig. 6. Rolling friction.

the wheel on the horizontal rail because the surfaces are continually distorted as illustrated by the hill along line CD. The deformations of the two surfaces produce internal friction in the two bodies. The force of rolling friction varies inversely as the radius of the roller, and it is less the more rigid the surfaces.

Rolling friction is ordinarily much smaller than sliding friction. Sliding friction on the axle of a wheel is replaced by rolling friction through the use of roller or ball bearings.

6-6. Fluid Friction. The friction encountered by solid objects in passing through fluids and the frictional forces set up within liquids and gases in motion are examples of fluid friction. The laws of fluid friction differ greatly from those of sliding and rolling friction. The amount of frictional resistance encountered by an object moving through a fluid depends on the size, shape, and speed of the moving object, as well as on the nature of the fluid itself.

The frictional resistance encountered by a man falling through the air increases with his speed until he reaches a terminal speed, about 120 mi/hr, at which the retarding force of friction equals his weight. When he opens his parachute, the greater surface it presents increases the retarding force of friction and reduces the terminal speed to, say, 25 ft/sec. In such descents the aviator reaches the

ground with the same speed whether he jumps from an altitude of 500 ft or from 5 mi, owing to the fact that fluid friction increases with speed.

6-7. Viscosity. Viscosity is that property of a fluid, its internal friction, which causes it

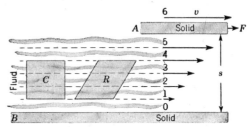

Fig. 7. Fluid friction.

to resist flow. Consider a layer of liquid in a shallow pan on the surface of which a flat plate A is placed (Fig. 7). A force F is required to maintain the plate at a constant speed v with respect to the other surface B.

On the surface of each solid, A and B, there will be a layer of liquid that adheres to the solid and has zero speed with respect to it. The next layer of liquid moves slowly over the first, the third layer moves slowly over the second, and so on. This distribution of speeds results in a continual deformation of the liquid. The portion of the liquid C, which is cubical in shape at one instant, is rhomboidal a moment later at R.

If the thickness s of the fluid between the surfaces is increased, application of the same force produces a greater speed: $v \propto s$. If the area A of the plate is increased, there is a corresponding decrease in speed: $v \propto 1/A$. An increase in the force produces a proportional increase in speed: $v \propto F$. Thus the speed is proportional to F, to s, and also to $1/A$. Hence we can write the equation

$$v = \frac{Fs}{\eta A}$$

or $$\eta = \frac{Fs}{Av} \tag{3}$$

where the factor η (eta) depends only on the

fluid and its temperature. This equation defines the *coefficient of viscosity* η of the liquid.

The absolute cgs unit of the coefficient of viscosity is called the *poise*.

From Eq. (3),

$$\eta = \frac{Fs}{Av}$$

$$1 \text{ poise} = \frac{1 \text{ dyne} \times 1 \text{ cm}}{1 \text{ cm}^2 \times 1 \text{ cm/sec}}$$

$$= 1 \text{ dyne-sec/cm}^2$$

A coefficient of viscosity of 1 poise is one that requires a tangential force of 1 dyne for each square centimeter of surface to maintain a relative velocity of 1 cm/sec between two planes separated by a layer of the fluid 1 cm thick.

The centipoise ($\frac{1}{100}$ poise) is the unit of viscosity commonly used.

In setting up this definition of coefficient of viscosity, we have chosen a case in which the application of forces to a fluid produces differences of speed between adjacent thin layers (laminae) within the fluid as indicated in Fig. 7. It is this laminar flow which is characterized by the proportionality between force and speed, which is expressed by Eq. (3). In the case of *turbulent* flow the lines of flow are complex and changing and Eq. (3) is not applicable.

The viscosity of liquids decreases with increase in temperature. A liquid that flows as slowly as the proverbial molasses in January at low temperature may pour freely at higher temperature. Lubricating oil may fail to form a protective film at low temperatures. Hence, when starting a car on a cold day, it is wise to allow the engine to idle for a time until the oil is warmed. The viscosities of gases, unlike those of liquids, increase with increase in temperature.

6-8. Nature of Viscosity. The internal friction of liquids is attributed to the cohesive forces between molecules. Our knowledge of the details of this mechanism is far from complete, but the picture of liquid viscosity just described does explain qualitatively the experimentally observed facts. On this basis, for example, one would expect a decrease in the viscosity of a liquid with increase in temperature. This is observed experimentally.

In the case of gases, whose molecules have relatively large separations, cohesive forces are small and some other mechanism must be sought for internal friction. One supposes that in the laminar flow of a gas there is a continual migration of molecules from one layer to another. Molecules diffuse from a fast-moving layer to a slower moving layer (5 to 4, Fig. 7), and from the slower moving layer to the faster. Thus each layer exerts a drag on the other. The amount of this drag depends on the mass of the molecules and their speeds and hence on the product *mv*. This description of gas viscosity accounts for the fact that an increase in temperature, which increases molecular speeds, results in an increase in the viscosity of a gas.

SUMMARY

Frictional force F is proportional to the normal force N pressing the two surfaces together, and is directed parallel to these surfaces

$$F = \mu N$$

The coefficient of friction μ is defined as the ratio of the frictional force to the normal force.

$$\mu_k = \frac{F}{N} \quad \text{and} \quad \mu_s = \frac{F_{max}}{N}$$

The coefficient of static friction μ_s may be calculated from the limiting angle of repose, θ.

Sliding friction is less than static friction, and rolling friction is less than sliding friction.

Fluid friction is measured in terms of the coefficient of viscosity η which is defined as the ratio of the tangential force per unit area of surface F/A to the velocity gradient v/s between two planes of fluid in laminar flow

$$\eta = \frac{Fs}{Av}$$

QUESTIONS   1. Name several types of mechanism in which friction is essential for proper operation.

2. What becomes of the energy expended against friction?

3. Why does a locomotive engineer shut off the power when the drive wheels begin to slip?

4. Why should one take short steps rather than long ones when walking on ice?

5. Friction being independent of area, why are broad belts used in driving heavy machinery, and why are automobile brake shoes of large area desirable?

6. Why does a high-pressure tire roll more easily than a low-pressure tire on a smooth pavement?

7. An automobile is moving along a concrete road with the same speed as that of a streetcar alongside of it. Which vehicle can stop in the shorter distance? (The coefficient of friction for rubber on concrete is 0.7, for steel on steel 0.2.)

8. A body rests on a rough horizontal plane. Show that no force, however great, applied toward the plane at an angle with the normal less than the limiting angle for friction, can push the body along the plane.

9. Can a moving automobile be stopped in shorter distance (a) by applying the brakes to "lock" the wheels or (b) by applying a braking force just short of that which causes the tires to slip?

10. A block is placed on an inclined plane. Under what condition will the force of friction be directed up the plane? Down the plane?

PROBLEMS   1. A force of 155 lb is required to start a sled whose weight is 800 lb, while a force of 54 lb is sufficient to keep it moving once it is started. Find the coefficients of starting and sliding friction.

2. A 500-lb piano is moved 20 ft across a floor by a horizontal force of 75 lb. Find the coefficient of friction. What happens to the energy expended?   *Ans.* 0.15

3. A horizontal force of 6.0 lb is applied to a 10-lb block, which rests on a horizontal surface. If the coefficient of friction is 0.40, find the acceleration.

4. A 350-gm block of wood on a horizontal plane is fastened to a cord passing over a frictionless pulley and attached to a 265-gm load. The coefficient of kinetic friction between block and plane is 0.45. (a) Determine the acceleration of the system after it is set in motion. (b) What is the force in the cord?
    Ans. 172 cm/sec^2; 2.14 newtons

5. A 1.0-kg block is placed on a horizontal slide and drawn across it by weights hung from a cord, which passes over a frictionless pulley at the end of the slide. When the block has a load of 9.0 kg on it, it is found that 2500 gm must be hung on the end of the cord to maintain uniform motion. If 7.0 kg are now removed from the block, what weight must be hung from the cord to keep the block in uniform motion?

6. A box weighing 150 lb is moved across a horizontal floor by dragging it by means of a rope attached to the front end. If the rope makes an angle of 30° with the floor and if the coefficient of friction between box and floor is 0.400, find the force exerted by the man pulling the rope.   *Ans.* 56.3 lb

7. A man holds a book weighing 3.0 lb between his hands and keeps it from falling by pressing his hands together horizontally. If the horizontal component of the force exerted by each hand is 7.5 lb, what is the coefficient of friction between book and hands?

8. A man holds a block from falling by pushing it horizontally against a vertical wall. If the block weighs 3.0 newtons and the coefficient of static friction between block and wall is 0.40, what force must he exert?   *Ans.* 7.5 newtons

9. An object having a weight of 10.0 lb is thrown forward on ice with a speed of 64 ft/sec. If the coefficient of friction between it and the ice is 0.10, how far will it go and after how many seconds will it stop?

10. A sled weighing 100 lb reaches the foot of a hill with a speed of 40 ft/sec. The coefficient of kinetic friction between the sled and the horizontal surface of the ice at the foot of the hill is 0.030. How far will the sled travel on the ice?
Ans. 830 ft

11. An object which is given an initial speed of 10 ft/sec on level ice comes to rest in 100 ft. What is the coefficient of kinetic friction between the object and the ice?

12. An automobile traveling at 50 mi/hr on a level road is stopped by sliding the wheels. If the coefficient of kinetic friction between tires and road is 0.75, what is the minimum distance in which the car can be brought to rest? *Ans.* 112 ft

13. A constant horizontal force of 25.0 newtons acting upon a 15.3-kg block causes it to slide 14.5 m along a level surface. If the block starts from rest and acquires a speed of 450 cm/sec, what is the retarding force of friction?

14. A loaded sled weighing 1250 lb is given a speed of 25.0 mi/hr while moving a distance of 140 ft from rest on a horizontal ice surface. If the coefficient of friction is 0.105, what constant force, applied horizontally, would be necessary to produce this motion?
Ans. 320 lb

15. If the coefficient of kinetic friction for the surfaces in contact is 0.20, what force parallel to a 30° incline is required to pull a 100-lb box up the incline with an acceleration of 2.0 ft/sec²?

16. A 200-lb box is drawn up a skid 40 ft long and 20 ft high by a rope parallel to the incline. Find the tension in the rope required to haul the box up with uniform motion if the coefficient of friction for the surfaces in contact is 0.30.
Ans. 152 lb

17. An 80-lb box rests on an inclined plane 10.0 ft long and 6.0 ft high for which the coefficient of sliding friction is 0.30. What force parallel to the plane is required to move the box with uniform speed up the plane? down the plane?

18. The coefficient of friction between a block and the surface on which it slides is 0.18 and the surface is inclined at an angle of 15° with the horizontal. If the block weighs 300 lb, what force is needed to drag it up the incline at uniform speed? What force is required to let it slide down the plane at uniform speed?
Ans. 130 lb; 26 lb

19. A 100-lb box slides down a skid 30 ft long and inclined at 60° to the horizontal. At the bottom of the skid it moves along a horizontal surface until it comes to rest. Assuming a uniform coefficient of kinetic friction of 0.20, calculate (*a*) the accelerating force along the incline, (*b*) the time taken to travel the first 20 ft, and (*c*) the distance moved along the horizontal surface at the foot of the incline.

20. A 100-lb box slides down a skid 20.0 ft long and inclined at an angle of 60° to the horizontal. At the bottom of the skid the box slides along a level surface. If the coefficient of kinetic friction throughout the motion is 0.100, how far will the box travel, and how long a time will elapse after it reaches the level surface before it comes to rest?
Ans. 162 ft; 10.1 sec

21. A body takes just twice as long to slide down a plane inclined at 30° to the horizontal as if the plane were frictionless. What is the coefficient of friction.?

22. A 540-lb safe is to be lowered at constant speed down skids 8.0 ft long from a truck bed 4.0 ft high. If the coefficient of friction is 0.40, (*a*) will the safe have to be held back or pulled down? (*b*) What force parallel to the plane is needed for motion at constant speed?
Ans. 82 lb

23. A sled weighing 45.0 lb slides from rest down an ice incline which is 64 ft high and 320 ft long. The sled reaches the foot of the incline with a speed of 50 ft/sec. What is the coefficient of friction?

24. A sled and rider together weigh 75.0 lb. Starting from rest, the sled coasts down a 30° incline which is 150 ft long. The coefficient of kinetic friction is 0.125. What speed will the sled have at the foot of the incline?   *Ans.* 61 ft/sec

25. A block weighing 25.0 lb slides from rest down a 20° incline, after having been given a slight push to start it. The coefficient of kinetic friction is 0.150. How long will it take for the block to acquire a speed of 75.0 ft/sec?

26. A coin lying on a foot ruler starts to slide when one end of the ruler is raised 4¼ in. above the horizontal. (*a*) What is the limiting angle for friction? (*b*) What is the coefficient of starting friction?   *Ans.* 21°; 0.38

27. A block is placed on an inclined plane and the inclination is gradually changed until the block begins to slide down. At an inclination of 30°, the body starts to slip and it then travels 900 cm down the plane in 6.0 sec. Find the coefficients of *kinetic* and *static* friction.

28. An inclined plane is 130 cm long and its upper end is 50 cm above the level of the lower end. A block *A* of mass 200 gm rests on the plane. A block *B* of mass 60 gm rests on *A*. The coefficient of friction between the blocks is 0.50, and between the lower block and the plane is 0.33. A force *F* upward and parallel to the plane is applied to the lower block. (*a*) What is the acceleration of the lower block when the upper block just starts to slip on it? (*b*) What is the maximum value of *F* before this slipping takes place?

Ans. 75 cm/sec²; 2.0 newton

29. A block *A* of mass 700 gm rests on an inclined plane that makes an angle of 36.9° with the horizontal (Fig. 8). The coefficient of sliding friction between

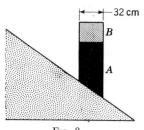

Fɪɢ. 8.

block and plane is 0.40. On the smooth horizontal top of *A* rests squarely a 100-gm block *B*. In the horizontal direction, in a plane parallel to the direction of motion, the blocks are 32 cm wide. How long after the system is released will block *B* fall off block *A*?

30. Two weightless rings can slide along a rough horizontal rod with coefficient of friction μ (Fig. 9). The rings are connected by a light, inextensible string

Fɪɢ. 9.

of length *a*, to the mid-point of which is attached a weight *W*. What is the greatest distance between the two rings consistent with equilibrium of the system?

Ans. $\mu a / \sqrt{1 + \mu^2}$

31. What range of accelerations may be given the cart in Fig. 10 during which m_2 will not slip on the cart?

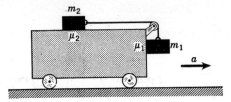

32. When a fluid is forced through a small-bore tube, the flow depends on the viscosity. Poiseuille showed that the volume V of fluid passing in time t through a tube of length L and internal radius r under a difference of pressure Δp between its ends is given by

$$V = \frac{\pi r^4 t}{8 L \eta} \Delta p$$

From this relation, calculate the viscosity of an SAE No. 10 motor oil which flows at the rate of 410 cm³/min through a tube of length 100 cm and internal diameter 0.20 cm under a pressure difference of 50 lb/in.²   *Ans.* 0.20 poise

33. What size bore is needed in a tube 80 cm long so that 1.0 liter of ethyl alcohol (viscosity 0.012 dyne-sec/cm²) will flow through it in 1.0 min under a pressure difference of 0.010 atmosphere (1.013×10^4 dynes/cm²)?

34. A steel shaft 2.50 cm in diameter and 20 cm long revolves 5.0 rev/sec inside a cylinder whose internal diameter is 2.60 cm. The two are separated by a uniform film of lubricating oil whose coefficient of viscosity is 4.0 poises. Calculate (*a*) the rate of shear v/s in the film and (*b*) the shearing stress F/A.

Ans. 790 (cm/sec)/cm; 3100 dynes/cm²

7. *Work and Power*

The rate of production of a man working with hand tools only is small, so small that production by these methods does not meet the demands of modern times. In order to increase the output, machines were devised. In them, the energy possessed by coal, gasoline, falling water, nuclear energy, or electricity is converted into useful work. The machine not only enables the operator to make articles that would not otherwise be possible, but it also enables him to convert energy into useful work at a much greater rate than he could by his own efforts. Each workman in a factory has at his disposal power much greater than he alone could develop.

7-1. Work. The term work, commonly used in connection with widely different activities, is restricted in physics to cases in which there is a force and a displacement along the line of the force. In this technical sense of the word work, a pier does no work in supporting a bridge, and a man does no external work if he merely holds up a suitcase, though he may experience muscular

fatigue. But in lifting the suitcase to a rack he would perform work.

Work is defined as the product of the force and the displacement in the direction of the force. The work dW done by the force F in Fig. 1 when the object is given an infinitesimal displacement ds is

$$dW = (F \cos \theta) \, ds \qquad (1)$$

If the force is constant, the work done in moving the body a distance s is

$$W = \int_0^s F \cos \theta \, ds = (F \cos \theta)s \qquad (2)$$

In the special case where the force is constant and has the same direction as the displacement, $\cos \theta = 1$, and the work done by the force is the product of the force and the displacement.

In the British system, the most common unit of work is the *foot-pound*, the work done by a force of 1 lb exerted for a distance of 1 ft. In the metric system, work is frequently expressed in terms of the *erg* (dyne-centimeter),

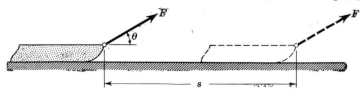

Fig. 1. Work = $(F \cos \theta)s$.

64

which is the work done by a force of 1 dyne exerted for a distance of 1 cm. In the mks system, the *newton-meter* is the work done by a force of 1 newton exerted for a distance of 1 m; 1 newton-meter is 1 joule. A joule is equal to 10^7 ergs. Another unit of work, used especially in electrical measurements, is the *kilowatt-hour* (Chap. 34).

Example: A box is pushed 15 ft along a horizontal floor against a frictional force of 50 lb. How much work is done?

$$W = Fs = (50 \text{ lb})(15 \text{ ft}) = 750 \text{ ft-lb}$$

Example: What work is performed in dragging a sled 50 ft horizontally when the force of 60 lb is transmitted by a rope making an angle of 30° with the ground (Fig. 1)?

The component of the force in the direction of the displacement is $F \cos 30°$.

$$W = (F \cos 30°)s$$
$$W = 60 \text{ lb} \times 0.866 \times 50 \text{ ft} = 2600 \text{ ft-lb}$$

7-2. Energy. The capacity for doing work is called *energy*. Though energy can be neither created nor destroyed, it can exist in many forms and can be transformed from one form to another. The energy possessed by an object by virtue of its motion is called *kinetic energy*, or energy of motion. Energy of position or configuration is called *potential energy*. In any case, the change in the kinetic energy or potential energy is equal to the work done on a body or group of bodies. It follows that the units in which energy is expressed are the same as the units for work.

Much of our everyday work is accomplished by using the energy from some source such as gasoline, coal, or impounded water. We often buy the privilege of having energy transformed on our premises. Thus electricity flowing through the grid of a toaster has its electric energy transformed into heat. Energy is transformed, not destroyed. We pay for the energy that is transformed (not for the electricity, for that flows back to the plant). The amount of energy transformed is the rate of transformation multiplied by the time.

7-3. Simple Machines. A machine is a device for applying energy to do work in a way suitable for a given purpose. No machine can create energy. To do work, it must receive energy from some source, and the maximum work it does cannot exceed the energy it receives.

Machines may receive energy in different forms, such as mechanical energy, heat, electric energy, or chemical energy. We are here considering only machines that employ mechanical energy, and do work against mechanical forces. In the so-called *simple machines*, the energy is supplied by a single *applied force* and the machine does useful work against a single *resisting force*. The frictional force which every machine encounters in action and which causes some waste of energy will be neglected for simplicity in treating some of the simple machines. Most machines, no matter how complex, are combinations of the lever and the inclined plane.

7-4. Actual Mechanical Advantage. The utility of a machine is chiefly that it enables a person to perform some desirable work by changing the amount, the direction, or the point of application of the force. The ratio of the output force F_o exerted by the machine on a load to the input force F_i exerted by the operator on the machine is defined as the *actual mechanical advantage* (AMA) of the machine.

$$\text{AMA} = \frac{F_o}{F_i} \qquad (3)$$

For example, if a machine is available that enables a person to lift 500 lb by applying a force of 25 lb, its actual mechanical advantage is 500 lb/25 lb = 20. For most machines the AMA is greater than unity. A machine that is designed to increase the force has an AMA greater than one; for example, a bench vise, a crowbar, or a block and tackle. A machine designed to increase speed has an AMA less than one; for example, a catapult, or the gear train in a hand grinding wheel, or the chain drive of a bicycle.

7-5. Ideal Mechanical Advantage. In any machine, because of the effects of friction, the useful work done *by* the machine is always less than the work done *on* the machine. The input work done by the applied force F_i is measured by the product of F_i and the distance s_i through which it acts. The output work is measured by the product of the output force F_o and the distance s_o through which it acts. Hence

$$F_o s_o < F_i s_i$$

If we divide each member of the inequality by $F_i s_o$, we obtain

$$\frac{F_o}{F_i} < \frac{s_i}{s_o} \qquad (4)$$

that is, the ratio of the forces F_o/F_i is less than the ratio of the distances s_i/s_o for any machine. If the effects of friction are very small, the value of the output work approaches that of the input work, or the value of F_o/F_i becomes nearly that of s_i/s_o. The *ideal mechanical advantage* (IMA) is defined as the ratio of the distance s_i through which the input force acts to the distance s_o through which the output force acts.

$$IMA = \frac{s_i}{s_o} \qquad (5)$$

Since the forces *move* these distances in equal times, the ratio s_i/s_o is also frequently called the *velocity ratio*. In a "frictionless" machine the inequality of Eq. (4) would become an equality.

Example: A pulley system is used to lift a 1000-lb block of stone a distance of 10 ft by the application of a force of 150 lb for a distance of 80 ft. Find the actual mechanical advantage and the ideal mechanical advantage.

$$AMA = \frac{F_o}{F_i} = \frac{1000 \text{ lb}}{150 \text{ lb}} = 6.67$$

$$IMA = \frac{s_i}{s_o} = \frac{80 \text{ ft}}{10 \text{ ft}} = 8.0$$

7-6. Efficiency. Because of the friction and other losses in all moving machinery, the useful work done by a machine is less than the energy supplied to it. From the principle of conservation of energy,

Energy input = energy output + energy wasted

assuming no energy is stored in the machine. *The efficiency of a machine is defined as the ratio of its output to its input work.* This ratio is always less than 1, and is usually multiplied by 100 per cent and expressed in per cent. A machine has a high efficiency if a large part of the energy supplied to it is expended by the machine on its load and only a small part wasted. The efficiency (eff.) may be as high as 98 per cent for a large electric generator and will be less than 50 per cent for a screw jack.

$$\text{Eff.} = \frac{\text{output work}}{\text{input work}} = \frac{F_o s_o}{F_i s_i} \qquad (6)$$

Also, since
$$\frac{F_o s_o}{F_i s_i} = \frac{F_o/F_i}{s_i/s_o}$$

$$\text{Eff.} = \frac{AMA}{IMA}$$

Note that the work input times the efficiency is equal to the work output

$$\text{Eff.} \times F_i s_i = F_o s_o \qquad (7)$$

Example: What is the efficiency of the pulley system (described in the previous example) which lifts a 1000-lb block of stone a distance of 10 ft by the application of a force of 150 lb for a distance of 80 ft?

$$\text{Eff.} = \frac{F_o s_o}{F_i s_i} = \frac{(1000 \text{ lb})(10 \text{ ft})}{(150 \text{ lb})(80 \text{ ft})} = 0.83 = 83\%$$

Also $\text{Eff.} = \dfrac{AMA}{IMA} = \dfrac{6.67}{8.0} = 0.83 = 83\%$

To calculate the mechanical advantage of a machine, one can imagine it to have carried out a chosen motion. Expressions are written separately for the input distance s_i and the output distance s_o. The ratio of these is the ideal mechanical advantage.

Example: A screw jack (Fig. 2) has a pitch of 0.25 in., a lever arm 18 in. long, and an efficiency of 40 per cent. Find the IMA and the AMA.

In one revolution of the lever arm the screw lifts

the weight W a distance 0.25 in., while the force F acts through $2\pi \times 18$ in.

$$\text{IMA} = \frac{2\pi \times 18 \text{ in.}}{0.25 \text{ in.}} = 4\bar{5}0$$

For 40 per cent efficiency, $0.40 \times F \times 2\pi \times 18$ in. $= W \times 0.25$ in.

$$\text{AMA} = \frac{W}{F} = \frac{0.40 \times 2\pi \times 18 \text{ in.}}{0.25 \text{ in.}} = 1\bar{8}0$$

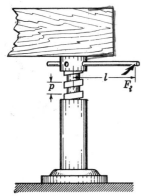

Fig. 2. Screw jack.

7-7. Power. In science and technology the word *power* is restricted to mean the *time rate of doing work*. The average power is the work performed divided by the time required for the performance. In measuring power P, both the *work W* and the *elapsed time t* must be measured

$$\text{Average power} = \frac{\text{work}}{\text{time}} \qquad \bar{P} = \frac{W}{t} \quad (8)$$

The power at any instant is the derivative of the work with respect to time

$$P = \frac{dW}{dt} \qquad (9)$$

or

$$W = \int P \, dt \qquad (10)$$

The same work is done when a 500-lb steel girder is lifted to the top of a 100-ft building in 2 min as is done when it is lifted in 10 min. However, the average power required is five times as great in the first case as in the second, for the power needed to do the work varies inversely as the time. If given sufficient time, a hod carrier can transfer a ton of bricks from the ground to the roof of a skyscraper. A hoisting engine can do this same work more quickly since it develops more power.

7-8. Units of Power. Common British units of power are the *foot-pound per second* and the *horsepower*. A horsepower is defined as 550 ft-lb/sec.

A metric unit of power is the *erg per second*, but since this is an inconveniently small unit, the joule per second, called the *watt*, is commonly used. The watt equals 1 newton-meter/sec and is the mks unit of power. The *kilowatt*, used largely in electrical engineering, is equal to 1000 watts.

TABLE 1. UNITS OF POWER

1 watt = 1 newton-meter per second = 1 joule per second = 10^7 ergs per second
1 horsepower = 550 foot-pounds per second = 33,000 foot-pounds per minute
1 horsepower = 746 watts
1 kilowatt = 1,000 watts = 1.34 horsepower

Example: By the use of a pulley a man raises a load of 120 lb to a height of 40 ft in 65 sec. Find the average horsepower required.

$$\bar{P} = \frac{W}{t} = \frac{Fs}{t} = \frac{(120 \text{ lb})(40 \text{ ft})}{65 \text{ sec}} = 74 \text{ ft-lb/sec}$$

$$\bar{P} = \frac{74 \text{ ft-lb/sec}}{550 \dfrac{\text{ft-lb/sec}}{\text{hp}}} = 0.13 \text{ hp}$$

Since work is the product of power and time, any power unit multiplied by a time unit may be used as a unit of work. Commonly used units of work formed in this manner are the watt-second (joule), the watt-hour, the kilowatt-hour, and the horsepower-hour.

7-9. Measurement of Mechanical Power. The mechanical power output of a rotating machine can be measured by equipping the machine with a special form of friction brake, which absorbs the energy output of the machine and converts it into heat. A simple style of brake suitable for small machines consists of a band that passes around the rotating pulley of the machine and is supported at the ends as shown in Fig. 3. Two screws W serve to tighten or loosen the band, thus regulating the load of the machine, and two spring balances show in terms of their readings, F and F', the forces exerted on the ends of the band. In operation the band is dragged around by friction at the rim of the

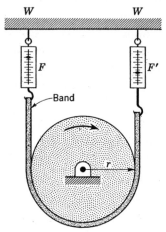

Fig. 3. A rope or band brake.

rotating pulley and remains slightly displaced. The effective force of friction is equal to the difference of the spring balance readings $F' - F$. The machine, in opposing friction, does an amount of work $(F' - F)(2\pi r)$ during each rotation, or $(F' - F)(2\pi rn)$ in 1 min, where n is the number of rotations that it makes per minute.

7-10. Human Power Output. A man who weighs 220 lb may be able to run up a 10-ft flight of stairs in 4.0 sec. If so, he is able to work at the rate of 1 hp, since

$$\frac{220 \text{ lb} \times 10 \text{ ft}}{4.0 \text{ sec}} \doteq 5\bar{5}0 \text{ ft-lb/sec} = 1.0 \text{ hp}$$

A 110-lb boy would have to climb the same height in 2 sec in order to develop the same power. Human endurance will not enable even an athlete to maintain this pace very long. In almost no other way can a man approximate a horsepower in performance. In sustained physical effort a man's power is seldom as great as $\frac{1}{10}$ hp.

Since the muscles of the body are only about 20 per cent efficient, the rate at which they perform useful work is only about one-fifth the rate at which they may be transforming energy. The remainder of the energy is converted into heat, which must be dissipated through ventilation and perspiration. Just as a mechanical engine may have to be "geared down" to match its power output to the requirements of the load, so we as human machines can often best accomplish work by long-continued application at a moderate rate.

7-11. Alternative Ways of Writing the Power Equation. The rate at which a machine works depends on several factors, which appear implicitly in Eq. (9). When a machine is working, the average power developed is

$$\bar{P} = \frac{\bar{F}s}{t} \tag{11}$$

where $\bar{F}$ is the average force that acts through a distance s in time t.

Equation (11) may be written $\bar{P} = \bar{F}(s/t)$, or

$$\bar{P} = \bar{F}\bar{v} \tag{12}$$

which shows that the average rate at which a machine works is the product of the average force and the average speed. A special use of Eq. (12) is that in which the force is applied by a moving belt.

The instantaneous power is

$$P = \frac{dW}{dt} = \frac{d}{dt}(Fs \cos \theta) \tag{13}$$

If the force is constant,

$$P = (F \cos \theta)\frac{ds}{dt} = (F \cos \theta)v \tag{14}$$

which shows that the instantaneous power is the product of the component of the force and the speed at the instant considered.

SUMMARY

Work is the product of force and the **displacement** in the direction of the force

$$dW = F \, ds \cos \theta$$

For a variable force

$$W = \int F(\cos \theta) \, ds$$

Energy is the capacity for doing work.

The *foot-pound* is the work done by a force of 1 lb exerted through a distance of 1 ft.

The *erg* is the work done by a force of 1 dyne exerted through a distance of 1 cm.

The *newton-meter* (*joule*) is the work done by a force of 1 newton exerted through a distance of 1 m. A joule is 10^7 ergs.

A *machine* is a device for applying energy at man's convenience.

The actual mechanical advantage (AMA) of a machine is the ratio of the output force F_o that the machine exerts to the input force F_i applied to the machine

$$AMA = \frac{F_o}{F_i}$$

The ideal mechanical advantage (IMA) of a machine is defined as the ratio of the distance s_i through which the input force acts to the distance s_o through which the output force acts

$$IMA = \frac{s_i}{s_o}$$

$$Eff. = \frac{\text{work output}}{\text{work input}} = \frac{F_o s_o}{F_i s_i} = \frac{AMA}{IMA}$$

Power is the time rate of doing work.

$$P = \frac{dW}{dt} = \frac{d(Fs \cos \theta)}{dt} = F \cos \theta \frac{ds}{dt}$$
$$= F(\cos \theta)v$$

A *horsepower* is 550 ft-lb/sec or 33,000 ft-lb/min.

A *watt* is 1 joule/sec.

One *horsepower* is equivalent to 746 watts.

QUESTIONS
1. Distinguish carefully between doing of work and the exertion of force. Give examples.

2. Show that no work is done on a body that moves with constant speed in a circle.

3. In a tug of war, team A is slowly giving ground to team B. Is any work being done? If so, by what force?

4. Does the use of a lever increase one's power?

5. What kind of machine would you select if you desired one having a mechanical advantage of 2? of 500 or more? Which machine would be likely to have the greater efficiency if both machines were as mechanically perfect as it is possible to make them?

6. Why does a road wind up a steep hill instead of going directly up the slope?

7. How does the IMA of an inclined plane vary with the angle θ of the plane, that is, what trigonometric function of θ gives the value of IMA?

8. Describe several machines in which the load moves at a greater speed than the applied force. Which is greater in each case, the applied force or the force exerted by the machine?

9. A screw jack used to support a heavy load will usually stay set without running back. Show that in raising a load by means of such a jack at least half the work is expended against friction in the jack.

10. In Fig. 4 are shown the three ways in which the applied force F_i, the load

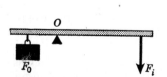
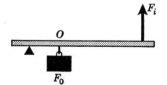
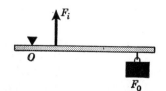

FIG. 4. Three types of lever.

F_o, and the fulcrum O can be arranged on a lever to suit the needs of a particular situation. In which case is the AMA less than 1?

PROBLEMS   **1.** How much work does a 160-lb man do against gravity in climbing a flight of stairs between floors 12 ft apart? Does this account for all the energy expended?

2. Find the work done in removing 300 gal of water from a coal mine 400 ft deep. Water weighs 8.34 lb/gal.   *Ans.* 1.00×10^6 ft-lb

3. What is the increase in the potential energy of a 1.0-kg body when it is lifted from the floor to a table 1.0 m high?

4. A box is pushed 3.0 ft along a floor by a horizontal force of 12 lb. The opposing force of friction is 8.0 lb. (*a*) How much work is done by the agent exerting the 12-lb force? (*b*) How much energy is converted into heat?

Ans. 36 ft-lb; 24 ft-lb

5. Find the work done in drawing a 100-lb box up a plane 20 ft long (Fig. 5) to a platform 12 ft high if the coefficient of friction is 0.20.

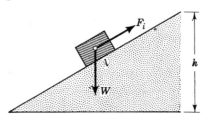

Fɪɢ. 5. Inclined plane.

6. A safe weighing 10 tons is to be loaded on a truck, 5.0 ft high, by means of planks 20 ft long. If it requires 350 lb to overcome friction on the skids, find the least force necessary to move the safe.   *Ans.* 5400 lb

7. A force of 3.0 lb is required to raise a load of 16 lb by means of a pulley system. If the load is raised 1.0 ft while the applied force is exerted through a distance of 8.0 ft, find (*a*) the IMA, (*b*) the AMA, and (*c*) the efficiency of the pulley system.

8. A man raises a 500-lb stone by means of a lever 5.0 ft long. If the fulcrum is 0.65 ft from the end that is in contact with the stone, what is the ideal mechanical advantage?   *Ans.* 6.7

9. Neglecting friction, what applied force is necessary in problem 8?

10. A man weighing 150 lb sits on a platform suspended from a movable pulley and raises himself by a rope passing over a fixed pulley. Assuming the ropes parallel, what force does he exert? (Neglect the weight of the platform.)

Ans. 50 lb

11. Compare the mechanical advantages of a block and tackle (Fig. 6) (*a*) when the end of the cord is attached to the upper block and (*b*) when it is attached to the lower block.

12. A block and tackle having three sheaves in each block is used to raise a load of 620 lb. If the efficiency of the system is 69%, what force is necessary?

Ans. 150 lb

13. A movable pulley is used to lift a 200-lb load. What is the efficiency of the system if a 125-lb force is necessary?

14. The lever arm of a screw jack (Fig. 2) is 3.0 ft long, and the pitch is 0.50 in. The efficiency is 13%. Calculate the IMA, the AMA, and the input force necessary to raise a load of 1.0 ton.   *Ans.* 450; 59; 34 lb

15. The pitch of a screw jack is 0.20 in., and the input force is applied at a radius of 2.5 ft. Find the IMA.

16. Assuming an efficiency of 30%, find the force needed to lift a load of 3300 lb with the screw jack of problem 15. *Ans.* 12 lb

17. A certain screw jack has a pitch of 0.20 in. and the bar used to turn the screw is 4.0 ft long. Find the IMA, the AMA, and the efficiency of this screw jack if a 50-lb force applied at the end of the bar will just raise a 5.0-ton load.

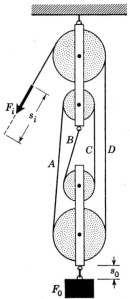

FIG. 6. Block and tackle.

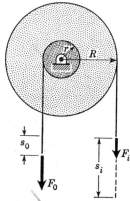

FIG. 7. Wheel and axle.

18. A load of 400 newtons is lifted by means of a screw whose pitch is 5.0 mm. The length of the lever is 20 cm, and the force applied is 5.0 newtons. Determine the efficiency of the machine. *Ans.* 32%

19. The radius of a wheel is 2.0 ft and that of the axle is 2.0 in. (Fig. 7). What force, neglecting friction, must be applied at the rim of the wheel in order to lift a load of 900 lb, which is attached to a cable wound around the axle?

20. A wheel and axle are used for raising a bucket up the shaft of a mine. The radius of the wheel is 20 in. and that of the axle is 4.0 in. The bucket weighs 120 lb and moves upward with uniform speed when the tangential force applied to the rim of the wheel is 30 lb. (*a*) What is the IMA of the wheel and axle? (*b*) What is the efficiency? (*c*) What would be the acceleration of the bucket if the force applied to the wheel were 32 lb? Assume AMA constant. *Ans.* 5.0; 80%; 2.1 ft/sec²

21. A 500-lb safe is suspended from a block and tackle and hoisted 20 ft in 1.5 min. At what rate is the work performed?

22. A horse walks at a steady rate of 3.0 mi/hr along a level road and exerts a pull of 80 lb in dragging a cart. What horsepower is he developing? *Ans.* 0.64 hp

23. How heavy a load can a 15-hp hoist lift at a steady speed of 240 ft/min?

24. Find the useful horsepower expended in pumping 5000 gal of water per minute from a well in which the water level is 40 ft below the discharge pipe.
Ans. 50 hp

25. The friction brake of Fig. 3 is applied to an electric motor. The following data are recorded by an observer: $r = 6.0$ in.; $F' = 55$ lb; $F = 20$ lb; and $n = 1800$ rev/min. Compute the horsepower at which the motor is working.

26. A 2000-lb load is moved at a speed of 15 mi/hr up a plane 100 ft long that makes a 30° angle with the horizontal. The frictional force is 500 lb. Find the work done and the necessary power.   *Ans.* 1.50×10^5 ft-lb; 60.0 hp

27. A 10-hp hoisting engine is used to raise coal from a barge to a wharf, an average height of 75 ft. Assuming an efficiency of 75%, how many tons of coal can be lifted in 20 min?

28. A locomotive developing 2500 hp draws a freight train 1.75 mi long at a rate of 10.0 mi/hr. Find the drawbar pull exerted by the engine.   *Ans.* 46.8 tons

29. A 3200-lb car is towed by a horizontal towrope with uniform speed along a level road. The tension in the towrope is 180 lb, and the car moves 450 ft in 30 sec. (*a*) How much work is done on the car in towing it the 450 ft? (*b*) What horsepower is utilized in towing the car?

30. Find the difference in the tensions of the two sides of a belt when it is running 2800 ft/min and transmitting 150 hp.   *Ans.* 1770 lb

31. A 2000-lb car travels 30 mi/hr up a grade that rises 1.0 ft in 20 ft along the slope. Find the horsepower expended.

32. Fifteen horsepower is required to maintain a car's speed at 30 mi/hr on a level road. What horsepower is required when the 2.0-ton car travels at the same speed up a 5° grade?   *Ans.* 43 hp

33. The engines of a patrol plane deliver 2100 hp to keep the plane in level flight at a speed of 200 mi/hr. What is the total force opposing the forward motion of the plane?

34. If it requires 25 hp to drive an automobile 20 mi/hr along a level road, what is the frictional force opposing the motion?   *Ans.* 470 lb

35. An express elevator makes an ascent of 750 ft in 1.0 min. Find the horse-power used in lifting each 150-lb passenger.

36. A motor operates at its rated load of 10 hp for 8.0 hr a day. Its efficiency is 87%. What is the daily cost of operation if electric energy costs 5 cents per kilowatt-hour?   *Ans.* $3.43

37. An unbalanced force of 10.0 newtons acts on a 20.0-kg body initially at rest. Compute (*a*) the work done in the first second, (*b*) in the third second, and (*c*) the instantaneous power at the end of the third second.

38. A screw jack with a 3.0-ft handle and a pitch of ⅝ in. is used to raise a load of 5000 lb. The jack has an efficiency of 35% and is being turned at the rate of 40 rev/min. Find (*a*) the IMA, (*b*) the AMA, (*c*) the force needed to operate the jack, (*d*) the power being supplied to the jack, and (*e*) the power wasted.
Ans. 360; 127; 39 lb; 0.89 hp; 0.58 hp

39. In the arrangement of Fig. 8, the radii of the wheel and axle are 18 in. and 6.0 in., respectively. The efficiencies are: lever 90%, wheel and axle 80%, pulley system 60%. Find (*a*) the IMA and AMA of each individual machine, (*b*) the IMA and AMA of the combination, (*c*) the force F needed to raise a 1.0-ton load, and (*d*) the power needed to raise the 1.0-ton load at a rate of 2.0 ft/sec.

40. A coal loader consists of an endless belt, driven by a gasoline engine, which moves coal 36 ft up an incline, lifting it 15 ft vertically. It delivers 12 tons of coal per minute to freight cars. (*a*) How much work does the machine do in 4.0 min? (*b*) If the loader were redesigned so as to be 40 ft long and 12 ft high, would the engine required to load coal at the same rate (with same efficiency) be larger or smaller, in power rating? Why?   *Ans.* 1.4 × 10⁶ ft-lb; smaller

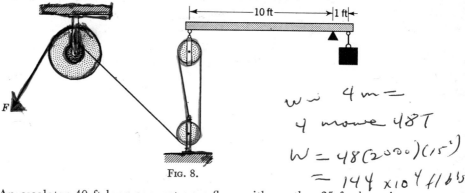

Fɪɢ. 8.

41. An escalator 40 ft long connects one floor with another 25 ft above it. The escalator is designed to carry 120 persons per minute, of average weight 160 lb each, at a constant linear speed of 2.0 ft/sec. (*a*) What power is needed to carry the maximum load? (*b*) If a 160-lb man walks up the escalator at a uniform speed so that he reaches the top in 10 sec, what work must the escalator do on him? (*c*) If the same 160-lb man rides at the middle of the slope, and walks down the escalator at the same rate as the escalator moves up, so that he remains at the same place, at what rate must the escalator motor work?

$$\frac{dw}{dt} = P = \frac{w}{T} = \frac{FS}{T} = Fv$$

$$eff = \frac{wo}{w_i} = \frac{F_o S_o}{F_i S_i}$$

$$W = FS$$

$$2B - FT$$

$$dynes - cm = ERG$$

$$NewTON - M = Joule$$

$$10^{-5} \, dynes = 1 \, newton$$

$$10^{-7} ergs = 1 \, joule$$

$$1 \, Joule/sec = WATT$$

8. Energy

Many problems in mechanics can be solved by the laws of motion discussed in Chap. 4. Given certain information about the initial status of an object and the forces to which it is subjected, we can predict its position and velocity at any future time. In some situations, however, as in the description of the motion of a pendulum, direct application of the laws of motion would require complicated calculations of forces and accelerations in order to obtain a relatively simple result. Consideration of the potential and kinetic energy involved and the relation between work and energy simplifies the solution of many problems in mechanics. Moreover, the concept of energy leads to the principle of the conservation of energy, which unifies a wide range of phenomena in the physical sciences.

8-1. Potential Energy. Energy is the capacity for doing work. *Potential energy* (PE) is energy which bodies possess by virtue of their positions or configuration. The most common form of potential energy is *gravitational* potential energy. Since the earth attracts every body, work is required to lift the body to a higher level. When a brick is carried to the top of a building, the work done on the brick (weight of brick times vertical distance) represents energy that can be recovered. By virtue of its position at the top of the building the brick possesses a capacity for doing work. It has potential energy. The work done on the

brick, and hence the potential energy gained, is the product of the weight W and the height h to which it is raised.

$$PE = Wh \qquad (1)$$
or
$$PE = mgh \qquad (2)$$

If W is in pounds and h in feet, the PE is given by Eq. (1) in foot-pounds. If m is in grams and h in centimeters, the PE is given by Eq. (2) in ergs. If m is in slugs and h in feet, the PE is given by Eq. (2) in foot-pounds. If m is in kilograms and h in meters, the PE is given by Eq. (2) in newton-meters (joules).

The gravitational potential energy is expressed relative to a specified arbitrary reference level. This reference level may be any point that is agreed upon by the people concerned. For example, the arbitrary reference for zero gravitational potential may be chosen as sea level, or floor level, or "at infinity," a point so far from the earth as to be effectively outside the earth's gravitational field.

Example: A 20-lb stone is carried to the top of a building 100 ft high. How much does its potential energy (PE) increase?

Friction being neglected, the increase in PE is just the amount of work done in lifting the stone, so that

$$PE = Fs = (20 \text{ lb})(100 \text{ ft}) = 2\bar{0}00 \text{ ft-lb}$$

In Eqs. (1) and (2) we have assumed that

when we elevate an object a distance h which is small compared to the radius of the earth, the gravitational force acting on that object remains constant. Consider, however, a missile sent far out from the earth's surface. The change in potential energy of the missile in going from a point on the earth's surface, $r = r_1$, to a distant point, $r = r_2$, can be computed from the work which would be done by an external agent in transporting the missile from r_1 to r_2. (The force must be applied in such a manner that it does not produce kinetic energy.) Then, from Eq. (6), Chap. 4,

$$W = \int_{r_1}^{r_2} F \, dr = GMm \int_{r_1}^{r_2} \frac{dr}{r^2}$$

$$= GMm \left(\frac{1}{r_1} - \frac{1}{r_2} \right)$$

where M is the mass of the earth, m the mass of the missile, and G the universal gravitational constant.

Example: A certain spring when elongated a distance s experiences a restoring force $F = -ks$. By how much is the potential energy of this spring increased when it is stretched from $s = s_1$ to $s = s_2$?

$$W = \int_{s_1}^{s_2} F \, ds = k \int_{s_1}^{s_2} s \, ds = \frac{k}{2} (s_2^2 - s_1^2)$$

8-2. Kinetic Energy. In addition to energy of position or state, objects may possess energy due to their motions. A car or bullet in motion, a stream of water, or a revolving flywheel possesses kinetic energy (KE). The kinetic energy of a moving object can be measured by the amount of work it will do if brought to rest, or by the amount of work originally needed to impart the velocity to it.

Consider a body with an initial speed v_1 on which a steady unbalanced force F acts as it moves a distance s. The body gains speed at a rate given by $a = F/m$ until it reaches a final speed v_2. The work done on the body by the unbalanced force that accelerated it appears as a change in its kinetic energy.

$$\Delta \text{KE} = Fs = mas$$

From Eq. (5), Chap. 3,

$$2as = v_2^2 - v_1^2$$

or

$$as = \frac{1}{2}(v_2^2 - v_1^2)$$

$$\Delta \text{KE} = \frac{1}{2}m(v_2^2 - v_1^2) = \frac{1}{2}mv_2^2 - \frac{1}{2}mv_1^2$$

If the body was initially at rest, $v_1 = 0$ and the gain in kinetic energy is the final kinetic energy. Thus

$$\text{KE} = \frac{1}{2}mv^2 \tag{3}$$

If m is expressed in slugs and v in feet per second, Eq. (3) gives the KE in foot-pounds. If m is in grams and v in centimeters per second, Eq. (3) gives the KE in ergs. If m is in kilograms and v in meters per second, Eq. (3) gives the KE in newton-meters (joules).

Although a steady force has here been assumed, the result is independent of the particular manner in which a body attains its velocity. The proof for nonuniform acceleration follows:

Consider a mass m accelerated by a force directed along the x axis but varying in magnitude. Let the mass start from rest at position $x = x_1$ and let it acquire speed v_2 by the time it reaches point $x = x_2$. Its kinetic energy will be given by the work done by the accelerating force

$$\text{KE} = \int_{x_1}^{x_2} F \, dx = \int_{x_1}^{x_2} ma \, dx = m \int_{x_1}^{x_2} \frac{dv}{dt} \, dx$$

$$= m \int_{t_1}^{t_2} \frac{dv}{dt} \frac{dx}{dt} \, dt = m \int_{t_1}^{t_2} v \frac{dv}{dt} \, dt = m \int_0^{v_2} v \, dv$$

$$= \frac{1}{2} mv_2^2$$

Example: What is the kinetic energy of a 3000-lb automobile which is moving at 30 mi/hr (44 ft/sec)?

$$m = \frac{W}{g} = \frac{3000 \text{ lb}}{32 \text{ ft/sec}^2} = 94 \text{ slugs}$$

$$\text{KE} = \frac{1}{2}mv^2 = \frac{1}{2} \times 94 \text{ slugs} \times (44 \text{ ft/sec})^2 = 9\bar{1},000 \text{ ft-lb}$$

When an accelerating force is applied to a body, the work done by that force produces a change in the kinetic energy of the body. If a resultant force F acts to start a body in motion or to stop one initially in motion

$$Fs = \tfrac{1}{2}mv^2 \qquad (4)$$

Example: What average force is necessary to stop a bullet of mass 20 gm and speed 250 m/sec as it penetrates wood to a distance of 12 cm?

The work done by the retarding force is equal to the initial kinetic energy of the bullet

$$Fs = \tfrac{1}{2}mv^2$$
$$F \times 12 \text{ cm} = \tfrac{1}{2}(20 \text{ gm})(25{,}\bar{0}00 \text{ cm/sec})^2$$
$$F = 5.2 \times 10^8 \text{ dynes}$$

This force is nearly 30,000 times the weight of the bullet.

The initial kinetic energy, $\tfrac{1}{2}mv^2 = 6.2 \times 10^9$ ergs $= 6\bar{2}0$ joules, is largely wasted in heat and in work done in deforming the bullet.

8-3. Stopping Distance. The fact that the kinetic energy of a moving object is proportional to the square of its speed has an important bearing upon the problem of stopping an automobile. Doubling the speed of the car quadruples the amount of work that must be done by the brakes in making a quick stop.

A consideration of the equation

$$v_2{}^2 - v_1{}^2 = 2as$$

shows that, if $v_2 = 0$ (indicating a stop), $s = -v_1{}^2/2a$, so that the distance in which an automobile can be stopped is likewise proportional to the square of the speed, assuming a constant deceleration. Actually, however, the deceleration accomplished by the brakes is smaller at high speed because of the effect of heat upon the brake linings, so that the increase in stopping distance with speed is even more rapid than is indicated by theoretical considerations.

Example: In what distance can a 3000-lb automobile be stopped from a speed of 30 mi/hr (44 ft/sec) if the coefficient of friction between tires and roadway is 0.70?

The retarding force furnished by the roadway can be no greater than

$$F_s = \mu N = (0.70)(3000 \text{ lb}) = 2\bar{1}00 \text{ lb}$$

Since the work done by this force is equal to the kinetic energy of the car, the stopping distance can be found by substituting in Eq. (4).

$$Fs = \tfrac{1}{2}mv^2$$
$$m = \frac{W}{g} = \frac{3000 \text{ lb}}{32 \text{ ft/sec}^2} = 94 \text{ slugs}$$
$$s = \frac{\tfrac{1}{2}mv^2}{F} = \frac{94 \text{ slugs } (44 \text{ ft/sec})^2}{2 \times 2\bar{1}00 \text{ lb}} = 43 \text{ ft}$$

8-4. Conservation of Energy. Energy is given to a body when work is done upon it. In this process there is merely a transfer of energy from one body to another. In such transfer no energy is created or destroyed; it merely changes from one form to another. This statement is known as the *law of conservation of energy*. It is true that in most processes some of the energy becomes unavailable. Work done against friction is converted into heat energy in such a form that it can seldom be used. Thus, although the energy is not destroyed, it is wasted as far as its usefulness in the process is concerned.

8-5. Transformations of Kinetic and Potential Energy. Very frequently there is an interchange of kinetic and potential energies. If a ball is held at the top of a building, it possesses potential energy. When it is released and falls, the kinetic energy increases as the potential energy decreases. The sum of the KE and PE remains constant and equal to the PE at the top.

Example: A 3000-lb automobile at rest at the top of an incline 30 ft high and 300 ft long is released and rolls down the hill. What is its speed at the bottom of the incline if the average retarding force is 200 lb?

The potential energy at the top of the hill is available to do work against the retarding force F and to supply kinetic energy.

$$Wh = Fs + \tfrac{1}{2}mv^2$$
$$m = \frac{W}{g} = \frac{3000 \text{ lb}}{32 \text{ ft/sec}^2} = 94 \text{ slugs}$$
$$3000 \text{ lb} \times 30 \text{ ft} = 200 \text{ lb} \times 300 \text{ ft} + \tfrac{1}{2}$$
$$\times 94 \text{ slugs} \times v^2$$

$$9\bar{0},000 \text{ ft-lb} - 6\bar{0},000 \text{ ft-lb} = \frac{1}{2} \times 94 \text{ slugs} \times v^2$$
$$v^2 = \frac{3\bar{0},000 \text{ ft-lb}}{47 \text{ slugs}} = 6\bar{4}0 \text{ ft}^2/\text{sec}^2$$
$$v = 25 \text{ ft/sec}$$

The motion of a pendulum furnishes another simple example of energy transformations. A small ball (Fig. 1) of weight W is suspended from a fixed point P by a string of

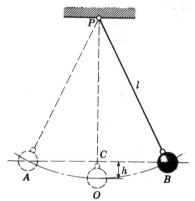

FIG. 1. Pendulum, an example of energy transformation.

length l. When the ball is pulled aside from O to position B, it is raised a distance h and hence given potential energy Wh. When the ball is released, it moves toward its lowest point, and its energy while remaining constant changes from potential to kinetic, the sum of the two forms always being equal to Wh. At point O all the energy will be kinetic. The ball will have a speed v obtained from

$$Wh = \frac{1}{2} mv^2 = \frac{1}{2} \frac{W}{g} v^2 \qquad (5)$$

or
$$v = \sqrt{2gh} \qquad (6)$$

This is the *speed* it would have acquired if it

had fallen freely through a vertical distance h. However, the *velocity* is directed toward the left at O. Under the constraint of the string the ball will continue to move along the arc BOA, gaining potential energy at the expense of its kinetic energy as it approaches A. If no energy is lost to its surroundings, the ball will reach point A at a height h above its lowest position. It will then retrace its path AOB, and the motion will be repeated.

Example: The bob of a pendulum has its rest point 100 cm below the support. The bob is pulled aside until the string makes an angle of 15° with the vertical. Upon release, with what speed does the bob swing past its rest point?

From the geometry of Fig. 1

$$h = l - \overline{PC} = l - l \cos 15° = l(1 - \cos 15°)$$
$$= 100(1.000 - 0.966) = 3.4 \text{ cm}$$
$$v = \sqrt{2gh} = \sqrt{2 \times 980 \text{ cm/sec}^2 \times 3.4 \text{ cm}}$$
$$= 81 \text{ cm}$$

SUMMARY

Energy is the capacity for doing work.

Potential energy is energy of position or configuration. For gravitational potential energy,

$$PE = Wh$$

or
$$PE = mgh$$

Kinetic energy is energy of motion

$$KE = \frac{1}{2}mv^2$$

For transformations between work and kinetic energy,

$$Fs = \frac{1}{2}mv^2 \qquad \text{or} \qquad \int F \, ds = \frac{1}{2}mv^2$$

Energy can be neither created nor destroyed, only transformed. This is the *principle of the conservation of energy*.

QUESTIONS

1. A man rowing a boat upstream is just able to hold his position with respect to the shore. Is he doing work? If so, on what?

2. Which performs work: the hammer or the nail? the powder or the bullet? the catcher or the baseball? the baseball or the bat? Explain your answers.

3. When a car is moving with constant speed along a level road there is no net force. Is any work being done on the car? Explain.

4. Is kinetic energy a vector or a scalar quantity?

5. Two boys are throwing and catching a ball on a moving train. Does the

kinetic energy of the ball at any instant depend on the speed of the train? Explain.

6. Two similar automobiles are driven up a slope, one to twice the height of the other. How do their potential energies compare? If they are driven on the level, one at twice the speed of the other, how do their kinetic energies compare?

7. Show that during the motion of a simple pendulum the work done by the tension in the string is zero.

8. Show that when a body of mass m is dropped from a height h, the sum of its kinetic and potential energies at any instant is constant and equals mgh.

9. Trace the changes in the energy of a roller coaster car.

10. Why is the safe driving speed at night limited by the range of the driver's headlights?

11. Suppose we change the arbitrary zero level for measuring the potential energy of a body. Is the potential energy of the body changed? Explain.

12. How can one calculate the minimum speed with which a projectile would have to be fired vertically in order to escape from the earth?

PROBLEMS   **1.** What is the potential energy of a 1600-lb elevator car at the top of the Empire State Building, 1248 ft above the street level? Take the potential energy at street level as zero.

2. A vertical spring is 10.0 in. long when under a load of 12 lb and 12.5 in. long when the load is increased to 35 lb. How much work is done in stretching this spring? Assume that the added force is proportional to the spring displacement.   *Ans.* 4.9 ft-lb

3. A vertical spring is 10.0 cm long when carrying a load of 20 kg and 12.0 cm long when carrying a load of 32 kg. How much work (*a*) in joules and (*b*) in foot-pounds is required to stretch the spring from 10.0 to 15.0 cm? Assume that the force is proportional to the spring displacement.

4. What is the kinetic energy of a 128-lb body moving with a speed of 110.0 ft/sec?   *Ans.* 2.42×10^4 ft-lb

5. An electron strikes the screen of a cathode-ray tube with a speed of 1.2×10^9 cm/sec. If the mass of an electron is 9.1×10^{-28} gm, compute its energy in ergs.

6. Which has greater kinetic energy: an airplane whose weight is 25 tons and which is flying at 250 mi/hr, or a plane whose weight is 50 tons and which is flying at 160 mi/hr?   *Ans.* 10.5×10^7 ft-lb; 8.6×10^7 ft-lb

7. A 100-lb stone is dropped from a height of 200 ft. Find its kinetic and potential energies at 0, 1.0, and 2.0 sec after being released, and also upon striking the ground. What do you notice concerning the sum of potential and kinetic energies?

8. Find the kinetic energy of a 5.0-kg mass moving with a speed of 4.0 m/sec.   *Ans.* 40 newton-m

9. A driver accelerates a car from 15 mi/hr to 35 mi/hr in 60 sec. The weight of the car is 2800 lb. Find (*a*) the change in kinetic energy of the car and (*b*) the accelerating force acting on the car.

10. A stream flows at a rate of 6.0 ft/sec. What is the kinetic energy associated with each cubic foot of water?   *Ans.* 35 ft-lb

11. A 110-lb body has its speed changed from 25 to 40 ft/sec in 1.8 sec. What average power is required?

12. A 144-lb body initially has kinetic energy of 6400 ft-lb. After 18 sec it has kinetic energy of 160,000 ft-lb. Find (*a*) the initial speed, (*b*) the acceleration,

(c) the accelerating force, and (d) the distance traveled during the 18 sec.

Ans. 53 ft/sec; 12 ft/sec²; 54 lb; 2$\overline{9}$00 ft

13. A constant force of 12 lb acts vertically upward upon a 10-lb body, originally at rest. What is the kinetic and potential energy after 10 sec have elapsed? What average horsepower is used?

14. The hammer of a pile driver weighs 500 lb and falls 12 ft, driving a post 4.0 in. into the ground. What mean force is applied to the post?

Ans. 1$\overline{8}$,000 lb

15. The 1.0-ton hammer of a pile driver is raised 15 ft above a pile and then released. What is the average force exerted by the hammer on the pile if the pile is driven 8.0 in. into the ground with each blow?

16. A pile is to be driven into the ground, which resists penetration with a force of 15,$\overline{0}$00 lb. If the pile is struck by a 300-lb hammer moving with an initial speed of 30 ft/sec, (a) how far will it be driven at each blow? (b) What average horsepower is expended? (Neglect energy loss due to heating.)

Ans. 0.28 ft; 4$\overline{1}$0 hp

17. A 120-gm ball is thrown vertically upward with a speed of 7.5 m/sec. (a) What is the maximum height it attains? (b) What is its speed when it returns to the initial point of release?

18. A 0.30-kg ball is thrown vertically upward with an initial speed of 7.5 m/sec. Find (a) the initial kinetic energy, (b) the potential energy of the ball at the highest point in its path, and (c) the maximum height reached above the point of release. *Ans.* 8.4 joules; 8.4 joules; 2.8 m

19. The V-2 rocket projectile weighed 27,300 lb and acquired a speed of 3600 mi/hr in 70 sec. (a) What energy did it possess on account of its motion? (b) What average power was expended in setting it into motion?

20. The "Big Bertha" gun fired by the German army in the First World War used a projectile weighing 264 lb and having an initial speed of 1.05 mi/sec. (a) Calculate its kinetic energy. (b) Compare this energy with that of the V-2 rocket of problem 19. *Ans.* 1.26 × 10⁸ ft-lb; 1/95

21. A 100-ton car is moving at a speed of 40 mi/hr. A constant force of 1.0 ton opposes the motion. Calculate (a) the time required to bring the car to rest, (b) the distance it will travel in stopping, (c) the energy expended in stopping it, and (d) the rate of expenditure of this energy, in horsepower.

22. If the coefficient of kinetic friction between road and tire is 0.40, how far will a car traveling 60 mi/hr go after application of the brakes if all four wheels are locked? *Ans.* 3$\overline{0}$0 ft

23. A box slides down a chute 12 ft high and 24 ft long onto a level platform. The coefficient of friction of the box on the chute or platform is 0.20. Find (a) the speed of the box as it leaves the chute and (b) the distance it travels on the level platform.

24. What kinetic energy does a 64-lb body acquire in sliding down a plane 100 ft long inclined at an angle of 30° with the horizontal, if the coefficient of sliding friction is 0.20? *Ans.* 2$\overline{1}$00 ft-lb

25. A sled, which with its load weighs 160 lb, is started into motion by a boy who exerts a constant force of 28.2 lb for a distance of 15 ft. The coefficient of sliding friction for the horizontal surface is 0.0200. Find the distance the sled travels after the boy stops pushing.

26. A 40-ton railway car moving 5.0 ft/sec strikes a spring bumper at the end of a siding. (a) What is the kinetic energy of the car before collision? (b) Through

what distance does it compress the spring if its elastic constant is 2.25 ×
10^4 lb/ft?   *Ans.* 3.1 × 10^4 ft-lb; 1.7 ft

27. A body slides from rest down a frictionless track which is a quadrant of a
circle of radius r (Fig. 2). (*a*) Find the speed at the bottom. (SUGGESTION: Since

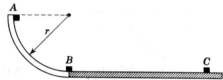

FIG. 2. A frictionless track *AB* and a surface *BC* having coefficient of sliding friction μ_k.

no energy is converted into heat, we can equate the change in kinetic energy to
the change in gravitational potential energy.) (*b*) How does the velocity acquired compare with the velocity which would be acquired in free fall through
a vertical height r?

28. A 0.50-lb block is released from rest at a point A on a track which is one
quadrant of a circle (Fig. 2) of radius 4.0 ft. It slides down the track and reaches
point B with a speed of 12 ft/sec. From B it slides along a level board a distance
of 6.0 ft to point C where it stops. (*a*) What is the coefficient of sliding friction on
the horizontal board? (*b*) How much energy was converted to heat as the block
slid from A to B?   *Ans.* 0.37; 0.9 ft-lb

29. A 2000-lb bomb falls freely for 30 sec and penetrates 6.0 ft into the
ground. What resisting force (assumed constant) does the earth exert?

30. A bicycle rider has to climb a hill whose crest is 10 ft higher than the base.
What must be his speed at the foot of the hill in order to save him from doing
one-tenth of the necessary work against gravity?   *Ans.* 8.0 ft/sec

31. How many miles per hour can a 500-hp engine pull a 180-ton train up a
2.0 per cent slope if the force of friction is 3000 lb?

32. A pendulum bob on a 10-ft string is displaced 30° from the vertical and
then released. What is the speed of the bob as it passes through the lowest point
in its path?   *Ans.* 9.3 ft/sec

33. An object of mass 20 kg hung by a cord 2.0 m long is drawn aside 30° from
the vertical and released. It is stopped in a vertical position by a uniform spring
which is compressed 3.0 cm. What is the maximum force exerted on the compressed spring? (Neglect energy lost due to heating.)

34. A wedge is 3.0 in. thick and 15 in. long. It is driven 0.25 in. into a log by
the impact of a hammer blow. (*a*) If there is an average force of 30 lb exerted on
the hammer for a distance of 4.0 ft, what is the ideal mechanical advantage of
the entire arrangement? (*b*) What is the average force exerted by the wedge
upon the log? (Neglect losses.)   *Ans.* 960; 29,000 lb

35. The engine delivers 30 hp to the propeller of a boat while it cruises at
20 mi/hr. If the boat were being towed at the same speed, what would be the
tension in the towline?

36. A locomotive traveling at 34 mi/hr exerts a drawbar pull of 10 tons. What
horsepower is it producing?   *Ans.* 1800 hp

37. A body of mass 2.0 slugs initially at rest on a smooth horizontal surface is
acted upon by a horizontal force of 24 lb. Find (*a*) the instantaneous power being
expended at the end of 1.0 sec, (*b*) at the end of 5.0 sec, and (*c*) the average
power expended during the first 5.0 sec. (*d*) Explain why the power is not
constant.

38. The engine of a 3600-lb automobile develops 30 hp to move the car at 30 mi/hr on a level road. (*a*) What is the retarding force of friction and wind? (*b*) What power is needed to drive the car at 30 mi/hr up a 10 per cent grade? (*c*) Down what grade would the car coast at 30 mi/hr?

Ans. 3$\overline{8}$0 lb; 59 hp; 10.4 per cent

39. A ski tow is to be operated on a 37° slope 800 ft long. The rope is to move 8.0 mi/hr and power must be provided for 80 riders at one time, each weighing, on the average, 150 lb. Estimate the horsepower required to operate the tow, assuming no losses.

40. A halfback, while throwing a quick pass, pushed on the ball with a constant force for 0.10 sec, while his hand moved forward a distance of 3.2 ft. The ball weighs 2.0 lb. (*a*) What was the acceleration of the ball? (*b*) What was the force exerted on the ball? (*c*) How much work was done on the ball? (*d*) What power was developed by the halfback while accelerating the ball?

Ans. 6$\overline{4}$0 ft/sec²; 40 lb; 1$\overline{3}$0 ft-lb; 2.3 hp

41. A guided missile weighing 12 tons is fired vertically, using a propellant which exerts a thrust of 33 tons for 10 sec. Determine the maximum height to which it will rise. Neglect the change in weight.

42. The coefficient of static friction between the tires and the road is μ_s. Find the minimum stopping distance for an automobile of mass m and speed v.

Ans. $v^2/2\mu_s g$

43. In Fig. 3, blocks A and B are connected by a weightless cord passing over a weightless, frictionless pulley. Block B has a mass of 16 kg and block A a mass

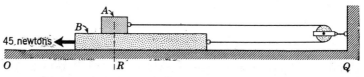

FIG. 3.

of 4.0 kg. The coefficient of sliding friction between blocks A and B is 0.25, and between block B and the horizontal surface OQ it is 0.10. A force of 45 newtons is applied to block B, parallel to OQ. Use $g = 10$ m/sec². (*a*) Draw two force diagrams, one showing the forces acting on block A, the other showing the forces acting on block B. (*b*) Calculate the acceleration of block A. (*c*) At time $t = 0$, block A is at point R and is moving to the right with an initial velocity of 5.0 cm/sec. How much work is done by the agent exerting the 45-newton force during the time interval between $t = 0$ and $t = 0.8$ sec? Assume block B is of sufficient length so that A never falls off. (*d*) What is the kinetic energy of block A at time $t = 0.8$ sec?

9. Torque

When a body is in equilibrium, it is either at rest or in uniform motion. Forces may act to change the linear motion of a body or to change the rotation of the body. If all the forces acting upon a body intersect at a common point and their vector sum is zero, they have no tendency to change either translation or rotation.

Since most bodies are acted upon by forces that do not act through a single common point, we must consider the effect of each force in changing the rotation as well as its effect in changing the linear motion of the body. The same force applied at different places or in different directions produces greatly different rotational effects. The engineer is very much concerned with these effects and must make allowances for them in the design of his structures.

9-1. Conditions for Equilibrium. Consider an arrangement in which two opposing forces equal in magnitude act on a block as in Fig. 1a. It is obvious that if the block is originally at rest it will remain so under the action of these two forces. We say, as before, that the vector sum of the forces is zero.

Now suppose that the forces are applied as in Fig. 1b. The vector sum of the forces is again zero; yet it is plain that under the action of these two forces, the block will rotate. In fact, when the vector sum of the applied forces is equal to zero, we can be sure only

that the body as a whole will have no change in its *linear* motion; we cannot be sure that there will be no change in its *rotary* motion. Hence complete equilibrium is not assured. In addition to the first condition for equilibrium previously stated (Chap. 2), a second

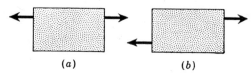

Fig. 1. Forces which are equal in magnitude and opposite in direction produce equilibrium when they have a common line of action (a), but do not produce equilibrium when they do not have the same line of action (b).

condition is necessary, a condition eliminating the possibility of a change in rotational motion. The example of Fig. 1b indicates that this second condition is concerned with the *placement* of the forces as well as their magnitudes and directions.

In order to study the factors that determine the effectiveness of a force in changing rotational motion, consider the familiar problem of turning a heavy wheel by pulling on a spoke (Fig. 2). It is a common experience that the wheel can be set into motion more easily and quickly by applying a force F perpendicular to a spoke at some point A far from the axis than by applying the same force at a point B nearer the axis. The effect of a given force upon the rotational motion of a body is greater the farther the *line of action* of the force is from the axis of rotation. The distance of the

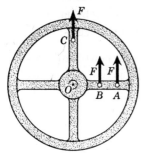

FIG. 2. An unbalanced force produces rotational acceleration if its line of action does not pass through the axis of rotation.

line of action from the axis is measured perpendicular to the line of action of the force. It is not merely the distance from the axis to the point of application of the force. If the same force F of Fig. 2 is applied at C rather than A, where $OC = OA$, there is no effect upon the rotation of the wheel, since the line of action of F passes through the axis and it merely pulls the wheel as a whole upward. Though the magnitude of the force, its direction, and the distance of its point of application from the axis are the same in the two examples, rotation is affected when the force is applied at A but it is not affected when the force is applied at C.

9-2. Moment Arm. The factor that determines the effect of a given force upon rotational motion is the *perpendicular distance from the axis of rotation to the line of action of the force.* This distance is called the *moment arm* of the force. In Fig. 3, the moment arm of the force F is indicated by the dotted line OP. The line of action of the force is a mere geometrical construction and may be extended indefinitely either way in order to intersect the perpendicular OP. It has nothing to do with the length of the force vector. The force F in Fig. 2 produces no change in the rotation when it is applied at C because its line of action passes through the axis of rotation and its moment

arm is therefore zero. The same force applied at A has a moment arm OA and, therefore, tends to change the rotation.

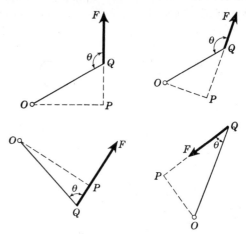

FIG. 3. Measurements of moment arm.

9-3. Torque. For a fixed moment arm, the greater the force the greater is the effect upon rotational motion. The two quantities, force and moment arm, are of equal importance. They can be combined into a single quantity, *torque* (also called *moment of force*), which measures the effectiveness of the force in changing rotation about the chosen axis. Torque will be represented by the symbol L.

The torque (moment of force) about a chosen axis is *the product of the force and its moment arm.*

$$L = Fs \qquad (1)$$

An axis must always be selected about which torques are to be measured. The value of the torque produced by a given force depends, of course, upon the axis chosen. The selection of an axis is quite arbitrary; it need not be any actual axle or fulcrum. In many cases, however, a wise selection of the axis about which torques are to be calculated greatly simplifies a problem, because it reduces to zero the torque due to a force whose magnitude or direction is unknown.

Since torque is a product of a force and a distance, its unit is a force unit times a distance unit, such as pound-foot, the usual unit in the British system. An mks unit of torque is the meter-newton. The cgs unit of torque is the centimeter-dyne. Any similar combination of force and distance units makes a suitable unit for torque.

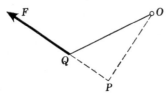

FIG. 4. A clockwise torque.

Torque is a vector quantity. The direction assigned to the vector is parallel to the axis of the torque. The consequences of the vector nature of torque will be discussed in more detail later in connection with rotary motion. For the present we shall confine our attention to cases in which all the forces act in the same plane. For these cases the axes, and therefore the torques, are parallel and only the algebraic signs of the torques need be considered.

The algebraic sign of such torques is determined by consideration of the direction of the rotation the torque tends to produce. For example, the torques in Fig. 3 tend to produce counterclockwise accelerations about O, while the torque in Fig. 4 tends to produce a clockwise acceleration. One may refer to these torques as positive and negative, respectively. Note that a given force may produce a clockwise torque about one axis, but a counterclockwise torque about another axis. The direction of a torque is not known from the direction of the force alone.

Example: A light horizontal bar is 4.0 ft long. A 3.0-lb force acts vertically upward on it 1.0 ft from the right-hand end. Find the torque about each end.

Since the force is perpendicular to the bar, the moment arms are measured along the bar.

About the right-hand end

$$L_r = 3.0 \text{ lb} \times 1.0 \text{ ft} = 3.0 \text{ lb-ft} \quad \text{(clockwise)}$$

About the left-hand end

$$L_l = 3.0 \text{ lb} \times 3.0 \text{ ft} = 9.0 \text{ lb-ft}$$
$$\text{(counterclockwise)}$$

The torques produced by this single force about the two axes differ in both magnitude and direction.

9-4. Concurrent and Nonconcurrent Forces. Concurrent forces are those whose lines of action intersect in a common point. If an axis passing through this point is selected, the torque produced by each force of such a set is zero. If any other axis is chosen in place of that through the common point, the sum of the torques will not, in general, be zero. For the special case in which the resultant of the concurrent forces is zero, the sum of the torques about any axis is zero. Hence a consideration of torque is not necessary in the study of a set of *concurrent* forces in equilibrium.

For a set of nonconcurrent forces, there exists no single axis about which no torque is produced by any of the forces. Therefore, in studying a set of nonconcurrent forces in equilibrium, it is essential to take into account the relation existing among the torques produced by such a set of forces. This relation is expressed in the second condition for equilibrium.

9-5. The Two Conditions for Equilibrium. We have previously considered (Chap. 2) the condition necessary for equilibrium under the action of concurrent forces, namely, that the vector sum of all the forces acting shall be equal to zero. This condition must also be fulfilled when the forces are not concurrent. This first condition may be expressed by the statement that the sum of the components in any two perpendicular directions shall be zero

$$\Sigma F_x = 0 \quad (2)$$
$$\Sigma F_y = 0 \quad (3)$$

For an object to be in equilibrium under the action of forces in a single plane, the algebraic sum of the torques (about *any* axis) acting upon the body must be zero. This statement is known as the *second condition for equi-*

librium. It may be represented by the equation

$$\Sigma L = 0 \qquad (4)$$

In the first and second conditions for equilibrium we have a complete system for solving problems involving forces that are all in a single plane. These same conditions are useful in certain problems involving uniform motion. If the first condition is satisfied, the vector sum of the forces is zero, and no translational acceleration is produced. If the second condition is satisfied, the algebraic sum of the torques is zero, and there is no rotational acceleration. This does not mean that there is no motion, but only that the forces applied to the body produce no *change* in its motion. While in equilibrium, the body may have a uniform motion including both translation and rotation.

9-6. Center of Gravity. The most common force acting upon a body is its weight. For every body, no matter how irregular its shape, there exists a point such that the entire weight may be considered as concentrated at that point. This point is called the *center of gravity* of the body. The center of gravity may be either within or outside the body. If a single force equal to the weight of the body and acting vertically upward could be applied at the center of gravity, it would support the body in equilibrium no matter how the body might be tipped about the center of gravity.

A knowledge of the position of the center of gravity is very useful in problems of equilibrium, for that is the point of application of the vector representing the weight. (It is never necessary and seldom convenient to break the weight up into parts.)

Example: A uniform bar, 9.0 ft long and weighing 5.0 lb, is supported by a fulcrum 3.0 ft from the left end as in Fig. 5. If a 12-lb load is hung from the left end, what downward pull at the right end is necessary to hold the bar in equilibrium? With what force does the fulcrum push up against the bar?

Consider the bar as an object in equilibrium.

The first step is to indicate clearly all the forces that act on it. Since the bar is uniform its center of gravity is at its mid-point and hence the weight of the bar, 5.0 lb, can be considered to be concentrated at its middle. A 12-lb force acts downward at the left end of the bar, a force R acts upward at

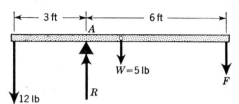

FIG. 5. The forces acting on a lever.

the fulcrum, and there is an unknown downward force F at the right end.

The first condition for equilibrium indicates that the vector sum of the forces applied to the bar is zero, or that

$$R - 12 \text{ lb} - 5.0 \text{ lb} - F = 0$$

Without further information we certainly cannot solve this equation, since it has two unknown quantities in it, R and F. Let us set it aside for a moment and employ the second condition for equilibrium, calculating the torques about some axis and equating their algebraic sum to zero.

The first thing we must do is to select an axis from which to measure moment arms. We shall choose an axis through the point A about which to calculate all the torques. Beginning at the left end of the bar, we have $(12 \text{ lb})(3.0 \text{ ft}) = 36$ lb-ft of torque, counterclockwise about A. Next, we see that the force R produces no torque, since its line of action passes through the point A. (Is it clear now why we decided to take A as an axis?) Third, the torque produced by the weight W of the bar is $(5.0 \text{ lb})(1.5 \text{ ft}) = 7.5$ lb-ft, clockwise. Finally, F produces a torque $F(6.0 \text{ ft})$, clockwise.

Taking the counterclockwise torque as positive and clockwise torque as negative and equating the algebraic sum of all the torques to zero, we write

$$\Sigma L = (12 \text{ lb})(3.0 \text{ ft}) + R(0) - (5.0 \text{ lb})(1.5 \text{ ft})$$
$$- F(6.0 \text{ ft}) = 0$$
$$36 \text{ lb-ft} + 0 - 7.5 \text{ lb-ft} - F(6.0 \text{ ft}) = 0$$
$$F(6.0 \text{ ft}) = 28.5 \text{ lb-ft}$$
$$F = 4.8 \text{ lb}$$

Substituting this value in the equation obtained

from the first condition for equilibrium, we find $R - 12$ lb $- 5.0$ lb $- 4.8$ lb $= 0$, or $R = 22$ lb.

Example: A chain C (Fig. 6) helps to support a uniform 200-lb beam, 20 ft long, one end of which is hinged at the wall and the other end of which

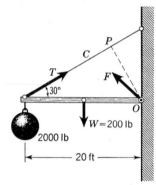

FIG. 6. The forces acting on a horizontal beam.

supports a 1.0-ton load. The chain makes an angle of 30° with the beam, which is horizontal. Determine the tension in the chain.

Since all the known forces act on the 20-ft beam, let us consider it as the object in equilibrium. In addition to the 200- and 2000-lb forces straight down, there are the pull of the chain on the beam, and the force F, which the hinge exerts on the beam at the wall. Let us not make the mistake of assuming that the force at the hinge is straight up, or straight along the beam. A little thought will convince us that the hinge must be pushing both up and out on the beam. The exact direction of this force, as well as its magnitude, is unknown. The second condition for equilibrium is an excellent tool to employ in such a situation, for if we use an axis through the point O as the axis about which to take torques, the unknown force at the hinge has zero moment arm and, therefore, causes zero torque. The remarkable result is that we can determine the tension T in the chain without knowing either the magnitude or the direction of the force at O.

The torques about O as an axis are,

$(200$ lb$)(10$ ft$) = 2\bar{0}00$ lb-ft

(counterclockwise)

$(2000$ lb$)(20$ ft$) = 4\bar{0},000$ lb-ft

(counterclockwise)

$T(20$ ft$) \sin 30° = T(10$ ft$)$

(clockwise)

(NOTE: The moment arm of T is $\overline{OP} = 20$ ft $\times \sin 30° = 10$ ft.) Then

$$-T(10 \text{ ft}) + 2,\bar{0}00 \text{ lb-ft} + 4\bar{0},000 \text{ lb-ft} + F(0) = 0$$

so that

$$T = 4\bar{2}00 \text{ lb} = 2.1 \text{ tons}$$

The problem of finding the magnitude and direction of the force at the hinge is left to the student. (SUGGESTION: Apply the first condition for equilibrium.)

The trick just used in removing the unknown force from the problem by taking torques about the hinge as an axis is a standard device in statics. The students should always be on the lookout for the opportunity to side-step (temporarily) a troublesome unknown force by selecting an axis of torques that lies on the line of action of the unknown force he wishes to avoid.

9-7. Couples. In general, the application of one or more forces to an object results in both translational and rotational acceleration. An exception to this result is the case in which a single force is applied along a line passing through the center of gravity of the object, in which case there is no rotational acceleration. Another special case is the one in which two forces equal in magnitude, opposite in direction, and not in the same line, are applied to the object as in Fig. $1b$. In this case there is no translational acceleration but there is a net torque and hence a rotational acceleration. A pair of forces equal in magnitude, opposite in direction, and not in the same line is called a *couple*. The torque produced by a couple is independent of the position of the axis and is equal to the product of one of the forces and the perpendicular distance between them.

Consider the torque produced by the couple shown in Fig. 7. About the axis O, the torque produced by F_1 is $F_1(\overline{OA})$, and that by F_2 is $-F_2(\overline{OB})$. Since $F_1 = F_2 = F$, the total torque is

$$F(\overline{OA}) - F(\overline{OB}) = F(\overline{OA} - \overline{OB}) = F(\overline{AB})$$

This verifies the statement that the torque produced by a couple is the product of one (either) of the forces and the perpendicular distance between them, a product independent of the location of the axis. A couple cannot be balanced by a single force but only by

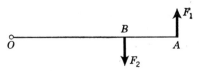

FIG. 7. Forces constituting a couple.

the application of another couple equal in magnitude and opposite in direction.

SUMMARY

The motion of a body is determined by the *placement* of the forces acting on it as well as the magnitude and direction of the forces.

The *moment arm* of a force is the perpendicular distance from the axis to the line of action of the force.

The *torque* produced by a force is equal to the product of the force and its moment arm

$$L = Fs$$

Torque is measured in pound-feet, meter-newtons, centimeter-dynes, or any similar combination of force and distance units.

Torque is a vector quantity.

For an object to be in equilibrium, it is necessary (1) that the vector sum of the forces applied to it be zero, and (2) that the algebraic sum of the torques (about any axis) acting on it be zero.

$$\Sigma F_x = 0$$
$$\Sigma F_y = 0$$
$$\Sigma L = 0$$

The *center of gravity* of a body is the point at which its weight may be considered as acting.

A *couple* consists of two forces equal in magnitude, opposite in direction and not in the same line. The torque produced by a couple is equal to the magnitude of one (either) of the forces times the perpendicular distance between them.

QUESTIONS   1. What are the advantages of an automobile brake drum with a large diameter over one with a smaller diameter?

2. Describe and explain the difference in the position of a man carrying a suitcase in one hand and that of a man carrying a suitcase in each hand.

3. A man wishes to check the weight of a purchase, but has available only a spring balance reading to about a third of the presumed weight of the object. Show how he could perform an accurate weighing with the spring balance and a yardstick.

4. How could one determine experimentally the location of the center of gravity of an irregular body?

5. How might one use the property of center of gravity to locate the geographic center of a state?

6. Discuss the stability of a body in equilibrium. How is stability related to potential energy? Give illustrations.

7. Is it possible to balance permanently a uniform bar on a knife edge? Explain.

8. A bar rests with one end on a frictionless table top. A string is attached at the other end. What must be the direction of the force in the string to hold the bar in equilibrium at an angle of 45° with the horizontal?

9. Justify the statement that in order for a body to be in equilibrium under the action of three nonparallel forces, these forces must be directed so that their lines of action intersect at a single point.

10. Show that if the resultant of a set of concurrent forces is zero, the sum of the torques, about any point, due to these forces must also be zero.

11. Archimedes is reputed to have said, "Give me a place to stand and I can lift the earth." Comment on this statement. What are some of the auxiliary devices that he would have needed for this cosmic experiment?

12. Show that a couple cannot be balanced except by another couple.

PROBLEMS

1. A rope is wound around a shaft 3.0 in. in diameter. If a pull of 160 lb is exerted on the rope, what torque is imparted to the shaft?

2. A bar 20 ft long makes an angle of 30° with the horizontal. A vertical force of 40 lb is applied 4.0 ft from the upper end. Calculate the torque due to this force about each end.   *Ans.* 5$\overline{5}$0 lb-ft; 1$\overline{4}$0 lb-ft

3. A motor with a pulley of diameter 18 in. is coupled to a machine by a belt that passes over a pulley 24 in. in diameter on the machine. The sides of the belt are under tensions of 45 and 60 lb. Calculate the torque exerted at each pulley.

4. A uniform board 20.0 cm × 10.0 cm has a mass of 200 gm. Masses of 50.0 gm and 80.0 gm are attached at two corners at the ends of one of the longer sides. Locate the center of gravity.

Ans. y = 1.97 cm; x = 0.91 cm from the intersection of the diagonals

5. A uniform board 10.0 cm square has a mass of 100 gm. Masses are attached at each corner in order around the square, 200 gm at A, 100 gm at B, 60 gm at C, and 40 gm at D. Find the center of gravity.

6. A uniform rod has a mass of 2.0 gm for each centimeter of its length. The rod is bent into the shape of a letter L with the longer arm 100 cm and the shorter 50 cm. Find the position of the center of gravity of the bent rod.

Ans. 8.3 cm from longer arm, 33 cm from shorter

7. Two uniform rods, each of 2.0 gm per centimeter length, are 40 and 60 cm long. The rods are joined with one end of the shorter rod 20 cm from an end of the longer and the two rods at right angles to each other. Find the position of the center of gravity of the combined rods.

8. The legs of a wheelbarrow are 3.0 horizontal ft from the axle. When the wheelbarrow is unloaded, a force of 12 lb applied to the handles 4.0 horizontal ft from the axle is needed to raise the legs from the ground. If a 120-lb box is placed in the wheelbarrow with its center of gravity 1.5 ft from the axle, what force must be applied to the handles to raise the legs from the ground?   *Ans.* 57 lb

9. A uniform plank 20.0 ft long and weighing 200 lb is supported in a horizontal position by two vertical ropes A and B, one at either end. Calculate the tension in each rope when a 140-lb man and a 160-lb man are standing 5.0 ft and 12.0 ft, respectively, from A.

10. A painter stands on a horizontal uniform scaffold hung by its ends from two vertical ropes A and B, 20 ft apart. The scaffold weighs 50 lb. The tension in A is 140 lb and that in B is 60 lb. (*a*) What is the weight of the painter? (*b*) How far from A is he standing?   *Ans.* 1$\overline{5}$0 lb; 4.7 ft

11. A 300-lb uniform beam 40 ft long is carried by three men, one at one end of the beam, the other two supporting a crossbar. Where must the crossbar be placed so that each man will support the same load?

12. A uniform pole 20 ft long and weighing 80 lb is supported by a boy 2.0 ft from end A and a man 5.0 ft from end B. At what point should a load of 100 lb be placed so that the man will support twice as much as the boy?

Ans. 8.8 ft from B

13. Where must a force of 100 lb be applied to a 20-lb uniform pole which is 10 ft long, if a man at one end supports 50 lb and a man at the other end supports the remainder? What force does the second man exert?

14. A uniform, 30-lb beam 10 ft long is carried by two men A and B, one at each end of the beam. (*a*) If A exerts a force of 25 lb, where must a load of 50 lb be placed on the beam? (*b*) What force does B exert?

Ans. 2.0 ft from B; 55 lb

15. A meter stick is balanced on a fulcrum at the 50.0-cm mark. A scale pan P at the 14.0-cm mark just balances a second pan Q at the 90.0-cm mark. When a load of 100 gm is added to pan Q, it must be moved to the 75.0-cm mark to maintain balance. Pan P remains unmoved. Calculate the masses of pans P and Q.

16. A nonuniform bar weighs 40 lb and is 12 ft long. When it is supported by a fulcrum at its mid-point, a load of 8.0 lb must be supplied at the small end to hold the bar in a horizontal position. Where is the center of gravity?

Ans. 4.8 ft from thicker end

17. A telephone pole weighs 300 lb and is 30.0 ft long. Its center of gravity is 10.0 ft from the thicker end. What force must be applied at the smaller end to maintain the pole in a horizontal position when it is supported at its mid-point?

18. A nonuniform bar of iron 16 ft long rests on two supports, one at either end. At end A, the support exerts a force of 200 lb, at end B, 160 lb. There is a load of 40 lb, 2.0 ft from B and another of 60 lb, 4.0 ft from A. Find the weight of the bar and the position of its center of gravity. *Ans.* 260 lb; 6.8 ft from A

19. A uniform horizontal beam 15 ft long has one end supported on a ledge in a vertical wall while the other end is supported by a rope, which makes an angle of 30° with the wall. The beam weighs 100 lb and supports a load of 200 lb at the outer end. Find the tension in the rope and also the vertical and horizontal forces at the wall.

20. A crane boom 30 ft long, weighing 200 lb, and having its center of gravity 10 ft from the bottom is hinged at the lower end and makes an angle of 30° with the vertical. It is held in position by a horizontal cable fastened at the upper end. The boom supports a 1000-lb load at its upper end. Find the tension in the cable, the horizontal and vertical components of the thrust at the hinge, and the resultant thrust there.

Ans. $6\overline{2}0$ lb; $6\overline{2}0$ lb; $1\overline{2}00$ lb; $1\overline{3}00$ lb, 63° above the horizontal

21. The uniform boom of a crane is 40.0 ft long and weighs 4.00 tons. The tie rope is horizontal and is attached 10.0 ft from the upper end of the boom, which makes an angle of 60° with the horizontal. If a 10.0-ton load is attached to the end of the boom, calculate the tension in the tie and the force exerted by the boom on its lower support.

22. The uniform boom of a crane is 40.0 ft long and weighs 400 lb. It is hinged at the bottom and held at an angle of 45° by a tie rope attached 10.0 ft from the upper end. The tie rope makes an angle of 60° with the vertical. A load of 3600 lb is supported at the end of the boom. Find (*a*) the tension in the tie rope, (*b*) the vertical and horizontal thrusts at the hinge, and (*c*) the resultant thrust at the hinge.

Ans. $37\overline{0}0$ lb; $21\overline{5}0$ lb; $32\overline{0}0$ lb; $38\overline{5}0$ lb, 33.8° above horizontal

23. A uniform rod 16 ft long and weighing 200 lb is pivoted at its upper end. It is drawn aside so that it makes an angle of 30° with a vertical wall by means of a rope fastened at its lower end and making an angle of 90° with the rod. Find the tension in the rope and the horizontal, vertical, and resultant forces at the pivot.

24. A uniform rod 30 ft long and weighing 200 lb is pivoted at its upper end. It is drawn aside so that it makes an angle of 60° with the vertical by means of a rope fastened at the lower end and making an angle of 90° with the rod. Find

(a) the tension in the rope, (b) the horizontal force at the pivot, (c) the vertical force at the pivot, and (d) the resultant force at the pivot.

Ans. 87 lb; 43 lb; 125 lb; 132 lb, 19° from the vertical

25. A uniform ladder 30.0 ft long weighing 50.0 lb rests on horizontal ground and leans against a smooth vertical wall. If the ladder makes an angle of 60° with the horizontal, calculate the frictional force between ladder and ground necessary to keep the ladder from slipping when a 150-lb man is 10.0 ft from the top of the ladder.

26. A uniform ladder 20 ft long and weighing 80 lb rests against a smooth vertical wall at an angle of 30° to the wall. A 150-lb man stands 12 ft up from the bottom of the ladder. Find the horizontal force necessary at the base to keep the ladder from slipping.   *Ans.* 75 lb

27. The foot of a 50-lb uniform ladder is 6.0 ft from a smooth vertical wall. The upper end rests against the wall at a point 30 ft from the ground. If a 150-lb man is halfway up the ladder, find (a) the force exerted by the ladder against the wall, (b) the vertical, and (c) the horizontal component of its force against the ground.

28. A uniform ladder 20.0 ft long weighing 30.0 lb rests on horizontal ground and leans at an angle of 60° with the horizontal against a smooth vertical wall. How far up the ladder may a 160-lb man go before the ladder slips if the coefficient of friction between ladder and ground is 0.433?   *Ans.* 15.9 ft

29. A 200-lb man stands on a 50-lb ladder which is 20 ft long. The ladder has one end resting on a horizontal floor. The other end is held up by a vertical rope so that the ladder makes an angle of 30° with the floor. The man is 4.0 ft away from the end of the ladder to which the rope is attached. A boy exerts a downward force of 25 lb perpendicular to the ladder at a point 8.0 ft from the end that rests on the floor. Determine (a) the tension in the rope and (b) the thrust exerted by the floor.

30. A uniform ladder stands against a smooth wall. The coefficient of static friction between the ladder and the horizontal floor is 0.40. What is the largest angle between the wall and the ladder for which the ladder will not slip?

Ans. 38.7°

31. A 20-lb uniform ladder stands against a smooth wall. The coefficient of static friction between the ladder and the horizontal floor is 0.40. What is the largest angle between the wall and the ladder for which a 50-lb boy can climb to the top of the ladder without slippage of the ladder?

32. A 20-lb farm gate is supported by two hinges 4.0 ft apart. The gate is 12.0 ft long. Its weight is entirely supported by the upper hinge. If the gate is of uniform construction, what forces are exerted (a) at the upper hinge and (b) at the lower hinge?   *Ans.* 36 lb, 56° from vertical; 30 lb, horizontally

33. A uniform 120-lb farm gate, 10.0 ft long, is supported by two hinges, one above the other and 3.0 ft apart. If the hinges share the weight equally, find the magnitude and direction of the force on each hinge when a 30-lb boy is on the end of the gate farthest from the hinges.

34. A uniform wire is bent at its mid-point so that the two halves are perpendicular to each other. The wire is supported at one end so that it is free to turn about that end. Find the angle between the upper segment of the wire and the vertical when the wire is in equilibrium.   *Ans.* 18.4°

35. A uniform wire is bent at its mid-point so that there is an angle θ between the two segments. The wire is supported at one end so that it is free to turn about this end. For what value of θ is the lower segment of the wire horizontal when the wire is in equilibrium?

36. A uniform rod 10.0 ft long weighs 8.0 lb. One end of the rod is placed at the intersection of the floor and one wall of a room. The rod lies across a smooth support 4.0 ft high placed 6.0 ft from the wall. Find the horizontal and vertical components of the force on the lower end of the rod. *Ans.* 2.6 lb, 4.2 lb

37. A 250-lb cubical block, 5.0 ft wide, rests on a horizontal floor against a small obstacle at one edge. In order to overturn the block most easily, (*a*) how should one push, and (*b*) what force must one apply? (*c*) How will this force vary as the block starts to tip?

38. A 30.0-lb sphere rests on a 30° incline where the coefficient of static friction is 0.95. (*a*) What is the minimum force that will keep the sphere in equilibrium? (*b*) How must this force be applied? *Ans.* 7.5 lb

10. Rotation of Rigid Bodies

The motion of a body may consist of translation, rotation, or a combination of translation and rotation. Let us first examine the ways in which rotary or angular motion can be described. We shall then see how the action of a torque in changing angular motion can be expressed by relations similar to Newton's laws for translational motion.

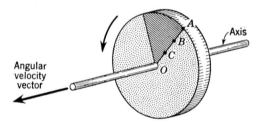

FIG. 1. Rotation about axis O. The angular speed is the same for all parts of the disk, but the linear speed increases as the radius increases.

10-1. Rotary Motion; Angular Speed. As a disk turns about its axis, not all points move with the same speed; as the disk makes one rotation, a point at the edge must move farther than one near the axis, and the points move these different distances in the same time. In Fig. 1 the point A has a greater speed than B, and B greater than C.

If we consider the line ABC rather than the points, we notice that the line as a whole turns about the axis. In a certain interval of time it will turn through an *angle* shown by the shaded area. The angle turned through

per unit time is called the *angular speed*

$$\text{Angular speed} = \frac{\text{angular displacement}}{\text{time}}$$

$$\bar{\omega} = \frac{\theta}{t}$$

where $\bar{\omega}$ (omega) is the average angular speed and θ is the angle turned through in time t.

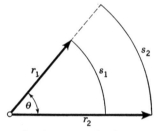

FIG. 2. The ratio of arc to radius is a measure of the angle

$$\theta = \frac{s_1}{r_1} = \frac{s_2}{r_2}$$

The angle may be expressed in degrees, in revolutions (1 rev = 360°), or in radians. The angular speed is then expressed in degrees per second, revolutions per second, or in radians per second.

The radian is a unit of angular measure which is based on the relative dimensions of a sector of a circle. In radian measure, there is a very simple relation between angular motion and the linear motion of the points. In Fig. 2, the ratio of length of arc to radius is the same for both concentric arcs. This ratio is used as a measure of the angle

$$\theta = \frac{s}{r}$$

where s is the length of the arc and r is the radius. The unit of angle in this system is the *radian*, which is the angle whose length of arc is equal to the radius. The length of the circumference is $2\pi r$. Hence

$$1 \text{ rev} = 360° = \frac{2\pi r}{r} = 2\pi \text{ radians}$$

$$1 \text{ radian} = \frac{360°}{2\pi} = 57.3° \quad \text{(approximately)}$$

If the time interval is taken shorter and shorter, the average angular speed approaches the instantaneous value; in the limit the instantaneous angular speed ω is given by

$$\omega = \frac{d\theta}{dt}$$

The distinction between speed and velocity, used in describing linear motion, applies also to angular motion. An angular velocity is represented by a vector along the axis of rotation pointing in the direction of the thumb of a right hand which grasps the axis with the fingers encircling the axis in the direction of rotation.

10-2. Angular Acceleration. As in the case of linear motion, angular motion may be uniform or accelerated. *Angular acceleration* α (alpha) is the time rate of change of angular velocity

Angular acceleration

$= \dfrac{\text{change in angular velocity}}{\text{time}} \quad \bar{\alpha} = \dfrac{\omega_2 - \omega_1}{t}$

where ω_1 is the initial and ω_2 the final angular velocity. The instantaneous angular acceleration is the derivative of ω with respect to t

$$\alpha = \frac{d\omega}{dt}$$

In studying uniformly accelerated angular motion, we treat it in a manner similar to that in which uniformly accelerated linear

motion was handled in Chap. 3. For solving problems in uniformly accelerated rotary motion, the following five equations are needed:

$$\theta = \bar{\omega}t \tag{1}$$
$$\omega_2 - \omega_1 = \alpha t \tag{2}$$
$$\bar{\omega} = \tfrac{1}{2}(\omega_1 + \omega_2) \tag{3}$$
$$\theta = \omega_1 t + \tfrac{1}{2}\alpha t^2 \tag{4}$$
$$\omega_2{}^2 - \omega_1{}^2 = 2\alpha\theta \tag{5}$$

Note that these equations become identical with Eqs. (1) to (5) of Chap. 3 if s is substituted for θ, v for ω, and a for α. These equations hold whatever the angular measure may be, as long as the same measure is used throughout a single problem. As in the case of linear motion, Eq. (1) holds for any type of angular motion while the other four are true only for uniformly accelerated angular motion.

When radian measure is used, there is a very simple relationship between angular and linear motions. These relationships are given by the equations

$$s = \theta r \tag{6}$$
$$v = \frac{ds}{dt} = r\frac{d\theta}{dt} = r\omega \tag{7}$$
$$a = \frac{dv}{dt} = r\frac{d\omega}{dt} = r\alpha \tag{8}$$

Example: A flywheel revolving at 200 rpm slows down at a constant rate of 2.00 radians/sec². What time is required to stop the flywheel and how many revolutions does it make in the process?

$\omega_1 = 200 \text{ rpm} = 200(2\pi) \text{ radians/min}$
$$= \frac{200(2\pi)}{60} \text{ radians/sec}$$

From Eq. (2) $\quad \omega_2 - \omega_1 = \alpha t$

$$0 - \frac{400\pi}{60} \text{ radians/sec} = (-2.00 \text{ radians/sec}^2)t$$
$$t = 10.5 \text{ sec}$$

From Eq. (5) $\quad \omega_2{}^2 - \omega_1{}^2 = 2\alpha\theta$

$$0 - \left(\frac{400\pi}{60} \text{ radians/sec}\right)^2$$
$$= 2(-2.00 \text{ radians/sec}^2)\theta$$
$$\theta = 110 \text{ radians} = \frac{110}{2\pi} \text{ rev} = 17.5 \text{ rev}$$

10-3. Moment of Inertia or Rotational Inertia. It has been found that a force is necessary to change the motion of a body, that is, to produce an acceleration. A greater force is required to give an acceleration to a body

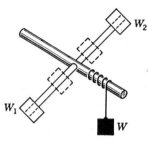

FIG. 3. Angular acceleration produced by a torque depends upon the distribution of mass.

of large mass than to cause the same acceleration in a smaller one. If the rotation of a body about an axis is to be changed, a *torque* about that axis must be applied. The angular acceleration produced by a given torque depends not only upon the mass of the rotating body but also upon the *distribution of mass* with respect to the axis. In Fig. 3, a bar with adjustable weights W_1 and W_2 is supported on an axle. If a string is wrapped around the axle and a weight W is hung on the string, the axle and rod will rotate. The rate of gain in speed of rotation will be much greater when W_1 and W_2 are near the axle, as shown by the dots, than when they are near the ends of the rod. The mass is not changed by this shift, but the distribution of mass is altered and the *rotational inertia* is changed.

If a small body of mass m is guided in a circular path at a distance r from an axis, a tangential force will give the body an acceleration $a = F/m$ along the circumference. The torque of force F about the axis is $L = Fr$, from which

$$L = mar = mr^2\alpha$$

The torque produces an angular acceleration proportional to the torque. The product mr^2 is characteristic of the configuration of the particle with respect to the chosen axis. The

moment of inertia I (also called the *rotational inertia*) of a small body about the chosen axis is the product of the mass and the square of the radius

Moment of inertia $=$ (mass)(radius)^2

$$I = mr^2 \quad (9)$$

In an extended body, each particle of matter in the body contributes to the moment of inertia an amount mr^2. The moment of inertia I of the body is the sum of the contributions of the individual elements

$$I = m_1r_1^2 + m_2r_2^2 + m_3r_3^2 + \cdots$$
or $\quad I = \Sigma mr^2 \qquad (10)$

The unit of moment of inertia is made up as a composite unit. In metric systems we have the kilogram-meter^2 or the gram-centimeter^2. In the British gravitational system that we have been using, where the weight is in pounds, we get the mass in slugs from W/g and the unit for I is the slug-foot^2.

For many regular bodies, the moment of inertia can be computed without difficulty and expressed in terms of the total mass of the body and the dimensions of the body. Note that the value of the moment of inertia depends upon the position of the axis chosen. The summation of Eq. (10) is replaced by an integral

$$I = \int r^2 \, dm \qquad (11)$$

where r is the distance of the mass element dm from the axis of rotation and the integral is taken over all the mass elements in the body.

Example: Find the moment of inertia of a solid cylinder about its axis of symmetry.

Consider the cylinder of Fig. 4. We shall select as an element of mass dm all particles that are at a distance r from the axis. This represents a shell of radius r, length l, and thickness dr. The volume dV of the shell is

$$dV = 2\pi r l \, dr$$

and the mass dm is $\rho \, dV$, where ρ is the mass per unit volume

$$dm = 2\pi \rho l r \, dr$$
and $\qquad dI = r^2 \, dm = 2\pi \rho l r^3 \, dr$

Integration between the limits of 0 and R gives

$$I = \int_0^R 2\pi\rho l r^3 \, dr = 2\pi\rho l \left[\frac{r^4}{4}\right]_0^R = 2\pi\rho l \frac{R^4}{4}$$

$$= \frac{1}{2}\pi\rho l R^4$$

But the mass m of the cylinder is

$$m = \pi R^2 l \rho$$

and $\qquad I = \frac{1}{2}\pi R^2 l \rho R^2 = \frac{1}{2}mR^2$

Moments of inertia of other regular bodies, calculated in the same way as that of the cylinder in the example, are given in Table 1.

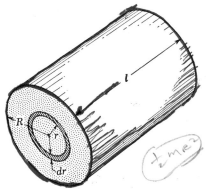

Fig. 4. Moment of inertia of a cylinder.

Example: What is the moment of inertia of a 50-lb cylindrical flywheel whose diameter is 16 in.?

For a cylinder about its axis

$$I = \frac{1}{2}mR^2$$

$$m = \frac{W}{g} = \frac{50 \text{ lb}}{32 \text{ ft/sec}^2} = 1.6 \text{ slugs}$$

$$R = 8.0 \text{ in.} = \frac{2}{3} \text{ ft}$$

$$I = \frac{1}{2}(1.6 \text{ slugs})(\frac{2}{3} \text{ ft})^2 = 0.35 \text{ slug-ft}^2$$

10-4. Parallel-axis Theorem. It is frequently desirable to be able to compute the moment of inertia of a body about an axis other than its common geometrical axis. This is relatively simple if the axes are parallel. We make use of the fact that the moment of inertia about an axis that is distant s from the center of gravity is the sum of the moment of inertia about the axis through the center of gravity and the moment of inertia of the body considered concentrated at the center of gravity about the new axis parallel to that through the center of gravity. That is, we must add ms^2 to the moment of inertia about the axis through the center of gravity.

Example: A solid cylinder rolls on a flat surface. Find the moment of inertia I_s of the cylinder about its line of contact with the surface.

From the parallel-axis theorem, and Table 1,

$$I_s = I_{c.g.} + mR^2$$
$$= \frac{1}{2}mR^2 + mR^2 = \frac{3}{2}mR^2$$

10-5. Radius of Gyration. In considering the moment of inertia of a body, it is frequently convenient to treat it as if all the mass were concentrated at a single distance from the axis. For each body a distance K can be found such that if all the mass were concentrated at that distance the moment of inertia would not be altered. This distance is called the *radius of gyration*. Its defining equation is

$$I = mK^2 \qquad (12)$$

The radius of gyration of a body with respect

TABLE 1. MOMENT OF INERTIA OF REGULAR BODIES

Body	Axis	Moment of inertia
Thin ring of radius R	Through center, perpendicular to plane of ring	mR^2
Thin ring of radius R	Along any diameter	$\frac{1}{2}mR^2$
Disk of radius R	Through center, perpendicular to disk	$\frac{1}{2}mR^2$
Disk of radius R	Along any diameter	$\frac{1}{4}mR^2$
Cylinder of radius R	Axis of the cylinder	$\frac{1}{2}mR^2$
Sphere of radius R	Any diameter	$\frac{2}{5}mR^2$
Uniform thin rod of length l	Perpendicular to rod at one end	$\frac{1}{3}ml^2$
Uniform thin rod of length l	Perpendicular to rod at the center	$\frac{1}{12}ml^2$

to any axis may be thought of as the radius of a thin ring which is centered on that axis and which has the same mass as the given body and the same moment of inertia. The radius of gyration is most useful for irregular bodies since the moment of inertia of such a body cannot be simply expressed in terms of its measurements. If, however, the radius of gyration of the irregular body is known, it can be used to compute the moment of inertia. For regular bodies such as those listed in Table 1, we can write an expression for the radius of gyration in place of the expression for the moment of inertia. For example,

for a disk $\qquad K = R/\sqrt{2}$
and for a sphere $\quad K = R\sqrt{2/5}$

Example: A 40-lb flywheel has a radius of gyration of 1.5 ft. What is its moment of inertia?

$$m = \frac{W}{g} = \frac{40 \text{ lb}}{32 \text{ ft/sec}^2} = 1.2 \text{ slugs}$$
$$I = mK^2 = 1.2 \text{ slugs } (1.5 \text{ ft})^2 = 2.8 \text{ slug-ft}^2$$

10-6. Newton's Laws for Angular Motion. Newton's laws for rotary motion are very similar to those for linear motion. The first law applies to a condition of equilibrium. *A body does not change its angular velocity unless it is acted upon by an external, unbalanced torque.* A body at rest does not begin to rotate without a torque to cause it to do so. Neither does a body that is rotating change its rotation or change its axis unless a torque acts. A rotating wheel would continue to rotate forever if it were not stopped by a torque such as that due to friction.

An unbalanced torque about an axis produces an angular acceleration, about that axis, which is directly proportional to the torque and inversely proportional to the moment of inertia of the body about that axis. In the form of an equation this becomes

$$L = I\alpha \qquad (13)$$

where L is the unbalanced torque, I is the moment of inertia, and α is the angular acceleration. Torque must always be referred to some axis as are also moment of inertia and

angular acceleration. In Eq. (13) we must be careful to use the same axis for all three quantities. As in the case of the force equation for linear motion, we must be careful to use a consistent set of units in Eq. (13). The angular acceleration must be expressed in radians per second per second.

Torque is a vector quantity. A vector representing a torque is drawn according to the same right-hand rule as used in representing an angular velocity.

The following sets of units apply to Eq. (13):

L	I	α
lb-ft	slug-ft^2	radians/sec^2
m-newton	kg-m^2	radians/sec^2
cm-dyne	gm-cm^2	radians/sec^2

Example: A flywheel, in the form of a uniform disk 4.0 ft in diameter, weighs 600 lb. What will be its angular acceleration if it is acted upon by a net torque of 225 lb-ft?

$$m = \frac{W}{g} = \frac{600 \text{ lb}}{32 \text{ ft/sec}^2} = 18.7 \text{ slugs}$$
$$I = \frac{1}{2}mR^2 = \frac{1}{2}(18.7 \text{ slugs})(2.0 \text{ ft})^2 = 38 \text{ slug-ft}^2$$
$$L = I\alpha$$
$$225 \text{ lb-ft} = (38 \text{ slug-ft}^2)\alpha$$
$$\alpha = 5.9 \text{ radians/sec}^2$$

In radian measure the angle is a ratio of two lengths and hence is a pure number. The unit "radian" therefore does not always appear in the algebraic handling of units.

Example: If the disk of the preceding example is rotating at 1200 rpm, what torque is required to stop it in 3.0 min?

From Eq. (2)
$$\omega_2 - \omega_1 = \alpha t$$
$$\omega_1 = 1200 \text{ rpm} = 20 \text{ rps} = 40\pi \text{ radians/sec}$$
$$t = 3.0 \text{ min} = 180 \text{ sec}$$
$$0 - 40\pi \text{ radians/sec} = \alpha(180 \text{ sec})$$
$$\alpha = -\frac{40\pi}{180} \text{ radians/sec}^2$$
$$L = I\alpha = (38 \text{ slug-ft}^2)\left(-\frac{40\pi}{180} \text{ radians/sec}^2\right)$$
$$= -26 \text{ lb-ft}$$

The negative sign is consistent with a retarding torque.

Example: A wheel and its axle (Fig. 5) have a total mass of 50 kg. The axle has a diameter of 10.0 cm. A 2.5-kg ball is fastened to a cord wrapped around the axle. When started from rest, the ball moves downward a distance of 2.8 m in

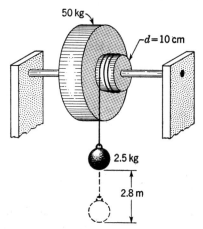

FIG. 5. Angular acceleration of a wheel.

7.0 sec. Find the radius of gyration of the rotating system. Neglect friction.

The linear acceleration of the ball is

$$a = \frac{2s}{t^2} = \frac{2(2.8 \text{ m})}{(7.0 \text{ sec})^2} = 0.114 \text{ m/sec}^2$$

The unbalanced force acting on the ball is the difference between its weight and the unknown tension T in the cord. From Newton's second law

$W = mg = (2.5 \times 9.8)$ newtons $= 24.5$ newtons
24.5 newtons $- T = (2.5 \text{ kg})(0.114 \text{ m/sec}^2)$
$$= 0.284 \text{ newton}$$
$$T = 24.2 \text{ newtons}$$

The torque L on the rotating system is

$L = Tr = 24.2$ newtons $\times 0.050$ m
$$= 1.21 \text{ m-newtons}$$

The angular acceleration

$$\alpha = \frac{a}{r} = \frac{0.114 \text{ m/sec}^2}{0.050 \text{ m}} = 2.28 \text{ radians/sec}^2$$

From Eq. (13), the moment of inertia of the wheel and its axle is

$$I = \frac{1.21 \text{ m-newtons}}{2.28 \text{ radians/sec}^2} = 0.53 \text{ kg-m}^2$$

The radius of gyration is therefore

$$K = \sqrt{\frac{I}{m}} = \sqrt{\frac{0.53 \text{ kg-m}^2}{50 \text{ kg}}} = 0.103 \text{ m}$$

For every torque applied to one body, there is a torque equal in magnitude and opposite in direction applied to another body. If a motor applies a torque to a shaft, the shaft applies an opposite torque to the motor. If the motor is not securely fastened to its base, it may turn in a direction opposite to that of the shaft. If an airplane engine exerts a torque to turn the propeller clockwise, the airplane experiences a torque tending to turn it counterclockwise and this torque must be compensated by the thrust of the air on the wings. For twin-engined planes, the two propellers turn in opposite directions and thus avoid a net torque.

10-7. Work, Power, Energy. If a constant torque L turns a body through an angle θ, work is done by the torque. The torque is the result of a force F acting at a distance r from the axis. The work done by the force is

$$\text{Work} = Fs$$

but the distance s in the direction of the force is the length of the arc $s = r\theta$, and $L = Fr$

$$\text{Work} = Fr\theta = L\theta \qquad (14)$$

Since power is work per unit time,

$$P = \frac{dW}{dt} = L\frac{d\theta}{dt} = L\omega = L \times 2\pi n \qquad (15)$$

The expression for the kinetic energy of rotation of a body can be derived from Eqs. (5) and (13) in the same manner that Eq. (3), Chap. 8, was derived to express the linear kinetic energy.

$$\text{KE} = \frac{1}{2}I\omega^2 \qquad (16)$$

Frequently a body has simultaneous linear and angular motions. For example, the wheel of an automobile rotates about its axle, but the axle advances along the road. It is usually easier to deal with the kinetic energy of such a body if we consider the two parts: (1) that due to translation of the center of mass ($\frac{1}{2}mv^2$)

and (2) that due to rotation about an axis through the center of mass ($\frac{1}{2}I\omega^2$)

Example: What is the kinetic energy of a 5.0-lb ball whose diameter is 6.0 in., if it rolls across a level surface with a speed of 4.0 ft/sec?

$$KE = \tfrac{1}{2}mv^2 + \tfrac{1}{2}I\omega^2$$
$$m = \frac{W}{g} = \frac{5.0 \text{ lb}}{32 \text{ ft/sec}^2} = 0.16 \text{ slug}$$
$$\omega = \frac{v}{R} = \frac{4.0 \text{ ft/sec}}{\frac{1}{4} \text{ ft}} = 16 \text{ radians/sec}$$

From Table 1

$$I = (\tfrac{2}{5})mR^2 = \tfrac{2}{5}(0.16 \text{ slug})(\tfrac{1}{4} \text{ ft})^2$$
$$= 0.0040 \text{ slug-ft}^2$$
$$KE = \tfrac{1}{2}(0.16 \text{ slug})(4.0 \text{ ft/sec})^2$$
$$+ \tfrac{1}{2}(0.0040 \text{ slug-ft}^2)(16 \text{ radians/sec})^2$$
$$= 1.3 \text{ ft-lb} + 0.5 \text{ ft-lb} = 1.8 \text{ ft-lb}$$

When energy is supplied to a body so that it is divided between energy of translation and energy of rotation, the way in which the energy is divided is determined by the distribution of mass. If two cylinders of equal mass, one being solid and the other hollow, roll down an incline, the solid cylinder will roll faster. Its moment of inertia is less than that of the hollow cylinder and hence the kinetic energy of rotation is smaller than that of the hollow cylinder; but its kinetic energy of translation is greater than that of the hollow cylinder. Hence the solid cylinder has a greater speed.

Example: A solid cylinder of 12.0-in. diameter at the top of an incline 6.0 ft high and 13 ft long is released and rolls down the incline. Find its linear and angular speeds at the bottom. Neglect energy losses due to friction.

The potential energy of the cylinder at the top of the incline is converted into kinetic energy of translation and rotation as the cylinder rolls down. At the bottom of the incline all the potential energy has been converted into kinetic energy.

$$PE = KE$$
$$Wh = \tfrac{1}{2}mv^2 + \tfrac{1}{2}I\omega^2$$

but
$$\omega = \frac{v}{R}$$

and
$$I = \tfrac{1}{2}mR^2$$

Then

$$Wh = \frac{1}{2}mv^2 + \frac{1}{2}\left(\frac{1}{2}mR^2\right)\left(\frac{v}{R}\right)^2$$
$$Wh = \tfrac{1}{2}mv^2 + \tfrac{1}{4}mv^2 = (\tfrac{3}{4})mv^2$$
$$Wh = mgh = (\tfrac{3}{4})mv^2$$
$$v^2 = (\tfrac{4}{3})gh$$
$$v = \sqrt{(\tfrac{4}{3})gh} = \sqrt{(\tfrac{4}{3})(32 \text{ ft/sec}^2)(6.0 \text{ ft})}$$
$$= 16 \text{ ft/sec}$$
$$\omega = \frac{v}{R} = \frac{16 \text{ ft/sec}}{0.50 \text{ ft}} = 32 \text{ radians/sec}$$

Note that the linear speed does not depend upon the size or weight of the cylinder.

10-8. Comparison of Linear and Angular Motions. In our discussion of motions and forces we have found the equations of angular motion to be quite similar to those of linear motion. They can be obtained directly from

TABLE 2. CORRESPONDING EQUATIONS IN LINEAR AND ANGULAR MOTION

	Linear	Angular
Velocity	$\bar{v} = \dfrac{s}{t},\ v = \dfrac{ds}{dt}$	$\bar{\omega} = \dfrac{\theta}{t},\ \omega = \dfrac{d\theta}{dt}$
Acceleration	$\bar{a} = \dfrac{v_2 - v_1}{t},\ a = \dfrac{dv}{dt}$	$\bar{\alpha} = \dfrac{\omega_2 - \omega_1}{t},\ \alpha = \dfrac{d\omega}{dt}$
Uniformly accelerated motion	$v_2 - v_1 = at$ $s = v_1 t + \frac{1}{2}at^2$ $v_2{}^2 - v_1{}^2 = 2as$	$\omega_2 - \omega_1 = \alpha t$ $\theta = \omega_1 t + \frac{1}{2}\alpha t^2$ $\omega_2{}^2 - \omega_1{}^2 = 2\alpha\theta$
Newton's second law	$F = ma$	$L = I\alpha$
Work	Work $= Fs$	Work $= L\theta$
Power	$P = Fv$	$P = L\omega$
Kinetic energy	$KE = \frac{1}{2}mv^2$	$KE = \frac{1}{2}I\omega^2$

the equations of linear motion if the following substitutions are made: θ for s, ω for v, α for a, L for F, I for m. In Table 2 is listed a set of corresponding equations.

SUMMARY

For a rotating body the *angular speed* is the angle turned through per unit time by a line that passes through the axis of rotation

$$\bar{\omega} = \frac{\theta}{t} \qquad \omega = \frac{d\theta}{dt}$$

Angular distance, in radians, is the ratio of the length of arc to its radius.

A *radian* is the angle whose length of arc is equal to the radius.

Angular acceleration is the rate of change of angular velocity,

$$\bar{\alpha} = \frac{\omega_2 - \omega_1}{t} \qquad \alpha = \frac{d\omega}{dt}$$

Equations of uniformly accelerated angular motion are similar to those for linear motion with angle substituted for distance, angular speed for linear speed, and angular acceleration for linear acceleration.

The *moment of inertia* (rotational inertia) of a body about a given axis is the sum of the products of the mass and square of the radius for each particle of the body

$$I = \Sigma mr^2 \qquad I = \int r^2 \, dm$$

The radius of gyration K of a body about an axis is the distance from that axis at which all the mass might be concentrated without altering the moment of inertia. It is defined by the equation

$$I = mK^2$$

For angular motion *Newton's laws* may be stated:

1. A body does not change its angular velocity unless it is acted upon by an external, unbalanced torque.

2. An unbalanced torque about an axis produces an angular acceleration about that axis, which is directly proportional to the torque and inversely proportional to the moment of inertia of the body about that axis

$$L = I\alpha$$

3. For every torque applied to one body there is a torque equal in magnitude and opposite in direction applied to another body.

In angular motion the *work* done by a torque L in turning through an angle θ is

$$\text{Work} = L\theta$$

The *power* supplied by a torque is

$$P = L\omega$$

Kinetic energy of rotation is given by the equation

$$\text{KE} = \tfrac{1}{2}I\omega^2$$

For a rolling body the total kinetic energy, both translational and rotational, is

$$\text{KE} = \tfrac{1}{2}mv^2 + \tfrac{1}{2}I\omega^2$$

In the last five equations the angles must be expressed in radian measure.

QUESTIONS 1. Show why the radian measure of angle is equally satisfactory for all systems of units.

2. Why is most of the mass of a flywheel placed in the rim?

3. Can you distinguish between a raw egg and one that has been hard-cooked in its shell by giving each a spin on a table top? Explain.

4. A solid cylinder rolls down an inclined plane. Its time of descent is noted. Then a hole is bored along the axis of the cylinder. When it is again allowed to roll down the incline, will it require more, less, or the same time to reach the bottom? Explain.

5. A solid cylinder, a hollow cylinder, and a solid sphere roll down an incline starting simultaneously from rest. In what order do they reach the bottom of the incline?

6. A bicycle wheel is supported by its axle on two inclined rods. It is allowed to roll down first with the axle free to turn on its bearings and second with the cones tightened so that the wheel must turn with the axle. In which case does it reach the bottom of the incline quicker? Explain.

7. Derive an expression for the linear acceleration of a sphere that starts from rest and rolls down a plane inclined at an angle θ to the horizontal.

8. Show that when a hoop rolls down an incline half the kinetic energy is rotational and half translational.

9. What portion of the total kinetic energy of a rolling solid disk is energy of translation and what portion is energy of rotation?

10. Show that the total kinetic energy of a rolling solid cylinder is independent of its radius. Is this true of other rolling bodies?

11. A hollow cylinder and a rectangular block are placed at the top of an incline. When they are released, the cylinder rolls down the incline without loss of energy while the block slides down with half its energy being used to do work against friction. Do they reach the bottom at the same time? If not, which arrives first?

PROBLEMS   **1.** A shaft of 6.0-in. diameter is to be turned on a lathe with a surface linear speed of 180 ft/min. What is its angular speed?

2. A pulley of 18.0-in. diameter makes 300 rev/min. What is the linear speed of the belt if there is no slippage? The belt passes over a second pulley. What must be the diameter of the second pulley if its shaft turns at a rate of 400 rev/min?   *Ans.* 1410 ft/min; 13.5 in.

3. A flywheel is brought from rest to a speed of 60 rev/min in 0.50 min. What is the angular acceleration? What is the angular speed at the end of 15 sec?

4. A wheel has its speed increased from 120 to 240 rev/min in 20 sec. (*a*) What is the angular acceleration? (*b*) How many revolutions of the wheel are required?   *Ans.* 0.63 radian/sec²; 60 rev

5. What is the angular acceleration of an automobile wheel 30 in. in diameter when the car changes speed from 15 to 30 mi/hr in 5.0 sec?

6. If a disk 3.0 ft in diameter starts from rest with an angular acceleration of 4.4 radians/sec², (*a*) what is its angular speed at the end of 10 sec? (*b*) What is the linear speed of a point on the circumference?   *Ans.* 44 radians/sec; 66 ft/sec

7. The armature of a motor revolving at 1800 rev/min comes to rest in 20.0 sec after the power is turned off. Calculate (*a*) the angular acceleration, (*b*) the number of revolutions that the motor makes before coming to rest, and (*c*) the angular distance traversed during the fifth second after the power is turned off.

8. A uniform circular disk 3.0 ft in diameter weighs 960 lb. What is its moment of inertia about its usual axis?   *Ans.* 34 slug-ft²

9. Considering the earth as a uniform sphere of 6.00×10^{21} tons and 4000 mi radius, calculate its moment of inertia about its axis of rotation.

10. A cylinder 12.0 cm in diameter having a mass of 3.00 kg rests on a horizontal plane. Compute the moment of inertia of the cylinder about an axis along the line of contact with the plane.   *Ans.* 1.62×10^5 gm-cm²

11. A sphere 30.0 cm in diameter, having a mass of 5.00 kg, rests on a horizontal plane. Compute its moment of inertia about an axis in the plane through the point of contact.

12. A disk 3.0 ft in diameter whose moment of inertia is 34 slug-ft² is caused to rotate by a force of 100 lb acting tangent to the circumference. What is the angular acceleration?   *Ans.* 4.4 radians/sec²

13. A uniform disk has a diameter of 20.0 cm and a mass of 3000 gm. It is free to rotate with negligible friction. A string wrapped around the disk is attached to an object of mass 100 gm. Determine the angular acceleration of the disk when the object is released.

14. What constant torque must be applied to a 200-lb flywheel having a radius of gyration of 2.0 ft in order to increase the angular speed by 1800 rev/min in 15 sec? Assume a constant frictional force of 20 lb acting on the 6.0-in. shaft. *Ans.* $3\bar{2}0$ lb-ft

15. The rotor of an electric motor has a moment of inertia of 25 slug-ft². If it is rotating at a rate of 1200 rev/min, what frictional torque is required to stop it in 1.0 min?

16. A 400-lb flywheel has a radius of gyration of 2.0 ft. (*a*) What constant torque is required to bring the wheel from rest to a speed of 120 rev/min in 30 sec? (*b*) How much work is done in this interval? *Ans.* 21 lb-ft; $4\bar{0}00$ ft-lb

17. A small object of mass 300 gm is arranged to revolve around an axis at a distance of 60.0 cm. What constant torque would cause the object to turn through 40.0 rev in 3.00 min, if it starts from rest and moves with uniform angular acceleration?

18. A uniform disk of 12.0-in. diameter and 50.0-lb weight is mounted on an axle having a diameter of 1.00 in. A string is wrapped around the axle, and a constant force of 1.00 lb is exerted on it. What speed will the wheel acquire in 3.00 min? *Ans.* 38.5 radians/sec

19. A flywheel weighing 500 lb has its mass largely concentrated in the rim, which has an average diameter of 2.00 ft and an outer diameter of 2.10 ft. A cord wrapped around the rim has maintained in it a constant force of 10.0 lb. Determine the angular speed of the wheel 30.0 sec after it is started from rest.

20. The belt which drives a 1600-lb flywheel of radius of gyration 2.00 ft passes over a pulley of 1.00-ft radius on the same shaft as the flywheel. The average pull of the tight belt exceeds that of the slack belt by 100 lb. How long will it take the flywheel to acquire an angular speed of 600 rev/min if it starts from rest? *Ans.* 125 sec

21. A solid, cylindrical shaft weighing 50 lb has a radius of 5.0 in. and rotates in a bearing with an angular speed of 1000 rev/min. The bearing exerts a frictional force of 2.5 lb tangentially. How many revolutions would the shaft make if the driving force were removed?

22. (*a*) What is the constant torque which must be applied to a flywheel weighing 400 lb and having a radius of gyration of 2.00 ft if, starting from rest and moving with uniform angular acceleration, it develops an angular speed of 1800 rev/min in 10.0 sec? (*b*) If the shaft on which the pulley is mounted has a radius of 6.00 in. and there is a tangential frictional force of 20.0 lb, how much must be the total torque? *Ans.* 942 lb-ft; 952 lb-ft

23. A small sphere rolls without loss of energy down a 20° incline. What is its linear acceleration?

24. A steel ball rolls down an incline 220 cm long, making an angle of 4.0° with the horizontal. It requires 3.00 sec for the ball to reach the bottom of the incline after starting from rest at the top. Calculate the value of *g* for this location. *Ans.* 980 cm/sec²

25. A belt-driven pulley 24 in. in diameter makes 300 rev/min. If the tension in the tight side of the belt exceeds that of the slack side by 80 lb, (*a*) how much work is done in 5.0 min? (*b*) What is the rate of working in horsepower?

26. What is the initial kinetic energy of rotation of a rotor that has a moment of inertia of 25 slug-ft² and is rotating at a rate of 1200 rev/min? What becomes of this energy when the rotor is stopped?   *Ans.* 2.0 × 10⁵ ft-lb

27. A motor running at a rate of 1200 rev/min can supply a torque of 4.4 lb-ft. What power does it develop?

28. A solid cylinder of mass 300 gm and radius 1.5 cm starts from rest and rolls down a plane 1470 cm long, inclined at 30° to the horizontal. How long will it take to descend, if there is no loss of energy due to friction? What will be its energy of rotation at the bottom?   *Ans.* 3.0 sec; 7.2 joules

29. A 16-lb bowling ball is rolling without slipping down an alley with a speed of 20 ft/sec. What is its kinetic energy (*a*) of translation and (*b*) of rotation? (*c*) What is its total kinetic energy?

30. A wheel of an automobile traveling 30.0 mi/hr has an external radius of 14.0 in. and weighs 80.0 lb. Assuming the radius of gyration to be 10.0 in., find (*a*) the kinetic energy of translation, (*b*) the kinetic energy of rotation, and (*c*) the total kinetic energy of the wheel.   *Ans.* 24$\overline{2}$0 ft-lb; 12$\overline{3}$0 ft-lb; 36$\overline{5}$0 ft-lb

31. A 25-lb solid cylinder is at the top of an incline 5.00 ft high and 13.0 ft long. What linear speed does the cylinder acquire in rolling down the incline?

32. A 25-lb solid sphere is at the top of an incline 5.00 ft high and 13.0 ft long. What linear speed does the sphere acquire in rolling down the slope?

Ans. 15.0 ft/sec

33. A 50.0-gm bullet, moving with a speed of 100 m/sec, strikes a projection on a wheel of moment of inertia 2.00 × 10⁵ gm-cm². The radius of the uniform disk is 30.0 cm. If 80% of the energy of the bullet is expended in producing rotation of the wheel, determine the angular speed imparted to it.

34. The extremity of the hour hand of a clock travels one-eighteenth as fast as the extremity of the minute hand. If the minute hand is 6.0 in. long, how long is the hour hand?   *Ans.* 4.0 in.

35. Calculate the moment of inertia of a meter stick, which has a mass of 320 gm, about an axis at right angles to the stick and located at the 25-cm mark.

36. A wheel starts from rest and reaches a rotational speed of 100 rev/min within 30 revolutions. Assuming a uniform angular acceleration, calculate (*a*) the angular acceleration and (*b*) the time required to reach this speed. (*c*) If the wheel has a radius of 2.0 ft, what is the speed of a point on the rim at 100 rev/min?   *Ans.* 3$\overline{3}$0π radians/min²; 36 sec; 6.7π ft/sec

37. A 40-gm hoop of 10.0-cm radius is suspended in a vertical plane on a 50-cm length of weightless cord. Find the moment of inertia of the hoop with respect to an axis through the point of suspension normal to the plane of the hoop and string.

38. A slender uniform rod is suspended from one end (point *O*). The mass and length of the rod are *m* and *l*, respectively. A point particle, also of mass *m*, is embedded in the rod at a distance *x* from the point *O*. It is observed that the radius of gyration of the system about an axis through *O* and perpendicular to the plane of the paper is *l*/2. The moment of inertia of the uniform rod alone, about the axis of rotation, is ⅓*ml²*. Evaluate the fraction *x*/*l*.   *Ans.* 0.41

39. Two solid wheels each 2.0 ft in diameter and weighing 24.0 lb are keyed to a solid axle 1.0 ft in diameter and weighing 32.0 lb. A string wrapped around the axle passes over a massless, frictionless pulley and down to a block weighing 160 lb. Find the acceleration of the center of mass of the spool described.

40. In the arrangement shown in Fig. 6, the solid disk and the pulley have the same radii, and the disk, pulley, and block have equal masses. The plane has a slope of 30.0°; the disk rolls on the incline without slipping or loss of energy. Find the acceleration of the hanging block.   *Ans.* $\frac{2}{5}g$

41. A hexagonal nut of mass 100 gm and radius of gyration 2.0 cm turns without friction down a vertical screw of 3.0 turns/cm. Starting from rest, how long does it take the nut to run down 10 cm of the screw?

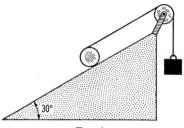

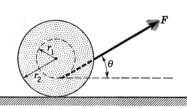

FIG. 6.   FIG. 7.

42. A spool of thread with an inner radius r_1 and an outer radius r_2 has a moment of inertia I_0 about the center of mass. The spool is pulled by a thread, as shown in Fig. 7, with a constant force F. (*a*) Find the linear acceleration of the spool if $\theta = 0°$. (*b*) At what angle θ will the linear acceleration vanish? (Assume that the spool rolls without slipping.)

Ans. $\dfrac{F(r_2{}^2 - r_1 r_2)}{I_0 + m r_2{}^2}$; $\cos \theta = \dfrac{r_1}{r_2}$

angular distance

$$\omega = \frac{\theta}{t}$$

α = angular acceleration

$$\alpha = \frac{W_2 - W_1}{t}$$

$$2as = v_2{}^2 - v_1{}^2$$

$$2\alpha\theta = W_2{}^2 - W_1{}^2$$

$$F = ma$$

$$L =$$

11. Momentum

In collisions between objects in motion the forces involved may be extremely large. When the bat strikes a baseball, both ball and bat are greatly distorted while they are in contact. If a heavy, fast-moving truck strikes a house, the force may be sufficient to move the building from its foundation.

While the force may be very great during the impact, the large force acts for only a very short time. The force is not constant during the contact, varying between wide limits. The way in which the force varies during the collision depends upon the elastic properties of each of the bodies involved as well as upon their speeds. Because of the complicated manner in which the forces vary it is usually convenient to study impact problems from the standpoint of momentum.

11-1. Momentum. If a passenger car traveling at the rate of 20 mi/hr is brought to rest in 1 sec, a large force is required. To bring a loaded truck traveling at the same speed to rest in the same time would require a much greater force. If the speed of the passenger car is 40 mi/hr instead of 20 mi/hr, the force would also be increased. The force required depends jointly upon the speed and mass of the moving object. The product of the *mass* and *velocity* of a body is called its *momentum*. The defining equation for momentum is

$$p = mv \tag{1}$$

where p is the momentum, m the mass, and v the velocity. Every object in motion has momentum.

The units for momentum are composite units made up from those of mass and velocity. In the cgs system the unit becomes the gram-centimeter per second. In the British system as usual we compute the mass in slugs from W/g, and the unit of momentum is the slug-foot per second. The corresponding mks unit is the kilogram-meter per second.

Example: What is the momentum of a 100-lb shell as it leaves the gun with a speed of 1200 ft/sec?

$$m = \frac{W}{g} = \frac{100 \text{ lb}}{32 \text{ ft/sec}^2} = 3.1 \text{ slugs}$$
$$p = mv = (3.1 \text{ slugs})(1200 \text{ ft/sec})$$
$$= 3700 \text{ slug-ft/sec}$$

Momentum is a vector quantity, its direction being that of the velocity. To find the momentum of a system of two or more bodies, we must add their momenta vectorially. Consider two 4-lb balls moving toward each other with equal speeds of 4 ft/sec as shown in Fig. 1. The mass of each is $\frac{4}{32}$ slug. The momentum of A is

$$p_A = (\tfrac{4}{32} \text{ slug})(4 \text{ ft/sec}) = 0.5 \text{ slug-ft/sec}$$

to the right while that of B is similarly 0.5 slug-ft/sec to the left. The vector sum of the two is zero, and hence the momentum of the *system* is zero.

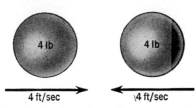

FIG. 1. Two balls of equal mass having velocities equal in magnitude but opposite in direction. The momentum of the system is zero.

11-2. Conservation of Momentum. According to Newton's first law of motion, the velocity of a body does not change unless it is acted upon by a net force. Since the mass of the body is constant, we find that the momentum does not change unless an external force acts upon the body. The statement that the momentum of a body, or system of bodies, does not change except when an external force is applied is known as the *law of conservation of momentum*. The use of the law enables us to explain simply the behavior of common objects.

If an external force does act upon a system of bodies, the momentum of the system is changed but, in the process, some other set of bodies must gain (or lose) an amount of momentum equal to that lost (or gained) by the system. In every process where velocity is changed the momentum lost by one body or set of bodies is equal to that gained by another body or set of bodies.

Momentum lost = momentum gained (2)

Let us consider further the balls shown in Fig. 1. If they continue to move toward each other, they will collide and in the collision each will exert a force on the other. The momentum of the system of two balls is zero before the impact. By the law of conservation of momentum it must be zero after the impact. If the balls are elastic, they will rebound and the conservation law requires that the speeds of recoil shall be equal to each other (but not necessarily equal to the original

speed) so that the momentum shall remain zero.

The recoil of a gun is an example of conservation of momentum. The momentum of gun and bullet is zero before the explosion. The bullet gains a forward momentum, and hence the gun must acquire an equal backward momentum so that the sum will remain zero.

Example: A 2.0-oz bullet is fired from a 10-lb gun with a speed of 2000 ft/sec. What is the speed of recoil of the gun?

The momentum of the system of gun and bullet is zero before the gun is fired and therefore must be zero after the firing. Hence the momentum of the gun is equal in magnitude but opposite in direction to that of the bullet.

$$m_1 v_1 = m_2 v_2$$

$$v_1 = \frac{m_2}{m_1} v_2$$

but $\quad m_1 = \dfrac{W_1}{g} \quad$ and $\quad m_2 = \dfrac{W_2}{g}$

$$\frac{m_1}{m_2} = \frac{W_1}{W_2}$$

$$v_1 = \frac{(\frac{2}{16})\ \text{lb}}{10\ \text{lb}}\ (2000\ \text{ft/sec}) = 25\ \text{ft/sec}$$

In the firing of the gun, forces are exerted, one on the gun and the other on the projectile. These forces, however, are *internal*, that is, they are within the system of the gun and bullet that we considered. If we consider the bullet alone, the force becomes an external force and causes a change in momentum of the bullet but, in accordance with Newton's third law, a force equal in magnitude but opposite in direction acts on the gun giving it a momentum equal in magnitude to that of the bullet but opposite in direction.

11-3. Impulse. The change in momentum caused by an external force depends upon the amount of the force and also upon the time the force acts. From Newton's second law

$$F = ma = m\frac{dv}{dt} = \frac{d(mv)}{dt} = \frac{dp}{dt} \quad (3)$$

Therefore, an alternative statement of Newton's second law is: *the rate of change of momentum of a body is proportional to the net force acting on the body.* From Eq. (3) it is seen that

$$F \, dt = dp \tag{4}$$

The product of the force and the time the force acts is called the *impulse*. The impulse is equal to the change in momentum produced by the force during the time interval.

No matter how the force varies during any time interval it is related to the total change in momentum by the equation

$$\int_{t_1}^{t_2} F \, dt = \int_{p_1}^{p_2} dp \tag{5}$$

If the force is constant during the interval Δt, Eq. (5) reduces to

$$F \, \Delta t = p_2 - p_1 \tag{6}$$

In Eq. (6) the force may also be interpreted as the average force during the interval even when the variation is very large. In an impact the force almost never is constant during the time of collision but varies over a wide range of values. Equation (6) can be used in such a case only to find the average force during the interval of contact. If it is necessary to know the force at any instant during the collision, it may be determined if the rate of change of momentum is known, for the force is equal to the rate of change of momentum. Since it is seldom possible to observe the rate of change of momentum, the forces can best be studied in terms of the deformations produced in the colliding bodies. The relation between force and deformation will be studied in Chap. 13.

Equations (4), (5), and (6) imply that no object can be stopped instantaneously and that the shorter the length of time required for stopping the greater must be the force. A bomb dropped from a height of several thousand feet has very great momentum just before it strikes its target. As it strikes the steel deck of a ship it must be stopped in a very short time or it will penetrate the deck. The ordinary steel deck of a ship is unable to supply the force necessary to stop the bomb.

Extremely large forces are involved where a rapidly moving body is stopped quickly.

Example: A 3000-lb car traveling with a speed of 30 mi/hr strikes an obstruction and is brought to rest in 0.10 sec. What is the average force on the car?

From Eq. (6)

$$F \, \Delta t = mv_2 - mv_1$$

$$m = \frac{W}{g} = \frac{3000 \text{ lb}}{32 \text{ ft/sec}^2} = 94 \text{ slugs}$$

$$v_1 = 30 \text{ mi/hr} = 44 \text{ ft/sec}$$

$$F = \frac{m(v_2 - v_1)}{\Delta t} = \frac{94 \text{ slugs} \, (0 - 44 \text{ ft/sec})}{0.10 \text{ sec}}$$

$$= -4\overline{1},000 \text{ lb}$$

The negative sign of the result indicates that the force is in a direction opposite to the initial velocity, a result which we should expect after careful consideration of the problem.

11-4. Elastic and Inelastic Collisions. In any collision between two bodies the relative velocity of recession is proportional to the relative velocity of approach. In symbols

$$e = \frac{u_2 - u_1}{v_1 - v_2} \tag{7}$$

where $v_1 - v_2$ is the relative velocity before impact and $u_2 - u_1$ is the relative velocity after the impact but with the sign changed. The ratio e is a constant for any two bodies, and it is called the *coefficient of restitution*. A collision is said to be perfectly elastic if $e = 1$. It is completely inelastic if $e = 0$, and in this case the two colliding bodies adhere and move as one body after the collision. For all other collisions the value of e is between zero and one.

For the special case of perfectly elastic collision, kinetic energy is conserved in the collision. From the law of conservation of momentum

$$m_1 v_1 + m_2 v_2 = m_1 u_1 + m_2 u_2 \tag{8}$$

or, by rearranging the terms we observe that the loss in momentum of the first body is equal to the gain in momentum of the second

$$m_1 v_1 - m_1 u_1 = m_2 u_2 - m_2 v_2 \qquad (9)$$

From Eq. (7), for a perfectly elastic collision

$$v_1 - v_2 = u_2 - u_1$$
or
$$v_1 + u_1 = u_2 + v_2 \qquad (10)$$

If we multiply Eq. (9) by Eq. (10), we obtain

$$m_1(v_1 - u_1)(v_1 + u_1) = m_2(u_2 - v_2)(u_2 + v_2) \qquad (11)$$

or
$$m_1 v_1{}^2 - m_1 u_1{}^2 = m_2 u_2{}^2 - m_2 v_2{}^2 \qquad (12)$$

and by multiplying by $\frac{1}{2}$ and rearranging terms we obtain

$$\tfrac{1}{2}m_1 v_1{}^2 + \tfrac{1}{2}m_2 v_2{}^2 = \tfrac{1}{2}m_1 u_1{}^2 + \tfrac{1}{2}m_2 u_2{}^2 \qquad (13)$$

Thus the kinetic energy before the collision is the same as that after the collision. In all inelastic collisions the kinetic energy after the impact is less than that before.

Example: A 2.0-lb ball traveling with a speed of 22 ft/sec overtakes a 4.0-lb ball traveling in the same direction as the first with a speed of 10 ft/sec. If the coefficient of restitution is 0.80, find the velocities of the two balls after the collision.

$$e(v_1 - v_2) = u_2 - u_1$$
$$0.80(22 \text{ ft/sec} - 10 \text{ ft/sec}) = u_2 - u_1$$
$$u_2 - u_1 = 9.6 \text{ ft/sec}$$
$$m_1 v_1 + m_2 v_2 = m_1 u_1 + m_2 u_2$$

Since $m = W/g$, we may make that substitution and multiply the equation by g to obtain

$$W_1 v_1 + W_2 v_2 = W_1 u_1 + W_2 u_2$$
$$2.0 \text{ lb} \times 22 \text{ ft/sec} + 4.0 \text{ lb} \times 10 \text{ ft/sec}$$
$$= (2.0 \text{ lb})\, u_1 + (4.0 \text{ lb})\, u_2$$
$$2u_2 + u_1 = 42 \text{ ft/sec}$$
and since
$$u_2 - u_1 = 9.6 \text{ ft/sec}$$
$$u_2 = 17.2 \text{ ft/sec}$$
$$u_1 = 7.6 \text{ ft/sec}$$

11-5. Collisions of Bodies Not Moving along the Same Line.

Thus far we have considered only those collisions in which each of the bodies initially moves along the same line. If the motions are not thus simply related, one must consider two components of momentum at right angles to each other and the corresponding components of velocity. From the law of conservation of momentum we may write two equations, one for each component, since the momentum in each of these directions must be conserved separately. Similarly, Eq. (7) gives two equations. These four equations do not have a unique solution for any real body since the directions of recoil depend upon the way the bodies collide as well as upon the initial momenta. If the direction of motion of one of the bodies after collision is known, the problem can be solved. A classic example of an analysis of this type is the problem of scattering of photons by electrons.

11-6. Angular Momentum. In motions of rotation *angular momentum* appears in much the same way as linear momentum appears in motions of translation. Just as linear momentum is the product of mass and velocity, the angular momentum of a body is defined as the product of its moment of inertia and its angular velocity.

$$\text{Angular momentum} = I\omega \qquad (14)$$

The units in which angular momentum is expressed can be determined by examination of Eq. (14). In the British system moment of inertia is expressed in slug-feet^2 and angular velocity in radians per second. Thus angular momentum is expressed in (slug-ft^2) (radians/sec) or slug-ft^2/sec. As usual the "radian" which represents a dimensionless ratio is dropped from the unit. In the cgs system I is in gm-cm^2 and ω in radians per second. Thus angular momentum is expressed in gm-cm^2/sec. Similarly in the mks system angular momentum is expressed in kg-m^2/sec.

11-7. Conservation of Angular Momentum. *The angular momentum of a body remains unchanged unless the body is acted upon by an external torque.* This is the law of *conservation of angular momentum.* The action of a flywheel, which helps to maintain constant speed of rotation in a motor, depends upon this principle. Since the moment of inertia of the flywheel is large, the torques acting on it do not produce rapid changes in its angular momentum. During the time the motor is speeding up, the flywheel supplies a resisting torque; when the motor slows down, the flywheel applies an aiding torque to maintain the speed.

If the distribution of mass of a rotating body is changed, the angular velocity must change

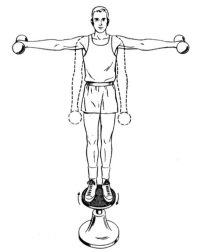

FIG. 2. Conservation of angular momentum.

to maintain the same angular momentum. Suppose a man stands on a stool that is free to rotate with little friction (Fig. 2). If he is set in rotation with his hands outstretched, he will rotate at a constant rate. If he lowers his arms, his moment of inertia is decreased and his rate of rotation increases.

Another consequence of the principle of conservation of angular momentum is that a rotating body maintains the same plane of rotation unless acted upon by a torque. A top does not fall over when it is spinning rapidly for there is not sufficient torque to cause that change in angular velocity. The rotation of the wheels helps maintain the balance of a bicycle or motorcycle. The barrel of a gun is rifled to cause the bullet to spin so that it will not "tumble."

If an unbalanced external torque is applied to a rotating body, the angular momentum will be changed. From Eq. (11), Chap. 10,

$$L = I\alpha$$
$$\bar{\alpha} = \frac{\omega_2 - \omega_1}{t} \qquad \alpha = \frac{d\omega}{dt}$$
$$Lt = I\omega_2 - I\omega_1 \qquad L\,dt = d(I\omega) \quad (15)$$

The product of torque and time is called *angular impulse*. Angular impulse is equal to change in angular momentum.

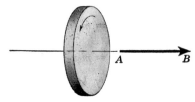

FIG. 3. Angular velocity is represented by a vector parallel to the axis.

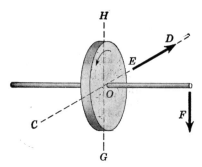

FIG. 4. Torque acting on a rotating disk.

11-8. Vector Properties in Angular Motion. Angular velocity, angular acceleration, angular momentum, and torque are all vector quantities. All rotary motion is referred to an axis. The vector representing the vector quantity is taken parallel to the axis of rotation. The *sense* along this line is given by a "right-hand rule." If, in imagination, one grasps the axis with the right hand, the fingers pointing in the direction the particles move around the axis, the thumb points in the direction of the vector. In Fig. 3 the angular velocity of the rotating disk is represented in magnitude and direction by the vector *AB* parallel to the axis. If a torque is applied to the disk in such a manner that the axis of the torque is the same as the axis of rotation of the disk, the direction of the torque will be parallel to *AB* and the resultant angular acceleration will also be parallel to AB. Hence such a torque will produce a change only in the *magnitude* of the angular velocity.

11-9. Precession. If a torque is applied to the disk by a vertical force on the end of the

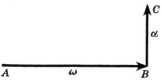

FIG. 5. Vector representation of angular velocity and angular acceleration.

axle as F in Fig. 4, the axis of the torque is a horizontal line such as CD and the torque is represented by the vector ED. The angular acceleration produced is in the direction CD. When the disk is viewed from above, its motion is described by the vectors drawn in Fig. 5, AB representing the original angular velocity of the disk and BC representing the angular acceleration produced by the torque. Since the angular acceleration is at right angles to the angular velocity, no change in angular speed is produced but only a change in direction. That is, the axis of rotation changes its direction, rotating in a counterclockwise sense. Note that the direction of motion of the end of the axle is at right angles to the original direction of the axle and also at right angles to the direction of the *force* applied. The direction of motion of the end of the axle is in the direction of the *torque* applied. Such shift in the axis of spin of a rotating body is called *precession*. The vertical axis GH about which the turning of the spin axis takes place is called the *axis of precession*. In Fig. 6 are shown the three axes involved in the motion. Each axis is perpendicular to the other two. The line AB is the axis of spin along which is drawn the vector representing the angular velocity ω of the rotating body; CD is the axis of torque along which is drawn the vector representing L; and GH is the axis of precession along which is drawn a vector representing the angular velocity of precession Ω.

The rate of precession, that is, the angular speed about the axis of precession, depends upon the angular momentum of the rotating body about the axis of spin and the torque applied. In Fig. 7, OA represents the original angular velocity ω, OB represents the angular

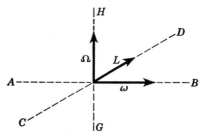

FIG. 6. Three axes describing precession: axis of spin AB, axis of torque CD, and axis of precession GH.

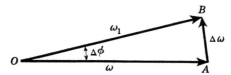

FIG. 7. Vector diagram for precession.

velocity ω_1, a short time Δt later, and AB represents the change $\Delta \omega$ in the angular velocity. The change in angular velocity is a change in direction only since the torque is at right angles to the initial angular velocity. If $\Delta \phi$ is small,

$$\Delta \omega = \omega \, \Delta \phi \qquad \text{(approximately)}$$

In the limit

$$d\omega = \omega \, d\phi \qquad \text{(exactly)}$$

From Eq. (15)

$$L \, dt = I \, d\omega = I\omega \, d\phi$$
$$L = I\omega \frac{d\phi}{dt}$$

But $d\phi/dt = \Omega$, the angular velocity of precession. Then

$$L = I\omega\Omega \qquad (16)$$

or

$$\Omega = \frac{L}{I\omega} \qquad (17)$$

The rate of precession is directly proportional

to the torque applied and inversely proportional to the angular momentum of the rotating body about the axis of spin.

Example: A disk with its axle has a weight of 4.0 lb and a moment of inertia of 0.0040 slug-ft². It is supported at one end of the axle (Fig. 8), the

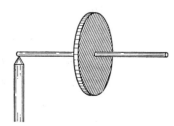

FIG. 8. A rotating disk supported at one end of its axle precesses.

support being 3.0 in. from the center of gravity. When the disk is turning at the rate of 1800 rpm, what is the rate of precession?

The weight, considered as concentrated at the center of gravity, produces a torque

$L = Ws = (4.0 \text{ lb})(0.25 \text{ ft})$
$\omega = 1800 \text{ rpm} = 30 \text{ rps} = 2\pi \times 30 \text{ radians/sec}$
$$\Omega = \frac{L}{I\omega} = \frac{(4.0 \text{ lb})(0.25 \text{ ft})}{(0.0040 \text{ slug-ft}^2)(2\pi \times 30 \text{ radians/sec})}$$
$\Omega = 1.3 \text{ radians/sec}$

11-10. Gyroscopes. A gyroscope is a rotating body that is so mounted as to be free to turn about any of three mutually perpendicular axes. Such a mounting is shown in Fig. 9. If the wheel spins with high angular speed about axis 1, the base may be turned in any manner without transmitting a torque, except for frictional torque, to the rotating wheel, which will therefore maintain its axis of rotation unchanged as the support is tilted in any manner so long as the wheel rotates rapidly. Since the angular momentum depends upon the moment of inertia and upon the angular velocity, a heavy wheel rotating at high speed would have a large angular momentum and correspondingly great stability. If a torque is applied perpendicular to the axis of spin, there will be precession of the axis as previously described.

The two principal characteristics of the behavior of gyroscopes are (1) stability of the axis and (2) precession. Both of these characteristics are employed in the many applications of gyroscopes. In those applications which require stability great care must be

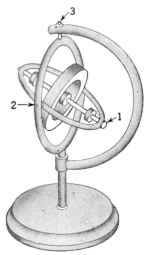

FIG. 9. A gyroscope has three axes of freedom.

taken in mounting the gyroscope wheel so that as little torque as possible is transmitted to the axis. In this class of application are the gyropilot, gyrohorizon indicator, directional gyro, and to some extent the gyrocompass. The latter, however, is so constructed that when it is in any position except that with its axis parallel to the axis of the earth there will be a torque which will cause a precession into that position.

Every rotating body shows gyroscopic action; the greater the angular momentum, the more marked will be the effect. Some of these effects are useful, others harmful. As a car turns a corner, the gyroscopic action of the wheels produces a torque tending to overturn the car. If the flywheel rotates counterclockwise as one looks forward in a car, the force on the front wheels decreases when the car turns to the right, but increases when the car turns to the left.

The gyrostabilizer may be used to reduce

the roll of a boat by exerting a torque opposite to the roll. The gyroscope wheel, spun at high speed by a motor, is mounted with its axis vertical in such a manner that the axis may be tilted forward or backward but not sideways. Assume that the spin of the gyroscope is counterclockwise as viewed from above. When the boat rolls, say to the right, a control gyro closes contacts of a motor which tilts the axis forward. There results a torque opposing the roll to the right. Similarly if the roll is to the left, the motor tilts the axis backward supplying a torque again opposing the roll.

SUMMARY

Momentum is the product of the mass and velocity of a body. It is a vector quantity.

$$p = mv$$

Common units of momentum are *slug-foot per second, gram-centimeter per second,* and *kilogram-meter per second.*

The law of *conservation of momentum* states that the momentum of a body or system of bodies does not change unless an unbalanced external force acts upon it.

An alternative statement of Newton's second law is represented by the equation

$$F = \frac{dp}{dt}$$

Impulse is the product of a force and the time it acts. Impulse is equal to the change in momentum

$$F \, \Delta t = p_2 - p_1 = mv_2 - mv_1$$

Some units of impulse are the pound-second, the newton-second, and the dyne-second.

The *coefficient of restitution* is the ratio of the relative velocity of recession to the relative velocity of approach in a collision. Its value is unity for a perfectly elastic collision, zero for a completely inelastic collision, and between zero and one for all others.

Angular momentum is the product of moment of inertia and angular velocity

$$\text{Angular momentum} = I\omega$$

The *law of conservation of angular momentum* states that the angular momentum of a rotating body remains unchanged unless it is acted upon by an external, unbalanced torque.

Angular momentum is a *vector quantity* as are also angular velocity, angular acceleration, and torque. The direction of the vectors representing these quantities is parallel to the axis in the sense given by the "right-hand rule."

Precession is the change in direction of the axis of spin of a rotating body under the action of a torque.

A gyroscope exhibits the properties of precession and stability of axis. These properties result in many useful applications.

QUESTIONS   1. Why does a gun appear to have a greater "kick" when fired with the butt held loosely against the shoulder than when held tightly?

2. Why does a heavy rifle not kick as strongly as a light rifle using the same cartridges?

3. Explain how the term *conservation* applies (*a*) to energy and (*b*) to momentum.

4. Compare the change in momenta produced by two equal forces acting for equal times on two unequal masses, one of which is at rest, the other initially in motion.

5. When one billiard ball strikes a second in such a manner that their centers of gravity are not in the line of motion of the first ball, their paths after collision do not lie on the same line. Draw a vector diagram to represent the momenta before and after such a collision if the angle between the paths is 100°.

6. Mercury is often shipped in small iron cylinders. Why is it easier to carry on the shoulder a full cylinder weighing 100 lb than one three-fourths full?

7. Prove that if the coefficient of restitution is less than one, the kinetic energy after a collision is less than that before the collision.

8. How may the speed of a rifle bullet be measured with simple apparatus?

9. How may a high diver turning somersaults in the air arrange on the way down to strike the water head first? What physical principle does he make use of?

10. A stone is dropped in the center of a deep vertical mine shaft. Will the stone continue in the center of the shaft or will it strike the side? If it strikes the side, will it be the north, south, east, or west side? Consider the linear speed of rotation of the earth and assume ideal conditions.

11. A projectile is fired due south in the Northern Hemisphere. When it strikes the ground will it be east or will it be west of the north-south line along which it started? Consider the speed of rotation of the earth. If the projectile is fired north, on which side of the line will it strike? On which side of an east-west line will it strike if fired east? if fired west?

12. A boy rolling a hoop finds he can control it by touching it lightly with a stick on the side toward which he wants it to turn. Explain.

13. Why is a rifle barrel "rifled"?

14. An airplane propeller rotates counterclockwise as viewed from behind. What effect does its gyroscopic action have when the plane is turning toward the right? when the plane is diving?

15. Explain the gyroscopic action of the front wheels of a car traveling at high speed when one turns toward the right.

16. Why does the axis of a spinning gyrocompass always point north?

PROBLEMS

1. What is the momentum of a 160-lb shell if its speed is 2000 ft/sec?

2. What is the momentum of a 5.0-ton truck when traveling at the rate of 60 mi/hr?   *Ans.* 28,000 slug-ft/sec

3. A 5.0-kg rifle fires a 10-gm bullet with a speed of 700 m/sec. What is the speed of recoil of the rifle?

4. What is the recoil speed of a 9.0-lb gun when it projects a 0.60-oz bullet with a speed of 2400 ft/sec?   *Ans.* 10 ft/sec

5. A 40-ton freight car moving with a speed of 15 mi/hr runs into a stationary car of the same weight. If they move off together after the collision, what is their speed?

6. A 10-ton freight car rolling freely at 6.0 mi/hr collides with and is coupled to a 7.0-ton car originally at rest. Calculate the speed with which the two cars roll away.   *Ans.* 3.5 mi/hr

7. An automobile weighing 3200 lb is moving at the rate of 60 mi/hr. (*a*) What is its momentum? (*b*) What constant retarding force would be required to stop this car in 2.5 sec? (*c*) How far would it travel in coming to rest?

8. A 5.0-oz baseball arrives at the bat with a speed of 160 ft/sec. It remains in contact with the bat for 0.020 sec, and leaves with the direction of its motion reversed and at a speed of 280 ft/sec. (*a*) What impulse does the bat impart to the ball? (*b*) What is the value of the average force exerted by the bat on the ball?   *Ans.* 4.3 lb-sec; $2\bar{2}0$ lb

9. A machine gun fires 10 bullets per second into a target. Each bullet weighs 0.50 oz and has a speed of 2400 ft/sec. Find the force necessary to hold the gun in position and that required to hold the target in position.

10. Two 5.0-lb balls *A* and *B* approach each other with speeds of 20 ft/sec and 30 ft/sec, respectively. Assuming a perfectly elastic collision, what will be their speeds after collision?   *Ans.* 30 ft/sec; -20 ft/sec

11. A 5.0-lb ball and a 10.0-lb ball approach each other with equal speeds of 20 ft/sec. What are their speeds after collision if the collision is perfectly elastic?

12. A 5.00-lb ball and a 10.0-lb ball have speeds of 10.0 ft/sec and 14.0 ft/sec, respectively, as they approach each other. Find their speeds after collision if the coefficient of restitution is 0.800.   *Ans.* -18.8 ft/sec; 0.40 ft/sec

13. Two elastic balls of mass 30.0 gm and 90.0 gm are supported by strings 100 cm long. The smaller ball is pulled aside until its center of gravity has been raised 5.00 cm and then released. Find the velocity of each ball after the impact, assuming it to be perfectly elastic. If the balls are undisturbed after the first impact, there will be a series of impacts. Find the velocity of each ball after the second impact.

14. Two balls of mass 30.0 gm and 90.0 gm are supported by strings 100 cm long. The larger ball is pulled aside until its center of gravity has been raised 5.00 cm and then released. Assuming the collision to be perfectly elastic, find the velocity of each ball after the collision.   *Ans.* 148 cm/sec; 49.4 cm/sec

15. A 50-gm ball A traveling east with a speed of 40 cm/sec collides with a 60-gm ball traveling north with a speed of 80 cm/sec. After the collision, ball B moves in a direction 11°N of E. Assuming the collision to be perfectly elastic, find the speed of each ball and the direction in which A moves.

16. A 120-gm ball A traveling east with a speed of 80 cm/sec collides with a 160-gm ball B traveling with a speed of 100 cm/sec in a direction 30°N of W. After the collision, ball A is found to move in a direction 27.3°N of W. Assuming the collision to be perfectly elastic, find the speed of each ball and the direction of B after the collision.   *Ans.* $1\bar{2}0$ cm/sec; 57 cm/sec; 7°N of E

17. A small rocket, fired horizontally, has a mass of 3.0 kg of which one-third is fuel. Assume that the fuel is all consumed at a uniform rate in 10.0 sec and that the thrust has a constant value of 20.0 newtons during that time. Find the horizontal velocity of the rocket at the end of that time. Neglect air resistance.

18. A rocket has a mass of 10.0 kg of which 4.0 kg is fuel. The rocket is fired vertically upward. Assume that the fuel is consumed at a constant rate and that it is exhausted at the end of 20.0 sec. Assume also that the thrust during that time has a constant net value of 49 newtons. What is the speed of the rocket at the instant the fuel is exhausted? How high will it rise? Neglect air resistance and the change in g.   *Ans.* 126 m/sec; $2\bar{1}00$ m

19. A 40-gm bullet is fired into a 10-kg block that is suspended by long cords so that it can swing as a ballistic pendulum. If the block is displaced so that its center of gravity rises 10 cm, what was the speed of the bullet?

20. A $5\frac{1}{4}$-oz baseball is thrown so that it is captured by the 11.7-lb block of a ballistic pendulum. The block is displaced so that its center of gravity is raised 2.7 in. With what speed was the ball pitched?   *Ans.* 95 mi/hr

21. A 4.41×10^{-3}-lb rifle bullet is fired into a 4.00-lb ballistic pendulum. The pendulum is 12.0 ft long and it rises 0.118 ft as a result of the impact. (*a*) What is the speed of the bullet just before the impact? (*b*) What is the percentage loss in its kinetic energy?

22. The rotor of an electric motor has a moment of inertia of 25 slug-ft². If it is rotating at a rate of 1200 rev/min, what is its angular momentum?
          Ans. $3\bar{1}00$ slug-ft²/sec

23. The rotor of an electric motor weighs 160 lb and has a radius of gyration of 9.0 in. What is its angular momentum when it is rotating at the rate of 1800 rev/min?

$$K.E = \tfrac{1}{2}mv^2$$

24. What torque is required to change the speed of the rotor of an electric motor from 600 rev/min to 1200 rev/min in 2.0 sec if the rotor has a moment of inertia of 25 slug-ft²? *Ans.* $7\overline{9}0$ lb-ft

25. What torque is required to change the speed of the rotor of a motor from 1800 to 600 rev/min in 3.0 sec if the rotor weighs 160 lb and has a radius of yration of 9.0 in.?

26. A torque of 0.24 lb-ft is required to rotate a cylindrical grindstone at uniform speed. The grindstone weighs 96.0 lb and has a radius of 2.00 ft. This grindstone is given an angular speed of 100 rev/min, is released, and is allowed to run until it stops. (*a*) What is its angular momentum at the instant it is released? (*b*) How long will it run? *Ans.* 20π slug-ft²/sec; 4.3 min

27. A 400-lb turntable which can be thought of as a solid disk of 10.0 ft radius is rotating freely about an axis through its center at an angular speed of 1.0 radian/sec. A 200-lb man is standing at the edge of the turntable. The man walks radially inward to a position 5.0 ft from the center. (*a*) What is the angular speed when the man is in this position? (*b*) Is the change in kinetic energy of the system an increase or a decrease? (*c*) What is responsible for this change?

28. A gyroscope wheel weighs 7.0 lb and has a radius of gyration of 4.0 in. It spins with its axis horizontal at a rate of 3000 rev/min, clockwise as viewed from the pivot. The gyroscope is supported by a pivot near one end of the axle 6.0 in. from the center of gravity (Fig. 8). What is the angular velocity of precession? When viewed from above is the precession clockwise or is it counterclockwise? *Ans.* 0.46 radian/sec

29. A top that weighs 12 oz has a radius of gyration of 0.80 in. The center of gravity is 2.0 in. from the point. The top spins at a rate of 2400 rev/min with its axis making an angle of 30° with the vertical. Find the angular velocity of precession. If the rotation of the top is clockwise as one looks downward along the axis, is the precession clockwise or is it counterclockwise?

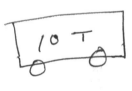
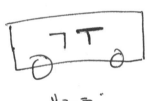

12. Uniform Circular Motion

Uniform motion along a straight line seems "natural"; no cause for such action is expected. However, if there is a change in the direction of the motion, some disturbing factor is at once assumed. Just as a force is required to change the speed of an object, so a force must act to cause a change in the *direction* of the motion. Whenever the net force on a body acts in a direction other than the original direction of motion, it changes the direction of the motion. Such acceleration is very common, for it is present whenever a car turns a corner, a plane changes its direction, a wheel turns, or in many other common motions. The simplest type of motion in which the direction changes is uniform circular motion, in which there is no change in speed but only a change in direction.

12-1. Central Acceleration. When an object is moving in a circular path with constant speed, its velocity is continually changing. The acceleration produces a change in direction but no change in speed. Therefore the acceleration must always be at right angles to the motion, since any component in the direction of the motion would produce a change in speed. The acceleration is always directed toward the center of the circle in which the body moves. It is constant in magnitude but continually changing direction. In Fig. 1 a body is moving with uniform speed v and constant angular speed ω in a circular path.

The linear speed and angular speed are related by the equation $v = \omega r$, where r is the radius of the circular path. The velocities of the body at the points A and B are, respectively, v and v_1, equal in magnitude but differing in direction by a small angle $\Delta\theta$. In

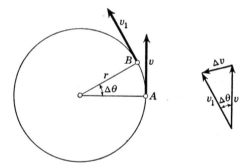

Fig. 1. Changing velocity in uniform circular motion.

the vector triangle, Δv represents the change in velocity in the time Δt required for the body to move from A to B. If the angle $\Delta\theta$ is small the chord is approximately equal to the arc and thus

$$\Delta v = v\,\Delta\theta \qquad \text{(approximately)}$$

But

$$\Delta\theta = \omega\,\Delta t$$

Hence

$$\Delta v = v\omega\,\Delta t = \omega^2 r\,\Delta t = \frac{v^2}{r}\,\Delta t$$

and

$$\frac{\Delta v}{\Delta t} = \omega^2 r = \frac{v^2}{r}$$

As Δt is made smaller, the approximation in this equation becomes less and less. Furthermore, the direction of Δv becomes more and more nearly perpendicular to that of v. In the limit as Δt approaches zero the instantaneous acceleration is found to be directed toward the center of the circle and is given by

$$a = \frac{dv}{dt} = \lim_{\Delta t \to 0} \frac{\Delta v}{\Delta t} = \omega^2 r = \frac{v^2}{r} \qquad (1)$$

This equation states that the acceleration increases as the speed is increased and, for a given speed, is greater for a shorter radius. The acceleration is at right angles to the velocity and hence is directed toward the center of the circle.

In Eq. (1) the angular speed ω must be expressed in radians per second and the units of a then depend upon the units in which r and v are expressed.

Example: A train whose speed is 60 mi/hr rounds a curve whose radius of curvature is 484 ft. What is its acceleration?

$$v = 60 \text{ mi/hr} = 88 \text{ ft/sec}$$
$$a = \frac{v^2}{r} = \frac{(88 \text{ ft/sec})^2}{484 \text{ ft}} = 16 \text{ ft/sec}^2$$

Example: What is the acceleration of a point on the rim of a flywheel 3.0 ft in diameter, turning at the rate of 1200 rev/min?

$$\omega = 1200 \text{ rpm} = 20 \text{ rps} = 20 \times 2\pi \text{ radians/sec}$$
$$r = 3.0 \text{ ft}/2 = 1.5 \text{ ft}$$
$$a = \omega^2 r = (20 \times 2\pi \text{ radians/sec})^2 (1.5 \text{ ft})$$
$$= 24{,}000 \text{ ft/sec}^2$$

12-2. Centripetal Force. According to Newton's laws of motion any object that experiences an acceleration is acted upon by an unbalanced force, a force which is proportional to the acceleration and in the direction of the acceleration. The net force that produces the central acceleration is called *centripetal force* and is directed toward the center of the circular path. Every body that moves in a circular path does so under the action of a centripetal force. A body moving with uniform speed in a circle is not in equilibrium.

From Newton's second law the magnitude of the centripetal force is given by

$$F_c = ma = m\frac{v^2}{r} = m\omega^2 r \qquad (2)$$

where m is the mass of the moving object, v is its linear speed, r is the radius of the circular path, and ω is the angular speed. If the mass is in kilograms, the radius in meters, and the speed in meters per second, the force is in newtons. If m is in grams, v in centimeters per second, and r in centimeters, F_c is in dynes. If m is in slugs, v in feet per second, and r in feet, F_c is in pounds.

Example: A 3200-lb car traveling with a speed of 60 mi/hr rounds a curve whose radius is 484 ft. Find the necessary centripetal force.

$$m = \frac{W}{g} = \frac{3200 \text{ lb}}{32 \text{ ft/sec}^2} = 100 \text{ slugs}$$
$$v = 60 \text{ mi/hr} = 88 \text{ ft/sec}$$
$$F_c = m\frac{v^2}{r} = (100 \text{ slugs})\frac{(88 \text{ ft/sec})^2}{484 \text{ ft}} = 1600 \text{ lb}$$

An inspection of Eq. (2) discloses that the centripetal force necessary to pull a body into a circular path is directly proportional to the square of the speed at which the body moves and inversely proportional to the radius of the circular path. Suppose, for example, that a 4.0-kg object is held in a circular path by a string 1.2 m long. If the object moves at a constant speed of 0.80 m/sec,

$$F_c = \frac{mv^2}{r} = \frac{(4.0 \text{ kg})(0.80 \text{ m/sec})^2}{1.2 \text{ m}}$$
$$= 3.2 \text{ newtons}$$

If the speed is doubled keeping the radius constant, F_c becomes four times as great, or 12.8 newtons. If, instead, the radius is decreased from 1.2 m to 0.60 m with the speed maintained at 0.80 m/sec, F_c increases to 6.4 newtons. If at any instant the string breaks, eliminating the centripetal force, the object will retain the velocity it has at the instant the string breaks and travel at constant speed along a line tangent to the circle. The paths taken by sparks from an emery

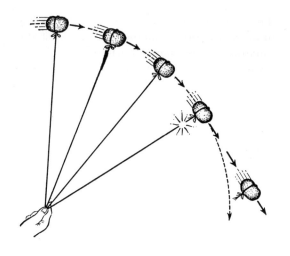

If the string breaks, the rock flies off.

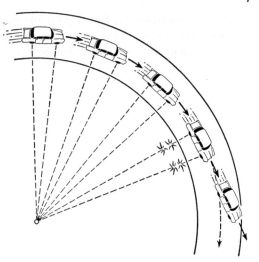

If friction "breaks," the car skids off.

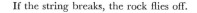

FIG. 2.

wheel are an illustration of this fact. This action is illustrated in Fig. 2.

A body can travel at uniform speed in a circular path only when the resultant of the forces acting on the body is constant in magnitude and always directed toward the center of the circle.

12-3. No Work Done by Centripetal Force. Work has been defined as the product of force and the displacement in the direction of the force. Since centripetal force acts at right angles to the direction of motion, there is no displacement in the direction of the centripetal force, and it accomplishes no work. Aside from the work done against friction, which has been neglected, no energy is expended on or by an object while it is moving at constant speed in a horizontal circular path. This conclusion is consistent with the observation that, if the speed is constant, the kinetic energy of the body also is constant.

12-4. Action and Reaction. Newton's third law expresses the fact that for every force that is exerted on one body there is a second force equal in magnitude but opposite in direction acting on a second body. When an object not free to move is acted upon by an external force, it is pushed or pulled out of its natural shape. As a consequence it exerts an *elastic* reaction in an attempt to resume its normal shape. On the other hand, the action of a force upon a free object results in an acceleration. The object exerts an inertial reacting force upon the agent of the accelerating force.

The elastic reacting force of a stretched body is equal in magnitude to the stretching force but opposite in direction. So also the inertial reacting force of an accelerated body is equal in magnitude to the accelerating force but opposite in direction. It should be remembered, however, that a force of reaction is exerted *by* the reacting object, not on it.

12-5. Centrifugal Reaction. A string that constrains an object to a circular path exerts on the object the centripetal force that changes its velocity. In reaction against this change of motion, the object pulls outward on the string with a force called the *centrifugal reaction*. This force, which is exerted by the object in its tendency to continue along a straight path, is just equal in magnitude to the inward (centripetal) force.

As the speed of a flywheel increases, the force needed to hold the parts of the wheel in circular motion increases with the square of the speed, as indicated by Eq. (2). Finally the cohesive forces between the molecules are no longer sufficient and the wheel disintegrates, the parts flying off along tangent lines like mud from an automobile tire. The inward directed force is greatest near the center of the

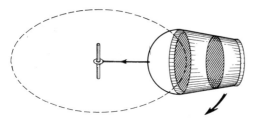

FIG. 3. Centripetal force on a liquid. The principle of the centrifuge.

wheel, for each ring must supply the force required to accelerate all rings farther from the axis.

When a container full of liquid is being whirled at a uniform rate, the pail exerts an inward force on the liquid sufficient to keep it in circular motion (Fig. 3). The bottom of the pail presses on the layer of liquid next to it; that layer in turn exerts a force on the next; and so on. In each layer the pressure (force per unit area) must be the same all over the layer or the liquid will not remain in the layer. If the liquid is of uniform density (mass per unit volume), each element of volume of mass m in a given layer will experience an inward force $(m)(v^2/r)$ just great enough to maintain it in that layer and there will be no motion of the liquid from one layer to another. If, however, the layer is made up of a mixture of particles of different densities, the force required to maintain a given element of volume in the layer will depend upon the density of the liquid in that element. Since the inward force is the same on all the elements in a single layer, there will be a motion between the layers. For those parts which are less dense than the average the central force is greater than that necessary to hold them in the layer; hence they are forced inward. For the parts more dense than the average the force is insufficient to hold them in the circu-

lar path and they will move to a layer farther out. As rotation continues, the parts of the mixture will be separated, with the least dense nearest the axis and the most dense farthest from the axis. This behavior is utilized in the centrifuge, a device for separating liquids of

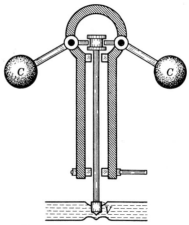

FIG. 4. A centrifugal governor.

different densities. The cream separator is the most common example of the centrifuge but it is very commonly used to separate mixtures of liquids or mixtures of solids in liquids. Very high speed centrifuges may be used to separate gases of different densities.

Airplane pilots sometimes pull out of a vertical dive at such high speed that the centripetal acceleration becomes several times as large as the gravitational acceleration. Under these circumstances, the flow of blood to the pilot's brain is decreased. This sometimes causes the pilot to lose consciousness during the period of maximum acceleration.

12-6. Centrifugal Governor. The speed of an engine can be controlled by centripetal force through a *governor* (Fig. 4). This device consists of a pair of masses C, C attached to arms hinged on a vertical spindle which rotates at a speed proportional to that of the engine. As the speed of rotation increases, the centripetal force necessary to maintain circular motion of the balls is increased and they move farther from the axis. This motion is used to actuate a valve V, decreasing the supply of steam or fuel. As the speed of the engine decreases, the balls descend, opening the throttle. Thus the engine speed may be kept reasonably constant under varying loads.

12-7. Banking of Curves. A runner, in going around a curve, leans inward to obtain

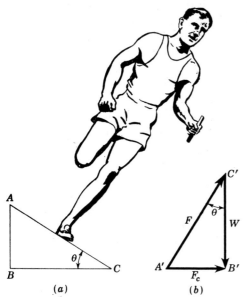

A

B

θ

C

(a)

C'

F θ W

A'

F_c

B'

(b)

FIG. 5. The advantage of banking curves.

the centripetal force that causes him to turn (Fig. 5a). The roadway must exert an upward force sufficient to sustain his weight, while at the same time it must supply a horizontal centripetal force. If the roadway is flat, the horizontal force is entirely frictional. In that case the frictional force may not be large enough to cause a sharp turn when the surface of the roadway is smooth.

If the roadway is tilted from the horizontal, a part of the horizontal force is still supplied by friction but the remainder is a result of the reaction of the surface. If the angle of banking is properly selected, the force the roadway exerts is perpendicular to its surface and no frictional force is necessary.

For this ideal case, as shown in Fig. 5b, the thrust F of the roadway is perpendicular to the surface AC. The weight W of the runner is directed vertically downward. The resultant

force F_c is the horizontal centripetal force. In the force triangle the angle θ is the angle of bank of the roadway

$$\tan \theta = \frac{F_c}{W} = \frac{mv^2/r}{mg} = \frac{v^2}{rg} \quad (3)$$

Equation (3) indicates that, since the angle of banking depends upon the speed, the curve can be ideally banked for only one speed. At any other speed the force of friction must be depended upon to prevent slipping. The banking of highway curves, by reducing the lateral force of friction on the tires, greatly reduces wear in addition to contributing to safety.

Example: A curve on a highway forms an arc whose radius is 150 ft. If the roadbed is 30 ft wide and its outer edge is 4.0 ft higher than the inner edge, for what speed is it ideally banked?

The tangent of the angle of bank is the ratio of the difference in elevation of the two edges and the width of the road.

$$\tan \theta = 4.0 \text{ ft}/30 \text{ ft}$$
$$\tan \theta = \frac{v^2}{rg} \quad \text{hence} \quad v^2 = gr \tan \theta$$

so that

$$v = \sqrt{\frac{(32 \text{ ft/sec}^2)(150 \text{ ft})(4.0 \text{ ft})}{30 \text{ ft}}} = 25 \text{ ft/sec}$$

Example: An unbanked curve has a radius of 242 ft. What is the maximum speed at which a car can make the turn if the coefficient of static friction μ_s is 0.81?

When a curve is not banked, the centripetal force must be supplied by friction between the wheels and the roadway. Since the normal force is the weight,

$$F_c = \mu_s W = m\frac{v^2}{r} = \frac{Wv^2}{gr}$$

whence $v^2 = \mu_s gr = (0.81)(32 \text{ ft/sec}^2)(242 \text{ ft})$
$$v = 79 \text{ ft/sec} = 54 \text{ mi/hr}$$

12-8. Curvilinear Motion. Frequently the net force acting upon a body is neither parallel to the direction of its motion nor at right angles to that direction. In this case neither the speed nor the direction remains constant.

Such motion may be readily studied by considering two components of the acceleration, one parallel to the original direction of motion, the other perpendicular to that direction.

One of the most common of such motions is planetary motion, in which the force on the moving body is inversely proportional to the square of the radius and always directed toward a fixed point. The body travels in an ellipse, the fixed point being at one focus. The speed is greatest when the moving body is near the focus, less when it is farther away. This motion is called planetary motion because the planets move in this manner in their journeys around the sun. The gravitational forces acting are inversely proportional to the square of the radius.

Since electrified particles show a similar law of attraction, we should expect them to behave in the same manner as those moving under the action of gravitational forces.

SUMMARY

In *uniform circular motion* (*a*) the speed *v* is constant; (*b*) the direction of the motion is continually and uniformly changing; (*c*) the acceleration a_c is constant in magnitude and is directed toward the center of the circular path. The magnitude of the *central acceleration* is given by

$$a_c = \frac{v^2}{r} = \omega^2 r$$

where *v* is the linear speed, *r* is the radius, and ω is the angular speed.

The *centripetal force*, the inward force that causes the central acceleration, is given by

$$F_c = m\frac{v^2}{r} = m\omega^2 r$$

The *centrifugal reaction* is the outward force exerted by the moving object on the agent of its centripetal force. The magnitude of the centrifugal reaction is equal to that of the centripetal force.

The proper banking of a curve to eliminate the necessity for a sidewise frictional force is given by the relation

$$\frac{v^2}{gr} = \tan \theta$$

Often in curvilinear motion the accelerating force is neither parallel nor perpendicular to the direction of motion. The acceleration produces change in both speed and direction.

QUESTIONS   1. Mention several practical devices, other than those mentioned in this chapter, that make use of central forces.

2. Show that the units of v^2/r are those of acceleration.

3. Why is the acceleration of a body moving in uniform circular motion always toward the center?

4. Explain the statement that "an aviator experiences 3 *g*'s in pulling out of a certain dive."

5. If a heavy bolt on the end of a string is revolved rapidly enough, the string will break. What force causes the string to break? Is the centripetal force ever greater than the centrifugal reaction?

6. A body at the end of a string moves in a vertical circle. If the string always pulls toward the center of the circle can the speed of the body be constant? Discuss any variation and the reasons for it.

7. A body at the end of a string moves in a vertical circle with uniform speed. Discuss the variation in magnitude and direction of the force that the string must exert. Is the tension in the string always directed toward the center of the circle?

8. Discuss the possibility of a passenger falling from an open plane during a loop.

9. Discuss the difference between an inside and an outside loop with an airplane.

10. A motorcycle is ridden on a circular track for which the angle of banking is gradually increased across the track until it ends in a vertical wall. Can the motorcycle ride against the vertical wall? Discuss the forces involved.

11. Can a motorcycle ride against the vertical wall of a circular track with the plane of the motorcycle horizontal? Discuss forces and torques involved.

12. Analyze clearly the reasons why an automobile overturns when going too fast around a curve. Which wheels leave the ground first?

PROBLEMS   **1.** An aviator loops the loop in a circle 400 ft in diameter. If he is traveling 120 mi/hr, how many g's does he experience?

2. What is the least speed at which an airplane can execute a loop of 400-ft radius so that there will be no tendency for the pilot to fall out at the highest point?   *Ans.* 110 ft/sec

3. At the equator the centripetal acceleration is about 3.0 cm/sec². How fast would the earth have to turn to make the apparent weight of a body zero?

4. Assuming the earth to be a sphere 13,000 km in diameter, how much is the acceleration due to gravity changed by the rotation of the earth (*a*) at the equator? (*b*) at 40° lattitude? (*c*) at the pole? Is this change an increase or a decrease in the value of *g*?   *Ans.* 3.4 cm/sec²; 2.6 cm/sec²; 0

5. A 5.0-lb ball is swung in a vertical circle at the end of a cord 3.0 ft long. What is the maximum speed at which it can swing if the cord can sustain a tension of 60 lb?

6. Compute the minimum speed that a pail of water must have in order to swing without splashing in a vertical circle of radius 3.8 ft.   *Ans.* 11 ft/sec

7. A car traveling at a speed of 30 mi/hr rounds a circular curve whose radius is 200 ft. What is the centripetal force acting on a 160-lb man riding in the car?

8. An automobile has a mass of 1500 kg. What centripetal force is necessary for this vehicle to make a uniform 90° turn at 60 km/hr in a distance of 628 m along the road?   *Ans.* 1040 newtons

9. A 2.50-kg body turns in a horizontal circle at the end of a cord 1.50 m long. At what angular speed will the cord break if it can support a load of 50 newtons?

10. A 3200-lb automobile is moving with a constant speed of 40 mi/hr on a curve of 100-ft radius. (*a*) What is its acceleration? (*b*) What is the centripetal force on the automobile? (*c*) What supplies this force?   *Ans.* 34 ft/sec²; 3400 lb

11. A ball weighing 2.5 lb is whirled in a circular path at a speed of 12 ft/sec. If the radius of the circle is 5.6 ft, what is the centripetal force?

12. A 2.0-lb ball is swung in a vertical circle at the end of a wire 3.0 ft long. Find the maximum and minimum tensions in the wire if the ball makes 45 rev/min.   *Ans.* 6.2 lb; 2.2 lb

13. A body whose mass is 0.600 kg is turned in a vertical circle at the end of a cord 0.300 m long at the uniform rate of 2.00 rev/sec. Find the tension in the cord when the body is (*a*) at the bottom of the circle, (*b*) at the top of the circle. (*c*) Find the angle of the cord with the horizontal and the tension in the cord when the body is at the same level as the center of the circle.

14. A 5.0-lb ball is swung at the end of a cord in a vertical circle of radius 2.0 ft at the rate of 2.0 rev/sec. What is the tension of the cord when the ball is (*a*) at the bottom, (*b*) at the top? (*c*) Find the tension in the cord and the angle

the cord makes with the horizontal when the body is at the level of the center.
Ans. 54 lb; 44 lb; 49 lb; 5.8°

15. A boy is sitting 4.0 ft from the center of a rotating platform. The coefficient of friction between the boy and the platform is 0.20. What is the greatest angular speed the platform may have without causing the boy to slide off?

16. A 100-lb boy is standing on a merry-go-round platform 10 ft from the center. The platform is turning at the rate of 4.0 rev/min. Find the boy's linear speed, his radial acceleration, the frictional force needed to prevent him from slipping off the platform, and the coefficient of static friction if he is on the verge of slipping at this speed.   *Ans.* 4.2 ft/sec; 1.8 ft/sec²; 5.6 lb; 0.056

17. A 3200-lb automobile is moving with a speed of 10 ft/sec on a level circular track having a radius of 100 ft. What coefficient of friction is necessary to prevent the car from skidding?

18. If the coefficient of friction between road and tire is 0.50, find the maximum speed with which a car can turn a corner on a horizontal road if the curve has a radius of 100 ft.   *Ans.* 27 mi/hr

19. A circular race track is a half mile long. If the track is horizontal and the coefficient of friction is 0.80, what is the maximum speed at which a car can stay on the track?

20. A ball rolls down an inclined track and around a vertical loop 40.0 cm in diameter that is built into the track. How high above the lowest point in the loop must the ball be released in order that it will just go over the loop if half the energy of the ball is expended in work against friction?   *Ans.* 108 cm

21. An amusement device has a mast with crossarms extending 20 ft from the center at the top. A car is suspended from the end of the crossarm by a rope 30 ft long. Find the angular speed in radians per second and in revolutions per minute that will cause the rope to make an angle of 30° with the vertical.

22. The governor of an engine has arms that are 30 cm long and stand at an angle of 30° with the vertical when the governor is in constant rotation. Find the angular speed, in rotations per minute, of the shaft of the governor.
Ans. 59 rot/min

23. A 40.0-gm body swings in a horizontal circle supported by a flexible string 20.0 cm long. Find the tension in the string and the angle it makes with the horizontal when the body is making 120 rev/min.

24. An 8.0-lb body swings in a horizontal circle at the end of a string 2.0 ft long at a rate of 72 rev/min. Find the tension in the string and the angle that the string makes with the horizontal.   *Ans.* 28 lb; 17°

25. A car whose wheels are spaced 48 in. laterally and whose center of gravity is 18 in. above the ground rounds a curve at a speed of 50 mi/hr. Assuming no slipping, find the radius of the sharpest curve that can be rounded at this speed without overturning.

26. A car whose wheels are 54 in. apart laterally and whose center of gravity is 18 in. above the road rounds a curve of 200-ft radius. Assuming no slipping of the wheels on the road, find the greatest speed at which the car can round the curve without tipping over.   *Ans.* 67 mi/hr

27. Find the angle of banking for a curve to be traversed at 30 mi/hr, if the radius is 40 ft.

28. On some roads the curves are banked so that there is no side thrust on the passengers in a car which takes the curve at 45 mi/hr. Find the angle of banking for a circular curve making a 90° turn in a distance of 314 ft along the road.
Ans. 34°

29. On a railroad the roadbed is designed for a speed of 60 mi/hr. If the bed of a curve is banked 12°25′, find the radius of the curve.

30. A 3200-lb automobile rounds a curve of 400 ft radius at a speed of 60 mi/hr. The curve is banked at an angle of 20° with the horizontal. What frictional force is necessary? What is the minimum coefficient of friction?   *Ans.* 730 lb; 0.20

31. A curve of 80 m radius is banked at an angle of 15°. What frictional force is necessary if a 1500-kg car rounds the curve at a speed of 60 km/hr? What is the necessary coefficient of friction?

13. Elastic Properties of Solids

When a structure or a machine is to be built, suitable materials must be chosen for the parts. An engineer bases his design on the laws of mechanics and a knowledge of the properties of the materials available. Some of the properties thus considered are weight, strength, hardness, elasticity, thermal expansion, and maximum safe operating temperature.

Much of the progress in the design of structures has resulted from the discovery, adaptation, or development of new structural materials. As stone, brick, steel, and reinforced concrete replaced the original structural materials, mud and wood, buildings became stronger and taller. Early tools were made of wood, bone, or stone, but the discovery of metals made possible the construction of more intricate and useful devices. The machine age depends largely upon the technology of metals.

13-1. Elasticity. Among the most important properties of materials are their elastic characteristics. If, after a body is deformed by some force, it returns to its original shape or size as the distorting force is removed, the material is said to be *elastic*. Every substance is elastic to some degree.

Consider a long steel wire fastened to the ceiling in such a manner that its upper end is held rigidly in place. To keep the wire taut suppose a stone of sufficient weight is fastened

to the lower end of the wire. The force per unit area of cross section of the wire is defined as the *tensile stress* in the wire. The pound per square inch or the newton per square meter are units in which this stress is commonly

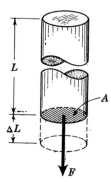

Fig. 1. Stress and strain in the stretching of a wire.

measured. The force per unit area is sometimes called *unit stress*.

Let L (Fig. 1) represent the length of the wire when just enough force has been applied to take the kinks out of it. Increasing the stretching force by an amount F will stretch or elongate the wire an amount ΔL. The ratio of the change in length ΔL to the total length L is called the *tensile strain*. Notice that the change in length must be measured in the same unit as the total length if the value of this ratio $\Delta L/L$ is to be independent of the units used.

13-2. Hooke's Law. Robert Hooke recognized (1676) and stated the law that is used to define the elastic properties of a body. In studying the effects of tensile forces, he observed that the increase in length of a body is proportional to the applied force over a rather wide range of forces. This observation may be made more general by stating that *the stress is proportional to the strain*. In this form the statement is known as *Hooke's law*.

If the stress is increased above a certain value, the body will not return to its original size (or shape) after the stress is removed. It is then said to have acquired a *permanent set*. The smallest stress that produces a permanent set is called the *elastic limit*. For stresses that exceed the elastic limit Hooke's law is not applicable.

The stretching of a given rod, cable, or spring is sometimes represented by an equation of the form

$$F = ks \qquad (1)$$

which states that the elongation s, beyond its no-load length, of the body in tension is directly proportional to the stretching force F. The constant k, or the ratio of the force to the elongation, is called the *force constant* and is expressed in pounds per foot, dynes per centimeter, or newtons per meter. It is equal numerically to the force required to produce unit elongation.

13-3. Elastic Potential Energy. When a spring is compressed or stretched, energy is stored in it. Changes in this potential energy are associated with changes in the shape of the elastic body. By arbitrarily calling the potential energy zero for a particular configuration of the body (Fig. 2a) one can calculate the potential energy when this body is deformed by application of a particular force, F_a in Fig. 2b.

The work which is done *against* the elastic forces in deforming a body, starting from the configuration of zero potential energy, is the elastic potential energy of the deformed body. This is the same as the work done *by* the ap-

plied forces which produce the deformation, provided these forces are increased gradually from zero to their final values. In this case the elastic body acquires no appreciable kinetic energy.

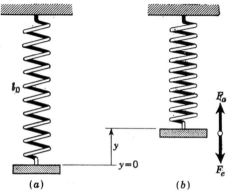

Fig. 2. Elastic potential energy: (a) spring in position of zero energy; (b) compressed spring has potential energy equal to $-\overline{F}_e y$.

Example: A spring loaded within its elastic limit has a length l_0. By application of a force F_a, upward, to the lower end of the spring it is compressed an amount s. Find the elastic potential energy of the spring.

From Hooke's law, the work dW to compress the spring a distance ds is $dW = -ks\, ds$. Hence the work done *against* the elastic force is

$$W = k \int_0^s s\, ds = \tfrac{1}{2} k s^2$$

The elastic potential energy of the spring is directly proportional to the force constant and to the square of the compression. The potential energy has the same value for an elongation of the same magnitude; in each case the same work is done against the elastic force to produce the deformation.

Although it is often of immediate interest to know the force constant for a particular object, it is also generally convenient to define elastic coefficients characteristic of a material. We shall discuss three of these coefficients.

13-4. Young's Modulus. A modulus of elasticity is defined as the ratio of a stress to the corresponding strain. This ratio is a constant, characteristic of the material. The ratio of the tensile stress to the tensile strain is called *Young's modulus*.

$$Y = \frac{\text{tensile stress}}{\text{tensile strain}} = \frac{F/A}{\Delta L/L} = \frac{FL}{A\,\Delta L} \quad (2)$$

Example: A steel bar, 20 ft long and of rectangular cross section 2.0 by 1.0 in., supports a load of 2.0 tons. How much is the bar stretched?

From Eq. (2) $\Delta L = \dfrac{FL}{YA}$

$F = 2.0$ tons $= (2.0 \text{ tons})(2000 \text{ lb/ton})$
$$= 4\bar{0}00 \text{ lb.}$$
$A = (2.0 \text{ in.} \times 1.0 \text{ in.}) = 2.0 \text{ in.}^2$
$$\Delta L = \frac{(4\bar{0}00 \text{ lb})(20 \text{ ft})}{(29 \times 10^6 \text{ lb/in.}^2)(2.0 \text{ in.}^2)} = 0.0014 \text{ ft}$$
$$= 0.017 \text{ in.}$$

Values of Y for several common materials are given in Table 1. Note that the physical dimensions of Y are those of force per unit area.

Although stretching a rubber band does increase the restoring force, the stress and strain do not vary in a direct proportion; hence Young's modulus for rubber is not a constant. Moreover, a stretched rubber band does not return immediately to its original length when the deforming force is removed. This failure of an object to regain its original size and shape as soon as the deforming force is removed is called *elastic lag* or *hysteresis* (a lagging behind).

Ordinarily stretching a wire cools it. Rubber gets warmer when stretched and cools when relaxed. This can be verified easily by stretching a rubber band and quickly holding it against the lips or tongue, which are very sensitive to changes in temperature. One would expect then that heating a rubber band would increase the stress. A simple experiment shows this to be true. Suspend a load by a long rubber band and apply heat to the band with a bunsen flame played quickly across the band so as not to fire the rubber. The band will contract, lifting the load. A wire under similar circumstances will expand, lowering the load. The modulus of elasticity of a metal decreases as the temperature increases.

13-5. Volume Elasticity. Bodies can be compressed as well as stretched. In this type of deformation also, elastic forces tend to restore the body to its original size.

Suppose that a rubber ball is placed in a liquid confined in a vessel and that a force is applied to the confined liquid, causing the ball to contract. The *volume stress* is the added normal force per unit area F/A and the *volume strain* is the fractional change $-\Delta V/V$ that is produced in the volume of the specimen. The ratio (volume stress)/(volume strain) is

TABLE 1. ELASTIC CONSTANTS

Material	Young's modulus, lb/in.²	Tension		Compression	
		Stress at elastic limit, lb/in.²	Breaking stress, lb/in.²	Breaking stress, lb/in.²	Hardness, Brinell number, kg/mm²
Aluminum, rolled......................	10×10^6	25,000	29,000	50,000	40
Aluminum alloy, 20% nickel.............	9.4	23,000	60,000	110,000	100
Copper, hard-drawn....................	14	.....	49,000		
Glass, silica..........................	10	.....	10,000	50,000	
Iron, wrought........................	27.5	23,500	47,000		
Lead, rolled..........................	2.2	.....	3,000		
Phosphor bronze......................	....	60,000	80,000	.....	50–200
Plastics, cast phenolic.................	1	.....	9,000	23,000	38
Plastics, polystyrene...................	0.4	.....	7,000	13,000	25
Rubber, vulcanized....................	2	500	2,500		
Steel, annealed.......................	29	40,000	75,000	.....	150

called the *coefficient of volume elasticity*, or *bulk modulus*.

$$B = \frac{\text{stress}}{\text{strain}} = \frac{F/A}{-\Delta V/V} \qquad (3)$$

This type of deformation, which involves only volume changes, applies to liquids as well as to solids. The bulk moduli of liquids and solids are large numbers of the same order of magnitude, expressing the familiar fact that large forces are needed to produce even minute changes in their volumes. Gases are more easily compressed and have correspondingly smaller bulk moduli. The *compressibility* of a material is represented by the reciprocal of its bulk modulus.

13-6. Elasticity of Shear. A third type of elasticity concerns changes in shape. This is called *elasticity of shear*. As an illustration of shearing strain, consider a cube of material (Fig. 3) fixed at its lower face and acted upon

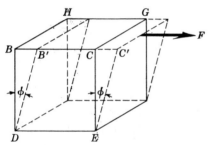

FIG. 3. Shearing of a cubical block through an angle ϕ by a force F.

by a tangential force F at its upper face. This force causes the consecutive horizontal layers of the cube to be slightly displaced or *sheared* relative to one another. Each line, such as BD or CE, in the cube is rotated through an angle ϕ by this shear. The shearing strain is defined as the angle ϕ, expressed in radians. For small values of the angle, $\phi = BB'/BD$, approximately. The shearing stress is the ratio of the force F to the area A of the face $BCGH$. The ratio, shearing stress divided by shearing strain, is the *shear modulus* or *coefficient of rigidity*, n.

$$n = \frac{F/A}{\phi} \qquad (4)$$

The volume of the body is not altered by shearing strain.

TABLE 2. BULK MODULI AND SHEAR MODULI

Material	B, lb/in.^{2}	n, lb/in.^{2}
Aluminum.........	10×10^6	3.6×10^6
Copper (hard)......	17	6.1
Cast iron.........	14	7.4
Glass.............	65	3.5
Rocks............	1.5–4	
Steel.............	23	11.6
Water............	0.30	0
Mercury..........	36	0

13-7. Ultimate Strength. The way in which samples of different materials are deformed by various loads is illustrated by Fig. 4. For each load the tensile strain is calculated as the ratio of the elongation to the

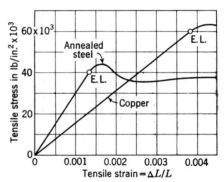

FIG. 4. Elastic behavior of certain metals.

original length. This is plotted against the tensile stress, and a curve is drawn through the points so obtained.

In the region below the elastic limit (EL) the sample obeys Hooke's law and returns to its original length when the stress is removed. The sample will support stresses in excess of the elastic limit, but when unloaded it is found to have acquired a permanent set.

If the applied stress is increased slowly, the sample will finally break. The maximum stress applied in rupturing the sample is called the *ultimate strength*. Although the ultimate strength of the sample lies far up on its strain-stress curve, it cannot safely be expected to carry such loads in structures. Axles and other parts of machines which are subject to repeated stresses are never loaded beyond the elastic limit.

Whenever a machine part is subjected to repeated stresses over a long period of time, the internal structure of the material is changed. Each time the stress is applied, the molecules and crystals realign. Each time the stress is removed, this alignment retains some permanent set. As this process continues, certain regions are weakened, particularly around areas where microscopic cracks appear on the surface. This loss of strength in a machine part because of repeated stresses is known as *fatigue*. Since failure due to fatigue occurs much sooner if flaws are present originally than in a perfect part, it is important to detect such flaws, even though they are very slight, before the part is installed. Great care is exercised in testing parts of airplane structures to detect original flaws. In many plants, x rays are used to detect hidden flaws.

13-8. Thermal Stresses. When a structure such as a bridge is put together, the design must take into account changes in shape due to changes in temperature. If such provision is not made, tremendous forces develop that may shatter parts of the structure. Anyone who has ever seen a concrete pavement shattered by these forces on a hot day realizes the violence of such a phenomenon.

The suitability of a material for a certain application may depend on properties other than the mechanical ones just discussed. Among those are flammability, moisture absorption, electrical conductivity, and thermal conductivity. For most structural purposes, however, materials are selected chiefly on the basis of their cost and their elastic properties.

13-9. Some Further Properties of Matter. Materials possess several characteristics that are closely related to the elastic properties. Among these are ductility, malleability, compressibility, and hardness.

The *ductility* of a material is the property

that represents its adaptability for being drawn into wire. *Malleability* is the property of a material by virtue of which it may be hammered or rolled into a desired shape. In the processes of drawing or rolling, stresses are applied that are much above the elastic limit so that a "flow" of the material occurs. For many materials the elastic limit is greatly reduced by raising the temperature; hence processes requiring flow are commonly carried on at high temperature.

The hardness of a substance was once determined from its ability to scratch other materials. The property of hardness of engineering materials is now commonly measured by the *Brinell number* or *Rockwell number*, based on two somewhat different test procedures.

The Brinell number is the ratio of load, in kilograms, on a sphere used to indent the material, to the spherical area, in square millimeters, of the indentation. The standard indentor is a hardened steel ball of 10 mm diameter and the usual load is 3000 kg, although 500-kg loads are used in testing some softer nonferrous materials.

In the Rockwell test, hardness is measured by the depth of penetration of a spherical-tipped conical indentor under certain specified conditions. The Rockwell number is read directly from a scale, lower numbers corresponding to soft materials, which suffer deeper penetration.

Hardness is not a fundamental property of materials but a composite one dependent on the elastic moduli, elastic limit, the hardening produced by "working" a metal, etc. Empirical relations are used to determine other properties from the easily measured hardness, but all such schemes are of doubtful or limited validity.

The useful life of a structure or a machine part depends quite as much on its surface properties as on its bulk properties. A glass fiber 0.003 mm in diameter may have a tensile strength 30 times that of a fiber 1 mm in diameter, owing to the greater freedom from surface flaws in the smaller fiber. The surface layers of metal tools, glass plates, and rubber tires may be treated so as to introduce compressive stresses in the surface, thereby greatly increasing the durability of the part.

13-10. Importance of Correct Testing Procedures. One difficulty encountered when attempting to measure the elastic properties of a material is that of providing a uniform or typical sample. If examined under sufficient magnification, no material is found to be uniform (homogeneous). Rock, brick, and concrete have structure that can readily be seen. Elastic constants for such materials should not be taken for samples that are not large compared to the size of the unit structure. Resistance to crushing varies from 800 to 3800 lb/in.² for concrete, while that of granite varies from 9700 to 34,000 lb/in.²

Equally as important as correct sampling is the choice of a testing procedure which permits measurement of a given property of the sample under the same conditions as those under which the material will be used. It may be convenient to measure the ultimate strength of a steel by subjecting a small polished cylinder to steadily increasing tension until rupture occurs. But such a test tells little about the possible failure of a machine part made of the same steel when that part has an unpolished surface and when it is subjected to rapidly recurring loads or to twisting and bending. A valid test must duplicate the conditions of actual use.

Many industries have developed laboratories and testing equipment with which to examine the properties of the materials they purchase and to control the quality of their products. Recommended procedures for making numerous tests have been developed cooperatively by industry and such organizations as the American Society for Testing Materials and the National Bureau of Standards.

SUMMARY

Elasticity is that property of a body which enables it to resist deformation and to recover after removal of the deforming force.

Tensile stress is the ratio of the force to the cross-sectional area.

Tensile strain is the ratio of the increase in length to the original length.

The smallest stress that produces a permanent deformation is known as the *elastic limit*.

Hooke's law expresses the fact that, within the limits of elasticity, stress is proportional to strain or the elongation s is proportional to the force F

$$F = ks$$

A *modulus of elasticity* is found by dividing the stress by the corresponding strain.

Young's modulus is the ratio of tensile stress to tensile strain

$$Y = \frac{F/A}{\Delta L/L}$$

The *coefficient of volume elasticity* or *bulk modulus* is the ratio of volume stress to volume strain

$$B = \frac{F/A}{-\Delta V/V}$$

The *shear modulus* or *coefficient of rigidity* is the ratio of shearing stress to shearing strain

$$n = \frac{F/A}{\phi}$$

Compressibility is the reciprocal of the bulk modulus.

Brinell hardness number is the ratio of the force applied on a hardened steel ball to the spherical area of indentation produced in a sample.

QUESTIONS   **1.** What is the purpose of the steel in a horizontal reinforced concrete beam? in a vertical column? Does concrete need reinforcement more under compressive or under tensile stresses? Why?

2. A horizontal concrete beam is to be reinforced with steel rods. Should they be embedded near the upper or near the lower side of the beam? Why?

3. Which is the more elastic, rubber or steel? air or water?

4. What kind of elasticity is utilized in a suspension bridge? an automobile tire? an automobile drive shaft? a coil spring? a water lift pump? rubber heels?

5. In what way do the numerical magnitudes of (*a*) strain, (*b*) stress, and (*c*) modulus of elasticity depend upon the units of force and length?

6. Two 40-ft wires of the same material have diameters whose ratio is *n*. How much more will the smaller wire be stretched under a given load?

7. An elevator is suspended by a heavy steel cable. If this cable were replaced by two steel cables each having the same length as the original one but half its diameter, how would the amount of stretch in the pair of thin cables compare with that of the original cable?

8. Can one use a slender wire in the laboratory to estimate the load capacity of a large cable on a bridge? Explain.

9. A certain force is required to break a piece of wire. What force is required to break a wire made of the same material which is (*a*) twice as long and (*b*) twice as large in diameter and the same length?

10. From Table 1, which material would be preferable for the spiral spring of a spring balance? Why?

PROBLEMS   **1.** When a 2.4-kg block is attached to the end of a spring hanging vertically, the spring experiences an elongation of 5.0 cm. What is the potential energy of the stretched spring?

2. A long wire hangs vertically with its upper end clamped. When a torque of 2.5 lb-ft is applied to the free end, it is twisted through an angle of 30°. What is the potential energy of the twisted wire?   *Ans.* 0.66 ft-lb

3. How much will a steel wire 20 ft long and 0.20 in. in diameter stretch when a load of 200 lb is hung on it?

4. How much will an annealed steel rod 100 ft long and 0.0400 in.² in cross section be stretched by a force of 1000 lb?   *Ans.* 1.03 in.

5. Young's modulus for steel is about 29×10^6 lb/in.² Express this value in dynes per square centimeter.

6. A wire 1000 in. long and 0.010 in.² in cross section is stretched 4.0 in. by a force of 2000 lb. What are (*a*) the stretching stress, (*b*) the stretching strain, and (*c*) Young's modulus?   *Ans.* 2.0×10^5 lb/in.²; 0.0040; 5.0×10^7 lb/in.²

7. A certain wire 0.70 mm in diameter and 2.0 m long was stretched 1.6 mm by a load of 2.0 kg. Find Young's modulus for the material.

8. A steel wire 100 cm long having a cross-sectional area of 0.025 cm² is stretched a distance of 0.30 cm. What is the stretching force?
    Ans. $\overline{3}40$ lb or 1.5×10^8 dynes

9. A hollow metal post is 10.0 ft long and the cross-sectional area of the metal is 2.5 in.² When a load of 25.0 tons is applied to it, the length decreases 0.010 ft. Compute (*a*) the stress, (*b*) the strain, and (*c*) Young's modulus.

10. A load of 9.0 tons is imposed on a vertical steel support 18 ft high having a cross-sectional area of 3.0 in.² How much is the column shortened by the load?
    Ans. 0.045 in.

11. A load of 60 tons is carried by a steel column having a length of 24 ft and a cross-sectional area of 10.8 in.² What decrease in length will this load produce?

12. Compute the elongations of the aluminum wire of 40-mil (0.040 in.) diameter and the 60-mil copper wire in Fig. 5. Young's modulus for copper is 14×10^6 lb/in.²   *Ans.* 0.0026 ft; 0.00040 ft

13. A steel wire 3.0 ft long and a copper wire 2.0 ft long, each 0.20 in.² in cross section, are fastened together end to end and are then subjected to a tension of 200 lb. Calculate the elongation of each wire. $Y_{Cu} = 14 \times 10^6$ lb/in.^{2}

14. A steel wire 8.0 ft long has a cross section of 0.050 in.^{2} When a stretching force of 1600 lb is applied, the wire increases 0.106 in. in length. (*a*) What is the stress in the wire? (*b*) What is Young's modulus for the wire?

Ans. $3\overline{2},000$ lb/in.^{2}; 2.9×10^7 lb/in.^{2}

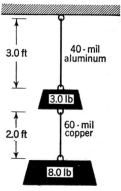

FIG. 5.

15. Many "high tension" cables have a solid steel core to support the aluminum wires that carry most of the current. Assume that the steel is 0.50 in. in diameter, that each of the 12 aluminum wires has a diameter of 0.13 in., and that the strain is the same in the steel and the aluminum. If the total tension is 1.0 ton, what is the tension sustained by the steel?

16. A seamless steel boiler drum is 48 in. in inside diameter and 50 in. in outside diameter. When tested at twice its normal operating pressure, the outer circumference of the drum expanded 0.080 in. What was the tensile force in the drum per foot of axial length? *Ans.* 1.8×10^5 lb

17. A steel wire 0.128 in. in diameter hangs vertically from a support. A load of 400 lb is applied to the lower end. (*a*) What elongation will take place per foot of length when the load is applied? (*b*) Will the wire return to its original length upon removal of the load?

18. A steel wire $\frac{1}{2}$ mi long hangs vertically in a deep well. How much does it stretch under its own weight? The density of steel is 7.85 gm/cm^2. (SUGGESTION: Find the elongation for each element; then integrate.) *Ans.* 0.408 ft

19. A circular rod 0.50 in. in diameter is made of an alloy which has a Young's modulus of 24×10^6 lb/in.^{2} If the elastic and breaking limits coincide at a stretch of 1 part in 1000, what force is needed to break the rod in tension?

20. An aluminum rod 300 cm long and 0.508 cm in diameter would normally contract 1.32 cm in cooling from 225°C to 25°C. What force would be required to prevent this contraction? *Ans.* $13\overline{8}0$ lb

21. Fibers of spun glass have been found capable of sustaining unusually large stresses. Calculate the breaking stress of a fiber 0.00035 in. in diameter, which broke under a load of 0.385 oz.

22. To maintain 200 in.^{3} of water at a reduction of 1% in volume requires a force per unit area of 3400 lb/in.^{2} What is the bulk modulus of the water?

Ans. 3.4×10^5 lb/in.^{2}

23. What increase in stress is required to produce a 1% increase in the density of glycerin, whose compressibility is 22×10^{-12} cm^2/dyne?

24. (*a*) Find the decrease in volume of 2.0 liters of water when subjected to 10 atm pressure. The compressibility of water is $1/B = 50 \times 10^{-12}$ cm²/dyne. A pressure of 1 atm is 1.013×10^6 dynes/cm². (*b*) From Table 2, what would be the change in volume for mercury and iron under the same circumstances?

Ans. 1.01 cm³; 0.084 cm³; 0.024 cm³

25. What is the change in volume of the water in a cylinder 3.0 ft long and 3.0 in. in diameter when there is a compressional force per unit area of 14.3 lb/in.² exerted on a tight piston in the cylinder?

26. If the density of sea water is 1.03 gm/cm³ at the surface, what is its density at a depth where the pressure is 10^9 dynes/cm²?   *Ans.* 1.08 gm/cm³

27. A 12-in. cubical block of sponge has two parallel and opposite forces of 2.5 lb each applied to opposite faces. If the angle of shear is 0.020 radian, calculate the relative displacement and the shear modulus.

28. A 4.0-ft square steel plate 1.0 in. thick is supported vertically with its lower edge fixed rigidly. Shear stress is applied, and the upper edge is observed to move parallel to the lower edge through 0.020 in. Find the shear strain.

Ans. 0.00042

29. A 2.0-in. cube of gelatin has its upper surface displaced ¼ in. by a tangential force of 1.0 oz. What is the shear modulus of gelatin?

30. A shearing force of 3.0 tons is distributed uniformly over the cross section of a pin 1.5 in. in diameter. Find the shear stress.   *Ans.* 1.7 tons/in.²

14. *Vibratory Motion*

Three types of motion have been treated in the earlier chapters. The simplest is that of an object in equilibrium, a motion consisting of constant speed and unchanging direction. The second type of motion, which is produced by the action of a constant force parallel to the direction of motion, is that in which the direction is constant and the speed increases uniformly. Projectile motion was discussed as a combination of these two simple types of motion. The third type of motion discussed is uniform circular motion, that produced by a (centripetal) force of constant magnitude directed inward along the radius of the circular path of the moving object.

It is clear that the forces we commonly observe are not always zero, constant in magnitude and direction, or constant in magnitude and of rotating direction; so that, consequently, the motions commonly observed are not always uniform rectilinear, uniformly accelerated, uniform circular, or even combinations of the three. In general, the forces acting on a body vary in both magnitude and direction, resulting in complicated types of nonuniformly accelerated motion, which cannot be investigated in an elementary physics course. However, there is one common and important type of nonuniformly accelerated motion that can be analyzed rather simply. This motion is called periodic motion.

14-1. Periodic Motion. A type of motion that is particularly important in mechanics is the to-and-fro or vibrating motion of objects stretched or bent from their normal positions and then released. Such an object moves back and forth along a fixed path, repeating over and over a fixed series of motions and returning to each position and velocity after a definite period of time. Such motion is called *periodic* motion or *harmonic* motion. This type of motion is produced by varying forces, and hence the body experiences varying accelerations. While many periodic motions are quite complicated, they can usually be studied as combinations of relatively simple types of vibration. It is fortunate that the simple vibrations, though produced by varying forces, can be analyzed rather easily and completely by elementary methods.

14-2. Simple Harmonic Motion. When an elastic spring is stretched by a force, the amount of the force required is proportional to the stretch. Suppose that an object of mass m (Fig. 1) hanging at the end of a spiral spring is pulled down a distance s below the equilibrium position. The spring exerts a restoring force on the object, tending to pull it back toward its original position. This force is proportional to the displacement s but opposite in direction to the displacement.

$$F = -Ks \qquad (1)$$

When the object is released, the restoring force produces an acceleration that is proportional to F and inversely proportional to the

mass m being accelerated

$$a = \frac{F}{m} = -\frac{K}{m}s = -ks \qquad (2)$$

Hence the acceleration is proportional to the displacement but opposite in direction.

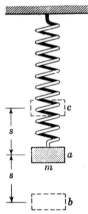

FIG. 1. An object supported by a spring vibrates with simple harmonic motion.

As the object moves toward its equilibrium position, its speed increases but the force, and consequently the acceleration, decreases until it becomes zero when the object reaches the initial position. Because of its inertia the object continues past the equilibrium position but at once a retarding force comes into being which increases until the object reaches c where it stops and begins its return trip. At all times during this motion the net force, and hence the acceleration, is proportional to the displacement and directed toward the equilibrium position. *The type of vibratory motion in which the acceleration is proportional to the displacement and always directed toward the equilibrium position is called simple harmonic motion* (SHM). This motion is always motion along a straight line, the acceleration and velocity constantly changing as the vibrating body moves through its series of positions. The direct proportionality of acceleration and displacement distinguishes simple harmonic motion from all other types of vibratory motion.

Very few vibrating bodies execute motion

that is strictly simple harmonic but many vibrate with a motion that is so nearly simple harmonic that it can be treated as such without appreciable error. Suppose that a steel ball is mounted on a flat spring that is clamped in a vise as in Fig. 2. Pull the ball

FIG. 2. A ball and spring in approximate simple harmonic motion.

sideways, bending the spring, and you will observe a restoring force that tends to move the ball back toward its initial position. This force increases as the ball is pulled farther away from its original position. The motion of the ball is only approximately SHM since it moves along the arc of a circle instead of along a straight line and the direction of the force is tangent to the circle rather than toward the initial position. However, if the displacement is small, the departure from SHM is so slight that no great error is introduced by assuming that the motion is simple harmonic. The motion of a pendulum is also approximately SHM.

14-3. Period, Frequency, and Amplitude. The *period* T of a vibratory motion is the time required for a complete to-and-fro motion or oscillation. In a complete oscillation the vibrating body moves from the equilibrium position to one end of the path, back to the equilibrium position, to the other end of the path, and back to the equilibrium position ready to repeat the cycle.

The *frequency f* of the vibratory motion is the number of complete oscillations per unit time. The frequency is the reciprocal of the period: $f = 1/T$.

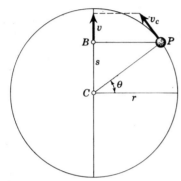

Fig. 3. Circle of reference for analyzing simple harmonic motion.

The *amplitude* of a vibratory motion is the maximum displacement from the equilibrium position.

14-4. The Circle of Reference. When a body moves with uniform speed in a circle, the projection of this motion on a diameter is simple harmonic motion. In Fig. 3, the body P is moving with uniform speed v_c and uniform angular speed ω in a circular path. The projection B moves up and down along the vertical diameter. Assume that the time is assigned a zero value when the body B passes through the equilibrium position C, moving upward. At any later time t the rotating body P will have moved through an angle $\theta = \omega t$. At this instant the projection B has a displacement

$$s = r \sin \theta = r \sin \omega t \qquad (3)$$

at this instant the velocity v of the vibrating body B is

$$v = \frac{ds}{dt} = r\omega \cos \omega t \qquad (4)$$

at the same instant the acceleration is

$$a = \frac{dv}{dt} = -r\omega^2 \sin \omega t \qquad (5)$$

But $r \sin \omega t = s$; hence

$$a = -\omega^2 s \qquad (6)$$

Thus the acceleration of B is proportional to the displacement but is opposite in direction. Hence the motion of B is SHM and the projection of uniform circular motion upon a diameter is SHM.

This example of simple harmonic motion is very useful in studying SHM since it can be used to determine relationships between velocity, acceleration, period, frequency, and amplitude. The circle used here is commonly called the *reference* circle.

In terms of the reference circle the period of the SHM is the same as the time of one revolution in the reference circle. The amplitude in SHM is the same as the radius of the reference circle, and the frequency is the number of revolutions per unit time in the reference circle. For every SHM a reference circle can be set up from these relationships.

14-5. Period and Frequency in SHM. The frequency f of the SHM is the same as the frequency or number of revolutions per unit time in the reference circle. The angular velocity ω is

$$\omega = 2\pi f = \frac{2\pi}{T} \qquad (7)$$

From Eq. (6)

$$a = -\omega^2 s = -\frac{4\pi^2}{T^2} s \qquad (8)$$

and

$$T^2 = -4\pi^2 \frac{s}{a}$$

$$T = 2\pi \sqrt{-\frac{s}{a}} \qquad (9)$$

The period can be expressed in terms of the force constant of the spring (or other agency) that supplies the restoring force. From Eq. (2)

$$-\frac{s}{a} = \frac{m}{K}$$

If we substitute this value of $-s/a$ in Eq. (9),

we obtain

$$T = 2\pi \sqrt{\frac{m}{K}} \qquad (10)$$

If the mass m is expressed in grams and the force constant K in dynes per centimeter, Eq. (10) gives the period in seconds. If the mass is expressed in kilograms and the force constant in newtons per meter, Eq. (10) gives the period in seconds. In the British system the mass is computed in slugs from W/g, and the force constant is expressed in pounds per foot. The resulting period is in seconds.

Equation (10) expresses the fact that the period in SHM depends upon only two factors, the mass of the vibrating body and the force constant of the spring (or other agent). It should be noted that the *period is independent of the amplitude.*

Reference to Eq. (10) will show that if the object is replaced by another whose mass is four times as great the period will be doubled. If, instead, the spring is replaced by another four times as stiff, the period is halved.

Example: A 5.0-lb ball is fastened to the end of a flat spring (Fig. 2). A force of 2.0 lb is sufficient to pull the ball 6.0 in. to one side. Find the force constant and the period of vibration.

$$K = \frac{F}{s} = \frac{2.0 \text{ lb}}{0.50 \text{ ft}} = 4.0 \text{ lb/ft}$$

$$m = \frac{W}{g} = \frac{5.0 \text{ lb}}{32 \text{ ft/sec}^2} = 0.16 \text{ slug}$$

$$T = 2\pi \sqrt{\frac{m}{K}} = 2\pi \sqrt{\frac{0.16 \text{ slug}}{4.0 \text{ lb/ft}}} = 1.2 \text{ sec}$$

14-6. Acceleration and Speed in SHM. At the position of greatest displacement, that is, at the end points of the motion, the vibrating object comes momentarily to a stop. It should be noticed that at the instant when its speed is zero, the object is acted upon by the maximum restoring force, so that the acceleration is greatest when the speed is zero. The restoring force (and therefore the acceleration) decreases as the object moves toward the equilibrium position. At the equi-

librium position the acceleration is zero and the speed is the greatest. The direction of the acceleration reverses as the object passes through the equilibrium position, increasing as the displacement increases, and reaching a maximum at the other extreme of displacement.

Example: A 2.0-lb body vibrates in SHM with an amplitude of 3.0 in. and a period of 5.0 sec. Find the acceleration and the speed (*a*) at the mid-point, (*b*) at the end of the path, and (*c*) at a point 2.0 in. from the mid-point. Find the force on the body and the kinetic energy of the body at the point 2.0 in. from the mid-point.

Since the amplitude is 3.0 in. the radius of the reference circle is 3.0 in. The angular speed in the reference circle is

$$\omega = \frac{2\pi}{T} = \frac{2\pi}{5.0 \text{ sec}} = 1.26 \text{ radians/sec}$$

At the mid-point $\theta = 0°$ (or 180°) and, from Eq. (4),

$$v = r\omega \cos\theta = 3.0 \text{ in.} \times 1.26 \text{ rad/sec} \times 1.00$$
$$= 3.8 \text{ in./sec} = 0.32 \text{ ft/sec}$$

From Eq. (5)

$$a = -r\omega^2 \sin\theta$$
$$= -3.0 \text{ in.} \times (1.26 \text{ rad/sec})^2 \times 0 = 0$$

At the end point of the path, $\theta = 90°$ (or 270°) and, from Eqs. (4) and (5),

$$v = r\omega \cos\theta = 3.0 \text{ in.} \times 1.26 \text{ rad/sec} \times 0 = 0$$

and

$$a = -r\omega^2 \sin\theta = -3.0 \text{ in.} \times (1.26 \text{ rad/sec})^2$$
$$\times 1.00 = -4.8 \text{ in./sec}^2 = -0.40 \text{ ft/sec}^2$$

At the point 2.0 in. from the equilibrium position, we see from Fig. 3 that $\sin\theta = 2.0/3.0 = 0.67$ and $\cos\theta = \sqrt{(3.0^2 - 2.0^2)}/3.0 = \sqrt{5.0}/3.0 = 0.75$. Then

$$v = r\omega \cos\theta = 3.0 \text{ in.} \times 1.26 \text{ rad/sec} \times 0.75$$
$$= 2.8 \text{ in./sec} = 0.23 \text{ ft/sec}$$

$$a = -r\omega^2 \sin\theta = -3.0 \text{ in.} \times (1.26 \text{ rad/sec})^2$$
$$\times 0.67 = -3.2 \text{ in./sec}^2 = -0.27 \text{ ft/sec}^2$$

From Newton's second law

$$F = ma = \frac{2.0}{32} \text{ slug} \times 0.27 \text{ ft/sec}^2 = 0.017 \text{ lb}$$

$$KE = \tfrac{1}{2}mv^2 = \frac{1}{2} \times \frac{2.0}{32} \text{ slug} \times (0.23 \text{ ft/sec})^2$$
$$= 0.0017 \text{ ft-lb}$$

An alternative method of using the reference circle is a direct application of the projections. At every position of the vibrating

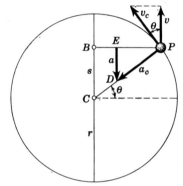

Fig. 4. Velocity and acceleration from the reference circle.

body, the velocity of the body is the component, taken parallel to the chosen diameter, of the velocity in the reference circle and, similarly, the acceleration in the vibration is the component, taken parallel to the diameter, of the acceleration in the circular path. Consider Fig. 4. The acceleration of the particle at P is a_c directed toward the center of the circle. The component a of the central acceleration of particle P parallel to the chosen diameter is the acceleration of B. The triangles PBC and PED are similar. Therefore

$$\frac{a}{a_c} = -\frac{s}{r} \qquad (11)$$

where a_c is the central acceleration, r is the radius, and s is the displacement of the particle B. The minus sign is used since s is measured upward while a is directed downward. Hence

$$a = -\frac{a_c}{r} s \qquad (12)$$

Example: Use the component method to solve the preceding example.

Since the amplitude is 3.0 in., the radius of the reference circle is 3.0 in. The speed v_c of the particle in the reference circle is

$$v_c = \frac{2\pi r}{T} = \frac{(2\pi)(3.0 \text{ in.})}{5.0 \text{ sec}} = 3.8 \text{ in./sec}$$

At the mid-point of the path, the particle in the reference circle is moving parallel to the chosen diameter and therefore the velocity of the vibrating body is the same as the velocity in the reference circle.

$$v_1 = v_c = 3.8 \text{ in./sec} = 0.32 \text{ ft/sec}$$

At the mid-point, the acceleration in the reference circle is perpendicular to the diameter, and hence the component parallel to the path of the vibrating body is zero. Therefore

$$a_1 = 0$$

At the end point, the velocity in the reference circle is perpendicular to the path of vibration and hence has no component in that direction.

$$v_2 = 0$$

At the end point, the acceleration in the reference circle is the same as the acceleration in the vibration

$$a_2 = a_c = \frac{v_c^2}{r} = \frac{(3.8 \text{ in./sec})^2}{3.0 \text{ in.}} = 4.8 \text{ in./sec}^2$$
$$= 0.40 \text{ ft/sec}^2$$

At the point 2.0 in. from the mid-point, we may find the acceleration by use of the similar triangles PBC and PED of Fig. (4).

$$\frac{a}{a_c} = \frac{-s}{r}$$
$$a = \frac{-a_c s}{r} = \frac{-(4.8 \text{ in./sec}^2)(2.0 \text{ in.})}{3.0 \text{ in.}}$$
$$= -3.2 \text{ in./sec}^2 = -0.27 \text{ ft/sec}^2$$

From Fig. 4, the velocity in the path of vibration is the component v of the velocity v_c in the reference circle. From the geometry of Fig. 4,

$$v = v_c \cos \theta$$
$$\cos \theta = \frac{BP}{CP} = \frac{\sqrt{(3.0 \text{ in.})^2 - (2.0 \text{ in.})^2}}{3.0 \text{ in.}} = 0.75$$
$$v = (3.8 \text{ in./sec})(0.75) = 2.8 \text{ in./sec}$$
$$= 0.23 \text{ ft/sec}$$

14-7. The Simple Pendulum. One of the most common of approximate simple harmonic motions is the motion of a pendulum. A pendulum consisting of a small relatively heavy bob at the end of a very light string is called a *simple pendulum*. If such a pendulum is

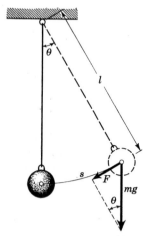

FIG. 5. A simple pendulum.

displaced as shown in Fig. 5, the weight *mg* of the bob supplies a restoring force

$$F = -mg \sin \theta$$

The displacement along the arc is $s = l\theta$. Hence, the force is proportional to $\sin \theta$ while the displacement is proportional to θ. The restoring force is not proportional to the displacement. Moreover, the restoring force is not directed toward the equilibrium position but rather it is tangent to the arc. Thus the motion is not simple harmonic. However, if θ is small, we may replace $\sin \theta$ by θ (in radians) without serious error. To this degree of approximation the motion may be considered as simple harmonic motion. Then

$$F = ma = -mg\theta = -\frac{mgs}{l}$$

and
$$-\frac{s}{a} = \frac{l}{g}$$

From Eq. (9)

$$T = 2\pi \sqrt{\frac{l}{g}} \qquad (13)$$

Equation (13) shows that to the degree of approximation involved the period depends only upon the length of the pendulum and the acceleration due to gravity. The period is independent of the mass of the bob. The period is also independent of the amplitude

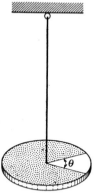

FIG. 6. A torsion pendulum. Simple angular harmonic motion.

when the amplitudes are small. If the amplitude is large, the period is greater than that for small amplitudes. It can be shown that the whole relation is

$$T = 2\pi \sqrt{\frac{l}{g}} \left(1 + \frac{1}{4} \frac{\sin^2 \theta}{2} + \frac{9}{64} \frac{\sin^4 \theta}{4} + \cdots \right)$$

For large amplitudes one can use as many terms of the series as are necessary to give the accuracy needed.

14-8. Simple Angular Harmonic Motion. If a heavy cylinder is supported at the end of a wire (torsion pendulum) and twisted through an angle θ (Fig. 6) about an axis along the wire, the wire supplies a restoring torque proportional to the angle of twist.

$$L = -K_0 \theta \qquad (14)$$

where the negative sign is introduced because L and θ are always opposite in sign. The constant K_0 is called the *moment of torsion* of the wire and depends upon the length, diameter, and material of the wire. This constant is of

considerable importance in the design of instruments in which the sensitivity depends
upon the twist of a wire or fiber.

When the pendulum is released, the restoring torque produces an angular acceleration
proportional to the angular displacement.
The motion produced is *simple angular harmonic motion*. The period depends upon the
moment of torsion of the support and upon
the moment of inertia of the oscillating system. By analogy to Eq. (10) we can write the
equation

$$T = 2\pi \sqrt{\frac{I}{K_0}} \qquad (15)$$

where K_0 is the moment of torsion of the supporting fiber and I is the moment of inertia of
the vibrating system about an axis along the
supporting fiber.

14-9. Resonance. Suppose that the natural
frequency of vibration of the system represented in Fig. 2 is 10 vib/sec. Now imagine
that, beginning with the system at rest, we
apply to it a to-and-fro force, say, 25 times
per second. In a short time this force will set
the system to vibrating regularly 25 times a
second, but with a very small amplitude, for
the ball and spring are trying to vibrate at
their natural rate of 10 vib/sec. During part
of the time, therefore, the system is, so to
speak, "fighting back" against the driving
force, whose frequency is 25 vib/sec. We call
the motion of the system in this case *forced
vibration*.

Now suppose that the alternation of the
driving force is gradually slowed down from
25 vib/sec to 10 vib/sec, the natural frequency of the system, so that the alternations

Fig. 7. Dangerous resonance. Excessive vibration caused the collapse of the bridge.

of the driving force come just as the system is ready to receive them. When this happens, the amplitude of vibration becomes very large, building up until the energy supplied by the driving force is just sufficient to overcome friction. Under these conditions the system is said to be in *resonance* with the driving force.

A small driving force of proper frequency can build up a very large amplitude of motion in a system capable of vibration. We have all heard car rattles that appear only at certain speeds, or vibrations set up in dishes, table lamps, cupboards, and the like by musical sounds of particular frequency. A motor running in the basement will often set certain pieces of furniture into vibration. This problem of resonant vibrations may become particularly important with heavy machinery. The problem is to find the part that is vibrating in resonance with the machinery and to change its natural frequency by changing its mass or its binding force (force constant).

A common example of resonance is furnished by radio circuits. When one tunes his receiver, he is in effect altering what corresponds to the spring constant of a mechanical system. By thus changing the natural frequency, one can bring the circuit into resonance with the desired electrical frequency transmitted by the sending station. The forced vibrations from all other frequencies have such small amplitudes that they do not produce any noticeable effect.

SUMMARY

Periodic motion is that motion in which a body moves back and forth over a fixed path, repeating over and over a fixed series of motions and returning to each position and velocity after a definite interval of time.

Simple harmonic motion is that type of vibratory motion in which the acceleration is proportional to the displacement and is always directed toward the position of equilibrium.

$$a = -\frac{K}{m}s = -ks$$

Simple harmonic motion is always motion along a straight line. Many vibrations that are not strictly simple harmonic are very close approximations and may be treated as such without serious error.

The motion of the projection on a diameter of a point that moves at constant speed on the "circle of reference" describes simple harmonic motion. The displacement, velocity, and acceleration in the SHM are related to the reference circle by the following equations:

$$s = r \sin \omega t$$
$$v = r\omega \cos \omega t$$
$$a = -r\omega^2 \sin \omega t$$

where t is the time elapsed after the vibrating body passes through the equilibrium position and ω is the angular velocity in the reference circle.

The *period* of a vibratory motion is the time required for one complete oscillation

$$T = 2\pi \sqrt{\frac{m}{K}}$$

The *frequency* is the number of complete oscillations per second

$$f = \frac{1}{T}$$

The *amplitude* of the motion is the maximum displacement from the equilibrium position. The radius of the reference circle is equal to the amplitude.

A *simple pendulum* is one which consists of a concentrated bob supported by a very light string. Its motion is approximately SHM and the period is given by the equation

$$T = 2\pi \sqrt{\frac{l}{g}}$$

A *torsion pendulum* vibrates with simple angular harmonic motion. Its period of oscillation is given by

$$T = 2\pi \sqrt{\frac{I}{K_0}}$$

The *moment of torsion* K_0 is the ratio of the

torque to the angle of twist produced by that torque. It depends upon the length, diameter, and material of the rod or wire.

Resonance occurs when a periodic driving force is impressed upon a system whose natural frequency of vibration is the same as that of the driving force. When this happens, the amplitude of vibration builds up until the energy supplied by the driving force is just sufficient to overcome friction in the system.

QUESTIONS

1. Why are approximate simple harmonic motions common in nature? Give some examples. Why are true simple harmonic motions extremely rare?

2. Describe clearly how the motion of the piston in the cylinder of a steam locomotive differs from simple harmonic motion.

3. How could one connect a piston to a rotor so that the motion of the piston would be simple harmonic?

4. Within a solid sphere of uniform density the gravitational force on an object varies directly with the first power of the distance from the center. Assuming that the earth were such a sphere and that a hole could be drilled completely through it from one pole to the other, what would happen to an object dropped into the hole?

5. Under what conditions does the addition of two simple harmonic motions produce a resultant that is simple harmonic?

6. What is the purpose of the pendulum of a clock or the balance wheel of a watch?

7. When a pendulum clock gains time, what adjustment should be made?

8. A 1-in. iron ball and a 1-in. wooden ball are supported by threads of equal length. When the two are set swinging, how will the periods compare? Is there any difference in their behavior? If so, what?

9. A simple pendulum has a period of 2.00 sec at sea level and 45° latitude. What will be the effect qualitatively on the period if the pendulum is at sea level (*a*) at the equator? (*b*) at latitude 60°? What will be the effect of taking it to elevation 5000 ft at latitude 45°?

10. A small ball is supported by a string that passes through a hole in the support. The ball is started swinging, and the string is pulled up through the hole. Describe and explain the motion of the ball. If its energy is increased what is the source of the increased energy?

11. Why do marching men break step when crossing a light bridge?

12. Use the standard method of maxima and minima to show that in SHM the acceleration is zero when the velocity is greatest and that the velocity is zero when the acceleration is greatest.

13. Describe several common phenomena in which resonance is an important factor.

PROBLEMS

1. What is the force constant of a spring that is stretched 11.0 in. by a force of 5.00 lb? What is the period of vibration of a 10.0-lb body if it is suspended by this spring?

2. A 1000-gm cage is suspended by a spiral spring. When a 200-gm bird sits in the cage, the cage is pulled 0.50 cm below its position when empty. Find the period of vibration of the cage (*a*) when empty and (*b*) when the bird is inside.

Ans. 0.32 sec; 0.35 sec

3. A 50.0-gm body hung on a spring causes it to elongate 2.00 cm. When a certain object is hung on the spring and set vibrating its period is 0.568 sec. What is the mass of the object attached to the spring?

4. A spring elongates 2.00 cm for a load of 15.0 gm. If a body of mass 294 gm

is attached to the spring and it is set into vibration with an amplitude of 10.0 cm, what will be (a) the force constant, (b) the period, and (c) the maximum speed of the vibrating body?   *Ans.* 7350 dynes/cm; 1.26 sec; 50.0 cm/sec

5. A 200-gm body elongates a spring 4.9 cm. (a) What will be the period of vibration of the spring when a 400-gm object is attached to it? (b) What will be the maximum speed of the vibrating object if the amplitude is 3.0 cm?

6. A spring is stretched 25.0 cm by a load of 200 gm. A 300-gm object is attached to the spring and displaced 10.0 cm from the equilibrium position. Find the potential energy of the system in this position. From consideration of energy find the speed of the object when it is 5.00 cm from the equilibrium position.   *Ans.* 3.92×10^5 ergs; 44.2 cm/sec

7. A spring is stretched 12.0 in. by a force of 5.00 lb. A 2.00-lb body is attached to the spring, displaced 4.00 in. and allowed to vibrate in SHM. Find (a) the force constant, (b) the period, (c) the maximum speed, and (d) the maximum kinetic energy. Compute the work done in stretching the spring 4.00 in. Compare this work with the maximum kinetic energy.

8. The drive wheels of a locomotive whose piston has a stroke of 2.00 ft make 185 rev/min. Assuming that the piston moves with SHM, find the speed of the piston relative to the cylinder head at the instant when the piston is at the center of its stroke.   *Ans.* 19.4 ft/sec

9. A 2.0-lb body is executing simple harmonic motion of amplitude 1.0 ft and period 0.80 sec. (a) What is its speed as it passes through the equilibrium position? (b) What is its kinetic energy at that instant?

10. A 4.0-kg body is caused to vibrate with SHM by means of a spring. If the amplitude is 30 cm and the time of a complete vibration is 0.60 sec, find (a) the maximum speed, (b) the maximum kinetic energy, (c) the minimum kinetic energy, and (d) the spring constant of the spring.
          Ans. 3.1 m/sec; 19 newton-m; 0; 4$\overline{4}$0 newtons/m

11. A 50-kg body vibrates with SHM of amplitude 25 cm and a period of 0.784 sec. (a) What is its maximum speed? (b) its maximum kinetic energy? (c) its minimum kinetic energy?

12. A tooth in the blade of a reaper describes approximate SHM of 1.5 in. amplitude and has a period of 0.20 sec. Find its speed when at a point 0.50 in. from the center of its path.   *Ans.* 44 in./sec

13. A load of 500 gm causes a spring to stretch 12.0 cm. An additional load of 100 gm is added, and the spring is set into vibration with an amplitude of 3.25 cm. Calculate (a) the frequency, (b) the speed when the displacement is 1.63 cm, and (c) the maximum kinetic energy of the system.

14. A body moves with SHM of an amplitude 24 cm and a period of 1.2 sec. (a) Find the speed of the object when it is at its mid-position, and when 24 cm away. (b) What is the magnitude of the acceleration in each case?
          Ans. 1$\overline{3}$0 cm/sec; 0; 0; 6$\overline{6}$0 cm/sec²

15. A body suspended from a coiled spring oscillates vertically with SHM through a distance of 2.0 ft. The time for one complete vibration is 3.0 sec. Find (a) the maximum speed of the body, (b) the speed of the body 0.38 sec after it has passed the lowest point in its path, and (c) the maximum acceleration of the body.

16. A 2.0-lb body vibrates in SHM with a period of 4.0 sec and an amplitude of 10.0 in. Find the maximum speed and the maximum acceleration. Find the speed and acceleration when the body is one-sixth period from the equilibrium position. Find the net force on the vibrating body at the latter position.
          Ans. 1.3 ft/sec; 2.0 ft/sec²; 0.65 ft/sec; 1.7 ft/sec²; 0.11 lb

17. A body vibrates in SHM with an amplitude of 6.0 in. and a frequency of 240 vib/min. Find the speed and acceleration when the body is 3.0 in. from the equilibrium position.

18. A body having simple harmonic motion of amplitude 5.0 cm has a speed of 50 cm/sec when its displacement is 3.0 cm. What is its period?   *Ans.* 0.50 sec

19. A body moving in SHM with an amplitude of 10.0 cm has an acceleration of 20.0 cm/sec² when the body is 8.00 cm from the equilibrium position. What is the period?

20. Find the restoring force on a 3.0-lb body in SHM at the instant its displacement is 0.50 in. The frequency of vibration is 180 vib/min and the amplitude is 1.5 in.   *Ans.* 1.4 lb

21. A tuning fork makes 256 complete vibrations per second with an amplitude of 0.50 mm. What is the acceleration of one of its prongs when it is displaced 0.40 mm from its equilibrium position?

22. A body of mass 60.0 gm is moving with a uniform angular speed in a vertical circle of radius 10.0 cm at the rate of 20.0 rev/sec. (*a*) What is the magnitude and direction of the centripetal force 0.00625 sec after the body passes a horizontal diameter going in the upward direction? (*b*) What is the velocity of a companion particle, executing SHM on a horizontal diameter of the circle?
Ans. 9.51 × 10⁶ dynes; 890 cm/sec

23. Find the period of a simple pendulum 3.00 ft long. What is the length of a pendulum with just half this period? (Use $g = 32.2$ ft/sec².)

24. At a certain place a simple pendulum 100 cm long makes 250 complete vibrations in 8.38 min. What is the length of a simple seconds pendulum at that place?   *Ans.* 99.0 cm

25. A simple pendulum is used to determine the value of *g*. When the length of the pendulum is 98.45 cm, the period is measured to be 1.990 sec. Find the value of *g*.

26. Calculate the length of a simple pendulum which has a period of 1.000 sec at a place where $g = 981$ cm/sec².   *Ans.* 24.8 cm

27. A simple pendulum is 45.00 in. long. At a place where $g = 32.17$ ft/sec², what will be the frequency of the pendulum?

28. A simple pendulum was accurately adjusted to have a period of 2.00 sec. The supporting fiber broke and was shortened 2.00 in. Find the change in period, assuming $g = 32.2$ ft/sec².   *Ans.* 0.05 sec

29. A solid disk of 30-cm radius and mass 9.0 kg is suspended as a torsion pendulum. In order to twist the disk completely around once, two forces, each of 22.5 × 10⁶ dynes, must be applied tangentially to the disk at opposite ends of a diameter. What is the moment of torsion and the period of oscillation?

30. A solid cylinder, whose weight is 16.0 lb and radius is 9.0 in., is supported along the axis by a wire 2.0 ft long. The cylinder is twisted through an angle of 120° by a torque of 4.0 lb-ft. Find the moment of torsion of the wire and the period of the pendulum when released.   *Ans.* 1.9 lb-ft/radian; 1.7 sec

31. A torsion pendulum consists of a vertical wire supporting a disk. A torque of 10.0 lb-ft twists the disk 7.5°. The frequency of the pendulum is 90 vib/min. What is the moment of inertia of the disk?

32. An irregularly shaped bar is supported by a wire which can be twisted 15.8° by a torque of 5.25 × 10⁶ cm-dynes. The system as a torsion pendulum vibrates with a period of 0.333 sec. What is the moment of inertia of the bar?
Ans. 5.34 × 10⁴ gm-cm²

33. An irregular body supported by a wire vibrates as a torsion pendulum with a period of 1.50 sec. When a ring whose moment of inertia is 5.25 × 10³ gm-cm² is added to the irregular body, the period becomes 1.80 sec. Find the moment of inertia of the irregular body.

34. A 200-gm sphere of radius 12.0 cm is supported by a wire as a torsion pendulum. The frequency of the pendulum is 0.250 vib/sec. Find the moment of torsion of the wire and the energy of the system when it is displaced 12.5° from its equilibrium position.   *Ans.* 2.85×10^4 cm-dynes/radian; 677 ergs

35. A watch has a balance wheel which moves with an angular acceleration of 41 radians/sec² when it is displaced 15° from its equilibrium position. What is its frequency?

36. A torsion pendulum begins moving with an angular acceleration of 15 radians/sec² when its displacement is 90°. What is the frequency of the pendulum?   *Ans.* 0.49 vib/sec

15. *Liquids at Rest*

Materials are commonly classified as solids, liquids, and gases. The class into which a substance falls depends upon the physical conditions surrounding it at the time of observation. Under varying conditions a single substance may be observed in any one of the three states. We are all familiar with water in its three states: ice, water, and vapor. Other substances such as iron and most other metals, which are not familiar in the liquid and gaseous states, nevertheless exist in those states if the temperature is sufficiently high. Those substances which are commonly observed as gases can all be liquefied and solidified if the temperature is lowered far enough and the pressure is made great enough.

Solids are bodies that maintain definite size and shape. A liquid has a definite volume, for it will fill a container to a certain level, forming a free surface, but it does not have a definite shape. Gases have neither definite shape nor definite volume, but completely fill any container no matter how small an amount of gas is put into it. The term "fluid" is applicable to both liquids and gases.

15-1. Density. One of the properties characteristic of every material is its density. We are all familiar with the fact that a small piece of one material may be heavier than a much larger piece of another material. The *mass per unit volume* of a substance is called its *density*,

$$\rho = \frac{m}{V} \tag{1}$$

Units of density are made up by dividing the chosen unit of mass by the unit of volume, as grams per cubic centimeter, kilograms per cubic meter, or slugs per cubic foot.

It is sometimes helpful to use another quantity called *weight-density* or weight per unit volume

$$D = \frac{W}{V} \tag{2}$$

Since $W = mg$, we have the simple relation between density and weight-density

$$D = \rho g \tag{3}$$

TABLE 1. DENSITIES AND WEIGHT-DENSITIES OF SOLIDS AND LIQUIDS

Substance	Density, gm/cm³	Weight-density, lb/ft³
Alcohol (ethyl) at 20°C.....	0.79	49.4
Water at 4°C.............	1.000	62.4
Water at 20°C............	0.998	62.3
Gasoline.................	0.68	42
Mercury.................	13.6	850
Oak.....................	0.8	50
Aluminum...............	2.7	169
Copper..................	8.89	555
Ice.....................	0.92	57
Iron, wrought...........	7.85	490

Weight-density is commonly used when we are concerned with effects depending upon force while density is used when mass is to be considered. Values of density for some substances are given in Table 1.

15-2. Specific Gravity. The *specific gravity* of a substance is the ratio of its density to that of some standard substance. The standard usually chosen is water at the temperature of its maximum density, 39.2°F (4°C). Thus, if ρ is the density of the substance and ρ_w the density of the water, the specific gravity (sp. gr.) of the substance is

$$\text{Sp. gr.} = \frac{\rho}{\rho_w} \tag{4}$$

also
$$\text{Sp. gr.} = \frac{D}{D_w} \tag{4a}$$

Since each of the two densities has the same unit, their quotient has no units. Specific gravity is often more convenient to tabulate than density, the values of which in the British and metric systems of units are different. One may easily compute density from specific gravity by the use of Eq. (4).

$$\rho = (\text{sp. gr.})\rho_w$$

The units of density thus obtained will be those of the system in which the density of water is expressed.

Since the density of water in the *cgs* system is 1 gm/cm³, the density in this system is *numerically* equal to the specific gravity.

15-3. Pressure. When a liquid is confined in a container, the liquid exerts force on every part of the area of the walls and bottom of the container which the liquid touches. If the liquid is at rest, this force is everywhere perpendicular to the containing surface. The normal *force per unit area* is called *pressure*.

$$P = \frac{F}{A} \tag{5}$$

Pressure is a scalar quantity.

The idea of pressure is not restricted to liquids but may be used whenever a force is applied over an area. A very large pressure may result from the application of even a moderate force if it acts on a small area. Such objects as pins and nails are made with sharp points so that high pressures may produce distortion of the surfaces they press against even when a relatively small force is applied.

A unit of pressure may be made from any force unit divided by an area unit. Pressures are commonly expressed in pounds per square inch, newtons per square meter, or dynes per square centimeter. Sometimes pressures are expressed in terms of certain commonly observed pressures as, for example, an *atmosphere*, representing a pressure equal to that exerted by the air under standard conditions, or a *centimeter of mercury*, representing a pressure equal to that exerted by a column of mercury 1 cm high. The concept of pressure is particularly useful in discussing the properties of liquids and gases.

Example: The end of a stake that is to be pushed into the ground has an area of 0.50 in.² What is the pressure under the stake when a force of 200 lb is applied?

$$P = \frac{F}{A} = \frac{200 \text{ lb}}{0.50 \text{ in.}^2} = 400 \text{ lb/in.}^2$$

If the force is not uniformly distributed over a surface, the pressure is not constant. At any point on the surface

$$P = \lim_{\Delta A \to 0} \frac{\Delta F}{\Delta A} = \frac{dF}{dA} \tag{6}$$

where ΔF represents the normal force acting on the element ΔA of area. Where the pressure varies over a surface, the total force on the surface is given by the equation

$$F = \int P \, dA \text{ (vector sum)} \tag{7}$$

where the integral is taken over the whole surface.

Example: The pressure on a triangular surface varies directly with the altitude h of the triangle in accordance with the equation $P = (2.5 \text{ lb/in.}^3)h$. The dimensions of the triangular surface are shown in Fig. 1. Find the force on the surface.

Consider an element of area of length s and height dh. The area is

$$dA = s\, dh = \frac{10.0 \text{ in.}}{5.0 \text{ in.}}\, h\, dh = 2.0h\, dh$$

$$F = \int_0^{5.0 \text{ in.}} P\, dA = \int_0^{5.0 \text{ in.}} (2.5 \text{ lb/in.}^3)h$$
$$\times (2.0h)\, dh$$

$$= \int_0^{5.0 \text{ in.}} (5.0 \text{ lb/in.}^3)h^2\, dh$$

$$= \left[(5.0 \text{ lb/in.}^3)\frac{h^3}{3} \right]_0^{5.0 \text{ in.}}$$

$$= 2\bar{1}0 \text{ lb}$$

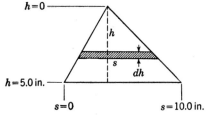

FIG. 1. To find the force due to a variable pressure on a triangular surface.

15-4. Pressure Due to Gravity.

The atoms and molecules of which a liquid is composed are attracted to the earth in accordance with Newton's law of universal gravitation. Hence, liquids collect at the bottoms of containers, and the upper layers exert forces on the ones underneath.

The pressure at a point in a liquid means the force per unit area of a surface placed at the point in question. Imagine a horizontal surface A (Fig. 2), which is 10 in. below the surface of the liquid. Because of its weight, the column of liquid directly above the surface exerts a force F on the surface. If the liquid is water, each cubic foot weighs 62.4 lb and each cubic inch weighs $(62.4/1728)$ lb $= 0.0361$ lb. If we take the area A as 2.0 in.^{2}, the volume above the area is $(10 \text{ in.})(2.0 \text{ in.}^2) = 20$ in.^{3} Hence the weight of water above the area is $(0.036 \text{ lb/in.}^3)(20 \text{ in.}^3) = 0.72$ lb and this is the force exerted on the surface. The pressure is the force divided by the area

$$P = \frac{F}{A} = \frac{0.72 \text{ lb}}{2.0 \text{ in.}^2} = 0.36 \text{ lb/in.}^2$$

15-5. Hydrostatic Pressure.

In order to find the pressure P due to the weight W of a column of liquid, it is sufficient to know the weight-density D and the depth h below the surface, for the force exerted on the area A is the weight of the column of liquid.

$$W = hAD$$
$$P = \frac{W}{A} = \frac{hAD}{A}$$
$$P = hD \qquad (8)$$

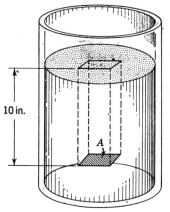

FIG. 2. Pressure in a liquid.

The pressure may also be expressed in terms of the density ρ of the liquid by substituting from Eq. (3)

$$P = h\rho g \qquad (9)$$

Example: Find the pressure at the bottom of a tank that is filled with gasoline to a depth of 8.0 ft.

From Table 1, $D = 42$ lb/ft^3

$$P = hD = (8.0 \text{ ft})(42 \text{ lb/ft}^3) = 3\bar{4}0 \text{ lb/ft}^2$$
$$= \frac{3\bar{4}0 \text{ lb/ft}^2}{144 \text{ in.}^2/\text{ft}^2} = 2.4 \text{ lb/in.}^2$$

Example: If the bottom of the tank of the previous example is 6.0 by 8.0 ft, what force is exerted on it?

$$F = PA = (3\bar{4}0 \text{ lb/ft}^2)(6.0 \text{ ft})(8.0 \text{ ft}) = 1\bar{6},000 \text{ lb}$$

Example: Find the pressure due to a column of mercury 74.0 cm high.

$$P = h\rho g = (74.0 \text{ cm})(13.6 \text{ gm/cm}^3)(980 \text{ cm/sec}^2)$$
$$= 98\bar{6},000 \text{ dynes/cm}^2$$

15-6. Pressure in Liquids at Rest.

The following general statements apply to the pressure in a liquid at rest:

1. Pressure exists at every point within the liquid.

2. As indicated by Eq. (8), the pressure is proportional to the depth below the surface.

3. At any point in a liquid the magnitude of the force (due to pressure) exerted on a surface is the same no matter what the orientation of the surface is. If this statement were not true, there would be a net force in one direction, and the liquid would be set in motion.

4. The pressure is the same at all points at the same level within a single liquid.

5. The force due to the pressure is everywhere perpendicular to the surfaces of the container.

6. The force on the bottom of a container is the pressure at that level times the area of the bottom. The force may be greater than, equal to, or less than the weight of the liquid in the

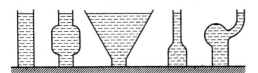

FIG. 3. The force on the base is not always equal to the weight of the liquid.

container. In Fig. 3 are shown several containers, each having the same base area and the same depth of liquid. The force the liquid exerts on the base is the same in each of these cases even though the weights of liquid are widely different. (How is the difference between weight of liquid in the container and the force on the base accounted for?)

Example: In a U-tube (Fig. 4) the right-hand arm is filled with mercury while the other arm is filled with a liquid of unknown density, the levels being as shown in the diagram. Find the density of the unknown liquid.

At the level of separation the pressure is the same in the two liquids. At that level the pressure in the mercury is

$$P_1 = h_1\rho_1 g$$

and the pressure in the unknown liquid is

$$P_2 = h_2\rho_2 g$$
$$P_1 = P_2$$
$$h_1\rho_1 g = h_2\rho_2 g$$
$$\rho_2 = \frac{h_1\rho_1}{h_2} = \frac{2.0 \text{ cm} \times 13.6 \text{ gm/cm}^3}{14 \text{ cm}}$$
$$= 1.9 \text{ gm/cm}^3$$

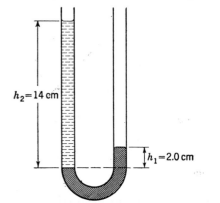

FIG. 4. Columns of unequal heights may produce equal pressures.

15-7. Buoyancy; Archimedes' Principle.

Everyday observation has shown us that when an object is lowered into water it apparently loses weight and indeed may even float on the water. Evidently a liquid exerts an upward, buoyant force upon a body placed in it. Archimedes (287–212 B.C.), a Greek mathematician and inventor, recognized and stated the fact that a *body wholly or partly submerged in a fluid experiences an upward force equal to the weight of the fluid displaced.*

Archimedes' principle can readily be verified experimentally. One can deduce this principle from a consideration of Fig. 5. Consider a block of rectangular cross section A, immersed in a liquid of weight-density D. On the vertical faces, the liquid exerts horizontal forces, which are balanced on all sides. On the top face it exerts a downward force h_1DA and on the bottom face an upward force h_2DA. The net upward force on the block is

$$h_2DA - h_1DA = hDA$$

which is just the weight (volume hA times weight-density D) of the liquid displaced by the block.

The control of submarines depends in part on Archimedes' principle. In submerging the boat, sea water is admitted into ballast tanks

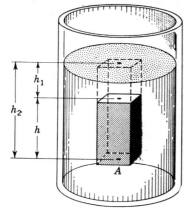

FIG. 5. The upward force on the bottom of the block is greater than the downward force on the top.

and the buoyant force balanced. The boat is brought to the surface by expelling the water from these tanks with compressed air.

15-8. Weight-density and Specific Gravity Measurements by Archimedes' Principle. This principle suggests a method for comparing the weight-density of a substance with that of some standard fluid, such as water. The measurement of specific gravity involves the following reasoning which is briefly stated in symbols:

$$\text{Sp. gr.} = \frac{\text{weight-density of substance}}{\text{weight-density of water}}$$
$$= \frac{W_s/V}{W_w/V} = \frac{W_s}{W_w}$$
$$= \frac{\text{weight of body in air}}{\text{apparent loss of weight in water}}$$

$$(10)$$

Since the volume of a submerged body is equal to the volume of the displaced water, the ratio of the weight-densities is the same as the ratio of the weight W_s of the sample of the substance to the weight W_w of an equal volume of water. These weights can be determined by weighing the sample in air and in water. The weight in water subtracted from the weight in air gives the apparent loss of weight in water, which is the weight of the water displaced (from Archimedes' principle). Therefore, the specific gravity can be deter-

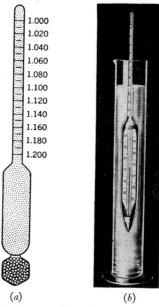

FIG. 6. A hydrometer float (a) floats at such a depth as to displace its own weight of the liquid (b).

mined by the measurements which are indicated in Eq. (10).

Example: A metal sphere weighs 35.2 oz in air and 30.8 oz when submerged in water. What is the specific gravity and the weight-density of the metal?

From Eq. (10)

$$\text{Sp. gr.} = \frac{\text{weight of sample in air}}{\text{apparent loss of weight in water}}$$

Loss of weight in water = 35.2 oz − 30.8 oz
$$= 4.4 \text{ oz}$$

$$\text{Sp. gr.} = \frac{35.2 \text{ oz}}{4.4 \text{ oz}} = 8.0$$

From Eq. (4a)

$$D = (\text{sp. gr.})D_w = (8.0)(62.4 \text{ lb/ft}^3) = 5\bar{0}0 \text{ lb/ft}^3$$

Quick determinations of the specific gravity of a liquid can be made with a hydrometer. This instrument (Fig. 6) is a glass bulb attached to a narrow stem and weighted so as to remain upright when floating in a liquid. **It** floats at such a depth as to displace exactly its own weight of the liquid (Archimedes' principle). The stem is calibrated to indicate the specific gravity of the solution, for the

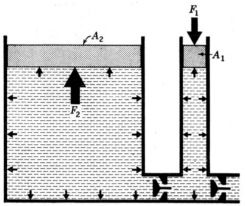

FIG. 7. Hydraulic press.

smaller this specific gravity the deeper the bulb sinks in the liquid.

15-9. External Pressure; Pascal's Law. The pressure previously discussed is that caused by the weight of the liquid. If any external pressure is applied to the liquid, the pressure will be increased beyond that given by Eq. (8). The most common of such external pressures is that due to the atmosphere.

Whenever an external pressure is applied to any confined fluid at rest, the pressure is increased at every point in the fluid by the amount of the external pressure. This statement is called *Pascal's law,* after the French philosopher (1623–1662) who first clearly expressed it. The practical consequences of Pascal's law are apparent in automobile tires, hydraulic jacks, hydraulic brakes, pneumatic drills, and air brakes.

15-10. Hydraulic Press. The fact that an external pressure applied to a liquid at rest increases the pressure at all points in the liquid by the amount of the external pressure has an important application in a machine called the *hydraulic press.* Small forces exerted on this machine cause very large forces exerted by the machine. In Fig. 7, the small

force F_1 is exerted on a small area A_1. This increases the pressure in the liquid under the piston by an amount P. The force that this increase of pressure will cause on the large piston will be $F_2 = PA_2$, since the pressure increase under both pistons is the same.

Simply by changing the ratio of A_2 to A_1, the force F_2 may be made as large as is safe for the big piston to carry. Larger pistons require more transfer of liquid and are correspondingly slower in action.

Example: In a hydraulic press the small cylinder has a diameter of 1.0 in. while the large piston has a diameter of 8.0 in. If a force of 120 lb is applied to the small piston, what is the force on the large piston, neglecting friction?

Since the pressure is increased the same amount at both pistons

$$P_2 = P_1$$
$$\frac{F_2}{A_2} = \frac{F_1}{A_1}$$
$$F_2 = \frac{A_2}{A_1} F_1 = \frac{\pi(4.0 \text{ in.})^2}{\pi(0.50 \text{ in.})^2} 120 \text{ lb} = 7700 \text{ lb}$$

SUMMARY

Density of a substance is mass per unit volume

$$\rho = \frac{m}{V}$$

Weight-density is weight per unit volume

$$D = \frac{W}{V}$$

The *specific gravity* of a substance is the ratio of its density to that of water.

Pressure is force per unit area

$$P = \frac{F}{A} \qquad P = \frac{dF}{dA}$$

At a depth h below the surface, the pressure due to a liquid of weight-density D is

$$P = hD = h\rho g$$

Archimedes' principle states that a body wholly or partly submerged in a fluid is buoyed up by a force equal to the weight of the fluid displaced.

Pascal's law states that an external pressure applied to a confined fluid increases the pressure at every point in the fluid by an amount equal to the external pressure.

QUESTIONS

1. In stating that the pressure at a point in a liquid is proportional to the depth, what is assumed regarding the density?

2. In some regions after a heavy rain, water backs up into basements of houses. When valves are inserted to prevent the flow into the house, the force on the floor is sometimes sufficient to break the floor. One household adviser recommended that the valve be replaced by a pipe at the drain high enough to reach above the water level. Comment on the effect of this device on the force that is exerted on the floor.

3. An open-tube manometer consists of a U-tube open to the air at one end and connected to a pressure chamber at the other. It can be filled with mercury, water, or an oil of specific gravity 0.60. Discuss the advantages and disadvantages of each. Under what circumstances would each be useful?

4. An open manometer has one tube twice the diameter of the other. How would this affect the operation of the manometer? Does it make any difference which end is connected to the pressure chamber?

5. A body is immersed in a liquid in such a manner that it is closely in contact with the bottom and there is no liquid beneath the body. Is there a buoyant force on the body? Explain.

6. If, when floating in water, you take a deep breath, will you float with more or less of your body out of water? Explain.

7. Does a ship wrecked in mid-ocean sink to the bottom or does it remain suspended at some great depth? Justify your opinion.

8. A can full of water is suspended from a spring balance. Will the reading of the balance change (a) if a block of cork is placed in the water and (b) if a piece of lead is suspended in the water? Explain.

9. Explain how to determine the specific gravity of a liquid by weighing a solid suspended in it.

10. A free balloon can be arranged to float at a constant elevation in the air, but this is not possible for a submarine in water. Show why this is the case.

11. To secure great sensitivity, is a narrow or wide hydrometer stem preferable? Why?

12. Discuss several important uses of the hydrometer.

13. On a hydrometer that is to be used for liquids lighter than water is the unit mark beginning the scale placed near the top or bottom of the stem? Why?

14. Two beakers partly filled with water are connected by a siphon. One beaker rests on each pan of a balance, which is initially balanced. Explain the changes that are observed in the position of the balance when (a) a block of wood is laid on the left pan, (b) the block of wood is floated in the left beaker, (c) an iron ball on a string is lowered until it is just submerged in the left beaker, and (d) the iron ball is allowed to rest on the bottom of the beaker.

PROBLEMS

1. An irregular gold nugget is found, but no balance is available to determine its mass. Water is poured into a graduate, and when the nugget is dropped into the water the reading increases by 3.75 cm³. What is the mass of the nugget? Specific gravity of gold = 19.3.

2. Uranium has a specific gravity of 18.7. (a) What is the weight of a cubic inch? (b) How large a volume could a man carry if he can lift a load of 200 lb?

Ans. 0.675 lb; 296 in.³

3. The heaviest element, osmium, has a specific gravity of 22.5. What is the weight of a cubic inch of osmium? What is the volume of 150 lb of the element?

4. To what pressure can a 150-lb man raise the air pressure in an automobile tire if he uses a simple pump without levers and the area of cross section of the piston is 3.0 in.²?   *Ans.* 50 lb/in.²

5. A vertical force of 0.20 oz pushes a phonograph needle against the record surface. If the point of the needle has an area of 0.0010 in.², find the pressure in pounds per square inch.

6. If the casing of an oil well 500 ft deep is full of water, what is the pressure at the bottom due to the weight of water?   *Ans.* 216 lb/in.²

7. An ocean depth of 35,400 ft has been measured off the island of Mindanao. What is the pressure at that depth? The specific gravity of sea water is 1.03.

8. The barometric pressure is 30.0 in. of mercury. Express this in pounds per square foot and in pounds per square inch.   *Ans.* 21$\overline{2}$0 lb/ft²; 14.7 lb/in.²

9. If the specific gravity of crude oil is 0.70, what is the minimum pressure needed at the bottom of an oil well 1.0 mi deep to force the oil to the top?

10. A V-shaped open manometer contains kerosene of specific gravity 0.700. Find the displacement of the liquid columns produced by a difference of pressure of 1.00 mm of mercury when the sides of the manometer make angles of 30° with the horizontal.   *Ans.* 3.88 cm, along the tube

11. A U-tube is used to determine the specific gravity of an oil that will not mix with water. Water is poured into the vertical tube and then the oil. The free surface of water is at 21.2 cm on the scale, that of oil is at 30.2 cm, and the surface of separation is at 12.5 cm. Find the specific gravity of the oil.

12. A vertical U-tube is partly filled with mercury and a solution of unknown specific gravity is poured into one arm. The surface of separation of the liquids is at 6.35 cm on the scale, the free surface of the mercury at 8.46 cm, and the free surface of the solution at 24.84 cm. Find the specific gravity of the solution.
                                                                      Ans. 1.55

13. A cylindrical tank 4.0 ft in diameter is filled with water to a depth of 10.0 ft. (*a*) What is the pressure at the bottom? (*b*) Find the total thrust on the bottom of the tank.

14. Find the force tending to crush an outside hatch of a submarine 2.00 ft² in area when the boat is 100 ft below the surface of the sea. Specific gravity of sea water is 1.03.   *Ans.* 12,$\overline{9}$00 lb

15. A pail 20 cm in diameter at the bottom, 30 cm in diameter at the top, 22 cm high, and having a mass of 1.5 kg stands full of water upon a table. The volume of the pail is 10.9 liters. Calculate the force due to the water on the bottom of the pail and the force of the pail and contents against the table.

16. A swimming tank 50 ft long and 20 ft wide has a sloping floor so that the water is 4.0 ft deep at one end and 7.0 ft deep at the other. Find the total force due to the water on the bottom and that on each end.
                        Ans. 3$\overline{4}$0,000 lb; 1$\overline{0}$,000 lb; 3$\overline{1}$,000 lb

17. A dam 20.0 ft high and 200 ft long backs up a lake 2 mi long. What is the total force of the water on the face of the dam?

18. In constructing a concrete wall of a basement, a form is built 15 ft high and 30 ft long. There is a space of 6.0 in. between the form and the earthen bank. After a heavy rain the 6.0-in. space fills with water to a depth of 8.0 ft. What is the total force on the form?   *Ans.* 6$\overline{0}$,000 lb

19. A tank has a triangular cross section with a base 8.0 ft wide and 10.0 ft long. The height is 6.0 ft. It is filled with a liquid of specific gravity 1.25. Find the force on the base and that on one end.

20. A dam 30 ft high is 100 ft long at the top and 70 ft long at the bottom. Find the force due to the water on the vertical face of the dam when the water is 20 ft deep at the face. *Ans.* $4\overline{7}0$ tons

21. A cylindrical tank 10.0 ft long and 6.0 ft in diameter is installed with its axis horizontal. What is the force on one end when the tank is half filled with gasoline?

22. A cylindrical tank 8.0 ft long and 4.0 ft in diameter is set with its axis horizontal. Find the force on one end when the tank is half filled with a liquid whose specific gravity is 1.25. *Ans.* $4\overline{1}0$ lb

23. A coal barge with vertical sides has a bottom 40 ft by 20 ft. When it is loaded with coal, it sinks 18 in. deeper than when empty. How much coal was taken on?

24. A barge has vertical sides and a flat bottom of 320 ft² area. When partly filled, the barge is immersed in fresh water to a depth of 2.00 ft. Upon removal of the load the barge rises 16.0 in. (*a*) What is the approximate weight of the barge? (*b*) What vertical displacement will result if a 10-ton truck is loaded on the barge? *Ans.* $13,\overline{3}00$ lb; 1.0 ft

25. The weight of a submarine is 200 tons, and it lies submerged and full of water at the bottom of the sea. If the specific gravity of the material is 7.80, find the total pull that must be exerted by the lifting chains in order to raise the vessel from the bottom. The specific gravity of sea water is 1.03.

26. A 2.0-lb iron ball is supported by a wire and immersed in oil of specific gravity 0.80. What is the tension in the wire? The specific gravity of iron is 7.8. *Ans.* 1.8 lb

27. A 20.0-kg body of specific gravity 5.00 is at the bottom of a lake 10.0 m deep. Calculate the amount of work required to lift it to the surface, assuming 5% of the force exerted is used to overcome friction.

28. A stone of specific gravity 2.50 starts from rest and sinks in a fresh-water lake. Allowing for a 25% frictional force, calculate the distance the stone sinks in 3.00 sec. *Ans.* $19\overline{8}0$ cm

29. A buoy is 75% submerged when floating in fresh water. A force of 62.4 lb is just sufficient to submerge it completely. (*a*) What is the volume of the buoy? (*b*) What is its approximate weight?

30. What volume of lead of specific gravity 11.3 must be placed on top of a 20.0-gm block of cork of specific gravity 0.240 to cause the cork to be barely submerged in water? *Ans.* 5.61 cm³

31. A block of wood 5.0 cm by 4.0 cm and 3.0 cm high floats in water immersed to a depth of 2.5 cm. What mass of aluminum (specific gravity 2.6) on top of the block would cause both to be completely immersed?

32. A diver and his suit weigh 220 lb. It requires 30.0 lb of lead to sink him in fresh water. If the specific gravity of lead is 11.3, what is the volume of the diver and his suit? *Ans.* 3.96 ft³

33. How many cubic feet of poplar (25 lb/ft³) must be used to construct a raft that will just support 10 persons whose average weight is 160 lb if 20 lb of iron (specific gravity 7.8) is used in the construction?

34. A stone weighs 30.0 lb in air, and 21.0 lb in water. What is its (*a*) specific gravity, (*b*) weight-density, and (*c*) volume? *Ans.* 3.33; 208 lb/ft³; 0.144 ft³

35. A block of lead weighs 3.30 lb. When suspended in water, it is found that the water and containing vessel gain 0.30 lb in weight. What is the specific gravity of the lead?

36. A solid of mass 120 gm is found to have an apparent mass of 90 gm when in water and 78 gm in a solution of zinc sulfate. What is the specific gravity of the solid and that of the solution?   *Ans.* 4.0; 1.4

37. A body that has a mass of 22.958 gm appears to have a mass of 19.756 gm in water of specific gravity 0.997, and 17.435 gm in a certain liquid. Calculate the density of the body and that of the liquid.

38. A piece of copper, specific gravity 8.9, has a mass of 523 gm and appears to have a mass of 447 gm in water. Is the body solid or hollow? If hollow, find the volume of the cavity.   *Ans.* 17 cm^3

39. A 23.40-gm hollow stopper is made of glass of specific gravity 2.50. Its apparent mass when immersed in water is 3.90 gm. What is the volume of the internal cavity?

40. A wooden block weighs 9.00 lb in air. A lead sinker is hung from the end of the block and is lowered into water until the lead only is immersed. The apparent weight of the system is found to be 15.00 lb. When the system is completely immersed in water, the apparent weight is 3.00 lb. Calculate (*a*) the weight-density of the wood, (*b*) the specific gravity of the wood, and (*c*) the apparent weight of the system if immersed in oil of specific gravity 0.800. Specific gravity of lead is 11.3.   *Ans.* 46.8 lb/ft^3; 0.750; 5.52 lb

41. A vessel contains water and a liquid of specific gravity 2.50. The two do not mix. A solid object floats with 70% of its volume in the water and the remainder in the denser liquid. Calculate the density of the solid.

42. A gold ring set with a diamond has a mass of 4.000 gm and appears to have a mass of 3.720 gm in water. Find the mass of the diamond if the specific gravity of the gold is 19.3 and that of the diamond is 3.50.   *Ans.* 0.310 gm

43. An ornament made of gold and silver has a mass of 76.8 gm and has a specific gravity of 18.0. Assuming the volume of the alloy to be equal to the combined volumes of its component parts, calculate the amounts of gold and silver in the ornament. The specific gravity of gold is 19.3; that of silver is 10.5.

44. The piston of a hydraulic lift for cars is 8.00 in. in diameter. The device is operated by water from the city system. What water pressure is necessary to raise a car if the total load lifted is 3142 lb?   *Ans.* 62.5 lb/in.^{2}

45. A hydraulic lift operated by water under pressure of 100 lb/in.^{2} has a plunger 16.0 in. in diameter and weighs 2000 lb. What load can it carry?

46. What size piston is used in a hydraulic lift, if the maximum load is 5000 lb and the water pressure is that due to a 100-ft head of water?
                                  Ans. 12.1 in. in diameter

47. A 100-kg man stands on a square, water-filled bellows which measures 20.0 by 20.0 cm. The bellows communicates with a vertical pipe which has a sectional area of 2.00 cm^2. How high will the water rise in the pipe?

48. A 100-kg man stands on a bellows having a circular shape of 10.0 cm radius. The bellows is connected to a vertical pipe and is filled with oil of specific gravity 0.800. How high will the oil rise in the pipe in order to support the man?
                                  Ans. 3.98 m

49. Two pistons of a hydraulic press have diameters of 1.00 ft and 1.00 in. (*a*) What is the force exerted by the larger piston when a 56.0-lb weight is placed on the smaller one? (*b*) If the stroke of the smaller piston is 1.50 in., through what distance will the larger piston have moved after 10 strokes?

50. The lever of a hydraulic press gives a mechanical advantage of 6.0. The sectional area of the smaller plunger is 1.0 in.^{2} and that of the larger plunger is 15 in.^{2} What load will the larger plunger sustain when a 60-lb weight is applied to the lever? *Ans.* 5400 lb

51. The lever of a certain hydraulic press gives a mechanical advantage of 5.0. The diameter of the smaller plunger is 2.0 in. and that of the larger is 10 in. What force is exerted by the press when a 40-lb force is applied to the handle?

16. Fluids in Motion

The harnessing of waterpower and the building of efficient steam turbines require knowledge of the behavior of fluids in motion. The designing of streamlined cars, trains, and airplanes is based on the study of problems involving fluids in motion—particularly air in motion. An understanding of the fundamental principles of flight and the operation of certain aircraft instruments follows from a logical extension of the principles of mechanics to fluids in motion.

We have seen that the properties of liquids at rest can be described by the simple concepts of pressure and weight-density, by Archimedes' principle of buoyancy, and by Pascal's law of the transmission of pressure. When liquids are in motion, new properties become apparent. In predicting what happens we cannot always rely on our previous experience or intuition. But careful consideration shows that the phenomena of fluids in motion can be described in terms of the familiar principles of mechanics. The term "fluid" is applicable to both liquids and gases and is used in considering their common properties.

16-1. Fluid Flow. Knowledge of the laws that govern fluid flow is important in providing for the distribution of water, gas, and oil in pipelines and the efficient transmission of energy in hydraulic machines. The rate of flow of a liquid through a pipe or channel is usually measured as the volume that passes a certain cross section per unit time, as cubic feet per second, liters per second, etc. If the average speed of the liquid at section S in Fig. 1 is v, the distance l through which the

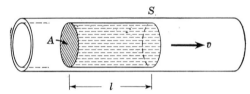

Fig. 1. Rate of flow of liquid through a pipe.

stream moves in time t is vt. This may be regarded as the length of an imaginary cylinder that has passed section S in time t. If A is the area of cross section, then the volume of the cylindrical section is $Al = Avt$, and the rate of flow of the liquid is given by

$$R = \frac{Avt}{t} = Av \qquad (1)$$

In a fluid at rest the pressure is the same at all points at the same elevation. This is no longer true if the fluid is moving. When water flows in a uniform horizontal pipe, there is a fall in pressure along the pipe in the direction of flow. The reason for this fall in pressure is that force is required to maintain motion against friction. If the liquid is being accelerated, additional force is required.

When the valve of Fig. 2 is closed, water

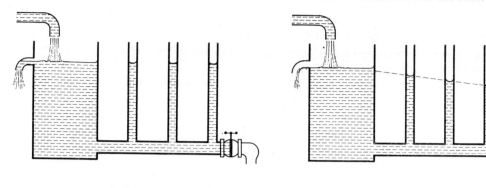

FIG. 2. Friction causes a fall in pressure along a tube in which a liquid flows.

rises to the same level in each vertical tube. When the valve is opened slightly to permit a small rate of flow, the water level falls in each tube, indicating a progressive decrease of pressure along the pipe. The pressure drop is proportional to the rate of flow. Frictional effects are very important when water is distributed in city mains or when petroleum is transported long distances in pipelines. Pumping stations must be placed at intervals along such lines to maintain the flow.

16-2. Streamlines and Tubes of Flow. We shall first consider steady flow. A fluid flowing in a pipe (Fig. 3) will have a certain

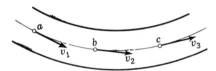

FIG. 3. Steady flow. Path *abc* is a streamline.

velocity v_1 at a, a velocity v_2 at b, and so on. If, as time goes on, the velocity of whatever fluid particle happens to be at a is still v_1, that at b is still v_2, etc., then the flow is said to be *steady* and the line abc which represents the path followed by a particle is called a *streamline*. It represents the fixed path followed by an orderly procession of particles. In streamline flow, all particles passing through b also pass through b and c. This is not the case in turbulent flow. When the flow is unsteady or turbulent, there are eddies and whirlpools in the motion and the paths of the particles are continually changing.

It is convenient to imagine the whole region in which flow occurs to be divided into tubes. A *tube of flow* is a tube that follows in form the streamlines on its surface. It may be thought of as made up of a bundle of lines of flow. The fluid in a tube of flow remains in that tube. It is assumed that all particles passing a given cross section in a tube of flow have the same velocity. In regions where the streamlines are crowded together the speed is increased (Fig. 4), since from Eq. (1) $A_a v_a = A_b v_b$.

FIG. 4. Steady flow. Volume *abc* is a tube of flow.

When a body moves through a fluid, turbulence increases the resistance offered by the fluid to the moving body. The streamlining of a car or a plane is intended to permit a steady flow of air past its surfaces so as to reduce the resistance or drag which turbulent flow would produce. Figure 5 shows a disk, a sphere, and a streamlined object of equal cross sections. They are placed in streams of fluid moving with the same speeds. The forces required to hold the objects stationary in the streams are indicated by the vectors. Note the reduction in force obtained by streamlining the object to reduce turbulence. A fighter plane may have a drag equivalent to that of a rectangular plate only 20 in. square, moving broadside.

16-3. Flow through a Constriction. When a liquid is flowing through a pipe of varying cross-sectional area (Fig. 6), there can be no accumulation between a and b, provided that the liquid is incompressible. Hence the mass of liquid passing through the cross section A_1 with speed v_1 must equal the mass passing in

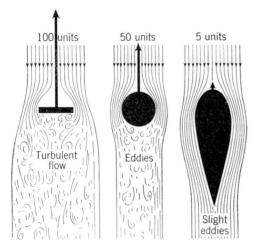

FIG. 5. Comparative drag.

the same time t through cross section A_2 with speed v_2

$$A_1 v_1 \rho t = A_2 v_2 \rho t \qquad (2)$$

where ρ is the density of the liquid.

Two important consequences are immediately apparent from this equation. Since $A_1 v_1 = A_2 v_2$, it follows that the speed of flow in a pipe is greater in those regions where there is a constriction in the cross-sectional area A. Furthermore, if as in Fig. 6 the speed is greater at b than at a, the liquid experiences an acceleration between a and b. This requires an accelerating force. This accelerating force

can be present only if the pressure at a is greater than the pressure at b. We conclude that in the steady flow of a liquid, the pressure is least where the velocity is greatest.

16-4. Bernoulli's Theorem. The preceding description of the steady flow of a liquid can be put in more definite form by an application of the principle of conservation of energy to the incompressible liquid flowing between the two planes a and b of Fig. 6. In any time t, the volume V that flows through a is the same as that which flows through b. Since the pressure is different at the two ends, work is done on the liquid of an amount $P_1 V - P_2 V$ (since work $= Fs = (PA)(vt) = PV$). The work done is equal to the change in energy (both potential and kinetic).

$$P_1 V - P_2 V = (mgh_2 - mgh_1)$$
$$+ (\tfrac{1}{2}mv_2^2 - \tfrac{1}{2}mv_1^2) \quad (3)$$

Since $V = m/\rho$

$$P_1 \frac{m}{\rho} - P_2 \frac{m}{\rho} = (mgh_2 - mgh_1)$$
$$+ (\tfrac{1}{2} mv_2^2 - \tfrac{1}{2} mv_1^2)$$

Simplifying and rearranging terms to group initial terms on one side of the equation and final terms on the other gives

$$\frac{P_1}{\rho g} + h_1 + \frac{v_1^2}{2g} = \frac{P_2}{\rho g} + h_2 + \frac{v_2^2}{2g} \quad (4)$$

Each term in Eq. (4) has the dimensions of a length. In the pressure-depth relation the depth h is frequently called the "head." In analogy then, each term of Eq. (4) is called a head; $P/\rho g$, the pressure head; $v^2/2g$, the velocity head; and h, the elevation head.

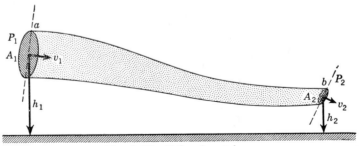

FIG. 6. Liquid flow in a tube.

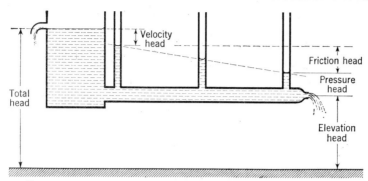

FIG. 7. As the friction head increases, the pressure head decreases.

Although Bernoulli's theorem is rigorously correct only for incompressible, nonviscous liquids, it is often applied to ordinary liquids with sufficient accuracy for many engineering purposes.

Example: Water flows at the rate of 300 ft³/min through an inclined pipe (Fig. 6). At a, where the diameter is 12 in., the pressure is 15 lb/in.² What is the pressure at b, where the diameter is 6.0 in. and the center of the pipe is 2.0 ft lower than at a?

$$A_1 v_1 = A_2 v_2 = \frac{300 \text{ ft}^3/\text{min}}{60 \text{ sec}/\text{min}} = 5.0 \text{ ft}^3/\text{sec}$$

$$\frac{A_1}{A_2} = \frac{v_2}{v_1} = \frac{\pi(6.0 \text{ in.})^2}{\pi(3.0 \text{ in.})^2} = 4.0$$

$$v_1 = \frac{5.0 \text{ ft}^3/\text{sec}}{\pi(\frac{1}{2} \text{ ft})^2} = 6.4 \text{ ft/sec}$$

$$v_2 = 4v_1 = 26 \text{ ft/sec}$$

$$P_1 = (15 \text{ lb/in.}^2)(144 \text{ in.}^2/\text{ft}^2) = 2\bar{2}00 \text{ lb/ft}^2$$

For water, $D = 62.4 \text{ lb/ft}^3$, and therefore $\rho = 1.94 \text{ slugs/ft}^3$. From Eq. (4)

$$\frac{P_1}{\rho g} + h_1 + \frac{v_1^2}{2g} = \frac{P_2}{\rho g} + h_2 + \frac{v_2^2}{2g}$$

$$P_2 = P_1 + \rho g(h_1 - h_2) + \frac{\rho}{2}(v_1^2 - v_2^2)$$

$$= 2\bar{2}00 \text{ lb/ft}^2 + (62.4 \text{ lb/ft}^3)(2.0 \text{ ft})$$
$$+ \frac{1.94 \text{ slug/ft}^3}{2}[(6.4 \text{ ft/sec})^2 - (26 \text{ ft/sec})^2]$$

$$= 2\bar{2}00 \text{ lb/ft}^2 + 1\bar{2}0 \text{ lb/ft}^2 - 6\bar{2}0 \text{ lb/ft}^2$$

$$= 1\bar{7}00 \text{ lb/ft}^2 = 12 \text{ lb/in.}^2$$

16-5. Effect of Friction on Flow. When friction is present, some of the energy of a flowing stream is converted into heat. There is a gradual reduction in pressure along the direction of flow (Fig. 7). By analogy with the other terms in Eq. (4), the pressure reduction due to friction is treated as a "friction head." Its effect at the outlet is to reduce the velocity head and the rate of discharge.

16-6. Pressure and Speed. When water flows through a pipe that has a constriction (Fig. 8), the water necessarily speeds up as it

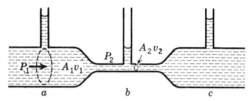

FIG. 8. Flow through a constriction. Decrease in pressure accompanies increase in speed.

enters the constriction, and as we have seen there is a decrease in pressure between a and b. Consider the case of a horizontal pipe. Applying Bernoulli's theorem, we get

$$\frac{P_1}{\rho} + \frac{v_1^2}{2} = \frac{P_2}{\rho} + \frac{v_2^2}{2} \qquad (5)$$

Combining Eq. (5) with Eq. (2) gives

$$P_1 - P_2 = \frac{\rho}{2}(v_2^2 - v_1^2)$$

$$= \frac{\rho v_1^2}{2}\left(\frac{A_1^2}{A_2^2} - 1\right) \qquad (6)$$

Equation (6) may be used to determine the rate of flow of the liquid, that is, the volume per second of liquid passing a.

A tube similar to that of Fig. 8 having a constricted throat section between larger diameter inlet and outlet sections is called a *venturi tube.* A meter that utilizes such a tube and is calibrated by the relation of Eq. (6) is called a *venturi flowmeter.*

Another important application of Bernoulli's principle is the orifice-type flow gage.

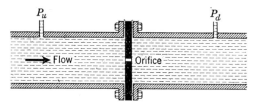

FIG. 9. An orifice-type flow gage.

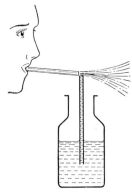

FIG. 10. Bernoulli's principle applied to a spray jet.

A polished disk with an accurately sized hole is placed in the stream whose flow rate is to be measured (Fig. 9). With a manometer or other gage the pressures are measured on the upstream and downstream sides of the orifice. From these measurements and the density and viscosity of the fluid its rate of flow is computed.

16-7. Airfoils. Imagine that the walls of a venturi tube are moved apart as suggested in Fig. 11. The result will be as shown at the right in Fig. 11. The nearby streamline follows the curved surface closely; at increasing distances above the surface the streamlines are less curved, and at a distance equal to four times the chord length the curvature is negligible. The increase in speed of the air on the upper curved surface results in a decreased pressure at that surface. Because the pressure below the section is greater than that above it, the section experiences a lift. Any such surface designed to obtain reacting force from the air through which it moves is called an *airfoil.* In this sense airplane wings, ailerons, rudders, and propellers are all airfoils.

When an airfoil is inclined upward a few degrees with respect to the wind direction, air will be deflected from the lower surface and the reacting force will produce a pressure at the lower surface greater than atmospheric by an amount indicated by the arrows in Fig. 12. At the upper surface the pressure is less than atmospheric, according to Bernoulli's principle. Both effects, but chiefly the second, constitute the lifting force L. Vectors representing the weight W of the wing, the drag D due to air friction, the propeller thrust, and the lift add to form a closed polygon (zero resultant) when the wing is moving with constant velocity.

16-8. Discharge from an Orifice. When liquid escapes from a small sharp-edged orifice in a vessel (Fig. 13), the outgoing liquid gains kinetic energy at the expense of the remaining liquid. In the absence of friction, the kinetic energy, if changed back to potential energy, should be sufficient to raise the escaping liquid to the level of the surface in the vessel.

Liquid of mass m in leaving the orifice with

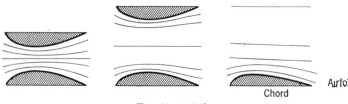

FIG. 11. Airfoils.

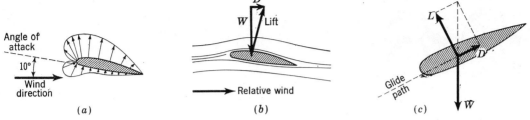

FIG. 12. Lift produced by air flow past an airfoil.

speed v has kinetic energy $\frac{1}{2}mv^2$. The potential energy of this same liquid when at the upper surface of the liquid is mgh. Equating these we get

$$\frac{1}{2}mv^2 = mgh \qquad \text{or} \qquad v^2 = 2gh \qquad (7)$$

This relation is known as *Torricelli's theorem*.

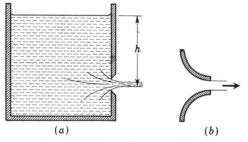

FIG. 13. Discharge from an orifice.

Since the pressure P at a depth h below the liquid surface is ρgh, Eq. (7) also can be expressed as

$$v^2 = \frac{2P}{\rho} \qquad (8)$$

This expression is also applicable to the escape of a gas at pressure P.

These results are only approximate. During the flow, the streamlines from all parts of the vessel crowd together at the orifice, and the stream contracts somewhat in cross section outside the orifice owing to the inertia and centrifugal force of the liquid as it follows the curved streamlines. The effect of frictional resistance is to decrease the rate of discharge to about 0.6 of that given by Eqs. (7) and (8). Contraction can be eliminated by the use of an orifice whose walls curve to fit the streamlines (Fig. 13b).

Example: A tank containing water has an orifice of 1.0 in.² in one vertical side, 9.0 ft below the free surface level in the tank. Find the velocity of discharge assuming that there is no wasted energy. Assuming the cross section of the stream contracts to 0.64 of the area of the circular orifice, find the flow.

From Eq. (7)

$$
\begin{aligned}
v &= \sqrt{2gh} \\
&= \sqrt{2 \times 32 \text{ ft/sec}^2 \times 9.0 \text{ ft}} \\
&= 24 \text{ ft/sec}
\end{aligned}
$$
$$
\begin{aligned}
\text{Rate of flow} &= (\text{area of cross section})(\text{speed}) \\
&= (0.64)(1.0 \text{ in.}^2)(24 \text{ ft/sec}) \\
&= (0.64)\left(\frac{1.0}{144} \text{ ft}^2\right)(24 \times 60 \text{ ft/min}) \\
&= 6.4 \text{ ft}^3/\text{min}
\end{aligned}
$$

16-9. Turbines. In a turbine the direction of flow of water, steam, or burning gases is changed by blades or buckets on a wheel, and

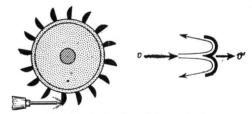

FIG. 14. Action in a Pelton wheel.

the force resulting from the change in momentum is used to rotate the wheel. For efficient operation turbine blades should be so formed that the impelling fluid flows smoothly over them. Also the fluid should be discharged from the turbine with as small a speed as possible. Figure 14 shows how this is accomplished in a Pelton wheel. If the velocities of

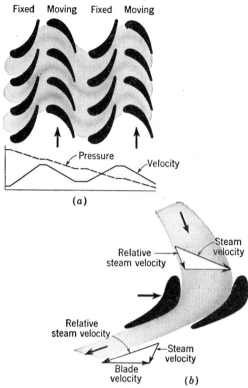

Fixed Moving Fixed Moving

Pressure

Velocity

(a)

Steam velocity

Relative steam velocity

Relative steam velocity

Steam velocity

Blade velocity   (b)

FIG. 15. The steam turbine. (a) In a reaction turbine steam expands in alternate rings of fixed and moving blades that act as jets. The diagram shows two stages. Steam pressure falls in both fixed and moving blades. As the steam expands, the direction of its motion is changed, and the reaction rotates the moving blades. Steam velocity referred to the earth increases in the fixed blades but decreases in the moving blades. (b) In the vector diagram, the horizontal arrows represent the velocity of the blades relative to earth. The flow lines are those which would be seen by an observer on the moving blades. The blades are shaped so that the velocity of the steam *relative to the moving blades* is parallel to the blade surfaces on entering and on leaving.

the jet and bucket are v and v', respectively, and if v' is half of v, then the velocity of the outgoing water relative to ground will be zero

and the whole of the kinetic energy of the water in the jet is converted into useful work. In practice, 70 to 90 per cent of this ideal work may be obtained. Figure 15 shows a steam turbine in which the direction of flow of high-speed steam is repeatedly changed by passage past alternate stator and rotor blades until much of its energy has been delivered to the rotor.

SUMMARY

The rate of flow of a liquid through a pipe is usually measured as the volume that passes a certain cross section per unit time

$$R = Av$$

In the steady flow of a liquid the pressure is least where the speed is greatest.

The steady flow of a liquid can be described by *Bernoulli's theorem* in the statement that the sum of the pressure head, the elevation head, and the velocity head remains constant,

$$\frac{P_1}{\rho g} + h_1 + \frac{v_1{}^2}{2g} = \frac{P_2}{\rho g} + h_2 + \frac{v_2{}^2}{2g}$$

Bernoulli's principle is applied in a venturi flowmeter to measure the rate of flow of a fluid.

An airfoil is any surface designed to obtain a reacting force from the air through which it moves.

The speed with which a liquid escapes from a vessel through an orifice is given by *Torricelli's theorem*

$$v = \sqrt{2gh}$$

In a turbine the change in momentum of a fluid as it is deflected by blades causes the shaft to rotate.

QUESTIONS   1. Why does the flow of water from a faucet decrease when someone opens another valve in the same building?
2. Discuss the statement, "Fluids have a zero coefficient of static friction."
3. Give a detailed description of the process of fluid flow. What are the causes of flow?
4. Describe four illustrations of Bernoulli's principle.
5. Why will marbles not fall vertically in a cylinder of water?

6. How is air drawn into a gas burner?

7. If a person is standing near a fast-moving railroad train, is there danger that he will fall toward it?

8. What makes a flag flutter? What makes a baseball curve?

9. How does the speed of flow of liquid from a small hole in a tank depend upon the depth of the hole below the liquid surface?

10. A jet of water strikes a surface and the water may be assumed to run off with a negligible speed. Derive an expression for the force exerted by the jet.

11. Why is a difference of pressure needed to force a liquid through a horizontal pipe of uniform diameter?

12. How will an increase in altitude affect the difference in pressure on the upper and lower surfaces of an airplane wing? Justify your answer by reference to Eq. (4).

13. A stretched elastic band is wrapped around a ping-pong ball. The ball is snapped forward by the elastic band, which also causes the top of the ball to spin in the forward direction. Will the ball "rise" or "drop"?

14. Explain how you would pitch a ball for an "incurve"; for a "drop."

15. Water flows in a horizontal conduit of nonuniform cross section. Does a typical small mass of the liquid remain in equilibrium as it passes through the pipe? Explain.

16. Explain by the aid of diagrams why a ball will remain spinning on the side of an air jet.

17. Two tall cylinders are filled with liquid to the same height. One contains water, the other mercury. In which cylinder is the pressure greater at a given depth? If small holes are opened in the wall halfway up the cylinders, from which will the liquid emerge at higher speed? Which jet will travel farther before striking the table top?

18. Can the action of a parachute in retarding a fall be explained on Bernoulli's principle?

19. Explain why water breaks into drops when falling freely, whereas it flows in a continuous stream down a vertical pipe.

PROBLEMS   **1.** Water flows from a pipe of 2.0 cm internal diameter at the rate of 8.0 liters/min. What is the speed of the water in the pipe?

2. Liquid flows in a pipe of inside diameter 1.5 in. at an average speed of 3.5 ft/sec. What is the rate of flow in gallons per minute? (1 gal = 231 in.^{3})

Ans. 19 gal/min

3. Oil flows in a 10-in. pipeline at a speed of 3.5 mi/hr. How many gallons of oil does the pipe deliver in one day?

4. What is the kinetic energy of each cubic foot of water in a stream that is moving with a speed of 64 ft/sec?   *Ans.* 4$\bar{0}$00 ft-lb

5. How much work is done in forcing 50 ft^3 of water through a $\frac{1}{2}$-in. pipe if the difference in pressure at the two ends of the pipe is 15 lb/in.^{2}?

6. Liquid of specific gravity 0.90 flows in a horizontal tube 6.0 cm in diameter. In a section where the tube is constricted to 4.2 cm in diameter the liquid pressure is less than that in the main tube by 16,000 dynes/cm^2. Calculate the speed of the liquid in the tube.   *Ans.* 1$\bar{1}$0 cm/sec

7. A venturi meter having a 5.0-in.^{2} throat is connected in a pipe of 12-in.^{2} cross section. The pressures are observed to be 22 lb/in.^{2} in the pipe and 16 lb/in.^{2} at the throat when water flows steadily through the meter. What is the rate of flow in cubic feet per second?

8. A horizontal pipe of cross section 4.0 in.^{2} has a constriction of cross section 1.0 in.^{2} Gasoline (weight-density 42 lb/ft^3) flows with a speed of 6.0 ft/sec in the large pipe where the pressure is 10.0 lb/in.^{2} Find (a) the speed, and (b) the pressure in the constriction.   *Ans.* 24 ft/sec; 7.5 lb/in.^{2}

9. Oil of specific gravity 0.85 flows in a tube 3.0 cm in diameter at a pressure of 1.6×10^6 dynes/cm^2. In a venturi constriction the tube has a 2.0 cm diameter and the pressure is 1.0×10^6 dynes/cm^2. Calculate the rate of flow of oil in the tube.

10. Water flows steadily through a pipe at the rate of 64 ft^3/min. A pressure gage placed on a section of the pipe where the diameter is 4.0 in. reads 16 lb/in.^{2} Determine the pressure in a section of the pipe where the diameter is constricted to 2.0 in.   *Ans.* 0.9 lb/in.^{2}

11. A venturi flowmeter shows a pressure difference of 7.5 lb/in.^{2} between the constriction, of inside diameter 0.25 in., and the normal section of 1.0-in. diameter. How many gallons does it pass per second?

12. Water flowing at 1.0 ft/sec in a pipe passes into a constriction (Fig. 8) whose area is one-tenth the normal pipe area. What is the decrease in water pressure in the constriction? The density of water is 62.4 lb/ft^3.

        Ans. 0.67 lb/in.^{2}

13. In a wind-tunnel experiment the pressure at the upper surface of an airfoil is found to be 12.95 lb/in.^{2} while the pressure at the lower surface is 13.05 lb/in.^{2} What is the lifting force of a wing of this design if it has a span of 24 ft and a width of 5.0 ft?

14. An airplane weighing 800 lb has a wing area of 120 ft^2. What difference in pressure on the two sides of the wing is required to sustain the plane in level flight?   *Ans.* 0.046 lb/in.^{2}

15. (a) With what speed does water flow from an opening that is 25 ft below the free surface? (b) Calculate the speed of discharge of water from this aperture if an added pressure of 20 lb/in.^{2} is applied to the surface of the water.

16. Water in a storage tank stands 9.0 ft above the level of a valve in the side of the tank. (a) With what speed will water come out of the valve, if friction is negligible? (b) To what height will this water rise if the opening in the outlet tube is directed upward?   *Ans.* 24 ft/sec; 9.0 ft

17. Water is maintained at a height of 24 ft in a tank. Calculate the diameter of a circular streamlined hole needed at the base of the tank to discharge water at the rate of 1.0 gal/min.

18. Water having an elevation head of 24 ft flows at the rate of 9.0 ft/sec in a sloping channel. Neglecting friction losses, what is the speed of the water at a place where the elevation head is 12 ft?   *Ans.* 29 ft/sec

19. The level of water in a tank is maintained 4.0 ft above the center of a sharp-edged orifice in the side of the tank. The orifice is 1.0 in. in diameter, but the stream contracts to two-thirds this diameter as it leaves the hole. What is the rate of discharge from the hole?

20. A stream of water escapes from a hole 6.0 ft above the base of a standpipe and strikes the ground at a horizontal distance of 48 ft. How far below the surface of the water is the hole?   *Ans.* 96 ft

21. A fire hose emits 32 lb of water per second in a horizontal jet which strikes a vertical wall at a speed of 75 ft/sec. If each particle of water rebounds with the same horizontal speed as it has when it strikes the wall, what is the total force exerted by the water on the wall?

22. A Pelton wheel is driven by a jet of water 3.0 in. in diameter moving 120 ft/sec. (a) How much energy is supplied per second? (b) Assuming an efficiency of 75%, what horsepower can the wheel develop?

Ans. 8̄3,000 ft-lb; 1̄10 hp

23. Castle Geyser at Yellowstone shoots a spire of water 250 ft into the air. By how much must the pressure at its base exceed atmospheric pressure?

24. A 1.0-kg pail will hold 10.0 kg of water. Water from a faucet fills the pail in 12.0 sec. At the instant the pail is half full, the scales on which it is supported read 6.5 kg. What is the velocity of the flowing water at that instant, assuming that no splashing takes place? *Ans.* 5.9 m/sec

25. During the construction of a building, mortar in a fluid state is pumped into a flexible hose of 5.0 in. diameter and discharged from a nozzle 3.0 in. in diameter on the second floor, 21.0 ft above the pump. The mortar weighs 150 lb/ft^3 and is discharged at the rate of 45 ft^3/min. As an approximation, assume a 50% energy loss due to friction and find (a) the speed of the mortar at the nozzle, (b) the speed of the mortar entering the hose, and (c) the pressure in the hose at the pump.

26. It is desired to refuel a plane at the rate of 50 gal/min (1.0 ft^3 = 7.5 gal). The fuel line is a 3.0-in. hose connected to a pump 3.0 ft above ground; a 2.0-in. nozzle delivers the gasoline (specific gravity 0.675) to the plane 15.0 ft above the ground. Find (a) the speed of the fuel at the nozzle, (b) the speed of the fuel in the line near the pump, and (c) the pressure in the line near the pump.

Ans. 5.1 ft/sec; 2.3 ft/sec; 3.6 lb/in.^{2}

27. Water flows down through a vertical pipe made of a heat-insulating material, which at one point narrows in a constriction to one-third its former cross-sectional area. The pressure and temperature of the water in the constriction are 1.0 atm and 20.00°C; at a point 10.0 m above the constriction the values are 4.5 atm and 19.90°C. What is the speed of the water in the constriction?

28. You and a movie starlet are shipwrecked on a South Sea Island. By chance, she finds a tin can of square cross section of 40 by 40 cm and height 70 cm lying on the beach. You decide to make a shower out of it by punching 20 holes, each of 0.10 cm^2 area into the bottom of the can. If she likes to stay in the shower for 5.0 min, does the can have sufficient capacity?

Ans. Yes, fill to a height of 69 cm.

29. At the base of a tank 10.0 ft square and 20.0 ft high, full of water, is a pump which is to deliver water 90.0 ft above the pump with an exit speed of 16.0 ft/sec. The pump and motor combination is 50% efficient. When the pump is started, the reading of a kilowatt-hour meter in the service line to the motor is 7308.9 kw-hr. What is the meter reading when the tank is empty?

30. A turbine is driven by water which falls from a height of 60 ft. If the flow rate is 480 ft^3/min, determine the maximum power that can be produced.

Ans. 54 hp

17. *Properties of Gases*

All matter, whether solid, liquid, or gas, consists of molecules that attract each other. In solids the molecules are relatively close to each other and the forces of attraction are great enough to hold the molecules in a regular pattern and thus maintain a definite volume and shape. In a liquid the molecules are, on the average, farther apart; the forces are therefore smaller and while the liquid maintains a definite volume it assumes the shape of its container. In a gas the distances between molecules are large compared to their size and the forces of attraction are small compared to those in solids and liquids. A gas therefore has neither shape nor volume of its own but assumes those of its container.

17-1. Air. The most common gas is air, a mixture of several gases but principally nitrogen and oxygen. Since the air is always present, we seldom notice the forces that air exerts unless these forces become so great that they produce inconvenience, discomfort, or destruction.

It is a common expression to characterize something as "light as air," but air is hardly "light." Air is attracted by the earth as is every other substance and the total weight of the air is tremendous, roughly 6×10^{15} tons. This huge weight is always pressing on the surface of the earth but since the forces come from all directions the resultant force is zero.

17-2. Air Pressure. Since air has weight, it exerts force on any object immersed in it. The force per unit area is the air pressure. This pressure under standard conditions is about 14.7 lb/in.^{2} As a result of this pressure very large forces are exerted on even moderately large areas. On an ordinary window, which measures say 3.0 ft by 6.0 ft, the force is $(14.7 \text{ lb/in.}^2)(36 \text{ in.})(72 \text{ in.}) = 3\bar{8},000 \text{ lb} = 19$ tons. Fortunately this large force is normally balanced by another force equal in magnitude but opposite in direction on the other side of the window for no ordinary window would of itself be able to withstand so great a force. If a container such as an ordinary tin can is closed tightly and air pumped out, it soon collapses because of the greater force on the outside. This action is used in certain types of conveyors. A spout is inserted into grain or other loose material, air is removed from the spout by means of a blower, and the outside air pushes the material up the spout. Freight cars or boats may be loaded or unloaded very quickly in this manner.

17-3. Buoyancy. The buoyant effect of air or other gas is by no means negligible. A balloon is supported as it floats in air by a buoyant force equal to the weight of air displaced. At the surface it may displace a weight of air greater than the combined weight of bag, gas contained in the bag, and

166

load. If this is the case, the balloon is accelerated upward. As the balloon rises, the external pressure decreases and the balloon expands; but at the same time the density of air becomes less so that the buoyancy per unit volume is decreased. The balloon will rise until the weight of air displaced in the new position is equal to the total weight of balloon and contents.

The buoyant force of air on solids is less important because it is only a small fraction of the weight of the solid. However, in accurate weighing buoyancy cannot be neglected.

TABLE 1. DENSITY AND SPECIFIC GRAVITY
OF SOME GASES
(0°C and 760 mm of mercury)

Gas	Density, gm/liter	Weight-density, lb/ft³	Specific gravity (relative to air)
Air..............	1.293	0.081	1.000
Carbon dioxide.....	1.977	0.123	1.529
Hydrogen.........	0.090	0.0056	0.069
Helium...........	0.178	0.011	0.138
Nitrogen..........	1.251	0.078	0.967
Oxygen...........	1.429	0.089	1.105
Steam, 100°C......	0.598	0.037	0.462

Example: Brass weights are used in weighing an aluminum cylinder whose approximate mass is 89 gm. What error is introduced if the buoyant effect of air ($\rho = 0.0013$ gm/cm³) is neglected?

$$\rho_{\text{brass}} = 8.9 \text{ gm/cm}^3$$
$$\rho_{Al} = 2.7 \text{ gm/cm}^3$$
$$V = \frac{m}{\rho}$$
$$V_B = \frac{89 \text{ gm}}{8.9 \text{ gm/cm}^3} = 10 \text{ cm}^3$$
$$V_{Al} = \frac{89 \text{ gm}}{2.7 \text{ gm/cm}^3} = 33 \text{ cm}^3$$

The difference in volume V of air displaced on the two pans of the balance is

$$V = V_{Al} - V_B = 33 \text{ cm}^3 - 10 \text{ cm}^3 = 23 \text{ cm}^3$$

Hence, the mass error

$$m = V\rho = 23 \text{ cm}^3 \times 0.0013 \text{ gm/cm}^3 = 0.030 \text{ gm}$$

The error introduced is only a small fraction of the total mass, but in many experiments where accuracy is important an error of 0.030 gm in 89 grams is too great to allow.

Example: A balloon is to operate at a level where the weight-density of air is 0.060 lb/ft³. How much load can it support if it has a volume of 800 ft³ at that level and is filled with hydrogen, $D = 0.0050$ lb/ft³? The weight W_b of the bag is 30 lb.

$$W = VD$$

Weight of air displaced

$$W_a = 800 \text{ ft}^3 \times 0.060 \text{ lb/ft}^3 = 48 \text{ lb}$$

Weight of hydrogen

$$W_h = 800 \text{ ft}^3 \times 0.0050 \text{ lb/ft}^3 = 4 \text{ lb}$$

The load supported

$$L = W_a - W_h - W_b = 48 \text{ lb} - 4 \text{ lb} - 30 \text{ lb}$$
$$= 14 \text{ lb}$$

17-4. The Mercury Barometer. If a long vertical tube is inserted into a liquid and air pumped from it, the liquid will be pushed up

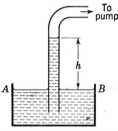

FIG. 1. When air is pumped from the tube, atmospheric pressure forces liquid into it.

into the tube by the air on the outside (Fig. 1). The liquid will rise until the pressure in the tube due to the remaining air and the column of liquid is the same as the pressure outside the tube at the same level in the liquid. At the level of the outside surface AB the pressure is the same as the air pressure. If we could remove all the air above the liquid, the height of the liquid column above the free surface would give a direct measure of atmospheric pressure. Such an instrument is called a *barometer*. The length of tube necessary for use as a barometer depends upon the density of the liquid used, for in the liquid $P = h\rho g$. The most satisfactory liquid for a barometer is mercury. Because of its high density (13.6 gm/cm³) the column supported by atmospheric pressure is only about 30 in. high, whereas water would require a tube over 30 ft in

FIG. 2. Principle of the mercury barometer.

length. Mercury has the added advantage that it does not vaporize readily at ordinary temperatures, and hence the pressure due to its vapor in the space above the liquid is very small.

A simple mercury barometer can be made by filling a 3-ft glass tube with mercury, carefully stoppering the end so that no air is trapped in the tube and inverting the tube in a dish of mercury as shown in Fig. 2. When the stopper is removed, some mercury runs out of the tube and the upper surface sinks to a position lower than the top of the tube. The height of the mercury column above the surface in the well is called the *barometric height* and is usually about 30 in. near sea level. If, while filling the tube, one allows air to get into the space above the mercury column, the barometer will read too low because of the pressure of the entrapped air.

A common type of mercury barometer is shown in Fig. 3. It consists essentially of a closed glass tube inserted into a well in which the level of the free surface is adjustable to bring it to the end of the *scale* shown by the

small pointer to the right of the tube. Graduations are marked on the scale only near the top where an indicator is placed to assist in making the reading. This type of barometer is used in technical laboratories, weather observatories, and even on ships for accurate reading of barometric pressure.

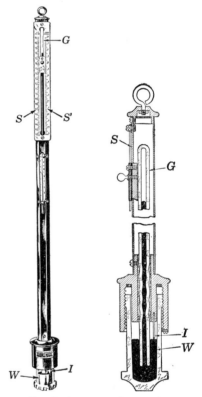

FIG. 3. A mercury barometer.

17-5. Atmospheric Pressure. Barometer readings are much lower at high altitudes than at sea level, since the weight of air above the measuring station is much less. The decrease as we go to higher altitudes is not uniform as it is in a liquid, since the density of air decreases with increase in altitude.

At any one level barometric pressure varies from day to day. Standard atmospheric pressure supports a column of mercury 76.00 cm (29.92 in.) in height at latitude 45° and at sea level. Barometric pressure is usually expressed in terms of the height of a mercury column,

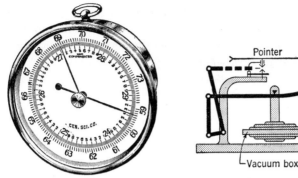

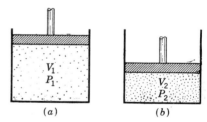

FIG. 4. An aneroid barometer.

but it can be converted into other pressure units by the use of the familiar relation

$$P = hD \text{ (or } P = h\rho g)$$

Example: Express standard atmospheric pressure in pounds per square inch and in dynes per square centimeter.

$$D = 13.60 \times 62.4 \text{ lb/ft}^3 \frac{1}{1728 \text{ in.}^3/\text{ft}^3}$$

$$P = hD = 29.92 \text{ in.} \frac{13.60 \times 62.4}{1728} \text{ lb/in.}^3$$

$$= 14.7 \text{ lb/in.}^2$$

$$P = h\rho g = 76.00 \text{ cm} \times 13.60 \text{ gm/cm}^3$$
$$\times 980 \text{ cm/sec}^2$$

$$= 1,01\overline{3},000 \text{ dynes/cm}^2$$

Since the dyne per square centimeter is a very small unit, a larger unit of pressure, the *bar*, is used. A bar is 1,000,000 dynes/cm². A more common unit, the *millibar*, is used in weather records. The millibar is a thousandth of a bar or 1000 dynes/cm². Standard atmospheric pressure is approximately 1013 millibars (mb).

17-6. The Aneroid Barometer.

The mercury barometer is the most reliable type of barometer, but it is not readily portable since its construction requires that it be kept in a vertical position. Whenever the use of a barometer requires portability, another type called an *aneroid* barometer is used. The essential feature of an aneroid barometer (Fig. 4) is a metallic box or cell, corrugated to make it flexible and partly exhausted of air. This cell tends to collapse under the pressure of air, but a strong spring balances the force due to air

pressure and prevents collapse. As the pressure of the air changes, the free surface of the cell moves in or out slightly, and this small movement is magnified by a system of levers and transmitted to a needle that moves over a dial.

17-7. Pressure in a Confined Gas; Boyle's Law.

Whenever a sample of gas is confined in a closed container, it exerts pressure. Consider a container such as that shown in Fig. 5,

FIG. 5. *P-V* relation; *t* constant.

one wall of which is a movable piston. In its initial position *a* there is a pressure P_1 when the volume is V_1. If, however, the piston is pressed down until it is in the new position shown in *b*, the volume has been decreased to V_2 while the pressure has been increased to P_2. If this change takes place so slowly that there is no change in temperature, the volume occupied by the gas is inversely proportional to the pressure

$$V \propto \frac{1}{P} \tag{1}$$

or the product of pressure and volume is always the same, that is

$$P_1V_1 = P_2V_2 \qquad (2)$$

This relationship is expressed in *Boyle's law*, named after the Irish physicist, Robert Boyle (1627–1691), who first stated it. It may be written as follows: If the temperature of a confined gas does not change, the product of the pressure and volume is constant. In symbols

$$PV = k \qquad (3)$$

Example: The volume of a gas under standard atmospheric pressure (76.0 cm of mercury) is 200 in.³ What is the volume when the pressure is 80 cm of mercury if the temperature is unchanged?

From Eq. (2)
$$P_1V_1 = P_2V_2$$
$$76 \text{ cm} \times 200 \text{ in.}^3 = 80 \text{ cm} \times V_2$$
$$V_2 = {}^{76}\!/_{80}\ 200 \text{ in.}^3 = 1\bar{9}0 \text{ in.}^3$$

Boyle's law is approximately true over considerable ranges of temperature and pressure. There are, however, conditions under which it cannot be applied. If the temperature is near that at which the gas will liquefy, there will be large deviations from the simple law. The change in volume is greater than that predicted by the law. Also if the pressure becomes very great, the deviation from Boyle's law is large, in this case the change in volume being less than that predicted by the law.

17-8. Pressure Gages. Several types of instruments may be used to measure the pressure of a gas. A few of these, such as the barometer, measure the whole pressure directly; others measure only the *difference between the gas pressure and atmospheric pressure.* This differential pressure is called *gage pressure.*

One of the simplest types of pressure-measuring device is a simple U-tube *manometer* such as is shown in Fig. 6. The excess pressure of the gas above atmospheric is indicated by the difference h in level of the liquid in the two tubes. The liquid may be mercury, in which case the reading is directly in centimeters of mercury, or any other liquid which

does not react with the gas and is not too volatile. The reading may be converted into centimeters of mercury by use of Eq. (7), Chap. 15,

$$h_{Hg}\rho_{Hg} = h_l\rho_l$$

where the subscripts Hg and l refer, respectively, to mercury and the liquid used.

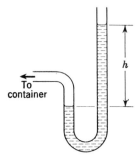

Fig. 6. A simple U-tube manometer.

Other pressure gages make use of the force exerted on the end of a piston by the gas, this force being balanced by a known weight. Still others make use of the deformation of an elastic membrane by the pressure.

Gage pressures cannot be used in Boyle's law. Whenever the pressure indicated is a gage pressure, atmospheric pressure must be added before using it in the law.

Example: An automobile tire whose volume is 1500 in.³ is found to have a pressure of 20.0 lb/in.² when read on the tire gage. How much air (at standard pressure) must be forced in to bring the pressure to 35.0 lb/in.²?

The 1500 in.³ of air in the tire at 20 lb/in.² is compressed into a smaller volume at 35.0 lb/in.²

$$P_1V_1 = P_2V_2$$
$$P_1 = 20.0 \text{ lb/in.}^2 + 14.7 \text{ lb/in.}^2 = 34.7 \text{ lb/in.}^2$$
$$P_2 = 35.0 \text{ lb/in.}^2 + 14.7 \text{ lb/in.}^2 = 49.7 \text{ lb/in.}^2$$
$$(34.7 \text{ lb/in.}^2)(1500 \text{ in.}^3) = (49.7 \text{ lb/in.}^2)V_2$$
$$V_2 = 10\bar{5}0 \text{ in.}^3$$

The volume of air added to the tire is

$$15\bar{0}0 \text{ in.}^3 - 10\bar{5}0 \text{ in.}^3 = 4\bar{5}0 \text{ in.}^3$$

when its gage pressure is 35.0 lb/in.²

The volume at atmospheric pressure will be found from Boyle's law

$$14.7 \text{ lb/in.}^2 \times V = 49.7 \text{ lb/in.}^2 \times 4\bar{5}0 \text{ in.}^3$$

$$V = \frac{49.7}{14.7} \, 4\bar{5}0 \text{ in.}^3 = 1\bar{5}00 \text{ in.}^3$$

17-9. Volume Elasticity of Gases. If the pressure on a confined gas is increased, the volume decreases in accordance with Boyle's law. When the pressure is released, the gas returns to its original volume. The gas has the property of volume elasticity.

If the temperature remains the same during compression and expansion, from Eq. (3), Chap. 13, the bulk modulus is

$$B = \frac{\text{stress}}{\text{strain}} = \frac{-\Delta P}{\Delta V/V} = -V\frac{\Delta P}{\Delta V} \quad (4)$$

The minus sign is introduced because an increase in P causes a decrease in V. For infinitesimal changes, Eq. (4) may be written

$$B = -V\frac{dP}{dV}$$

From Boyle's law $PV = k$. If we differentiate with respect to V

$$\frac{d(PV)}{dV} = P + V\frac{dP}{dV} = 0$$

$$-V\frac{dP}{dV} = P = B \quad (5)$$

Thus at constant temperature the bulk modulus of a gas is equal to its pressure.

17-10. The Siphon. The *siphon* (Fig. 7) is a simple device commonly used to transfer liquid from one container to another. It consists essentially of an inverted U-tube completely filled with liquid. An external pressure P due to the atmosphere tending to force the liquid in A up the tube and over into B is diminished in the tube by the pressure $h\rho g$ of the column of liquid. The same external pressure P tending to force the liquid over to A is diminished by $h_1\rho g$. There is a net pressure $h_1\rho g - h\rho g$, causing the liquid to flow from

A to B since the liquid level is higher in A than in B. The siphon will not operate if the height h is greater than the column the atmosphere can support ($h = P/\rho g$).

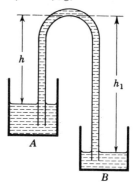

Fig. 7. A siphon.

SUMMARY

Molecules of a gas are relatively far apart and do not attract each other sufficiently to maintain a definite volume or shape. A gas takes the shape and volume of its container.

Air has weight and hence exerts pressure.

The buoyant force of a gas is equal to the weight of the gas displaced.

The *barometer* is an instrument for the measurement of air pressure. There are both mercury and aneroid types of barometer.

Standard barometric pressure is 76.00 cm (29.92 in.) of mercury at sea level and 45° latitude. This is equivalent to about 14.7 lb/in.² Pressure decreases as the altitude increases and varies from time to time at a single place. Pressure is also expressed in *millibars*. A millibar is 1000 dynes/cm².

Boyle's law states that if the temperature of a confined gas is unchanged the product of pressure and volume is constant

$$PV = k$$

Gage pressure is the excess pressure above atmospheric. Gage pressure cannot be used in Boyle's law.

QUESTIONS   **1.** State some of the relative advantages and disadvantages of the mercury *vs.* the aneroid type of barometer.

2. Show clearly why the constant k in the Boyle's-law equation $PV = k$ is not a pure number, but has the dimensions of work.

3. Why cannot the door of a closet be slammed shut?

4. Why is there more danger in the failure of an air storage tank in which the pressure is 100 lb/in.² than in the failure of a water tank in which the pressure is 100 lb/in.²?

5. Why is the work of digging a tunnel under a river done in a high-pressure chamber? What determines how high the pressure should be in the chamber? What danger is involved if the pressure becomes too low? too high?

6. In a common type of drinking fountain a large bottle of water is inverted into a small reservoir. Why does the water not all run out?

7. Could a balloon be constructed that would rise until it reached the moon?

8. In certain instruments pressure must be transmitted for considerable distance and to various levels. What advantages are there in using a gas as a transmitting medium rather than a liquid? What disadvantages?

9. Cite the physical principle involved in the operation of (*a*) a hydrometer, (*b*) hydraulic brakes, (*c*) an aspirator, (*d*) a mercury barometer, and (*e*) an airship.

PROBLEMS

1. The barometric pressure is 30 in. of mercury. Express this in pounds per square foot and in pounds per square inch.

2. What is the net lifting ability of a balloon containing 400 m³ of hydrogen, the mass of the balloon without gas being 250 kg, if the density of air is 1200 gm/m³?   *Ans.* 194 kg

3. Find the mass (corrected for buoyancy) of a sample of balsa wood (density = 0.12 gm/cm³) that is balanced by a 0.500-kg brass weight (density = 8.5 gm/cm³) at 20°C.

4. A block of material whose specific gravity is 2.50 is found to have a mass of 32.240 gm when measured by an equal-arm balance with brass weights. Find the correction for buoyancy of the air and the true mass.

Ans. 0.011 gm; 32.251 gm

5. A cylindrical glass jar of 5.0 cm radius is covered with a closely fitting glass plate of mass 200 gm. What total force is required to lift the plate off if the inside of the vessel is exhausted to a pressure of 68 cm of mercury?

6. A gas occupies 2.0 ft³ under a pressure of 30 in. of mercury. What volume will it occupy under 25 in. of mercury pressure? Assume that the temperature is unchanged.   *Ans.* 2.4 ft³

7. To what fraction of its original volume is the air compressed in a diving bell when it is lowered to a depth of 60 ft in salt water of specific gravity 1.026, the height of the barometer being 30 in.? What air pressure would keep the water out of the bell?

8. A uniform air column is 50 cm long at atmospheric pressure. It is compressed to 40 cm length by an added pressure of 18 cm of mercury. What is the atmospheric pressure?   *Ans.* 72 cm of mercury

9. To what depth must a diving bell 5.0 ft high be immersed in order that the water may rise 3.0 ft within it? The barometric reading is 30 in. of mercury.

10. The volume of an air bubble increases tenfold in rising from the bottom of a lake to its surface. If the height of the barometer is 30.0 in., and if the temperature of the air bubble is constant, what is the depth of the lake?

Ans. 306 ft

11. A bicycle tire has a capacity of 200 in.³ when fully inflated to a pressure of 3.0 atm. If the tire is initially quite flat, find the volume of air at atmospheric pressure required to fill it.

12. A tube 120 cm long, closed at one end, is half filled with mercury and then inverted into a mercury trough in such a way that no air escapes from the tube. If the barometric pressure is 75 cm, what is the height of the mercury column inside the tube?   *Ans.* 27 cm

13. A uniform capillary tube sealed at one end and placed in a horizontal position contains a column of air 24 cm long trapped between the closed end and a slug of mercury 36 cm in length. Barometric pressure is 72 cm of mercury. What is the length of the entrapped column of air if the tube is turned into a vertical position (*a*) with the closed end pointing downward? (*b*) with the closed end pointing upward?

14. A barometer, which has not been completely freed of air, reads 76.0 cm when the correct barometric height is 77.0 cm. The internal height of the top of the barometer tube above the surface of the mercury in the cistern is 85 cm. Find the true barometric height when the height of the mercury in the defective instrument is 75.0 cm.   *Ans.* 75.9 cm

15. A barometer has a little air in the space at the top of the mercury column and hence reads only 28.0 in. when the barometric pressure is 29.0 in. When the barometer reads 29.0 in., the correct pressure is 30.2 in. What is the correct value of the atmospheric pressure when it reads 26.0 in.?

16. An open U-tube manometer is used to measure the pressure of gas in a tank. The manometer contains oil of specific gravity 0.80. What is the gas pressure on a day when the mercury barometer reads 75.0 cm and the oil stands 20 cm higher in the open arm of the manometer than in the arm which communicates to the confined gas?   *Ans.* 76.2 cm of mercury

17. In a J-tube a volume of 5.0 cm³ of air is trapped when the level of the mercury on the open side is 60 cm higher than on the closed end. If the barometric height is 72 cm, what will be the difference in levels to cause the air to have a volume of 6.0 cm³?

18. The volume of a tire is 1500 in.³ when the pressure is 30 lb/in.² above atmospheric pressure. (*a*) What volume will this air occupy at atmospheric pressure? Assume that atmospheric pressure is 15 lb/in.² (*b*) How much air will come out of the tire when the valve is removed?   *Ans.* 4500 in.³; 3000 in.³

19. An air bubble occupies a volume of 12 cm³ when submerged 8.0 m below the surface of an oil vat. The oil has a specific gravity of 0.80, and the air above it is at normal atmospheric pressure. What is the buoyant force upon the bubble when it is just below the surface of the oil?

20. An oxygen tank has a volume of 1.5 ft³, and its pressure gage indicates 200 lb/in.² After opening the valve for a time, the gage reads 150 lb/in.² How many cubic feet will the escaped oxygen occupy at atmospheric pressure? Assume temperature constant.   *Ans.* 5.0 ft³

21. Water is pumped into the bottom of an airtight tank holding 1000 gal, compressing the air above it until a pressure gage reads 60.0 lb/in.² (*a*) How much water does the tank then contain? (*b*) If 200 gal of water are drawn off, what will the gage pressure then be? Assume atmospheric pressure is 15.0 lb/in.²

22. A tank containing 24 ft³ of oxygen at 150 lb/in.² absolute pressure is connected through a small tube with a second tank containing 48 ft³ of nitrogen at 120 lb/in.² absolute pressure. Assuming both tanks are at the same temperature, the volume of the connecting pipe is negligible, and no temperature change occurs, what is the pressure of the gases when mixed?   *Ans.* 130 lb/in.²

23. A bubble 1.0 cm³ in size leaves an air hose 30 ft under water. How large will the bubble be when it reaches the surface, assuming its temperature to remain constant?

24. A flask from which the air is to be exhausted contains 2400 cm³ at a pressure of 76 cm of mercury. An air pump removes 160 cm³ of air during its first upward stroke. What will be the pressure in the flask at the end of the fifth upward stroke?   *Ans.* 55 cm of mercury

25. The pressure in a vacuum system used for aluminizing telescope mirrors is read on a McLeod gage as 5.0×10^{-2} mm of mercury. Express this in (*a*) millibars and (*b*) atmospheres.

26. A glass capillary tube closed at one end contains dry air and a slug of mercury 2.4 cm long which acts as a piston enclosing the air. When the tube is held vertically with closed end down, the length of air column is 36.0 cm. When the tube is inverted, the mercury descends until the length of air column is 38.6 cm. Find the atmospheric pressure.   *Ans.* 69.0 cm of mercury

27. A cartesian diver consists of an inverted test tube, containing water and air, floating in a jar of water whose top is covered by a rubber sheet made airtight. The test tube floats with 0.60 cm length extending above the water when the length of air column in the tube is 3.6 cm. How much must the pressure on top of the liquid be increased (by pressing on the rubber sheet) in order to submerge the test tube, if the barometer reads 72 cm of mercury?

18. Molecular Theory of Matter

In our discussion of the properties of liquids and those of gases we assumed that the fluids are composed of small particles called *molecules* and that liquids and gases differ in the spacing and forces between the molecules. These assumptions are in accord with present ideas of the structure of matter.

Most of the conclusions that we reach regarding the molecular nature of matter are the result of indirect observations, since the molecules are much too small to see and in all except a few experiments the effects of individual molecules are too small to observe. From observation of the effects of *large groups* of molecules, we make up a picture or theory of the arrangement and behavior of the molecules. We then *test by experiment* the results predicted by the theory. Observation can be made only on large numbers of molecules at one time or on the average effects of individual molecules. Hence only *average* effects are subject to observation.

18-1. Fundamental Assumptions. In building a theory of the molecular nature of matter, we start with a set of assumptions. The assumptions are considered valid if the results predicted are verified by experiment.

We assume that all matter is composed of distinct particles called molecules. In the case of a pure substance, these molecules are alike in all respects. The *chemical* properties are determined by the character of the molecules; but the *physical* properties depend also upon the forces the molecules exert on each other, and the relation of these forces to the distances between molecules. Also the motion of the molecules must be taken into account.

We assume that the molecules obey Newton's laws of motion. Except in very special circumstances, we assume that collisions between molecules are elastic, that is, that both momentum and kinetic energy are unchanged.

It is assumed further that the molecules are continually in motion. The average speed is dependent upon the temperature.

From observation of the physical properties of solids, liquids, and gases, we can state some conclusions about the forces which molecules exert upon each other. In order to pull a solid apart, it is necessary to exert rather large forces of tension. Hence there must be forces of attraction between the molecules when they are at the distances existing in solids. Much smaller forces are required to separate parts of liquids, and in gases the molecules if left to themselves separate without external forces. These facts indicate that as the distance between molecules increases, the force of attraction decreases rapidly. On the other hand, we find that very large forces of compression are necessary to reduce the volume of a solid or a liquid. We must therefore conclude that when the distance between the molecules is very small, there are forces of repulsion and that these forces increase very rapidly as the distance between the molecules decreases. The forces must vary in a manner something like that shown in Fig. 1. As the molecules approach each other from distances

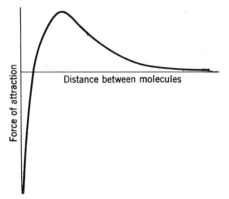

FIG. 1. Variation of attractive force with distance between molecules.

which are large compared to their own dimensions, the forces exerted on one another are at first extremely small; then on closer approach a force of attraction develops which reaches a maximum value, decreases to zero, and finally becomes a repulsive force which increases very rapidly as the distance is further reduced.

18-2. Pressure in a Gas. If our picture of the molecular nature of matter is correct, it must lead to the laws which are observed in the behavior of gases.

Consider the gas contained in a cubical box the length of each edge being l (Fig. 2). Suppose there are n molecules in each unit volume of the gas. Consider one of the moving molecules. Its velocity v may be divided into three rectangular components v_x, v_y, and v_z related by the equation

$$v^2 = v_x{}^2 + v_y{}^2 + v_z{}^2 \qquad (1)$$

Consider the x component of the motion. When the molecule strikes the yz face of the box, it rebounds with its speed unchanged but moving in the opposite direction, that is, $v_x = -v_x'$. If the x component of the mo-

mentum before the collision was mv_x, that after the collision is $-mv_x$. The change in this component of momentum is therefore $2mv_x$. As the molecule moves, the distance it moves in the x direction between collisions with *this* face is $2l$. The time between impacts with this

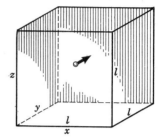

FIG. 2. Pressure in a gas is related to molecular motion.

face is $2l/v_x$, and hence there are $v_x/2l$ collisions per unit time. The change in momentum per unit time at this face is

$$2mv_x \times v_x/2l = mv_x{}^2/l$$

Since the change in momentum per unit time is the force, in accordance with Newton's second law, this one molecule exerts a force F_1 on this face (and the opposite one as well) given by

$$F_1 = \frac{mv_x{}^2}{l} \qquad (2)$$

But if n is the number of molecules per unit volume there are nl^3 molecules in the box. The average total force on the yz face is given by

$$F_{yz} = (nl^3)\frac{\overline{mv_x{}^2}}{l} = nl^2 m \overline{v_x{}^2} \qquad (3)$$

where $\overline{v_x{}^2}$ is the average of the squares of the x components of the velocities.

From Eq. (1) we may express the kinetic energy $\tfrac{1}{2}mv^2$ of the molecule by the relation

$$\tfrac{1}{2}mv^2 = \tfrac{1}{2}mv_x{}^2 + \tfrac{1}{2}mv_y{}^2 + \tfrac{1}{2}mv_z{}^2$$

We may associate the energy with the three components of velocity. On the average the energy for all the molecules will be equally divided among the three components of motion.

$$\tfrac{1}{2}m\overline{v^2} = \tfrac{1}{2}m\overline{v_x^2} + \tfrac{1}{2}m\overline{v_y^2} + \tfrac{1}{2}m\overline{v_z^2}$$

and $m\overline{v_x^2} = m\overline{v_y^2} = m\overline{v_z^2} = (\tfrac{1}{3})m\overline{v^2}$ (4)

From Eq. (3)

$$F_{yz} = \tfrac{1}{3}nl^2m\overline{v^2} \quad (5)$$

Pressure is force per unit area. The area of the side of the box is l^2.

Hence $P = \dfrac{F_{yz}}{l^2} = \dfrac{(\tfrac{1}{3})nl^2m\overline{v^2}}{l^2}$

$$P = (\tfrac{1}{3})nm\overline{v^2} \quad (6)$$

In Eq. (6) we use the average of the squares of the speeds of the molecules. In any gas the speeds of the individual molecules are widely different. The speed used in Eq. (6) is the square root of the average square of the speeds and is called the *root-mean-square* (rms) value of v.

In terms of the average kinetic energy we may write Eq. (6) as

$$P = (\tfrac{2}{3})n(\tfrac{1}{2}m\overline{v^2}) \quad (7)$$

In a volume V of gas the number of molecules is $N = Vn$. If we multiply both sides of Eq. (7) by V, we obtain

$$PV = \tfrac{2}{3}N(\tfrac{1}{2}m\overline{v^2}) \quad (8)$$

If we assume that the temperature is associated with the average kinetic energy, the right-hand side of Eq. (8) is a constant for a given temperature and Eq. (8) then reduces to Boyle's law.

Example: Compute the rms speed of the molecules of oxygen at 76.0 cm of mercury pressure and 0°C, when the density of oxygen is 0.00143 gm/cm³.

From Eq. (6)

$P = \tfrac{1}{3}nmv^2$

Since

$nm = \rho \qquad P = \dfrac{1}{3}\rho v^2 \quad \text{or} \quad v^2 = \dfrac{3P}{\rho}$

$P = h\rho g = 76.0 \text{ cm} \times 13.6 \text{ gm/cm}^3$
$\qquad\qquad\qquad\qquad\qquad \times 980 \text{ cm/sec}^2$
$\quad = 1,01\overline{3},000 \text{ dynes/cm}^2$

$$v^2 = \frac{3P}{\rho} = \frac{3 \times 1,01\overline{3},000 \text{ dynes/cm}^2}{0.00143 \text{ gm/cm}^3}$$

$$v = \sqrt{\frac{3 \times 1,013,000}{0.00143}} \text{ cm/sec} = 45,\overline{7}00 \text{ cm/sec}$$

This speed approximates that of a rifle bullet.

18-3. Cohesion and Adhesion. The force with which like molecules attract each other is called *cohesion*. Within a solid the forces of cohesion are large since the molecules are close together. If the solid is broken, it is difficult to force the molecules close enough together for these forces to become large again. When an iron bar is broken, the pieces may be fitted together, but they will not cohere. However, by heating the iron until it softens and pounding it with a hammer, the molecules may be again brought close enough to cohere and the bar is welded. Local heating until the metal flows also serves to bring the molecules close enough for cohesion. Two ordinary plates of glass or two blocks of steel, when brought together, show little evidence of cohesion because they touch at only a few points. It is possible, however, to grind these surfaces flat enough so that when they are brought into contact the cohesive forces become very large. The highest grade gage blocks will thus cohere and can be pulled apart only with considerable difficulty.

At the surface between two different substances, or in a mixture, unlike molecules attract each other. The attraction of unlike molecules is called *adhesion*. Glue adheres to wood; solder adheres to brass. Adhesive forces may be greater than cohesive forces; in fact, the relative magnitude of the cohesive and adhesive forces determines the nature of the surface between two substances in contact.

18-4. Surface Phenomena. Suppose a straight piece of wire hangs in a horizontal position from a spring attached to the midpoint of the wire. The spring is stretched by the weight of the wire. If now the wire is dipped into a liquid that wets the wire and is then pulled up just above the surface as in Fig. (3), it will be found that the spring is stretched more than it was before. Evidently the film of liquid that extends over the wire exerts a force F on the wire. If the length of the wire is increased, F is found to increase proportionately. Thus the force appears to be proportional to the length of the film. From

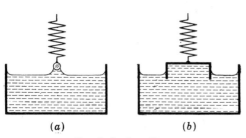

(a)   (b)

FIG. 3. Surface film.

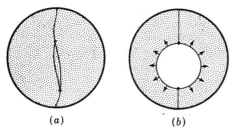

(a)   (b)

FIG. 4. Force of surface film at right angles to boundary.

Fig. (3) we see that there is a film on each side of the wire. We might assume that the length of the film is twice the length of the wire. We may test this assumption by using first a ring of wire in which there will be a film on each side of the wire and then a flat disk of the same radius. For the disk there is only a single film around the edge. If we perform these experiments, we find that the force due to the film is twice as great for the ring as for the disk, which confirms our assumption. If several liquids are used, one after the other, the force is found to depend upon the liquid used. The force also depends upon the gas above the liquid.

If a thread with a small loop is tied across a wire frame (Fig. 4a) and the frame is dipped into soap solution, the film will cover the whole frame and the loop may be of any shape. If, however, the film is broken within

the loop, the loop immediately becomes circular in shape as in Fig. 4b.

18-5. Surface Tension. These experiments suggest that the surface film exerts a force perpendicular to any line in the surface. Such a force must be a result of molecular forces. If

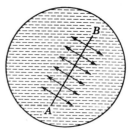

FIG. 5. Forces across an imaginary line in a surface.

the surface is flat, the force across the line in one direction is just equal in magnitude to that in the opposite direction and there is equilibrium (Fig. 5). However, if the film is broken on one side (Fig. 4b) or if the surface is so shaped that the forces are not in opposite directions, the surface forces do not themselves produce equilibrium.

The force per unit length across such a line in the surface is called the *surface tension*

$$T = \frac{F}{L} \qquad (9)$$

where F is the force across the line of length L. The unit of surface tension may be any force unit divided by any length unit. Since the forces are small it is customary to use the force in dynes and the length in centimeters so that T is given in dynes per centimeter. Surface tension is the cause of several phenomena that would not be expected of liquids at rest. A steel needle has a density so high that the buoyant force of water upon it is not sufficient to support its weight. However, if it is oiled slightly so that the water will not wet it and it is laid very carefully upon the surface so that the film is not broken, it will float (Fig. 6). Note that the surface is depressed under the needle so that the film is able to exert an upward force.

Example: The maximum force, in addition to the weight, required to pull a wire frame (Fig. 3) 5.00 cm long from the surface of water at temperature 20°C is 728 dynes. Calculate the surface tension of water.

There is a film on either side of the wire and hence the length of the film is twice the length of the wire.

$$T = \frac{F}{L} = \frac{F}{2l} = \frac{728 \text{ dynes}}{2 \times 5.00 \text{ cm}} = 72.8 \text{ dynes/cm}$$

TABLE 1. SURFACE TENSION FOR PURE LIQUIDS IN CONTACT WITH AIR

Liquid	Temperature, °C	T, dynes/cm
Benzene.............	20	27.6
	50	24.7
Carbon tetrachloride...	20	26.8
Ethyl alcohol.........	20	22.3
	50	19.8
Methyl alcohol........	20	22.6
	50	20.1
Mercury..............	20	465
Water................	10	74.2
	20	72.8
	50	67.9
Liquid lead...........	400	445
Liquid tin............	400	520

Consider a rectangular wire frame (Fig. 7) one side of which is movable. If the frame is dipped into soap solution so that there is a film on the inside of the rectangle, there will be a force on the movable side so as to decrease the area of the loop. To hold the movable side in equilibrium a force F must be applied. Since there is a film on either side of the wire

$$F = LT = 2lT \tag{10}$$

where l is the length of the movable wire. If the movable wire is pulled slowly a distance s so as to increase the area, the force F remains constant as the area of the film increases. In this process work is done. The work done in moving the wire is

$$W = Fs = 2lsT \tag{11}$$

But the increase in area A of the double film (front and back) is $2ls$.

Thus $$W = AT$$

or $$T = \frac{W}{A} \tag{12}$$

Thus the surface tension may also be regarded as the work done per unit area in increasing the area of the film. The surface tension can thus be expressed in ergs per square

FIG. 6. The force due to surface tension is sufficient to support a needle.

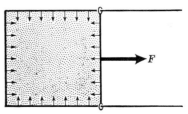

FIG. 7. Force per unit length and work per unit area in a film.

centimeter. This unit is equivalent to a dyne per centimeter.

The surface under tension will always tend to contract until its area is the smallest possible for the conditions present. The film of Fig. 7 tends to contract until its area becomes zero. A droplet takes the shape that will make its surface area least, that is, a spherical shape if the drop is undisturbed by its weight.

18-6. Pressure Due to Surface Tension. Within a liquid droplet the pressure is greater than the pressure outside. Its spherical shape is one indication of the pressure difference. Consider the droplet of Fig. 8. The excess pressure ΔP inside the droplet causes a force on each element of the surface perpendicular to that surface element. The resultant of these forces is a force perpendicular to a cross section of the droplet and given by the excess

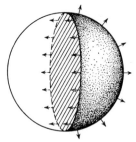

Fig. 8. Forces that produce pressure within a droplet.

pressure times the area of the cross section

$$F = \Delta P \times \pi r^2$$

This force is supplied by the film pulling across the perimeter of this cross section

$$F = 2\pi r T$$

Thus

$$\Delta P \times \pi r^2 = 2\pi r T$$

or

$$\Delta P = \frac{2T}{r} \qquad (13)$$

18-7. Contact of Liquids, Solids, and Gases. At the boundary of the surface of a liquid in a vessel there are three substances in contact. We may consider that there is a surface effect at each surface of separation and that there is a force parallel to each such surface. In addition there is a force of adhesion between the molecules of the liquid and those of the solid. This adhesive force is perpendicular to the wall of the container. The point where the three substances are in contact is in equilibrium under the action of four forces and the liquid surface will set itself so that this condition is realized. The liquid surface near this point of contact will, in general, be

curved. Two such combinations are shown in Fig. 9. In Fig. 9a the adhesive force is relatively large, the liquid wets the solid, and the liquid surface is concave upward. In Fig. 9b the adhesive force is relatively smaller, the liquid does not wet the solid, and the liquid surface is concave downward. If a line is drawn tangent to the surface, it makes an angle θ with the wall. This angle is called the *angle of contact*. When the liquid wets the solid the angle of contact will be less than 90°; when the liquid does not wet the solid the angle of contact is greater than 90°. Certain angles of contact are given in Table 2.

TABLE 2. ANGLES OF CONTACT BETWEEN PURE LIQUIDS AND CLEAN SOLIDS

Solid	Liquid	θ, degrees
Glass...............	Water	0
Glass...............	Ethyl alcohol	0
Glass...............	Mercury	128
Paraffin.............	Water	107

18-8. Capillarity. It is a common observation that water rises in fine glass tubes. If a string lies over the edge of a pan of water, the water will rise in the string over the top and down the outside. These effects are caused by surface tension.

In the tube shown in Fig. 10, the liquid wets the tube making an angle of contact θ. The liquid rises in the tube until the force due to surface tension is equal to the weight of the liquid lifted up.

$$F = W$$

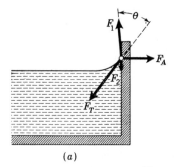

(a)

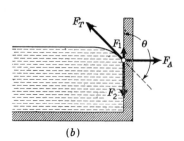

(b)

Fig. 9. Angle of contact θ. F_1, F_2, and F_T represent surface forces. F_A represents adhesive force.

The upward force F is the product of the length of the film, that is, the circumference $2\pi r$ of the tube and the upward component $T \cos \theta$ of the surface tension.

$$F = 2\pi r T \cos \theta \quad (14)$$

The weight of liquid lifted is the product of the volume $\pi r^2 h$ and the weight per unit volume ρg.

$$W = \pi r^2 h \rho g \quad (15)$$

$$2\pi r T \cos \theta = \pi r^2 h \rho g$$

$$h = \frac{2T \cos \theta}{r \rho g} \quad (16)$$

We note that if the angle of contact is greater than 90°, the cosine is negative and the liquid

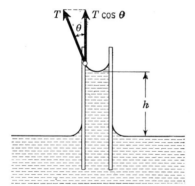

FIG. 10. Rise of liquid in a capillary tube.

goes down in the tube. That is, if the liquid does not wet the tube, it descends.

Example: The tube of a mercury barometer is 3.0 mm in diameter. What error is introduced into the reading because of surface tension?

For mercury

$$\theta = 128° \qquad \cos \theta = -0.616$$

$$h = \frac{2T \cos \theta}{r \rho g}$$

$$h = \frac{2(465 \text{ dynes/cm})(-0.616)}{0.15 \text{ cm} \times 13.6 \text{ gm/cm}^3 \times 980 \text{ cm/sec}^2}$$

$$= -0.286 \text{ cm} = -2.86 \text{ mm}$$

The negative sign indicates that the reading is lower than the correct reading.

The curved surface of the liquid in the capillary tube indicates that the pressure in-

side the liquid is not the same as that outside. The difference in pressure is

$$\Delta P = \frac{F}{A} = \frac{2\pi r T \cos \theta}{\pi r^2} = \frac{2T \cos \theta}{r} \quad (17)$$

also

$$\Delta P = h \rho g \quad (18)$$

Hence

$$h \rho g = \frac{2T \cos \theta}{r}$$

$$h = \frac{2T \cos \theta}{r \rho g} \quad (19)$$

Equation (19) is identical with Eq. (16).

At the surface of separation between two liquids, there is also a tension similar to surface tension. It is called *interfacial tension*.

18-9. Diffusion. If a bottle of ammonia is opened in one corner of a closed room, the odor is soon apparent in all parts of the room even though there are no air currents. The ammonia molecules reach the observer because of their own motion. The molecules in the air of the room are relatively far apart. As the ammonia molecules move, they pass between the molecules of the air with occasional collisions. Some of the molecules reach every part of the enclosure in a short time. The process of one substance mixing with another because of molecular motion is called *diffusion*. If the gas is confined in a small container and the pressure is reduced, diffusion takes place more rapidly, for the gas molecules are farther apart and collisions are less frequent.

Diffusion occurs in liquids as well as in gases. This may be shown by dropping a few copper sulfate crystals into a jar of water. As the crystals dissolve, the blue color appears first at the bottom and slowly spreads upward. After a period of some weeks, all the liquid will be colored. Since the copper sulfate solution is denser than water, the spreading cannot be caused by convection currents as it would be if the crystals were suspended near the top. If this were done, the mixing would be quite rapid.

Diffusion of gases or liquids through solids is also common. A light gas such as hydrogen passes quite readily through porous earthenware. Such a porous jar, arranged as at *A* in Fig. 11 with a tube extending into a flask of

FIG. 11. Diffusion of gas through a porous cup.

water, is filled with air. When a container of hydrogen is lowered over the porous jar, the hydrogen diffuses into the jar faster than air diffuses out. Hence the pressure is increased inside the system, and water is forced out.

18-10. Osmosis. Some substances, such as parchment or vegetable materials, have the property of allowing some molecules to diffuse through but not others. Suppose a piece of parchment is fastened over a thistle tube and some sugar sirup placed inside (Fig. 12). When this is immersed in water, the water molecules diffuse in through the parchment, but the larger sugar molecules cannot diffuse out. This process is called *osmosis*. The liquid rises in the tube until the pressure, due to the liquid, is sufficient to stop the diffusion or the membrane breaks. The pressure set up by this one-way diffusion is called *osmotic pressure*.

Osmosis is an important process in animal and vegetable life since it determines the flow of liquids through membranes. When fruit or vegetables are placed in fresh water, the skin becomes stretched and may even burst because water passes in through the skin. If, however, the fruit or vegetable is placed in a sugar or salt solution, liquid may pass out through the skin with resultant shriveling.

18-11. Brownian Movement. Individual molecules are too small to be visible, but it is possible to observe the effects of collisions of

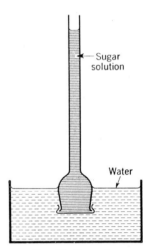

FIG. 12. Osmosis.

molecules with small particles, which can be seen with the aid of a microscope. If some gamboge, a gum, is dissolved in alcohol and a small amount poured into a dish of water, a very fine suspension is formed. When this is viewed by means of a microscope, the particles are seen to be in very erratic motion. This motion is called *Brownian motion* after the man who first observed it (1827). The motion is due to collisions of molecules with the particles. Each impact imparts a motion to the particle, and since it is struck first from one direction and then another, the motion is quite erratic. Brownian motion constitutes one of the most direct pieces of evidence for the belief in the motion of molecules.

SUMMARY

The *molecular theory* of matter is based upon a set of assumptions. Predictions made upon the basis of these assumptions are tested experimentally to determine whether the theory is tenable.

The fundamental assumptions are that all matter is made up of molecules which are in constant motion. Newton's laws of motion are assumed to hold. In collisions between molecules, the laws of conservation of momentum and conservation of kinetic energy hold. The molecules exert forces upon each other, which depend upon the distance between them.

The *pressure* of a gas is given by the expression

$$P = \frac{1}{3}nm\overline{v^2}$$

Cohesion is the attraction between like molecules, while *adhesion* is the attraction between unlike molecules.

At the surface of a liquid there is a *surface tension*. It is expressed as the force per unit length of the surface film

$$T = \frac{F}{L}$$

Surface tension is usually expressed in dynes per centimeter.

Liquids rise or are depressed in fine tubes. The height to which they rise is given by the expression

$$h = \frac{2T \cos \theta}{r\rho g}$$

Diffusion takes place because the molecules of a gas or liquid move between the molecules of the substance into which it is penetrating.

Osmosis is one-way diffusion through a semipermeable membrane.

Brownian movements are motions of small particles that are bombarded by molecules.

QUESTIONS

1. What reasons have you for believing in the existence of molecules?

2. What is the evidence that the molecules of a gas are in motion?

3. Discuss the reasons for believing that the molecules of a liquid are in motion.

4. How is the motion of the molecules in a gas different from that of the molecules in a liquid? in a solid?

5. Show that the kinetic energy per mole (gram-molecular weight) is the same for all gases at the same temperature.

6. When bits of camphor gum are dropped on water, they move about erratically. Explain.

7. Explain why the meniscus for certain liquids in a capillary tube is convex upward whereas for others it may be concave.

8. Molten lead is poured through a sieve at the top of a shot tower and is caught in water at the bottom. Why are the shot spherical?

9. Show that the surface tension of a film, defined as the force per unit length, also may be interpreted as the potential energy per unit area of the film.

10. Show that surface tension causes a pressure inside a liquid droplet given by $P = 2T/r$.

11. Show that the pressure due to surface tension in a bubble is given by $P = 4T/r$.

12. Should the reading of a barometer be corrected for capillary depression? Explain.

13. If two soap bubbles of radii 10 cm and 20 cm, respectively, could be joined by a tube without bursting, what would happen? Why?

14. When water rises in a capillary tube, how does the pressure inside the liquid at the top of the column compare with the pressure outside the liquid? Is there any visual evidence of a difference?

15. What effect has the looseness of the soil on the loss of water by evaporation from a garden plot in summer?

16. What is the importance of capillary action in the success of an irrigation system?

17. What physical principles are applied when candle wax is removed from clothing by covering the spot with blotting paper and then passing a hot iron over the paper?

18. Water will not run from the upper end of a short capillary tube the lower end of which dips below the surface of water, but sap runs from the end of a maple branch that has been cut off. Explain.

19. Why may alcohol escape from an automobile radiator that will hold water?

20. A glass rod is sometimes placed against the mouth of a bottle when pouring liquid from it into another vessel. Explain the usefulness of the rod.

21. Suggest a design for a dripproof cream pitcher or sirup dispenser.

22. Is diffusion important in determining the composition of the air at various levels?

23. Show how osmosis and capillarity can play important parts in feeding a plant.

24. In Brownian movement small particles are set into random motion by bombardment by gas molecules. Are large bodies ever set into motion by bombardment by gas molecules? If so, give examples.

PROBLEMS

1. There are 6.02×10^{23} molecules in a mass of any gas equal numerically to its molecular mass. How many molecules are there in a cubic centimeter of nitrogen under standard conditions?

2. Copper has atomic mass 63.6 and specific gravity of 8.9. What is the average volume per atom?   *Ans.* 1.2×10^{-23} cm³

3. Compute the rms speed of oxygen molecules at 0°C and 76.0 cm of mercury when the density is 1.429 gm/liter.

4. Compute the rms speed of helium molecules under standard conditions. The density of helium is 0.178 gm/liter.   *Ans.* 1.30×10^5 cm/sec

5. If the mean distance between collisions of carbon dioxide molecules under standard conditions is 6.29×10^{-4} cm, what is the time between collisions?

6. Under normal conditions the average distance a hydrogen molecule travels between collisions is 1.83×10^{-5} cm. Compute (*a*) the time between collisions and (*b*) the frequency of collisions.

Ans. 1.00×10^{-10} sec; 1.00×10^{10}/sec

7. A 1.00-liter flask contains 2.68×10^{22} molecules of oxygen each of mass 5.31×10^{-23} gm and having an rms speed of 4.61×10^4 cm/sec. Compute the pressure in the flask, and reduce it to atmospheres.

8. A needle is 2.5 in. long. Assuming that the needle is not wetted, how heavy can it be and still float on water?   *Ans.* $9\overline{2}0$ dynes

9. A wire frame 4.0 cm long (Fig. 3) is dipped into a soap solution, $T = 30$ dynes/cm, and lifted 2.0 cm above the surface of the liquid. How much extra work is done because of the film?

10. How high will water rise in a capillary tube of 0.50 mm radius?

Ans. 3.0 cm

11. To what height will a liquid of specific gravity 0.80 and surface tension 30 dynes/cm rise in a tube of 0.60 mm internal diameter? (The contact angle is 0°.)

12. The tube of a mercury barometer has an internal diameter of 5.0 mm. How much error does surface tension introduce in the readings?   *Ans.* -1.7 mm

13. Some distilled water in a capillary tube becomes mixed with an impurity that does not appreciably affect its density or surface tension but does change the angle of contact from 0 to 20°. If the tube has a diameter of 0.30 mm, what change in height will the water experience?

14. Find the internal diameter of a glass tube in which water rises to a height of 4.5 cm.   *Ans.* 0.066 cm

15. A liquid of specific gravity 0.85, for which the angle of contact is zero, rises to a height of 12.0 mm in a capillary tube of 2.0 mm diameter. Find the surface tension of the liquid.

16. A certain oil whose angle of contact against glass is 24° and density 0.90 gm/cm^3 rises 3.2 cm in a glass capillary tube 1.0 mm in diameter. What is the surface tension of the oil?   *Ans.* 77 dynes/cm

17. Two vertical glass plates 1.0 mm apart are dipped into water. How high will the water rise between the plates?

18. Two flat plates of glass are held in a vertical position 0.80 mm apart with their lower edges in alcohol, specific gravity 0.79 and surface tension 22.3 dynes/cm. How high will the alcohol rise between the plates?   *Ans.* 0.72 cm

19. Carbon tetrachloride, specific gravity 1.60, $T = 26.8$ dynes/cm, is poured into an open U-tube. One arm of the tube has a diameter of 0.80 mm, the other 0.80 cm. What is the difference in level of the liquid in the two tubes when the tubes are vertical? The angle of contact for CCl_4 and glass is 0°.

20. A U-tube is made with the internal diameter of one arm 1.0 cm and that of the other arm 2.0 mm, and mercury is poured into the tube. If the angle of contact of mercury with glass, after exposure to air, is 60°, what will be the difference in level of the surfaces in the two tubes?   *Ans.* 2.8 mm

21. The surface tension of a soap solution is 25 dynes/cm. How much work must be done in blowing a soap bubble 4.0 cm in diameter?

HEAT

19. *Temperature Measurement; Thermal Expansion*

In many industrial operations it is necessary to heat the material that enters into a process. In such cases a major factor in the success of the procedure is knowledge of when to stop. In many modern industrial processes the attainment of a uniform product having desirable properties requires precise measurement and control of temperature during the operation. For example, in the metallurgical industries the characteristics of the metal being treated are vitally affected by its temperature history.

The comfort and efficiency of human beings is influenced by the temperature of their surroundings. Ideal air conditioning requires measurement and control of temperature.

The most common type of temperature-measuring device utilizes the expansive properties of certain materials.

19-1. Temperature Sensation. We can tell something about the temperature of an object by feeling it. If it is very hot, we can sense this even without touching it. But under some conditions our temperature sense is a very unreliable guide. For example, if the hand has been in hot water, tepid water will feel cold; whereas, if the hand has been in cold water, the same tepid water will feel warm. If we go outdoors on a cold day and pick up a piece of wood, it will feel cold. Under the same conditions a piece of steel will feel even colder.

Both of these examples suggest that our sensations of hot or cold depend on the transfer of heat to or away from the hand. The steel feels colder than the wood because it is a better conductor of heat and takes heat from the hand much more rapidly than does the wood.

19-2. Temperature Level. The sense we possess for judging whether a thing is hot or cold cannot be used to measure temperature, but it does suggest to us what temperature is. *The temperature of an object is that property which determines the direction of flow of heat between it and its surroundings.* If heat flows away from an object, we say that its temperature is above that of the surroundings. If the reverse is true, then its temperature is lower. To answer the question of *how much* higher or lower requires a standard of measure and some kind of instrument calibrated to read temperature difference in terms of that standard. Such an instrument is called a *thermometer*.

19-3. Thermometers. There are many possible kinds of thermometers, since almost all the properties of material objects (except mass) change as the temperature changes. The amount of any such change may be used to measure temperature. To be useful, the amount of the change must correspond in some known manner to the temperature change that induces it. The simplest case is the one in which equal changes in the property correspond to equal changes in the temperature. This is approximately true for the length of a column of mercury in a glass capillary connected to a small glass bulb.

When a mercury thermometer is heated, the mercury expands more than the glass bulb and rises in the capillary tube. The position of the mercury in the capillary when the bulb is in melting ice is taken as a reference point. Such a reference temperature, chosen because it is easily reproducible, is called a *fixed point*.

If the bulb is placed in contact with something else and the mercury goes above the fixed point set by the melting ice, then that material is at a higher temperature than the melting ice. If the mercury goes below the fixed point, then the temperature is lower. The answer to how much higher or how much lower can be obtained only by selecting another fixed point so that the interval between the two can be divided into a convenient number of units in terms of which temperature changes can be compared, or, as we say, measured.

The other fixed point chosen is the boiling point of water. This is the temperature of the water vapor above pure water which is boiling under a pressure of one standard atmosphere. Since the temperature at which water boils depends upon the pressure, it is necessary to define this fixed point in terms of a standard pressure.

Many other easily reproducible temperatures may be used as fixed points. For example, the boiling point of oxygen, a very low temperature, and the melting point of platinum, a very high temperature, are sometimes used. The temperatures of such fixed points are based on the primary temperature interval between the freezing point of water and the (standard) boiling point of water.

19-4. Common Thermometer Scales. Two thermometer scales are in common use: one, the *centigrade* scale, which divides the standard interval into 100 equal parts called *degrees centigrade;* and the other, the *Fahrenheit* scale, which divides the standard interval into 180 equal parts called *degrees Fahrenheit* (Fig. 1). The centigrade degree represents a larger temperature interval than a Fahrenheit degree. One Fahrenheit degree is equal to five-ninths of a centigrade degree. A reading on the centigrade scale indicates directly the interval between the associated temperature and the lower fixed point, since the latter is marked zero. The Fahrenheit scale is more cumbersome, not only because the standard interval is divided into 180 parts instead of 100, but also because the base temperature, that of melting ice, is marked 32°. The Fahrenheit scale is used in many English-speaking countries, while nearly all others use the centigrade scale. Having the two temperature scales is something of a nuisance, but it is comparatively easy to convert temperatures from one scale to the other.

For any two temperature scales that use the freezing point and boiling point of water as fixed points, the temperature may be converted from one to the other by means of a simple proportion. For centigrade and Fahrenheit scales this relation is

$$\frac{C - 0°}{F - 32°} = \frac{100° - 0°}{212° - 32°} \qquad (1)$$

This equation reduces to

$$\frac{C}{F - 32°} = \frac{100}{180} = \frac{5}{9}$$

This may be solved for either C or F to give

$$C = \tfrac{5}{9}(F - 32°) \qquad (2)$$
$$F = \tfrac{9}{5}C + 32° \qquad (3)$$

Several numerical examples will serve to illustrate the process.

Example: A centigrade thermometer indicates a temperature of 36.6°C. What would a Fahrenheit thermometer read at that temperature?

The number of degrees centigrade above 0°C is 36.6. This temperature will be (9/5)36.6 or 65.9 Fahrenheit degrees above the freezing point of water. The Fahrenheit reading will be 32.0°F added to this, or 97.9°F.

Example: A Fahrenheit thermometer indicates a temperature of 14°F. What is the corresponding reading on the centigrade scale?

The temperature of 14°F is 32° − 14° = 18 F° below the freezing point of water. A temperature interval of 18 F° is equivalent to 5/9(18°) = 10 C°. Hence the reading on the centigrade scale is 10 deg below the freezing point of water, or

$$0° − 10° = −10°C$$

Example: A comfortable room temperature is 72°F. What is this temperature expressed in degrees centigrade?

$$C = \tfrac{5}{9}(72° − 32°) = \tfrac{5}{9}(40°) = 22°C$$

19-5. Temperature Intervals. From the manner in which the standard interval is subdivided in the two scales (Fig. 1), it is evident that 100 C° = 180 F°. Dividing each side of this equation by 180 F° and 100 C° in turn, we obtain

$$\frac{5\ C°}{9\ F°} = 1 = \frac{9\ F°}{5\ C°} \qquad (4)$$

These conversion factors, which are equal to unity, as are all conversion factors, may be used for the convenient transfer of temperatures from one type of scale to another.

When expressing *a temperature*, we write after the number one of the common symbols °C, °F, etc.; here when expressing *a difference of temperature* we have used the symbols C° and F° for the words *centigrade degrees* and *Fahrenheit degrees*.

Example: Over a period of 50 years, the extremes of temperature in New York differed by 116 Fahrenheit degrees. Express this range in centigrade degrees.

$$116\ F° = \tfrac{5}{9}(116)\ C° = 64.4\ C°$$

19-6. Expansion Thermometers. The property most commonly used in thermometers is expansion. The expansion may be that of a liquid, a solid, or a gas. Mercury-in-glass thermometers may be used over a range from the freezing point of mercury (−38.9°C) to the softening temperature of glass (about 500°C). For temperatures below the freezing point of mercury, other liquids, such as alcohol, or pentane, may be used. The expansion of a solid or of a gas may be used over a much greater range of temperatures.

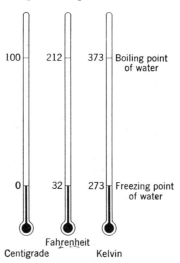

Fig. 1. Fixed points on various temperature scales.

19-7. Resistance Thermometers. Electrical methods of measuring temperature are applicable over a wide range and are capable of high precision. The variation of electrical resistance with temperature is often used in temperature measurements. A resistance thermometer (Fig. 2) consists of a small coil of wire, usually platinum, encased in a suitable protecting tube. By measuring the resistance of the coil at several known temperatures one can plot a resistance-temperature curve and thus calibrate the coil as a thermometer. The most accurate method of temperature measurement, resistance thermometry, can measure temperatures with an uncertainty of only 0.01 C° and can detect a difference in temperature of 0.0001 C°.

19-8. Thermoelectric Thermometers. In another electrical method, temperatures are measured by the variation of electric current

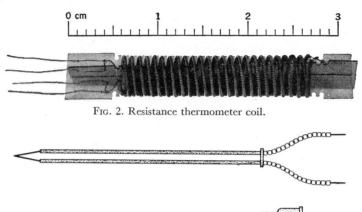

FIG. 2. Resistance thermometer coil.

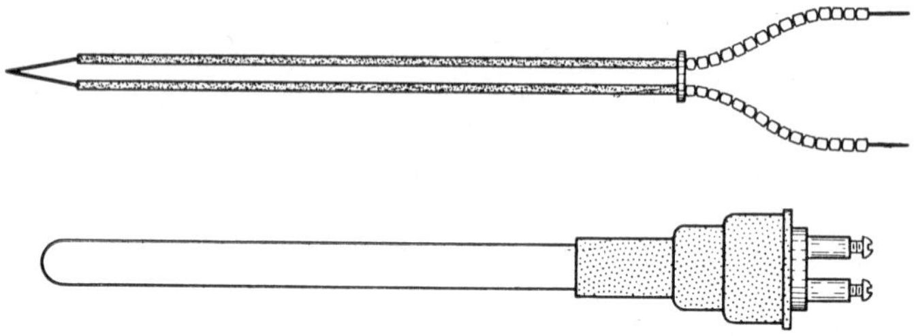

FIG. 3. Thermocouple.

in a thermocouple (Fig. 3). If wires of two different metals are joined at their ends and one of these junctions is maintained at a different temperature from the other, electricity will flow around the circuit. This current depends on the *difference* in temperatures at the two junctions. One junction may be held

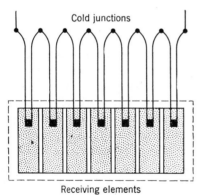

FIG. 4. Thermopile.

at 0°C in an ice bath, and the electrical measuring instrument calibrated to indicate directly the temperature of the other junction. Thermocouples have high sensitivity and a wide range. With them, temperatures can be measured at any convenient distance from the test body. Thermocouples are sufficiently rugged and inexpensive to find numerous uses in industry. Several tiny thermocouples may be connected in series to form a *thermopile* (Fig. 4) capable of measuring the radiation from a star.

19-9. Optical Pyrometer. At very high temperatures special thermometers, called *pyrometers*, are used. In an optical pyrometer (Fig. 5) the brightness of the hot object (inside of a furnace, for example) is matched against the brightness of the filament of a standard lamp. The temperature is determined from the electric current needed to heat the lamp filament to match the brightness of the hot object.

The color of an object also changes with temperature. As the temperature rises, the object first becomes a dull red, at a higher temperature a bright red, and finally white at very high temperatures. These changes in color may be used to measure temperature.

19-10. Linear Expansion. Nearly all materials expand with an increase in temperature. A solid changes all its linear dimensions and thus its volume. Liquids and gases have no shapes of their own, and therefore only volume expansion has meaning. For solids we are primarily concerned with linear expansion.

The *coefficient of linear expansion* (or the *linear expansivity*) is defined as the change in length per unit length per degree rise in tempera-

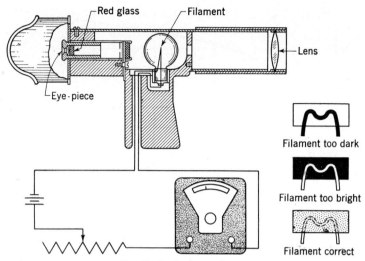

FIG. 5. Optical pyrometer.

ture. In symbols

$$\bar{\alpha} = \frac{L_t - L_0}{L_0 \, \Delta t} \qquad (5)$$

where $\bar{\alpha}$ is the average linear expansivity for the region about temperature t; L_0 and L_t are the initial and final lengths, respectively.

Measurements of the change in length and the total length are always expressed in the same unit of length; hence the value of the expansivity will be independent of the length unit used, but it will depend on the temperature unit used. The value of the expansivity must be specified as "per degree centigrade" or "per degree Fahrenheit" as the case may be. If we let ΔL represent the change in length of a bar, then

$$\Delta L = \alpha L_0 \, \Delta t \qquad (6)$$

The final length will be

$$L_t = L_0 + \Delta L = L_0 + \alpha L_0 \, \Delta t$$
$$= L_0(1 + \alpha \, \Delta t) \qquad (7)$$

Example: A copper bar is 8.0 ft long at 68°F and has an expansivity of 0.0000094 per F°. What is its increase in length when heated to 110°F?

$$\Delta L = L_0 \alpha \, \Delta t = (8.0 \text{ ft})(0.0000094/\text{F}°)$$
$$(110°\text{F} - 68°\text{F}) = 0.0032 \text{ ft}$$

Example: A steel plug has a diameter of 10.000 cm at 30.0°C. At what temperature will the diameter be 9.986 cm?

$$\Delta L = L_0 \alpha \, \Delta t$$
$$\Delta t = \frac{9.986 \text{ cm} - 10.000 \text{ cm}}{(10.000 \text{ cm})(0.000011/\text{C}°)} = -1\bar{3}0 \text{ C}°$$

Hence the required temperature

$$t = 30.0°\text{C} - 1\bar{3}0°\text{C} = -1\bar{0}0°\text{C}$$

Precise measurements show that for a given value of $\bar{\alpha}$, Eqs. (6) and (7) are inadequate to describe the expansion of a material over all ranges of temperature (Fig. 6). More exact expressions are obtained by introducing terms with higher powers in the right-hand member of Eq. (7). Thus, with rearrangement of L_0, we can write

$$\frac{L_t - L_0}{L_0} = a_1(t - t_0) + a_2(t - t_0)^2$$
$$+ a_3(t - t_0)^3 + \cdots \qquad (8)$$

where a_1, a_2, etc., are constants characteristic of the material and the reference temperature t_0 at which the length is L_0. Equation (8) may be written also as

$$\frac{\Delta L}{L_0} = a_1 \, \Delta t + a_2(\Delta t)^2 + a_3(\Delta t)^3 + \cdots \qquad (9)$$

For the limiting case, for the region about any

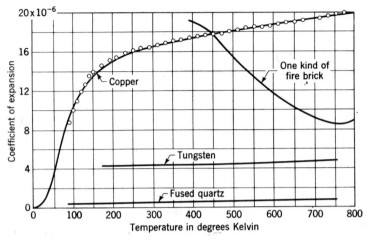

FIG. 6. Variation of linear expansivity for several materials.

temperature t, we can write

$$\alpha_t = \left(\frac{1}{L}\frac{dL}{dt}\right)_t \qquad (10)$$

As t approaches zero, α_t becomes the a_1 of Eq. (8). Hence a_1 is precisely the *linear expansivity* at t_0.

When the temperature of a solid is raised, it expands in all directions. Certain crystals are found to have different expansivities along different axes. However, many of the common materials have the same properties in all directions. These are called *isotropic* substances.

The facts that different solids have different expansivities, and that the expansivity for a given material may vary somewhat with temperature, lead to many industrial problems. If a structure, for example a furnace, can be made of materials that expand equally over wide ranges in temperature, the structure will hold together much better than if such materials cannot be found. When it is impossible to find suitable materials with approximately equal expansivities, allowance must be made for the large forces that arise, owing to the fact that different parts of the structure expand at different rates. Some materials that go together well at one temperature may be quite unsatisfactory at others because their expansivities may change considerably as the temperature changes.

Tungsten is a metal that expands in a manner similar to that of many glasses. Tungsten, platinum, and Dumet (an alloy) are metals often used to seal electrodes through the glass of electric light bulbs, x-ray tubes, and the like, since the expansion of these metals can be matched with that of appropriate glasses.

TABLE 1. LINEAR EXPANSIVITIES (AVERAGE)

Material	Per C°	Per F°
Aluminum	0.000022	0.000012
Brass	0.000019	0.000011
Copper	0.000017	0.0000094
Glass, ordinary	0.0000095	0.0000053
Glass, pyrex	0.0000036	0.0000020
Invar (nickel-steel alloy)	0.0000009	0.0000005
Iron	0.000012	0.0000067
Oak, along grain	0.000005	0.000003
Platinum	0.0000089	0.0000049
Fused quartz	0.00000059	0.00000033
Steel	0.000011	0.0000061
Tungsten	0.0000043	0.0000024

Figure 7 shows the close agreement of the cooling curves of Fernico and 705-AO glass from the annealing temperature down to room temperature. This means that if this combination of glass and metal is joined together at the annealing temperature the glass and metal will contract at the same rate as

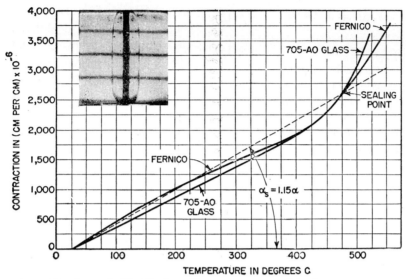

FIG. 7. Contraction of Fernico and 705-AO glass. The average expansivity between room temperature and sealing temperature is represented by α_s. (*From Robert L. Weber, Heat and Temperature Measurement, copyright, 1950, by Prentice-Hall, Inc., Englewood Cliffs, N.J., p. 16., reproduced by permission of the publisher.*)

they cool, and be free from strain both during cooling and after reaching room temperature. The insert gives a photoelastic stress pattern (Chap. 48) of a test seal made with these materials. The lines are straight within one-hundredth of a fringe, showing that the stress is less than 0.002 newton/mm².

19-11. Volume Expansion. *The volume expansivity for a material is the change in volume per unit volume per degree rise in temperature.* In symbols

$$\bar{\beta} = \frac{V_t - V_0}{V_0 \, \Delta t} \qquad (11)$$

where $\bar{\beta}$ is the average volume expansivity, V_t is the volume at temperature t, V_0 the volume at 0°C (32°F), and Δt is the temperature change.

There is a simple approximate relation between the linear expansivity for an isotropic solid and the corresponding volume expansivity:

$$\beta = 3\alpha \qquad \text{(approximately)} \qquad (12)$$

This relation can be derived by consideration of the expansion of a cube of the material.

TABLE 2. VOLUME EXPANSIVITIES OF LIQUIDS

Substance	Per C°	Per F°
Alcohol (ethyl).........	0.0011	0.00061
Mercury..............	0.00018	0.00010
Water (15–100°C).......	0.00037	0.00020

Example: Find the change in volume of an aluminum sphere of 5.0 cm radius when it is heated from 0 to 300°C.

$$V_0 = \tfrac{4}{3}\pi r^3 = \tfrac{4}{3}\pi(5.0 \text{ cm})^3 = 5\bar{2}0 \text{ cm}^3$$

From Eq. (11)

$$V_t - V_0 = \beta V_0 \, \Delta t$$
$$\beta = 3\alpha = 3(2.2 \times 10^{-5}/\text{C}°)$$

Hence the change in volume is

$$V_t - V_0 = 3(2.2 \times 10^{-5}/\text{C}°)(5\bar{2}0 \text{ cm}^3)(300 \text{ C}°)$$
$$= 10 \text{ cm}^3$$

The change in volume of the sphere is the same whether it be a solid sphere or a hollow spherical shell.

The more precise relations for volume expansion are similar to those just described for linear expansion.

$$\frac{\Delta V}{V_0} = b_1 \Delta t + b_2 \Delta t^2 + b_3 \Delta t^3 + \cdots \qquad (13)$$

$$\beta_t = \left(\frac{1}{V}\frac{dV}{dt}\right)_t \qquad (14)$$

If $t \doteq 0$, the β_t of Eq. (14) is the b_1 of Eq. (13).

Generally a liquid expands when its temperature is raised. Water is an important exception to this rule, since in the region from 0 to 4°C water contracts when its temperature is raised (Fig. 8). Above 4°C water expands with increasing temperature.

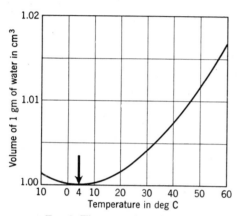

FIG. 8. The expansion of water.

19-12. Expansion of Gases. The behavior of a gas when its temperature is changed can be examined in the apparatus shown in Fig. 9. Suppose that the gas is confined in the bulb B, which is connected to a U-tube manometer M in which the mercury level may be adjusted by raising or lowering the reservoir R.

With the bulb surrounded by an ice bath, the mercury levels may be adjusted to zero on the scale. The pressure of the gas P_0 is then just atmospheric pressure. If the temperature of the bulb is raised to t, both the volume and the pressure of the gas will increase as indicated by the change in levels of the mercury. It is convenient to keep either the pressure or the volume constant in order to study the variation in the other factor with change in temperature. By raising the reservoir the level of mercury in the left-hand column may be restored to the index 0. The gas then occupies

its original volume. Its pressure P_t can be found by measuring the difference in levels of the mercury columns and adding to it the atmospheric pressure.

Let us define γ the *coefficient of pressure change* at constant volume as

$$\gamma = \frac{P_t - P_0}{P_0 \Delta t} \qquad (15)$$

Substitution of the observed values of P_t, P_0, and Δt in Eq. (15) gives the value of γ for the particular gas used. Experiments of this type

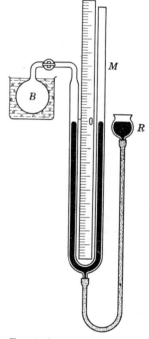

FIG. 9. A gas thermometer.

performed carefully with many different gases give the interesting result that the value of γ is roughly the same for all gases, provided the pressure of the gas is not too high. The value found for γ is

$$\gamma = \frac{1}{273}/C° = 0.00366/C°$$

That is, the pressure of any gas at constant volume will change by $\frac{1}{273}$ of its pressure at 0°C for each centigrade degree change in temperature.

The apparatus can be modified to hold a

gas at constant pressure while its change in volume is read from the displacement of mercury. The volume expansivity β at constant pressure may then be obtained by Eq. (11). It is found that, when the pressure of the gas is not too high, the value of β is approximately the same for all gases, and is the same as the value for γ,

$$\beta = \tfrac{1}{273}/C° = 0.00366/C°$$

It is apparent from their behavior that gases can be used as thermometric substances. Gas thermometers (Fig. 9), usually of the constant-volume type, filled with dry air, nitrogen, hydrogen, or helium have been widely used in scientific work where their accuracy outweighs the disadvantage of cumbersome equipment. A gas thermometer is calibrated by observing the pressure P_0 at the ice point and then the pressure P_s at the steam point. An unknown temperature t is then determined from the pressure P_t of the gas at that temperature; thus

$$t = \frac{P_t - P_0}{P_s - P_0} 100°C \qquad (16)$$

19-13. Absolute Temperature Scale. An important consequence of the experiments that showed that all gases have approximately the same values of the coefficients β and γ is the establishment of a scale of temperature known as the *absolute gas scale* of temperature. The derivation of this scale is suggested by rewriting Eq. (15), putting in the numerical value for γ

$$P_t = P_0 \left(1 + \frac{t}{273}\right) \qquad (17)$$

$$P_t = \frac{P_0}{273} (273 + t)$$

A new scale is adopted in which the size of the degree is the same as the centigrade degree and the temperature T of the gas is given by

$$T = 273 + t \qquad (18)$$

Then Eq. (17) becomes

$$P_t = \frac{P_0}{273} T \qquad \text{(volume constant)} \qquad (19)$$

showing that the pressure of a gas at constant volume is proportional to its absolute temperature. The defining equation for temperatures on the absolute gas scale, Eq. (18), could be derived equally well for a constant-pressure gas thermometer using Eq. (11) and $\beta = \tfrac{1}{273}$

$$V_t = \frac{V_0}{273} T \qquad (20)$$

An examination of Eq. (19) and the graph of pressure *vs.* centigrade temperature (Fig. 10) suggests a question of fundamental importance: Is there an absolute zero of temperature? An answer is not possible from a

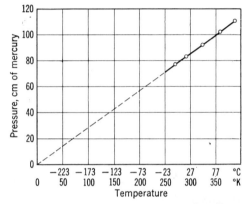

FIG. 10. The pressure of a gas at constant volume as a function of temperature.

consideration of the behavior of gases alone. The extrapolation of the pressure-temperature curve in Fig. 10 suggests the existence of a lowest temperature: that at which a gas would have zero pressure, that is, no motion of its molecules. This point would be near $-273°C$, according to the graph. But all gases become liquids and even solids at temperatures above absolute zero, and furthermore γ and β are not constant for gases near the temperatures at which they liquefy.

We need a temperature scale that is independent of the properties of particular substances. There is such a scale, known as the *Kelvin scale* or the *absolute thermodynamic scale*. It is an ideal scale based on certain fundamental laws (Chap. 22). Fortunately, temperatures on the thermodynamic scale are identical with those on the absolute gas scale. Temperatures on the centigrade absolute scale are designated by the symbol °K.

Absolute temperature can also be expressed in terms of the Fahrenheit degree by the relation

$$R = \frac{9}{5}K \qquad (21)$$

where R represents the temperature on the Fahrenheit absolute, or Rankine, scale. Thus the temperature of the ice point on the Fahrenheit absolute scale is

$$R = \frac{9}{5}(273) = 492°R \qquad (22)$$

Since the temperature of the ice point on the Fahrenheit scale is 32°F, a temperature F on the Fahrenheit scale is converted to the Fahrenheit absolute (Rankine) scale by the equation

$$R = 492° + (F - 32)$$
$$R = 460° + F \qquad (23)$$

Example: Express 20°C and −20°C on the centigrade absolute (Kelvin) scale.

$$K = 273° + 20° = 293°K$$
$$K = 273° + (-20°) = 253°K$$

Example: Express 68°F and −5°F on the Fahrenheit absolute (Rankine) scale.

$$R = 460° + 68° = 528°R$$
$$R = 460° + (-5°) = 455°R$$

19-14. The Gas Laws. We have found that pressure, volume, and temperature of a gas are related. In Chap. 17 we considered the relation between pressure P and volume V when the temperature remains constant, namely, that the product of pressure and volume is constant.

$$PV = k \qquad (24)$$

This relation is known as *Boyle's law.*

We have now found that there are relationships between temperature and pressure if the volume remains unchanged and between temperature and volume if the pressure is constant. These relations are expressed simply if an *absolute* (Kelvin or Rankine) temperature scale is used.

From Eq. (19)

$$\frac{P}{T} = k_1 \qquad \text{(at constant volume)} \qquad (25)$$

and from Eq. (20)

$$\frac{V}{T} = k_2 \qquad \text{(at constant pressure)} \qquad (26)$$

These two equations express *Charles's laws. If the volume of a confined gas is constant, the pressure is directly proportional to the absolute temperature,* or

$$\frac{P_1}{T_1} = \frac{P_2}{T_2} \qquad (27)$$

If the pressure of a confined gas is unchanged, the volume is directly proportional to the absolute temperature, or

$$\frac{V_1}{T_1} = \frac{V_2}{T_2} \qquad (28)$$

TABLE 3. VOLUME EXPANSIVITIES OF GASES

Substance	Temperature, °C	Pressure, cm of mercury	Volume expansivity, per C°	Pressure coefficient, per C°
Air....................	0–100	0.6	....	376.66×10^{-5}
	0–100	25	....	365.80
	0–100	76	367.1×10^{-5}	366.50
	0–100	100	367.28	367.44
	0–100	2000	....	388.66
Hydrogen...............	0–100	76.4	366.00	365.04
Carbon dioxide..........	0–100	100	374.10	372.48
Sulfur dioxide...........	0–100	76	390.3	384.5

19-15. The General Gas Law. The three gas laws just stated can be combined into a single law that applies to changes in conditions of a gas whether the factors change one at a time or simultaneously. The *general gas law* may be written in equation form as

$$PV = RT \qquad (29)$$

where R is a constant, usually applied to one gram-molecular mass of gas.

$$R = 8.317 \text{ joules/gm-mole K}°$$

The equation can also be written in such a form that it deals with changes in mass as well as changes in pressure, volume, and temperature. In this form it is written as

$$PV = mR'T \qquad (30)$$

where m is the mass of gas being considered and R' is a constant referred to unit mass of gas.

If we introduce the restrictions stated in the special laws, the general gas law reduces to the simpler expressions. If mass and temperature are constant, Eq. (30) reduces to $PV = k$ (Boyle's law). If m and V are constant, $P/T = k_1$; while if P and m are constant, $V/T = k_2$. These are Charles's laws.

In using the general gas law it may be convenient to write it in other forms. If we divide both sides of Eq. (30) by mT and express the result in terms of initial and final conditions, we have

$$\frac{P_1 V_1}{m_1 T_1} = \frac{P_2 V_2}{m_2 T_2} \qquad (31)$$

or, since the density $\rho = m/V$,

$$\frac{P_1}{\rho_1 T_1} = \frac{P_2}{\rho_2 T_2} \qquad (32)$$

The general gas law can be used to study any changes in the conditions of the gas so long as *absolute* temperatures and *complete* pressures are used. Gage pressures cannot be used in the gas law.

Example: A 5000-cm³ container holds 4.90 gm of a gas when the pressure is 75.0 cm of mercury and the temperature is 50°C. What will be the pressure if 6.00 gm of this gas are confined in a 2000-cm³ container at 0°C?

From Eq. (31)

$$\frac{P_1 V_1}{m_1 T_1} = \frac{P_2 V_2}{m_2 T_2}$$

$$\frac{P_1 \times 2000 \text{ cm}^3}{6.00 \text{ gm} \times 273°\text{K}}$$
$$= \frac{75.0 \text{ cm of mercury} \times 5000 \text{ cm}^3}{4.90 \text{ gm} \times 323°\text{K}}$$

$$P_1 = 194 \text{ cm of mercury}$$

Example: The weight-density of air at 32°F and 29.92 in. of mercury pressure is 0.081 lb/ft³. What is its weight-density at an altitude where the pressure is 13.73 in. of mercury and the temperature is $-40°$F?

From Eq. (32)

$$\frac{P_1}{D_1 T_1} = \frac{P_2}{D_2 T_2}$$
$$T_1 = 32° + 460° = 492°\text{R}$$
$$T_2 = -40° + 460° = 420°\text{R}$$

$$\frac{29.92 \text{ in.}}{0.081 \text{ lb/ft}^3 \times 492°\text{R}} = \frac{13.73 \text{ in.}}{D_2 \times 420°\text{R}}$$
$$D_2 = 0.044 \text{ lb/ft}^3$$

Example: Air at pressure 14.7 lb/in.² is pumped into a tank whose volume is 42.5 ft³. What volume of air must be pumped in to make the gage read 55.3 lb/in.² if the temperature is raised from 70 to 80°F in the process?

$$P_1 = 14.7 \text{ lb/in.}^2$$
$$P_2 = 14.7 \text{ lb/in.}^2 + 55.3 \text{ lb/in.}^2 = 70.0 \text{ lb/in.}^2$$
$$T_1 = 70° + 460° = 530°\text{R}$$
$$T_2 = 80° + 460° = 540°\text{R}$$

Since m is constant,

$$\frac{P_1 V_1}{T_1} = \frac{P_2 V_2}{T_2}$$
$$\frac{14.7 \text{ lb/in.}^2 \times V_1}{530°\text{R}} = \frac{70.0 \text{ lb/in.}^2 \times 42.5 \text{ ft}^3}{540°\text{R}}$$
$$V_1 = 199 \text{ ft}^3$$

Since 42.5 ft³ of air were in the tank at the beginning, the volume the added air would occupy at atmospheric pressure is

$$V = 199 \text{ ft}^3 - 42.5 \text{ ft}^3 = 157 \text{ ft}^3$$

SUMMARY

The *temperature* of an object is that property which determines the direction of flow of heat between it and its surroundings.

A thermometer scale is established by choosing as *fixed points* two easily reproducible temperatures (ice point and steam point), dividing this interval into a number of equal subintervals, and assigning an arbitrary zero.

Conversions between centigrade and Fahrenheit scale readings are made by the relations

$$F = \tfrac{9}{5}C + 32°$$
$$C = \tfrac{5}{9}(F - 32°)$$

The *expansivity* is the fractional change (in length or in volume) per degree change in temperature. The units, per C° or per F°, must be expressed.

$$\alpha = \frac{L_t - L_0}{L_0 \Delta t}$$

$$\beta = \frac{V_t - V_0}{V_0 \Delta t}$$

The expansion of a material is equal to the product of the expansivity, the original size (length or volume), and the temperature change. Symbolically

$$\Delta L = \alpha L_0 \Delta t \qquad \text{and} \qquad \Delta V = \beta V_0 \Delta t$$

The pressure coefficients of expansion and the volume expansivities of all gases are approximately equal to $\tfrac{1}{273}$ per C°.

Conversions to the centigrade absolute (Kelvin) and Fahrenheit absolute (Rankine) scales are made from the relations

$$K = 273° + C$$
$$R = 460° + F$$

The general gas equation is

$$\frac{P_1 V_1}{m_1 T_1} = \frac{P_2 V_2}{m_2 T_2}$$

QUESTIONS   **1.** List several methods of measuring temperatures and mention the factors that limit the range of each. What means are available for measuring the highest attainable temperatures?

2. What factors must be taken into account in the design of a sensitive thermometer?

3. What precautions are necessary to ensure accurate readings when using a liquid-in-glass thermometer?

4. Outline carefully the logical steps in the definition of a temperature scale.

5. How do you account for the fact that solids and liquids generally expand when heated?

6. Would the linear expansivity be different if the inch were used as the unit of length rather than the centimeter? If the Fahrenheit scale were used rather than the centigrade scale? Explain.

7. An observation made on the expansion of a liquid contained in a bulb or tube does not give the true expansion of the liquid. Explain.

8. Would the error introduced by the expansion of the container be larger in a liquid thermometer or in a gas thermometer? Explain why.

9. Suggest several practical uses of the differential expansion of two different materials. In what cases is differential expansion undesirable?

10. Describe the action of a temperature-compensated balance wheel in a watch.

11. In the early manufacture of light bulbs platinum wire was sealed through the glass. By reference to Table 1, show why this was feasible.

12. A steel plug fits into a hole in a brass plate. What will be the effect on the closeness of fit if the plug alone is heated? If the plate alone is heated? If both are heated equally?

13. Show that the area expansivity is approximately twice the linear expansivity and that the volume expansivity is approximately three times the linear expansivity.

14. Describe briefly the expansion of water near 4°C. What are some consequences of this behavior of water?

PROBLEMS   **1.** Liquid oxygen freezes at $-218.4°C$ and boils at $-183.0°C$. Express these temperatures on the Fahrenheit scale.

2. Convert $-14°C$, $20°C$, and $60°C$ to Fahrenheit readings. Convert $98°F$, $-13°F$, and $536°F$ to centigrade readings.

Ans. $6.8°F$; $68°F$; $140°F$; $37°C$; $-25°C$; $280°C$

3. What is the approximate temperature of a healthy person in degrees centigrade?

4. Calculate the temperature at which the readings of a Fahrenheit and a centigrade thermometer are the same.   *Ans.* $-40°$

5. A temperature interval of $25°$ on the centigrade scale is equal to what interval on the Fahrenheit scale?

6. A thermometer with an arbitrary scale of equal divisions registers $-20°$ at the ice point and $+90°$ at the steam point. Compute (*a*) the centigrade temperature corresponding to $50°$ on this thermometer (*b*) the Fahrenheit temperature corresponding to a reading of $-10°$ on this thermometer.

Ans. $64°C$; $48°F$

7. On a temperature scale proposed by Andreas Celsius in 1742, the 0 reading referred to the boiling point of water and the 100 reading to the temperature of melting ice. Convert a temperature of $68°F$ to this Celsius scale.

8. On a hypothetical temperature scale X, the ice point is assigned the reading $40°$ and the steam point $160°$. For another scale Y, the assigned values are $-20°$ and $180°$, respectively. Convert a reading of $20°X$ to the Y scale.

Ans. $-53°Y$

9. An iron steampipe joins two points 100 m apart. The temperature of the pipe varies between -20 and $+180°C$. If the linear expansivity of the iron is 12×10^{-6} per C°, what must be the range of motion of an expansion joint to be placed in the line?

10. The lower end of a vertical steampipe 50 ft long is supported rigidly by a hanger attached to the basement ceiling. When the pipe is at $40°F$, a steam radiator attached rigidly to the upper end of the pipe rests on the attic floor. Find the distance the radiator is lifted off the floor when the iron steampipe is at $220°F$.   *Ans.* 0.72 in.

11. A steel bridge is 200 ft long at $0°C$. The temperature has an annual variation from -25 to $45°C$. What is the difference in length of the bridge at these two temperature extremes?

12. The brass scale of a mercury barometer gives the correct length of the mercury column at $0°C$. If the barometer reads 740 mm at $25°C$, what is the reading when corrected for expansion of the brass scale and the expansion of the mercury (which decreases its density)? The volume expansivity of mercury is 1.82×10^{-4} per C° and the linear expansivity of brass is 1.84×10^{-5} per C°.

Ans. 737 mm

13. An aluminum piston whose diameter is 3.000 in. at $0°C$ is placed in a steel cylinder. The clearance (difference in radii) at this temperature is 0.0050 in. At what temperature of the piston and cylinder would the clearance be zero? The linear expansivity of steel is 12×10^{-6} per C°, of aluminum 24×10^{-6} per C°.

14. A wheel is 3.000 ft in circumference. An iron tire measures 2.992 ft around its inner face. How much must the temperature of the tire be raised in order that it may just slip onto the wheel?   *Ans.* $\bar{2}00$ C°

15. Measurements are made at $25°C$ upon a brass tube by a steel scale correct at 0°C. The result is 645.00 cm. Find the length that would have been obtained if the tube and scale had been at 0°C.

16. A steel tape correct at 0°C is used to measure land when the temperature is 25°C. What percentage error will result in length measurements due to the expansion of the tape?   *Ans.* 0.028%

17. The ends of a 2.00-ft steel rod having a cross section of 1.00 in.^{2} are clamped to rigid supports when the rod is at 212°F. If the rod is allowed to cool to 92°F without shortening, what will be the tension in the rod? Young's modulus for steel is 30×10^6 lb/in.^{2} and its linear expansivity is 6.1×10^{-6} per F°.

18. A steel rod at 25°C is clamped in a vise. The rod is subjected to a compressive stress of 5400 lb/in.^{2} To what temperature must the rod be brought in order that the stress be reduced to zero? Assume distance between jaws of vise remains constant. Young's modulus for steel is 30×10^6 lb/in.^{2} Its linear expansivity. is 12×10^{-6} per C°.   *Ans.* 10°C

19. A thin brass sheet at 10°C has the same surface area as a thin steel sheet at 20°C. At what common temperature, if any, will the two sheets have the same area? The linear expansivities are, for steel 12×10^{-6} per C° and for brass 20×10^{-6} per C°.

20. A vertical cylindrical glass tube 100 cm long is closed at its lower end. To what height must it be filled with mercury in order that the volume of the tube above the mercury shall remain constant as the temperature changes? For the glass, $\alpha = 8.0 \times 10^{-6}$ per C°, for mercury $\beta = 182 \times 10^{-6}$ per C°.
                                                                   Ans. 13 cm

21. In an incandescent lamp, the lead-in wires consist of a copper sleeve soldered to a nickel-steel core. The linear expansivities are 16.6×10^{-6} per C° and 5.9×10^{-6} per C°, respectively. The lamp-stem glass has an expansivity of 9.2×10^{-6} per C°; each figure is an average for the range from 0 to 300°C. What is the expected ratio of core diameter to wire diameter so that the lead-in wire shall have the same radial expansivity as the glass? (Disregard any effects that might arise if the copper and steel did not expand freely along the length of the wire.)

22. A thin-walled aluminum hoop is to be swung from a pivot at its circumference during a change in temperature. Calculate the percentage change in its moment of inertia per centigrade degree rise in temperature, at a temperature of 20°C.   *Ans.* 0.0044%

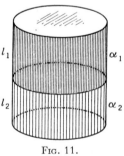

Fig. 11.

23. A cylindrical container is constructed of two parts, as shown. The linear expansivity of the top and bottom sections are α_1 and α_2, respectively. The container is filled to the brim with a liquid of volume expansivity β. Deduce an equation that gives the amount of liquid overflowing if the vessel is heated.

24. A 50-gal steel drum is filled with gasoline when the temperature is 50°F. How much of the gasoline will overflow when the temperature becomes 110°F? The linear expansivity of steel is 10×10^{-6} per C°; the volume expansivity of gasoline is 0.00096 per C°.   *Ans.* 1.6 gal

25. A gas occupies 200 cm³ at 100°C. Find its volume at 0°C, assuming constant pressure.

26. A tire gage registers 32 lb/in.² when air in a certain tire is at 10°C. After running for a time the tire heats up to 30°C. Calculate the pressure that would be registered then by the gage.   *Ans.* 35 lb/in.²

27. The volume expansivity of air at atmospheric pressure is 0.0037 per C°. What volume would 10 cm³ of air at 0°C occupy at 100°C? at −100°C? at 200°C?

28. On a hot day, temperature 35°C, the tires on a car are inflated to a pressure of 30 lb/in.² What will be the pressure of the air in the tires in the evening when the temperature drops 20 C°?   *Ans.* 28 lb/in.²

29. A gas occupies 2.0 ft³ under a pressure of 30 in. of mercury. What volume will it occupy under 25 in. of mercury pressure? Assume that the temperature is unchanged.

30. A gas occupies 50 cm³ at 100°C. Find its volume at 20.0°C, assuming constant pressure.   *Ans.* 39 cm³

31. Given 200 cm³ of oxygen at 5°C and 76 cm of mercury pressure, find its volume at 30°C and 80 cm of mercury pressure.

32. A cylinder is sealed at one end and is closed at the other end by a piston. A volume of 2.0 ft³ of dry air trapped in the cylinder exerts a pressure (absolute) of 15 lb/in.² when the temperature is 68°F. The piston compresses the air to a volume of 0.20 ft³ and the temperature rises momentarily to 180°F and then slowly decreases to 68°F. (*a*) What pressure does the air exert when the temperature has returned to 68°F? (*b*) What is the approximate value of the maximum pressure attained?   *Ans.* 1̄50 lb/in.²; 1̄80 lb/in.²

33. The volume of a tire is 1500 in.³ when the pressure is 30 lb/in.² above atmospheric pressure. What volume will this air occupy at atmospheric pressure (15 lb/in.²)? How much air will come out of the tire when the valve is removed?

34. Compare the densities of the air at the bottom and the top of a mine shaft when the temperatures and pressures are, respectively, 5°C and 31 in. of mercury at the bottom and 20°C and 30 in. of mercury at the top.

Ans. $\rho_b/\rho_t = 1.09$

35. A mass of gas has a volume of 6.0 ft³ at 40°C and 76 cm of mercury pressure. Find its volume at −15°C and 57 cm of mercury pressure.

36. The density of oxygen is 1.43 gm/liter at 0°C and a pressure of 1.0 atm. If a 20-liter cylinder is filled with oxygen at a pressure of 25 atm and temperature 27°C, what is the mass of oxygen in the cylinder?   *Ans.* 6̄50 gm

37. The pressure of the gas in a gas thermometer is 76.5 cm of mercury at 27.0°C. By how much will the pressure increase when the temperature rises 1.0 C°?

38. An oxygen tank is filled with oxygen at an absolute pressure of 1000 lb/in.² at 17°C. The internal volume of the tank is 1.00 ft³. The oxygen is used in high-altitude flying at an absolute pressure of 10 lb/in.² and temperature −27°C. How many cubic feet of oxygen can be supplied by the tank under these conditions?   *Ans.* 84 ft³

39. The temperature of air supplied to a furnace is increased from 27 to 77°C.

If the mass of oxygen in each cubic foot of air supplied is to remain the same, by what per cent must the pressure of the air be changed?   *Ans.* Increased 17%

40. (*a*) Express the boiling point of oxygen, $-183°C$, on the Kelvin scale and on the Rankine scale. (*b*) What is the melting point of silver, 961°C, on each of these scales?   *Ans.* 90°K; 162°R; 1234°K; 2221°R

41. (*a*) Change 40°C and $-5°C$ to the Kelvin scale. (*b*) Change $-45°F$ and 50°F to the Rankine scale.

20. *Heat Quantities*

After the concept of temperature became understood, there were many years of scientific development before the real nature of *heat* was established. Even today there are many people who do not carefully observe the distinction between these important technical terms. It was early recognized that a temperature difference between two objects results in a flow of heat when they are placed in thermal contact. The real nature of the "thing" that flows under such circumstances was not clearly identified until about 1840. This development depended on the *measurement* of heat quantities.

20-1. Meaning of Heat. To raise the temperature of an object, it is necessary either to add heat to it from some source at a higher temperature or to do work on it. It is possible to warm your hands by rubbing them together. The work done against friction is transformed into heat and raises the surface temperature of the hands. When a wire is broken by bending it back and forth rapidly, some of the work is transformed into heat and the wire gets hot. When a nail is pulled out of a board, work is needed because of the friction between the wood and the nail. The work produces heat, which warms the wood and the nail. Pumping up an automobile tire with a hand pump takes work. Some of this work produces heat, which warms the pump, tire, and air. *Heat is a form of energy* that molecules

of matter possess because of their motion. Heat must not be confused with temperature, which determines the direction of transfer of heat.

Suppose we dip a pail of water from the ocean. Its temperature is the same as that of the ocean, but the amount of heat (energy) in the pail of water is infinitesimal compared with the amount in the ocean. Heat may be measured in terms of any unit that can be used to measure energy, such as the joule or the kilowatt-hour. Historically, however, heat quantities have been measured in calories or British thermal units, whose definitions were suggested by early experiments involving heat. Temperature must be measured in terms of an independently established standard.

20-2. Units of Heat. One effect of the addition of heat to water, or any other substance, is a rise of temperature. The amount of heat necessary to raise the temperature of one pound of water one degree Fahrenheit is nearly constant throughout the interval between 32 and 212°F. This fact suggests a convenient unit to use in measuring heat. It is called the *British thermal unit* (Btu) and is the amount of heat needed to raise the temperature of one pound of water one Fahrenheit degree.

In the metric system the corresponding unit of heat is called a *calorie*. The calorie is the heat necessary to raise the temperature of one gram of water one centigrade degree. One Btu is equivalent to approximately 252 calories.

The mks unit of heat is the *kilocalorie* (kcal), or kilogram-calorie,[1] the amount of heat necessary to raise the temperature of one kilogram of water one centigrade degree.

Since the amount of heat required to raise the temperature of unit mass of water one degree is not quite constant throughout the temperature range, the definitions of the Btu and the calorie may be regarded as the average values in the region from freezing to boiling.

20-3. Specific Heat. The heat needed to change the temperature of unit mass of a substance one degree is a characteristic of that substance. The *specific heat*[2] of a substance is defined as the heat per unit mass per degree change in temperature

$$c = \frac{Q}{m \, \Delta t} \qquad (1)$$

where c is the specific heat, Q the heat added to the material of mass m, and Δt is its rise in temperature. In the British system[3] the specific heat is expressed in British thermal units per pound per Fahrenheit degree, and in the metric system in calories per gram per centigrade degree. Because of the way the Btu and the calorie are defined, the specific heat of a substance in metric units is the same numerically as that expressed in the British system. This means, for example, that the specific heat of salt, which is 0.204 Btu/lb F°,

---

[1] Nutritionists, in discussing food metabolism, use the term "Calorie" (often capitalized to distinguish it from the "small calorie") for what we have defined as the kilocalorie. Their statement that "there are 63 Calories in a slice of white bread" means that about 63 kilocalories will be liberated when the dried sample of bread is completely burned in an atmosphere of oxygen in a calorimeter.

[2] Some authors call this quantity the *thermal capacity* of the substance and define specific heat as the ratio of the thermal capacity of the substance to that of water.

[3] Note that in the British system the m of Eq. (1) is replaced by *weight*.

is also 0.204 cal/gm C°. Water has a specific heat much larger than that of most common materials.

TABLE 1. SPECIFIC HEATS

Substance	cal/gm C° or Btu/lb F°
Alcohol	0.60
Aluminum	0.212
Brass	0.090
Carbon (graphite)	0.160
Copper	0.092
Ethylene glycol (Prestone)	0.528
Glass (soda)	0.16
Gold	0.0316
Hydrogen (at 15°C, constant pressure)	3.389
Ice	0.51
Iron	0.117
Lead	0.030
Mercury	0.033
Silver	0.056
Water (by definition)	1.00
Water vapor (at 100°C, constant pressure)	0.482
Zinc	0.093

Knowing the specific heat c of a material, one can calculate the heat Q necessary to change the temperature of a mass m from an initial value t_i to a final value t_f from the relation

$$Q = mc(t_f - t_i) \qquad (1a)$$

Example: How much heat is necessary to raise the temperature of 2.5 lb of alcohol from room temperature (68°F) to its boiling point (173°F)?

$$Q = (2.5 \text{ lb})(0.60 \text{ Btu/lb F°})(173°F - 68°F)$$
$$= 160 \text{ Btu}$$

20-4. Method of Mixtures. The experimental determination of the specific heat of a metal by the method of mixtures consists essentially of adding a known mass of metal at a known high temperature to a known mass of water at a known low temperature and determining the equilibrium temperature that results. The heat absorbed by the water and containing vessel can be equated to the heat given up by the hot metal. From this equation the unknown specific heat can be computed.

$$\text{Heat lost} = \text{heat gained} \qquad (2)$$

The heat lost by the warm object is $m_x c_x \Delta t_x$, where m_x is the mass of the object, c_x the specific heat of the object, and Δt_x the change in its temperature. The heat gained by the container and water will be $m_c c_c \Delta t_c + m_w c_w \Delta t_w$, where m_c and c_c are the mass and specific heat of the container, and m_w and c_w are the mass and specific heat of the water in the container. The temperature change Δt_c refers to the container, and Δt_w is the change in the temperature of the water. To minimize the exchange of heat with the surroundings, a double-walled vessel (Fig. 1) is usually used in calorimetric experiments. Such a container is called a calorimeter.

Example: When 2.00 lb of brass at 212°F are dropped into 5.00 lb of water at 35.0°F, the resulting temperature is 41.2°F. Find the specific heat of brass.

Heat lost by brass = heat gained by water
$$m_B c_B \, \Delta t_B = m_w c_w \, \Delta t_w$$
$$(2.00 \text{ lb}) c_B (212°F - 41.2°F) = (5.00 \text{ lb})$$
$$\times (1.00 \text{ Btu/lb F°})(41.2°F - 35.0°F)$$
$$c_B = \frac{(5.00 \text{ lb})(1.00 \text{ Btu/lb F°})(41.2°F - 35.0°F)}{(2.00 \text{ lb})(212°F - 41.2°F)}$$
$$= 0.091 \text{ Btu/lb F°}$$

Example: Eighty grams of iron shot at 100.0°C are dropped into 200 gm of water at 20.0°C contained in an iron vessel of mass 50 gm. Find the resulting temperature.

In this mixture heat is lost by the shot and heat is gained by the water and its container.

Heat lost by shot = heat gained by water
$$+ \text{ heat gained by vessel}$$
$$(80 \text{ gm})(0.12 \text{ cal/gm C°})(100.0°C - t)$$
$$= (200 \text{ gm})(1.00 \text{ cal/gm C°})(t - 20.0°C)$$
$$+ (50 \text{ gm})(0.12 \text{ cal/gm C°})(t - 20.0°C)$$
$$t = 24°C$$

20-5. Change of State. Not all the heat that an object receives necessarily raises its temperature. Surprisingly large amounts of energy are needed to do the work of separating the molecules when solids change to liquids and liquids change to gases. Water will serve as a familiar example. The solid phase of water is ice. Ice has a specific heat of about 0.5 cal/gm C°. Water has a specific heat of 1 cal/gm C°.

To raise the temperature of 1 gm of ice from −1 to 0°C requires ½ cal of heat energy. To raise the temperature of 1 gm of water in the liquid phase from 0 to 1°C requires 1 cal. To melt a gram of ice requires 80 cal, although the temperature does not change while this large amount of heat is being added. The heat per unit mass needed to

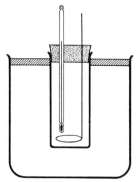

FIG. 1. Double-walled calorimeter.

change a substance from the solid to the liquid state at its melting temperature is called the *heat of fusion*.

$$L_f = \frac{Q}{m} \tag{3}$$

The heat of fusion L_f is expressed in Btu per pound or in calories per gram. The heat of fusion of ice is about 144 Btu/lb, or 80 cal/gm. Whereas specific heats are numerically the same in British and metric units, the numerical value of a heat of fusion in the metric system is ⅝ that in the British system.

20-6. Heat of Vaporization. Once a gram of ice is melted, 100 cal are required to raise the temperature of the gram of water from the melting point to the boiling point. As we continue to add heat at the boiling point, the temperature remains the same until the liquid is changed entirely to vapor. The steps by which a gram of ice is heated through fusion and vaporization are shown to scale in Fig. 2. The amount of heat per unit mass necessary to change a liquid from the liquid

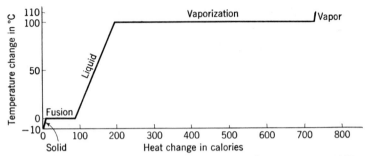

Fig. 2. Heat required to change 1 gm of ice at $-10°C$ to steam at $110°C$.

to the vapor phase without changing the temperature is called the *heat of vaporization.*

$$L_v = \frac{Q}{m} \qquad (4)$$

The heat of vaporization is usually measured at the normal boiling point of a liquid. But occasionally L_v is measured under other conditions of temperature and pressure, and its value depends on those conditions. For water the heat of vaporization L_v is approximately 540 cal/gm, or 970 Btu/lb. This is over five times as much energy as is needed to heat water from the melting to the boiling point. Where this energy goes in a change of state may be better understood if we think of the liquid as made up of a myriad of molecules packed closely but rather irregularly, compared to the neat arrangement in the crystals that make up the solid. One gram of water occupies 1 cm³ of space as a liquid. The same amount of water (and therefore the same number of molecules) in the vapor state at 1 atm of pressure and a temperature of 100°C fills 1671 cm³ instead of 1 cm³. The work to vaporize the water has been done in performing external work against the atmosphere and in separating the molecules to much larger distances than in the liquid state.

Example: How much heat is required to change 50 lb of ice at 15°F to steam at 212°F?

Heat to raise temperature of ice to its melting point
$$= (50 \text{ lb})(0.51 \text{ Btu/lb F°})(32°F - 15°F)$$
$$= 4\bar{3}0 \text{ Btu}$$
Heat to melt ice = $(50 \text{ lb})(144 \text{ Btu/lb})$
$$= 7\bar{2}00 \text{ Btu}$$

Heat to warm water to its boiling point
$$= (50 \text{ lb})(1.0 \text{ Btu/lb F°})(212°F - 32°F)$$
$$= 9\bar{0}00 \text{ Btu}$$
Heat to vaporize water = $(50 \text{ lb})(970 \text{ Btu/lb})$
$$= 4\bar{8},000 \text{ Btu}$$

Total heat required:

$$Q = (4\bar{3}0 + 7\bar{2}00 + 9\bar{0}00 + 4\bar{8},000) \text{ Btu}$$
$$= 6\bar{4},000 \text{ Btu}$$

Note that in this summation the $4\bar{3}0$ is negligible and may be disregarded, since there is a doubtful figure in the thousands place in $4\bar{8},000$.

20-7. Measurement of Heat of Fusion. Heats of fusion and vaporization, like specific heats, are determined by calorimetric experiments. The only change needed in Eq. (2) is the addition of a term giving the amount of heat required to change the state.

Example: When 150 gm of ice at 0°C are mixed with 300 gm of water at 50.0°C the resulting temperature is 6.7°C. Calculate the heat of fusion of ice.

The heat gained by the ice will be the heat to melt it (it is at 0°C when put into the calorimeter), plus the heat to warm it to the final temperature once it is all melted. This is

$$Q_g = m_i L_i + m_i c_w (t_f - 0)$$

where Q_g represents heat gained by the mass m_i of melting ice whose heat of fusion L_i is to be measured, c_w is the specific heat of the water which was ice before it melted, and t_f is the final temperature. The heat lost by the calorimeter (considered negligible) and the water in it will be

$$Q_l = m_c c_c \, \Delta t_c + m_w c_w \, \Delta t_w$$

where the symbols have meanings analogous to those following Eq. (2).

Heat lost by water
= $(300 \text{ gm})(1.00 \text{ cal/gm C}°)(50.0°C - 6.7°C)$
= $13,\bar{0}00$ cal

Heat to melt ice = $(150 \text{ gm})L_i$

Heat to raise temperature of ice water to final temperature
= $(150 \text{ gm})(1.00 \text{ cal/gm C}°)(6.7°C - 0°C)$
= $1\bar{0}00$ cal

Heat lost = heat gained
$13,\bar{0}00 \text{ cal} = (150 \text{ gm})L_i + 1\bar{0}00 \text{ cal}$
$L_i = 80.0 \text{ cal/gm}$

Any method of mixtures problem may be solved by choosing at will some standard state and then calculating the heat that would be gained or lost by each material in going from its initial condition to the standard state.

Example: If 150 gm of ice at 0°C are added to 200 gm of water in a 100-gm aluminum cup at 30°C, what is the resulting temperature?

Here let us choose water at 0°C as the standard state. Next compare the heat gained by the ice in going to the standard state with the heat lost by the water and cup in cooling to 0°C.

Heat gained by ice in melting
= $(150 \text{ gm})(80.0 \text{ cal/gm}) = 12,\bar{0}00$ cal
Heat lost by cup
= $(100 \text{ gm})(0.212 \text{ cal/gm C}°)(30°C - 0°C)$
= $6\bar{4}0$ cal
Heat lost by water
= $(200 \text{ gm})(1.0 \text{ cal/gm C}°)(30°C - 0°C)$
= $6\bar{0}00$ cal

Since the melting of *all* the ice would require more heat ($12,\bar{0}00$ cal) than that available from the water and cup ($6\bar{6}00$ cal), not all the ice will melt. The final temperature will then be 0°C. The amount of ice remaining is given by

$$m = \frac{(12,\bar{0}00 - 6\bar{6}00) \text{ cal}}{80.0 \text{ cal/gm}} = 67 \text{ gm}$$

20-8. Vaporization. *Vaporization* is the change of a substance into the state of a vapor or a gas. Vaporization may occur in three ways. When a liquid is confined in a closed vessel an equilibrium state is reached: molecules are continually leaving the surface of the liquid and forming a vapor; the vapor molecules are continually striking the liquid surface and entering it again. When the number of molecules leaving the liquid surface equals the number returning in the same time, the vapor is said to be *saturated*. The pressure of the saturated vapor is called the vapor pressure; it is characteristic of the substance and the temperature but independent of the volume of the vapor.

Evaporation is the vaporization of a liquid at its surface only. This proceeds without visible disturbance. Liquids left in uncovered dishes generally disappear in time by evaporation. The rate of evaporation depends on the material and such factors as the temperature, the surface area, amount of ventilation, and the pressure exerted on the surface. Evaporation is a cooling process, since it is the more energetic molecules that are able to escape from the liquid. Rapid evaporation may cool the remaining liquid enough to freeze it.

Boiling is the vaporization of a liquid in bubbles in the body of the liquid as well as at the free surface. It is accompanied by agitation of the liquid as the bubbles rise, expand, and burst. The boiling point of a liquid is the temperature at which its vapor pressure is equal to the pressure exerted on the liquid. The temperature at which a liquid boils at standard pressure, 76.0 cm of mercury, is called its normal boiling point.

Sublimation is the changing of a solid directly into a vapor without passing through a liquid state. Clothes hung to dry on a cold day may freeze and then dry. Solid carbon dioxide sublimes without wetting its container; hence its trade name "dry ice." The odor of solid camphor and naphthalene (moth balls) is evidence that they sublime at room temperature.

20-9. The Effect of Pressure on a Change of State. It is a familiar fact that at high altitudes where the atmospheric pressure is reduced water boils at temperatures lower than at sea level. On the other hand, if the pressure on the liquid surface is increased in a steam boiler or in a pressure cooker, boiling occurs at temperatures higher than the normal boiling point. Boiling can be brought about either by increasing the temperature of a liquid until its vapor pressure is equal to the pressure on the liquid, or by reducing the pressure on the liquid to the value of the saturated vapor pressure. The vaporization curve of Fig. 3 represents conditions of equilibrium between the liquid and vapor states of water.

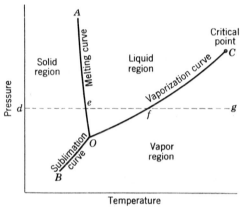

FIG. 3. Triple-point diagram for a substance such as water. (Not drawn to scale.)

The vaporization of water results in a large increase in the volume occupied by the molecules. An increase in pressure therefore raises the boiling point. Water can be boiled under reduced pressure at temperatures less than 100°C, as suggested by curve OC in Fig. 3.

The freezing of a liquid is accompanied by a change of volume, although this change is much smaller than that which occurs on vaporization. For the few substances which, like water, expand on freezing, an increase in pressure lowers the freezing point. The line OA in Fig. 3 is the fusion curve for water. Each point on it represents a pressure and a temperature at which ice and water can exist together in equilibrium, the relative amounts of each remaining the same if no heat is added or removed.

In ice skating or skiing a layer of ice or snow is melted even though the temperature is below 0°C owing to the momentary increase in pressure. The water film lubricates the skate or ski and refreezes as soon as the pressure is reduced, since its temperature is below 0°C. This process is called *regelation*.

20-10. Triple Point. Three cases of equilibrium have been discussed, those between liquid and vapor, between solid and liquid, and between solid and vapor. In each case the temperature of equilibrium depends on the pressure. This dependence can be represented conveniently in an equilibrium graph in which the coordinates of the points plotted represent temperatures and the corresponding pressures for equilibrium between two states of the substance.

In Fig. 3, the equilibrium curve OC shows the raising of the boiling point of the substance with increase of pressure. Curve BO shows the raising of the sublimation point with increase of pressure. Curve OA is typical of a substance, which, like water, expands on freezing, and shows for such a substance the lowering of the melting point with increase of pressure.

It can be shown that for any substance the three equilibrium curves intersect at a common point, O in Fig. 3, called the *triple point*, at which conditions of temperature and pressure the three phases, solid, liquid, and saturated vapor, can exist together in equilibrium. For water the triple point is at 0.0075°C and 4.62 mm of mercury pressure. If these conditions are changed, one of the phases will disappear. If the temperature is raised, for example, the ice will melt and the state of the system (water and saturated vapor) will be represented by a point on curve OC.

Consider a solid substance kept under constant pressure while its temperature is gradually increased. At each temperature its state will be represented by a point on the line dg in Fig. 3. The substance will remain solid from d to e. At e, which represents the melting temperature, the solid substance can exist in equilibrium with the liquid. From e to f the substance will be in the form of liquid. At f the liquid and saturated vapor can exist together. This is the boiling point for the substance at the pressure chosen. At higher temperatures, along fg, the vapor will be superheated and no longer saturated.

20-11. Critical Point. An instructive experiment can be performed, with suitable precautions, using a strong glass tube in which liquid carbon dioxide and carbon dioxide vapor have been sealed. As the tube is slowly heated, the meniscus (liquid-vapor boundary) can be observed to remain practically stationary, becoming flatter as the temperature increases. At 31°C the meniscus vanishes. The density of the liquid has decreased with rising temperature and the density of the vapor has increased, until they became equal at 31°C. The temperature at which the liquid and vapor densities of a substance become equal is called its *critical temperature*. The pressure of the saturated vapor at this temperature is called the *critical pressure*.

A vapor kept above its critical temperature will never form a meniscus, that is, it will never liquefy no matter how greatly it is compressed. Above the critical temperature and under high pressure the vapor may become as dense and as incompressible as the liquid at lower temperatures. The vaporization curve OC of Fig. 3 or Fig. 4 *terminates* at the critical point C. For water the critical point is at 374°C and 218 atm pressure.

When a substance in the gaseous state is below its critical temperature it is called a *vapor;* when above that temperature it is called a gas. Only gases well above the critical temperature obey the gas laws. Near the critical temperature there are marked departures from the gas laws. For saturated vapors the pressure is independent of volume.

20-12. Humidity. At all times water is present in the atmosphere in one or more of its physical forms—solid, liquid, and vapor. The invisible vapor is always present in amounts that vary over a wide range while

water drops (rain or cloud) or ice crystals (snow or cloud) are usually present.

If a shallow pan of water is allowed to stand uncovered in a large room, the liquid will soon disappear although the water will still be present as invisible vapor. If a similar pan of water is placed in a small enclosure, evaporation begins as before but after a time stops or becomes very slow and droplets begin to condense on the walls of the enclosure. The air is said to be *saturated*. When this condition

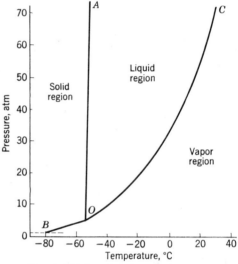

FIG. 4. Triple-point diagram for CO_2.

has been reached, the addition of more water vapor merely results in the condensation of an equal amount. The amount of water vapor required for saturation depends upon the temperature (Table 2); the higher the temperature, the greater is the amount of water vapor required to produce saturation. If the air is not saturated, it can be made so either by adding more water vapor or by reducing the temperature until that already present will produce saturation. The temperature to which the air must be cooled, at constant pressure, to produce saturation is called the *dew point*. If a glass of water collects moisture on the outside, its temperature is below the dew point.

When the temperature of the air is reduced

to the dew point, condensation takes place if there are present nuclei on which droplets may form. These may be tiny salt crystals, smoke particles, or other particles that readily take up water. In the open air such particles

TABLE 2. SATURATED WATER VAPOR

Showing pressure P and density ρ of aqueous vapor saturated at temperature t; or showing boiling point t of water and density ρ of steam corresponding to a pressure P.

t, °C	P, mm of mercury	ρ, gm/cm³
−10	2.0	2.2×10^{-6}
−5	3.0	3.3
0	4.6	4.9
5	6.5	6.8
10	9.2	9.4
12	10.5	10.7
14	12.0	12.1
16	13.6	13.6
18	15.5	15.6
20	17.6	17.3
22	19.8	19.4
24	22.4	21.8
26	25.2	24.4
30	31.8	30.4
40	55.1	51.1
50	92.3	83.2
60	149.2	130.5
70	233.5	198.4
80	355.1	298.8
90	525.8	424.1
95	634.0	505
96	657.7	523
97	682.1	541
98	707.3	560
99.0	733.3	579
100.0	760.0	598
101	787.5	618
102	815.9	639
110	1074.5	827
120	1489	1122
200	11,650	7840

are almost always present. In a closed space where such particles are not present, the temperature may be reduced below the dew point without consequent condensation. The air is then said to be *supersaturated*.

In a mixture of gases, such as air, the pressure exerted by the gas is the sum of the partial pressures exerted by the individual gases. The portion of the atmospheric pressure due to water vapor is called its *vapor pressure*. When the air is saturated, the pressure exerted by the water vapor is the *saturated vapor pressure*.

The mass of water vapor per unit volume of air is called the *absolute humidity*. It is commonly expressed in grains per cubic foot or in grams per cubic meter. *Specific humidity* is the mass of water vapor per unit mass of air and is expressed in grams per kilogram, grains per pound, etc. Specific humidity is more useful since it remains constant when pressure and temperature change, while the absolute humidity varies because of the change in volume of the air involved.

20-13. Relative Humidity. *Relative humidity* is defined as the ratio of the actual vapor pressure to the saturated vapor pressure at that temperature. It is commonly expressed as a percentage. At the dew point the relative humidity is 100 per cent. From a knowledge of the temperature and dew point the relative humidity can be readily determined by the use of the table of vapor pressures.

Example: In a weather report the temperature is given as 68°F and the dew point 50°F. What is the relative humidity?

To use Table 2, we must change the temperatures to the centigrade scale.

$$C = \tfrac{5}{9}(F - 32°)$$
$$C_1 = \tfrac{5}{9}(68° - 32°) = \tfrac{5}{9}(36°) = 20°C$$
$$C_2 = \tfrac{5}{9}(50° - 32°) = \tfrac{5}{9}(18°) = 10°C$$

From the table we find the vapor pressures

$P_1 = 17.6$ mm of mercury
$\qquad\qquad$ = pressure of saturated vapor
$P_2 = \;\;9.2$ mm of mercury = actual vapor pressure

$$\text{Relative humidity} = \frac{P_2}{P_1} = \frac{9.2 \text{ mm of mercury}}{17.6 \text{ mm of mercury}}$$
$$= 0.52 = 52\%$$

Whenever the temperature of the air is reduced to the dew point, condensation occurs.

When the dew point is above the freezing point, water droplets are formed; when it is below, ice crystals are formed. The formation of dew, frost, clouds, and fog are examples of this process. The cooling may be caused by contact with a cold surface, by mixing with cold air, or by expansion in rising air.

20-14. Phases of Matter. Among the common materials are many that do not have definite melting points; for example, glass and butter. In a furnace, glass will gradually soften until it flows freely even though at ordinary temperatures it is quite solid. When it is solid it may be thought of as a supercooled liquid; it flows, but very slowly. Since it does not have a definite melting point, it does not have a heat of fusion.

The specific heat of glass changes as the temperature rises. Such changes indicate transitions in the arrangement of the molecules. Specific heat measurements may be used by the ceramic engineer in studying the changes in these products as the temperature is varied.

Many materials decompose at high temperatures and therefore do not exist in liquid and gaseous states. Some may exist in the liquid state but decompose before reaching the gaseous state.

Since the chemical elements cannot be decomposed by heating, they are all capable of existing in the solid, liquid, and gaseous states. Many of them have more than one solid state, as in the case of phosphorus, which is known in three solid phases: black, formed at very high pressures, and the more familiar red and yellow forms. Powdered sulfur results from a direct transition of sulfur vapor to the solid state. If this powder is melted and then cooled, it solidifies normally.

SUMMARY

Heat is a form of energy.

The most commonly used units of heat are the *calorie* and the *British thermal unit.*

The *calorie* is the amount of heat required to change the temperature of 1 gm of water 1 C°.

The *British thermal unit* is the amount of heat required to change the temperature of 1 lb of water 1 F°.

The *specific heat* of a substance is the heat per unit mass per degree required to change the temperature of the substance (Units: cal/gm C° or Btu/lb F°).

The specific heat of water varies so slightly with temperature that for most purposes it can be assumed constant (1 cal/gm C°) between 0 and 100°C.

The heat lost or gained by a body when the temperature changes is given by the equation

$$Q = mc \, \Delta t$$

In a *calorimeter* the heat lost by the hot bodies is equal to the heat gained by the cold bodies.

The *heat of fusion* is the heat per unit mass required to change a substance from solid to liquid at its melting point.

The heat of fusion of ice is approximately 80 cal/gm, or 144 Btu/lb.

The *heat of vaporization* is the heat per unit mass required to change a substance from liquid to vapor.

The heat of vaporization of water at its normal boiling point is approximately 540 cal/gm, or 970 Btu/lb. It depends on the temperature at which vaporization takes place.

The boiling point of a liquid is the temperature at which its vapor pressure is equal to the pressure exerted on the liquid.

The boiling point of a liquid is raised by an increase in pressure.

The freezing point of water and of the few other materials which expand on freezing is lowered by an increase in pressure. The freezing point of substances which contract on freezing is raised by an increase in pressure.

The *triple point* is the condition of pressure and temperature at which the three phases can coexist in equilibrium.

The *critical point* is the condition of pressure and temperature at which a liquid and its vapor are indistinguishable. The critical temperature is the highest temperature at which a gas can be liquefied by pressure alone.

Absolute humidity is the mass of water vapor per unit volume of air. *Specific humidity* is the mass of water vapor per unit mass of air.

Relative humidity is defined as the ratio of the actual vapor pressure to the saturated vapor pressure at that temperature.

The *dew point* is the temperature to which the air must be cooled, at constant pressure, to produce saturation.

QUESTIONS

1. What is the distinction between quantity of heat and temperature?

2. What is the experimental evidence for considering heat to be a form of energy? To what general principle does this lead?

3. What is the physical distinction between a solid, a liquid, and a gas? What is the distinction between a vapor and a gas?

4. Which produces a more severe burn, boiling water or steam? Why?

5. Which would be liable to explode with greater violence, a high-pressure steam boiler or a tank containing air at the same pressure? Why?

6. At how low a temperature can water be made to boil?

7. What value would you expect to find approximately for the heat of vaporization of water at 0°C?

8. A tall vertical pipe is closed at the bottom, filled with water, and heated at the bottom by a bunsen burner. Water and steam erupt from the tube as from a geyser. Explain.

9. One sometimes places a tub of water in a fruit storage room to keep the temperature above 30°F during a cold night. Explain.

10. Assume that to determine the temperature of a bunsen flame in the laboratory you heat an iron washer in the flame and then drop the washer into water. (*a*) List the measurements you would make. (*b*) What physical constants would you look up before calculating? (*c*) Assign symbols to items in (*a*) and (*b*) and write the equation from which you would calculate the temperature *t*. (*d*) Would you expect the temperature determination to be accurate? Explain, briefly.

11. Why should foundation walls extend below the frost line?

12. In terms of molecular theory what happens when a liquid is evaporating? Why is a liquid cooled by evaporation?

13. A piece of blotting paper is placed in a beaker of ether with part of the blotter protruding over the edge of the beaker. Soon "frost" is noticed on the protruding portion of the blotter. Explain.

14. How is regelation involved in the motion of a glacier?

15. Why do water pipes occasionally burst in winter?

16. The temperature at the bottom of deep bodies of water is nearly constant. What temperature would you expect to find at the bottom of Lake Erie? Explain.

17. What condition must be satisfied before a gas may be liquefied by pressure?

18. In a heating system that circulates hot air in a house, it is usually desirable to add moisture to the air. Explain why this is necessary.

19. What precisely is the dew point and what does it indicate? Is the dew point a fixed point in the sense that the freezing point is?

PROBLEMS

1. How much heat is required to raise the temperature of 500 lb of iron from 32°F to 212°F?

2. A cylindrical water tank 3.0 m in diameter is filled with water to a depth of 4.5 m. What will be the rise in temperature per hour if 1.5 cal/sec enter through each square centimeter of the bottom? Neglect the heat supplied to the tank itself.   *Ans.* 12 C°/hr

3. If 1000 liters of air at 27°C and pressure of 1.0 atm have a mass of 1115 gm and have a specific heat at constant pressure of 0.24 cal/gm C°, how much heat is required to raise the temperature of this gas from 27 to 177°C at constant pressure?

4. How much heat is required to raise the temperature of 1.5 lb of water in an 8.0-oz aluminum vessel from 48°F to the boiling point, assuming no loss of heat to the surroundings?   *Ans.* 260 Btu

5. Calculate the amount of energy required to heat the air in a house 30 by 50 by 40 ft from 10 to 70°F. The density of air is about 0.080 lb/ft³ and its specific heat at constant pressure is approximately 0.24 Btu/lb F°. Discuss the assumptions made in your calculations.

6. A 45-gm metal strip has a specific heat of 0.10 cal/gm C° and a linear expansivity of 8.4×10^{-6} per C°. The strip is heated to 200°C and then placed in 40 gm of water which is initially in equilibrium with 4.0 gm of ice in a 50-gm container. When equilibrium is reestablished, the length of the strip L, in terms of its length L_0 at 200°C, is found to be $L = L_0(1 - 1.6 \times 10^{-3})$. Find the specific heat of the container.   *Ans.* 0.19 cal/gm C°

7. A tank of 10.0-ft³ capacity is half filled with glycerin. The weight-density of the glycerin is 78.6 lb/ft³ and its specific heat is 0.57 Btu/lb F°. (*a*) How much heat is needed to raise the temperature of the glycerin from 40 to 70°F? (*b*) If heat is supplied to the glycerin at the rate of 750 Btu/min, at what rate does its temperature rise?

8. A 3.0-lb lead ball at 160°F is dropped into 5.0 lb of oil (specific heat 0.60 Btu/lb F°) at 70°F contained in a 4.0-lb copper vessel. Assuming heat exchanges to be restricted to this system, what temperature will be reached finally by the mixture?   *Ans.* 72°F

9. A 100-lb casting was cooled from 1300°F (red hot) to 200°F by placing it in water whose initial temperature was 50°F. How much water was used? The specific heat of iron is approximately 0.12 Btu/lb F° for this temperature range. What heat effect is neglected in your calculations?

10. There are 100 gm of water in a brass calorimeter of mass 200 gm. It is found that 590 cal are required to raise the temperature of water and container 5.0 C°. What is the specific heat of brass?   *Ans.* 0.090 cal/gm C°

11. When 200 gm of aluminum at 100°C are dropped into an aluminum calorimeter of mass 120 gm and containing 150 gm of kerosene at 15°C, the mixture reaches a temperature of 50°C. What is the specific heat of kerosene?

12. Find the resulting temperature when 80 gm of iron shot at 100.0°C are dropped into 200 gm of water at 20.0°C contained in an iron vessel of mass 50 gm (specific heat 0.12 cal/gm C°).   *Ans.* 24°C

13. A 30-gm piece of ice at -20°C is dropped into a 25.0-gm calorimeter of specific heat 0.20 cal/gm C° containing 100 gm of water at 35.0°C. The final equilibrium temperature, corrected for thermal leakage, is found to be 7.2°C. What is the specific heat of the ice?

14. A 150-gm iron ball at 95°C is dropped into a cavity in a block of ice. The cavity is then found to contain 21.0 gm of water. Calculate the heat of fusion of ice.   *Ans.* 79.4 cal/gm

15. The temperature of a sample of molten lead, near its temperature of solidification, is falling at the rate of 6.0 C°/min. If the lead continues to lose heat at this same rate and takes 35.0 min to solidify completely, what is the heat of fusion of lead? The specific heat of molten lead is 0.030 cal/gm C°.

16. When 1.445 gm of coal are completely burned in a special calorimeter, the temperature of the 2510 gm of water is raised from 74.85 to 82.65°F. (*a*) How much heat is given to the water as a result of the combustion of the coal? (*b*) What is the heat of combustion of the coal?   *Ans.* 10,$\bar{9}$00 cal; 75$\bar{4}$0 cal/gm

17. A 1.0-lb iron ball at 210°F is dropped into a cavity in a block of ice. If it melts 0.14 lb of ice cooling to the temperature of the ice, what is the specific heat of the iron?

18. How much energy must be removed by the refrigerator coils from a 0.50-lb aluminum tray containing 3.0 lb of water at 70°F to freeze all the water, and then to cool the ice to 10°F?   *Ans.* 5$\bar{8}$0 Btu

19. A certain refrigerator contains 2500 gm of water and 5000 gm of food (specific heat 0.90 cal/gm C°). Find the mass of ice required to cool the contents of the refrigerator from 30 to 10°C if the ice water drains out at 0°C.

20. A 2.0-lb aluminum pail contains 20 lb of water at 70°F. What mass of ice at the melting point must be placed in the pail to cool the water to 50°F, assuming the heat exchanges to be limited to pail and its contents?   *Ans.* 2.5 lb

21. Water is heated in a boiler from 100 to 284°F where, under a pressure of 52.4 lb/in.², it boils. The heat of vaporization of water at 284°F is 511.5 cal/gm, or 920.7 Btu/lb. How much heat is required to raise the temperature and to evaporate 500 gal of water?

22. How many calories are needed to change 20.0 gm of water at 25°C to steam at 150°C? Assume the numerical value for the specific heat of steam to be 0.50.   *Ans.* 1$\bar{3}$,000 cal

23. A certain industrial process requires that 40 kg of water per minute have its temperature increased from 10 to 60°C by condensing steam in a coil of copper pipe immersed in the water. If the steam enters the coil at a temperature of 120°C and leaves the coil as water at a temperature of 82°C, how many kilograms of steam must pass into the coil per minute?

24. How many Btu's are needed to change 50 lb of ice at 12°F to steam at 232°F?   *Ans.* 6$\bar{6}$,000 Btu

25. A copper vessel weighing 0.50 lb and containing 2.0 lb of ice, all at a temperature of 20°F, is placed in a calorimeter of negligible heat capacity containing 6.0 lb of water at 70°F. What mass of steam at 212°F would have to be condensed in the calorimeter to heat the mixture to 70°F?

26. In a room where the temperature is 24°C an experiment shows the dew point to be 12°C. What is the relative humidity?   *Ans.* 47%

27. In which case does the air hold more water vapor: (*a*) temperature 32°F, dew point 32°F, or (*b*) temperature 80°F, dew point 50°F? What is the relative humidity in each case?

28. Air at a temperature of 22°C and relative humidity 70% is cooled to 18°C. What is then its relative humidity?   *Ans.* 90%

29. The relative humidity in a certain room is 60% at 20°C. (*a*) Calculate the relative humidity if the temperature drops to 15°C. (*b*) What is then the dew point?

30. What is the value of the relative humidity in a room where the temperature is 26°C and in which dew begins to form on the outside of a pitcher of iced water at a temperature of 10°C?   *Ans.* 37%

31. Calculate the pressure due to dry air when the relative humidity is 85%, the temperature 22°C, and the barometric reading 745.5 mm of mercury.

32. The pressure of saturated water vapor at 23.0°C and 12.0°C is equal to 21.0 and 10.5 mm of mercury, respectively. What is the relative humidity when the temperature is 23.0°C, the dew point is 12.0°C, and the height of mercury in the barometer is 30 in.?   *Ans.* 50%

33. How many pounds of water must be evaporated in an auditorium 50 ft by 20 ft by 100 ft to raise the relative humidity from 20 to 60%, the temperature remaining constant at 70°F? The weight density of saturated water vapor at 70°F is 0.00112 lb/ft³.

34. How many grams of water must be evaporated into a room 20 by 40 by 6.0 m to raise the relative humidity from 10 to 60%, with the temperature constant at 20°C?   *Ans.* 42 kg

35. Outdoor air at 30°C and 90% relative humidity is drawn into an air-conditioning system where it is first chilled to 12°C in a water spray and then allowed to warm to 22°C without the addition of moisture. (*a*) What is the relative humidity of the conditioned air? (*b*) How much moisture is removed from each cubic meter of air treated?

36. An airtight room contains 65 m³ of air at a temperature of 22°C, 760 mm of mercury pressure, and 20% relative humidity. (*a*) What is the dew point in the room? (*b*) How much water must be added to the air of the room to raise the relative humidity to 50%? (*c*) If all the water vapor in the air of the room were removed, what would be the pressure exerted by the air, if the temperature remained at 22°C?   *Ans.* $-2°C$; $3\bar{8}0$ gm; 756 mm of mercury

37. A small drop of water is noticed on top of the mercury column of a barometer at 25°C. (*a*) What correction must be applied to the barometer reading? (*b*) Suppose that 1.0×10^{-5} gm of water had been trapped in the 5.0-cm³ volume above the mercury, what would the correction have been? (*c*) How much would the correction have to be changed for a 1° rise in temperature from 25°C, in each case?

38. An airtight cylinder 300 cm long is divided into two parts by a freely moving, airtight, heat-insulating piston. When the temperatures in the two chambers are equal to 27°C, the piston is located 100 cm from one end of the cylinder. How far will the piston move if the gas in the smaller part of the cylinder is heated to 74°C and the temperature in the larger section remains constant? Assume ideal gas laws hold.   *Ans.* 10 cm

39. Two 5.0-liter flasks are connected by a short tube with a stopcock. First the flasks are evacuated and the stopcock closed. Then helium at 27°C is admitted into one flask until the pressure in that flask rises to 130 mm of mercury. Into the other flask nitrogen is admitted until at 77°C the pressure in that flask is 210 mm of mercury. The stopcock is then opened; after equilibrium has been reached the stopcock is closed again and one of the flasks is brought back to the temperature of 27°C. What is now the pressure in that flask?

21. *Heat Transfer*

Heat is the most common form of energy. Every object that we see or feel possesses heat energy. Heat is continually being transferred from one body to another.

The engineer is concerned with heat and its flow. Sometimes he wants to get it from one place to another. Heat must be transferred from the firebox to the water in a boiler, or from the automobile engine to the surrounding air. In other cases the engineer tries to prevent the flow of heat, as from the firebox to the surrounding room or from the welder's tongs to his hand. In the first problem he is confronted with the fact that there are no perfect conductors of heat. The second problem, that of heat storage, is complicated by the fact that there are no perfect heat insulators, so that one cannot confine heat. In order to utilize heat to the best advantage, it is necessary to know the laws that govern heat transfer.

21-1. Heat Flow. Heat is always being transferred in one way or another, wherever there is any difference in temperature. Just as water will run downhill, always flowing to the lowest possible level, so heat, if left to itself, flows down the temperature hill, always warming the cold objects at the expense of the warmer ones. The rate at which heat flows depends on the steepness of the temperature hill as well as on the properties of the materials through which it has to flow. The differ-

ence of temperature per unit distance is called the *temperature gradient* in analogy to the idea of steepness of grade, which determines the rate of flow of water.

21-2. Types of Heat Transfer. There are three ways in which heat is transferred. Since heat itself is the energy of molecular activity, the simplest mode of transfer of heat, called *conduction*, is the direct communication of molecular disturbance through a substance by means of the collisions of neighboring molecules. Metals contain so-called "free" electrons which make them good conductors of electricity; these electrons also contribute to the conduction of heat, so metals have high thermal conductivities (Table 1).

Convection is the transfer of heat from one place to another by actual motion of the hot material. Heat transfer is accomplished also by a combination of *radiation* and *absorption*. In radiation, thermal energy is transformed into radiant energy, similar in nature to light. In fact, a part of such radiant energy is light. While in the form of radiation, the energy may travel a tremendous distance before being absorbed or changed back into heat. For example, energy radiated from the surface of the sun is converted into heat at the surface of the earth only eight minutes later.

21-3. Conduction. The amount of heat that flows through any body by conduction depends upon the time of flow, the area through which it flows, the temperature gradient, and the kind of material. Stated as an equation

$$Q = kAt \frac{\Delta T}{\Delta L} \qquad (1)$$

where k is called the *thermal conductivity* of the material, A is the area measured at right

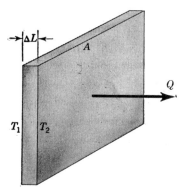

Fig. 1. Heat conduction through a thin plate.

angles to the direction of the flow of heat, t is the time the flow continues, and $\Delta T/\Delta L$ is the average temperature gradient. The symbol ΔT represents the difference in temperature between two parallel surfaces distant ΔL apart (Fig. 1).

In the British system these quantities are usually measured in the following units: Q in Btu, A in square feet, t in hours, ΔT in F°, and ΔL in inches. The thermal conductivity k is then expressed in Btu/(ft² hr F°/in.). The corresponding unit of k in the metric system is cal/(cm² sec C°/cm).

Example: A 3.0-in. wall of fire brick, $k = 8.0$ Btu/(ft² hr F°/in.), has one surface at 335°F, the other at 80°F. Find (*a*) the temperature gradient in the brick, and (*b*) the heat conducted through an area of 1.0 ft² in 1 day.

(*a*) Temperature gradient $\Delta T/\Delta L$
$$= \frac{335°F - 80°F}{3.0 \text{ in.}} = 85 \text{ F}°/\text{in.}$$

(*b*) Heat transferred $Q = \dfrac{kA(T_1 - T_2)t}{L}$

$$= \frac{8.0 \text{ Btu}/(\text{ft}^2 \text{ hr F}°/\text{in.}) \; 1.0 \text{ ft}^2 \times 255 \text{ F}° \times 24 \text{ hr}}{3.0 \text{ in.}}$$
$$= 1\overline{6}000 \text{ Btu}$$

Example: Heat is conducted through a compound wall composed of parallel layers of two different conductivities, 0.32 and 0.14 cal/(cm² sec C°/cm), and of thicknesses 3.6 and 4.2 cm, respectively (Fig. 2). The temperatures of the outer faces of the wall are 96° and 8.0°C. Find (*a*) the temperature T_i of the interface and (*b*) the temperature gradient in each section of the wall.

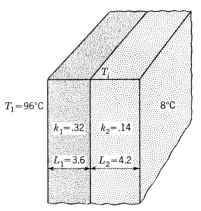

Fig. 2. Heat conduction through a compound wall.

For steady flow, the same quantity of heat per unit area passes through the first layer per unit time as passes through the second layer.

$$\frac{1}{A} \frac{\Delta Q}{\Delta t} = \frac{k_1(T_1 - T_i)}{L_1} = \frac{k_2(T_i - T_2)}{L_2}$$

or

$$\frac{k_1 L_2}{k_2 L_1}(T_1 - T_i) = T_i - T_2$$

$$\frac{0.32}{0.14} \times \frac{4.2}{3.6}(96° - T_i) = T_i - 8.0°$$

$$T_i = 72°C$$

Temperature gradient in first layer
$$= \frac{(96 - 72)C°}{3.6 \text{ cm}} = 6.7 \text{ C}°/\text{cm}$$

Temperature gradient in second layer
$$= \frac{(72 - 8)C°}{4.2 \text{ cm}} = 15 \text{ C}°/\text{cm}$$

A general equation for steady, one-dimensional flow of heat can be inferred from Eq. (1)

$$\frac{dQ}{dt} = -kA \frac{dT}{ds} \qquad (2)$$

where the minus sign is introduced because the temperature decreases in the direction of heat flow.

Example: Find the rate of flow of heat dQ/dt through a section of cylindrical pipe insulation of length L, in terms of the inside and outside temperatures.

Consider the thin cylindrical shell, shown shaded in Fig. 3. Here the area $A = 2\pi rL$. For

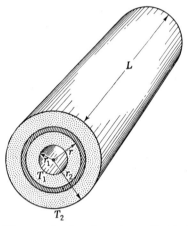

Fig. 3. Heat conduction through a cylindrical shell.

steady flow, dQ/dt is constant; call it P. Then in Eq. (2) $A = 2\pi rL$ and $s = r$ and the equation may be written as

$$P\frac{dr}{r} = -2\pi kL\, dT$$

$$P\int_{r_1}^{r_2}\frac{dr}{r} = -2\pi kL\int_{T_1}^{T_2} dT$$

$$P\left(\ln\frac{r_2}{r_1}\right) = 2\pi kL(T_1 - T_2)$$

$$P = \frac{2\pi kL(T_1 - T_2)}{\ln(r_2/r_1)}$$

There are large differences in the thermal conductivities of various materials. Gases have very low conductivities. Liquids also are, in general, quite poor conductors. The conductivities of solids vary over a wide range, from the very low values for asbestos fiber or brick to the relatively high values for most metals. Fibrous materials such as hair felt or asbestos are very poor conductors (or good insulators) when dry; if they become wet, they conduct heat rather well. One of the difficult problems in using such materials for insulation is to keep them dry.

TABLE 1. THERMAL CONDUCTIVITIES (NEAR 20°C)

Substance	cal/(cm² sec C°/cm)	Btu/(ft² hr F°/in.)
Silver	0.990	2870
Copper	0.918	2660
Aluminum	0.504	1460
Steel	0.11	320
Oak, across grain	0.048	140
Concrete	0.0041	12.0
Glass	0.0025	7.2
Brick	0.0017	5.0
Water	0.0014	4.1
Hydrogen	0.00038	1.1
Corkboard	0.00010	0.30
Glass wool	0.00009	0.27
Air	0.000053	0.15

21-4. Convection. The transfer of heat by convective circulation in a liquid or a gas is associated with pressure differences, most commonly brought about by local changes in density. A rise in temperature is accompanied by a decrease in density in most fluids. Hence if heat is applied at the bottom of a sample, the less dense fluid at the bottom is continually displaced by fluid of greater density from above. Heat transfer accompanies this motion, called *natural* or *free convection*. The primary circulation of the earth's atmosphere is an example of natural convection, as is also the circulation of water in an ordinary hot-water heating system in a house. Sometimes the pressure differences are produced mechanically by a pump, or blower, in which case the heat transfer is said to occur by *forced convection*. In all cases of convection, heat is transferred into or out of the fluid stream somewhere in its path.

Since convection is a very effective method of heat transfer, it must be considered in designing a system of insulation. If large air spaces are left within the walls of a house, convection currents are set up readily and much heat is lost. If, however, the air spaces are broken up into small, isolated regions, no major convection currents are possible and little heat is lost by this method. For this reason the insulating material used in the walls of a refrigerator or in a house is a porous material—cork, rock wool, glass wool, or other materials of like nature. They are not only poor conductors in themselves but they leave many small air spaces, which are very poor conductors and at the same time are so small that no effective convection currents can be set up.

21-5. Effect of Surface Films on Heat Transfer. When a cool fluid flows along a heated wall, heat is transferred from the wall to the fluid. Langmuir (1912) dealt with this situation by assuming that heat is transferred by conduction through a thin layer of fluid close to the wall, comprising roughly the laminar-flow region, to a region in which the ambient temperature is maintained by turbulent flow. A convective heat transfer of this type is treated approximately in the same manner as heat conduction, using the relation

$$\frac{dQ}{dt} = Ah\,\Delta T \qquad (3)$$

where ΔT is the temperature difference between the wall and the fluid at some distance from it and h is called a *film coefficient* or *convection* coefficient. It represents the conductivity of the fluid divided by the effective thickness of the conducting layer.

The conducting layer is assumed to extend from the wall to the region where the temperature of the main body of fluid is reached, assuming that the temperature gradient across the conducting layer is constant and is equal to that actually existing at the wall. The thickness of the conducting layer is somewhat greater than the thickness of the laminar-flow region. The film coefficient is found experimentally to depend on many factors: the nature of the fluid-wall surface (including curvature and orientation); the speed, density, viscosity, specific heat and thermal conductivity of the fluid; and the occurrence of evaporation or condensation at the fluid-wall surface.

In the steady-flow passage of heat through a wall separating two fluids (say water, steel, air), the heat passes through the three layers in succession, at the same rate

$$\frac{dQ}{dt} = k_1 \frac{\Delta T_1}{L_1} A = k_2 \frac{\Delta T_2}{L_2} A = k_3 \frac{\Delta T_3}{L_3} A$$

where subscripts 1 and 3 refer to the fluid films and 2 to the wall. If ΔT is the total temperature difference across the three layers, the resulting heat flow is

$$\frac{dQ}{dt} = \frac{A\,\Delta T}{1/h_1 + L_2/k_2 + 1/h_3} \qquad (4)$$

If there were no films present, Eq. (4) would reduce to the simpler form of Eq. (1).

Example: Compute the heat conducted per hour through a plate-glass window of area 15 ft² and thickness $\frac{1}{4}$ in., when the inside temperature is 70°F and the outside temperature is 20°F. The thermal conductivity of the glass is 5.8 Btu/(hr ft² F°/in.) and the film coefficient for air is about 2 Btu/(hr ft² F°).

From Eq. (4)

$$\frac{dQ}{dt} = \frac{15 \text{ ft}^2\ (70-20)\text{F}°}{\dfrac{2}{2 \text{ Btu/(hr ft}^2 \text{ F}°)} + \dfrac{\frac{1}{4} \text{ in.}}{5.8 \text{ Btu/(hr ft}^2 \text{ F}°/\text{in.})}}$$
$$= 7\overline{2}0 \text{ Btu/hr}$$

Note that if the air films were neglected, we should get for the rate of heat conduction the unrealistic figure 1$\overline{7}$,000 Btu/hr.

21-6. Radiation. The transfer of heat by radiation does not require a material medium for the process. Energy traverses the space between the sun and the earth and, when it is absorbed, it becomes heat energy. Energy emitted by the heated filament of an electric lamp traverses the space between the filament and the glass even though there is no gas in the bulb. Energy of this nature is emitted by all bodies. A body, which absorbs this radiant energy, converts the energy into heat, with a resulting increase in the random motion of its molecules.

All hot bodies emit radiant energy. Radiant energy travels out from a hot stove until it encounters some object where, in general, it is partly reflected, partly absorbed, and partly transmitted. In every way it behaves in the same manner as light except that it does not produce the sensation of sight. Heat radiation differs from light only in being of longer wavelengths.

There are large differences in the transparency of various substances to heat radiations. Certain materials, such as hard rubber, nickel oxide, special glasses, or a deep-black solution of iodine in carbon disulfide, which are opaque to light, are almost perfectly transparent to heat radiation. Ordinary window

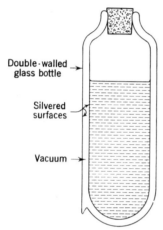

Double-walled glass bottle

Silvered surfaces

Vacuum

FIG. 4. Dewar, or thermos, flask.

glass, quite transparent optically, absorbs heat radiations. The glass roof of a greenhouse is transparent to the visible and near infrared radiations received from the sun and admits them. Their energy is converted into heat when they are absorbed by the objects inside the greenhouse. These objects become warmer and themselves radiate energy. But since their temperatures are not high, the heat radiation they emit is not identical with the radiation that entered. Glass does not transmit this heat radiation, and hence the energy radiated by the bodies in the greenhouse cannot get out. A greenhouse thus acts as an energy trap and, since heat losses by radiation and convection are largely prevented, the temperature inside

is greater than the temperature outside when the greenhouse receives direct sunlight.

21-7. The Ideal Radiator. An ideal *blackbody* is defined as one which absorbs all the radiation which falls upon it. No perfect blackbody is known, but a surface coated with lampblack is a very good approximation. A hole bored through the wall of a metal tube appears darker than the surrounding surface because almost all the light entering the hole is absorbed. Thus a cavity having only a small aperture is almost a blackbody in the technical sense of absorbing all radiation incident upon it.

Objects whose surfaces are in such condition that they are good absorbers of radiation are also good radiators. If two silver coins one of which has been blackened are placed in a small furnace, the blackened surface will absorb more radiation than the bright surface. The blackened surface will also radiate faster than the polished surface if the two are held at the same temperature. A blackbody is the ideal radiator.

21-8. Theory of Exchanges. The rate at which a body radiates energy depends only on its temperature and the nature of its surface. The rate of radiation increases very rapidly as the temperature rises. But all objects radiate. Prevost stated in the form of a theorem the idea that all objects continuously radiate heat to their surroundings and receive heat from their surroundings. When the temperature of a body remains constant, it is receiving heat at the same rate as that at which it is radiating. A piece of metal left in the sun rises in temperature until it loses heat at the same rate at which it absorbs heat. A piece of ice radiates energy less rapidly than one's hand held near it and thus seems cold, while a heated iron radiates energy faster than the hand and thus seems warm.

A thermos bottle (Fig. 4) illustrates how the principles of heat transfer may be used to decrease the amount of heat flowing into (or out of) a container. It consists of two bottles, one inside the other, touching each other only at the neck. The space between the two bottles is evacuated and the surfaces are silvered. Transfers by conduction are minimized by using a very small area of a poorly conducting material; those due to convection are lessened by removing the air. The transfer by radiation is made small because the polished silver acts as a poor emitter for one surface and a poor absorber for the other.

21-9. Rate of Radiation. The law that expresses the total energy of all wavelengths radiated from a blackbody at a given temperature was stated originally by Stefan on the basis of careful measurements of the energy radiated from a blackbody cavity. Subsequently Boltzmann derived the same law from thermodynamic theory. The rate P at which energy is radiated by a blackbody is proportional to the area of the body and to the fourth power of its absolute temperature

$$P = \sigma A T^4 \tag{5}$$

The relation expressed by Eq. (5) is called the *Stefan-Boltzmann law.* If the power P is in watts, the area A in square centimeters, and the absolute temperature T is in degrees Kelvin, the constant σ has the value 5.70×10^{-12} watt/cm^2(K$^\circ$)^4. It is important to note that a non-blackbody will radiate at a smaller rate.

A blackbody at temperature T radiates energy and also receives energy from its surroundings at temperature T_0. According to Prevost's theorem of heat exchanges, the *net* rate at which the body loses heat by radiation is the difference between the rate at which it receives energy and the rate at which it loses energy

$$P = \sigma A(T^4 - T_0^4) \tag{6}$$

For the case of small temperature differences, the rate of cooling, due to conduction, convection, and radiation combined, is proportional to the difference in temperature

$$P = bA(T - T_0) \tag{7}$$

This is *Newton's law of cooling.* It is a valid approximation in the transfer of heat from a radiator to a room, the loss of heat through the walls of a room, or the cooling of a cup of coffee on the table.

Example: What power is radiated from a tungsten filament 20 cm long and 0.010 mm in diameter when the filament is kept at 2500°K in an evacuated bulb? The tungsten radiates at 30 per cent of the rate of a blackbody at the same temperature. Neglect conduction losses.

$$A = \pi(0.0010 \text{ cm})(20 \text{ cm}) = 0.0628 \text{ cm}^2$$
$$T^4 = (2500°K)^4 = 39.1 \times 10^{12}(°K)^4$$

From Eq. (5)

$$P = 0.30 \, \sigma A T^4$$
$$P = (0.30)[5.70 \times 10^{-12} \text{ watt/cm}^2(K°)^4]$$
$$(0.0628 \text{ cm}^2)[39.1 \times 10^{12}(K°)^4] = 4.2 \text{ watts}$$

SUMMARY

Heat is the most common form of energy.

The three ways in which heat may be transferred from one place to another are *conduction, convection,* and *radiation-absorption.*

Conduction is heat transfer from molecule to molecule through a body, or through bodies in contact.

Temperature gradient is temperature difference per unit distance along the direction of heat flow. Its units may be centigrade degrees per centimeter, Fahrenheit degrees per inch, etc.

Thermal conductivity k is a quantity that expresses how well a substance conducts heat. It may have units of calories per square centimeter per second for a gradient of 1 C°/cm or Btu per square foot per hour for a gradient of 1 F°/in.

$$k = \frac{Q}{At(\Delta T/\Delta L)}$$

Convection is heat transfer due to motion of matter.

The passage of heat through a surface film is described by the relation

$$\frac{dQ}{dt} = Ah \, \Delta T$$

where the film coefficient h represents the conductivity of the fluid divided by the effective thickness of the conducting layer.

In the process of *radiation* energy is transferred, without the aid of a material medium, from one body to another where, upon *absorption*, it again becomes energy of thermal motion. Radiant energy travels as an electromagnetic wave.

Good absorbers of radiation are also good radiators. A *blackbody* is a perfect absorber of radiation and an ideal radiator.

The total energy radiated per unit time by a blackbody is proportional to the fourth power of its absolute temperature (Stefan-Boltzmann law)

$$P = \sigma A T^4$$

QUESTIONS

1. What kinds of bodies are good insulators? Why?
2. Why does iron seem colder to the touch than wood in winter weather?
3. A piece of paper wrapped tightly on a brass rod may be held in a gas flame without being burned. If wrapped on a wooden rod, it burns quickly. Explain.
4. Explain why a moistened finger may freeze quickly to a piece of metal on a cold day but not to a piece of wood.
5. Can you suggest an apparatus to demonstrate the differences in thermal conductivities of various metals, which gives results that do not depend also on differences in the specific heats?
6. What is the role of molecular action in convection and in conduction?
7. Why does a chimney "draw" poorly when a fire is first lighted?
8. Does warm air over a fire rise, or is it pushed up? Explain.
9. Why is a hollow wall filled with rock wool a better insulator than when filled with air alone?
10. What is the purpose of the inert gas in modern tungsten filament lamps?
11. A test tube filled with water is inclined so that the flame of a bunsen burner reaches only the upper part of the tube. It is found that the lower part of the tube can be held in the hand painlessly indefinitely. If, however, the positions of hand and flame are interchanged, the tube cannot long be held. What do you conclude from these observations?
12. Conduits for hot-air heating systems are frequently made of bright sheet metal. The addition of a layer of asbestos paper on the conduit may actually increase the loss of heat through the surface. Explain.
13. Explain how a thermos flask minimizes energy losses from convection, conduction, and radiation.
14. Describe a means for detecting radiant energy.
15. How do you account for the effectiveness of glasshouses in keeping plants warm?

PROBLEMS

1. How much heat is conducted in 1.0 hr through an iron plate 2.0 cm thick and 1000 cm² in area, the temperatures of the two sides being kept at 0 and 20°C?
2. An icebox made of wood 5.0 cm thick has an effective area of $1\overline{2},000$ cm² and thermal conductivity of 0.00027 cal/(cm² sec C°/cm). How much ice inside the box would be melted each 24-hr day if the outside temperature is 25° and the temperature inside the box is 5°C?   *Ans.* 13 kg
3. A pond is covered by a sheet of ice 2.0 cm thick [thermal conductivity 0.0040 cal/(cm² sec C°/cm)]. The temperature of the lower surface of the ice is 0°C and that of the upper surface is −10°C. At what rate is heat conducted

through each square meter of the ice? What is the direction of this flow of energy?

4. A copper kettle, the bottom of which has an area 0.20 ft² and thickness 0.062 in., is placed over a gas flame. Assuming that the average temperature of the outer surface of the copper is 300°F and that the water in the kettle is at its normal boiling point, how much heat is conducted through the bottom in 1.0 min? The thermal conductivity of copper is 2480 Btu/(ft² hr F°/in.).

Ans. 11.7×10^3 Btu

5. At what rate is heat conducted through a sheet of plate glass, $k = 0.0024$ cal/(cm² sec C°/cm), which is 2.0 m by 3.0 m and 5.0 mm thick, when the temperatures of the surfaces are 20 and $-10°C$, respectively? Why is considerably less heat transmitted through a window glass of these dimensions when *room* temperature is 20°C and the outdoor temperature is $-10°C$?

6. The value of a thermal conductivity is known in cal/(cm² sec C°/cm). By what factor should this value be multiplied to express it in Btu/(ft² hr F°/in.)?

Ans. 2901

7. A certain thermal conductivity is expressed in the units Btu/(ft² sec F°/in.). Derive expressions for expressing its value (*a*) in cal/(cm² sec C°/cm) and (*b*) in joules/(cm² sec C°/cm).

8. A copper rod whose diameter is 2.0 cm and length 50 cm has one end in boiling water, the other end in a jacket cooled by flowing water which enters at 10°C. The thermal conductivity of the copper is 1.02 cal/(cm² sec C°/cm). If 200 gm of water flow through the jacket in 6.0 min, by how much does the temperature of this water increase?

Ans. 10 C°

9. If the thermal conductivity of oak is 1.02 Btu/(ft² hr F°/in.), how much heat will pass in 24 hr through a door 3.0 by 7.0 ft whose thickness is 1.5 in., when the inside and outside temperatures are 72° and 10°F, respectively?

10. When one end of a copper rod 30 cm long and 8.0 mm in diameter is kept in boiling water at 100°C and the other end is kept in ice, it is found that 1.2 gm of ice melt per minute. What is the thermal conductivity of the rod?

Ans. 0.96 cal/(cm² sec C°/cm)

11. A cast-iron skillet has a bottom area of 250 cm² and is 5.0 mm thick. The iron has a thermal conductivity of 0.11 cal/(cm² sec C°/cm). If a temperature difference of 10.0 C° is maintained between the bottom surfaces, how many calories are transmitted through the bottom in 5.0 min?

12. Approximate values of the thermal conductivities of the following materials are: oak, 1.02 Btu/(hr ft² F°/in.); brick, 4.5; concrete, 7.5. What thickness of each would have the same insulating value as 0.50 in. of corkboard (conductivity 0.30)?

Ans. 1.7 in., 7.5 in., 12.5 in.

13. The thermal insulation of a woolen glove may be regarded as being essentially a layer of quiescent air 3.0 mm thick, of conductivity 5.7×10^{-5} cal/(cm² sec C°/cm). How much heat does a person lose per minute from his hand, of area 200 cm² and skin temperature 35°C, on a winter day at $-5°C$?

14. A bar has a length L when at a uniform temperature T_0. If one end of the bar is maintained at T_0 while the other end is heated to temperature T_1, find an expression for the change in length of the bar when a steady state is reached. The bar is thermally insulated along its length and the linear expansivity is α.

Ans. $\frac{1}{2}L\alpha(T_1 - T_0)$

15. A steam pipe has an outside diameter of 7.0 cm. Its outer surface is maintained at 96°C; the temperature of the surrounding air is 18°C. The convection coefficient for such a pipe is $1.00 \times 10^{-4} \, (\Delta T/\text{diameter})^{1/4}$. How much heat is delivered from 1.0 m of pipe to the surrounding air by free convection in 1.0 hr?

16. A copper rod whose diameter is 2.0 cm and whose length is 50 cm has one end in boiling water and the other in a block of ice. The thermal conductivity of the copper is 1.02 cal/(cm² sec C°/cm). How much ice will be melted in 1.0 hr if 25% of the heat escapes during transmission?   *Ans.* $2\bar{2}0$ gm

17. A ship has a steel hull 2.54 cm thick whose thermal conductivity is 0.11 cal/(cm² sec C°/cm). A layer of insulating material 5.0 cm thick having a thermal conductivity of 10×10^{-5} cal/(cm² sec C°/cm) lines the hull. When the temperature inside the ship is 25.0°C and the temperature of the surrounding water is 5.0°C, what is the temperature on the inside surface of the steel hull? What is the difference in temperature between the inside and outside of the insulating layer? How many calories are transmitted through each square meter of the hull per minute?

18. What will be the rise in temperature in 30 min of a block of copper of 500-gm mass if it is joined to a cylindrical copper rod 20 cm long and 3.0 mm in diameter when there is maintained a temperature difference of 80 C° between the ends of the rod? The thermal conductivity of copper is 1.02 cal/(cm² sec C°/cm). Neglect heat losses.   *Ans.* 11.3 C°

19. On a winter day, the air temperature is 20°F. The temperature directly beneath a 3.0-in. concrete highway is 5°F. (*a*) Calculate the steady heat flow per square foot through the concrete. What is the direction of this flow? The thermal conductivity of concrete is 6.0 Btu/(hr ft² F°/in.). (*b*) How thick must a layer of ice on this concrete be in order to reduce the steady heat flow per square foot to 75% of its original value? The thermal conductivity of ice is 12 Btu/(ft² hr F°/in.).

20. A composite wall consists of three layers each one inch thick whose thermal conductivities are 0.010, 0.020, and 0.030 Btu/(ft² sec F°/in.), respectively. What conductivity should a single layer of material 3.0 in. thick have to transmit the same heat flow for the same temperature difference?
        Ans. 0.016 Btu/(sec ft² F°/in.)

21. The wall of an industrial refrigerator is made of concrete 8.0 in. thick which has a conductivity of 7.5 Btu/(ft² hr F°/in.), lined with 2.0 in. of corkboard having a conductivity of 0.32 Btu/(ft² hr F°/in.). The temperature inside the refrigerator is maintained at 40°F while the outside temperature is 80°F. Find (*a*) the temperature of the outer surface of the corkboard, and (*b*) the heat conducted through each square foot of wall in one day.

22. An insulated chest for storing "dry ice" consists of a pine box lined with glass wool. The outside dimensions of the cubical box are 2 ft 4 in. The wood is 0.50 in. thick and has a conductivity of 0.78 Btu/(ft² hr F°/in.). The layer of glass wool is 1.5 in. thick and has a conductivity of 0.29 Btu/(ft² hr F°/in.). How much heat is conducted into the box (−97°F) from the room (72°F) in one day?
        Ans. $1\bar{7},000$ Btu

23. A solid sphere is placed in an evacuated chamber whose walls are held at 100°C. The walls behave like a blackbody, but the relative rate of radiation from the sphere is only half as much (that is, its emissivity is 0.5). (*a*) Compare the rate of energy radiation from the solid sphere with the rate of energy absorption after a long time has elapsed. (*b*) Compare the rate of energy radiation per unit area by the small sphere with the rate of energy radiation per unit area by the walls of the enclosure. (*c*) Suppose the temperature of the walls is increased to 200°C. After a long time, how will the rate of radiation from the small sphere compare with the rate under the original conditions?

24. The temperature of the sun is about 6000°K and when the sun is directly overhead its radiation is equivalent to about 2.0 cal/(cm² min). Calculate the decrease in this rate of heat transfer if the sun's temperature should drop 500 C°. *Ans.* 0.59 cal/(cm² min) or 29%

25. At what rate does the sun lose energy by radiation? The temperature of the sun is about 6000°K, and its radius is 4.3×10^5 mi.

26. A tungsten filament in a lamp reaches a temperature of 2000°K when its power consumption is 16 watts. Assuming that the filament radiates heat as a blackbody, what power must be supplied to maintain a filament temperature of 3000°K? *Ans.* 81 watts

27. The earth receives energy from the sun at an average rate of 0.135 watt/cm². The mean temperature of the earth's surface is 15°C. Assuming the earth to radiate as a blackbody, compute the temperature of interstellar space. Comment on the result.

28. The operating temperature of a tungsten filament in an evacuated lamp bulb is 2450°K. Find the surface area of the filament of a 25-watt lamp if the tungsten radiates at 0.30 the rate of an ideal (blackbody) radiator.
Ans. 0.41 cm²

29. How many calories per second will be radiated from a spherical blackbody 15.0 cm in diameter at a temperature of 800°C?

30. A blackened sphere of copper (density 8.9 gm/cm³, specific heat 0.093 cal/gm C°) of diameter 10.0 cm is cooled in an evacuated enclosure whose walls are kept at 0°C. How long does it take for the sphere to cool from 228° to 227°C? Take b in Eq. (7) to be 3.36×10^{-4} cal/cm² sec (K°). *Ans.* 18 sec

31. A can filled with water and containing an electric heating element rises to a temperature 80 F° above its surroundings when the power supplied to the heater is 120 watts. The can and water are equivalent to 3.0 lb of water. What will be the inital rate of cooling when the heater is turned off?

32. Calculate the radiation, in watts per square centimeter, from a block of copper at 200C°, and at 1000°C. The oxidized copper surface radiates at 0.60 the rate of a blackbody. *Ans.* 0.17 watt/cm²; 9.0 watts/cm²

33. A small body whose temperature is $T_0 + \Delta T$ is placed in a furnace, the walls of which are kept at a temperature T_0; $\Delta T \ll T_0$. How long will it take for the temperature of the body to fall to $T_0 + \frac{1}{2}\Delta T$?

34. Derive an expression for the radial flow of heat through the material of a hollow sphere of inside radius r_1, outside radius r_2, and thermal conductivity k.
$$Ans.\ \frac{dQ}{dt} = \frac{4\pi k r_1 r_2 (T_1 - T_2)}{r_2 - r_1}$$

22. *Thermodynamics*

Thermodynamics deals with the quantitative relations between heat and other forms of energy, particularly mechanical energy. In each application, thermodynamics treats a clearly defined *system* (a gas confined by a cylinder and piston, an electrochemical cell, etc.) which is made to interact with its surroundings and thus perform some useful function.

22-1. Thermodynamic Processes. The condition of a system may be expressed in terms of certain quantities (for example, pressure, volume per unit mass, temperature) called *variables of state*. By a *thermodynamic process* or a *change of state* is meant any change in the system (however small) that involves changes in these variables. A change of *phase*, however, refers to a more fundamental change of physical form, as from a liquid to a vapor, or a change from one crystalline form to another. Thermodynamics is not concerned with detailed assumptions about atomic structure or the exact mechanisms by which energy is exchanged; its predictions are independent of such assumptions about the system.

That thermodynamics is a practical subject is illustrated by the studies of Sadi Carnot (1796–1832) in an attempt to improve the efficiency of steam engines. A steam engine converts heat (in the working substance, steam) into useful mechanical energy. We wish to know the relation between heat and mechanical energy, and how much of the original energy of the steam can be converted into useful work. These questions may be answered by the two laws of thermodynamics. Both laws are simple and general. They apply not only to heat engines but also to many processes such as chemical reactions and electrical transformations where the system is practically in equilibrium with its surroundings.

22-2. Work and Heat. In many familiar processes work is done against friction and heat is produced. Brakes become heated in stopping an automobile or a train. A tool held against a grinding wheel becomes hot.

The continuous evolution of heat during the boring of a cannon suggested to Count Rumford (1753–1814) the idea of a definite relationship between the mechanical energy expended in the process and the heat produced. About 1800 he made some measurements and compared the *mechanical work* expended in turning a blunt drill with the *heat* produced, as measured by the warming of water. He found that the two quantities were in a constant ratio and he concluded that heat is a form of energy, obtained in his experiments by a transformation of mechanical energy.

Rumford's insight into the true nature of heat as a form of energy was confirmed by experiments of improved accuracy performed

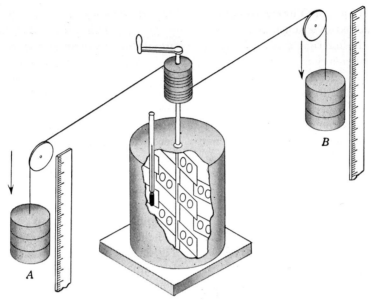

Fig. 1. Joule's apparatus for demonstrating equivalence of heat and mechanical work.

during the years that followed by Joule, Rowland, Callendar, and Barnes. Joule (1843) arranged a set of paddles, which could be rotated in water by a pair of falling bodies (*A* and *B*, Fig. 1). The churning of the water produced heat. The heat produced was calculated from the rise in temperature of the water and its container. The mechanical work performed in driving the paddles was calculated from the weights of the falling bodies and the distance they descended. In a series of experiments with this apparatus, Joule found that the ratio of the number of units of work to the number of units of heat produced was always the same.

The number of units of work per unit of heat is called the *mechanical equivalent of heat.* Thus, if work W is converted into heat Q,

$$W = JQ \qquad (1)$$

where J (after Joule) is a constant, independent of the magnitude of W or Q, but whose value depends on the units in which W and Q are expressed. Experimentally determined values for J are 4.19 joules/cal and 778 ft-lb/Btu. These values give the following relationships:

$$
\begin{aligned}
4.19 \times 10^7 \text{ ergs} &= 1 \text{ calorie} \\
4.19 \text{ joules} &= 1 \text{ calorie} \\
1 \text{ newton-meter} &= 1 \text{ joule} \\
&= 0.239 \text{ calorie} \\
778 \text{ foot-pounds} &= 1 \text{ Btu} \\
1055 \text{ joules} &= 1 \text{ Btu}
\end{aligned} \qquad (2)
$$

To an increasing extent, heat quantities are expressed in joules, the same unit used for electrical and for mechanical work.

Example: Ribbon Falls, in Yosemite, has a height of 1612 ft. What would be the rise in temperature of the water in this fall if its potential energy were converted into heat without loss?

Energy transformed per pound of water
$$= (1.00 \text{ lb})(1612 \text{ ft}) = 16\overline{1}0 \text{ ft-lb}$$

$$\text{Heat produced} = \frac{16\overline{1}0 \text{ ft-lb}}{778 \text{ ft-lb/Btu}} = 2.06 \text{ Btu}$$

Rise in temperature $\Delta t = \dfrac{Q}{mc}$

$$= \frac{2.06 \text{ Btu}}{(1.00 \text{ lb})(1.00 \text{ Btu/lb F}^\circ)} = 2.06 \text{ F}^\circ$$

Note that, as mentioned in Sec. 20-3, in the British system specific heat is expressed in terms of unit weight.

22-3. First Law of Thermodynamics.

When heat is added to a substance, there is an increase in the internal energy. This increase in internal energy is manifest by a rise in temperature, an increase in pressure, or a change in phase. If at the same time the substance is allowed to perform external work, by expanding for example, the heat Q required will be the heat necessary to change the internal energy of the substance from U_1

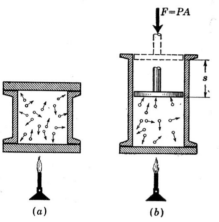

$F = PA$

s

(a)   (b)

FIG. 2. Specific heat of a gas (a) at constant volume; (b) at constant pressure.

in the first state to U_2 in the second state plus the heat equivalent of the external work W performed

$$Q = U_2 - U_1 + W \qquad (3)$$

In applying Eq. (3), all quantities must be expressed in the same units; Q is positive for heat entering the system, W is positive for energy leaving the system as external work. An arbitrary value may be assigned to the internal energy U in some standard reference state; its value in any other state is then defined since $Q - W$ is the same for all processes connecting the states.

The *first law of thermodynamics* states that when heat is transformed into any other form of energy, or when other forms of energy are converted into heat, the total amount of energy (heat plus other forms) is constant. The first law is extended to apply to interchanges of all forms of energy, and thus extended becomes the law of the conservation of energy. This means that kinetic energy, gravitational potential energy, heat, electric and magnetic energy, and the energy of chemical reaction are in principle convertible into one another without loss or gain of energy. Although the law of conservation of energy cannot be proved directly, it is in accord with a wide range of experience and the many scientific conclusions based on this principle have been confirmed by experiment.

22-4. Specific Heats of a Gas.

The heat necessary to raise the temperature of a gas depends on how the gas is confined. If the gas is held at constant volume, as indicated in Fig. 2a, the heat received is converted entirely into internal energy, in the form of molecular kinetic energy, thus raising the temperature. The heat per unit mass per degree required to raise the temperature of the gas under these conditions is called the *specific heat at constant volume, c_v*.

When the gas is confined in a cylinder under a piston that maintains constant pressure (Fig. 2b), the gas will expand on being heated. It does work in moving the piston. Hence heat must be supplied to change the internal energy of the gas and to perform external work. The heat per unit mass per degree required to raise the temperature of the gas under constant pressure is called the *specific heat at constant pressure, c_p*. Since the change of internal energy is the same in both cases, the specific heat at constant pressure c_p is greater than the specific heat at constant volume c_v because external work is also performed when the gas expands at constant pressure. For air and for diatomic gases such as hydrogen, nitrogen, and oxygen, the ratio of the specific heats $\gamma = c_p/c_v$ is 1.40. For other gases the value of γ lies between 1.00 and 1.67.

The work done by a gas in moving a piston a distance ds against a constant pressure P (Fig. 2b) is

$$dW = F\,ds = PA\,ds$$

But *Ads* is the change in volume dV of the gas. Hence the work done by a gas expanding at constant pressure is

$$W = P dV \qquad (4)$$

From Eqs. (3) and (4), at constant pressure,

$$dQ_p = dU + mR' \, dT$$

$$c_p = \frac{1}{m} \frac{dQ_p}{dT} = \frac{1}{m} \frac{dU}{dT} + \frac{mR'}{m} \frac{dT}{dT}$$

$$c_v = \frac{1}{m} \frac{dQ_v}{dT} = \frac{1}{m} \frac{dU}{dT}$$

hence

$$c_p = c_v + R' \qquad (5)$$

22-5. Work Done by Expanding Gas.

As an example of the transformation of heat into work, consider a process in which a gas is heated and caused to do external work as it expands from state 1 to state 2, Fig. 3. The expansion can be regarded as made up of infinitesimal expansions, shown shaded, in any one of which pressure can be assumed constant. The work dW in an infinitesimal expansion is the product $P \, dV$, from Eq. (4). The work done during the entire expansion is the sum of the areas of all the vertical elements under the curve

$$W = \int_{V_1}^{V_2} P \, dV \qquad (6)$$

Three important types of expansion will be treated, and for each the amount of work done by the expanding gas will be computed from Eq. (6).

Isothermal expansion occurs when the gas expands without change of temperature. For a gas expanding isothermally, the ideal gas law becomes

$$PV = mR'T = \text{constant} = K \qquad (7)$$

The work done in an infinitesimal expansion dV can be written $dW = P \, dV = (K/V) \, dV$, and during expansion from volume V_1 to volume V_2 the work is

$$W = \int_{V_1}^{V_2} P \, dV = K \int_{V_1}^{V_2} \frac{dV}{V} = K \Big[\ln V \Big]_{V_1}^{V_2}$$

$$= PV \ln \frac{V_2}{V_1} \qquad (8)$$

Reference to Eq. (7) suggests an alternate form for Eq. (8):

$$W = mR'T \ln \frac{V_2}{V_1} = 2.303 mR'T \log \frac{V_2}{V_1} \qquad (9)$$

Example: Two moles of an ideal gas are compressed slowly and isothermally from a volume of 4.0 ft³ to 1.0 ft³, at a temperature of 300°K. How much work is done?

From Eq. (9)

$$W = 2.30(2.0 \text{ moles})(8.31 \text{ joules/mole K}°)$$
$$\times (300°\text{K}) \log \tfrac{1}{4}$$

$$W = -6.9 \text{ joules}$$

The negative sign indicates that this work was done *on* the gas by an external agent.

Adiabatic expansion occurs without the addition or withdrawal of heat. When an ideal gas

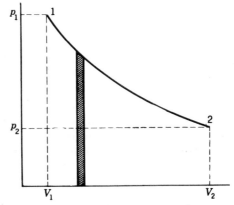

FIG. 3. The area under a pressure-volume curve represents work.

undergoes an adiabatic expansion, $dQ = 0$.

$$dU + dW = mc_v \, dT + P \, dV = 0$$

Differentiation of the general gas law gives

$$P \, dV + V \, dP = mR' \, dT$$

Elimination of dT between the last two equations gives

$$P \, dV + V \, dP = - \frac{mR'P \, dV}{mc_v}$$

or, from Eq. (5),

$$(c_v + R')P \, dV + c_v V \, dP = 0$$

$$\frac{dP}{P} + \frac{c_p}{c_v}\frac{dV}{V} = 0$$

If we denote the ratio c_p/c_v by γ and integrate the last equation we get

$$PV^\gamma = \text{constant} \qquad (10)$$

Equation (3) applied to an adiabatic process states that, since $dQ = 0$, $dW = -dU$ and $P\,dV = -mc_v\,dT$, where m is the mass of the gas, c_v is the specific heat at constant volume, and dT is the temperature change accompanying the expansion. The performance of external work is at the expense of a decrease in internal energy, evidenced by a decrease in the temperature of the gas. The work done by the expanding gas is

$$W = \int_{V_1}^{V_2} P\,dV = -mc_v \int_{T_1}^{T_2} dT$$
$$= mc_v(T_1 - T_2) \qquad (11)$$

Since this expression involves the difference between the initial temperature T_1 of the gas and its final temperature T_2, the temperatures need not be expressed on an absolute scale. The units commonly used for c_v will give W in calories or in Btu's, but the work is still represented by the area under the pressure-volume curve and can be converted into other units (say, joules) by using the proper value for J, the mechanical equivalent of heat.

Expansion at constant pressure is represented by a horizontal line in Fig. 3, and the work done is represented by the area under that line.

$$W = \int_{V_1}^{V_2} P\,dV = P\int_{V_1}^{V_2} dV$$
$$= P(V_2 - V_1) \qquad (12)$$

Example: Air which occupies 5.0 ft³ at 15 lb/in.² gage pressure is expanded isothermally to atmospheric pressure and then cooled at constant pressure until it reaches its initial volume. Compute the work done by the gas.

The volume V_B of the gas after expansion is obtained from Boyle's law

$$V_B = \frac{P_A V_A}{P_B} = \frac{(15 + 14.7)(144)\text{lb/ft}^2(5.0\text{ ft}^3)}{14.7 \times 144\text{ lb/ft}^2}$$
$$= 10\text{ ft}^3$$

The work done during the isothermal expansion is, from Eq. (8),

$$W_{AB} = PV \ln \frac{V_B}{V_A}$$
$$= (14.7 \times 144)\text{ lb/ft}^2 \times 10\text{ ft}^3 \ln\frac{10}{5}$$
$$= 1\overline{5},000\text{ ft-lb}$$

The work done during change in volume at constant pressure is, from Eq. (12),

$$W_{BC} = P_B(V_B - V_C)$$
$$= (14.7 \times 144)\text{ lb/ft}^2(10 - 5)\text{ ft}^3$$
$$= 1\overline{1},000\text{ ft-lb}$$

Hence the net work done by the gas is

$$W_{AC} = 1\overline{5},000 - 1\overline{1},000 = \overline{4}000\text{ ft-lb}$$

22-6. Throttling Process. James Joule in collaboration with William Thomson (Lord Kelvin) investigated the forces between the molecules of a gas by means of a throttled expansion of the gas through a porous plug. Consider a gas forced by a pump to circulate as shown in Fig. 4. Follow a sample of gas between imaginary pistons shown dashed in Fig. 4b. As the gas passes through the plug or throttling valve, work equal to P_1V_1 is done on the chosen sample by the gas back of it on the high pressure side. As it passes through the valve, the gas does work equal to P_2V_2 on the gas ahead of it. The expansion takes place in a thermally insulated chamber. The stream velocities on the two sides of the valve are the same. Hence the first law of thermodynamics gives

$$Q = U_2 - U_1 + W = 0$$

But the net work is $W = P_2V_2 - P_1V_1$; hence

$$U_1 + P_1V_1 = U_2 + P_2V_2 = \text{constant} \qquad (13)$$

This result applies to all fluids and is of great importance in steam engineering and in refrigeration. The quantity $U + PV$, is called the *enthalpy*. The enthalpy per unit mass is tabulated for steam and for many refrigerants. The throttling process is the important one in the action of a refrigerator; it is the process that causes the drop in temperature needed for refrigeration. Liquids undergo a drop in

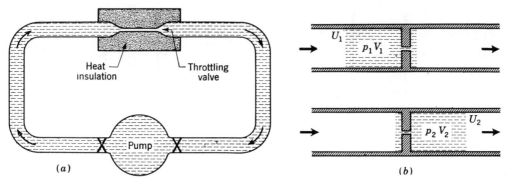

FIG. 4. Throttling process.

temperature and partial vaporization in a throttling process. However, a Joule-Thomson expansion of a gas may result in either cooling or heating, depending on the gas used and the initial temperature and pressure. Cooling is readily interpreted as due to the fact that work is done against the attractive forces between molecules. Heating is associated largely with changes that occur in PV during flow through the valve. The work P_1V_1 done on the gas about to enter the valve may be greater than the work P_2V_2 done by this gas on emerging from the valve.

22-7. Reversible and Irreversible Processes. Any process that can be made to go in the reverse direction by an infinitesimal change in the conditions is called a *reversible process*. No actual change is *fully* reversible, but many processes when carried out slowly are *practically* reversible.

The slow compression of a spring is practically a reversible process. If the compressing force is slightly decreased, the spring expands and performs work equal to the work done in compressing it. The slow evaporation of a substance in an insulated container is practically reversible, for if the temperature is slightly lowered condensation can be made to occur, returning energy to the heater until both it and the substance are in their original condition. The slow compression of a gas can be altered to expansion by a slight decrease in the force applied to the piston; hence this process, too, is reversible.

Any process that is not reversible is irreversible. All changes which occur suddenly or which involve friction or electrical resistance are inherently irreversible. An explosion is a highly irreversible change. Another type of irreversible process is represented by the following experiment. Let a flask containing air at atmospheric pressure be connected through a tube and stopcock with a second flask, which has been evacuated. If now the stopcock is opened, air rushes into the evacuated flask until the pressures in the two flasks become equal. No external work is done by the gas in expanding under these conditions, yet the gas cannot be restored to its original container and condition without energy from an outside source. The process is irreversible.

A cycle is a succession of changes that ends with the return of the body or system to its initial state. A reversible cycle is a cycle all of whose changes are reversible.

22-8. The Carnot Cycle. Carnot made important thermodynamic studies using an ideal, reversible heat engine, which operated through a sequence of isothermal and adiabatic steps now known as a *Carnot cycle*. The engine may be a cylinder (Fig. 5) fitted with a piston and filled with any substance that expands with rising temperature and decreasing pressure. We shall consider the working substance to be an ideal gas. The initial state of this working substance is represented by point A in Fig. 6. As a first step, the cylinder is placed in contact with a reservoir of heat and

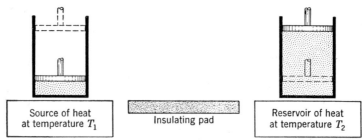

FIG. 5. Equipment for operation of a Carnot cycle.

the gas allowed to expand at constant temperature T_1 taking in heat Q_1, this change being represented by the isothermal curve AB. Next, the cylinder is insulated and expansion allowed to continue. This expansion is adiabatic, along BC, and the temperature drops from T_1 to T_2. The cylinder is then placed on a heat reservoir at temperature T_2, and the gas is compressed isothermally, along CD, the heat of compression Q_2 being transferred to the low temperature reservoir. Finally the cylinder is again insulated and the compression continued adiabatically, along DA, the gas now being heated to its original temperature T_1.

Let us examine the significance of the Carnot cycle diagram (Fig. 6).

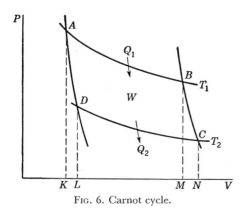

FIG. 6. Carnot cycle.

The area $ABMKA$ represents the energy Q_1 taken from the hot source and converted into work W in moving the piston.

The area $BCNMB$ represents the energy taken from the working substance in cooling it from T_1 to T_2.

The area $CNLDC$ represents the energy taken from the external machinery and given as heat Q_2 to the cool reservoir.

The area $ADLKA$ represents the energy taken from the external machinery and given to the working substance, heating it from T_2 to T_1.

The work done *by* the gas ($\int P\,dV$) in expanding from A to B to C equals the area under the upper curves, $ABCNKA$. The work done *on* the gas during compression from C to D to A equals the smaller area under the lower curves, $CDAKNC$. Area $ABCDA$ = the net useful work done by the heat engine during one cycle. This work is the difference between Q_1 the energy received from the hot reservoir and Q_2 the energy given to the cool reservoir.

$$\text{Eff.} = \frac{\text{output work}}{\text{input work}} = \frac{\text{area } ABCDA}{\text{area } ABMKA}$$

$$= \frac{Q_1 - Q_2}{Q_1} \quad (14)$$

We have thought of the working substance as an ideal gas, as an aid in visualizing the Carnot process. However, the results [Eq. (14)] are independent of the nature of the working substance.

22-9. Second Law of Thermodynamics. In each of the heat engine cycles described, we have seen that not all of the heat supplied to the engine is converted into useful work; some heat is always rejected to some outside reservoir. This is true of all heat engines and leads to an important generalization known as the *second law of thermodynamics: It is impossible for an engine unaided by external energy to* *transfer heat from one body to another at a higher temperature.*

Heat of its own accord will always flow from high temperature to low temperature. It is impossible to utilize the immense amount of heat in the ocean, for example, to run an engine unless there can be found a reservoir at a lower temperature into which the engine can discharge heat.

Whenever heat is transferred from low temperature to higher temperature, an expenditure of energy is required from some external source. This takes place in a refrigerator in which electrical energy is used to pump heat from the cool interior to the warmer room.

It follows from the second law of thermodynamics that a Carnot (reversible) heat engine has a greater efficiency than any other heat engine operating between the same temperature limits. If we assumed the contrary, then the more efficient engine could be used to run the reversible engine as a heat pump and we would have a self-acting pair transferring heat from low to high temperature. But this is contrary to experience. As a result of this type of reasoning we may conclude that the efficiency of a Carnot (reversible) engine represents the maximum efficiency any heat engine can have with the given temperatures.

22-10. The Absolute or Kelvin Temperature Scale. In each of the methods for measuring temperature that were discussed in earlier chapters, the results depend on the particular thermometric substance used. Most of the phenomena of heat depend on the properties of the particular substances involved. The efficiency of an ideal heat engine is unique in that it does not depend on the working substance or the particular mechanical device used.

Lord Kelvin (1827–1907) recognized the possibility of using an ideal heat-engine cycle to define a temperature scale which would be "absolute" in the sense that it did not depend on the thermometric substance. He suggested that temperatures on the absolute scale be

defined from the relation

$$\text{Eff.} = \frac{Q_1 - Q_2}{Q_1} = \frac{T_1 - T_2}{T_1} \quad (15)$$

giving

$$\frac{Q_2}{Q_1} = \frac{T_2}{T_1} \quad (16)$$

This equation states that any two temperatures are in the same ratio as the heat quantities absorbed and ejected in a Carnot cycle operated between those two temperatures.

Consider a Carnot cycle operating between two fixed temperatures, say, the boiling point of water (373°K) and the freezing point (273°K). There will be a certain area representing useful work (Fig. 7). We can define the temperature (323°K) midway between the boiling point and the freezing point as the temperature at which a Carnot engine operating between the boiling point and the midpoint does the same work, represented by area A, as the work represented by area B, done by a Carnot engine operating between the midpoint and the ice point. Obviously the interval so defined can be subdivided in the same manner, and the scale can be extended to

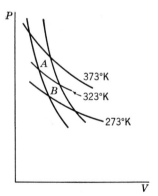

Fig. 7. Definition of absolute temperature from a Carnot cycle.

higher or lower temperatures. The temperature at which a Carnot engine ejects no heat would be the zero on the absolute temperature scale. Absolute zero may be thought of as the sink temperature T_2 of a Carnot engine operating at an efficiency of 100%.

The Kelvin or thermodynamic temperature scale is the same as the absolute scale determined by a perfect gas. Temperatures on this absolute scale are determined in practice with a gas thermometer, the readings being corrected for the deviation of the particular gas from the ideal gas law as calculated from certain other experiments.

22-11. The Efficiency of Heat Engines. The ideal or thermodynamic efficiency of a heat engine is defined from Eq. (15)

$$\text{Ideal efficiency} = \frac{T_1 - T_2}{T_1} = 1 - \frac{T_2}{T_1} \quad (17)$$

Owing to heat losses and friction, no actual engine ever attains the efficiency defined by Eq. (17). The ideal efficiency remains as an upper limit to the efficiency of any heat engine.

Example: A simple steam engine receives steam from the boiler at 180°C (about 150 lb/in.² gage pressure) and exhausts directly into the air at 100°C. What is the upper limit of its efficiency?

Ideal efficiency
$$= \frac{(180 + 273)°\text{K} - (100 + 273)°\text{K}}{(180 + 273)°\text{K}} = 0.176$$
$$= 17.6\%$$

SUMMARY

Energy is neither created nor destroyed, but it may be transformed from one form into another.

When mechanical energy is converted into heat, the amount of heat is proportional to the energy transformed

$$W = JQ$$

where J is called the *mechanical equivalent of heat*. Values of J are 4.19 joules/cal and 778 ft-lb/Btu.

The *first law of thermodynamics* states that

when heat is transformed into any other form of energy the total amount of energy is constant

$$Q = U_2 - U_1 + W$$

The specific heat of a gas at constant pressure is greater than its specific heat at constant volume, $c_p = c_v + R$.

An *isothermal* process is one occurring at constant temperature. For isothermal expansion of an ideal gas, $PV = $ constant. The work done in isothermal expansion of an ideal gas is

$$W = PV \ln \frac{V_2}{V_1}$$

An adiabatic process is one in which there is no exchange of heat with the surroundings. For adiabatic expansion of an ideal gas, $PV^\gamma = $ constant. The work done in adiabatic expansion of an ideal gas is

$$W = mc_v(T_1 - T_2)$$

A *reversible* process is one that is in equilibrium at each instant.

The *second law of thermodynamics* states that a heat engine cannot transfer heat from a body to another at higher temperature unless external energy is supplied to the engine.

Work can be obtained from a source of heat energy only by a process that transfers some of the heat to a reservoir at a temperature lower than that of the source.

The *Kelvin* or absolute temperature scale is independent of the thermometric substance, being based on the efficiency of an ideal heat engine.

The maximum efficiency of a heat engine supplied with heat at temperature T_1 and delivering heat to a reservoir at T_2 is

$$\text{Eff.} = \frac{T_1 - T_2}{T_1}$$

QUESTIONS   **1.** When is the conduction of heat a reversible process? when an irreversible process?

2. Why does air released through a tire valve feel cool to the hand?

3. Heat is transferred from the cool interior of an electric refrigerator to warmer surroundings. Show that this **is not a** violation of the second law of thermodynamics.

4. Trace the successive transformations by which sunlight is changed into the energy of an electric lamp.

5. Which of the following properties is most important in the selection of a refrigerant for a cyclic process refrigerator: (*a*) large specific heat, (*b*) high specific gravity, (*c*) large heat of vaporization, or (*d*) high vapor pressure?

6. Which is the most important characteristic of a material suitable for use as a working substance in a turbine: (*a*) a low viscosity, (*b*) a low freezing point, or (*c*) a high boiling point?

7. What becomes of wasted energy?

8. What becomes of work done by a pump in compressing air?

9. It is said that 3000 kg-cal in food are required every day for an average adult. What becomes of this energy?

10. What determines the efficiency of heat engines? Why is it generally so low?

11. Discuss the reasoning which leads to the idea of an absolute temperature. Explain the steps needed in defining an absolute scale. Can there be more than one absolute scale of temperature?

12. It has been asserted that the temperature of interstellar space is 2°K. What meaning is to be attributed to this statement?

13. Describe the condition of a "gas" at the absolute zero of temperature.

14. Explain how very low temperatures can be obtained with compressed gases.

15. In making a freezing bath or vapor trap, why does one put acetone or alcohol on the "dry ice"?

16. Of what practical value is liquid air? liquid helium?

17. How hot can a given mass be heated? How cold can a given mass be cooled?

18. Two samples of a gas initially at the same temperature and pressure are compressed from a volume V to a volume $\frac{1}{2}V$, one isothermally, the other adiabatically. In which sample is the pressure greater?

19. In which form will a given kind of fuel produce the greatest amount of heat if combustion is started at the same temperature and if equal quantities of fuel are completely burned: (*a*) a finely divided solid, (*b*) a liquid, and (*c*) a vapor?

PROBLEMS   **1.** A calorimeter of copper, specific heat 0.10 cal/gm C° and mass 300 gm, contains 120 gm of ice water and 50 gm of ice. The mixture is stirred by a rotating paddle which requires a torque of 10^8 cm-dynes to drive it. What would be the number of revolutions necessary to bring the mixture to 25°C?

2. Compute a value for the mechanical equivalent of heat from the following data obtained with apparatus similar to that of Fig. 1. Total mass allowed to fall = 2600 gm. Distance of fall = 160 cm. Number of descents = 20. The rise in temperature was 0.30 C° in the calorimeter which was thermally equivalent to 630 gm of water. Would experimental errors be likely to lead to a value for J which was too large or too small? Why?   *Ans.* 4.3 joules/cal

3. A 250-gm copper calorimeter contains 550 gm of oil. The oil is stirred by a 300-gm steel paddle. A couple of moment 6.0×10^6 cm-dynes is applied to rotate the paddle. Calculate the rise in temperature produced after 1000 revolutions. The specific heats are as follows: copper, 0.092; oil, 0.511; and steel, 0.114 cal/gm C°.

4. A 5.0-lb lead ball of specific heat 0.032 Btu/lb F° is thrown downward from a 50-ft building with an initial vertical speed of 20 ft/sec. If half of its energy at the instant of impact with the ground is converted to heat and absorbed by the ball, what will be its rise of temperature?   *Ans.* 1.1 F°

5. Mercury falls from a height of 12 m on a nonconducting surface. How much is the temperature of the mercury raised? The specific heat of mercury is 0.033 cal/gm C°.

6. At what speed must a lead bullet at 20°C strike an iron target in order that the heat produced on impact be just sufficient to melt the bullet assuming no heat is lost to the surroundings? Lead has a specific heat of 0.032 cal/gm C°, its melting point is 327°C, and the heat of fusion is 5.4 cal/gm.   *Ans.* $3\bar{6}0$ m/sec

7. A cylindrical brass tube closed at the ends has an internal length of 150 cm and is filled with 175 gm of water. The tube contains 36 gm of lead shot. Starting from the vertical position, the tube is rapidly reversed end for end 250 times. Find the rise in temperature of the water. Neglect the thermal capacity of the brass and the space occupied by the lead.

8. What quantity of butter (6000 cal/gm) would supply the energy needed for a 160-lb man to ascend to the top of Mt. Washington, elevation 6288 ft?

Ans. 0.12 lb

9. The brakes are set on a car weighing 2.5 tons so that it coasts down a hill at a uniform speed. How much heat is developed in the brakes if the car descends a vertical distance of 400 ft?

10. A 200-ton train has its speed reduced from 40 to 30 mi/hr in 0.50 min. If the whole of the work done against the frictional resistance of the brakes is converted into heat, find the heat developed.   *Ans.* $1\bar{2}$,000 Btu

11. In drilling a hole in a casting, power is supplied at the rate of 0.40 hp for 2.5 min. How many Btu of heat are developed?

12. How much heat (expressed in Btu) is produced in stopping by friction a 112-lb flywheel rotating 1.0 rev/sec, if the mass is concentrated in the rim of mean radius 2.0 ft?   *Ans.* 0.35 Btu

13. A portable power plant develops 15 kw-hr of electric energy, while its gasoline engine consumes 2.0 gal of fuel whose heating value is 13×10^4 Btu/gal. What is the efficiency of the power plant?

14. How many tons of coal per hour are consumed by a locomotive working at the rate of $3\bar{0}00$ hp if the heat of combustion of the coal is 12,000 Btu/lb and the over-all efficiency is 9.0%?   *Ans.* 3.5 tons

15. What is the cost of the coal needed to produce a kilowatt-hour of electric energy, if the coal costs 1.0 cent per kilogram, the heat of combustion is 9500 cal/gm, and the over-all efficiency is 25%?

16. A steam engine operates at an over-all efficiency of 15%. How much heat must be supplied per hour in order to develop 3.0 hp?   *Ans.* 5.1×10^4 Btu

17. What is the actual efficiency of a gas engine which consumes 22 ft³ of gas per hour when delivering 1.1 hp, the gas having a heating value of 550 Btu/ft³?

18. If the energy of the fuel were fully utilized, how many gallons of gasoline of heat of combustion $2\bar{1}$,000 Btu/lb would be needed to propel a 3600-lb car to the top of a 5000-ft mountain? The weight of 1.0 gal of gasoline is 6.2 lb.

Ans. 0.18 gal

19. A 10,000-ton ship is raised 16 ft in the locks of a canal. (*a*) What is the thermal equivalent (in Btu) of the work done? (*b*) How much coal (heating value 12,000 Btu/lb) would be required to produce this energy?

20. On test a steam plant was found to use 2.0 lb of coal ($1\bar{2}$,000 Btu/lb) for every horsepower-hour supplied by the engines. What proportion of the heat obtained from the coal was turned into work? What became of the rest of the heat?   *Ans.* 11%

21. A volume of 1500 cm³ of air at 20°C and 76 cm of mercury pressure is confined in a cylinder provided with a frictionless piston. How much external work is done by the trapped air in expanding at constant pressure as its temperature is raised to 100°C? Of the heat which must be supplied to effect this change, how much goes into external work? The specific heat of air at constant pressure is 0.237 cal/gm C°.

22. The weight-density of steam at 212°F is 0.0373 lb/ft³. What is the heat equivalent of expanding water (weight-density 60 lb/ft³ at 212°F) into steam against the force due to atmospheric pressure? What fraction of the total heat of vaporization does this represent?   *Ans.* 73 Btu/lb; 7.5%

23. A certain quantity of air at 76 cm of mercury pressure is compressed adiabatically to two-thirds of its initial volume. Calculate the final pressure.

24. A quantity of air at a pressure of 76 cm of mercury is suddenly compressed to half its volume. (*a*) Calculate the new pressure. (*b*) What would the pressure be if the change were isothermal?

Ans. 2̄00 cm of mercury; 1̄50 cm of mercury

25. Compute the work done in the adiabatic expansion of an ideal gas from state (P_1V_1) to state (P_2V_2).

26. A certain gas at constant temperature obeys the equation

$$\left(P + \frac{a}{V^2}\right)(V - b) = K = \text{constant}$$

Calculate the work done when this gas expands from V_1 to V_2.

$$\text{Ans. } K \log_e \frac{V_2 - b}{V_1 - b} - a\left(\frac{1}{V_1} - \frac{1}{V_2}\right)$$

27. Derive an expression for converting a temperature from the Fahrenheit scale to the Kelvin scale.

28. At what temperature are the readings on the Fahrenheit scale and the Kelvin scale the same?   Ans. 574°

29. What is the thermodynamic efficiency of a steam engine which operates with a boiler temperature of 177°C and a condenser temperature of 77°C?

30. A combination mercury-steam turbine takes saturated mercury vapor from a boiler at 875°F and exhausts it to heat a steam boiler at 460°F. The steam turbine receives steam at this temperature and discharges it to a condenser at 100°F. What is the maximum efficiency of the combination?   *Ans.* 58.0%

31. An ideal gas engine operates in a Carnot cycle between 227°C and 127°C. It absorbs 5.0 × 10⁴ cal at the higher temperature. What amount of work (joules) is this engine theoretically capable of performing?

32. The temperature of steam from the boiler of an engine of 10 hp is 390°F and the condenser temperature is 176°F. How much heat must leave the boiler per hour if the efficiency is 20% of that of a reversible engine working between the same limits of temperature?   *Ans.* 5.1 × 10⁵ Btu

33. An engine works in a Carnot cycle between the temperatures 105°C and 15°C. If the work done in the cycle is 1200 newton-m, how much heat is taken in at the higher temperature?

34. In a mechanical refrigerator the low-temperature coils are at a temperature of −37°C, and the compressed gas in the condenser has a temperature of 62°C. What is the theoretical maximum efficiency?   *Ans.* 30%

35. Consider a mechanical refrigerator as a heat engine transferring heat from the cooling coils at $-10°C$ to the room whose temperature is 20°C. How many kilowatt-hours of electric energy are needed to form 4.0 lb of ice at $-10°C$ from water at 20°C?

36. Consider an ideal, reversible heat engine which transfers heat from a room at 17°C to the outdoors at $-5°C$. (*a*) What is the maximum efficiency of this engine? (*b*) If the heat engine is reversed and is used to pump heat from outdoors into the room, energy being supplied by an electric motor, how many joules of heat will be delivered to the room for the expenditure of 1.0 joule of electric energy?   *Ans.* 0.076; 13 joules

37. A one-cylinder four-cycle gas engine operates at an average effective pressure of 175 lb/in.^{2} It has a 6.0-in. stroke, a piston area of 12.0 in.^{2}, and a speed of 2600 rev/min. What is the indicated horsepower of the engine?

SOUND

23. *Wave Motion*

One of the problems of modern industry is the transportation of energy from the place at which it is available to the place at which it can be used most effectively. The principal methods by which energy is transferred from place to place are by motion of particles, by a bodily motion of large masses of material, and by *wave motion*. Each of these types of transmission is of great importance in its proper place.

The transfer of electric energy by wire is an example of particle transmission. Charged particles (electrons) move through the wire to supply energy to any point in the circuit. Heat energy is conducted through a metal bar by the collisions between molecules as they are agitated in the metal. Air currents set up by unequal heating of the surface of the earth transmit energy that can be harnessed at any place the wind blows. The ocean tides are another source of energy of a fluid body.

Energy from the sun reaches us in large amounts. By far the greatest part of this comes as a wave motion. Radiant energy traverses the space between sun and earth with neither particles nor bodily motion of a fluid. Sounds reach our ears by means of waves in the air around us. Radio signals are waves that are used to transmit music or speech. Waves in strings or air columns are used in producing musical sounds. All waves have certain properties in common.

23-1. Waves. If a stone is dropped into a quiet pool of water, a disturbance is created where the rock enters the liquid. However, the disturbance is not confined to that place alone but spreads out so that it eventually reaches all parts of the pool.

When the stone enters the water, it sets into motion the particles of water with which it comes in contact. These particles set into motion neighboring particles. They in turn produce similar motion in others and so on until the disturbance reaches particles at the edge of the pool. In all this disturbance no particle moves far from its initial position. Only the disturbance moves through the water. This behavior is characteristic of all wave motions. The particles move over short paths about their initial positions and as a result a wave moves through the medium. *A wave is a disturbance that moves through a medium.* The medium as a whole does not progress in the direction of motion of the wave.

The motion of the wave through the medium is a result of the action of the particles of the medium on each other. Hence a particle wave can travel only in an *elastic* medium. If the particles were entirely independent of each other, no wave could pass through.

There are several types of waves, their classification being made in accordance with the motion of the individual particles. The most common types are *transverse* waves and *longitudinal* waves but other types are frequently observed.

23-2. Transverse Waves. When the motions of the individual particles of the medium are perpendicular to the direction in which the wave advances, the wave is called a *transverse* wave. Such a wave travels along a stretched cord if one section is displaced slightly in a direction at right angles to the cord and then released. In Fig. 1 are depicted

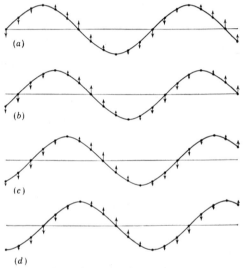

FIG. 1. Particle motion in a transverse wave.

several successive stages in the motion of the particles of a medium through which a transverse wave is passing. Each particle is assumed to be vibrating with simple harmonic motion about its equilibrium position on the straight line, the path of vibration being perpendicular to that line. From left to right, each successive particle is behind the previous one in phase in its vibration. The arrows indicate the magnitude and direction of the velocity of each of the particles pictured. In Fig. 1a the position and velocity of selected particles of the medium are shown at a given instant. Starting at the left, the first three particles shown are moving downward, the fourth is at the end of its path and momentarily at rest, the next five are moving upward, and so on. In Fig. 1b, c, and d are shown the positions and velocities of these same particles at successive *equal* intervals of time after a. We note that while no single particle moves to the right, the *shape of the medium*, that is, the wave, moves to the right. As the up-and-down motion of the particles continues, the wave moves farther and farther to the right. The wave is thus a transverse wave.

It is only when the particles are close enough to exert relatively large forces on one another that they are able to set each other into this type of vibration. In a gas the molecules are too far apart to transmit such motion, and hence a transverse wave does not travel through a gas.

23-3. Longitudinal Waves. When the motions of the individual particles of the medium are *parallel* to the direction in which the wave travels, the wave is called a *longitudinal* wave. In Fig. 2, successive positions of selected particles are shown. In a, the particles are in their equilibrium positions. Their positions at some instant after they start to vibrate with simple harmonic motion are shown in b. Successive positions after equal intervals of time are shown in c, d, and e. We note that while

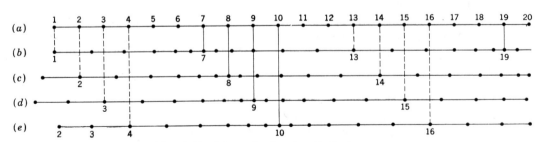

FIG. 2. Particle motion in a longitudinal wave.

each particle merely vibrates about its equilibrium position a *configuration,* ·or arrangement of particles, moves steadily to the right. The longitudinal wave moves to the right through the medium.

In *b, c, d,* and *e,* the distribution of particles is not uniform. In places they are closer together than normal and in others they are farther apart than normal. These *compressions* and *rarefactions* follow each other through the medium. This type of wave is also called a *compressional wave.* Sound waves are longitudinal (compressional) waves. Note that maximum or minimum compression does not coincide with maximum displacement. In Fig. 2*b* maximum pressure is seen to be at particles 7 and 19, but for these particles the displacement is zero. So also we find maximum pressure and zero displacement at particles 8 and 20 of *c,* 9 of *d,* and 10 of *e.* Likewise minimum pressure is observed where the displacement is zero as at *b* 1 and 13, *c* 2 and 14, *d* 3 and 15, *e* 4 and 16. The pressure wave, that is, the wave in which the pressure is considered as the property that varies, is out of phase with the displacement wave by 90° or a quarter wave.

Any elastic medium is able to transmit a compressional wave. Solids, liquids, and gases are all suitable mediums for the propagation of compressional waves. Elastic waves in gases and liquids are longitudinal; in solids they may be either longitudinal or transverse, or both.

23-4. Water Waves. In a liquid the motion of the particles may be neither purely transverse nor purely longitudinal but a combination of the two. In the latter case the path followed by the particle is either a circle or an ellipse. In Fig. 3 are shown the paths of selected particles, their positions and the wave shape at two different times, the wave having traveled to the right between these instants. Waves in deep water are of this type.

23-5. Wave Properties. In observing waves, we note several of their characteristics. Waves travel uniformly with a definite speed through a uniform medium. Also, if we watch a single spot we see that waves pass that spot at regular intervals of time. In the wave motion such factors as wave speed, frequency, phase, wavelength, and amplitude must be considered.

23-6. Wave Speed. The speed of a wave is the distance it advances per unit time. The speed depends upon the type of wave, properties of the medium, and, in some cases, the frequency of the wave. A few cases are of sufficient interest to warrant consideration of the factors that determine the wave speed.

One common type of wave is a transverse wave in a flexible cord. If the cord is fastened at one end and the other is held so that the tension is small, when the cord is plucked the wave travels slowly down the cord. If the tension is increased, the wave is observed to travel faster. If a heavy cord is used, the wave is observed to travel more slowly than when a lighter cord is used. The speed of this type of wave is determined by two factors, the tension in the cord and the mass per unit length of the cord.

$$v = \sqrt{\frac{F}{m/l}} \qquad (1)$$

where v is the speed of the wave, F is the tension in the cord, and m/l is the mass per unit length of the cord. In the cgs system of units, F is expressed in dynes, m/l in grams per centimeter, and hence v is in centimeters per

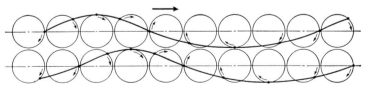

FIG. 3. Particle motion in a water wave.

second. In the usual British units, m is in slugs (W/g), F is in pounds, l in feet, and v in feet per second. In the mks system, m is in kilograms, l is in meters, F is in newtons, and v is in meters per second.

Example: A cord 80 cm long has a mass of 0.288 gm. What is the speed of a transverse wave in this cord when it is stretched by a load of 2.0 kg?

$$v = \sqrt{\frac{F}{m/l}}$$

$$\frac{m}{l} = \frac{0.288 \text{ gm}}{80 \text{ cm}} = 0.0036 \text{ gm/cm}$$

$$F = mg = 2000 \text{ gm} \times 980 \text{ cm/sec}^2$$

$$v = \sqrt{\frac{2000 \text{ gm} \times 980 \text{ cm/sec}^2}{0.0036 \text{ gm/cm}}}$$

$$= 2.3 \times 10^4 \text{ cm/sec} = 2\bar{3}0 \text{ m/sec}$$

The speed of a compressional wave in an elastic medium depends only on the modulus of elasticity E of the medium and its density ρ. The speed is given by the expression

$$v = \sqrt{\frac{E}{\rho}} \qquad (2)$$

For an extended medium (liquid or gas), E represents the bulk modulus. For a solid rod, E represents Young's modulus. In the metric system, if E is expressed in dynes per square centimeter and ρ in grams per cubic centimeter, Eq. (2) gives the speed in centimeters per second. In the British system, E is expressed in pounds per square foot rather than pounds per square inch. The density ρ, (D/g), must be expressed in slugs per cubic foot. The speed will then be in feet per second. In the mks system E is in newtons per square meter, ρ in kilograms per cubic meter, and v in meters per second.

Example: Find the speed of a compressional wave in an iron rod whose specific gravity is 7.7 and whose Young's modulus is 27.5×10^6 lb/in.^{2}

$$v = \sqrt{\frac{E}{\rho}} = \sqrt{\frac{Eg}{D}}$$

$$E = (27.5 \times 10^6) \text{ lb/in.}^2$$
$$= (27.5 \times 10^6 \times 144) \text{ lb/ft}^2$$
$$D = (7.7 \times 62.4) \text{ lb/ft}^3$$

$$v = \sqrt{\frac{27.5 \times 10^6 \times 144 \text{ lb/ft}^2 \times 32 \text{ ft/sec}^2}{7.7 \times 62.4 \text{ lb/ft}^3}}$$

$$= 1\bar{6},000 \text{ ft/sec}$$

23-7. Phase, Frequency, Period, and Wavelength. All the particles of the medium in which there is a wave motion vibrate about their respective positions of equilibrium in the same manner, but they reach corresponding positions in their paths at different times. These relative positions represent the *phase* of the motion. Two particles are in the same phase if they have the same displacement and are moving in the same direction. In Fig. 1*a* the second and the fourteenth particles are the same distance above the axis and both are moving downward and hence they are in the same phase. In the successive diagrams, these two particles are always in phase. Similarly the third and fifteenth are in phase, the fourth and sixteenth, etc. The twelfth particle is the same distance from the axis as the second but is below the axis rather than above. Hence these particles are not in the same phase. If two waves are moving through the same medium, they are said to be in phase if the motions of the particles due to the two waves are in phase.

If we observe the waves as they pass a point, we note that they are regularly spaced in time. The number of waves which pass a point per unit time is the *frequency f* of the wave motion. The time required for a single wave to pass is called the *period T* of the wave motion. The frequency is thus the reciprocal of the period

$$f = \frac{1}{T} \qquad (3)$$

The phase of the vibrating particle can be expressed in terms of the period of vibration. It is that fraction of the period that has elapsed since the particle passed through its position of equilibrium moving in the positive direction. Phase may be expressed in time, that is, as a fraction of a period, or in angular measure where one complete cycle represents $360°$ or 2π radians. Thus in Fig. 1*a* the seventh and nineteenth particles are passing through the equilibrium position and moving in the positive direction. The phase of each of these particles is zero. One-twelfth of a period has elapsed since the sixth particle was in the equilibrium position. Its phase is thus one-twelfth period or 30° or $2\pi/12$ radian ahead of the seventh in phase. Similarly particle four has a phase of one-fourth period or 90° or $\pi/2$ radians. The eighth particle is one-twelfth period behind the seventh in phase. Its phase would be negative one-twelfth period or $-30°$ or $-\pi/6$ radian.

The displacement of the particle can be expressed in terms of the phase angle. If y represents the displacement of a given particle and A the maximum displacement

$$y = A \sin \theta \qquad (4)$$

The angle θ is zero when the phase is zero as defined above. Since θ changes from 0 to 2π in the time of one period T, we may write

$$\theta = \frac{2\pi}{T} t$$

or $\theta = 2\pi ft$. Then

$$y = A \sin \frac{2\pi}{T} t = A \sin 2\pi ft \qquad (5)$$

where t is the time in seconds after zero phase.

The *wavelength* is the distance between two successive particles that are in the same phase. In Fig. 1, the wavelength is the distance from the second to the fourteenth particle, from the third to the fifteenth, etc. We shall represent wavelength by the Greek letter λ (lambda).

There is a simple relationship between speed, frequency, and wavelength, which holds true for all types of waves. It is given by the important equation

$$v = f\lambda \qquad (6)$$

If the wave passes from one medium into another, the speed changes. In this process the frequency remains the same, but the wavelength will change in proportion to the speed; if v increases, λ also increases.

Example: What is the wavelength in an iron rod, $v = 1.6 \times 10^4$ ft/sec, for a compressional wave whose frequency is 250 per sec? What will be the wavelength of this compressional wave when it emerges into air where the speed is 1.1×10^3 ft/sec?

In iron

$$\lambda = \frac{v}{f} = \frac{1.6 \times 10^4 \text{ ft/sec}}{250/\text{sec}} = 64 \text{ ft}$$

In air

$$\lambda = \frac{v}{f} = \frac{1.1 \times 10^3 \text{ ft/sec}}{250/\text{sec}} = 4.4 \text{ ft}$$

23-8. Amplitude; Transmission of Energy. The amplitude of a wave is identical with the amplitude of vibration of the particles of the medium. The *amplitude* is the maximum displacement of the particle from its equilibrium position. In a study of wave motion, consideration of amplitude is important because of its relation to the transmission of energy.

In all waves energy travels through the medium in the direction in which the wave travels. Each particle of the medium has energy of vibration and passes energy on to the succeeding particles.

In simple harmonic motion, where there is no damping, the energy of the vibrating particle changes from kinetic to potential and back, with the total energy constant. We may get this constant energy by finding the maximum kinetic energy

$$W = \frac{1}{2} m(v_{max})^2 = \frac{1}{2} m \left(\frac{2\pi A}{T}\right)^2 = \frac{1}{2} m(2\pi fA)^2 = 2\pi^2 mf^2 A^2 \qquad (7)$$

where A is the amplitude of vibration, T is the period, f is the frequency, and m is the mass of the vibrating particle.

As a wave passes through a medium the energy per unit volume in the medium is the energy per particle times the number n of particles per unit volume

$$\frac{W}{V} = n2\pi^2 mf^2 A^2 \qquad (8)$$

But nm is the density ρ of the medium; hence

$$\frac{W}{V} = 2\pi^2\rho f^2 A^2 \qquad (9)$$

The transfer of energy per unit time per unit area perpendicular to the direction of motion of the wave is called the *intensity I* of the wave. The energy that travels through such an area per unit time is that contained in a cylinder of unit cross section and of length numerically equal to the speed v of the wave. From Eq. (9)

$$I = 2\pi^2 v\rho f^2 A^2 \qquad (10)$$

We see that the intensity is directly proportional to the square of the amplitude and to the square of the frequency.

When a wave travels out in a uniform medium from a point source, the energy at some instant is passing through the surface of a sphere. At a later instant the same energy is passing through a larger spherical surface. The amount of energy per unit area per second, the intensity, is less at the second surface than at the first. Since the total energy per unit time is the same at the two surfaces, the intensity is inversely proportional to the area $4\pi r^2$ of the surface.

$$I = \frac{k_1}{4\pi r^2} = \frac{k_2}{r^2} \qquad (11)$$

Equation (11) expresses the fact that the intensity of a wave from a small source varies inversely as the square of the distance from the source when the wave diverges uniformly in all directions.

If in place of a point source we have a line source, the energy is spread over a cylindrical surface. Again the energy spreads over successively larger surfaces and the intensity is inversely proportional to the area $2\pi rl$ of the cylindrical surface

$$I = \frac{k_3}{2\pi rl} = \frac{k_4}{r} \qquad (12)$$

For cylindrical divergence, the intensity is inversely proportional to the first power of the distance.

If a plane source is large, that is, large compared to the distance from the source, the surface over which the energy spreads is a plane and the areas of successive planes are the same. In this case the intensity is independent of the distance.

As a wave passes through any material medium, energy is absorbed by the medium. Thus the energy passing through each surface, and hence the intensity, decreases faster than is expected from the change in area alone. The decrease in intensity due to absorption is called *damping* and a wave whose intensity decreases for this reason is called a *damped* wave.

23-9. Certain Characteristics of Wave Motion. Whenever a wave moves out from a source in a uniform medium, it *travels in straight lines*. In judging the position of an object by sight or sound we always assume this characteristic of the light or sound wave. At the boundary of a single medium the wave may be *reflected*. Water waves are reflected at the banks of the pool; sound waves are reflected at walls or other large surfaces; light waves are reflected by mirrors.

If a wave passes from one medium to another in which there is a different speed, the direction of travel is changed. This phenomenon is known as *refraction*. Refraction also occurs within a single nonuniform medium. The bending of light as it passes from air into the glass of a lens and emerges into air again is an example of refraction.

When two waves travel simultaneously through a single medium, each wave proceeds as though the other were not present. In this sense the waves do not interfere with each other. However, at each point in the medium, the disturbance produced is the resultant of the individual disturbances. At points where the two waves arrive in phase with each other the disturbance is the sum of the two and there is a maximum; at those points where the two waves arrive out of phase by 180° the disturbance is the difference of the two and at these points there is a minimum of disturbance. This phenomenon is known as *interference*. Where the waves arrive in phase the interference is *constructive;* where they arrive 180° out of phase the interference is *destructive*.

The bending of a wave around an obstacle is called *diffraction*. Diffraction is readily observed as water waves bend around a stick placed in water or as sound passes from one room through the door and spreads into a second room.

Straight-line propagation, reflection, refraction, interference, and diffraction are characteristics common to all waves. Their presence or absence may serve as a test as to whether a phenomenon has a wave nature.

23-10. Standing Waves. When two wave trains, of the same frequency and amplitude and having proper phase relations, travel in opposite directions through a medium, *standing* or *stationary waves* are set up. Standing waves can be set up by waves from two separate sources traveling in the same medium. They are more common, however, when waves from a single source are reflected. For example, one may tie one end of a string to a hook in a wall and set up waves in the string by moving the free end. The waves that travel toward the wall are reflected at the fixed end and travel away from the wall. If the string is of suitable length, the two sets of traveling waves produce standing waves.

The production of standing waves in this manner is shown in Fig. 4. In this diagram waves traveling toward the right are represented by dotted curves and those traveling to the left by dashed curves. The resultant wave is shown by the heavy solid line. In *a* the two waves are coincident and the resultant displacement of the cord at each point is the sum of the two displacements due to the individual waves. The resultant displacement curve is similar to the individual curves but of double amplitude. A quarter period later (*b*), each wave has progressed a quarter wavelength; the displacements at each point are equal in magnitude but opposite in direction and the

resultant displacement is everywhere zero. Figure 4c and *d* show the individual and resultant displacements of the cord at one-half and three-quarters of a period. The resultant displacements for a whole period are shown in Fig. 4e. It is seen that at certain points,

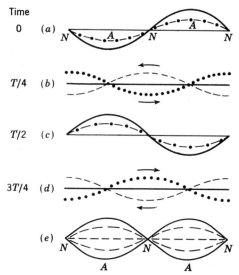

Fig. 4. Production of standing waves by two progressing waves traveling in opposite directions; curves *a*, *b*, *c*, and *d* show displacements of the particles due to the two waves and the resultant displacement at fractions of a period 0, $T/4$, $T/2$, and $3T/4$; curve *e* shows the position of the nodes N and the antinodes A in the stationary wave.

marked N, there is no displacement of the cord at any time. These points of no vibration are called *nodes*. At other points, marked A, the displacement varies from zero to a maximum. These points of maximum vibration are called *antinodes* or *loops*. At the nodes the initial and reflected waves always cancel the effects of each other, while at the antinodes the two waves add up to give maximum disturbance. Nodes and antinodes exist only in *standing* waves. The distance between a node and an adjacent antinode is a quarter wavelength; the distance between two successive nodes or between two successive antinodes is a half wavelength. Most vibrating bodies vibrate normally in such a manner that standing waves are set up in the body. In musical instruments the strings or the air column or other vibrating members have sets of standing waves with their nodes and antinodes.

SUMMARY

A *wave* is a disturbance that travels through a medium.

Energy is transmitted by waves.

In *transverse* waves, the particles of the medium vibrate in paths perpendicular to the direction the wave moves. In *longitudinal* waves, the paths in which the particles vibrate are parallel to the direction of motion of the wave.

The *speed* of a wave is the distance it moves per unit time. The speed depends upon the kind of wave and the properties of the medium. For a transverse wave in a string

$$v = \sqrt{\frac{F}{m/l}}$$

For a longitudinal or compressional wave

$$v = \sqrt{\frac{E}{\rho}}$$

Frequency is the number of waves per second which pass a point.

Period is the time required for one wave to pass the point in question.

$$f = \frac{1}{T}$$

Wavelength λ is the distance between two adjacent particles in the same phase.

Two particles are in the same *phase* if they have the same displacement from the equilibrium position and are moving in the same direction.

The displacement at a time t is given by

$$y = A \sin \frac{2\pi}{T} t = A \sin 2\pi f t$$

Speed v, frequency f, and wavelength λ are related by the expression

$$v = f\lambda$$

Amplitude is the maximum displacement of a particle in the wave motion.

The *intensity* of a wave is the transfer of energy per unit time per unit area perpendicular to the direction of motion of the wave. The intensity is proportional to the square of the amplitude

$$I = 2\pi^2 v\rho f^2 A^2$$

When waves travel uniformly in all directions from a small source, the intensity varies inversely as the square of the distance.

All waves show the following characteristics: straight line propagation, reflection, refraction, interference, diffraction.

Standing waves may be set up when two waves of equal frequency and equal amplitude travel in opposite directions through a medium. In the standing wave, there are nodes and antinodes. A *node* is a point of no vibration, while an *antinode* is a point of maximum vibration. The distance between successive nodes (or antinodes) is a half wavelength.

QUESTIONS   1. Describe a simple experiment that illustrates longitudinal waves; transverse waves. Of what does each wave consist?

2. Wind blowing over a wheat field sets up a series of waves. Describe the motion of the waves and that of the heads of grain.

3. Draw a diagram representing some form of wave motion, and indicate five characteristics of a wave. Define each.

4. Could a wave motion be set up in which the parts of the medium vibrate with angular simple harmonic motion? If so, describe such a wave.

5. In discussing transverse and longitudinal waves, it was assumed that the particles vibrate in simple harmonic motion. Could either type of wave exist if the vibratory motion were not simple harmonic?

6. If a single disturbance sends out both transverse and longitudinal waves

that travel with known speeds in the medium, how could the distance to the point of disturbance be determined?

7. Draw a diagram showing two transverse waves (*a*) having the same wavelength but amplitudes in the ratio of 2/1, (*b*) with the same amplitudes but wavelengths in the ratio of 1/2, and (*c*) with the same amplitude and the same wavelength but differing in phase by 90°.

8. As water waves spread out over the surface of a pond, how does the intensity vary with the distance from the source? How does the amplitude vary?

9. When two waves interfere, does one change the progress of the other? Explain.

10. What happens to a wave motion when it comes to the boundary of a medium? Distinguish between the effects at a "free" and at a "fixed" boundary.

11. Assuming that the solid wall between two rooms will not transmit a sound wave, is it possible for sound produced in one room to be heard in the other? If so, what wave processes are involved?

12. When a new phenomenon is observed in which there is a transfer of energy, there may be a question as to whether it is a particle or a wave phenomenon. What experiments could be used as tests?

13. Can more than one set of standing waves be present simultaneously within a single medium?

14. How might one locate the positions of nodes and antinodes in a vibrating body?

15. If a uniform metal plate is held at its mid-point and the edge stroked by a rosined bow it will vibrate. How might sand on such a plate be used to show the positions of the nodes?

16. How might fine dust on the body of a violin be used to show how the violin is vibrating?

PROBLEMS   **1.** A 50-ft rope weighs 2.0 lb and is stretched by a force of 150 lb. A wave is started down the rope by plucking it. What is the speed of the wave? If the stretching force were doubled how would the speed be changed?

2. A piano string is 2.5 ft long and weighs 6.0 oz. If it is stretched by a force of 1000 lb, what is the speed of the wave set up when the hammer strikes the string?   *Ans.* 460 ft/sec

3. A 16-lb steel wire, 100 ft long, is stretched between two poles under a tension of 500 lb. If the wire is struck transversely at one end, how long will it take for the wave to travel to the far end and return?

4. Find the speed of a compressional wave in an aluminum rod.
                                                    Ans. 1.7×10^4 ft/sec

5. Find the speed of a compressional wave in mercury. The specific gravity of mercury is 13.6 and the bulk modulus is 36×10^6 lb/in.^{2}.

6. From the speed of a compressional wave in water, 4750 ft/sec at 20°C, compute the adiabatic bulk modulus for water. Compare it with the isothermal value listed in Table 2, Chap 13.   *Ans.* 0.31×10^6 lb/in.^{2}

7. What must be the stress in a stretched steel wire in order for the speed of longitudinal waves to be equal to 100 times the speed of transverse waves?

8. Two waves whose frequencies are 20.0 and 30.0/sec travel out from a common point. How will they differ in phase at the end of 0.75 sec? *Ans.* 180°

9. Two waves whose frequencies are 500 and 511/sec travel out from a common point. Find their difference in phase after 1.40 sec.

10. A wave has a frequency of 13/sec and an amplitude of 2.0 in. Assuming the motion of the particles of the medium to be simple harmonic, find the displacement and the speed of the particle 0.33 sec after it is in the equilibrium position.   *Ans.* 1.9 in.; 40 in./sec

11. A wave has a period of 0.030 sec and an amplitude of 0.50 cm. Assuming the motion of the particle to be simple harmonic, find the displacement and speed of the particle at the instant that the phase is 60°.

12. The adiabatic bulk modulus of water is 2.14×10^{10} dynes/cm². Find the speed of a compressional wave in water. What is the wavelength in water of a compressional wave whose frequency is 400/sec?   *Ans.* 1.46×10^5 cm/sec; 365 cm

13. A string 2.0 ft long weighs 1.2 oz. Find the speed of a transverse wave in the string when the tension is 100 lb. If the wavelength is twice the length of the string, what is the frequency of vibration?

14. The adiabatic bulk modulus for a gas is γP. What is the wavelength in air at 0°C and 760 mm of mercury of a compressional wave whose frequency is 250/sec?   *Ans.* 132 cm

15. Compute the wavelength in hydrogen at standard temperature and pressure of a compressional wave whose frequency is 600/sec.

16. A compressional wave with frequency 300/sec travels through air at standard temperature and pressure with a speed of 331 m/sec. What is the amplitude of vibration when the intensity of the wave is 1.0×10^{-10} watt/cm²?   *Ans.* 3.6×10^{-6} cm

17. Two waves whose frequencies are 200 and 220/sec travel through a medium with a speed of 330 m/sec. If the sources are in phase, how do the waves differ in phase 2.00 m from the sources?

18. Two waves each of frequency 540/sec travel at a speed of 330 m/sec. If the sources are in phase, what is the phase difference of the waves at a point that is 4.40 m from one source and 4.00 m from the other?   *Ans.* 236°

19. Compute the intensity of a compressional wave in air, at 0°C and 76 cm of mercury, if its frequency is 1056/sec and its amplitude is 0.00120 cm. The speed of the wave in air is 331 m/sec.

20. A string 4.0 ft long is attached to the prong of a tuning fork that vibrates at right angles to the string with a constant frequency of 50/sec. The weight of the string is 0.064 lb. What stretching force is necessary for the string to vibrate in four segments? What would be the effect of turning the fork so that it vibrates parallel to the length of the string?   *Ans.* 5.0 lb

21. A 3.6-gm string is 64 cm long. What should be the tension in the string in order for it to vibrate in one segment with a frequency of 256/sec?

22. A string which weighs 1.0 oz for 16 ft is attached to a transverse vibrator whose constant frequency is 80/sec. How long must the string be in order for it to vibrate in two segments when the stretching force is 16.0 lb?   *Ans.* 4.5 ft

23. A brass rod ($Y = 9.0 \times 10^{11}$ dynes/cm² and density 8.6 gm/cm³) is clamped in the middle so that there is a node at that point and antinodes at the ends. If the rod is 90 cm long, what is the frequency of the compressional vibrations in the rod?

24. *Sound Waves*

We learn much about the world around us by means of sound. Minute amounts of energy carried by sound waves stimulate the sensation. Three stages are necessary in the production of a sensation of sound. The process must be started by a vibrating source which in its vibration supplies energy to the surrounding medium. The medium transmits this energy from the source to the receiver by means of a sound wave. When the wave arrives at a receiver, energy is transferred to the receiver. If the receiver is the ear, a sensation of sound may be produced.

24-1. Nature of Sound. Sound may be defined psychologically or physically. In the first aspect it is said to be the *sensation* produced when the proper disturbance comes to the ear. From the second viewpoint sound is the *stimulus* capable of producing the sensation of sound. Whether an observer is necessary for sound to exist depends entirely upon which of the two definitions is used. For our purposes we shall use the second, or physical, definition.

As an aid in visualizing the production of sound, suppose a small rubber balloon is partly inflated and attached to a bicycle pump. If the piston is pushed downward quickly, the balloon expands and the layer of air next to it is compressed. This layer of air will, in turn, compress the layer beyond it and so on. The compression that was started by

the expansion of the balloon will thus trave away from the source in the surrounding medium. If the piston is drawn upward, the balloon contracts and the adjacent layer of air is rarefied. As in the case of the compression, the rarefaction travels out from the source. If

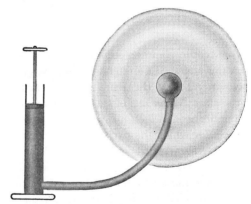

Fig. 1. Compressional waves produced by an expanding and contracting balloon.

the piston is moved up and down at regular intervals, a succession of compressions and rarefactions will travel out from the source (Fig. 1). Such a regular succession of disturbances traveling out from a source constitutes a wave motion. The compression and the following rarefaction make up a compressional wave.

If the up-and-down motion of the piston is

253

made rapid enough, an observer in the neighborhood will be able to hear a sound as the disturbance reaches his ear. These compressional waves are able to cause the sensation of hearing and are referred to as *sound waves*.

24-2. Vibrating Sources. Any body that has the properties of inertia and elasticity may be set into vibration. Most, but not all, bodies may vibrate in more than one manner and for each of these modes of vibration there is an associated frequency. In each of these modes of vibration a set of standing waves is set up in the body. Such standing waves may be transverse or longitudinal depending upon the

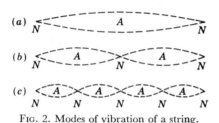

Fig. 2. Modes of vibration of a string.

shape and characteristics of the vibrating body.

One of the common sources of sound is a vibrating string. If a stretched cord is plucked, waves travel along the string and are reflected at the ends. Many sets of standing waves can be established; in fact, all standing waves are possible for which the two ends are nodes. In Fig. 2 are shown three such waves. For each there is a node at each end. In *a* there is no other node and hence the length of the string is a half wavelength. In *b* there is a node in the middle as well and the length of the string is a whole wavelength, while in *c* it is two wavelengths. The length of the string determines the wavelengths of the standing waves that can be set up in it. These wavelengths are those for which the length *l* of the string is an integral number of half-wavelength segments

$$l = n \frac{\lambda}{2} \qquad (1)$$

where *n* is any whole number.

Since the speed is the same for all the waves,

$$v = f\lambda$$

$$f = \frac{v}{\lambda} = \frac{v}{2l/n} = \frac{vn}{2l}$$

The possible frequencies of vibration are a lowest frequency $v/2l$, when n is 1, and all multiples of this lowest frequency. Many of these frequencies are present simultaneously when a string vibrates to produce sound.

The frequencies represented by the lowest frequency, called the fundamental, and all its multiples are called *harmonics*. They are called first, second, third, etc., harmonics in accordance with the number of the multiple n. The fundamental is the first harmonic. The higher harmonics are called *overtones*. In the case of the vibrating string the first overtone is the second harmonic.

Example: A string 80 cm long has a mass of 0.064 gm and is stretched by a force of 9.6×10^6 dynes. What is the frequency of the fundamental vibration?

From Eq. (1), Chap. 23,

$$v = \sqrt{\frac{F}{m/l}} = \sqrt{\frac{9.6 \times 10^6 \text{ dynes}}{0.064 \text{ gm}/80 \text{ cm}}}$$

$$= 1.09 \times 10^5 \text{ cm/sec}$$

$$f = \frac{v}{\lambda} = \frac{1.09 \times 10^5 \text{ cm/sec}}{2 \times 80 \text{ cm}} = 680 \text{ vib/sec}$$

A string usually vibrates in several different modes simultaneously. The relative amplitudes of the various modes depend upon the stiffness of the string, the point at which it is set into vibration, and how it is excited.

Another common source of sound is a vibrating air column. Such a column may be open at one end and closed at the other or it may be open at both ends. Organ pipes and wind instruments are common examples of vibrating air columns.

When an air column vibrates, waves are reflected at both open and closed ends and standing waves are set up. In the pipe the closed end must be a node N while an open end must be an antinode A. In Fig. 3 are shown several possible sets of nodes and anti-nodes for a pipe closed at one end. In *a* there is a node at one end and an antinode at the other. Since the distance from a node to the adjacent antinode is a quarter wavelength

$$l = \frac{\lambda}{4} \quad \text{or} \quad \lambda = 4l$$

In *b* the length is three-fourths the wavelength, in *c* five-fourths. Since

$$v = f\lambda$$

$$f = \frac{1v}{4l} \quad \text{or} \quad f = \frac{3v}{4l} \quad \text{or} \quad f = \frac{5v}{4l}$$

The possible frequencies are a lowest value $v/4l$ and the *odd* multiples of this lowest fre-

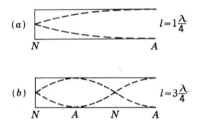

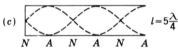

FIG. 3. Vibration of air column in a closed tube.

quency. Only odd harmonics are present and the first overtone is the third harmonic.

For an air column that is open at both ends there must be an antinode at each end (Fig. 4). In *a* the length is one half wavelength

$$l = \frac{\lambda}{2} \quad \lambda = 2l$$

In *b* the length is two half wavelengths and in *c* three half wavelengths. As in the case of the vibrating string, a lowest frequency and all its multiples are possible.

In each vibrating body whether string, air column, rod, plate, bell, or other body a set of nodes and antinodes is present in the body.

24-3. Forced Vibration and Resonance. Whenever a vibrating body is coupled to a second body in such a manner that energy can

be transferred, the second body is made to vibrate with a frequency equal to that of the original vibrator. Such a vibration is called a *forced vibration*. If the base of a vibrating tuning fork is set against a table top, the table top is forced to vibrate. This combination radiates energy faster than the fork could alone. Similarly, a vibrating string is inefficient in transferring energy to surrounding air unless it is coupled to some sounding board.

Whenever the coupled body has a natural frequency of vibration equal to that of the source, there is a condition of *resonance* (Chap. 14). Under this condition the vibrator releases more energy per unit time and the

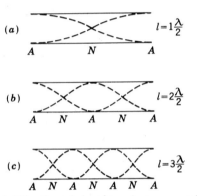

FIG. 4. Vibration of air column in an open tube.

sound is greatly reinforced. Hence the external power supplied to a resounding system must be increased, otherwise its vibrations will be quickly damped.

The reinforcement of sound by resonance with its accompanying release of large amounts of energy has many useful and many obnoxious consequences. Resonance of a radio loud-speaker to certain frequencies produces an objectionable distortion of speech or music. But the resonance of the air column in an organ pipe amplifies the otherwise almost inaudible sound of the vibrating air jet.

24-4. Transmitting Medium. The motion of a vibrating source sets up waves in a surrounding elastic medium. Whether the vibration of the source is transverse or longitudinal, the wave set up in the surrounding medium is a compressional wave whose frequency is the same as the frequency of vibration of the source. If the frequency is within the range to which the ear is sensitive, the wave is a sound wave.

Since a sound wave involves compression and expansion of some material, sound can be transmitted only through a material medium having mass and elasticity. No sound can be transmitted through a vacuum. This fact can be demonstrated experimentally by mounting an electric bell under a bell jar and pumping the air out while the bell is ringing (Fig. 5).

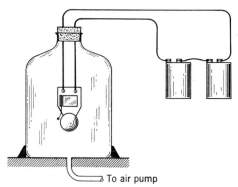

FIG. 5. Sound is not transmitted through a vacuum.

As the air is removed, the sound becomes fainter and fainter until it finally ceases, but it again becomes audible if the air is allowed to reenter the jar.

Sound waves will travel through any elastic material. We are all familiar with sounds transmitted through the windows, walls, and floors of a building. Submarines are detected by the underwater sound waves produced by their propellers. The sound of an approaching train may be heard by waves carried through the rails as well as by those transmitted through the air. In all materials the alternate compressions and rarefactions are transmitted in the same manner as they are in air.

24-5. Speed of Sound. If one watches the firing of a gun at considerable distance, he will see the smoke of the discharge before he hears the report. This delay represents the time required for the sound to travel from the gun to the observer (the light reaches him almost instantaneously). The speed of sound may be found directly by measuring the time required for the waves to travel a measured distance. The speed of sound varies greatly with the material through which it travels. Table 1 shows values for the speed of sound in several common substances.

TABLE 1. SPEED OF SOUND AT 0°C (32°F) IN VARIOUS MEDIUMS

Medium	ft/sec	m/sec
Air.....................	1,087	331.5
Hydrogen..............	4,167	1,270
Carbon dioxide.........	846	258.0
Water.................	4,757	1,450
Iron..................	16,730	5,100
Glass.................	18,050	5,500

Since sound waves are longitudinal (compressional) waves, the speed v is given by Eq. (2), Chap. 23,

$$v = \sqrt{\frac{E}{\rho}} \qquad (2)$$

where E is the bulk modulus for fluids or Young's modulus for solid rods, and ρ is the density of the medium.

If E is expressed in dynes per square centimeter and ρ in grams per cubic centimeter, Eq. (2) gives the speed in centimeters per second. If E is expressed in pounds per square foot and ρ, (D/g), in slugs per cubic foot, Eq. (2) gives the speed in feet per second. If E is in newtons per square meter and ρ in kilograms per cubic meter, Eq. (2) gives the speed in meters per second.

In a gas at constant temperature, the bulk modulus (Chap. 17) is the pressure P of the gas. When sound waves travel through a gas, the compressions and rarefactions (Fig. 6) occur so rapidly that the changes are practically adiabatic. The adiabatic modulus of elasticity is γ times the isothermal modulus P, where γ is the ratio of the specific heat of the gas at constant pressure to the specific heat at

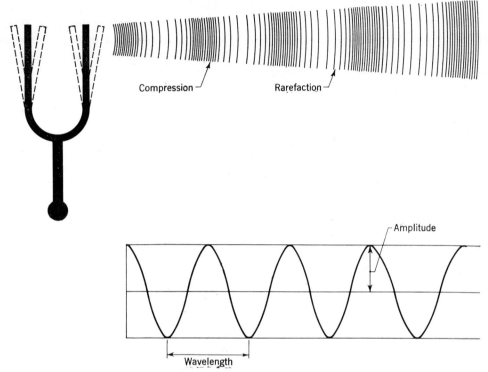

Fig. 6. Representation of a sound wave.

constant volume ($\gamma = 1.40$ for air and other diatomic gases). For gases, then

$$v = \sqrt{\frac{E}{\rho}} = \sqrt{\gamma \frac{P}{\rho}} \qquad (3)$$

Example: Compute the speed of sound in the steel rails of a railroad track. The weight-density of steel is 490 lb/ft³, and Young's modulus for steel is 29×10^6 lb/in².

$$v = \sqrt{\frac{Y}{\rho}} = \sqrt{\frac{Yg}{D}}$$

$$= \sqrt{\frac{(29 \times 10^6 \text{ lb/in.}^2)(144 \text{ in.}^2/\text{ft}^2)(32 \text{ ft/sec}^2)}{490 \text{ lb/ft}^3}}$$

$$v = 1\bar{6},000 \text{ ft/sec}$$

Example: Find the theoretical speed of sound in hydrogen at standard atmospheric pressure and 0°C.

From Table 1, Chap. 17, the density of hydrogen is 0.090 gm/liter.

$\rho = 0.090$ gm/liter $= 0.000090$ gm/cm³

$P = 76.0$ cm of mercury $= 76.0$ cm $\times 13.6 \frac{\text{gm}}{\text{cm}^3}$

$$\times 980 \frac{\text{cm}}{\text{sec}^2} = 1.01 \times 10^6 \frac{\text{dynes}}{\text{cm}^2}$$

$$v = \sqrt{\gamma \frac{P}{\rho}} = \sqrt{\frac{1.40(1.01 \times 10^6 \text{ dynes/cm}^2)}{0.000090 \text{ gm/cm}^3}}$$

$$v = 1\bar{2}0,000 \text{ cm/sec} = 1\bar{2}00 \text{ m/sec}$$

The speed of sound varies with the temperature of the medium transmitting it. For solids and liquids this change in speed is small and usually can be neglected. For gases, however, the change is rather large. The general gas law gives a relation between pressure, temperature, and density

$$\frac{P}{\rho} = RT$$

By substituting this for P/ρ in Eq. (3), we find that the speed of sound in a gas varies according to the relation

$$\frac{v_1}{v_2} = \sqrt{\frac{T_1}{T_2}} \qquad (4)$$

where v_1 and v_2 are the speeds at the *absolute* temperatures T_1 and T_2, respectively.

Example: What is the speed of sound in air at 25°C?

From Table 1, the speed at 0°C is 1087 ft/sec.

$$\frac{v_{25°C}}{1087 \text{ ft/sec}} = \sqrt{\frac{273° + 25°}{273°}} = \sqrt{\frac{298°K}{273°K}}$$

$$v_{25°C} = (1087 \text{ ft/sec}) \sqrt{\frac{298°}{273°}} = 11\overline{4}0 \text{ ft/sec}$$

For small differences in temperature we can consider the change in speed to be a constant amount for each degree change in tempera-

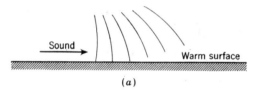

(a)

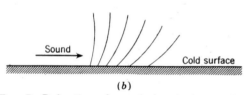

(b)

Fig. 7. Refraction of sound due to temperature difference.

ture. In air this is about 2 ft/sec per C° (1.1 ft/sec per F°) for temperatures near 0°C. The change is to be added if the temperature increases and subtracted if the temperature decreases.

24-6. Refraction of Sound. In a uniform medium at rest sound travels with constant speed in all directions. If, however, the medium is not uniform, the sound will not spread out uniformly but the direction of travel changes because the speed is greater in one part of the medium. The bending of sound due to change of speed is called refraction.

The nonuniform spreading of sound in the open air is an example of this effect. If the air were at rest and at a uniform temperature throughout, sound would travel uniformly in all directions. Rarely, if ever, does this occur, for the air is seldom at rest and almost never is the temperature uniform. On a clear summer day the surface of the earth is heated and the air immediately adjacent to the surface has a much higher temperature than do the layers above. Since the speed of sound increases as the temperature rises, the sound travels faster near the surface than it does at higher levels. As a result of this difference in speed the wave is bent away from the surface, as shown in Fig. 7a. To an observer on the surface, sound does not seem to travel very far on such a day since it is deflected away from him.

On a clear night the ground cools more rapidly than the air above, hence the layer of air adjacent to the ground may become cooler than that at a higher level. As a result of this condition sound travels faster at the higher level than at the lower level and consequently is bent downward, as shown in Fig. 7b. Since the sound comes down to the surface, it seems to travel greater distances than at other times.

Wind is also a factor in refraction of sound. In discussing the speed of sound in air, we assume that the air is stationary. If the air is moving, sound travels through the moving medium with its usual speed *relative to the air* but its speed relative to the ground is increased or decreased by the amount of the speed of the air, depending upon whether the air is moving in the same direction as the sound or in the opposite direction. If the air speed is different at various levels, the direction of travel of sound is changed, as shown in Fig. 8. Friction causes the wind speed to be lower at the surface than at a higher level, hence sound traveling against the wind is bent upward and leaves the surface while that traveling with the wind is bent downward. As a result, the observer on the surface reports that sound travels farther with the wind than against the wind.

Combinations of the two phenomena just discussed may cause some effects that seem very peculiar. Sound may carry over a mountain and be heard on the other side while similar sounds are not transmitted in the opposite direction. Frequently sound "skips" a region, that is, it is audible near the source and also at a considerable distance but at intermediate distances it is not audible. Such an effect is quite troublesome in the operation of such devices as foghorns. Refraction effects

1100 ft/sec, will go the 110 ft from the observer to the reflector and back in 0.1 sec.

Use is made of the reflection of sound waves in the determination of ocean depths (Fig. 9). A sound pulse is sent out under water from a ship. After being reflected from the sea bottom, the sound is detected by an underwater receiver also mounted on the ship, and the time interval is recorded by a special device. If the elapsed time and the speed of sound in water are known, the depth of the sea at that

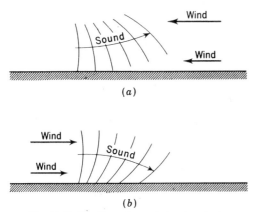

Fig. 8. Refraction of sound due to wind.

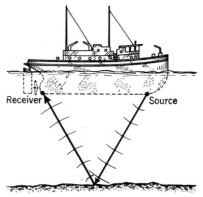

Fig. 9. Measuring ocean depth.

increase the difficulties in locating airplanes, guns, or submarines by means of sound waves.

24-7. Reflection of Sound Waves. Sound waves are reflected from surfaces such as walls, mountains, clouds, or the ground. A sound is seldom heard without accompanying reflections, especially inside a building where the walls and furniture supply the reflecting surfaces. The "rolling" of thunder is largely due to successive reflections from clouds and land surfaces.

The ear is able to distinguish two sounds as separate only if they reach it at least 0.1 sec apart; otherwise, they blend in the hearing mechanism to give the impression of a single sound. If a sound of short duration is reflected back to the observer after 0.1 sec or more, he hears it as a repetition of the original sound, an *echo*. In order that an echo may occur, the reflecting surface must be at least 55 ft away, since sound, traveling at a speed of

point can be computed. Measurements may thus be made almost continuously as the ship moves along.

Sound waves may be reflected from curved surfaces for the purpose of making more energy travel in a desired direction, thus making the sound more readily audible at a distance. The curved sounding board placed behind a speaker in an auditorium throws forward some of the sound waves that otherwise would spread in various directions and be lost to the audience. In the same way, a horn may be used to collect sound waves and convey their energy to an ear or other detector.

24-8. Interference of Waves; Beats. Whenever two wave motions pass through a single region at the same time, the motion of the particles in the medium will be the result of the combined disturbances of the two sets of waves. The effects due to the combined

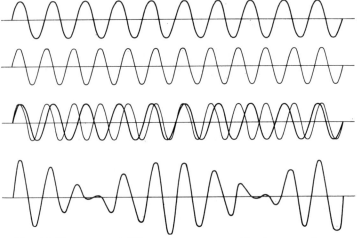

Fig. 10. Two waves of different frequency combined to cause beats.

action of the two sets of waves are known in general as *interference* and are important in all types of wave motion.

If a shrill whistle is blown continuously in a room whose walls are good reflectors of sound, an observer moving about the room will notice that the sound is exceptionally loud at certain points and unusually faint at others. At places where a compression of the reflected wave arrives at the same time as a compression of the direct wave their effects add together and the sound is loud; at other places where a rarefaction of one wave arrives with a compression of the other their effects partly or wholly cancel and the sound is faint.

Contrasted with the phenomenon of interference in space, we may have two sets of sound waves of slightly *different frequency* sent through the air at the same time. An observer will note a regular swelling and fading of the sound, a phenomenon called *beats*. Since the compressions and rarefactions are spaced farther apart in one set of waves than in the other, at one instant two compressions arrive together at the ear of the observer and the sound is loud. A little later a compression of one set of waves arrives with the rarefaction of the other and the sound is faint. The number of beats occurring each second is equal to the difference of the two frequencies. Thus, in Fig. 10, two sets of waves of frequencies

10 vib/sec and 12 vib/sec combine and give a resultant wave that fluctuates in amplitude 12 minus 10, or 2 times per second. Beats are readily demonstrated by sounding identical tuning forks, one of which has been loaded by placing a bit of soft wax on one prong, thus slightly reducing the frequency of this fork.

24-9. Absorption of Sound. As a wave motion passes through a medium, some of the regular motion of particles in the wave motion is converted into irregular motion (heat). This constitutes *absorption* of energy from the wave. In some materials there is very little absorption of sound as it passes through, in others the absorption is large. Porous materials, such as hair felt, are good absorbers of sound, since much of the energy is changed to heat energy in the pores. Whenever it is necessary to reduce the sound transmitted through walls or floors or that reflected from walls, a material should be used that is a good absorber. Rugs, draperies, porous plasters, felts, and other porous materials are used for this purpose.

24-10. Doppler's Principle of Frequency Shift. Anyone who has stood by the track and heard the bell or whistle of a passing train or who has listened to the horn of a passing automobile may have noticed the remarkable fall in pitch that occurs as the source of sound passes him. It is the relative motion of the source of sound and the observer that causes this change in pitch. Doppler (1845) clarified the principles underlying this effect for sound. The Doppler effect can occur in any wave motion, and indeed it leads to particularly important consequences in the study of light.

The relative motion responsible for the Doppler effect may be produced by motion of the sound source or by motion of the observer (or by both). If source and observer approach each other, the apparent frequency is increased while if they recede from each other it is decreased.

SUMMARY

Sound is a disturbance of the type capable of being detected by the ear. The disturbance is produced by the *vibration* of some material body.

Vibration may be set up in bodies that have the properties of inertia and elasticity. Those frequencies of vibration are possible for which standing waves can be set up within the body. The vibration of lowest frequency is called the *fundamental*. All others are called *overtones*. The vibrations whose frequencies are integral multiples of the frequency of the fundamental are called *harmonics*. The fundamental is the first harmonic.

Forced vibrations are set up in an elastic body when it is coupled to a vibrating body. If a natural frequency of the coupled body is the same as that of the vibrator, there is *resonance*. For resonance there is a rapid transfer of energy and a resultant louder sound.

Sound is transmitted through air or other material in the form of *compressional* (longitudinal) waves.

The speed of sound in air at ordinary temperatures is about 1100 ft/sec. The speed of sound in a gas depends on the particular gas and the temperature. It is independent of pressure and frequency.

$$v = \sqrt{\frac{\gamma P}{\rho}}$$

The speed of sound in a gas at constant pressure is proportional to the square root of the absolute temperature.

$$\frac{v_1}{v_2} = \sqrt{\frac{T_1}{T_2}}$$

A sound wave may be *refracted* if the speed is not the same in all parts of the medium or if parts of the medium are moving. It may also be refracted as it passes from one medium to another.

An *echo* occurs when a reflected sound wave returns to the observer 0.1 sec or more after the original wave reaches him, so that a distinct repetition of the original sound is perceived.

Two sets of waves of the same frequency may mutually reinforce or cancel each other at a given place. This is called *interference*.

Beats occur when two sources of slightly *different* frequencies are sounded at the same time. The resultant sound periodically rises and falls in intensity as the waves alternately reinforce and cancel each other.

Absorption occurs when the regular motion of the particles in a wave is converted into irregular motion (heat).

The apparent frequency of a source of sound is changed if there is relative motion between source and observer. This statement is called *Doppler's principle*. The frequency is raised when source and observer approach, lowered if they recede.

QUESTIONS   **1.** Explain why stroking the tip of a fingernail across a linen book cover produces a musical tone.

2. Explain how windows may be broken by an explosion several miles away.

3. What indications are there that standing waves exist in a vibrating body?

4. Is the wave in a vibrating string a sound wave? If not what kind of wave is it?

5. Explain the vibration in an organ pipe. What kind of wave is there within the pipe?

6. Explain how the distance, in miles, of a thunderstorm may be found approximately by counting the number of seconds elapsing between the flash of lightning and the arrival of the sound of the thunder and dividing the result by five.

7. Why does sound travel faster in solids than in gases?

8. (*a*) If a person inhales hydrogen and then speaks, how will the characteristics of his voice be changed? (*b*) How would the situation be changed if carbon dioxide were used?

9. Why does the speed of a sound wave in a gas change with temperature?

10. Give some common examples of resonant vibrations.

11. Mention some illustrations of the importance of resonance in musical instruments.

12. Under what circumstances should resonance be avoided in musical instruments?

13. Is it true that we can hear better on a cool, damp day than on a hot, dry day? Explain.

14. Explain clearly, using suitable diagrams, the conditions that are necessary for "skipping" of sound.

15. How can energy of a sound wave be brought to a focus?

16. In Statuary Hall of the Capitol at Washington, a person standing a few feet from the wall can hear the whispering of another person who stands facing the wall at the corresponding point on the opposite side 50 ft away. At points between, the sound is not heard. Explain.

17. How are beats useful in tuning a musical instrument?

18. The intensity of the sound from a small source diminishes as the square of the distance. How does absorption in the medium affect this relation?

19. From a consideration of Fig. 11*a*, show that the apparent frequency f' of a source moving with speed v_s toward a stationary receiver is

$$f' = \left(\frac{v_0}{v_0 - v_s}\right) f$$

where v_0 is the speed of sound.

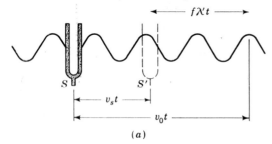 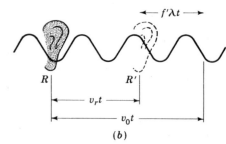

FIG. 11. Doppler's principle of frequency shift.

20. Show that for an observer moving with speed v_r away from a stationary sound source (Fig. 11*b*) the apparent frequency is

$$f' = \left(\frac{v_0 - v_r}{v_0}\right) f$$

PROBLEMS   *Assume the temperature to be 20°C unless it is stated otherwise.*

1. A stretched steel wire vibrates with a fundamental frequency of 240 vib/sec. What is the frequency of vibration if the tension in the wire is doubled?

2. A string 36 in. long subjected to a tension of 30 lb vibrates 500 times per second. What will be the rate of vibration of the string if the tension is reduced to 15 lb? *Ans.* $3\bar{5}0$ vib/sec

3. The prong of a tuning fork vibrates 50.0 times per second in a direction at right angles to a string attached to the prong, causing the string to vibrate in one segment when it is under a tension supplied by a 400-gm body suspended at the other end. (*a*) What stretching force would be needed to give four segments in the vibrating string? (*b*) What would be the stretching force and frequency of the string if it were vibrating in one segment when attached to the fork at right angles to the prong?

4. Calculate the tension in a stretched cord that is vibrating with a frequency whose third overtone is equal to the frequency of the second overtone produced when the tension is 12 lb. *Ans.* 6.8 lb

5. Calculate the tension in a stretched string for which the frequency of the fundamental vibration equals the frequency of the second overtone when the tension is 4.96×10^5 dynes.

6. What is the frequency of the tone emitted by a chime if it produces resonance in a tube 8.0 in. long when the tube is closed at one end?
Ans. $4\bar{1}0$ vib/sec

7. A string 40.0 cm long has a mass of 0.125 gm. What is the frequency of its fundamental vibration when the tension is 5.00×10^5 dynes? What is the wavelength of the sound in the surrounding air?

8. A string 60 cm long has a mass of 0.125 gm. What must be the tension in the string so that the fundamental frequency will be 250 vib/sec? What is the wavelength in air of the sound produced? *Ans.* 1.9×10^6 dynes; $1\bar{3}0$ cm

9. The sound of a gun is heard by an observer 6.0 sec after the flash of the gun is seen. Calculate the distance from gun to observer. The temperature is 20°C.

10. Thunder was heard 2.0 sec after the lightning. If the temperature was 24°C, how far away was the lightning? *Ans.* $2\bar{3}00$ ft

11. A stone is dropped into a mine shaft 400 ft deep. How much later will the impact be heard?

12. A plane flies east through clouds at 250 mi/hr at a height of 8000 ft. At a certain instant the sound of the plane appears to an observer on the ground to come from a point directly overhead. What is the approximate position of the plane? *Ans.* $2\bar{7}00$ ft east of the observer

13. In foggy weather a lighthouse sends sound signals simultaneously under water (0°C) and through the air (10°C). A vessel is 1000 m from the lighthouse. How much later does one signal arrive than the other?

14. The sound of the torpedoing of a ship is received by the underwater detector of a patrol vessel 18 sec before it is heard through the air. How far away is the ship? Take the speed of sound in sea water to be 4800 ft/sec. *Ans.* 4.9 mi

15. By means of Eq. (4) verify the statement that the speed of sound in air increases about 2 ft/sec for each centigrade degree rise in temperature from 0°C.

16. The density of oxygen is 16 times that of hydrogen. For both $\gamma = 1.40$. If the speed of sound is 1041 ft/sec in oxygen at 0°C, what is the speed in hydrogen? *Ans.* $41\bar{6}0$ ft/sec

17. (*a*) Compute the frequency of the tone produced when air is blown through the holes of a rotating disk if there are 20 holes and the disk is turning at the rate of 1800 rev/min. (*b*) What is the wavelength of this sound in air when the speed of sound is 1120 ft/sec?

18. A tuning fork vibrates 200 times per second and sends out a compressional wave that travels with a speed of 1100 ft/sec. Find (*a*) the period and (*b*) the wavelength.   *Ans.* 0.00500 sec; 5.50 ft

19. A sounding tuning fork is held over a vertical glass tube into which water is slowly poured. The shortest column of air in the tube which produces resonance is found to be 6.0 in. (*a*) What is the wavelength of the sound produced by the fork? (*b*) What is the frequency of the tuning fork?

20. A whistle closed at one end has a fundamental frequency of 160 vib/sec. What is the frequency of the first possible overtone?   *Ans.* 480 vib/sec

21. A musical instrument produces a fundamental tone C = 264 vib/sec. Assuming the speed of sound to be 336 m/sec, what is the shortest closed tube that will resonate to the first overtone (second harmonic) C′ emitted by the instrument?

22. The first overtone of an open organ pipe has the same frequency as the first overtone of a closed pipe 12 ft in length. What is the length of the open pipe?
Ans. 16 ft

23. A signaling bell produces a tone of 440 vib/sec. A resonance tube closed at one end is used to reinforce the sound. (*a*) What is the wavelength of the sound produced by the bell? (*b*) What is the length of the resonant air column in the closed tube?

24. A pipe open at one end is closed at the other by a movable plunger. A vibrating rod is held near the open end. The air column resonates when the plunger is in any of several positions spaced 11.0 cm apart. The speed of sound in air is 333 m/sec at the temperature of observation. What is the frequency of vibration of the rod?   *Ans.* $15\overline{1}0$ vib/sec

25. When a sound wave enters a medium of different acoustical density, its speed changes, but the frequency remains constant. What will be the change in wavelength when sound of frequency 1000/sec passes from air to carbon dioxide?

26. The echo of a gunshot is heard 5.0 sec after the gun is fired by the hunter. How far from him is the surface that reflects the sound?   *Ans.* $2\overline{8}00$ ft

27. A boat approaches a high vertical cliff. When the anchor is dropped, an echo is heard 1.5 sec later. How far is the boat from the cliff?

28. A depth-measuring device emits a signal of frequency 36,000 vib/sec in water. The impulse is reflected from the ocean bed and returned to the device 0.60 sec after the signal is emitted. (*a*) What is the depth of the water? (*b*) What is the wavelength of the wave in water? (*c*) What is the frequency of the wave in air? (*d*) What is the wavelength of the wave in air?
Ans. $1\overline{4}00$ ft; 0.13 ft; $3\overline{6}{,}000$ vib/sec; 0.031 ft

29. A device for determining ocean depths produces a signal of 60,000 vib/sec in water. The speed of the wave in water is 4600 ft/sec. An impulse is reflected from the ocean floor and returns to the device 0.75 sec after the signal is emitted. (*a*) What is the depth of the water? (*b*) What is the wavelength of the wave in water? (*c*) What is the frequency of this wave in air?

30. An experimenter connects two rubber tubes to a box containing an electrically driven tuning fork and holds the other ends of the tubes to his ear. One tube is gradually made longer than the other, and when the difference in length is 7.0 in., the sound he perceives is a minimum. What is the frequency of the fork? (Use v = 1100 ft/sec.)   *Ans.* $9\overline{4}0$ vib/sec

31. A siren disk has a ring of holes, uniformly spaced. When the siren is rotating at either 1674 or 1686 rev/min, it produces 2.0 beats per second with a sound of constant frequency. What is the frequency of the constant source?

25. Acoustics

The science of *acoustics* includes the production and transmission of sound and their relation to our sense of hearing. We have already discussed problems in production and transmission of sound and are now primarily interested in these phenomena in so far as they affect our sense of hearing.

The hearing mechanism is able to receive compressional waves within the range to which it is sensitive and to convert the stimulus into a sensation of hearing. The ear is able to analyze the waves that come to it, distinguishing between two or more sounds that arrive simultaneously when the sounds differ in one or more of the characteristics: *pitch*, *quality* (timbre), and *loudness*. Each of these characteristics is closely associated with the *physical* characteristics of the sound wave that comes to the ear. Pitch is primarily associated with *frequency*, quality with the *complexity* of the wave, and loudness with the *rate* at which *energy* is transmitted to the ear. These are the principal associations between characteristics of sound and those of the waves. However, each of the three sound characteristics depends to a limited extent upon the other two physical characteristics not primarily related to it.

Not all compressional waves are able to excite the sensation of hearing. Some waves may not transmit sufficient energy to excite the sensation although this threshold is re-markably low (Fig. 5). Others may transmit too much energy and the sensation becomes one of pain rather than one of sound. If the frequency is too low, no sensation of sound is produced but one can feel the changes in pressure. Compressional waves whose frequency is less than that to which the ear is sensitive are called *infrasonic* waves. On the other hand, if the frequency is too high, no sensation of sound is produced. It is possible to detect these high-frequency waves by means other than the ear and extensive studies of them have been made. These waves are called *ultrasonic* waves.

25-1. Musical Tones. The sensation that we describe as a *musical tone* is produced by a *regular succession* of compressions and the following rarefactions that come to the ear. If the vibrations of the source are regularly spaced, that source will produce a musical tone; it has a fixed frequency. Other vibrating sources may not maintain a single frequency and hence they do not produce musical tones even though they cause a sensation of sound. If a jet of air is directed toward the outer, evenly spaced holes in the disk shown in Fig. 1, a regular succession of puffs of air will come through the holes as the disk is rotated. A sound wave is produced that will give rise to a musical tone. If the air jet is directed toward the inner circle where the holes are unevenly spaced, the puffs will be irregular and an *un-*

pitched sound is produced. Other sounds cannot be classed as musical tones because they are of such short duration that the ear is unable to distinguish a regular succession of pulses. Such sounds as that produced by a rifle shot or a sharp blow on a table top with a ruler fall in this class. There is no sharp dividing line between such sounds and musical tones. When a single small piece of wood is dropped on a table, there is little evidence of tone, but when a succession of sticks of varying lengths is dropped one after the other, the ear readily detects the variation in sound.

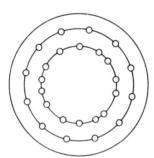

FIG. 1. A siren disk.

A *noise* may be defined as *any undesired sound*. On the basis of this definition, any sound can be a noise to some observer whether or not it is a musical tone.

25-2. Pitch and Frequency. *Pitch* is the characteristic of sound by which the ear assigns it a place in a musical scale. The ear assigns such a place to each musical tone but not to other sounds. When a stretched string is plucked, sound is produced that causes a given pitch sensation. If the tension of the string is increased, the pitch becomes higher. We have found that increasing the tension in a string increases its frequency of vibration. The principal physical characteristic associated with pitch is the *frequency* of the sound wave.

The range of frequency to which the human ear is sensitive varies considerably with the individual. For the average normal ear, it is from 20 to 20,000 vib/sec. These limits are determined by testing a large number of seem-

ingly normal individuals. The upper limit decreases, in general, as the age of the individual increases.

The satisfactory reproduction of speech and music does not require a range of frequencies as great as that to which the ear is sensitive. To have satisfactory fidelity of reproduction a range from 100 to 8000 vib/sec is required for speech and from 40 to 14,000 vib/sec for orchestral music.

The frequency range of most sound-reproducing systems, such as radio, telephone, and phonograph, is considerably less than that of the hearing range of the ear. A good radio transmitter and receiver in the broadcast band may cover the range from 40 to 8000 vib/sec. This limited range allows it to reproduce speech faithfully but it does detract from the quality of orchestral music. If the frequency range is further restricted, the quality of reproduction is correspondingly reduced.

Although pitch is associated principally with frequency, other factors also influence the sensation. Increase in intensity raises the pitch of a high-frequency tone but lowers the pitch of a low-frequency tone. The pitch of a complex tone depends upon its overtone structure; in some cases the pitch corresponds to a frequency that is not present. Tones of very short duration have a lower pitch than those of longer duration for the same frequency.

25-3. Quality and Complexity. It is a fact of experience that a tone of a given pitch sounded on the piano is easily distinguished from one of exactly the same pitch sounded, for example, on the clarinet. The difference in the two tones is said to be one of *tone quality*. This characteristic of sound is associated with the *complexity* of the sound wave that arrives at the ear.

We have found (Chap. 24) that sound waves are produced by vibrating bodies. In a few cases the body vibrates with a single frequency but most bodies vibrate in a very complex manner. The sound wave that is sent out from such a vibrating body is a combination of all the frequencies present in the vibration.

If we plot a curve of change in pressure (that is, difference between the pressure in the wave and the normal pressure in the air) against time for the wave sent out by a tuning fork, the curve is that shown in Fig. 2. Since the tuning fork vibrates with only a single frequency, the curve is a simple sine curve whose frequency is the same as that of the fork. If a second fork whose frequency is three times as great as the first but with amplitude only half as great is sounded with the first, the two waves combine as shown in Fig. 3. The pressure at each point is the algebraic sum of the individual pressures. By adding the ordinates of *a* and *b* at each point, we get the ordinate of the complex wave *c*.

Every body that vibrates with more than one frequency sends out a complex wave. The complexity, which determines the quality of the sound, is controlled by the number and relative intensity of the overtones that are present. A "pure" tone (no overtones) may not be as pleasing as the "rich" tone of a violin, which contains ten or more overtones. Any complex wave can be resolved into a number of simple waves. The more complex the wave, the greater is the number of overtones that contribute to it.

In Fig. 4 are shown the wave forms and overtone structure of sound produced by different instruments. Such wave forms can be obtained by means of a cathode-ray oscilloscope (Chap. 39). The sound wave is received by a microphone, which converts the pressure changes into electrical impulses. These in turn are amplified and cause motion of a spot on a sensitive screen to make a record of the wave form.

25-4. Loudness and Intensity. The *loudness* of a sound is the magnitude of the auditory sensation produced by the sound. The associated physical quantity, *intensity*, refers to the rate at which sound energy flows through unit area. Intensity may also be expressed in terms of the changes in pressure, since the rate of flow of energy is proportional to the square of the pressure change.

The loudness of sound depends upon both intensity and frequency. For a given fre-

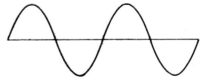

FIG. 2. When pressure is plotted against time for a sound wave of a single frequency, a simple sine curve is obtained.

quency an increase in intensity produces an increase in loudness but the sensitivity of the ear is so different in the various frequency ranges that equal intensities produce far different sensations in the different regions. In Fig. 5 is shown a diagram giving the relations between frequency, intensity, and hearing. Intensities below the line indicating the threshold of hearing are insufficient to produce any sensation of hearing. The curve indicates that the normal ear is most sensitive in the frequency range 2000 to 4000 vib/sec, that is, in this range it requires the least energy to cause a sensation of sound. The intensity

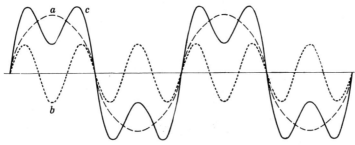

FIG. 3. Compounding of two simple waves *a* and *b* to form a complex wave *c*.

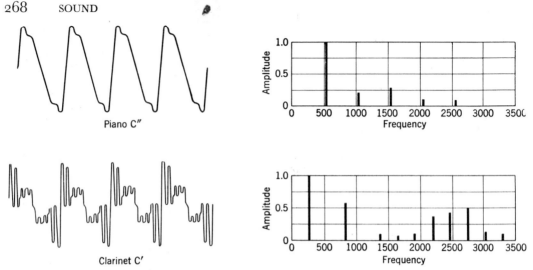

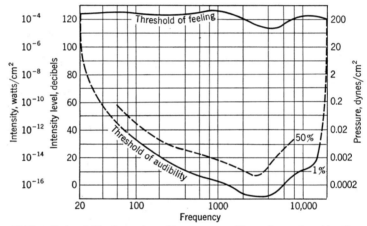

FIG. 4. Wave forms and frequency distribution in sounds produced by musical instruments.

FIG. 5. Limits of audibility. Only within the region of frequency and intensity enclosed by the curves is the sensation of sound excited.

necessary for hearing in the regions near the high and low limits of audibility is many times as great as that necessary in the region of greatest sensitivity.

The smooth threshold curve represents the average of many individuals. For a single person the curve would not be smooth but would show numerous dips and peaks. The threshold curve in Fig. 5 is one for the most sensitive ears. Of a large group tested only 1 per cent were able to hear sounds of intensity less than this threshold. The broken line indicates thresholds below which 50 per cent of the group were unable to hear.

If the intensity becomes too great, the sensation becomes one of feeling or pain rather than of hearing. This is indicated by the upper curve showing the threshold of feeling. Only in the region of intensity and frequency bounded by the two curves is there a sensation of hearing.

In the region of maximum sensitivity, the ear is able to hear sounds over an extremely wide range of intensity. At the threshold of audibility the intensity at the ear is almost unbelievably small, about 10^{-16} watt/cm². At the threshold of feeling, the maximum intensity that the ear records as sound is about

10^{-4} watt/cm². The maximum intensity in this range is thus a thousand billion times the minimum. The sensitivity of the ear to pressure changes is very great. At the threshold of audibility the pressure in the wave varies from normal only by about 0.0002 dyne/cm², and for the most intense sounds by about 200 dynes/cm². For the most intense sounds the pressure change is about a million times as great as for the least intense.

In a sound wave the particles of air that take part in the vibration move neither far nor fast. Using Eq. (10), Chap. 23, we can calculate the amplitude of the particles at a moderate frequency, say 2000 vib/sec. For the most intense sounds (threshold of feeling) the displacement is only about 5.4×10^{-3} cm, while at the threshold of hearing it is about a millionth of this value. The corresponding maximum speed calculated from simple harmonic motion is about 68 cm/sec.

The measurement of loudness is important for practical purposes but is a difficult one to achieve. There is an approximate law of psychology which states that the magnitude of a sensation is proportional to the logarithm of the intensity.

$$S = k \log \frac{I}{I_0} \qquad (1)$$

where S represents the magnitude of the sensation (for sound loudness), I the intensity, and I_0 the intensity at a reference level. This law is called the Weber-Fechner law. It does not exactly represent the relationship between loudness and intensity for sound, but is a fair approximation for pure tones at most frequencies. For complex tones, however, there is no simple relationship.

In place of the sensation S, we may use *intensity level* α, defined by the equation

$$\alpha = \log \frac{I}{I_0} \qquad (2)$$

There is a gain of one unit in intensity level when the actual *power* of the second sound is 10 times as great as the first. Hence it is now customary to state the differences in the intensity levels of two sounds as the *exponent* of 10, which gives the ratio of the powers. The unit exponent is called the *bel*, for Alexander Graham Bell (1847–1922), whose researches in sound are famous. If one sound has 10 times as much power as a second sound, the difference in their intensity levels is 1 bel. The bel is an inconveniently large unit and hence the *decibel* (0.1 bel) is the unit that is generally used in practice. A 26 per cent change in intensity alters the level by 1 db (decibel). This is practically the smallest change in intensity level that the ear can ordinarily detect. Under the best laboratory conditions a 10 per cent (0.4 db) change is detectable.

Intensity level is measured from an arbitrarily chosen intensity. An intensity of 10^{-10} μwatt/cm² is chosen as zero level or 0 db. It is roughly the intensity of the threshold of audibility for tones between 500 and 2500/sec. The intensity levels of various sounds are given in Table 1.

TABLE 1. INTENSITY LEVELS OF
CERTAIN SOUNDS

Source	Decibels
Average threshold of hearing	0
Quiet home, average living room	40
Ordinary conversation (3 ft)	70
Street corner traffic, large city	80
Boiler factory	100
Threshold of pain	120
DC4 take-off (150 ft)	120
F3D take-off (J34 engine)	140
J-57-type engine	160–170

Example: A small source of sound radiates acoustic energy uniformly in all directions at a rate of 1.5 watts. Find the intensity and the intensity level at a point 25 m from the source if (*a*) there is no absorption and (*b*) if 2 per cent of the energy is absorbed in each 5 m.

$$(a) \quad I = \frac{P}{A} = \frac{1.5 \text{ watts}}{4\pi(2500 \text{ cm})^2}$$

$$= 1.9 \times 10^{-8} \text{ watt/cm}^2$$

$$\alpha = \log \frac{I}{I_0} = \log \frac{1.9 \times 10^{-8} \text{ watt/cm}^2}{10^{-16} \text{ watt/cm}^2}$$

$$= \log (1.9 \times 10^8)$$

$$= 8.3 \text{ bels} = 83 \text{ db}$$

(*b*) If there is 10 per cent absorption,

$$I = 0.90 \times 1.9 \times 10^{-8} \text{ watt/cm}^2 = 1.7 \text{ watt/cm}^2$$

$$\alpha = \log \frac{1.7 \times 10^{-8}}{10^{-16}} = \log (1.7 \times 10^8)$$

$$= 8.2 \text{ bels} = 82 \text{ db}$$

25-5. The Ear. The ear is essentially a device which transmits and magnifies the pressure changes which come to it in sound waves. It consists of three sections, the outer ear, the middle ear, and the inner ear (Fig. 6). The

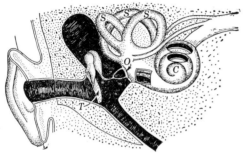

FIG. 6. Diagram of the ear. The parts of the ear are not drawn to scale.

outer section consists of the external ear or pinna and the canal. The canal is separated from the middle ear by a membrane called the *eardrum* T. In the middle ear are three small bones, the *hammer*, the *anvil*, and the *stirrup*, which transmit the pressure changes to the inner ear. The hammer is attached to the eardrum, the stirrup to a membrane O that separates the middle and inner ear. The three bones make up a system of levers that is so arranged as to increase the force. In addition, the area of the stirrup bearing on the mem-

brane at the inner ear is much smaller than the eardrum. By these means the pressure changes are increased 30 to 60 times. The inner ear is filled with liquid. The semicircular canals S are organs of balance and take no part in hearing. The cochlea C is really the end organ of hearing where the nerve enters. Here the pressure changes in vibrations excite the sensation of sound.

It is possible for sound vibrations to bypass the outer and middle ear and be conducted through the bone directly to the inner ear. One type of hearing aid is designed to make use of such bone transmission. Others are amplifiers that increase the energy that reaches the eardrum.

25-6. Voice Sounds. Voice sounds are formed by passage of air through the vocal cords, lips, and teeth. As the air stream passes through the vocal cords, they are set in vibration. The cavities of the nose and throat impress resonant characteristics on these vibrations to produce speech sounds. All the vowel sounds and some of the consonant sounds are produced in this manner. Other sounds called unvoiced sounds, for example, f, s, th, sh, t, and k are produced by passage of air over the teeth and tongue without use of the vocal cords. Voiced consonants, such as b, d, g, j, v, and z, are combinations of the two processes.

The various vowel sounds are made by changing the shape of the resonant chamber so that different frequencies are enhanced. Each of the vowel sounds has certain characteristic frequency groups as shown in the frequency chart in Fig. 7 and in Table 2.

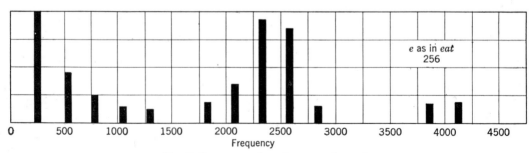

FIG. 7. Frequency chart for a vowel sound.

The values given are average values and there is considerable variation for different individuals and for a single individual at different times. If one of these speech sounds is passed through a sound filter that absorbs frequencies in the neighborhood of one of the characteristic frequencies, the vowel sound is no longer recognizable.

TABLE 2. CHARACTERISTIC FREQUENCIES OF VOWEL SOUNDS

Vowel sound	Low frequency	High frequency
a (tape)......	550	2100
a (father).....	825	1200
e (eat).......	375	2400
e (ten).......	550	1900
i (tip)........	450	2200
o (tone)......	500	850
u (pool)......	400	800

25-7. Musical Scales. The simplest music consists of a succession of musical tones of the same or different pitches. This constitutes a melody. Any succession of pitches can be chosen but it is found that the effect is most pleasing if the ratio of the frequencies of succeeding tones is a ratio of small integers. By use of this fact we construct a *musical scale* and in the melody only frequencies that appear in the scale are used.

Two tones sounded in succession or together constitute an *interval*. The ear recognizes intervals in the musical scale by ratios of frequencies rather than by differences in frequency. The interval between frequencies 600 and 1200/sec is the same as the interval between 150 and 300/sec since the ratio in each case is $2/1$. This is the simplest ratio other than $1/1$. Other simple ratios used in our common musical scale are $3/2$, $4/3$, $5/3$, $5/4$, $9/8$, and $15/8$.

25-8. A Diatonic Scale. A diatonic scale is made up of eight notes, which have frequencies such that the intervals between the first note and the others are those just given. The frequency of the first note may be chosen arbitrarily. The others are then fixed. Suppose middle C on the piano is fixed at 256 vib/sec. Then, the frequencies and intervals are those given in Table 3.

We note that there are three intervals between successive notes, $9/8$ the major tone, $10/9$ the minor tone, and $16/15$ the semitone. Intervals between the basic frequency and the other frequencies are also given names. Since the ratio $2/1$ occurs at the eighth note, this interval is called the *octave*. Similarly, the ratio $5/4$ is called the major third, $4/3$ the fourth, $3/2$ the major fifth, and $5/3$ the major sixth.

The ear recognizes as harmonious three notes when the frequencies are proportional to the three numbers, 4, 5, and 6. This combination is called a *major triad*. The major diatonic scale is made up of three major triads as indicated in Table 3.

TABLE 3. FREQUENCIES AND INTERVALS IN THE DIATONIC SCALE

Note...........	C	D	E	F	G	A	B	C′
Frequency, scientific pitch...	256	288	320	341	384	427	480	512
concert pitch..	264	297	330	352	396	440	495	528
Ratio to C......	1	$9/8$	$5/4$	$4/3$	$3/2$	$5/3$	$15/8$	2
Ratio to preceding frequency..		$9/8$	$10/9$	$16/15$	$9/8$	$10/9$	$9/8$	$16/15$
Triads..........	$\{4$	(6)	5	4	6	5	5	6

25-9. Consonance and Dissonance. When two notes are sounded together or consecutively, they seem pleasing if the interval is a simple ratio. Such a combination is a *consonance*. All other combinations are *dissonances*. There is no sure test as to whether the ratio of frequencies is "simple" since the decision depends upon the past training of the observer. What seems dissonance to one observer may seem consonance to another.

Dissonances appear when beat frequencies between about 10 and 50 are formed as the two notes are sounded together. The beat frequency may be formed by the fundamental frequencies or by *any pair* of overtones present

TABLE 4. FREQUENCY INTERVALS IN MUSICAL SCALES

Interval	Note												
	C	Db C#	D	Eb D#	E	F	Gb F#	G	Ab G#	A	Bb A#	B	C'
Diatonic interval.........	1.000	.....	1.125	1.200	1.250	1.333	.....	1.500	1.600	1.667	.....	1.895	2.000
Tempered interval.......	1.000	1.059	1.122	1.189	1.260	1.335	1.414	1.498	1.587	1.682	1.782	1.888	2.000

in the complex tones. Dissonances thus will not be present in pure tones except at low frequencies. Consonance represents the absence of dissonance.

25-10. Evenly Tempered Scale. The intervals of the diatonic scale are larger than is desirable in much music. However, if we try to split the larger intervals by semitones, it is not possible to find a single frequency that will divide the interval satisfactorily. For example, the semitone above G would not have the same frequency as the semitone below A. In other words, on this scale G$^{\#}$ would differ from A$^{\flat}$. To overcome this difficulty, a scale of 12 equal intervals or semitones is set up. If x represents the semitone interval, then $(x)^{12} = 2$ or $x = 2^{1/12} = 1.059$, approximately. This scale of even intervals is called the *evenly tempered* scale and is that actually used in music at the present time. Bach wrote his compositions for the "well-tempered clavichord" to demonstrate the usefulness of the evenly tempered scale in changing from one key to another. Only a very acute ear will recognize the difference between the evenly tempered and diatonic scales. In Table 4 is a comparison of the intervals.

25-11. Sound Production. Any vibrating body whose frequency is within the audible range will produce sound provided that it can transfer to the medium enough energy to reach the threshold of audibility. Even though this limit is reached it is frequently necessary to amplify the sound so that it will be readily audible where the listener is stationed. For this purpose sounding boards and loud-speakers may be used, the purpose of each being to increase the intensity of the sound.

When a sounding board is used, the vibrations are transmitted directly to it and force it to vibrate. The combined vibrations are able to impart greater energy to the air than the original vibration alone. If the sounding board is to reproduce the vibrations faithfully, there must be no resonant frequencies, for such resonance will change the quality of sound produced.

The loud-speaker is used to increase the intensity of sound sent out, either by electrical amplification or by resonance. Two general types are used: the direct radiator, such as the cone loud-speaker commonly used in radios, and the horn type. The direct radiator is used more commonly because of its simplicity and the small space required. The horn speaker consists of an electrically or mechanically driven diaphragm coupled to a horn. The air column of the horn produces resonance for a very wide range of frequencies and thus increases the intensity of the sound emitted. The horn loud-speaker is particularly suitable for large-scale public address systems.

25-12. Sound Detectors. The normal human ear is a remarkably reliable and sensitive detector of sound, but for many purposes mechanical or electrical detectors are of great use. The most common of such detectors is the microphone in which the pressure variations of the sound wave force a diaphragm to vibrate. This vibration, in turn, is converted into a varying electric current by means of a change of resistance or generation of an electromotive force. For true reproduction the response of the microphone should be uniform over the whole frequency range. Such an ideal condition is never realized but a well-designed instrument will approximate this response. Microphones are used when it is necessary to reproduce, record, or amplify sound.

Parabolic reflectors may be used as sound-gathering devices when the intensity of sound is too small to affect the ear or other detectors or where a highly directional effect is desired. The sound is concentrated at the focus of the reflector and a microphone is placed there as a detector. Such reflectors should be large compared to the wavelength of the sound received and hence they are not useful for low frequencies.

25-13. Location of Sound. Although a single ear can give some information concerning the direction of a source of sound, the use of two ears is necessary if great accuracy is desired. The judgment of direction is due to a difference between the impression received at the two ears, these differences being due to the differences in loudness or in time of arrival. This is sometimes called the *binaural* effect. Certain types of sound locators exaggerate this effect by placing two listening trumpets several feet apart and connecting one to each ear. The device is then turned until it is perpendicular to the direction of the sound. In this way the accuracy of location is increased.

25-14. Reverberation; Acoustics of Auditoriums. A sound, once started in a room, will persist by repeated reflection from the walls until its intensity is reduced to the point where it is no longer audible. If the walls are good reflectors of sound waves—for example, hard plaster or marble—the sound may continue to be audible for an appreciable time after the original sound stops. The repeated reflection that results in this persistence of sound is called *reverberation*.

In an auditorium or classroom, excessive reverberation may be highly undesirable, for a given speech sound or musical tone will continue to be heard by reverberation while the next sound is being sent forth. The practical remedy is to cover part of the walls with some sound-absorbent material, usually a porous substance like felt, compressed fiberboard, rough plaster, or draperies. The regular motions of the air molecules, which constitute the sound waves, are converted into irregular motions (heat) in the pores of such materials, and consequently less sound energy is reflected.

Suppose a sound whose intensity is one million times that of the faintest audible sound is produced in a given room. The time it takes this sound to die away to inaudibility is called the *reverberation time* of the room. Some reverberation is desirable, especially in concert halls; otherwise the room sounds too "dead." For a moderate-sized auditorium the reverberation time should be of the order of 1 to 2 sec. For a workroom or factory it should, of course, be kept to much smaller values, as sound deadening in such cases results in greater efficiency on the part of the workers, with much less attendant nervous strain.

The approximate reverberation time of a room is given by the expression,

$$T = \frac{0.049V}{\Sigma(kA)} \tag{3}$$

where T is the time in seconds, V is the volume of the room in cubic feet, and ΣkA is the *total absorption* of all the materials in it. The total absorption is computed by multiplying the area A, in square feet, of each kind of material in the room by its *absorption coefficient* k (see Table 5) and adding these products together.

The absorption coefficient is merely the fraction of the sound energy that a given material will absorb at each reflection. For example, an open window has a coefficient of 1, since all the sound that strikes it from within the room would be lost to the room. Marble, on the other hand, is found to have a value of 0.01, which means it absorbs only 1 per cent of the sound energy at each reflection. Equation (3) usually gives satisfactory results except for very large or very small halls, for rooms with very large absorption, or for rooms of peculiar shape.

By means of Eq. (3) we can compute the amounts of absorbing materials needed to reduce the reverberation time of a given room to a desirable value. The absorbing surfaces may be placed almost anywhere in the room, since the waves are bound to strike them many times in any case. In an auditorium, however, they should not be located too close to the performers.

TABLE 5. ABSORPTION COEFFICIENTS FOR SOUNDS OF MEDIUM PITCH

Open window	1.00
Ordinary plaster	0.034
Acoustic plaster	0.20–0.30
Carpets	0.15–0.20
Painted wood	0.03
Hair felt, 1 in. thick	0.58
Draperies	0.40–0.75
Marble	0.01

In addition to providing the optimum amount of reverberation, the designer of an auditorium should make certain that there are no undesirable effects due to regular reflection or focusing of the sound waves.

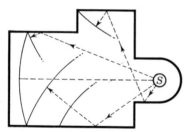

FIG. 8. Ripple-tank model of an auditorium showing reflections from the walls.

Curved surfaces of large extent should in general be avoided, but large flat reflecting surfaces behind and at the sides of the performers may serve to send the sound out to the audience more effectively. Dead spots, due to interference of direct and reflected sounds, should be eliminated by proper design of the room.

The acoustic features of the design of an auditorium may be investigated before the structure is built by experimenting with a sectional model of the enclosure in a ripple tank (Fig. 8). In this way the manner in which waves originating at the stage are reflected can be observed and defects in the design remedied before actual construction is undertaken.

SUMMARY

Sounds differ in *pitch*, *quality*, and *loudness*.

A *musical tone* is produced by a regular succession of compressions and the following rarefactions.

An *unpitched sound* is produced by an irregular succession of compressions and rarefactions or by a disturbance of such short duration that the ear is unable to distinguish a regular succession.

A *noise* is any undesired sound.

The *pitch* of a sound is associated with the physical characteristic of *frequency* of vibration. The average human ear is sensitive to frequencies over a range of 20 to 20,000 vib/sec.

The *quality* of a sound depends upon the *complexity* of the wave, that is, upon the number and relative prominence of the overtones.

The *loudness* of sound is the magnitude of the auditory sensation.

The *intensity* of sound is the energy per unit area per unit time.

Intensity level is the logarithm of the ratio of the intensity of a sound to an arbitrarily chosen intensity. The *bel* and *decibel* are units of intensity level. One bel is the change in intensity level which represents a tenfold ratio of *power*

$$\alpha = \log \frac{I}{I_0}$$

A *musical scale* is a succession of tones which bear a simple relation to each other.

Reverberation is the persistence of sound in an enclosed space due to repeated reflection of waves. It may be reduced by distributing sound absorbing material about the enclosure.

QUESTIONS   **1.** Not all compressional waves can be called sound waves. In what respects can they differ from sound waves?

2. If two pure tones have the same frequency and amplitude, can the ear distinguish one from the other?

3. Draw a simple wave and its first harmonic overtone along the same axis, making the amplitude of the latter half as great as that of the fundamental. Combine the two graphically by adding the ordinates of the two curves at a number of different points, remembering that the ordinates must be added algebraically. If the resulting curve is taken to represent a complex sound wave, what feature of the curve reveals the quality of the sound?

4. Draw a simple wave and its first harmonic overtone, making the latter 45° out of phase with the fundamental and the amplitude half that of the fundamental. Combine the two graphically by adding the ordinates at a number of different points. Compare the curve obtained with that of question 3. Is the wave form the same? Is the complexity the same? Will the two combinations ordinarily be distinguishable?

5. By what means can the overtones of a musical note be isolated and identified?

6. What is the purpose of the horn that is sometimes used as a hearing aid?

7. A noise meter is calibrated in decibels. What does the meter measure?

8. What advantages has the evenly tempered scale over the diatonic scale?

9. Why is the absorption of sound waves an important consideration in architecture? What is the physical meaning of absorption? How is it accomplished? What becomes of the energy of the sound wave absorbed?

10. In an auditorium with wooden seats how does the presence of a large audience affect (a) the reverberation and (b) the average loudness of the sound?

11. Which of the following actions would be more effective in decreasing the reverberation time in an auditorium in which the audience occupies wooden chairs: (a) requiring the audience to rise from their seats, (b) opening the windows, or (c) opening doors to adjoining rooms?

12. One hall is considered ideal for music, another for speaking. Which hall is likely to have the longer period of reverberation?

13. If the period of reverberation in an auditorium is too long, how can it be shortened appreciably?

PROBLEMS   **1.** The human ear can respond to sound waves over a range of frequencies from about 20 cycles/sec to about 20,000 cycles/sec. Calculate the wavelengths corresponding to these frequencies (a) for sound waves in air and (b) for sound waves in water.

2. What is the wavelength in air of sound to which the ear is most sensitive?

Ans. 0.36 ft

3. In a certain concrete grandstand the distance from one riser back to the next is 30 in. If a person claps his hands in front of this grandstand, what is the frequency of the note that comes back to him?

4. Sound of a single frequency is reinforced by reflection from stone steps each 18 in. deep. If the speed of sound is 1080 ft/sec, what is the frequency of the reflected note?   *Ans.* 360 cycles/sec

5. Calculate the amplitude in air under standard conditions of a sound wave whose frequency is 400/sec at (a) the threshold of audibility and (b) the threshold of feeling.

6. Calculate the amplitude in air under standard conditions of a sound wave whose frequency is 1200/sec at the intensity level of ordinary speech.

Ans. 2.90 × 10⁻⁶ cm

7. A relation between the maximum gage pressure P (pressure amplitude) and the displacement amplitude A for a sound wave in a gas may be written $P = 2\pi vf\rho A$. The pressure amplitude of a sound wave of frequency 100/sec just detectable by a person of good hearing is about 0.010 dyne/cm². (*a*) What is the displacement amplitude of the wave in air? The pressure amplitude of the loudest tolerable sound wave of frequency 100/sec is about 200 dynes/cm². What is its displacement amplitude (*b*) if the wave is in air and (*c*) if the wave is in water?

8. Two sounds of the same frequency have intensities of 10⁻¹⁶ and 10⁻¹² watt/cm². What is the difference between the intensity levels of these sounds?

Ans. 40 db

9. At a certain point the power received from one loud-speaker is 100 times as great as that from a second. What is the difference in intensity level between the two sounds at that point?

10. The intensity level at unit distance from a small source is 50 db. Assuming that the sound travels uniformly in all directions, what will be the intensity level at a distance of 10 units? Neglect absorption.   *Ans.* 30 db

11. (*a*) What is the ratio of the sound intensity measured 2.0 ft from a small whistle to the sound intensity measured 20 ft from the whistle? (*b*) What is the difference in intensity levels?

12. For ordinary conversation the intensity level is given as 60 db. What is the intensity of the wave?   *Ans.* 10⁻¹⁰ watt/cm²

13. The intensity level of a certain sound of frequency 200/sec lies 30 db above the threshold of audibility. What is the intensity of this sound?

14. A small source ($f = 200$/sec) radiates uniformly in all directions at a rate of 0.0050 watt. If there is no absorption, how far from the source is the sound audible?

Ans. 2.0 km

15. A small source ($f = 1500$/sec) radiates uniformly in all directions at a rate of 5.0 milliwatts. If there is no absorption, how far from the source is this sound audible?

16. The first note of a diatonic scale has a frequency of 480/sec. Compute the frequencies of the other seven notes.   *Ans.* 540, 600, 640, 720, 800, 900, 960/sec

17. Compute the frequencies of the major diatonic scale based on E as 320/sec. What notes of this scale are common to the scale based on C as 256?

18. A minor diatonic scale is made up of three triads each having frequency ratios of 10/12/15. Compute the frequencies of each of the notes in an octave if the lowest note is 256/sec.   *Ans.* 256, 288, 307, 341, 384, 410, 461, 512/sec

19. Compute the frequencies of an evenly tempered scale starting with E as 320/sec.

20. What is the reverberation period of a room of $10\bar{0},000$-ft³ volume and $20,\bar{0}00$-ft² area if the average absorption coefficient of the surfaces is 0.20?

Ans. 1.2 sec

21. A classroom 30 by 25 by 12 ft has a cork tile floor (absorption coefficient 0.030) and plastered walls. (*a*) What is the reverberation time for this room? (*b*) How many square feet of draperies (absorption coefficient 0.60) must be placed on the walls of the room to make the reverberation time 2.0 sec?

22. What is the reverberation time of a hall whose volume is $100,\bar{0}00$ ft³ and whose total absorption is 2000 ft²? How many square feet of acoustic wallboard of absorption coefficient 0.60 should be used to cover part of the present walls (ordinary plaster) in order to reduce the reverberation time to 2.0 sec, assuming that Eq. (3) holds for this hall?   *Ans.* 2.5 sec; 800 ft²

23. A concert hall whose volume is 30,000 ft³ has a reverberation time of 1.50 sec when empty. If each member of an audience has a sound absorption equivalent to 4.0 ft² of ideal absorbing material (absorption coefficient unity), what will the reverberation time be when 200 people are in the hall, assuming that Eq. (3) holds for this hall?

24. An auditorium is rectangular in shape, 115 by 75 ft, and 30 ft high. It has plaster walls and ceiling, a wood floor, and 750 seats, each with an equivalent complete absorption area of 0.10 ft². (*a*) Find the reverberation time of the empty auditorium. (*b*) What is the reverberation time when the auditorium is filled if each auditor has an equivalent area of 4.0 ft²?   *Ans.* 13 sec; 3.2 sec

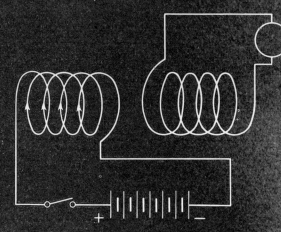

ELECTRICITY
AND MAGNETISM

26. Electric Charges and Fields

Gasoline trucks dangle chains along the road to prevent static electric charges from accumulating to dangerous proportions. Lightning rods are effective in discharging the electricity from low-hanging clouds and thus minimizing damage caused by lightning. Huge machines are today used for building up high voltages for "atom-smashing" experiments. Electricity stored temporarily in capacitors may be removed in a millionth of a second and replaced in the next instant, thus giving rise to electric and magnetic disturbances, which hurtle out through space with the speed of light and actuate our radio receivers. The phenomena of electricity at rest are both historically and practically of great significance in the development of science.

26-1. Electrification. If a piece of sealing wax, hard rubber, or one of many other substances is brought into intimate contact with wool or cat's fur, it acquires the ability to attract light objects such as bits of cork or paper. The process of producing this condition in an object is called *electrification*, and the object itself is said to be *electrified* or charged with electricity.

There are two kinds of electrification. If two rubber balls, electrified by being brushed against fur, are brought near each other, they will be found to repel each other (Fig. 1*a*). But a glass ball rubbed with silk will attract either of the rubber balls (Fig. 1*b*), although two such glass balls will repel each other. The charge on the glass is evidently unlike that on the rubber. These facts suggest the first law of electrostatics: *objects that are similarly charged repel each other; bodies with unlike charges attract each other*.

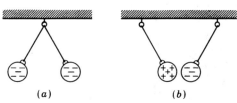

Fig. 1. (*a*) Like charges repel; (*b*) unlike charges attract.

The electrification produced in a glass rod by stroking it with silk is arbitrarily called *positive* electrification, while that produced in the rubber rod by contact with wool is called *negative* electrification. It is ordinarily assumed that uncharged objects contain equal amounts of positive and negative electricity. When glass and silk are rubbed together, some negative electricity is transferred from the glass to the silk, leaving the glass rod with a net positive charge, and the silk with an equal net negative charge. Similarly, hard rubber receives negative electricity from the wool with which it is in contact, causing the rod to be negatively charged and leaving the wool positive. Though a similar explanation

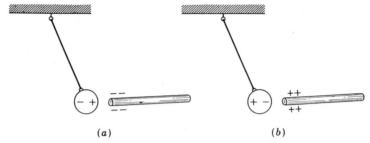

(a)   (b)

FIG. 2. A charged body brought near an insulated conductor causes charges in the conductor to separate. This results in an attraction of the conductor by the charge.

could be made by assuming a transfer of positive electricity, it has been shown that in solids only negative electricity is transferred.

The effect of a charged object on one that is uncharged is illustrated in Fig. 2. Separation of positive and negative electricity within the uncharged object is produced by the charged rod, which exerts a force of repulsion on the like portion of the charge and an attraction on the unlike. In case *a* the negatively charged rubber rod causes the adjacent side of the uncharged object to become positively charged, while the opposite side becomes negatively charged. Because the unlike charge is nearer the rod, the force of attraction will exceed that of repulsion and produce a net attraction of the uncharged object by the rod. In *b* is shown the case in which a positively electrified glass rod is used. It should be remembered that the separation of the charges described here does not alter the total amounts of positive and negative electricity in the uncharged object. No charge is gained or lost; all that occurs is a shift of negative electricity toward one side of the object, making that side predominantly negative

and leaving the other side predominantly positive.

26-2. Electron Theory and Atomic Structure. According to modern theory all matter is composed of *atoms*, tiny particles that are the building blocks of the universe. There are many kinds of atoms, one or more for each chemical element. Each atom consists of a *nucleus*, a small, tightly packed, positively charged mass, and a number of larger, lighter, negatively charged particles called *electrons*, which revolve about the nucleus at tremendous speeds (Fig. 3). The centripetal force necessary to draw these electrons into their circular or elliptical paths is supplied by the electrical attraction between them and the nucleus. The nucleus consists of a number of *protons*, each with a single positive charge, and (except for hydrogen) one or more *neutrons*, which have no charge. Thus the positive charge on the nucleus depends upon the number of protons that it contains. This number is called the *atomic number* of the atom. An ordinary, uncharged atom contains equal numbers of electrons outside the nucleus and protons within the nucleus. Each

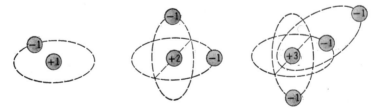

FIG. 3. Each atom consists of a positively charged nucleus surrounded by electrons. The three simplest atoms, hydrogen, helium, and lithium, are represented diagrammatically.

electron carries a single negative charge of the same magnitude as the positive charge of a proton, so that the attraction between the nucleus of an atom and one of the electrons will depend on the number of protons in the nucleus. An electron has a mass of 9.106×10^{-28} gm. Since the mass of a proton or a neutron is about 1837 times that of an electron, the mass of the atom is almost entirely concentrated in the nucleus. The chemical properties of the atom are determined by the number and arrangement of the extra-nuclear electrons.

26-3. Conductors and Insulators. A solid piece of material consists of an extraordinarily large number of atoms clinging together. Though these atoms may be vibrating about their normal positions as a result of thermal agitation, their arrangement is not permanently altered by this motion. Also present in solids are numbers of *free electrons*, so called because they are temporarily detached from atoms. The number and freedom of motion of these electrons determine the properties of the material as a conductor of electricity. A good conductor is a material containing many free electrons whose motion is not greatly impeded by the atoms of which the material is composed. As a result of the repulsive forces between them, free electrons spread throughout the material, and any concentration of them in any one region of the material will tend to be relieved by a motion of the electrons in all directions away from that region until an equilibrium distribution is again reached.

In the best conductors the outer electrons of the atoms can easily be removed, so that a free electron colliding with an atom often causes an outer electron to leave the atom. When this happens, the ejected electron becomes a free electron, moving on, while its place in the atom is taken by another free electron that encounters the atom. An *insulator*, or poor conductor, is a substance that contains very few free electrons and whose atoms have no loosely held orbital electrons.

TABLE 1. ELECTRICAL CONDUCTORS

Good conductors	Poor conductors	Insulators (very poor conductors)
Silver	Tap water	Glass
Copper	Moist earth	Mica
Other metals	Moist wood	Paraffin
Carbon (graphite)	Dry wood	Hard rubber
Certain solutions	Leather	Amber

In Table 1 some common substances are arranged roughly in the descending order of their electrical conductivities.

The reason for describing electrification as occurring through the *transfer of negative electricity* now can be seen. An uncharged object contains a large number of atoms (each of which normally contains an equal number of electrons and protons), but with some electrons temporarily free from atoms. If some of these free electrons are removed, the object is considered to be positively charged, though

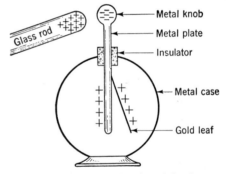

FIG. 4. Leaf electroscope, showing deflection caused by proximity of charged glass rod.

actually this means that its negative charge is below normal. If extra free electrons are gained by an object, it is said to be negatively charged, since it has more negative charge than is normal. The positive charges in atoms are firmly bound in the nucleus and do not participate in ordinary conduction in solids.

26-4. The Leaf Electroscope. A common device to study electrostatic phenomena is the *leaf electroscope* (Fig. 4). This instrument consists essentially of a strip of very light gold leaf or other thin metal foil hanging from a contact on a flat metal plate which terminates in a ball at the upper end. This plate is carefully insulated from the metal case, which has glass windows for observation.

When a charged body of either sign is brought near the knob of the electroscope, the leaf diverges from the plate. This is because the charge in the body causes a separation of the charges in the electroscope plate. When the charging body is removed, the charges in the plate flow together and the leaf collapses. To charge the electroscope permanently, one could touch the knob with a charged rod. If the charging rod has a positive charge, some electrons will leave the plate and flow into the charged rod. When the rod is withdrawn, the leaf will remain diverged for a considerable time because of the positive charge on the electroscope. A negatively charged body touching the knob will leave the electroscope negatively charged since some of the extra electrons on the body will flow into the plate. Note the fact that in this process of *charging by conduction* the sign of the charge left on the electroscope is the same as that of the charging body. Electroscopes can be made which have an amazingly high sensitivity, so that noticeable deflections can be observed from exceedingly small charges, for example, those met with in radioactive phenomena.

26-5. Force between Charges. *The quantity of electricity* or *charge Q* possessed by a body is simply the aggregate of the amount by which the electrons exceed (or are less than) the positive charges in the body. The phenomena of charges at rest constitute the subject of *electrostatics*. Later it will be noted that charges in motion constitute electric currents, with their varied effects.

Coulomb (1736–1806) was the first investigator to place the law of force between electrostatic charges upon an experimental basis. His relatively rough experiments established the law, now known as Coulomb's law

of electrostatics, that the force F between two charges Q and Q' varies directly with each charge, inversely with the *square* of the distance s between the charges, and is a function of the nature of the medium surrounding the charges. In symbols, Coulomb's law is

$$F = k \frac{QQ'}{s^2} \tag{1}$$

where the dimensional factor k is introduced to take care of the units of F, Q, and s, and also to provide for the properties of the medium around the charges, in so far as these properties affect the force between the charges. It must be noted that this k is not a dimensionless proportionality constant. The dimensions of k are force $\times$ distance^2/charge^2.

26-6. Systems of Units Used in Electrostatics. Two families of units are useful in the field of electrostatics, the mks system and the electrostatic system. The electrostatic system is a cgs family and is based upon Coulomb's law [Eq. (1)], with a unit of charge so defined as to make k have a numerical value of unity for empty space. This electrostatic unit (esu) of charge is called the statcoulomb. The *statcoulomb* is a charge of such a magnitude that it is repelled with a force of 1 dyne if placed 1 cm away from an equal charge in a vacuum. This charge is tiny, in terms of the mks unit, the coulomb. One coulomb is approximately 3×10^9 statcoulombs. Although the statcoulomb is much too small for most purposes in conventional electricity, it is a very convenient unit for many electrostatic problems and a much larger unit than that which might seem to be a natural basic unit of quantity of electricity, namely, the charge of one electron. This charge is 4.803×10^{-10} statcoulomb, or 1.60×10^{-19} coulomb. A proton has a similar charge, of positive sign. (The mass of an electron is 9.11×10^{-31} kg and the mass of a proton is 1.67×10^{-27} kg.)

Example: A charge A of $+250$ statcoulombs is placed on a line between two charges B of $+50.0$

statcoulombs and C of -300 statcoulombs. The charge A is 5.00 cm from B and 10.0 cm from C. What is the force on A?

Force on A due to $B = F_1$

$$= \frac{(1.00 \text{ dyne cm}^2/\text{statcoulomb}^2)(250 \times 50.0) \text{ statcoulombs}^2}{(5.00 \text{ cm})^2}$$

$$= 500 \text{ dynes} \qquad (\text{toward } C)$$

Force on A due to $C = F_2$

$$= \frac{(1.00 \text{ dyne cm}^2/\text{statcoulomb}^2)(250 \times 300) \text{ statcoulombs}^2}{(10.0 \text{ cm})^2}$$

$$= 750 \text{ dynes} \qquad (\text{toward } C)$$

Since these two component forces are in the same direction, the resultant force is their arithmetical sum.

$$F_1 + F_2 = 1250 \text{ dynes} \qquad (\text{toward } C)$$

When the mks system of units is used in Coulomb's law, the charge is in coulombs, the force is in newtons, and the distance is in meters. The property of the medium around the charges that affects the force between them is called the *permittivity* of the medium and is represented in Coulomb's law by the symbol ϵ (Greek epsilon).

$$F = \frac{1}{4\pi\epsilon} \frac{QQ'}{s^2} \qquad (1a)$$

Permittivity may be considered roughly as a measure of the ease with which the effects of an electric charge permeate the medium around the charge. For empty space the symbol ϵ_0 is used. In the mks system ϵ_0 has the value 8.85×10^{-12} coulomb^2/newton-m^2. The factor $1/(4\pi\epsilon_0)$ has a value of 8.98740×10^9 newton-m^2/coulomb^2; this number is usually rounded off to the approximate 9.0×10^9. The permittivity of some commonly used insulators (rubber, mica, glass) ranges from two to ten times that of empty space. The value of ϵ for air is practically identical with ϵ_0 for empty space.

In calculations involving electrostatic forces it is often convenient to use the microcoulomb

as a unit of charge [micro $(\mu) = 10^{-6}$]. One microcoulomb equals approximately 3000 statcoulombs.

Example: What is the force between a charge of -50 μcoulombs and another of $+25$ μcoulombs when they are 50 cm apart, in a vacuum?

$$F = \frac{1}{4\pi\epsilon_0} \frac{QQ'}{s^2}$$

$$= 9.0 \times 10^9 \frac{\text{newton-m}^2}{\text{coulomb}^2}$$

$$\times \frac{(50 \times 10^{-6} \text{ coulomb})(25 \times 10^{-6} \text{ coulomb})}{(0.50 \text{ m})^2}$$

$$= 45 \text{ newtons}$$

It must be understood that Coulomb's law applies only to *point* charges, or to those that act as if they are concentrated at a point. For example, if charges are uniformly distributed over the surface of a sphere, their effect on other charges at a great distance from the sphere is the same as if the charges were concentrated at the center of the sphere.

26-7. Electric Fields. The region in the vicinity of a charged body possesses special properties because of the presence of the charge. For example, another charge brought into this region will experience a force. Such a space is known as an electric field. An *electric field* is defined as any region in which there would be a force upon a charge brought into the region.

The direction of an electric field at any point is defined as the direction of the force upon a positive charge placed at that point.

26-8. Electric Field Intensity. *The intensity (or strength) of the electrostatic field* at a point is defined as the force per unit positive charge at that point. The symbolic defining equation is

$$\mathcal{E} = \frac{F}{+q} \qquad (2)$$

where $\mathcal{E}$ is the electric field intensity[1] and F is the force exerted upon the charge q. Note that field intensity is a vector quantity. The

---

[1] The symbol script $\mathcal{E}$ is used here rather than the italic E to avoid confusion when the latter symbol is used for electromotive force.

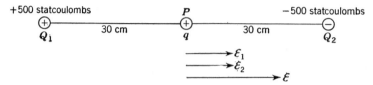

FIG. 5. Electric field intensity midway between two charges.

electrostatic unit of electric field intensity is the dyne per statcoulomb. In the mks system the unit of electric field intensity is the newton per coulomb.

Example: A charge of 30 statcoulombs is placed in an electric field of intensity 5.2 dynes/statcoulomb. What is the force on the charge?

$$F = \mathcal{E}q = (5.2 \text{ dynes/statcoulomb})$$
$$\times 30 \text{ statcoulombs} = 1\overline{6}0 \text{ dynes}$$

Example: The electric field in the space between the plates of a discharge tube is 3.25×10^4 newtons/coulomb. What is the force of the electric field on a proton in this field? Compare this force with the weight of the proton, if the mass of the proton is 1.67×10^{-27} kg and its charge is 1.60×10^{-19} coulomb.

$$F = \mathcal{E}q = 3.25 \times 10^4 \frac{\text{newtons}}{\text{coulomb}} \times 1.60$$
$$\times 10^{-19} \text{ coulomb}$$
$$= 5.20 \times 10^{-15} \text{ newton}$$

The weight of the proton is given by

$$W = mg = 1.67 \times 10^{-27} \text{ kg} \times 9.80 \text{ m/sec}^2$$
$$= 1.64 \times 10^{-26} \text{ newton}$$

Hence

$$\frac{F}{W} = \frac{5.20 \times 10^{-15} \text{ newton}}{1.64 \times 10^{-26} \text{ newton}} = 3.17 \times 10^{11}$$

This emphasizes the fact that the force caused by an electric field may be much greater than that due to a gravitational field.

The electrostatic unit of electric field intensity is a larger unit than the mks unit. The following conversion may be made:

$$\frac{1 \text{ newton}}{1 \text{ coulomb}} = \frac{10^5 \text{ dynes}}{3 \times 10^9 \text{ statcoulombs}}$$
$$= \frac{1}{3 \times 10^4} \frac{\text{dyne}}{\text{statcoulomb}}$$

or 1 esu of electric field intensity is 3×10^4 as large as the corresponding mks unit, since 1 dyne/statcoulomb is 3×10^4 newtons/coulomb.

26-9. Electric Field Intensity Near an Isolated Point Charge. A useful expression for the electric field intensity near an isolated point charge Q may be obtained as follows: Imagine a small positive charge q placed at a distance s from Q. The force between these charges, by Coulomb's law, is

$$F = k\frac{Qq}{s^2}$$

From the definition of electric field strength

$$\mathcal{E} = \frac{F}{q} = k\frac{Qq/s^2}{q} = k\frac{Q}{s^2} \qquad (3)$$

Since electric field intensity is a vector quantity the resultant of two or more field intensities is obtained by taking the vector sum of the various field intensities. When there are a number of charges near a point, the electric field intensity at that point is obtained by taking the *vector* sum of the various component intensities.

Example: Two charges are 60 cm apart, in air. One charge Q_1 is $+500$ statcoulombs, the other Q_2 is -500 statcoulombs. What is the electric field intensity at a point P midway between the charges?

Imagine a test charge q to be placed at P (Fig. 5). The resultant force per unit charge at point P is the vector sum of the component fields $\mathcal{E}_1$ and $\mathcal{E}_2$. Both of these fields are in the same direction. Since k for air is numerically equal to unity, Eq. (3) gives

$$\mathcal{E} = k\frac{Q_1}{s_1^2} + k\frac{Q_2}{s_2^2} = \frac{1.00 \text{ dynes cm}^2}{(\text{statcoul})^2} \times \frac{500 \text{ statcoul}}{30^2 \text{ cm}^2}$$
$$+ \frac{1.00 \times 500}{30^2} \frac{\text{dynes}}{\text{statcoulomb}} = 1.11 \frac{\text{dynes}}{\text{statcoulomb}}$$

This resultant field is directed along the line from Q_1 to Q_2.

Example: Equal charges of $+250$ μcoulombs are placed in air at the corners of an equilateral triangle. (*a*) What is the electric field intensity produced by one of the charges at a point 18 cm

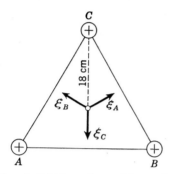

FIG. 6. Electric field intensity equidistant from three equal charges.

from each corner? (*b*) What is the resultant field intensity at this point? (See Fig. 6.)

$$\mathcal{E} = k\frac{Q}{s^2} = 9.0 \times 10^9 \frac{\text{newton-m}^2}{\text{coulomb}^2}$$

$$\times \frac{250 \times 10^{-6} \text{ coulomb}}{(0.18 \text{ m})^2}$$

$$= 1.25 \times 10^7 \text{ newtons/coulomb}$$

This field is directed away from the charge, along the line joining the center point and the charge in question. From the symmetry of the vector figure it is clear that the resultant field at the mid-point is zero.

26-10. Lines of Force. The direction of electric fields at various points may be represented graphically by lines of force. A *line of force* in an electric field is a line so drawn that a tangent to it at any point shows the direction of the electric field at that point.

As an example of this definition consider the isolated positive charge Q placed on sphere A, Fig. 7. A small, positive charge q at b would experience a force of repulsion. Hence the region at b is an electric field. From symmetry it is evident that the direction of the force upon a positive charge anywhere near A would be radially *away from A*.

Hence the lines of force are drawn in these directions. If A were the location of an isolated negative charge, the electric field would extend everywhere radially *toward A*.

The diagram of Fig. 8 shows a plane section of the electric field near a pair of charges

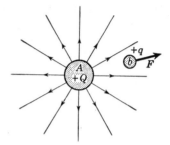

FIG. 7. Electric field near a charge.

equal in magnitude but of opposite sign. The field at any point is the resultant of the superposition of the two component fields due to the charges at A and B. For example, at point b the direction of the resultant force on a positive charge would be along the vector

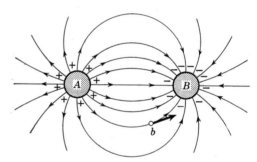

FIG. 8. Electric field near two equal charges of opposite sign.

drawn tangent to the line of force at that point.

26-11. Lines of Force and Electric Field Intensity. It is frequently convenient to represent graphically the intensity as well as the direction of the electric field by means of lines of force ("flux"). This is done by the conventional agreement that the intensity of the field will be represented by a number of lines of force per unit area normal to the field.

The number of lines per unit area is proportional to the intensity of the field. Where the field intensity is large, the lines of force are closely spaced, as in the regions near A and B in Fig. 8. Where the field is less intense, the lines are more widely spaced, as at b in Fig. 8.

Our conventional agreement concerning this electric "flux density" can be expressed by the relation

$$D = \frac{\psi}{A_n} = \epsilon \mathcal{E} \qquad (4)$$

Where D is the "density" of the lines, ψ (Greek psi) is the number of lines of force crossing the surface, and A_n is the area perpendicular to the electric field at the point considered. In the mks system an electric field intensity of 1 newton/coulomb is conventionally represented by $1/(4\pi k)$ lines of force through a square meter that is normal to the field. In the electrostatic system a field of 1 dyne/statcoulomb is conventionally represented by one line of force per square centimeter that is normal to the field.

SUMMARY

Objects may be *electrified* or *charged* either *positively* or *negatively* by the removal or addition of *electrons*.

Like charges repel; unlike charges attract.
Coulomb's law for the force between charges is expressed by the equation

$$F = k\frac{QQ'}{s^2}$$

In the cgs electrostatic system of units the dimensional factor k is arbitrarily assigned a numerical value of unity for empty space. In the mks family $k = 1/(4\pi\epsilon)$, where ϵ is the permittivity of the medium around the charges. For empty space $\epsilon_0 = 8.85 \times 10^{-12}$ coulomb²/newton-m² and $1/4\pi\epsilon_0 = $ approximately 9×10^9 newton-m² per coulomb².

The *coulomb* may be arbitrarily defined or it may be defined in terms of the ampere. One coulomb is approximately 3.0×10^9 statcoulombs.

The *electrostatic unit charge* (statcoulomb) is one that will act upon a similar charge with a force of 1 dyne when the charges are 1 cm apart, in empty space.

An *electric field* is a region in which a force is exerted upon a charge placed in the field.

The *direction of an electric field* is the direction of the force on a positive charge placed at the point considered.

Electric field intensity is force per unit positive charge

$$\mathcal{E} = \frac{F}{+q}$$

The *electric field intensity* near an isolated point charge is given by

$$\mathcal{E} = \frac{kQ}{s^2}$$

The electrostatic unit of electric field intensity is the dyne per statcoulomb; the mks unit is the newton per coulomb.

A *line of force* in an electric field is a line so drawn that a tangent to it at any point shows the direction of the electric field at that point. By conventional agreement the magnitude of $\mathcal{E}$ is represented by a number of lines of force per unit area normal to the field. This number of lines is proportional to $\mathcal{E}$.

QUESTIONS   **1.** Mention a number of cases (other than those given in this book) in which static electricity is illustrated.

2. When a charged rod is brought near bits of cork dust, the cork will at first cling to the rod. Very quickly thereafter the bits of cork will fly off from the rod. Explain why this is true.

3. A positively charged rod is brought near a ball suspended by a silk thread. The ball is attracted by the rod. Does this indicate that the ball has a negative charge? Justify your answer. Would an observed force of repulsion be a more conclusive proof of the nature of the charge on the ball? Why?

4. Will a solid metal sphere hold a larger electric charge than a hollow sphere of the same diameter? Where does the charge reside in each case?

5. Explain why it is so much easier to remove an electron from an atom of large atomic weight than it is to remove a proton.

6. As one gets out of an automobile, he sometimes gets a "shock" when he touches the car. Why is this? Is it likely to happen on a rainy day? Why?

7. A positively charged rod is brought near the terminal of a charged electroscope and the leaves collapse as the rod approaches the terminal. When the rod is brought still closer (but not touching), the leaves again diverge. What is the sign of the charge on the electroscope? Explain its action.

8. Make a rough sketch to show the main forces which act on the leaf of a charged electroscope when it is in equilibrium.

9. Describe and explain an experiment in which a large and massive body can be set into motion by the use of the charge on a rubber rod. State the reasoning involved.

10. Explain clearly why the "constant" k in the coulomb-law equation is not the same type of constant that is found in Newton's second law of motion $F = kma$.

11. In the definition of electric field intensity (force per unit charge) it is assumed that the test charge on which the force acts does not appreciably distort the field. For what charge would this statement be rigorously true? Write a calculus defining equation for $\mathcal{E}$.

12. What proportionality constant would have to be introduced into Eq. (2) if the force were given in pounds and the other quantities were in mks units?

13. State some similarities and some differences between the phenomena of electric fields and gravitational fields.

14. Sketch the appearance of the lines of force (*a*) between two charged plates, one positive and the other negative, and (*b*) between a small positive charge and a negatively charged plate.

15. Sketch an approximate curve to show how the electric field intensity near an isolated point charge varies as the distance away from the charge is increased.

16. A pith ball gilded with metallic paint is attracted by a glass rod that has been rubbed with silk. Does this experiment show that the pith ball has a positive, negative, or zero charge? Explain fully by the aid of diagrams.

17. A copper wire is connected to a brass sphere that has a large positive charge. The wire is touched in turn to equal-sized glass, hard rubber, and aluminum spheres. The spheres are carefully insulated from the ground. Compare the charges that the spheres receive.

18. Three charges of $+20$, $+30$, and $+40$ μcoulombs are placed at the corners of an equilateral triangle. At the center of the triangle toward which charge is the electric field most nearly directed?

19. Derive an expression for the total number of electric lines of force that emanate from a charge Q.

PROBLEMS   *The term "insulated" used in a number of these problems means that the object is not supposed to gain or lose charge by leakage through its supports. Unless otherwise stated, it should also be assumed that the charges are concentrated as point charges.*

1. Two charges of 0.300 μcoulomb and 0.500 μcoulomb are 12.5 cm apart, in air. What force is there between them?

2. Two similar small conducting spheres have charges of $+25$ and -10 statcoulombs, respectively. They are placed in contact and then separated until their centers are 8.0 cm apart. What is the force between them at this position?

Ans. 0.88 dyne

3. Two small conducting spheres of equal radii carry charges of $+0.600$ μcoulomb and -0.400 μcoulomb. If the spheres are brought into contact and their centers are then separated by 110 cm in air, what force is exerted by one sphere on the other?

4. A small charged body, placed 3.0 cm vertically over a charge of $+100$ statcoulombs, has its apparent weight increased by 49 dynes. What is the sign and magnitude of the charge on the body?   *Ans.* -4.4 statcoulombs

5. When a charged ball is hung 15.0 cm above a charge of $+0.300$ μcoulomb, its apparent weight is reduced 1.22 newtons. What is the sign and magnitude of the charge on the ball?

6. Calculate the position of the point in the neighborhood of two point charges of 1.67 and -0.600 μcoulombs, situated 0.40 m apart, where a third charge would experience no force.   *Ans.* 0.60 m from the second charge

7. How much force, in tons, would there be between two charges each of 1.00 coulomb, placed 30 cm apart, in air? Is such a thing feasible? Why?

8. Assuming that a person could count two each second, how long would it take for a million people to count the electrons in 1 coulomb? Assume that the people work in 10-hr shifts and the charge on an electron is 1.60×10^{-19} coulomb.   *Ans.* 2.37×10^5 years

9. Assume that the electron of charge e and mass m in the hydrogen atom revolves in a circular orbit of radius r and that the centripetal force is supplied by electrostatic attraction between the electron and the nucleus. Derive the expression for the speed v of the electron.

10. Two small spheres having a mass of 300 milligrams (mg) each and having equal charges are suspended from the same point by silk strings 100 cm long. When the spheres are kept 15.0 cm apart by electrostatic repulsion, what is the charge on each?   *Ans.* 0.0235 μcoulomb

11. Two small spheres, each having a mass of 150 mg and having equal charges, are suspended from the same point by silk threads 25 cm long. If the threads make an angle of 10° with each other, what is the charge on each sphere?

12. Two gilded pith balls each having a mass of 100 mg are suspended in air by threads 30.0 cm long attached to a common point. When the balls are given equal charges, they are repelled to a distance of 1.80 cm from each other. (*a*) What is the force of repulsion? (*b*) What is the charge on each ball?

          Ans. 2.94×10^{-5} newton; 1.03×10^{-3} μcoulomb

13. Two small metal spheres are supported from a common point by insulating cords 75 cm long. The spheres are charged with 0.060 μcoulomb each. Their electrostatic repulsion forces them to remain apart a distance of 35 cm between the centers of the spheres. Calculate the mass of one of the spheres.

14. What is the intensity of the electric field which will just support a water droplet having a mass of 10 micrograms (μg) and a charge of 1.0×10^{-7} μcoulomb?   *Ans.* 9.8×10^5 newtons/coulomb

15. A charge of -0.050 μcoulomb is situated in an electric field of intensity 9.0×10^4 newtons per coulomb, directed horizontally toward the right. What is the magnitude and direction of the force on this charge?

16. Three points A, B, and C are on the corners of an equilateral triangle. At A there is a point charge of $+0.100$ μcoulomb. What is the magnitude of the electric field intensity at a point midway between B and C, if BC is 10.0 cm?

          Ans. 1.20×10^5 newtons/coulomb

17. Charges Q and $-Q$ of equal magnitudes are placed at points A and B which are a distance s apart, in air. Derive the symbolic expression for the electric field intensity at a point C midway between the charges. A line CD is normal to AB. Derive the symbolic equation for the electric field intensity at point D which is at a distance r from C.

18. Calculate the number of lines of force through a circle of 1.00 mm radius normal to the electric field at a point midway between two charges, one of +500 statcoulombs, the other of −200 statcoulombs, placed 50.0 cm apart, in air. What force would be exerted upon a charge of +20.0 statcoulombs at that point? *Ans.* 0.0352; 22.4 dynes

19. Two charges are 36 cm apart. One charge is +125 μcoulombs; the other is +500 μcoulombs. At what place is there no net force on a positive charge situated on a line that joins the two charges?

20. A charge A of 400 μcoulombs is 12.0 m from a charge B of −100 μcoulombs. (*a*) What is the strength of the electric field at a point C that is 5.00 m from B and 13.0 m from A? (*b*) How many lines of electric force pass through an area of 1.00 cm² normal to the field at C?

Ans. 3.42 × 10⁴ newtons/coulomb at an angle of 35° from line BC; 3.03 × 10^{-11} lines/m²

21. Derive a measure of the ratio of the mks to the electrostatic unit of electric field strength.

22. A hydrogen atom consists of a proton and an electron that revolves in a circular orbit around the proton with a radius of 5.30 × 10^{-9} cm. At what speed must the electron move so that its centrifugal force is just equal to the electrostatic force? *Ans.* 2.20 × 10⁶ m/sec

23. Calculate the ratio of the electrostatic and gravitational forces between two electrons that are 1.00 m apart, in air.

24. How many electrons are there in a coulomb? in a statcoulomb?

Ans. 6.25 × 10¹⁸; 2.10 × 10⁹

25. Compare the acceleration of an electron in an electric field of strength 1250 newtons/coulomb with its acceleration due to the earth's gravity.

27. *Electric Potential*

The most basic concept in physics is energy. We define energy as that property of a system by virtue of which work may be done. In electricity there are numerous ways in which energy in some form is converted into electric energy. For example, a battery transforms chemical energy into electric energy. In other cases electric energy is transformed into another type of energy. For instance, the electric motor converts electric energy into mechanical energy.

In electrical phenomena the concept that is of primary importance in all energy transfers is that known as potential difference. This concept is analogous to gravitational potential. Work must be done to lift a body above the earth against gravitational force. Similarly work must be done to move an electric charge in an electric field. Hence points in the region around charges have potential differences that are associated with the electric field.

27-1. Potential Difference. The *potential difference* between two points is the work done per unit charge when a charge is moved from one point to the other. The defining equation is

$$\text{Potential difference} = \frac{\text{work}}{\text{charge}}$$

$$PD = \frac{W}{q} \quad (1)$$

Conventionally q is always understood to be a

positive charge, thus making definite the algebraic sign of the PD in any particular case.

The unit of PD in the mks system is the volt. One *volt* is defined as the PD between points in an electric field such that one joule of work must be done to move a charge of one coulomb between the points considered.

Small potential differences are often expressed in millivolts (1 mv = 10^{-3} volt) or microvolts (1μv = 10^{-6} volt). Large potential differences can be expressed in kilovolts (1 kv = 10^3 volts) or megavolts (1 Mv = 10^6 volts).

Since the difference of potential between two points is expressed in volts, the PD is often referred to as the *voltage* between these points. Thus if an electric power line has a voltage of 120 volts it follows that 120 joules of work have to be expended for each coulomb of electricity which is transferred through any apparatus connected between the two wires.

Example: A cyclotron produces a PD of 150 megavolts. What is the energy of an electron (charge 1.60×10^{-19} coulomb) that has been accelerated in this machine?

From the definition of PD

$W = PD \times q = 1.50 \times 10^8 \text{ volts} \times 1.60$
$\times 10^{-19} \text{ coulomb} = 2.40 \times 10^{-11} \text{ joule}$

In the cgs family of electrostatic units the unit of PD is the statvolt. One *statvolt* is the

PD between points in an electric field when an energy of one erg must be expended to move a charge of one statcoulomb between the points considered.

The relationship between the volt and the statvolt is calculated as follows:

$$1 \text{ volt} = \frac{1 \text{ joule}}{1 \text{ coulomb}} = \frac{10^7 \text{ ergs}}{3 \times 10^9 \text{ statcoulombs}}$$
$$= \frac{1 \text{ erg}}{300 \text{ statcoulombs}}$$

Since 1 erg/statcoulomb is 1 statvolt, it follows that 1 volt = $\frac{1}{300}$ statvolt, or 1 *statvolt = 300 volts.*

Consider the simple electric field illustrated in Fig. 1. The charge $+Q$ produces an electric field with lines of force extending radially outward. A small test charge $+q$ at any point in the field will be acted upon by a force. Hence it will be necessary to do work to move q between any such points as B and C. The work done per unit positive charge is a measure of the potential difference between these points.

Example: Two points in an electric field have a potential difference of 3.0 volts. What work is required to move a charge of 5.0 coulombs between these points?

$$\text{PD} = \frac{W}{q}$$

or $\quad W = \text{PD} \times q = 3.0 \text{ volts} \times 5.0 \text{ coulombs}$
$$= 15 \text{ joules}$$

Since both work and charge are scalar quantities it follows that *PD is a scalar quantity.* The algebraic sign of a PD is positive when energy must be expended in moving a positive test charge from one point to another. If energy can be obtained *from* the electric field by moving a positive charge from one point to another the PD is conventionally given a negative sign. Thus in Fig. 1 the PD between B and C is positive, while the PD between C and B is considered negative.

27-2. Potential Difference Independent of Path. From the conservation of energy principle it must follow that the work done in moving a charge from one point to another in an electric field is independent of the path over which the charge is transported. Otherwise energy could be created or destroyed by moving a charge from one point such as B in Fig. 1 to C by path a, requiring an amount of work and returning by path b requiring a different amount of work.

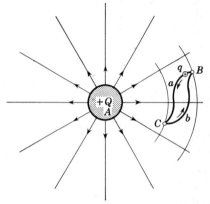

Fig. 1. Potential difference in an electric field.

27-3. Reference Point for Potential Difference. In our study of gravitational effects on the earth we noted the fact that there is need for an *arbitrary* choice of the zero of gravitational potential ("level"). The conventional choice of this zero is usually taken as sea level. We then speak of a body as having a particular height above sea level. At other times we consider the difference of level between two points, neither of which is at sea level. Similarly in electricity we find it convenient to agree upon an arbitrarily selected zero of potential. This zero reference potential is frequently taken as the potential of the earth. For other purposes the zero of potential is considered as the potential of a point greatly distant from all charges (at "infinity"). When a conducting body is connected to the earth ("grounded"), its potential difference above the earth automatically becomes zero. There are often large potential differences between the earth and portions of the atmosphere. Lightning is an example of an electrical discharge that often takes place between the earth and clouds that have potential differences of billions of volts or more.

27-4. Potential at a Point. Instead of considering the potential difference between two points we sometimes wish to consider the potential V_A at a particular point. The *potential at a point* is the difference between the potential of the point and an arbitrarily selected zero of potential. The *potential at a point* is therefore the work done per unit charge when a charge is moved from the zero reference level to the point in question. This work equals the increase in the potential energy of the charge. Hence the definition of the potential of a point is equivalent to the statement: the potential at a point is the ratio of the potential energy of a test charge placed at that point to the magnitude of the test charge

$$\text{Potential} = \frac{\text{potential energy}}{\text{charge}} \qquad V_A = \frac{W}{q}$$

$$(2)$$

It will be noted that Eqs. (1) and (2) are alike and that the respective terms are measured in the same units.

Example: A 120-volt battery is connected to a high-resistance wire 300 in. long. The center of the wire is grounded. What is the potential of the center and each end of the wire?

$$\text{Potential at center} = 0$$
$$\text{Potential at one end} = +60 \text{ volts}$$
$$\text{Potential at other end} = -60 \text{ volts}$$

27-5. Electric Potential Near an Isolated (Point) Charge. Consider the point A at a distance r from an isolated charge Q (Fig. 2).

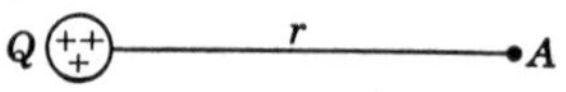

$$Q \oplus \!\!\!\!\!\!\!\!\!\! \underline{\qquad\qquad r \qquad\qquad} \bullet A$$

Fig. 2. Electric potential near isolated point charge.

We shall determine the work done in moving a test charge q from a point outside the electric field of Q (that is, from "infinity") up to the point A. The work per unit charge is the potential of the point considered.

The work done in moving q an infinitesimal distance ds is $dW = F \, ds \cos \theta$. Let $ds \cos \theta = dr$, the displacement in the direction of the electric field. Then

$$dW = -F \, dr$$

where F is the force on q in the direction of the electric field. The negative sign is used because F and dr are in opposite directions. When the value of F from Coulomb's law is inserted in the equation for dW, we obtain

$$W = \int_\infty^s -k\frac{Qq}{r^2}\,dr = kQq\int_\infty^s -\frac{dr}{r^2}$$
$$= kQq\left[\frac{1}{r}\right]_\infty^s = k\frac{Qq}{s}$$

It may be noted that this expression gives the potential energy of the test charge at point A. If we divide this equation by q, we obtain

$$\frac{W}{q} = V_A = k\frac{Q}{s} \qquad (3)$$

The quantities in Eq. (3) are easily handled in electrostatic units. In this system k is numerically equal to unity for empty space, Q is in statcoulombs, and s is in centimeters.

Example: A small brass sphere has a charge of 25 statcoulombs. What is the potential of a point 3.0 cm from the center of the sphere?

$$V = \frac{kQ}{s} = 1.00 \frac{\text{dyne cm}^2}{\text{statcoul}^2} \times \frac{25 \text{ statcoul}}{3.0 \text{ cm}}$$
$$= 8.3 \text{ statvolts}$$

If mks units are used, we substitute for k its equivalent $1/(4\pi\epsilon_0)$, which gives

$$V_A = \frac{1}{4\pi\epsilon_0}\frac{Q}{s} \qquad (3a)$$

In the mks system V is in volts, Q in coulombs, and s in meters. The value of $1/4\pi\epsilon_0$ is 9.0×10^9 newton-m^2/coulomb^2.

Example: The brass sphere in the preceding example had a charge of 25 statcoulombs. Calculate the potential, using mks units, at a point 3.0 cm from the center of the sphere.

$$V_A = \frac{1}{4\pi\epsilon_0} \frac{Q}{s} = 9.0 \times 10^9 \frac{\text{newton-m}^2}{\text{coulomb}^2}$$

$$\times \frac{25 \text{ statcoulombs}}{3.0 \times 10^9 \text{ statcoulombs/coulomb}}$$

$$\times \frac{1}{0.030\text{m}} = 2\bar{5}00 \frac{\text{newton-m}}{\text{coulomb}}$$

$$= 2\bar{5}00 \frac{\text{joules}}{\text{coulomb}} = 2\bar{5}00 \text{ volts}$$

This value agrees with the answer obtained in the preceding example, since 8.3 statvolts × 300 volts/statvolt = $2\bar{5}00$ volts.

If the point A in Fig. 2 were situated near a number of charges, each charge would contribute a share to the resultant potential of the point A. The resultant potential of a point situated near a number of charges is the algebraic sum of all such component potentials; in symbols this may be stated

$$V_A = \sum k\left(\frac{Q}{s}\right) \tag{3b}$$

Example: In Fig. 3 is shown a charge A of $+800$ statcoulombs situated 30 cm from a charge B of -300 statcoulombs. (a) What is the potential at point D which is 10 cm from B and 20 cm from A? (b) What is the potential at point C which is 5.0 cm from A and 25 cm from B? (c) How much work is required to move a charge of $+50$ statcoulombs from C to D?

$$V_D = \sum\left(k\frac{Q}{s}\right) = +\frac{1.0 \times 800}{20} - \frac{1.0 \times 300}{10}$$

$$= +40 - 30 = +10 \text{ statvolts}$$

$$V_C = \sum\left(k\frac{Q}{s}\right) = +\frac{1.0 \times 800}{5.0} - \frac{1.0 \times 300}{25}$$

$$= +1\bar{6}0 - 12 = +1\bar{5}0 \text{ statvolts}$$

$$W_{CD} = q(V_D - V_C)$$

$$= 50 \text{ statcoulombs}$$

$$\times (+10 - 150) \text{ statvolts} = -7\bar{0}00 \text{ ergs}$$

The negative sign of this work indicates the fact that energy is supplied *by* the system in this move.

Example: On a line ABC is situated a charge of $+0.0125$ μcoulomb at point B that is 5.00 cm from A and a charge of -0.0250 μcoulomb at point C that is 25.0 cm from B. What is the potential at A?

$$V_A = \sum \frac{1}{4\pi\epsilon_0}\frac{Q}{s} = 9.0 \times 10^9 \frac{\text{newton-m}^2}{\text{coulomb}^2} \times$$

$$\left(\frac{0.0125 \text{ } \mu\text{coulomb}}{0.050 \text{ m}} - \frac{0.0250 \text{ } \mu\text{coulomb}}{0.300 \text{ m}}\right)$$

$$\times 10^{-6} \frac{\text{coulomb}}{\mu\text{coulomb}}$$

$$= 15\bar{0}0 \frac{\text{newton-m}}{\text{coulomb}} = 15\bar{0}0 \text{ volts}$$

27-6. Equipotential Surfaces. It is easily possible to find in an electric field a large number of points all of which have the same potential. If a line or a surface is so drawn that it includes such points only, the line or surface is known as an equipotential line or surface. An *equipotential surface is defined as a surface all points of which have equal potentials.*

27-7. Lines of Force Perpendicular to Equipotential Surfaces. Equipotential surfaces in an electric field are always perpendicular to the lines of force. This must be true because of the fact that the line of force shows, by definition, the direction of the force upon a test charge and there can be no force normal to this direction. Hence there is no work done in producing a small displacement of a test charge normal to a line of force, and this normal is therefore an equipotential line. Hence, if the equipotential lines can be drawn the lines of force can be immediately constructed, since they are at all points perpendicular to the equipotential lines which they intersect. For example, in Fig. 4 there are shown the lines of force and the equipotential lines in a plane surface containing two charges of equal magnitude and opposite sign.

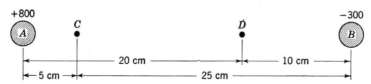

FIG. 3. Potentials of points near two charges.

27-8. Charging by Induction. An insulated conductor may be given a permanent charge by induction. This process takes no charge from the object which induces the charge in the conductor, as there is no electrical connection between them. The method of charging by induction will be illustrated for the case of the leaf electroscope (Fig. 5). When a positively charged glass rod is brought

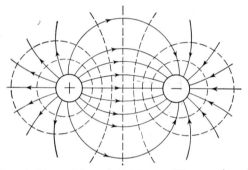

FIG. 4. Lines of force (solid lines, with arrows) and equipotential lines (shown broken) near two equal charges of unlike sign.

near the electroscope, the electrons are attracted to the knob, leaving the leaf positively charged (case *a*). The net charge on the leaf and plate is zero, since no charge has been transferred to or from the surroundings. However, the potential of the entire plate and leaf is some positive value, since this conductor is situated near the positively charged glass rod. The second step in the process is shown in *b*, where the plate is grounded. Electrons flow up from the ground, attracted by the positively charged glass rod. This flow

of electrons will cease in an instant when the previous positive potential of the plate has been reduced to zero. This potential must be zero since the plate and ground have a common potential which, by conventional agreement, is taken as zero. The third phase at *c* consists of breaking the ground connection. This does not change the potential or the charge. But when the charged glass rod is removed in *d* and the electrons in the knob redistribute themselves over the plate and leaf, the electroscope is left negatively charged and having a negative potential. Note that the sign of the final charge is opposite to that of the charging body, unlike the case of charging by conduction. The source of the energy stored up in the charged electroscope is represented by the additional work done in pulling the positively charged glass rod away from the negative charge on the electroscope.

27-9. Potential Gradient. The *gradient* of a quantity is the space rate of its increase from one point to another. The concept of a gradient is important in such cases as temperature gradient, pressure gradient, and the gradient of a roadway. *Electric potential gradient* is the rate of change of potential with distance, dV/ds. The mks unit is the volt per meter and the electrostatic unit is the statvolt per centimeter.

There is a direct relationship between electric field intensity and potential gradient. This relationship may be derived as follows: Consider two points A and B (Fig. 6) on

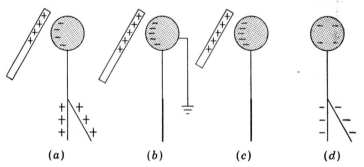

(a)   (b)   (c)   (d)

FIG. 5. Successive steps in charging an electroscope by induction.

some path in an electric field. These points are separated by an infinitesimal distance ds. The electric field intensity $\mathcal{E}$ is practically constant in the region ds. When the test charge $+q$ is moved from A to B, the work done is given by

$$dW = -q\mathcal{E} \cos \theta \, ds$$

The negative sign indicates the fact that the work is negative; that is, that the field supplies

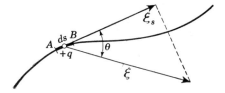

FIG. 6. Work done in moving a test charge in an electric field.

the energy when the positive test charge is moved in a direction that has a component in the same direction as the field intensity. From the definition of potential

$$dV = \frac{dW}{q} = -\mathcal{E} \cos \theta \, ds$$

The component of $\mathcal{E}$ in the direction of ds will be designated $\mathcal{E}_s$. It is therefore apparent that

$$\mathcal{E}_s = -\frac{dV}{ds} \qquad (4)$$

This equation leads to the statement: the electric field intensity in a particular direction at any point in an electric field is equal to the negative of the potential gradient in that direction.

Example: A "point" source of electrons is situated midway between two large metal plates 1.5 cm apart (one of which is maintained at a potential of 2500 volts above that of the other). What is the potential gradient at the source (a) measured at right angles to the plates, (b) measured along a line from the source to a point 15 cm away on one plate?

(a) Potential gradient $= \dfrac{dV}{ds} = \dfrac{2500 \text{ volts}}{0.0150 \text{ m}}$
$= 166 \text{ kv/m}$

(b) Potential gradient $= \dfrac{2500 \text{ volts}}{0.300 \text{ m}} = 8.33 \text{ kv/m}$

27-10. Distribution of Charge on Irregular Conductor. It has previously been assumed that the charges on a conductor, such as a sphere, were uniformly distributed over the surface. This assumption is not always true, particularly in the case of an irregular body. A familiar illustration is the case of an irregularly shaped conductor, such as that

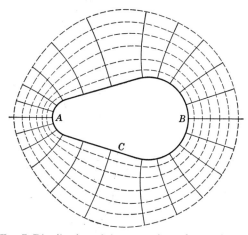

FIG. 7. Distribution of charges on irregular conductor.

shown in Fig. 7. It can be shown, both theoretically and experimentally, that there is a greater density of charge on regions of large curvature and a lower charge density on surfaces of small curvature (large radius of curvature). A common experiment to test these facts is the procedure of using a small metal disk on an insulating handle ("proof plane") to touch a given part of the conductor and then to transfer the charge thereby captured to an electroscope. Such an experiment demonstrates the fact that the charge density is greatest at A, smaller at B, and least at C.

Since the electric field intensity near a point charge is proportional to the charge, it must be true that the electric field will be greatest near the places where the charge density is highest. Lines of force may be sketched in accordance with these facts, spacing them more closely together where the charge density is larger. Equipotential lines are shown in Fig. 7 as dashed lines. They are everywhere normal to the lines of force. The surface of the conductor is an equipotential surface and hence the lines of force are normal to the surface. It is often true that the potential gradient near a pointed surface that is charged becomes so great that the air in this vicinity becomes ionized and conduction takes place rapidly to reduce the charge at the point. This effect is used widely to reduce the accumulation of static electricity in such devices as lightning rods, airplane structures, moving belts, and printing presses. The electric discharge from such points is known as a "*corona* discharge."

It is a fact of considerable importance that all portions of a conductor in an electrostatic field are everywhere at the same potential if the charges are at rest. This must be true, for otherwise there would be a flow of charge from points of higher potential to points of lower potential. Furthermore, all points of a conductor or inside a hollow conductor are at the same potential regardless of the shape of the conductor.

Another item of significance in this connection is the fact that there can be no electric field inside a conductor in an electrostatic field. If such a field existed, the free charges within the conductor would continue to move, thus producing an electric current. Such a current is not possible in electrostatics, as by definition the charges must be at rest in an electrostatic field. It therefore follows that the excess charges on a conductor in an electrostatic field must reside on the outside surface of the conductor. This statement is true regardless of whether the conductor is solid or hollow. In electric shielding, use is made of the fact that external electric fields do not produce an electric field inside a conductor. For example, radio tubes are shielded from external electric fields by placing the tubes inside a conducting "can." A room full of apparatus may be shielded by the use of a wire-mesh cage around all sides of the room.

27-11. The Faraday Ice-pail Experiments. Several significant experiments, originally performed by Faraday with a metallic ice pail and an electroscope, are useful in illustrating some of the facts stated above. The pail is connected to the electroscope by a conducting wire, as in Fig. 8a. When a charged ball, held by an insulating thread, is lowered into the pail, the leaves of the electroscope diverge, showing that they possess an induced charge (Fig. 8b). No change in the divergence of the leaves is noticed when the charged ball is moved to various places inside the pail. This shows that the number of induced charges inside the pail is just equal to the charge on the ball. Now if the ball is touched to a wall of the pail no change in the divergence of the leaves is observed (Fig. 8c). The ball is found to have lost its charge and the outside of the pail and the electroscope have gained the charge lost by the ball (Fig. 8d). When the ball touches the wall, its charge just neutralizes the charges of opposite sign that were on the inside of the pail.

If the ball is again similarly charged and reintroduced into the pail and touched to the pail, it will be found that the pail acquires an additional charge, equal in magnitude and sign to the original charge. This procedure

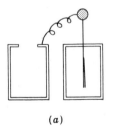 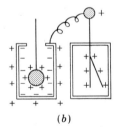 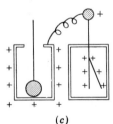 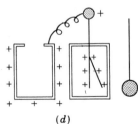

(a)   (b)   (c)   (d)

FIG. 8. Faraday ice-pail experiments.

can be continued until the pail is charged to a very high potential, as is described in Sec. 27-12.

27-12. The Van de Graaff Generator. Use is often made of high-voltage electrostatic sources for the production of "atom-smashing" devices that are useful in experiments in nuclear physics. One such generator was designed by Robert J. Van de Graaff and further developed with his associate John G. Trump.

A highly simplified schematic diagram of this generator is shown in Fig. 9. A large metal sphere S is supported by an insulating tube T. A wide belt AB of some insulating material is motor driven by pulley C; at the upper end it passes over the idler pulley D. A series of needle points at F is kept at a high negative potential (10 to 50 kv) by the source E and a corona discharge sprays electrons onto the belt as it moves upward from C. Another series of needle points at G transfers some of the electrons from the belt to the sphere S, giving it a continually increasing negative charge. Other electrons from the belt charge the pulley D to a sufficiently high negative potential so that positive charges are attracted to the belt from the needle points at H. The belt carries these positive charges downward where they are collected by the grounded terminal I.

Thus there is a steady transfer of negative electricity up the belt to the sphere and a downward flow of positive charges from the sphere to the ground. This results in giving the sphere a high negative potential with respect to the ground. Some large machines of this type have produced potentials up to 10 megavolts and commercial models of various sizes are currently available for a variety of uses. The limiting potential is determined by various leakages including the surrounding air and the supporting insulators.

SUMMARY

Potential difference is the work done per unit charge when a charge is moved from one

point to another

$$PD = \frac{W}{q}$$

The mks unit of PD is the volt. One *volt* is the PD between points when one joule of work must be done to move one coulomb of charge between the points.

The electrostatic unit of PD is the statvolt. One *statvolt* is the PD between points when

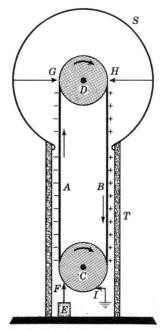

FIG. 9. Van de Graaff generator.

one erg of work must be done to move one statcoulomb of charge between the points.

Potential difference is a scalar quantity.

The PD between two points is independent of the path.

The *potential at a point* is the PD between the point and an arbitrarily selected zero of potential. This zero is frequently taken as the earth ("ground"). If the reference zero of potential is chosen as a point very distant from all charges, the PD between this distant point (at "infinity") and the point in question is called the *absolute potential* of the point. The potential at a point may also be defined as the ratio of the potential energy of a test charge at the point considered to the magnitude of the charge

$$V_A = \frac{W}{q} \quad \text{or} \quad V_A = \frac{dW}{dq}$$

The potential at a point near an isolated point charge is given by

$$V_A = k\frac{Q}{s} \quad \text{or} \quad V_A = \frac{1}{4\pi\epsilon_0}\frac{Q}{s}$$

The work done in moving a charge from point B to point A, which are at different potentials, is given by

$$W_{BA} = q(V_A - V_B)$$

An *equipotential surface* is a surface on which all points have the same potential. The surface is everywhere perpendicular to the lines of force. A charge may be moved anywhere on an equipotential surface without work being performed on or by the field.

Electric potential gradient is the rate of change of potential with distance, dV/ds. Units are the volt per meter and the statvolt per centimeter.

Electric field intensity is equal to the negative of the potential gradient of the field in the given direction

$$\mathcal{E}_s = -\frac{dV}{ds}$$

The *charge density* of charges on an irregular conductor is largest on regions of large curvature (sharp surfaces). The electric fields near such conductors are most intense near the sharp surfaces, thus leading to *corona discharges*.

All portions of a conductor in which the charges are at rest are at the same potential.

There can be no electric field inside a conductor in which there is no charge.

High-voltage electrostatic generators are made by utilizing the phenomena of electrostatic induction.

QUESTIONS   1. State some good analogies between gravitational and electric fields, with reference to field intensity and to potential.

2. Explain clearly why electric potential is not identical with energy. Is it correct to say that PD is the work required to move unit charge between the points considered?

3. Why is it logical to say that the potential of a grounded object is zero? What can be said about the charge on the earth?

4. A brass sphere, mounted on an insulating support, has a positive potential with respect to the earth. Does this fact indicate clearly whether the sphere has a net charge that is zero, positive, or negative? Explain reasoning fully by the aid of diagrams.

5. Draw a curve to portray the variation of electric potential with distance near an isolated point electric charge.

6. Can two lines of force cross in an electric field? Can two equipotential lines intersect? Why?

7. Given a positively charged, insulated sphere, how could you charge two other spheres, one positively, the other negatively, without changing the charge on the first sphere? What is the source of the energy represented by the charges acquired by the spheres?

8. A glass ball and a copper ball are mounted on hard rubber insulating rod supports. Each is rubbed with a silk cloth. The electrification of each is tested at various places by means of a proof plane and an electroscope. Describe how the electrification is found to vary.

9. An insulated and uncharged metallic sphere is brought near a glass rod that had been rubbed with silk. The sphere is grounded for a short time, then the ground connection is broken, and the glass rod is removed. What should

one expect concerning (*a*) the charge and (*b*) the potential of the sphere while it is grounded? After the ground connection is broken and the glass rod is removed?

10. In Fig. 10 is shown a positively charged sphere *A* and an insulated cylinder *B*. The conductor *B* was uncharged before it was brought near to *A*. (*a*) Compare the charges at *C*, *D*, and *E*. (*b*) Compare the potentials of these points.

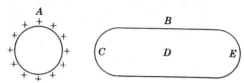

FIG. 10. Charges and potentials at different places on a conductor near a charged body.

11. Can an electric potential exist at a point in a region where the electric field has zero value? Can the potential be zero at a place where the electric field intensity is not zero? Give examples to illustrate your reasoning.

12. Draw a rough figure to show the lines of force and the equipotential lines near one corner of a large charged rectangular box.

PROBLEMS   **1.** There is a PD of 150 volts between the two conductors of a power line. A charge of 600 coulombs is carried from one conductor to the other. What work is required? If the time necessary to transport the charge is 1.25 sec, how much power is used?

2. What is the difference of potential between *A* and *B* if 125 ergs of work must be done to carry a charge of 6.40 statcoulombs from *B* to *A*?

Ans. 19.5 statvolts

3. Two point charges of opposite sign, each of 0.0045 μcoulomb, are placed 60 cm apart, in air. What is the electric potential at a point on the line joining the charges if the point is 20 cm from the negative charge?

4. Two similar charges of 250 statcoulombs are situated on small spheres 15.0 cm apart. What is the electric field intensity midway between the spheres? What is the potential at this point?   *Ans.* zero; 66.7 statvolts

5. Determine the potential in empty space midway between two point charges 24 cm apart when the charges are (*a*) +60 and −60, (*b*) +60 and +60, and (*c*) +80 and −60 statcoulombs, respectively.

6. Calculate the potential midway between two point charges, one of +500 statcoulombs, the other of −200 statcoulombs, placed 50.0 cm apart, in air. What work would be required to bring a charge of +23.5 statcoulombs to this point from a very distant point?   *Ans.* 12.0 statvolts; 282 ergs

7. At point *A* there is a charge of 400 statcoulombs. At point *B*, 80.0 cm away, there is a charge of −800 statcoulombs. What is the potential at point *C* situated midway between *A* and *B*? Point *D* is 30.0 cm away from *C*, on a line perpendicular to *AB*. How much work is required to move a charge of 60 statcoulombs from *D* to *C*?

8. Compute the work required to bring a charge of 5.0 statcoulombs from a point 24 cm from a charge of 60 statcoulombs to a point 3.0 cm from it.

Ans. 88 ergs

9. A small spherical conductor in air has a charge of +200 statcoulombs. How much work is done in moving a unit positive charge from a point 50 cm from the center of the sphere to a point 10 cm from the center of the sphere?

10. At each corner of a square 20 cm on a side is a small charged body. Going around the square, these charges are +60, −30, +60, and −30 statcoulombs. Find (a) the field intensity and (b) the electrostatic potential, at the center of the square.   *Ans.* zero; 4.3 statvolts

11. Charges of 1.00, 2.00, 3.00, and −4.00 statcoulombs, respectively, are placed at the corners of a square, taken in order. If the length of each side of the square is 2.00 cm, find the potential at the middle point of the side joining charges 1 and 2.

12. The distance between concentrated charges of 125 statcoulombs and 150 statcoulombs is changed from 75.0 to 25.0 cm. How much work is done?

Ans. 500 ergs

13. There is an electric field intensity of 7.50 dynes/statcoulomb at a point A near a charge of 35.0 statcoulombs. A charge of 67.5 statcoulombs is placed so that the field at A is made zero. Locate A relative to both charges. What is the potential of the point A?

14. Calculate the potential energy of a system composed of four charges of 0.0125 μcoulomb each that are situated at the corners of a square which is a meter on each side.   *Ans.* 7.64×10^{-6} joule

15. A charge of 8.00 statcoulombs is moved 30.0 cm against a field that increases uniformly from 12.0 to 50.0 dynes/statcoulomb over that distance. How much work is done to move the charge?

16. A pair of large parallel plates 5.25 mm apart are charged until they have a PD of 1.50 kv. What is the electric field intensity between the plates?

Ans. 2.86×10^{5} newtons/coulomb

17. A hollow spherical brass shell has a radius of 18.0 cm and a charge of 0.300 μcoulomb. What is the electric field intensity and the potential (a) at a point 27.0 cm from the center of the sphere, (b) at the surface of the sphere, and (c) at a point 9.0 cm from the center of the sphere?

18. The electric field intensity directed downward between two large horizontal plates 3.00 cm apart is 2.50×10^{4} newtons/coulomb. How much energy is required to move a charge of 6.35 μcoulombs (a) from the lower to the upper plate, (b) 10.0 cm horizontally, and (c) 4.30 cm at an angle of 25° above the horizontal?   *Ans.* 4.78×10^{-3} joule; zero; 2.87×10^{-3} joule

19. A Van de Graaff generator has a potential of 5.0 megavolts built up when the charging belt carries negative charge upward at a rate of 1.25 millicoulombs/sec and positive charge downward at a like rate. What power is required to maintain this flow?

28. *The Electric Current*

We live in an age of electricity. Homes and factories are lighted by electricity; communication by telegraph, telephone, radio and television depends upon the use of electricity; and the industrial applications of electricity extend from the delicate instruments of measurement and control to giant electric furnaces and powerful motors. Electricity is a useful servant of man—a practical means of transforming energy to the form in which it serves his particular need. The effects of electricity both at rest and in motion are well known, and the means to produce these effects are readily available.

This chapter is designed to give a preliminary and necessarily superficial preview of the major sources and effects of electric currents. The student is not expected immediately to become thoroughly familiar with all of these. But it has been found helpful to survey the field broadly before beginning more detailed studies of the individual portions.

28-1. Electric Currents, Charges in Motion. In Chaps. 26 and 27 the phenomena of electricity at rest were considered. When there is a flow of electricity through a substance, such as a copper wire, an *electric current* is said to exist in the wire. Such a current constitutes one of the most widely used means of transmitting energy in the modern world. The effects of electric currents are quite different from those of static electricity, just as the phenomena of water in motion differ from those of water at rest. A famous American physicist Henry Rowland (1889) was the first to prove that electric charges in motion produce the characteristic effects of electric currents, many of which were known at the time of his experiments. Some of the ways of producing electric currents and the effects of such currents are described in this chapter.

In Chap. 26, the electron theory of the constitution of matter was discussed. This theory enables us to describe in very simple terms the main phenomena associated with electric currents. Conductors differ from insulators in the ease with which electrons leave their "parent" atoms and move through the conductor to constitute an electric current. Some of the details of the exact mechanism of the flow of electricity in solid conductors are not yet entirely clear. But in general physicists are agreed that the main facts of current electricity are described in terms of the flow of electrons through the conductor.

28-2. Electric Current. Consider a circular loop of copper wire. The wire consists of a tremendous number of copper atoms along with a large number of free electrons. If energy is supplied to make these free electrons move around the circuit continuously, an *electric current* is said to be produced in the wire. It is to be emphasized that a *source of electric current is simply a device for causing elec-*

tricity to move around a circuit. The electrons themselves are already in a metallic circuit, hence a source of electric current merely causes a motion of electrons but does not produce them. Since electrons repel each other, a motion of those in one part of the circuit will cause those next to them to move, relaying the motion around the circuit. The individual

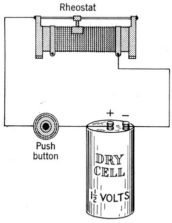

Fig. 1. A simple electric circuit.

electrons in a current-carrying wire move with a relatively low speed (about 0.01 cm/sec for a current of 1 amp in a copper wire 1 mm in diameter), but the impulse of the electron movement travels around the circuit with a speed approaching that of light (186,000 mi/sec).

28-3. Chemical Sources of Electric Current. Let us consider some of the methods by which electrons can be caused to move around a circuit. In Fig. 1 is shown an electric circuit consisting of a dry cell, a push button, and a rheostat. A conventional wiring diagram for this circuit is shown in Fig. 2. The positive terminal of a cell is usually represented by a long, thin line and the negative terminal by a shorter (often heavier) line. The electrons are forced out of the negative terminal of the cell and around the circuit, returning to the positive terminal of the cell. Since the electrons leaving the cell must push those just ahead (and thus those on around the circuit), the cell furnishes the driving force for the elec-

trons throughout the circuit by propelling each as it comes through. The cell thus does work on the electrons, communicating to them the energy released in the interaction of chemicals within it. This phenomenon is often known as the *voltaic effect.*

There are many types of these *chemical sources of electric current.* Cells that must have

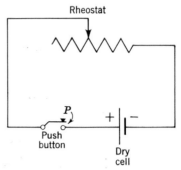

Fig. 2. A schematic diagram of the simple circuit.

their elements renewed after they have supplied a given amount of energy to an external circuit are called *primary cells.* Such sources of electric energy are quite expensive. This fact greatly hampered the industrial utilization of electric currents until other and vastly more economical electric "generators" were invented.

A widely used chemical source of electric current is the *storage cell.* This type of source differs from the primary cell in that it can be recharged by the use of a reverse current from an outside source. This cell transforms electric energy into chemical energy during the charging process. During discharge, chemical energy is transformed into electric energy, as in the case of the primary cell.

28-4. The Dry Cell. The most commonly used voltaic cell is the so-called *dry cell* (Fig. 3). The positive electrode of this cell is a carbon rod and the negative terminal is the zinc container for the cell. A layer of paper moistened with ammonium chloride (NH_4Cl) is placed in contact with the zinc, while the space between this and the central carbon rod is filled with manganese dioxide and granulated carbon moistened with ammonium chloride solution. The ammonium chloride is the electrolyte and in the chemical reaction hydrogen is liberated at the carbon electrode. The hydrogen reduces the effectiveness of the cell for two reasons: (1) the gas increases the internal resistance of the cell, and (2) the

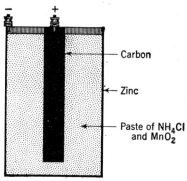

FIG. 3. A dry cell.

hydrogen produces a reverse emf at the carbon electrode. The latter effect is known as *polarization*. The manganese dioxide acts as a depolarizing agent by reacting with the hydrogen to form water. The cell polarizes when it is used but recovers slowly as the manganese dioxide reacts with the hydrogen. Because of this behavior, the cell should not be used continuously. The voltage of the dry cell is slightly more than 1.5 volts.

28-5. Storage Batteries. Some voltaic cells can be recharged or restored to their original condition by using some other source to maintain a current in the reverse direction in them. This "charging" current reverses the chemical changes that occur on discharge. Such a cell is called a *storage* cell. Only those voltaic cells in which the chemical reaction is readily reversed by changing the direction of the current can be used as storage cells. The most common type of storage cell is the lead cell (Fig. 4), which is used for automobiles and many other purposes. Both plates are lead grids into which the active material is pressed. The active material is lead oxide (PbO_2) for the positive plate and finely divided metallic

lead for the negative electrode. Dilute sulfuric acid is used as the electrolyte.

A lighter and more rugged type of storage battery is made up of *Edison* cells. The positive plate of the Edison cell is nickel oxide (NiO_2), the negative plate is iron, and the solution is potassium hydroxide. It is more

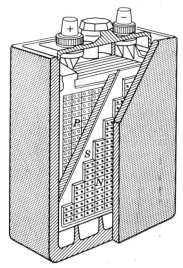

FIG. 4. A lead storage cell.

readily portable than the heavy lead cell and can be allowed to stand uncharged for long periods of time without damage. However, it is more expensive than the lead cell, and its voltage is lower (1.3 volts). It is commonly used in installations where charging is irregular or where weight is an important factor, as in field radio sets and miners' lamps. Its long life and ruggedness have made it a favorite cell for the electrical laboratory.

When a storage battery is charged, *chemical energy* is stored up in the cells. The amount of energy that can be stored depends upon the size of the plates. A large cell has exactly the same voltage as a small cell but the energy available in it when fully charged is much greater than that in the small cell.

28-6. Direction of Electric Current. The modern picture for the mechanism of an electric current in a metallic conductor postulates a flow of electrons in the circuit. Since they are negatively charged, their direction of motion, in the aggregate, is from the negative terminal of the source, through the external circuit, and back into the positive terminal. For many years before this picture became established, the direction of the flow was assumed to be that of positively charged particles. We now know that we do have this flow of positive electricity in many cases of gaseous and electrolytic conduction. But in the

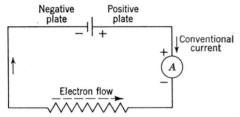

FIG. 5. Directions of electron flow and conventional current.

more common cases of metallic conduction the current is believed to be mainly a flow of electrons from the negative toward the positive. Any current direction is a convention, and the choice is arbitrary. In this book the common custom will be followed of regarding *the direction of the conventional current* as that of the flow of *positive* electricity. The electron flow and the direction of the conventional current are schematically represented in Fig. 5.

An ammeter is placed in series in a circuit to measure the current. The positive terminal of a d-c ammeter is ordinarily marked with a + sign, the negative terminal often being indicated by a number equal to the range

(full-load current) of the instrument. The electrons enter the negative terminal and leave the positive terminal of the ammeter, while the conventional current is from the positive to the negative.

28-7. Thermoelectric Source of Electric Current. A commonly used source of electric current in which heat is transformed into electric energy is shown in the thermocouple illustrated in Fig. 6. In the diagram there is

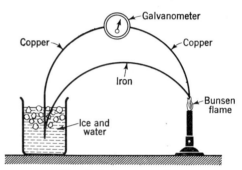

FIG. 6. A thermocouple.

shown a loop consisting of a piece of iron wire joined to a piece of copper wire. One of the junctions is heated by a flame, causing electrons to flow around the circuit. The flow will continue as long as one junction is at a higher temperature than the other junction. Such a device, consisting of a pair of junctions of dissimilar metals, is called a *thermocouple*. The main commercial use of thermocouples is for the measurement and control of temperature.

28-8. Electromagnetic Generators of Current. The principle upon which the main source of electric currents depends is illustrated by the following. If one end of a bar

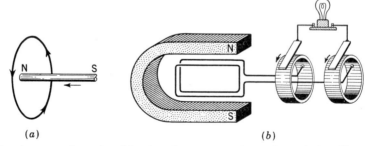

(a)   (b)

FIG. 7. (a) An electric current is produced by thrusting a magnet into a loop of wire. (b) A simple generator.

magnet is plunged into a loop of wire, the electrons in the wire are caused to move around the loop, though their motion continues only while the magnet is moving (Fig. 7a). If the magnet is withdrawn, the electrons move around the loop in the opposite direction. The discovery of this means of producing an electric current with a moving magnet led to the development of the *electric generator*. A very simple generator is shown in Fig. 7b. It consists of a stationary magnet between whose poles a coil of wire is rotated. The two ends of the coil are joined, through rotating contacts, to an incandescent lamp. During one-half of a rotation of the coil the electrons move in one direction through the lamp filament, while during the next half rotation they move in the opposite direction. Such a generator is said to produce an *alternating* current. In the generator there is a transformation of mechanical into electric energy. This energy is expended in forcing the electricity through the circuit.

28-9. Photoelectric Sources of Electric Current. If light falls on a clean surface of certain metals, such as potassium or sodium, electrons are emitted by the surface. This phenomenon is called the *photoelectric* effect. If such a metallic surface is made a part of an electric circuit, such as that in Fig. 8, the electric current in the circuit is controlled by the light. If the light is bright, the current will be larger than if the light is dim. This device is known as a *photoelectric cell* and serves as a basis for most of the instruments that are operated or controlled by light such as television, talking motion pictures, wire or radio transmission of pictures, and many industrial devices for counting, rejecting imperfect pieces, and control. The photoelectric cell is an example of a device that transforms radiant energy into electric energy.

Electrification by contact, as described in Chap. 26, can bring about transfers of small quantities of electricity; yet it is not commercially important as a means of sustaining an electric current.

28-10. Piezoelectric Sources. In recent years another source of electric current has become of importance in such devices as microphones, oscillators, phonograph pickups, and frequency stabilizers. These instruments utilize crystals which, when slight pressures are applied, produce tiny voltages which may be amplified and used. This is known as the *piezoelectric* effect.

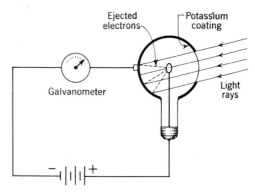

FIG. 8. A photoelectric cell.

In all these sources of electric current some type of energy is used to set the electrons in motion. Chemical, mechanical, thermal, or radiant energy is transformed into electric energy.

28-11. Effects of Electric Current. The circuit in Fig. 9 consists of a battery E in series with a piece of high-resistance wire R; an incandescent lamp L; an electrolytic cell Z containing metal electrodes (a and b) immersed in water to which a few drops of sulfuric acid have been added; and a key K, which opens and closes the circuit. A magnetic compass C is directly over the wire.

If the key K is closed, the battery produces a flow of electrons from its negative terminal through L, R, K, and back to the positive terminal of the battery. In the electrolytic cell Z the flow of electricity includes positive ions traveling in the direction of the conventional current and negative ions moving in the opposite direction. As a result of the flow, several changes occur in the various parts of the circuit. The wire R becomes warm, and

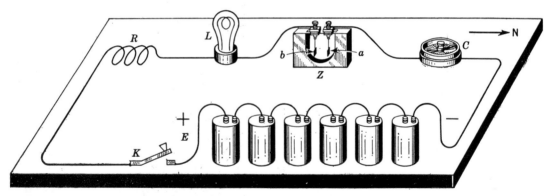

FIG. 9. A circuit showing three effects of an electric current.

the filament of wire in the incandescent lamp becomes so hot that it begins to glow. The water in Z presents a very interesting appearance. Bubbles of gas come from the surfaces of the electrodes a and b (twice as much from a as from b). Tests show that hydrogen gas is being given off at a, and oxygen at b. Since oxygen and hydrogen are the gases that combine to form water and since the water in Z is disappearing, it is natural to conclude that the water is being divided into its constituents (hydrogen and oxygen) by the action of the electric current.

The compass C, which points north (along the wire in Fig. 9) when the key is open, is deflected slightly when the key is closed. This indicates that a magnetic effect is produced in the vicinity of an electric current. A phenomenon so simple as the deflection of a compass needle hardly indicates the importance of the magnetic effect of an electric current, but it is this magnetic effect that makes possible the operation of electric motors as devices by means of which electric currents perform mechanical work. The magnetic effect makes possible also the radio, telephone, telegraph, and countless other important electric devices.

The heat produced in R and L, the decomposition of water in the cell Z, and the deflection of the compass needle can be accomplished only by the expenditure of energy. By means of the electrons that it drives

around the circuit, the battery E communicates energy to the various parts of the circuit. Electrons forced through R and L encounter resistance to their motion because of their collisions with the atoms of the material in R and L. These collisions agitate the atoms, producing the atomic-molecular motion whose energy we call *heat*. In ways that will be discussed later, the current causes the decomposition of the water in Z and the deflection of the compass C, and the energy that is expended in these processes is furnished by the battery.

Various other effects of electric currents might be mentioned, but they can be classified as combinations of the three main effects. For example, the *optical effect* observed in light sources such as electric lamps, advertising signs, and fluorescent lights is caused chiefly by heating effects. The *physiological* effects that one experiences when he receives an electric "shock" are caused by a combination of heating and chemical effects.

28-12. Unit of Electric Current. Any one of the major effects of the electric current could be used to define the unit of current. Both the heating effect and the chemical effect have been used for this purpose. The ampere is now defined in terms of the forces between parallel current-carrying conductors (Sec. 31-10). The *ampere* is a current that, when it is maintained in two infinitely long conductors, parallel to each other and 1 m apart in a vacuum, will cause a force on each conductor of exactly 2×10^{-7} newton per meter length.

28-13. Quantity of Electricity; Charge. Having established the ampere as the unit of current, we may now use it to define the unit of quantity of electricity, or charge. Quantity and current are related by

Quantity of electricity = current $\times$ time
$$Q = It \qquad (1)$$

One *coulomb* is the charge which in one second traverses a conductor in which there is a constant current of one ampere.

If the current is not constant, Eq. (1) must be modified into the form

$$Q = \int i \, dt \qquad (1a)$$

in which all the infinitesimal values of the charge $i \, dt$ are integrated, or summed up, between the time limits considered.

28-14. Faraday's Laws of Electrolysis. Quantitative measurements made by Faraday (1833) contributed to the understanding of the processes occurring in electrolytic cells and showed a striking relation between the electrolytic behavior and the chemical properties of various substances. Faraday established by experiment the following two laws of electrolysis:

FIRST LAW: The mass of a substance separated in electrolysis is proportional to the quantity of electricity that passes.

SECOND LAW: The mass of a substance deposited is proportional to the chemical equivalent of the ion, that is, to the atomic mass of the ion divided by its valence.

Faraday's laws may be expressed by the following symbolic statements:

$$m \propto Q \qquad (Q = It)$$
$$m \propto c \qquad \left(c = \frac{\text{atomic mass}}{\text{valence}} \right)$$

whence

$$m = kcQ = zQ = zIt \qquad (z = kc) \quad (2)$$

where k is a proportionality constant, whose value depends only upon the units involved, m is the mass deposited, and z is a constant for a given substance (but different for different substances), which is known as the *electrochemical equivalent* of the substance considered.

The electrochemical equivalent of a substance is the mass deposited per unit charge, that is, it is numerically the number of grams deposited in 1 sec by an unvarying current of 1 amp.

Example: How long will it take to electroplate 3.00 gm of silver onto a brass casting by the use of a steady current of 15.0 amp?

$$m = zIt$$
$$3.00 \text{ gm} = 0.001118 \frac{\text{gm}}{\text{coulomb}} \, 15.0 \text{ amp} \times t$$
$$t = 178 \text{ sec}$$

28-15. Calculations of Electrochemical Equivalents. From Faraday's second law and the standard value of z for silver, the value of z for any other substance can be calculated if its chemical equivalent is known. From Faraday's second law the following proportion is valid:

$$\frac{\text{Unknown electrochemical equivalent}}{\text{Electrochemical equivalent of silver}}$$
$$= \frac{\text{chemical equivalent of the substance}}{\text{chemical equivalent of silver}}$$

In symbols $\qquad \dfrac{z}{z_{Ag}} = \dfrac{c}{c_{Ag}}$

From the standard values for silver,

$$z = 0.00111800 \frac{\text{gm}}{\text{coulomb}} \frac{c}{107.9}$$
$$= \frac{c}{107.9/0.001118} \frac{\text{gm}}{\text{coulomb}}$$
$$z = \frac{c}{96{,}500} \frac{\text{gm}}{\text{coulomb}} \qquad \text{(approximately)} \quad (3)$$

Example: Calculate the electrochemical equivalent of copper.

$$z = \frac{c}{96,500} = \frac{31.8 \text{ gm}}{96,500 \text{ coulombs}}$$

$$= 0.000329 \frac{\text{gm}}{\text{coulomb}}$$

28-16. The Faraday. The mass m deposited by any charge Q is given by the equation $m = zQ$. From Eq. (3), it follows that a charge of 96,500 coulombs will deposit a mass of any substance numerically equal to its chemical equivalent, since

$$c = z \times 96,500 \text{ coulombs}$$

The mass equal to the chemical equivalent expressed in grams is called the gram equivalent. The *faraday* is the charge that will deposit one gram equivalent of any substance. Its value is approximately 96,500 coulombs.

Some electrochemical data are listed in Table 1.

TABLE 1. ELECTROCHEMICAL DATA

Element	Atomic mass	Valence	Electrochemical equivalent, gm/coulomb
Aluminum...	27.1	3	0.0000936
Copper......	63.6	2	0.0003294
Copper......	63.6	1	0.0006588
Gold.......	197.2	3	0.0006812
Hydrogen...	1.008	1	0.0000105
Iron........	55.8	3	0.0001929
Iron........	55.8	2	0.0002894
Lead.......	207.2	2	0.0010736
Nickel......	58.68	2	0.0003041

28-17. Difference of Potential, Voltage. The concept of potential difference, also called *voltage*, was considered in Chap. 27. The practical unit of potential difference is the *volt*. The legal volt is defined as an arbitrary fraction of the voltage of a Weston standard cell, of specified constitution. This value was selected so as to make the legal volt the potential difference between two points which are so situated that 1 joule of work per coulomb of charge is required to transport electricity from one point to the other. Familiar examples of voltage are those be-

tween the terminals of the dry cell, about 1.5 volts, and household electric circuits of about 110 to 120 volts.

28-18. Resistance. The electric resistance R of a conductor is the ratio of the potential difference between its terminals to the current produced in it

$$R = \frac{V}{I}$$

The practical unit of electric resistance is the *ohm*, which is the resistance of a conductor in which a current of 1 amp can be maintained by a potential difference of 1 volt. The ohm, therefore, is merely another name for the volt per ampere. The legal ohm is defined in terms of the resistance of an arbitrarily selected column of mercury of specified characteristics. These specifications were chosen to make the legal ohm identical with the legal volt per ampere.

28-19. Ohm's Law. One of the most widely used principles of practical electricity is known as *Ohm's law*. This law is the statement of the observed fact that, if the temperature and other physical conditions of a metallic conductor are unchanged, *the ratio of the potential difference to the current is a constant*. In symbols

$$\frac{V}{I} = R \qquad \text{(a constant)} \qquad (4)$$

Example: The difference of potential between the terminals of an incandescent lamp is 6.0 volts. If the current is 1.5 amp, what is the resistance?

From the definition $R = \frac{V}{I}$ it is seen that

$$R = \frac{6.0 \text{ volts}}{1.5 \text{ amp}} = 4.0 \text{ ohms}$$

Now suppose that one wishes to determine what current will be maintained in the lamp if the difference of potential is increased to 8.0 volts. Ohm's law indicates that the resistance R will remain the same (4.0 ohms) when the voltage is increased; hence we can write

$$I = \frac{V}{R} = \frac{8.0 \text{ volts}}{4.0 \text{ ohms}} = 2.0 \text{ amp}$$

Note that it is impossible to solve this problem without using Ohm's law, that is, the fact that R is constant.

Example: It is desired to maintain a current of 5.00 amp in an electric iron of 24.0 ohms resistance. What voltage is required?

$$V = IR = 5.00 \text{ amp} \times 24.0 \text{ ohms} = 120 \text{ volts}$$

28-20. Systems of Electrical Units. The group of electrical units used in this chapter is the legal system in the United States. The ampere, volt, and ohm are each independently defined, by act of Congress, in terms of practical working standards.

In Chap. 1 it was pointed out that a complete set of units for mechanics could be developed in terms of three arbitrarily chosen fundamental units. Also mention was made of the mks system of units, which has gained international recognition. For mechanics the basic mks units are the meter, the kilogram, and the second. By adding one fundamental electrical unit to these three a complete set of electrical units can be established. The ampere serves nicely for this additional unit and nas the advantage of making the practical system identical with the mks system.

SUMMARY

An *electric current* exists when there are charges in motion.

In metallic conductors the current is essentially a stream of electrons forced through the circuit by the source. The direction of the ,*conventional* current is from positive to negative.

Cells are commonly used as sources of currents when limited amounts of energy are required. Cells transform chemical energy into electric energy.

Thermocouples transform heat energy into electric energy. They are used extensively in thermoelectric thermometers.

The most important source of electric current is the *electromagnetic generator*. Generators transform mechanical energy into electric energy.

Photoelectric cells transform light energy into electric energy.

Piezoelectric sources transform the energy of compression of crystals into electric energy.

The chief effects of electric currents are the *magnetic, heating,* and *chemical* effects.

The *ampere* is the unit of electric current.

The *coulomb* is the unit quantity of electricity (charge). One coulomb is the charge transmitted by a constant current of one ampere in one second

$$Q = It \qquad 1 \text{ coulomb} = 1 \text{ amp} \times 1 \text{ sec}$$

Electrolysis is the chemical action which is connected with the passage of electricity through an electrolyte.

Faraday's laws of electrolysis are as follows:

1. The mass of a substance deposited by an electric current is proportional to the amount of electric charge transferred.

2. For the same quantity of electricity transferred, the masses of different elements deposited are proportional to their atomic masses, and inversely proportional to their valences

$$m = zIt$$

The *electrochemical equivalent* of a substance is the mass per unit charge

$$z = \frac{m}{Q}$$

The *faraday* is the quantity of electricity, approximately 96,500 coulombs, which will deposit a gram equivalent of any substance. From this it follows that

$$z = \frac{c}{96,500} \frac{\text{gm}}{\text{coulomb}}$$

The *potential difference, or voltage,* between two points is the work per unit charge expended in moving a quantity of electricity between the points considered

$$V = \frac{W}{q} \qquad 1 \text{ volt} = \frac{1 \text{ joule}}{1 \text{ coulomb}}$$

One *volt* is the PD between points such that

one joule of work is required to transfer one coulomb of charge between the points considered.

Electric *resistance* is the ratio of the voltage to the current

$$R = \frac{V}{I} \qquad 1 \text{ ohm} = \frac{1 \text{ volt}}{1 \text{ amp}}$$

One *ohm* is the resistance of the conductor which requires a PD of one volt to maintain a current of one ampere in the conductor.

Ohm's law states that the ratio of the voltage to the current in a resistor is constant when the physical characteristics of the circuit are unchanged.

QUESTIONS

1. What happens when two initially charged conducting bodies are connected by a wire? What determines the direction of the current? How long will it continue?

2. What determines which one of the terminals of a rheostat is positive when it is connected in a circuit? Illustrate your answer by a diagram.

3. Although the cost of electric energy from dry cells is very high such sources are widely used. Why is this true?

4. Arrange the following sources in the order of relative amounts of electric energy which they might ordinarily supply: (*a*) electrostatic generator, (*b*) electromagnetic generator, (*c*) battery, (*d*) thermocouple, (*e*) photoelectric cell, and (*f*) piezoelectric source.

5. Does a storage cell store up electricity? Why is it properly called a storage cell?

6. Does an electric heater "use up" current? What happens to the current in such a device as time goes on? What is "used up" in the heater?

7. A battery is connected through an ammeter to two plates which dip into a vessel of distilled water. What current is observed? What would happen if a little acid were poured into the water? Explain. What would be noticed at the plates?

8. The oceans contain incredibly large quantities of such materials as gold, silver, and many other valuable substances. Explain why the precious metals are not obtained from sea water by electrolysis when such substances as chlorine, caustic soda, and magnesium are so made in large quantities.

9. A pair of platinum plates is inserted into a solution of copper sulfate and connected to a battery. Describe the electrochemical actions which take place. Will this process continue indefinitely? Why?

10. How does the voltage of a tiny flashlight dry cell compare with that of the large dry cell commonly used in the electrical laboratory? Compare their ampere-hour ratings.

11. A person standing on damp earth sometimes gets a shock by touching electric apparatus. Why is this? Would one get a similar shock if he were standing on a dry floor? Why?

12. Why is it more dangerous to touch a 500-volt line than a 110-volt line? Why is it dangerous to have an electric switch within reach of a bathtub?

13. Which is likely to be more dangerous, touching an automobile battery terminal when it is delivering a current of 200 amp or touching a 200-volt generator terminal? Why?

14. In a research laboratory a sign reading "Danger: Ten thousand ohms," was placed upon some apparatus. Comment upon the scientific appropriateness of this sign.

15. The voltage applied to a rheostat is doubled, then trebled. What happens to the resistance of the rheostat?

16. Plot a curve to show how the reading of the voltmeter in Fig. 10 varies as the slider is moved from A to C. What is the significance of the slope of this curve?

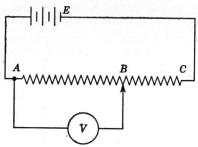

FIG. 10. Potential drop along a slide wire.

17. Plot a curve to show the variation of the ammeter reading in Fig. 11 as afunction of the rheostat resistance. Interpret the shape and intercepts of this curve.

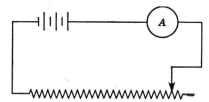

FIG. 11. Variation of current with resistance.

18. From the definition of quantity of electricity in terms of current ($q = \int i\, dt$) justify the fact that $i\, ds = v\, dq$, where v is the speed of the charges flowing through a conductor of length ds.

19. The curves in Fig. 12 show the variation of current as a function of voltage for three typical classes of conductors. (a) How does the resistance change with current in each case? (b) Discuss the validity of Ohm's law for each of these cases.

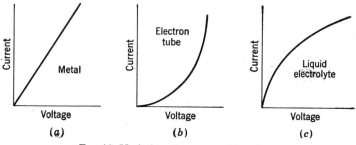

FIG. 12. Variation of current with voltage.

PROBLEMS   *Unless otherwise stated, in all the following problems the electrochemical equivalent of silver may be taken as known and atomic data may be assumed as known, but other values should be worked out as a part of the problem. For silver, $z = 0.00111800$ gm/coulomb; atomic mass = 107.9; valence = 1.*

1. A current of 1.25 amp is maintained in a wire for 5.00 min. What quantity of electricity flows through the wire?

2. The current in a common electric heater is 5.0 amp. What quantity of electricity flows through the heater in 8.0 min?   *Ans.* 2400 coulombs

3. A charge of 3600 coulombs passes through an electric lamp in 3.0 min. What is the current in the lamp?

4. A charge of 600 coulombs flows through a rheostat in which a steady current is maintained for 120 sec. What is the current?   *Ans.* 5.00 amp

5. What current is required to deposit 500 mg of silver from a silver-plating cell in 1.00 hr?

6. A steady current of 4.00 amp is maintained for 10.0 min in a solution of silver nitrate. Find how much silver is deposited on the cathode.   *Ans.* 2.68 gm

7. How long will it take for a current of 5.0 amp to produce 1.00 liter of hydrogen by electrolysis of water? The density of hydrogen is 0.000090 gm/cm³.

8. How much hydrogen is liberated each day in an acidulated-water cell in which a current of 30.0 amp is maintained?   *Ans.* 27.2 gm

9. A current of 700 ma is maintained in a $CuSO_4$ cell. How much copper will be deposited in 20.0 min?

10. How long will it take a current of 10 amp in an electroplating bath to deposit a layer of copper 0.10 mm thick on a casting having a surface area of 200 cm²? The specific gravity of copper is 8.9.   *Ans.* 5400 sec

11. A 6.00-volt battery is connected to a rheostat of 30 ohms resistance. What quantity of electricity flows in 10 min?

12. A charge of 15.0 coulombs is sent through an electric lamp when the difference of potential is 120 volts. What energy is expended?   *Ans.* 1800 joules

13. It requires 2880 joules of work to maintain a current of 3.25 amp in a circuit for 4.50 min. What is the voltage of the circuit?

14. A battery which has a terminal voltage of 6.00 volts is connected in series with a rheostat and an ammeter which reads 5.00 amp. Neglecting the resistance of the ammeter, what must be the resistance of the rheostat?

Ans. 1.20 ohms

15. An incandescent lamp is designed for a current of 0.600 amp. If a potential difference of 110 volts is necessary to maintain that current, what is the resistance of the lamp?

16. In a certain rheostat there is a current of 0.45 amp when the difference of potential between the terminals is 60 volts. What is the resistance of the rheostat?

Ans. 130 ohms

17. A dry cell having a negligible resistance developed a PD of 1.56 volts. When it was short-circuited through an ammeter, it furnished a current of 30 amp. What was the resistance of the ammeter?

18. A certain wire used in electric heaters has a resistance of 1.75 ohms per foot. How much wire is needed to make a heating element for a toaster which takes 8.25 amp from a 115-volt line?   *Ans.* 7.98 ft

19. A battery connected to a rheostat furnishes a certain current. When a lamp of resistance 150 ohms is inserted in series, the current is reduced to one-third of its former value. What is the resistance of the rheostat?

20. A simple series circuit consists of a cell, an ammeter, and a rheostat of resistance R. The ammeter reads 5 amp. When an additional resistance of 2 ohms is added, the ammeter reading drops to 4 amp. Determine the resistance of the rheostat R.   *Ans.* 8 ohms

21. A uniform wire 2.00 m long and having a resistance of 11.0 ohms is connected in series with a battery having a terminal voltage of 6.00 volts and a rheostat that has a resistance of 1.00 ohm. What is the reading of a voltmeter that is placed across 60.0 cm of wire?

22. A fan motor is designed to operate at a current of 3.50 amp at a potential difference of 115 volts. It is desired to use this motor in another city where the line voltage is 125 volts. How large a resistor must be placed in series with the motor to maintain the rated current?   *Ans.* 2.86 ohms

23. A battery having a voltage of 3.00 volts is connected through a rheostat to a uniform wire 100 cm long. The wire has a resistance of 2.00 ohms. What must the resistance of the rheostat be in order that the voltage per millimeter of the wire shall be exactly 1 mv?

24. One electron has a charge of 1.60×10^{-19} coulomb. How many electrons flow each day through an electric lamp in which there is a current of 1.25 amp?   *Ans.* 6.75×10^{23}

25. Measurements show that there are about 10^{22} electrons per milliliter that take part in the conduction of electricity through a wire. Calculate the average speed of the electrons that maintain a current of 2.50 amp in the wire leading to an electric lamp if the wire has a diameter of 0.645 mm.

26. An electron (charge 1.60×10^{-19} coulomb) moves with a speed of $\frac{1}{100}$ the speed of light (3.0×10^{10} cm/sec) in a photoelectric tube. If the plate which collects the photoelectrons is 5.0 cm from the emitting surface, how long does it take for an electron to travel this distance? How many such electrons per second arrive at the collecting plate when there is a current of 9.6×10^{-12} amp?
Ans. 1.7×10^{-8} sec; 6.0×10^{7} electrons/sec

27. In a certain a-c circuit the variation of the current with time is given by the equation $i = 12.5 \sin 377t$, where i is the instantaneous current, in amperes, and t is the time, in seconds, since the current was zero. What charge is conducted during the first $\frac{1}{120}$ sec? If the current were constant, what would its value be for the same charge and time?

28. A current of 2.00 amp is maintained in two coulombmeters, in series, one of silver, the other an "unknown" metal of atomic mass 55.0. In 2.00 hr, 2.73 gm are deposited from the "unknown." How much silver is deposited, and what is the valence of the other metal?   *Ans.* 16.1 gm; 3

29. Derive the numerical relationship between (*a*) the ampere-hour and the coulomb and (*b*) the ampere-hour and the faraday.

29. *Electric Circuits*

The practical applications of electricity are almost entirely those which depend upon the effects produced by the flow of electricity, that is, electric current. In order to apply and to control the heating, chemical, or magnetic effects the engineer must control the current.

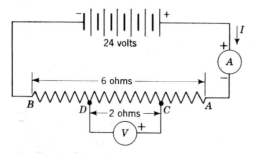

FIG. 1. Ohm's law applied to a circuit.

One of the most widely used of the laws related to electric current is Ohm's law. From this law and its extensions vital circuit relationships can be determined. From the point of view of practical electricity, series and parallel circuits are of primary importance. The electrician, the electrical engineer, the physicist, and many others are concerned with the relationships involved in the series and parallel connection of various pieces of equipment.

29-1. Ohm's Law. In Chap. 28 Ohm's law was discussed briefly. This law is a basis for study of an entire circuit or a part of a circuit containing only resistance. For ex-

ample, consider the circuit shown in Fig. 1. Ohm's law applied to a resistor gives

$$I = \frac{V}{R} \tag{1}$$

Using the subscripts AB to refer to the particular part of the circuit in Fig. 1, the current in this part is obtained from

$$I_{AB} = \frac{V_{AB}}{R_{AB}} = \frac{24 \text{ volts}}{6 \text{ ohms}} = 4 \text{ amp}$$

When this current is maintained in the resistor, there is a fall of potential or potential drop from A to B. The point A has a higher potential than C, C higher than D, and D higher than B. If the resistance between C and D is 2 ohms

$$V_{CD} = I_{CD} \times R_{CD} = 4 \text{ amp} \times 2 \text{ ohms}$$
$$= 8 \text{ volts}$$

The current in CD is the same as that in AB. A voltmeter connected across CD would read 8 volts while one across AB would read 24 volts. Whenever there is a current in a resistor, there is a resultant drop in potential.

29-2. Potential Difference and EMF. In our study of electricity at rest, we noted that whenever a charge Q is moved from one point to another and these points are maintained at a potential difference V work must be done in amount $W = VQ$. If there is a continuous flow of charge, that is, a steady current, energy must be supplied continuously by some *source* of energy. Such a source is a device that converts energy from some other form of energy (mechanical, chemical, heat, light, etc.) into electric energy. For every unit of charge that moves through the source a definite amount of energy is supplied by the source. The *energy per unit charge* thus supplied is called the *emf E* of the source. The abbreviation emf represents electromotive force. But the use of "force" in this term is so misleading that it is desirable to use the abbreviation emf without any thought of the original term.

If the source is part of a complete circuit the energy per unit charge (the emf) of the source is just the work per unit charge used in maintaining the flow of charges in the circuit. That is, the emf E must equal the fall in potential around the circuit. If the circuit is composed entirely of resistors, then by Ohm's law $(E/I = R_t)$ the fall in potential over the entire group of resistors is given by

$$E = IR_t \qquad (2)$$

where the IR_t includes all potential drops inside and outside the source.

An alternative definition of E is the work per unit charge done in taking a charge once around the entire circuit, since that is equal to the work per unit charge supplied by the source.

Many devices that are sources of emf are also able to convert energy from electric energy to some other form when they are reversed in the electric circuit. A storage battery is an example. Such a device is known as a *sink* of electric energy.

In our study of electricity we shall be careful to use the term emf and the designation E to refer only to those special values of work per unit charge that are associated with sources in which some form of energy is converted into electric energy or sinks in which electric energy is converted into some form of energy other than heat.

29-3. Ohm's Law in Complete and Partial Circuits. Ohm's law is applicable either to an entire circuit or to any part of a circuit that does not include a source or sink of energy.

Whenever the law is applied to a complete circuit, the voltage used is the emf E and the resistance is the total resistance R_t of the circuit, $E/I = R_t$. Whenever only part of the

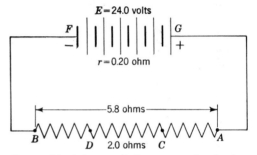

FIG. 2. Ohm's law applied to a part of a circuit.

circuit is considered, the voltage V is the drop in potential across that part and the resistance R is the resistance of that part only

$$\frac{V}{I} = R \qquad (3)$$

This equation (3) can *never* be applied to a part of a circuit that contains a battery, generator, motor, or other device that supplies an emf.

In Fig. 2 the circuit is similar to that of Fig. 1 except for the fact that part of the resistance in the circuit is in the battery itself. Considering the entire circuit, Eq. (2) gives

$$I = \frac{E}{R_t} = \frac{24.0 \text{ volts}}{6.0 \text{ ohms}} = 4.0 \text{ amp}$$

For the part of the circuit AB, Eq. (3) gives

$$V_{AB} = IR_{AB} = 4.0 \text{ amp} \times 5.8 \text{ ohms}$$
$$= 23 \text{ volts}$$

or for CD

$$V_{CD} = IR_{CD} = 4.0 \text{ amp} \times 2.0 \text{ ohms}$$
$$= 8.0 \text{ volts}$$

In the part of the circuit from F to G there is a battery and Eq. (3) cannot be applied.

29-4. Resistors in Series. Suppose that a box contains three coils of wire whose resistances are R_1, R_2, and R_3 which are connected in series as shown in Fig. 3. If one were asked to determine the resistance of whatever is inside the box without opening it, he might place it in the circuit shown, and measure the current I in the box and the voltage V across it. He would then write $R = V/I$, where R is the resistance of the part of the circuit inside the box.

Let us now determine the relation of R, the combined resistance, to the individual resistances R_1, R_2, and R_3. The current in each of

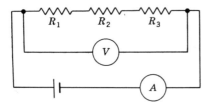

FIG. 3. Resistors in series.

the resistors is I, since the current is not divided in the box. The voltages across the individual resistors are

$$V_1 = IR_1 \qquad V_2 = IR_2 \qquad \text{and} \qquad V_3 = IR_3$$

The sum of these three voltages must be equal to V, the voltage across the box; thus

$$V = V_1 + V_2 + V_3 \qquad \text{or}$$
$$V = IR_1 + IR_2 + IR_3$$

This can be written

$$V = I(R_1 + R_2 + R_3) \qquad \text{or}$$
$$R_1 + R_2 + R_3 = \frac{V}{I}$$

but this is identical with $R = V/I$, so that

$$R = R_1 + R_2 + R_3 \qquad (4)$$

The following facts may therefore be noted for series connection of resistors:

1. The *current* in all parts of a series circuit *is the same.*

2. The *voltage* across a group of resistors connected in series is equal to the *sum of the voltages* across the individual resistors.

3. The *total resistance* of a group of conductors connected in series is equal to the *sum of the individual resistances.*

Example: The resistances of four rheostats are 10.0, 4.0, 6.0, and 5.0 ohms. These rheostats are connected in series to a battery, which produces a potential difference of 75 volts across its terminals. Find the current in each rheostat and the voltage across each.

The total resistance is

$$R = (10 + 4 + 6 + 5) \text{ ohms} = 25 \text{ ohms}$$

so that

$$I = \frac{V}{R} = \frac{75 \text{ volts}}{25 \text{ ohms}} = 3.0 \text{ amp}$$

The voltage across each rheostat is the product of its resistance and the current. Thus

$$V_1 = (3.0 \text{ amp})(10 \text{ ohms}) = 30 \text{ volts}$$
$$V_2 = (3.0 \text{ amp})(4.0 \text{ ohms}) = 12 \text{ volts}$$
$$V_3 = (3.0 \text{ amp})(6.0 \text{ ohms}) = 18 \text{ volts}$$
$$V_4 = (3.0 \text{ amp})(5.0 \text{ ohms}) = 15 \text{ volts}$$

29-5. Resistors in Parallel. Suppose that a box contains a group of three resistors in

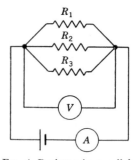

FIG. 4. Resistors in parallel.

parallel, of resistances R_1, R_2, and R_3, as shown in Fig. 4. The resistance of the combination will be $R = V/I$, where V is the voltage across the terminals of the box and I is the total current in it. Since the voltage across each of the resistors is V, the voltage across the terminals of the box, the currents in the individual resistors are,

$$I_1 = \frac{V}{R_1} \qquad I_2 = \frac{V}{R_2} \qquad I_3 = \frac{V}{R_3}$$

The sum of these three currents must be the total current I, so that

$$I = I_1 + I_2 + I_3$$

or

$$I = \frac{V}{R_1} + \frac{V}{R_2} + \frac{V}{R_3}$$

This can be written

$$I = V\left(\frac{1}{R_1} + \frac{1}{R_2} + \frac{1}{R_3}\right)$$

or

$$\frac{I}{V} = \frac{1}{R_1} + \frac{1}{R_2} + \frac{1}{R_3}$$

Since $V/I = R$, we know that $I/V = 1/R$, so that

$$\frac{1}{R} = \frac{1}{R_1} + \frac{1}{R_2} + \frac{1}{R_3} \tag{5}$$

For parallel connection of resistors, the following conditions obtain:

1. The currents in the various resistors are different and are inversely proportional to the resistances. The total current is the sum of the separate currents.

2. The voltage across each resistor of a parallel combination is the same as the voltage across any other resistor. Moreover, the voltage across each separate resistor is identical with the voltage across the *whole group* considered as a unit.

This statement may become clearer from a consideration of the fact that the terminals of each resistor are connected to a common point, that is, each conductor has its beginning at a common potential and its end at another (different) common potential. Hence the PD's across all conductors in parallel must be identical.

This fact provides the basis of the best method we have for calculating the currents in the separate branches of a parallel group of resistors. Consequently, its importance is emphasized because this type of problem is one of the most common in elementary electricity.

3. The reciprocal of the total resistance of a number of resistors connected in parallel is equal to the sum of the reciprocals of the separate resistances.

Example: The values of three resistances are 10, 4.0, and 6.0 ohms. What will be their combined resistance when connected in parallel?

$$\frac{1}{R} = \frac{1}{R_1} + \frac{1}{R_2} + \frac{1}{R_3} = \frac{1}{10 \text{ ohms}} + \frac{1}{4.0 \text{ ohms}}$$
$$+ \frac{1}{6.0 \text{ ohms}}$$
$$= (0.10 + 0.25 + 0.17)/\text{ohm} = 0.52/\text{ohm}$$
$$\frac{1}{R} = 0.52/\text{ohm} \qquad R = \frac{1}{0.52} \text{ ohms} = 1.9 \text{ ohms}$$

Note that the resistance of the combination is smaller than any one of the individual resistances.

It is important to note that connecting additional resistors in series *increases* the total resistance, while connecting additional resistors in parallel *decreases* the total resistance. For example, in an ordinary house installation, when we "turn on" more lamps, we are inserting additional resistors *in parallel*. We thus *reduce* the total resistance of the house circuit, and hence (since the voltage is constant) we *increase* the current in the mains.

As exercises and as an aid in the solution of problems involving the series and parallel arrangement of resistors the student may derive the following relations:

1. The total resistance offered by N equal resistors arranged in series is equal to NR, where R is one of the resistances.

2. The total resistance offered by N *equal* resistors arranged in parallel is equal to R/N, where R is one of the resistances.

NOTE: It should be borne in mind that (1) and (2) apply only in the exceptional cases of *equal* resistances.

3. The total resistance offered by *two* (and only two) separate resistors of resistances R_1 and R_2 when arranged in parallel is given by $R = R_1R_2/(R_1 + R_2)$, that is, their product divided by their sum. *This statement is not true for three or more resistances.*

Example: Determine the current in each of the resistors in Fig. 5.

For the parallel group, Eq. (5) gives

$$\frac{1}{R_{BC}} = \frac{1}{6.0 \text{ ohms}} + \frac{1}{9.0 \text{ ohms}} + \frac{1}{18.0 \text{ ohms}}$$
$$= \frac{6.0}{18.0 \text{ ohms}}$$

$$R_{BC} = \frac{18.0}{6.0} \text{ ohms} = 3.0 \text{ ohms}$$

$$R_{AC} = R_{AB} + R_{BC} = 4.0 \text{ ohms} + 3.0 \text{ ohms}$$
$$= 7.0 \text{ ohms}$$

The current I_t in the circuit is obtained from

$$I_t = \frac{V_{AC}}{R_{AC}} = \frac{35 \text{ volts}}{7.0 \text{ ohms}} = 5.0 \text{ amp} \qquad (a)$$

This total current is the same as that in the 4-ohm resistor.

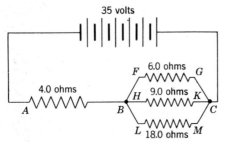

35 volts

F   6.0 ohms   G

4.0 ohms   H   9.0 ohms   K

A   B   C

L   18.0 ohms   M

FIG. 5. Currents in a divided circuit.

The voltage across the parallel group V_{BC} is equal to the resistance of the entire parallel group multiplied by the current in the entire parallel group, that is,

$$V_{BC} = R_{BC}I_{BC} = R_{BC}I_t = 3.0 \text{ ohms} \times 5.0 \text{ amp}$$
$$= 15 \text{ volts} \quad (b)$$

Note that Ohm's law was applied in Eq. (a) to the total current, total voltage, and total resistance; while in Eq. (b) the law was applied consistently to the current, voltage, and resistance, *all of the part BC.*

Since the voltage across BC is identical with that across FG, HK, and LM, the currents in each of these resistors may be calculated, namely,

$$I_{FG} = \frac{V_{FG}}{R_{FG}} = \frac{15 \text{ volts}}{6.0 \text{ ohms}} = 2.5 \text{ amp}$$

$$I_{HK} = \frac{V_{HK}}{R_{HK}} = \frac{15 \text{ volts}}{9.0 \text{ ohms}} = 1.7 \text{ amp}$$

$$I_{LM} = \frac{V_{LM}}{R_{LM}} = \frac{15 \text{ volts}}{18.0 \text{ ohms}} = 0.83 \text{ amp}$$

Note that

$$I_t = (2.5 + 1.7 + 0.8) \text{ amp} = 5.0 \text{ amp}$$

29-6. Line Drop. The voltage between the conductors at a generating source is always greater than that at any distant place where the power is used. This is caused by the fact that there must be a loss of potential in the line wires as a result of their resistance. This drop of potential is given by

$$V_l = I_l R_l$$

where the subscripts refer to the line values: V_l is the "line drop," I_l the current in the line, and R_l the resistance of the line.

A voltmeter placed across the line at the transmitting end reads the terminal voltage V_t at the source. Because of the line drop the voltage V which would be read at the receiving end of the line is less than V_t and is given by

Voltage at receiving end
    = voltage at transmitting end − line drop

This line drop is very objectionable, and every effort is made to minimize its effects. In long-distance transmission lines this is done by "stepping up" the voltage and correspondingly "stepping down" the current (see Chap. 35). When power is to be transmitted for short distances, the line drop is reduced by the use of large wire of low resistance. This is necessarily expensive.

One effect of line drop is noticed when a device taking a large current is turned on in a household where there is an electric lamp in operation. The lamp becomes slightly dimmer. This is caused by the reduced voltage at the lamp terminals due to the increased line drop.

29-7. EMF and Internal Resistance. A battery or other source supplies a potential difference for the circuit to which it is connected. Every such source has *within* it some resistance called *internal* resistance. When there is no current in the battery, the potential difference E between its terminals is a maximum that is called its *emf*, or no-load voltage. The emf is the total work per unit charge supplied by the source in moving a charge through the entire circuit including internal resistance. The work is obtained by the conversion of some other form of energy into electric energy. In Fig. 6, a battery of emf E and internal resistance r is shown connected to a voltmeter. With the switch open the voltmeter reads a value nearly equal to E, since it may be assumed that the voltmeter current is negligible.

When the switch is closed, the battery will maintain a current I and the voltage V across

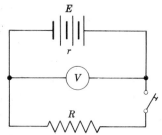

Fig. 6. Terminal potential difference and emf.

its terminals will be less than the emf by the amount of the internal drop of potential Ir across the internal resistance. The terminal potential difference is given by

$$V = E - Ir \qquad (6)$$

For any battery or other source of constant emf the terminal voltage decreases as the current increases. However, a battery of low internal resistance can supply a large current without much decrease in its terminal voltage.

Example: What is the potential difference across the terminals FG of the battery shown in Fig. 2?

It was noted above that the equation $V = IR$ cannot be used here as there is a *source* of electric energy in a battery. However, Eq. (6) can be used, and hence we may write

$V_{FG} = E - Ir = 24.0$ volts
$\qquad - (4.0 \text{ amp} \times 0.20 \text{ ohm})$
$\qquad = 24.0 \text{ volts} - 0.8 \text{ volt}$
$\qquad\qquad = 23.2 \text{ volts}$

29-8. Terminal Potential Difference with Reverse Current. In Fig. 7, a storage

battery of emf E is being charged by a generator which maintains a voltage V. In order to produce the reverse current necessary to charge the battery, the voltage at the terminals of the battery must be *higher* than the emf by the amount of the internal drop. This is indicated by the equation

$$V = E + Ir \qquad (7)$$

The charging of a storage battery is an example of a sink of energy, referred to above.

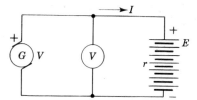

Fig. 7. Terminal potential difference of battery with reverse current.

By the use of Ohm's law, Eqs. (2) and (3), and its extensions, Eqs. (6) and (7), a complete simple circuit or any of its parts can be studied.

Example: The generator in Fig. 7 is charging a storage battery having an emf of 50 volts and an internal resistance of 0.60 ohm. What voltage must the generator maintain to charge the battery with a current of 15 amp?

$V = E + Ir = 50 \text{ volts} + 15 \text{ amp} \times 0.60 \text{ ohm}$
$\qquad\qquad\qquad = 59 \text{ volts}$

29-9. Applications to an Entire Circuit. If one traces completely any closed path in a circuit, returning to the starting point, the sum of the various emf's of the batteries (or generators) in the path (counted negative if they oppose the current) is equal to the sum of the voltages across the resistors in the path, that is,

$$\Sigma E = \Sigma(IR) \qquad (8)$$
$\Sigma E = E_1 + E_2 + E_3 + \cdots \qquad$ and
$\Sigma(IR) = I_1R_1 + I_2R_2 + I_3R_3 + \cdots$

Consider the circuit of Fig. 8. Let us begin at A and follow the path of the current through E_1, R_1, R_2, E_2, and R_3, returning to A

$$\Sigma E = \Sigma(IR),$$

or $E_1 + E_2 = I_1R_1 + I_2R_2 + I_3R_3$

where I_1 is the current in R_1, etc. Since $I_1 = I_2 = I_3$,

$$E_1 + E_2 = I_1(R_1 + R_2 + R_3)$$

Note that E_2 will be a negative number, since it is the voltage across a reversed battery.

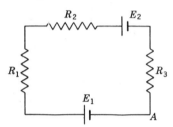

FIG. 8. A series circuit, $\Sigma E = \Sigma IR$.

Example: Find the current in the circuit of Fig. 8 if $E_1 = 6$ volts, $E_2 = -2$ volts, $R_1 = 2$ ohms, $R_2 = 4$ ohms, $R_3 = 2$ ohms.

From the preceding discussion

$$E_1 + E_2 = I_1(R_1 + R_2 + R_3)$$

so that

$$I_1 = \frac{E_1 + E_2}{R_1 + R_2 + R_3} = \frac{(6 - 2) \text{ volts}}{(2 + 4 + 2) \text{ ohms}}$$

$$= \frac{4 \text{ volts}}{8 \text{ ohms}} = 0.5 \text{ amp}$$

29-10. Batteries. A group of cells may be connected together *in series* or *in parallel*, or in a *series-parallel* combination. Such a grouping of cells is known as a *battery*, although this word is often loosely used to refer to a single cell.

29-11. Cells in Series. Cells are said to be connected in series when they are joined end to end so that the same quantity of electricity must flow through each cell. In the ordinary series connection of cells the positive terminal of one cell is connected to the negative terminal of the next, the positive of the second to the negative of the third, etc., the negative of the first and the positive of the last being joined to the ends of the external resistor (see Fig. 9).

For a series arrangement of cells, the following statements apply:

1. The emf of the battery is equal to the sum of the emf's of the various cells.

2. The current in each cell is the same and is identical with the current in the entire series arrangement.

3. The total internal resistance is equal to the sum of the individual internal resistances.

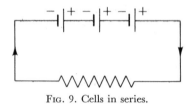

FIG. 9. Cells in series.

Example: If each of the cells in Fig. 9 has an emf of 2 volts and an internal resistance of 0.4 ohm, what will be the current in the middle cell when the battery is connected to an 18.8-ohm external resistor?

The emf of the battery is $(2 + 2 + 2)$ volts = 6 volts. The internal resistance of the battery is $(0.4 + 0.4 + 0.4)$ ohms = 1.2 ohms.

$$\text{Total current} = \frac{\text{total emf}}{\text{total resistance}}$$

$$= \frac{6 \text{ volts}}{(18.8 + 1.2) \text{ ohms}} = 0.3 \text{ amp}$$

Since the current in each of the cells is the same and is identical with the current in the entire series arrangement, it follows that the current in the middle cell is also 0.3 amp.

29-12. Cells in Parallel. Cells are connected in parallel when the current is divided between the various cells. In the normal parallel connection of cells all the positive poles are connected together and all the negative poles are connected together. Connection is made to an external resistor from the positive and negative terminals at any point along the wires connecting the various cells (see Fig. 10).

For a parallel arrangement of identical cells, the following statements are true:

1. The emf of the battery is the same as the emf of a single cell.

2. The reciprocal of the total internal resistance is equal to the sum of the reciprocals of the resistances of the individual cells.

3. The current in the external circuit is divided equally among the cells.

Example: Compare the currents maintained in a 3.0-ohm resistor by *each cell* of the following arrangements: (*a*) a single cell, (*b*) three cells in series, and (*c*) three cells in parallel. Each cell has an emf of 2.0 volts and a negligible internal resistance.

The emf of the first arrangement is 2.0 volts; of the second, 6.0 volts; and of the third, 2.0 volts. Hence, the total current in each case is given by

$$I_{total} = \frac{E_{total}}{R_{total}}$$

$$I_a = \frac{2.0 \text{ volts}}{3.0 \text{ ohms}} = 0.67 \text{ amp}$$

$$I_b = \frac{6.0 \text{ volts}}{3.0 \text{ ohms}} = 2.0 \text{ amp}$$

$$I_c = \frac{2.0 \text{ volts}}{3.0 \text{ ohms}} = 0.67 \text{ amp}$$

Note that the *total* current in case (*a*) is the same as that in case (*c*). Since there is only one cell in arrangement (*a*), the current in that cell is the same as the current in the entire circuit, namely, 0.67 amp. Since the cells in case (*b*) are all joined in series, and are in series with the external resistor, the currents in the various cells must be identical and equal to the total current, namely, 2.0 amp. In case (*c*), the total current is divided equally among three cells; hence the current in any single cell is (0.67/3) amp = 0.22 amp.

29-13. Optimum Methods of Connecting Cells. Cells may be connected in series regardless of the emf's of the individual cells, but this is not true for a parallel connection. In the latter case, the cells should have exactly the same emf's; otherwise there will be circulating currents in the local branches formed by the cells. These currents do not contribute to the current in the external resistor and serve only to waste away the cells.

Cells are connected in series when the external resistance is comparatively high. They are connected in parallel when the external resistance is comparatively low. The series

connection gives a sufficiently high emf to produce the desired current. In the parallel connection the large circuit current is divided among the several cells. For example, suppose it is necessary to maintain a current of 0.20 amp in a resistor of 50 ohms resistance using cells each of emf 2 volts and negligible

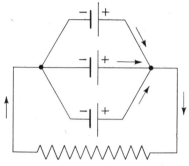

FIG. 10. Cells in parallel.

internal resistance. By Ohm's law the required voltage is

$$V = RI = 50 \text{ ohms} \times 0.20 \text{ amp} = 10 \text{ volts}$$

Hence five cells in series could be used.

Next suppose it is desired to produce a current of 20 amp in a rheostat, which has a resistance of 0.1 ohm. By Ohm's law, the required voltage is

$$V = RI = 0.1 \text{ ohm} \times 20 \text{ amp} = 2 \text{ volts}$$

Hence one 2-volt cell could be used. But not all cells could maintain a current of 20 amp without being damaged. It would be better, therefore, to use, say, four 2-volt cells in parallel. In this case, each cell would deliver 5 amp, a current which could reasonably be carried by one cell.

Sometimes a series-parallel combination of cells is desirable. Such an arrangement of three rows in parallel with each row comprising four cells in series is shown in Fig. 11. In such a case, assuming the cells are all identical, the emf of the battery is NE, where N is the number of cells in a row and E is the emf of each cell. This sort of arrangement is used when a fairly high voltage and high current are required in the external circuit.

Example: The emf of each cell in Fig. 11 is 1.50 volts and the internal resistance is 0.60 ohm. The external resistance is 17.2 ohms. Determine the terminal voltage of *one* of the cells in the battery.

Since $V = E - Ir$ it is seen that it is necessary to calculate the current in one of the cells. To do this, the total current must be obtained. The emf of the battery is 4×1.50 volts $= 6.00$ volts. The

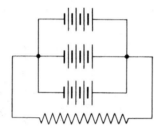

FIG. 11. Cells in a series-parallel combination.

internal resistance of each row of cells is 4×0.60 ohm $= 2.4$ ohms. The internal resistance of the 3 rows in parallel is 2.4 ohms/3 $= 0.80$ ohm. Hence the total current is

$$I_t = \frac{E_t}{R_t} = \frac{6.00 \text{ volts}}{(17.2 + 0.80) \text{ ohms}} = 0.333 \text{ amp}$$

The current in one cell is the same as the current in each row, which is one-third of the total current. Hence $I = 0.333$ amp/3 $= 0.111$ amp. Therefore

$$V = E - Ir = 1.50 \text{ volts} - 0.111 \text{ amp} \\ \times 0.60 \text{ ohm} = 1.43 \text{ volts}$$

In general, if a maximum current is to be maintained in a given external resistor by a given number of cells, the cells should be arranged in such a manner that their total internal resistance will most nearly equal the external resistance. This may frequently necessitate a series-parallel arrangement.

29-14. Simplification of Electrical Networks. A complex circuit including sources of emf, resistors in series and parallel, and other electrical devices is known as a *network*. In many cases complicated-appearing networks can be simplified by steps taken in turn so that the solution of circuit problems becomes comparatively easy. The order in which these steps can be taken is illustrated in the following example.

Example: In Fig. 12 the cells are all alike. Each has an emf of 1.50 volts and an internal resistance of 0.30 ohm. Determine the terminal PD of one of the cells in the parallel groups, the terminal PD of the reversed cell, and the current in the 2.00-ohm resistor.

In order to solve this problem it is necessary to obtain E_t, the total emf, and R_t, the total resistance of the circuit. The total resistance is obtained

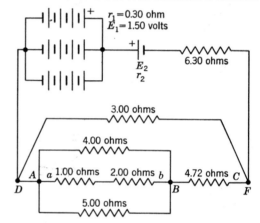

FIG. 12. Electrical network problem.

by finding the equivalent resistance of each parallel group and then using these equivalent resistances as single resistances in series.

The emf of the entire battery will first be obtained. Each row of cells has an emf of 4×1.50 volts $= 6.00$ volts. Hence the emf of the series-parallel group is also 6.00 volts. The emf of the single cell is opposite in sense to that of the large group. Hence the total emf of the entire circuit is $6.00 - 1.50 = 4.50$ volts.

The internal resistance of each row of cells is $4 \times 0.30 = 1.20$ ohms. Since there are three rows in parallel, the total internal resistance of the parallel groups of cells is $1.20/3 = 0.40$ ohm.

The resistance of the parallel group AB is obtained from

$$\frac{1}{R_{AB}} = \frac{1}{4.00} + \frac{1}{3.00} + \frac{1}{5.00} \qquad R_{AB} = 1.28 \text{ ohms}$$

Next, $R_{AC} = 1.28 + 4.72 = 6.00$ ohms

and $\quad \dfrac{1}{R_{DF}} = \dfrac{1}{6.00} + \dfrac{1}{3.00} \qquad R_{DF} = 2.00$ ohms

This gives for the entire external resistance

$$R = 2.00 + 6.30 = 8.30 \text{ ohms}$$

and for the total resistance of the circuit

$$R_t = R + r_1 + r_2 = 8.30 + 0.40 + 0.30$$
$$= 9.00 \text{ ohms}$$

Note the fact that the total emf and the total resistance of the circuit have now been reduced to a single emf and a single resistance. Hence we can consider the network a simple series circuit. The current in the entire circuit is given by

$$I = \frac{E}{R_t} = \frac{4.50 \text{ volts}}{9.00 \text{ ohms}} = 0.500 \text{ amp}$$

The current in each of the cells of the series-parallel group is one-third of the total current. Hence the terminal PD of one of these cells is

$$V_1 = E_1 - I_1 r_1 = 1.50 - \frac{0.500}{3} \times 0.30$$
$$= 1.45 \text{ volts}$$

The terminal PD of the reversed cell is

$$V_2 = E_2 + I_2 r_2 = 1.50 + 0.500 \times 0.30$$
$$= 1.65 \text{ volts}$$

The PD across the parallel group DF is

$$V_{DF} = I_{DF} \times R_{DF} = 0.500 \text{ amp} \times 2.00 \text{ ohms}$$
$$= 1.00 \text{ volt} \qquad (\text{since } I_{DF} = I_t)$$

The current in the branch AC is therefore

$$I_{AC} = \frac{V_{AC}}{R_{AC}} = \frac{1.00 \text{ volt}}{6.00 \text{ ohms}} = 0.167 \text{ amp} \qquad (\text{since}$$
$$V_{AC} = V_{DF})$$

$$V_{AB} = I_{AB} \times R_{AB} = I_{AC} \times R_{AB}$$
$$= 0.167 \text{ amp} \times 1.28 \text{ ohms} = 0.213 \text{ volt}$$

But the current in the 2.00-ohm resistor is equal to the current in the branch ab

or $\qquad I_{ab} = \dfrac{0.213 \text{ volt}}{3.00 \text{ ohms}} = 0.071 \text{ amp}$

SUMMARY

Ohm's law may be applied either to an entire circuit or to a part of a circuit containing resistance only, provided that the proper voltages, currents, and resistances are used. For the entire circuit

$$\frac{E}{I} = R_t$$

and for a part of a circuit having resistance only

$$\frac{V}{I} = R$$

For resistors in series

$$I = I_1 = I_2 = I_3 = \cdots$$
$$V = V_1 + V_2 + V_3 + \cdots$$
$$R = R_1 + R_2 + R_3 + \cdots$$

When resistors are connected in parallel,

$$I = I_1 + I_2 + I_3 + \cdots$$
$$V = V_1 = V_2 = V_3 = \cdots$$
$$\frac{1}{R} = \frac{1}{R_1} + \frac{1}{R_2} + \frac{1}{R_3} + \cdots$$

The maximum potential difference generated by a cell or generator is called its emf. When the cell is maintaining a current, its terminal voltage is reduced according to the equation

$$V = E - Ir$$

Whenever there is a reverse current in a battery, the terminal voltage is given by

$$V = E + Ir$$

For an entire series circuit

$$\Sigma E = \Sigma(IR)$$

When cells are connected in series,

$$E = E_1 + E_2 + E_3 + \cdots$$
and $\qquad r = r_1 + r_2 + r_3 + \cdots$

For identical cells in parallel

$$E = E_1 = E_2 = E_3 = \cdots \qquad \text{and} \qquad r = \frac{r_1}{N}$$

QUESTIONS   **1.** A battery is connected to a long resistance wire. One terminal of a voltmeter is connected to one end of the wire. The other terminal of the voltmeter is connected to a sliding contact, which is then moved along the wire. Describe the way in which the voltmeter reading varies as the contact is placed at different points on the wire.

2. A string of Christmas-tree lights is frequently made of miniature lamps connected in series. For an 8-amp 120-volt set what is the voltage across each lamp? If one lamp were removed, what would happen? The voltage across the empty socket becomes equal to the line voltage. Why is this?

3. A resistor forms part of a series circuit. How is the resistance of the circuit affected if a second resistor is connected (*a*) in series with the first? (*b*) in parallel with the first?

4. A piece of copper wire is cut into 10 equal parts. These parts are connected in parallel. How will the joint resistance of the parallel combination compare with the original resistance of the single wire?

5. As one turns on more lamps in an ordinary household circuit, what happens to the current in the first lamp? to the line current? to the line voltage? Why is it not customary to connect household electric lamps in series?

6. What are some of the advantages and disadvantages of series *vs.* parallel strings of miniature lamps used for Christmas trees?

7. Resistors *A*, *B*, and *C* are connected in series to a battery. To find the current in resistor *A*, is it satisfactory to divide the terminal voltage of the battery by the resistance of *A*? Why? Answer the same question for these resistors connected in parallel.

8. When a dry cell is connected to an external resistor, what happens to the terminal voltage of the cell? Why? Describe how this effect differs in a fresh cell of low internal resistance and an old cell of very high internal resistance.

9. Explain why a good-quality voltmeter connected to a cell does not read the correct emf of the cell. What characteristics should a voltmeter have so that its reading will closely approximate the emf of the cell? Describe how one might use a voltmeter of known resistance to measure the internal resistance of a cell of known emf.

10. Plot a curve that shows the variation of the TPD of a high-resistance cell as a function of the current delivered to an external circuit. Carefully interpret the significance of the shape and the slope of this curve. Show how the curve reveals (*a*) the emf of the cell, (*b*) the short-circuit current, and (*c*) the internal resistance.

11. Draw a curve to show how the terminal voltage of a cell varies as the external resistance is varied from zero to "infinity." Carefully interpret the significance of the slope and the intercepts of this curve. Show why the internal resistance is equal to the external resistance when the terminal voltage is just one-half the emf of the cell.

12. As electrons flow through a resistor connected to a cell, the electric energy decreases. The energy increases as the electrons go through the cell. Show the source and sink of this energy.

13. Most automobiles have an ammeter with a center zero mounted on the instrument panel. Show how and why the readings of this meter change when the car is (*a*) moving slowly, (*b*) moving rapidly, (*c*) standing still (with the engine idling), and (*d*) standing still with the lights turned on.

14. Suppose a voltmeter with a center zero to be connected across a storage battery. Describe how the pointer on the meter changes for the following cases: (*a*) battery connected to the voltmeter only, (*b*) battery connected to a high-resistance rheostat, (*c*) battery connected to a low-resistance rheostat, (*d*) battery short-circuited, and (*e*) battery being charged.

15. Show why the lamps in a trolley car become dimmer as the car goes up a hill. Is it because "the current in the line is low'? Is this the same effect observed in automobile lamps when the starter is operated? Explain.

16. For the circuit shown in Fig. 8, plot a graph to show how the electric potential varies as one goes around the circuit.

17. Four 1.5-volt dry cells connected in series have a total emf of 6.0 volts. Could they be substituted satisfactorily for the 6.0-volt lead storage battery in an automobile? Explain.

18. In connecting two identical cells in parallel, by error one of the cells is connected with polarity reversed from the normal direction. How would this affect the total internal resistance? What other effect would be observed?

19. Compare the "short-circuit" current of (a) a single cell, (b) two cells in series, and (c) two cells in parallel. (Assume identical cells of appreciable resistance.)

20. An external resistor is to be connected to one or more identical cells each having an internal resistance equal to the external resistance. Which arrangement furnishes the largest current: (a) 1 cell, (b) 10 cells in series, or (c) 10 cells in parallel?

21. A battery is made up of N rows of cells, with n cells in each row, as shown in Fig. 11. The cells have identical emf's E and internal resistances r. Derive the equation for the current I which is furnished to an external resistor of resistance R.

PROBLEMS　　　**1.** A battery of emf 3.0 volts and internal resistance 0.10 ohm is connected through an ammeter of resistance 0.05 ohm to a 5.00-ohm rheostat by wires having a total resistance of 0.85 ohm. What is the current in the circuit? What percentage error is made by neglecting all the resistance except that of the rheostat?

2. A dry cell of internal resistance 0.0624 ohm when short-circuited will furnish a current of 25.0 amp. What is its emf?　　　　　*Ans.* 1.56 volts

3. Three rheostats having resistances of 5.0, 10.9, and 21.3 ohms, respectively, are connected in series. What is their combined resistance?

4. Two lamps need 50 volts and 2.0 amp each in order to operate at a desired brilliancy. They are to be connected in series across a 120-volt line. What is the resistance of the rheostat which must be placed in series with the lamps?
Ans. 10 ohms

5. A 6.0-volt battery is connected to a group of 3 resistors in series which have resistances of 2.0, 3.0, and 13.0 ohms, respectively. What is the current in the 13-ohm resistor? By what percentage is the current changed when an ammeter of resistance 0.6 ohm is introduced?

6. A battery of 12.0 volts terminal PD is connected to a group of three resistors, joined in series. One resistance is unknown; the others are 3.00 ohms and 1.00 ohm. A voltmeter connected to the 3.00-ohm resistor reads 6.00 volts. Determine the value of the unknown resistance.　　　　*Ans.* 2.00 ohms

7. A wire 200 cm long has a resistance of 16.0 ohms. It is connected in series with a resistance box of 8.00 ohms to a battery having a terminal PD of 8.00 volts. A poorly calibrated voltmeter connected across 150 cm of the wire reads 3.84 volts. What is the percentage error of the reading of the voltmeter?

8. A battery of 1.5 ohms internal resistance is connected to two resistors in series of 2.0 and 3.0 ohms. The voltage across the 2.0-ohm resistor is 8.0 volts. What is the emf of the battery?　　　　　*Ans.* 26 volts

9. Find the resistance of a combination formed by 5.0 ohms and 7.0 ohms in parallel.

10. Three conductors whose resistances are 20.0 ohms, 30.0 ohms, and 40.0

ohms, respectively, are connected in parallel. What is the joint resistance of this group? *Ans.* 9.25 ohms

11. Five identical lamps are connected in parallel on a 100-volt lighting circuit of a house. If the resistance of each lamp is 400 ohms, what current is there in the group?

12. Sketch the outline of a cube. Imagine that each of the 12 edges represents a conductor having a resistance of 1.0 ohm. What is the resistance between corners diagonally opposite each other? *Ans.* $\frac{5}{6}$ ohm

13. Calculate the value of R_x in Fig. 13 which makes the total resistance of the circuit also equal to R_x.

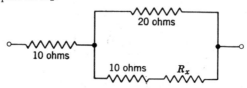

Fig. 13. Unknown resistor in series-parallel circuit.

14. Two rheostats of resistances 10.0 and 3.00 ohms are connected in parallel and joined to a battery of negligible internal resistance. There is a current of 0.200 amp in the 10.0-ohm resistor. Determine (*a*) the current in the 3.00-ohm resistor and (*b*) the emf of the battery. *Ans.* 0.667 amp; 2.00 volts

15. From the curve of Fig. 14 determine (*a*) the emf of the cell, (*b*) the short-circuit current, and (*c*) the internal resistance.

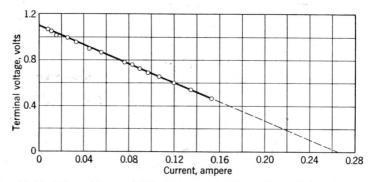

Fig. 14. Variation of terminal PD with current delivered by a high-resistance cell.

16. The terminal voltage of a battery is 9.0 volts when supplying a current of 4.0 amp and 8.5 volts when supplying 6.0 amp. Find its internal resistance and emf. *Ans.* 0.25 ohm; 10.0 volts

17. A battery has an emf of 10.0 volts and an internal resistance of 3.0 ohms. When connected across a rheostat of resistance 12 ohms, what current will it furnish? What is the terminal PD of the battery?

18. A small generator gives a potential reading of 100 volts when a voltmeter is placed across a resistor of 100.0 ohms resistance connected in series with the generator. When the 100.0-ohm resistor is replaced by a 200.0-ohm resistor, the voltmeter reads 105.0 volts. Calculate the internal resistance and the emf of the generator. *Ans.* 10.5 ohms; 111 volts

19. An electric circuit consists of two batteries and an external resistor in series. One battery has an emf of 2.00 volts and an internal resistance of 1.0 ohm; the other battery has an emf of 2.40 volts and internal resistance of 0.80 ohm.

The external resistance is 7.0 ohms. (*a*) Find the reading of voltmeters across each element of this circuit. (*b*) What would the voltmeters read if one of the batteries were reversed?

20. A 12.0-volt battery is to be charged from a 110-volt line. (*a*) If the internal resistance of the battery is 0.500 ohm, how much resistance must be put in series with the battery in order that the charging current shall be 5.00 amp? (*b*) What will be the difference in potential between the terminals of the battery?
Ans. 19.1 ohms; 14.5 volts

21. A battery of emf 120 volts and internal resistance 2.0 ohms is connected to a rheostat of such resistance that the terminal PD is just one-half the emf of the battery. What is the resistance of the rheostat?

22. A cell of internal resistance 0.20 ohm is connected to two coils of resistances 6.00 and 8.00 ohms, joined in parallel. There is a current of 0.200 amp in the 8.00-ohm coil. Find the emf of the cell.   *Ans.* 1.69 volts

23. A wire of resistance 41.2 ohms is connected in series with a group of three rheostats in parallel whose resistances are 5.0, 10.0, and 30.0 ohms. What is the resistance of the combination?

24. A pair of resistors of 5.0 ohms and 7.0 ohms are connected in parallel. This group is connected in series with another pair in parallel whose resistances are 4.0 and 3.0 ohms. What is the total resistance?   *Ans.* 4.6 ohms

25. A 4.0-ohm conductor and a 6.0-ohm conductor are connected in parallel. This combination is connected in series with a resistance group of two parallel branches. The resistance of one branch is 12 ohms. The second branch has resistors of 6.0 and 8.0 ohms in series. Calculate the total resistance of the group.

26. A battery having an emf of 12.0 volts and an internal resistance of 0.51 ohm is connected in series with the following: a 20.0-ohm coil and a parallel group consisting of three branches having resistances of 20, 40, and 60 ohms. Find (*a*) the current in the 40-ohm coil and (*b*) the PD at the terminals of the battery.   *Ans.* 104 ma; 11.8 volts

27. A cell *A* of emf 2.20 volts and internal resistance 0.30 ohm and a cell *B* of emf 1.08 volts and internal resistance 0.60 ohm have like poles connected. (*a*) What is the PD at the terminals of each cell? (*b*) What external resistance connected to this battery produces a maximum terminal PD and what is this voltage? (*c*) What external resistance gives a maximum current in the external circuit and what is this current?

28. Two resistors of 6.00 and 2.00 ohms are connected in parallel. This arrangement is connected in series with a 4.00-ohm resistor and a battery having an internal resistance of 0.500 ohm. The current in the 2.0-ohm resistor is 0.800 amp. Determine the emf of the battery.   *Ans.* 6.40 volts

29. What would the resistance of a power line have to be in order that the line drop shall not exceed 2% of the rated voltage of 120 volts when the current is changed from zero to 40 amp?

30. The voltage between the line wires entering a house is kept nearly constant at 115.0 volts. A line leading to the laundry has a resistance of 0.35 ohm. What is the voltage across a lamp in the laundry in which there is a current of 1.5 amp? What does this voltage become when a 10-amp iron near the lamp is turned on?   *Ans.* 114.5 volts; 111.0 volts

31. Three batteries of emf 2.0, 4.0, and 6.0 volts with internal resistances 0.10, 0.20, and 0.30 ohm, respectively, are connected in series and the resulting battery is connected to an external circuit of resistance 23.4 ohms. What is the terminal PD of the 4.0-volt battery?

32. A storage battery consists of 12 lead cells connected in series. Each cell has an emf of 2.1 volts and an internal resistance of 0.050 ohm. (*a*) What external voltage must be impressed on the terminals of the battery in order to charge it with a 15-amp current? (*b*) What is the PD between the terminals of the battery when it is being discharged at a rate of 30 amp?   *Ans.* 34.2 volts; 7.2 volts

33. Two cells have emf's of 2.00 and 1.50 volts, and internal resistances of 0.050 and 0.200 ohm, respectively. If connected with like poles together, what current will there be? What will be the terminal PD of each cell? (Note that the circuit is equivalent to two cells in series with the current reversed in one of them.)

34. Two cells have emf's of 2.0 and 4.0 volts and internal resistances of 0.10 and 0.20 ohm, respectively. The two are connected in series with each other and with a resistance of 2.7 ohms. Find the difference of potential between the terminals of the 2.0-volt cell (*a*) when the two cells are in helping series and (*b*) when they are in opposing series.   *Ans.* 1.8 volts; 2.1 volts

35. A cell of emf 2.00 volts and internal resistance 0.500 ohm is joined in series with a cell of emf 1.00 volt and internal resistance 0.300 ohm. These are connected in series with a parallel battery of three cells, each of emf 1.50 volts and internal resistance 0.600 ohm. In series with this arrangement there is connected a group of three parallel resistors of 4.00, 5.00, and 6.00 ohms. The circuit is closed through a 2.88-ohm resistor. Determine (*a*) the current in the top 1.50-volt cell, (*b*) the current in the 5.00-ohm resistor, and (*c*) the terminal PD of the 2.00-volt cell.

36. A battery is made up of two parallel groups, each of six cells connected in series. Each cell has an emf 2.0 volts and an internal resistance of 0.40 ohm. The battery is connected to an external circuit comprising an 8.8-ohm resistor connected in series with a group of three resistors of 20, 30, and 60 ohms, connected in parallel. Calculate (*a*) the current in the 20-ohm resistor, (*b*) the current in one cell, and (*c*) the terminal PD of the battery.

Ans. 0.30 amp; 0.30 amp; 11 volts

37. Twelve storage cells, each of emf 1.00 volt and internal resistance 0.10 ohm, are arranged in two rows, each row having six cells in series and the rows being connected in parallel. In series with this arrangement are connected three cells joined in series, each of emf 2.00 volts and of negligible internal resistance. The entire battery is connected by wires of 2.00 ohms total resistance to a parallel group of three resistors of 2.00, 5.00, and 10.0 ohms. Calculate the current in one of the cells in the parallel group and the current in the 5.00-ohm resistor.

38. It is desired to illuminate a building with 300 lamps, operating in parallel. The lamps have a hot resistance of 200 ohms each and should operate at 110 volts. A battery of storage cells is to be used, each of which has an emf of 2.20 volts and an internal resistance of 0.00400 ohm. The cells should discharge continuously at the rate of about 28.0 amp. What is the minimum number of cells that can be used and how should they be arranged?

Ans. 6 rows of 53 cells each

39. A current of 10 amp is to be maintained in an external circuit of 0.40-ohm resistance by the use of similar batteries. The batteries may be connected either all in series or all in parallel. Each battery has an emf of 6.0 volts and an internal resistance of 0.40 ohm. What is the minimum number of batteries required and how should they be arranged?

40. Six Daniell cells, each of emf 1.08 volts and internal resistance 2.00 ohms, are to be connected to a 6.00-ohm external resistor. Compare the currents delivered to the external resistor and the total life of the cells for each of the following arrangements: (*a*) all the cells in series, (*b*) two rows of cells in parallel, each row consisting of three cells in series, (*c*) what is the terminal PD of the entire battery in each case? (*d*) which arrangement is better? (State reasons.)

Ans. 360 ma; 360 ma; 2.16 volts

41. An automobile battery has an emf of 6.50 volts and an internal resistance of 0.025 ohm. The lamps when turned on normally take a current of 12 amp. With the lamps "on," the starter is operated, taking a current of 75 amp in the starter motor. Calculate the approximate value of the current taken by the lamps when the starter is operating.

42. A battery is made up of two groups of cells connected in a series-parallel arrangement. There are three cells in series, each of emf 1.2 volts and 0.20-ohm internal resistance. A second group of three similar cells in series is connected in parallel with the first group. In series with this battery is connected a coil of resistance 1.3 ohms and a group comprising three coils of resistances 4.0, 6.0, and 12 ohms, connected in parallel. Sketch the circuit. Find (*a*) the current in the 6-ohm coil, (*b*) the current in one of the cells, and (*c*) the PD at the terminals of the battery.   *Ans.* 0.33 amp; 0.50 amp; 3.3 volts

30. *Electrical Measurements*

Much of the rapid advance in the understanding and use of electricity is the result of the precision and definiteness with which electrical measurements can be made. These measurements have provided a quantitative basis for determining and utilizing important electrical phenomena. Also, electrical measurements frequently serve as convenient and

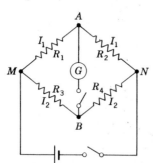

FIG. 1. Conventional diagram of a Wheatstone bridge.

accurate means of measuring other physical quantities such as temperature, pressure, distance, and time. Certain electric instruments or circuits designed primarily to measure a specific electric property have become versatile methods of measuring a variety of important related quantities.

The electric quantities most frequently measured are current, voltage, and resistance. From the measurement of these quantities and their variations many other physical properties may be determined.

30-1. The Wheatstone Bridge. One of the most convenient, precise, and widely used instruments for measuring resistance is the Wheatstone bridge. It consists of a battery, a galvanometer, and a network of four resistors, three of which are known and the fourth to be determined. In Fig. 1, the conventional diagram of a Wheatstone bridge is illustrated. The combination is called a *bridge* because the galvanometer circuit is bridged across the two parallel branches MAN and MBN. In general, the current divides unequally between the two branches. By adjusting the values of the resistances the current in the galvanometer is made zero as indicated by zero deflection. The bridge is then said to be balanced, that is, the points A and B are at the *same potential*. When the bridge is balanced, the fall in potential from M to A is the same as that from M to B and similarly the potential difference between B and N is identical with that between A and N.

For the balanced bridge, let the current in the resistors R_1 and R_2 be called I_1, and the current in the resistors R_3 and R_4 be called I_2.

Since the fall of potential over MA equals the fall over MB

$$R_1 I_1 = R_3 I_2 \qquad (1)$$

Similarly

$$R_2 I_1 = R_4 I_2 \qquad (2)$$

If we divide Eq. (2) by Eq. (1), we obtain

$$\frac{R_2}{R_1} = \frac{R_4}{R_3} \qquad (3)$$

or

$$R_2 = R_1 \frac{R_4}{R_3} \qquad (4)$$

Hence, if any three resistances are known, the fourth resistance can be computed.

From Eq. (4) it will be noted that it is not necessary to know the values of R_4 and R_3 but merely their ratio in order to determine R_2. Commercial bridges are built with a known adjustable resistance that corresponds to R_1 and ratio coils that can be adjusted at will to give ratios that are convenient powers of 10, usually from 10^{-3} up to 10^3. In some instruments both battery and galvanometer are built into the same box as the resistors, with binding posts for connection to the unknown resistor.

Example: A typical commercial Wheatstone bridge has the resistance R_1 variable from 1.00 to 9999 ohms and the ratio R_4/R_3 variable from 0.00100 to 1000. What are the maximum and minimum values of unknown resistances that can be measured by this bridge? Are these values feasible in practice? Why?

$$R_2 = R_1 \frac{R_4}{R_3} = 9999 \times 1000 = 9{,}99\overline{9}{,}000 \text{ ohms}$$

or $R_2 = 1.00 \times 0.00100 = 0.00100$ ohm

either of the extreme values in this example is ible in practice. Insulation leakage resistance the accuracy of the higher range, and con- and lead wire resistances introduce serious s in the lower range. In practice the bridge is suitable for measuring resistances in the e from 1 to 100,000 ohms.

-2. Resistance Boxes. Resistors are able in resistance boxes of wide varieties. he internal construction of a common type of plug box is shown in Fig. 2. The coils are wound with manganin wire whose resistance is practically independent of temperature. These coils are wound on spools attached to brass blocks mounted in a hard rubber sheet. The free ends of the wires are soldered to the brass blocks, which can be connected together by well-fitting brass plugs inserted in the holes between the blocks. The removal of a plug inserts the given resistor into the circuit. When the plug is firmly seated, its coil is short-circuited, thereby removing that resistance from the circuit. Hence the resistance

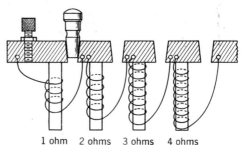

1 ohm   2 ohms   3 ohms   4 ohms
Fig. 2. Plug-type resistance box.

in this type of plug box (Fig. 3a) is the sum of the values marked at the vacant holes. In Fig. 2, the total resistance is 9 ohms.

Dial-switch resistance boxes are also widely used and offer convenient and rapid manipulation. A common type of this resistance box is the decade type shown in Fig. 3b.

30-3. Factors upon Which the Resistance of a Conductor Depends. Georg Simon Ohm, who formulated the law that bears his name, also reported the fact that the resistance of a metallic conductor *varies directly with its length, inversely with its cross-sectional area, and is a characteristic of the material.*

From the study of resistors in series, one would expect that the resistance of a piece of uniform wire is directly proportional to its length, since it can be thought of as a series of small pieces of wire whose total resistance is the sum of the resistances of the individual pieces.

Consider a wire 1 ft in length and having a cross-sectional area of 0.3 in.² By thinking of this as equivalent to three wires (1 ft in length) each having cross-sectional area of 0.1 in.² *connected in parallel,* we may infer that

$$\frac{1}{R} = \frac{1}{R_1} + \frac{1}{R_2} + \frac{1}{R_3}$$

or since $R_1 = R_2 = R_3$,

$$\frac{1}{R} = \frac{3}{R_1} \quad \text{and} \quad R_1 = 3R$$

showing that the resistance of one of the small wires is three times as great as that of the large wire. This suggests (but does not prove) that the resistance of a wire is inversely proportional to the cross section, a fact that was verified experimentally by Ohm.

Using $R \propto l$ and $R \propto 1/A$, as indicated at the beginning of this section, we can write $R \propto l/A$, where l is the length and A the cross-sectional area of a uniform conductor. This relation can be written in the form of an equation

$$R = \rho \frac{l}{A} \tag{5}$$

where ρ is a quantity, characteristic of the material of the conductor, called the *resistivity* of the substance. (The term *specific resistance* is sometimes used instead of resistivity.)

From Eq. (5)

$$\rho = R \frac{A}{l} \tag{6}$$

If A and l are given values of unity, it is seen that ρ is *numerically equal to the resistance of a conductor having unit cross section and unit length.*

If R is in ohms, A in square centimeters, and l in centimeters, then ρ is in ohm-(centimeters)^2/centimeter or simply ohm-centimeters. This unit is somewhat more convenient for most use than the mks unit, the ohm-meter.

Example: The resistance of a copper wire 2500 cm long and 0.090 cm in diameter is 0.67 ohm at 20°C. What is the resistivity of copper at this temperature?

From Eq. (6)

$$\rho = R \frac{A}{l} = \frac{(0.67 \text{ ohm})}{2500 \text{ cm}} \times \frac{\pi (0.090 \text{ cm})^2}{4}$$
$$= 1.7 \times 10^{-6} \text{ ohm-cm}$$

The unit of resistivity in the British engineering system of units differs from that just given, in that different units of length and area are employed. The unit of area is the *circular mil*, the area of a circle 1 mil (0.001 in.) in diameter, and the unit of length is the foot. In this system of units the resistivity of a substance is numerically equal to the resistance of a sample of that substance 1 ft long and 1 circular mil in area, and is expressed in

FIG. 3. Precision forms of resistance boxes. (a) Plug type; (b) dial decade type.

ohm-circular mils per foot. The area of a circle in circular mils is equal to the square of its diameter in mils (thousandths of an inch), $A = d^2$.

The abbreviation CM is often used for circular mils. This should not be confused with the abbreviation used for centimeters (cm).

Example: Find the resistance of 100 ft of copper wire whose diameter is 0.024 in. and whose resistivity is 10.3 ohm-circular mils/ft.

$$d = 0.024 \text{ in.} = 24 \text{ mils}$$
$$A = d^2 = 24^2 \text{ CM}$$
$$R = \rho \frac{l}{A} = \frac{(10.3 \text{ ohm-circular mils/ft})(100 \text{ ft})}{24^2 \text{ CM}}$$
$$= 1.8 \text{ ohms}$$

30-4. Conductance and Conductivity. Since the reciprocal of resistance $1/R$ occurs so often in parallel circuits it is frequently convenient to designate this concept as the *conductance* of the resistor. The symbol used for conductance is G and the unit is the *mho*. In a parallel circuit the total conductance is given by $G = G_1 + G_2 + G_3$. Less often the reciprocal of resistivity $1/\rho$ is used and this concept is called the *conductivity* of the material. The symbol for conductivity is σ and the unit is 1/ohm-cm or mho/cm.

30-5. Change of Resistance with Temperature. The electric resistance of all substances is found to change more or less with changes of temperature. Three types of change are observed. The resistance may increase with increasing temperature. This is true of all pure metals and most alloys. The resistance may decrease with increase of temperature. This is true of carbon, glass, and many electrolytes. The resistance may be independent of temperature. This is approximately true of many special alloys, such as manganin (Cu 0.84, Ni 0.12, Mn 0.04).

Experiments have shown that for a moderate temperature range, the change of resistance with temperature of conductors can be represented by the equation

$$R_t = R_0 + R_0\alpha t = R_0(1 + \alpha t) \qquad (7)$$

where R_t is the resistance at temperature t, R_0 is the resistance at 0°, and α is a quantity characteristic of the substance and known as the temperature coefficient of resistance. The defining equation for α is obtained by solving Eq. (7), giving

$$\alpha = \frac{R_t - R_0}{R_0 t} \qquad (8)$$

The temperature coefficient of resistance is defined as the change in resistance per unit resistance per degree rise in temperature, based upon the resistance at 0°.

Although Eq. (7) is only approximate, it can be used over medium ranges of temperature for all but very precise work.

Since $(R_t - R_0)$ and R_0 have the same units, their units will cancel in the fraction of Eq. (8). Hence, the unit of α depends only upon the unit of t. For instance, for copper $\alpha = 0.004$ per C°, but only $5/9 \times 0.004$ per F°.

Example: A silver wire has a resistance of 1.25 ohms at 0°C and a temperature coefficient of resistance of 0.00375 per C°. How much must the temperature be increased to double the resistance?

From Eq. (7)

$$t = \frac{R_t - R_0}{R_0 \alpha}$$
$$= \frac{(2.50 - 1.25) \text{ ohms}}{1.25 \text{ ohms} \times 0.00375/\text{C}°} = 266°\text{C}$$

It should be clearly understood that R_0 in the above equations ordinarily refers to the resistance at 0° and not to the resistance at any other temperature. A value of α based upon the resistance at room temperature, for example, is appreciably different from the value based upon 0°. This may be made clearer by a graphic analysis of the variation of resistance with temperature.

In Fig. 4, the resistance R_t of a conductor at any temperature t is plotted. For a pure metal, this curve gives a linear relation (approximately). Note the fact that the curve does not pass through the origin, that is, at 0° the resistance is not zero. Hence we cannot say that $R \propto t$. The slope of the curve $\Delta R/\Delta t$

is a constant. Since

$$\alpha = \frac{\Delta R/\Delta t}{R_0} = \frac{slope}{R_0}$$

it is clear that the value of α depends upon the base temperature chosen for R_0. In computations involving temperature variation of resistance, the value of R_0 must first be obtained by using Eq. (7).

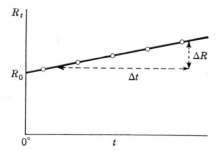

FIG. 4. Variation of resistance with temperature.

Example: A tungsten (wolfram) filament has a resistance of 133 ohms at 150°C. If $\alpha = 0.00450$ per C°, what is the resistance of the filament at 500°C?

From Eq. (7)

$$R_0 = \frac{R_t}{1 + \alpha t} = \frac{133 \text{ ohms}}{1 + (0.00450/\text{C}°) \times 150°\text{C}}$$
$$= 79.0 \text{ ohms}$$

$$R_{500} = R_0(1 + \alpha t_{500})$$
$$= 79.0 \text{ ohms } [1 + (0.00450/\text{C}°) \times 500°\text{C}]$$
$$= 257 \text{ ohms}$$

Since it is the resistivity factor that changes with temperature, Eqs. (7) and (8) may be written with ρ in place of R

$$\rho_t = \rho_0(1 + \alpha t)$$

It is interesting to note the fact that the value of α for all pure metals is roughly the same, namely, $\frac{1}{273}$, or about 0.004, per centigrade degree. Observe that this value is the same as the coefficient of expansion of an ideal gas. It suggests that at the absolute zero of temperature $(-273°\text{C})$, a conductor would have zero resistance, that is, a current once started would continue indefinitely without

the expenditure of any energy to keep it going. The complete disappearance of all electric resistance in the case of mercury at a temperature of 4°K was discovered by the Dutch physicist Onnes in 1911. Other pure metals also show this phenomenon of *superconductivity* at temperatures slightly above absolute zero.

TABLE 1. RESISTIVITIES AND
TEMPERATURE COEFFICIENTS

Material	ρ (at 20°C), microhm-cm	ρ (at 20°C), ohm-circular mils/ft	Temperature coefficient of resistance (based upon resistance at 0°C), per C°
Copper, commercial.	1.72	10.5	0.00393
Silver.	1.63	9.85	0.00377
Aluminum.	2.83	17.1	0.00393
Iron, annealed.	9.5	57.4	0.0052
Tungsten (wolfram). .	5.5	33.2	0.0045
German silver (Cu, Zn, Ni).	20–33	122–201	0.0004
Manganin.	44	266	0.00000
Carbon, arc lamp. . . .	3500	. . . .	−0.0003
Paraffin.	3×10^{24}		

30-6. Semiconductors. In recent years important discoveries have been made concerning the peculiar properties of certain semiconductors. These materials show an increase of conductivity as the temperature is raised. Prominent examples are silicon, germanium, and a variety of oxides and sulfides. It is now known that semiconductors have very few free electrons at low temperatures but that the number of these "conduction" electrons increase very rapidly at higher temperatures, thus reducing the resistance of the material.

When a semiconductor, such as copper oxide, is placed in contact with a metal, say copper, charges accumulate at the interface and interfere with the passage of electricity.

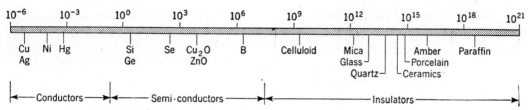

FIG. 5. Resistivities (ohm-centimeters) vary over the enormous range of about 10^{25}.

These *barrier layers* decrease when a voltage in one direction is applied, but increase when the potential is in the opposite sense. Hence such a device may be used as a *rectifier* to produce a unidirectional current from an alternating current. These *varistors* are finding wide application in modern electrical devices, particularly in the communication industry.

Another application of semiconductors is the *transistor*, described in Chap. 39. The wide range in the resistivities of materials extending from good conductors, through semiconductors, to the best insulators, is illustrated in Fig. 5.

30-7. Resistance Thermometer. On account of the accuracy and ease with which resistance measurements may be made and the well-known manner in which resistance varies with temperature, it is common to use this variation to indicate changes in temperature. Devices for this purpose are called *resistance thermometers*. Platinum wire is frequently used in these instruments because it does not react with chemicals and because of its high melting temperature. A coil of fine platinum wire contained in a porcelain tube is placed in the region whose temperature is to be measured. The resistance of the coil is measured by a Wheatstone bridge. Often these instruments are made to record temperatures on a chart and they are also frequently linked with devices to control temperatures at predetermined values. They can be made to measure temperatures with great precision from exceedingly low temperatures to about 1200°C.

30-8. The Potentiometer Principle. The potentiometer, as the name implies, is a device for measuring potential differences. The essential principle of the potentiometer is the balancing of one voltage against another in parallel with it. In the diagram of Fig. 6a a branched circuit is shown in which there is a current, because of the PD along the slide-wire AC to which it is connected. In Fig. 6b a cell has been introduced into the lower branch. Depending upon the voltage of this cell the current in the lower branch may now be in either direction, as indicated by the arrows. As a very special case, the current in the lower branch may be zero when the emf of the cell just equals the PD between A and B and the positive terminal of the cell is connected to the same end of the slide-wire as the positive terminal of the working battery W. In the actual potentiometer the unknown emf, which is to be measured, is balanced against a potential drop along a calibrated slide-wire.

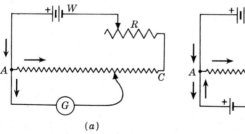
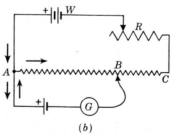

(a) (b)

FIG. 6. (a) A potential divider; (b) a simple slide-wire potentiometer.

A great advantage of the potentiometer is that at the moment of balance there is no current in the cell under test. Hence the lead wires do not carry any current, so that errors due to line drop or contact resistances do not occur. But even more important is the fact that the true emf of the cell is obtained and not just the terminal PD, which differs from the true emf by the drop of potential over the internal resistance of the cell in accordance with the equation $V = E - Ir$, where V is the terminal PD of the cell of emf E and internal resistance r when there is a current I in the cell. At the moment of balance $I = 0$ and hence $V = E$, regardless of the value of the internal resistance of the cell. For instance, an old dry cell may have such a high internal resistance that its apparent emf as read by a voltmeter may be very small, while the potentiometer will give an emf as high as 1.4 volts in many cases.

By the use of comparatively simple additional apparatus the potentiometer may be utilized to make measurements not only of emf but also of current, resistance, and power. Such devices are therefore widely used in commercial laboratories for the calibration of many electric meters and instruments.

Potentiometers are used in automatic indicating, recording, and control devices for the measurement and control of a wide variety of industrial processes. A typical case would be the measurement and regulation of the temperature of a group of furnaces at a distance from the control station.

SUMMARY

A *Wheatstone bridge* is a device for the comparison of resistances. The working equation is

$$R_2 = R_1 \frac{R_4}{R_3}$$

The resistance of a conductor

1. Varies directly with the length
2. Varies inversely with the area of cross section

3. Depends upon the nature of the material and the temperature

The resistance of a wire is given by

$$R = \rho \frac{l}{A}$$

The defining equation for *resistivity* is

$$\rho = R \frac{A}{l}$$

Resistivity is measured in ohm-centimeters in the metric system and in ohm-circular mils per foot in the British system. (The cross-sectional area of a wire in circular mils is found by squaring its diameter expressed in mils.)

Conductance, the reciprocal of resistance, $G = 1/R$, is measured in mhos.

Conductivity, the reciprocal of resistivity, may be measured in 1/ohm-cm or mho/cm.

The resistivity and hence the resistance of a conductor varies with temperature. For many materials this variation may be expressed, over a moderate temperature range, by

$$\rho_t = \rho_0(1 + \alpha t) \qquad \text{and} \qquad R_t = R_0(1 + \alpha t)$$

The *temperature coefficient of resistance* is defined by

$$\alpha = \frac{R_t - R_0}{R_0 t}$$

For all pure metals, α is roughly $\frac{1}{273}$ per C°. Near absolute zero many metals have negligible resistance.

Semiconductors show an increase of conductivity with temperature rise. Major uses of semiconductors are the *varistor*, for rectifying current, and the *transistor*, for replacing vacuum tubes.

The basic *potentiometer* principle is the balancing of one voltage against another. An advantage of the potentiometer over a voltmeter is the fact that the potentiometer takes no current from the source being measured and hence gives a reading of terminal voltage equal to the emf.

QUESTIONS   **1.** What is the effect of the internal resistance of the battery used with a Wheatstone bridge on the precision of the measurements? How is the precision altered by using similar galvanometers of different resistances? Is contact resistance important in (*a*) the battery circuit, (*b*) the galvanometer circuit, (*c*) the circuit containing the known resistance, and (*d*) the circuit containing the unknown resistance?

2. When a galvanometer is selected for optimum sensitivity for use with a Wheatstone bridge, is a high current sensitivity or a high voltage sensitivity desired? Give reasons.

3. A Wheatstone bridge is balanced in the usual manner. The galvanometer and the working battery are then interchanged. Describe how the galvanometer then would behave when the switches are closed.

4. In using a slide-wire Wheatstone bridge it is desirable to adjust the known resistance so that the final balance is obtained when the contact on the slide wire is near the center of the scale. Why is this desirable?

5. Mention some of the advantages of the box form of the Wheatstone bridge, in comparison with the slide-wire form. In the box form of Wheatstone bridge two keys are used, marked *BA* and *GA*. What are the meanings of these symbols? Which key is to be closed first? Give reason.

6. Which one of the following factors has the greatest effect on the setting of a slide-wire Wheatstone bridge when it is used to determine an unknown resistance: (*a*) the temperature of the slide wire, (*b*) irregularities in the diameter of the slide wire, and (*c*) variable resistance between the movable contact and the slide wire?

7. A piece of wire is cut into four equal parts. How will the resistance of each part compare with the original resistance? If the four parts are placed in parallel, how will the joint resistance compare with the resistance of the original wire?

8. A piece of wire is redrawn by pulling it through smaller dies until its length is doubled. Compare the new resistance with the original value.

9. Why is copper or aluminum used in electric bus bars rather than a less expensive material such as iron? Silver was extensively used for this purpose at Oak Ridge during the Second World War. What are some of the advantages of this metal for this purpose?

10. Why is wire for household appliance cords made of many stranded wires when the wire used in the house wiring is only a single strand?

11. Explain clearly the difference between the *ohm-centimeter* and the *ohm per centimeter cube* as units of resistivity. Show why one cannot define resistivity as the resistance of a cubic centimeter of a material.

12. Show how one might compute the area in circular mils of a bus bar if the length and width of the rectangular cross section are known.

13. Describe an experiment in which a Wheatstone bridge is used to measure the resistivity of a material. Show how the experiment could be extended to measure the temperature coefficient of resistivity.

14. The resistance of a metal like copper at widely differing temperatures is only approximately given by Eq. (7). A more exact equation is $R = R_0 (1 + \alpha t + \beta t^2)$, where β is a constant considerably smaller than α. Draw rough graphs to show the difference between the curve given by this equation and that given by Eq. (7).

15. Sketch approximate curves to show the variation of resistance of copper as ordinates with temperature as abscissas when the temperature is plotted

(a) in degrees centigrade, (b) in degrees Fahrenheit, and (c) in degrees Kelvin. Discuss the values of the slopes and intercepts of each of these curves.

16. A current once established in a circuit maintained at absolute zero would continue almost indefinitely. If a motor were included as a part of such a circuit, would this statement still be true? Why?

17. Two electric lamps, of equal rating, are simultaneously connected to the power line. One lamp has a tungsten (wolfram) filament, the other a carbon filament. Which lamp will first reach its equlibrium temperature? Give reasons for your answer.

18. Some Christmas-tree lamps are made to operate in series, with eight bulbs on a 112-volt line. Why is it important that such bulbs be identical? In certain of these sets the lamps have tungsten (wolfram) filaments; in other cases the filaments are of carbon. The resistance of the carbon lamps is about twice that of the tungsten lamps. Explain what would happen if a string of lamps were used with half of the bulbs having carbon filaments and the other half having tungsten filaments.

19. Mention some advantages of a resistance thermometer, in comparison with the conventional mercury type.

20. State some ways in which a potentiometer is superior to a voltmeter in the measurement of voltages. In what respects is the voltmeter more desirable?

21. Describe how one might determine the internal resistance of a cell by measuring its emf with a potentiometer and its terminal PD with a voltmeter of known resistance.

PROBLEMS   *Unless otherwise stated, use the values of ρ and α given in Table 1.*

1. A slide-wire Wheatstone bridge has resistor *MBN* (Fig. 1) in the form of a uniform wire 1.00 m long, with the galvanometer contact *B* continuously adjustable along *MBN*. The bridge is balanced with the known resistor at 450 ohms and the slider on the 42.8-cm mark. What is the value of the unknown resistance?

2. The slide-wire Wheatstone bridge of Prob. 1 is balanced when the slider is 45.8 cm from the known-resistor end of the slide wire. If the known resistance is 5.60 ohms, what is the unknown resistance?   *Ans.* 6.62 ohms

3. A precision box form of Wheatstone bridge has ratio coils which are accurate to $\frac{1}{20}\%$. Which ratio should be used for maximum precision in measuring an unknown resistance of approximately 3 ohms? Neglecting all other errors, what numerical error, in ohms, would the error of the ratio coils introduce into the measurement of the unknown resistance?

4. A Wheatstone bridge of the slide-wire type uses a 1-m wire of resistance 4.50 ohms for the resistors R_3 and R_4 of Fig. 1. In this bridge there is contact resistance where the wire is attached to the junctions M and N. If the contact resistance is 0.15 ohm at M and 0.25 ohm at N, what percentage error is introduced when the slider B is at (a) 50 cm and (b) 20 cm? What fact does this problem emphasize?   *Ans.* 4%; 9%

5. The Wheatstone bridge shown in Fig. 1 is balanced for the following values: $R_1 = 12$ ohms, $R_2 = 15$ ohms, $R_3 = 60$ ohms, $R_4 = 75$ ohms, $R_G = 125$ ohms, voltage of battery $= 2.48$ volts. Calculate the following: V_{MA}; V_{MB}; V_{AN}; V_{BN}; V_{AB}.

6. A wire has a resistance of 0.00325 ohm/m. If the diameter is 0.260 cm, what is its resistivity?   *Ans.* 1.72 microhm-cm

7. What is the resistance of a wire 238 ft long and 0.0500 in. in diameter, the wire being made of copper of resistivity 10.5 ohm-circular mils/ft?

8. Find the resistance of 5000 ft of copper wire of diameter 0.0110 in. The resistivity of the copper is 10.3 ohm-circular mils/ft. *Ans.* 425 ohms

9. How much copper wire of radius 0.0250 in. and having a resistivity of 10.5 ohm-circular mils/ft will be needed to make a coil of resistance 2.23 ohms?

10. It is desired to maintain a current of 40.0 amp in a 1000-ft wire with a maximum of 5.00 volts line drop. Copper of resistivity 10.5 ohm-circular mils/ft is to be used. What is the minimum diameter wire that can be used?
Ans. 290 mils

11. A generator maintains a constant PD of 125 volts at its terminals. At a distance of 1500 ft from the generator there is a motor which takes a current of 35 amp. What size wire must be used so that the line drop is not more than 5%?

12. Forty lamps connected in parallel have a voltage drop of 115 volts across each lamp. At this voltage each lamp takes 0.64 amp. The generator that is supplying the power is 500 ft from the lamps. If copper wire is used and there is a 10% line drop, what must be the diameter of the wire used? The resistivity of copper is 10.4 ohm-circular mils/ft. *Ans.* 145 mils

13. A power line is to be made from a cable which has an area of 10^6 circular mils. If there are 150 wires composing the cable, what is the diameter of each wire?

14. A 300-ft cable is made up of 25 strands of copper wire each of which has a diameter of 0.0125 inch. What is the resistance of the cable? *Ans.* 0.807 ohm

15. The legal standard of resistance (ohm) is defined as the resistance of a cylindrical column of mercury 106.3 cm long with a cross-sectional area of 1.00 mm^2 at a temperature of 0°C. What is the resistance between the opposite faces of an inch cube at the same temperature?

16. A copper tube has an inside diameter of 1.00 cm and an outside diameter of 1.10 cm. Its length is 100 cm and its resistivity is 10.0 ohm-circular mils/ft. Determine its resistance. *Ans.* 1.01 milliohms

17. Show that a resistivity of 9.85 ohm-circular mils/ft is equivalent to approximately 1.63 microhm-cm.

18. A certain wire has a resistivity of 1.750 microhm-cm. Calculate its resistivity in the usual British units, namely, ohm-circular mils per foot.
Ans. 10.52 ohm-circular mils/ft

19. What is the resistance between the faces of a copper cube that has a mass of 75 gm? (See tables for any necessary physical properties.)

20. The resistivity of pure iron is 9.70×10^{-8} ohm-meter. Determine its resistivity in ohm-circular mils per foot. *Ans.* 58.2 ohm-circular mils/ft

21. Calculate the conductivity of the wire of Prob. 20; express the result in both mks and British units.

22. Large electromagnets are sometimes wound with wire of square cross-section, in order to conserve space. Calculate the width of a square wire that has the same area as a cylindrical wire of area 1.33×10^{-5} cm^2. *Ans.* 1.44 mils

23. A cylindrical copper wire 1000 ft long with diameter 40.3 mils has a resistance of 6.38 ohms. What width of square wire of the same length would have the same resistance?

24. At 0°C the resistance of the armature of a motor was 0.500 ohm. After operating the motor, the resistance increased to 0.600 ohm. What was the rise in temperature of the copper wire in the armature? *Ans.* 50.8 C°

25. A platinum thermometer has a resistance of 25.00 ohms at 0°C. What is the temperature of the thermometer when it has a resistance of 32.20 ohms if the temperature coefficient of resistance of platinum is 0.00392 per C°?

26. A carbon filament has a resistance of 105 ohms at 0°C. What must be the resistance of an iron filament placed in series with the carbon so that the combination has the same resistance at all temperatures?   *Ans.* 6.1 ohms

27. In defining the temperature coefficient of resistance, the resistance at 0°C is usually taken as the reference base. What percentage change would be made in the value of this coefficient for aluminum if the base temperature were taken as 20°C instead of 0°C?

28. Wire having a radius of 0.0300 in. and resistivity 10.8 ohm-circular mils/ ft at 40°C is used to make a coil having a resistance of 7.00 ohms at 100°C. What is the resistance of this copper wire at 0°C? How much wire is used?

Ans. 5.02 ohms; 19$\overline{3}$0 ft

29. What is the resistivity of a wire 20 m long and 0.030 cm in diameter if it has a resistance of 25 ohms at 0°C? What would be the resistivity of this wire at 70°C if it has a temperature coefficient of resistance of 0.0050 per C°?

30. Copper wire of radius 0.0250 in. and resistivity 10.3 ohm-circular mils/ft at 0°C is to be used to make a wire of resistance 4.46 ohms. (*a*) How long a wire is necessary? (*b*) What would be the resistance of the wire at 70°C?

Ans. 108$\overline{0}$ ft; 5.7 ohms

31. A copper wire has a diameter of 0.500 mm and a resistivity of 1.60 × 10^{-6} ohm-cm at 0°C. How much of this wire would be necessary to make a 10.0-ohm coil? If heated from 0 to 100°C, what would be its resistance?

32. How much wire of diameter 0.0250 in. and resistivity 10.5 ohm-circular mils/ft at 25°C is needed to make a coil having a resistance of 6.00 ohms at 95°C, the temperature coefficient of resistance being 0.00405 per C°?

Ans. 290 ft

33. A power cable 5000 ft long has a resistance of 2.4 ohms per 1000 ft at 20°C. The metal of which the cable is made has a temperature coefficient of 0.0040 per C° at 20°C. If the temperature falls to −5°C, by how much does the resistance of the cable decrease?

34. A laboratory furnace with a platinum-wire heating coil is designed for 110 volts and is rated at 6.0 amp when operating at 500°C. If the wire has a temperature coefficient of resistance of 0.0039 per C°, what is the current rating of the smallest fuse which can be used in the 110-volt line to which the furnace is connected?   *Ans.* 18 amp

35. In a 1-m slide-wire Wheatstone bridge one branch is a coil of german silver wire and the other branch is a coil of iron wire. The temperature coefficients of resistance for iron and german silver are 0.0050 per C° and 0.0040 per C°, respectively. The slide wire is of manganin of negligible temperature coefficient of resistance. At 0°C, the bridge balances at 50.0 cm. Where will it balance at 25°C?

36. A slide-wire Wheatstone bridge has a meter wire of negligible temperature coefficient of resistance. At a temperature of 0°C, the bridge is balanced at the 55.0 cm mark when there is a known resistance of 27.0 ohms in one arm and an unknown coil of wire in the other arm. The temperature of the unknown is then raised to 80°C, giving a new balance point of 50.0 cm. Calculate α for the unknown coil.   *Ans.* 0.0029 per C°

37. A simple potentiometer comprises a battery connected to the ends of a uniform straight wire *AC* and a parallel circuit consisting of a standard cell of emf 1.018 volts and a galvanometer connected in series between A and a contact B which slides along AC. When B is at 30.0 on the scale AC, there is no current in the galvanometer. When the cell is replaced by an unknown emf, B must be shifted to the 75.0 mark for zero galvanometer deflection. (a) What is the value of the unknown emf? (b) If the position B of balance is read to the nearest 0.1 division, what is the uncertainty in determining the unknown emf?

38. A potentiometer is used to measure the voltage of a cell. On open circuit the cell shows a voltage of 2.218 volts. When the cell is connected to a resistor of 12.0 ohms the potentiometer reading is found to be 2.154 volts. What is the internal resistance of the cell? *Ans.* 0.36 ohm

39. An aluminum wire 1000 ft long and of diameter 0.0403 in. has a resistance of 10.5 ohms. (a) What is its resistivity? (b) Calculate the resistance of an aluminum wire that has the same weight but has a diameter of 0.0806 in.

40. A simple slide-wire potentiometer is made by using a wire 2.00 m long that has a resistance of 5.25 ohms. The working battery has a terminal voltage of 6.50 volts. A Weston cell is connected to make $AB = 1018.3$ mm (Fig. 6b) and the rheostat is adjusted to balance the potentiometer. What must the resistance of the rheostat be in order for the PD per millimeter of the slide-wire to be 1.00 mv? *Ans.* 11.8 ohms

41. A slide-wire potentiometer is to be made from a 2-m wire of resistance 4.00 ohms, in series with a rheostat and a working battery of emf 10.75 volts and internal resistance 0.50 ohm. If the potentiometer is to be direct reading, that is 1 mv/mm, what must be the resistance of the rheostat?

42. In the circuit of a potentiometer, which is not direct reading, AB and BC (Fig. 6b) are adjusted to 64.0 and 36.0 cm, respectively, in order to produce zero deflection of the galvanometer when a standard cell of emf 1.0183 volts is in the circuit. When the terminals are connected to the grid and cathode, respectively, of a radio vacuum tube (in operation), AB is changed to 95.0 cm in order to reestablish the condition of zero deflection. What is the potential difference between the elements of the radio tube? *Ans.* 1.51 volts

31. *Magnetic Effects of Electric Current*

Some facts of magnetism have been known for many centuries. The ancient Greeks observed that "lodestone" (Fe_3O_4) has the ability to attract bits of iron. Long narrow pieces of magnetized material are found to set themselves in an approximate north-south position and hence we have the magnetic compass. In both these observations we deal with *magnets*.

The fact that electric currents (electric charges in motion) exert magnetic effects was first observed by the Danish scientist Hans Christian Oersted in 1820. He found that a compass needle is deflected from its normal north-south orientation when a current-bearing conductor is parallel to the compass and above or below it.

Ampère (1820) observed that two current-bearing conductors exert forces on each other and suggested that the magnetic condition of magnets is caused by currents within the body of the magnet. These *Amperian currents* may now be identified with the motion of electrons in the atoms of the magnetic material.

31-1. Magnetic Force on a Moving Charge; Magnetic Induction. When electric charges are at rest, they exert electrostatic forces of attraction or repulsion on each other. When the charges are in motion, they still exert these electrostatic forces but, in addition,

magnetic forces appear because of the motion. The force of a current on a magnet is one example of this force.

A *magnetic field* is a region in which there is a force on a moving charge in addition to the Coulomb forces between charges. This force depends upon the charge q, the speed v of the moving charge, the direction of the motion, and some property of the field. This property of the field we call magnetic induction. The *magnetic induction B* is a vector quantity defined from the equation

$$B = \frac{F}{qv \sin \theta} \tag{1}$$

The direction of B is taken as the direction in which the force F on the moving charge is zero. The angle θ is then the angle between B and the direction of motion of the charge. Then the factor $v \sin \theta$ is the component of the velocity of the charge in a direction perpendicular to B.

If a small compass needle is brought into a magnetic field, it will set itself parallel to the direction here defined. Thus we observe that the orientation of the compass needle is an indication that there is a magnetic field associated with the earth. We may use the compass needle to indicate the positive sense of the magnetic induction. The N end of the com-

344

pass (the end that seeks the north in the earth's field) points in the positive direction of the magnetic induction.

The direction of the force F on the moving charge is perpendicular to B and to the component $v \sin \theta$ of the motion of the charge (Sec. 32-8).

If the charge q is moving along a conductor, Eq. (1) may be rewritten in terms of the current I and the length l of the conductor on which there is the force F

$$B = \frac{F}{Il \sin \theta} \qquad (2)$$

A unit for B may be defined from Eq. (1) or Eq. (2). In the mks system this unit is the newton per ampere-meter. In the cgs system where the force is in dynes, the current in abamperes (1 abampere $= 10$ amp), and the length in centimeters, the unit of B is the dyne per abampere-centimeter.

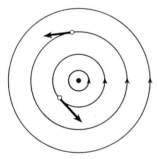

FIG. 1. Magnetic field around a conductor carrying a current "out" of the plane of the page.

Magnetic fields are observed in the neighborhood of magnetized materials and near currents. When the region near a current in a long straight conductor is explored by the small compass needle, it is found that the needle sets itself tangent to some circle with the center at the conductor. A set of such circles is shown in Fig. 1. A vector tangent to one of the circles shows the direction of the field. The sense of the magnetic field around a current is given by a right-hand rule: if the conductor is grasped by the right hand with the thumb in the direction of the (conventional) current, the fingers encircle the conductor in the direction of the field.

31-2. Magnetic Flux; Flux Density. In a manner similar to that used for electric fields, the magnetic induction B can be represented by *lines of induction*. A line of induction is a line so drawn that it is everywhere parallel to the direction of the magnetic field. The lines of induction are called *magnetic flux*. The selection of the number of lines to represent the magnetic induction quantitatively is arbitrary and the choice made sets up the system of units to be used. The usual choice is to take the number of lines of induction per unit area passing through a surface perpendicular to the flux as equal to B. In the mks system a magnetic induction of 1 newton/amp-m is represented by one line of induction per square meter. A line thus defined is called a *weber*.

The magnetic induction B is the flux per unit area of the surface perpendicular to B and hence magnetic induction is also called *flux density*. For a normal surface area ΔA

$$B = \frac{\Delta \Phi}{\Delta A} \quad \text{or} \quad B \, \Delta A = \Delta \Phi \qquad (3)$$

In the mks system flux density is measured in webers per square meter. From the way in which the weber is defined, 1 w/m² = 1 newton/amp-m.

When cgs electromagnetic units are used, the lines of induction are selected so that the number of lines of induction per square centimeter of the area normal to the field is equal to B. The unit of flux thus defined is called the *maxwell*. The corresponding unit of flux density, the maxwell per square centimeter, is called the *gauss:* 1 gauss = 1 dyne/abamp-cm. It follows that 1 w/m² = 10⁴ gauss.

In a uniform magnetic field the lines of induction are straight lines and uniformly spaced. For this type of field the flux through any plane area A is

$$\Phi = BA \cos \alpha \qquad (4)$$

where α is the angle between B and the normal to the surface.

31-3. Current and Flux Density. Each

element of a current contributes to the magnetic induction at all points in the field about the conductor. This contribution dB depends upon the current I in the element, the length dl of the element, the distance s from the ele-

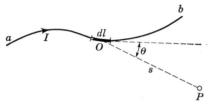

FIG. 2. Laplace's law for the magnetic flux density near a current.

ment to the point P considered, and the angle θ between the tangent to the conductor at the element and the line joining the element with P (Fig. 2).

$$dB = K \frac{I \sin \theta \, dl}{s^2} \qquad (5)$$

The factor K depends upon the properties of the medium between O and P as well as upon the units used. The flux density at P is the sum of the contributions from all the elements of the wire, that is,

$$B = \int K \frac{I \sin \theta \, dl}{s^2} \qquad (6)$$

where the integration is taken over the whole length of the conductor. The direction of the flux is at right angles to the plane determined by dl and the line joining P and dl.

The factor K may be related to the magnetic properties of the material around a current. Use of this factor K is similar to the way permittivity was used in Coulomb's law to give consideration to the dielectric properties of the medium around a charge. In the mks system

$$K = \frac{\mu_0}{4\pi} = 10^{-7} \frac{\text{weber}}{\text{amp-m}}$$

where μ_0 is called the *permeability* of free space (vacuum) or

$$\mu_0 = 4\pi \times 10^{-7} \text{ weber/amp-m}$$

We may use Eq. (6) to find expressions for B for various current arrangements.

31-4. Magnetic Induction at the Center of a Circular Current (Coil).

One of the most direct applications of Eq. (6) is the case of a current in a circular wire or a coil of a few closely wound turns. When the coil is placed

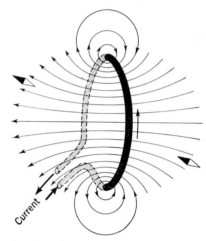

FIG. 3. Magnetic flux through a circular current.

at right angles to the plane of the paper, the field that is produced has something of the appearance shown in Fig. 3. It is clear that the field is not at all uniform. However, the value of B at the center of the coil can be obtained from Eq. (6). Since s is everywhere perpendicular to the wire, the angle θ is $90°$ and $\sin \theta = 1$. Also s is constant and equal to the radius r of the coil. From Eq. (6)

$$B = \frac{\mu_0}{4\pi} \int \frac{I \, dl}{r^2} = \frac{\mu_0 I}{4\pi r^2} \int dl$$

The integral $\int dl$ is simply the length of the circular conductor. For N turns $\int dl = 2\pi rN$. Thus the flux density at the center of a circular coil is

$$B = \frac{\mu_0 I}{4\pi r^2} 2\pi rN = \frac{\mu_0 NI}{2r} \qquad (7)$$

The direction of B is perpendicular to the plane of the coil in the direction given by the right-hand rule. At other points in the plane of the coil B is perpendicular to the plane but Eq. (7) gives the value only at the center.

Example: There is a current of 30 amp in a flat circular coil having 15 closely wound turns with a radius of 20 cm. What is the flux density at the center of the coil?

$$B = \mu_0 \frac{NI}{2r}$$

$$= (4\pi \times 10^{-7} \text{ weber/amp-m}) \frac{15 \times 30 \text{ amp}}{2 \times 0.20 \text{ m}}$$

$$= 1.4 \times 10^{-3} \text{ weber/m}^2$$

31-5. Flux Density Near a Long Straight Current.

In Fig. 4 an infinitely long straight

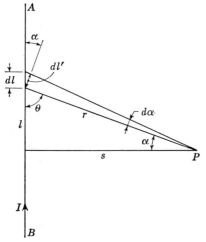

Fig. 4. Biot-Savart law.

wire AB carries a current I. The flux density at a point P distant s from the wire may be found from

$$dB = \frac{\mu_0}{4\pi} \frac{I \, dl \sin \theta}{r^2}$$

Since α and θ are complementary angles, we may write

$$dB = \frac{\mu_0}{4\pi} \frac{I \, dl \cos \alpha}{r^2}$$

By construction, $dl' = dl \cos \alpha$ and $d\alpha = dl'/r$. Hence

$$dl \cos \alpha = dl' = r \, d\alpha$$

Also

$$r = \frac{s}{\cos \alpha}$$

When these values are substituted, we obtain

$$dB = \frac{\mu_0}{4\pi} \frac{I \cos \alpha \, d\alpha}{s}$$

The total flux density at P is the sum of the contributions from all the elements, that is, the integral when α varies from $-90°$ to $+90°$.

$$B = \frac{\mu_0}{4\pi} \frac{I}{s} \int_{-90°}^{90°} \cos \alpha \, d\alpha = \frac{\mu_0}{4\pi} \frac{I}{s} \left[\sin \alpha \right]_{-90°}^{90°}$$

$$B = \frac{\mu_0}{2\pi} \frac{I}{s} \tag{8}$$

This equation is valid only for an infinitely long current, but it applies satisfactorily to shorter wires if the distance from the wire is not too great. Equation (8) is sometimes known as the *law of Biot and Savart*.

The field due to a long straight conductor is not a uniform field, even at a given distance from the conductor. Although the *magnitude* of the field may be constant, the *direction* changes from point to point and hence the field is not a uniform one.

Example: There is a current of 25.0 amp in a long straight wire. What is the flux density at a point 3.00 cm from the wire?

$$B = \mu_0 \frac{I}{2\pi s}$$

$$= (4\pi \times 10^{-7} \text{ weber/amp-m}) \frac{25.0 \text{ amp}}{2\pi \times 0.0300 \text{ m}}$$

$$= 1.67 \times 10^{-4} \text{ weber/m}^2$$

31-6. Flux Density on the Axis of a Coil.

Consider the case of a concentrated coil of N turns and radius r, with its plane normal to the plane of the paper (Fig. 5). When there is a current I in the coil, there will be a magnetic field at all points nearby. We shall determine the flux density at a point P on the

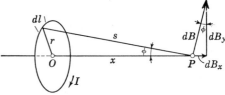

Fig. 5. Magnetic flux density on the axis of a coil.

axis of the coil at a distance x from the center O.

From Eq. (5) the contribution of the element dl to the flux density at P is given by

$$dB = \frac{\mu_0}{4\pi} \frac{I \, dl}{s^2}$$

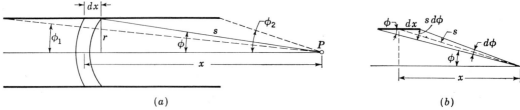

Fig. 6. Magnetic flux density on the axis of a solenoid.

since s is normal to dl. This flux density dB is perpendicular to s. It may be resolved into a component dB_y perpendicular to x and a component dB_x parallel to x. When the effect of an entire turn in the coil is considered, it may be seen that each component such as dB_y may be paired off against another one that is equal in magnitude but opposite in direction, due to the oppositely directed element of current in a portion of the wire at the other end of the diameter from dl. But the elements of field dB_x are all in the same direction and hence add up to give the resultant B, directed along x. The value of dB_x may be obtained from

$$dB_x = dB \sin \phi = \frac{\mu_0}{4\pi} \frac{I \, dl}{s^2} \frac{r}{s}$$

$$B = \frac{\mu_0}{4\pi} \frac{Ir}{s^3} \int_0^{2\pi r N} dl$$

$$B = \mu_0 \frac{NIr^2}{2s^3}$$

If we substitute $s^2 = r^2 + x^2$, we obtain

$$B = \mu_0 \frac{NIr^2}{2(r^2 + x^2)^{3/2}} \qquad (9)$$

It will be seen that Eq. (9) reduces to Eq. (7) when $x = 0$, that is, for a point at the center of the coil.

Example: A flat circular coil of 120 turns has a radius of 18 cm and carries a current of 3.0 amp. What is the magnitude and direction of the flux density at a point on the axis of the coil at a distance from the center equal to the radius of the coil?

$$B = \mu_0 \frac{NIr^2}{2(r^2 + x^2)^{3/2}} =$$

$$(4\pi \times 10^{-7} \text{w/amp-m}) \frac{120 \times 3.0 \text{ amp} \times (0.18\text{m})^2}{2(0.18^2\text{m}^2 + 0.18^2\text{m}^2)^{3/2}}$$

$$= 9.6 \times 10^{-5} \text{ weber/m}^2$$

The direction of the flux density is along the axis of the coil and directed away from the coil when the current in the coil is counterclockwise as viewed by an observer at P (Fig. 5).

31-7. Flux Density on the Axis of a Solenoid. Consider the case of a closely wound helical coil of N turns, which has an axial length l and radius r in which there is a current I. In an element of the solenoid of length dx (Fig. 6) there will be $(N/l) \, dx$ turns. In accordance with the equation derived above for the field on the axis of a coil, the field at P due to the element dx is given by

$$dB = \mu_0 \frac{NIr^2 \, dx}{2ls^3}$$

To integrate this expression, it is convenient to express dx and s in terms of the single variable ϕ. From Fig. 6b it is seen that

$$\sin \phi = \frac{s \, d\phi}{dx}$$

from which

$$dx = \frac{s \, d\phi}{\sin \phi}$$

Since $\sin \phi$ also equals r/s, we may write the equation for dB as

$$dB = \mu_0 \frac{NI}{2l} \sin \phi \, d\phi$$

The resultant field at P due to the whole solenoid is given by

$$B = \mu_0 \frac{NI}{2l} \int_{\phi_1}^{\phi_2} \sin \phi \, d\phi$$

$$B = \mu \frac{NI}{2l} (\cos \phi_1 - \cos \phi_2) \qquad (10)$$

For the center of a long solenoid, when l is large in comparison with r, $\phi_1 = 0$ and $\phi_2 = 180°$. Hence $\cos \phi_1 - \cos \phi_2 = 2$ and the field at the center of the solenoid is given by

$$B = \mu_0 \frac{NI}{l} \qquad (11)$$

Example: A closely wound solenoid of 1250 turns has an axial length of 98 cm and a radius of 1.50 cm. When there is a current of 1.30 amp in the solenoid, what is the flux density on the axis (a) at the center and (b) at one end of the solenoid?

At the center

$$B_c = \frac{\mu_0 NI}{l}$$

$$= (4\pi \times 10^{-7}\,\text{weber/amp-m}) \frac{1250 \times 1.30\,\text{amp}}{0.98\,\text{m}}$$

$$= 2.09 \times 10^{-3}\,\text{weber/m}^2$$

At one end

$$B_e = \mu_0 \frac{NI}{2l} (\cos \phi_1 - \cos \phi_2)$$

$$= (4\pi \times 10^{-7}\,\text{weber/amp-m})$$

$$\times \frac{1250 \times 1.30\,\text{amp}}{2 \times 0.98\,\text{m}} (\cos 1.8° - \cos 90°)$$

$$= 1.04 \times 10^{-3}\,\text{weber/m}^2$$

It will be noticed from this example that for a solenoid which has a length that is large in comparison with its radius, the flux density at the end is one-half that at the center.

The symbol n is often used for the number of turns per unit axial length of a solenoid ($n = N/l$). When this notation is used, Eq. (11) is written

$$B = \mu_0 nI \qquad (12)$$

In problems dealing with the design of electromagnetic machinery Eqs. (11) and (12) are highly important. Although it should be clearly understood that these equations apply strictly to an infinitely long solenoid, it is found that reasonably satisfactory results are obtained for shorter solenoids if the radius of the circular turns is small in comparison with the axial length of the helix. The equations are almost exactly valid for a closed solenoid

such as the ring-wound *toroid* illustrated in Fig. 7 where l is the mean circumference of the toroid, $2\pi R$. Here the field is nearly uniform within the coils and does not flare out anywhere as it does at the ends of an open solenoid. Such toroids are frequently used for laboratory measurements where a calculable uniform field is desired.

Example: A toroidal coil has 3000 turns. The inner and outer diameters are 22 cm and 26 cm, respectively. Calculate the flux density inside the coil when there is a current of 5.0 amp.

The mean radius R is 12 cm.

$$B = \frac{\mu_0 NI}{l}$$

$$= (4\pi \times 10^{-7}\,\text{weber/amp-m}) \frac{3000 \times 5.0\,\text{amp}}{2\pi \times 0.12\,\text{m}}$$

$$= 0.025\,\text{weber/m}^2$$

It should be noted that the field referred to in the case of the solenoid is the field *within* the solenoidal winding. If the turns are closely packed (not as shown in Fig. 7), there will be little "flux leakage" and the field outside the cross section of the windings will be

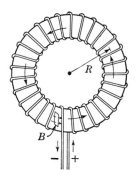

FIG. 7. A solenoid wound in the form of a toroid.

nearly zero. Students are warned not to confuse the (zero) field at the center of the toroid with the case of the field at the center of a circular coil.

The field caused by a flat *coil* (Fig. 3) and that produced by a solenoid (Fig. 8) should not be confused. To differentiate, we can think of a coil as a concentrated winding of very short axial length, while a solenoid

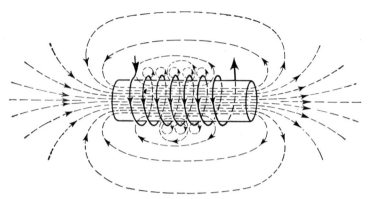

FIG. 8. Magnetic flux about a solenoid.

should have many closely wound turns extending over a considerable axial length.

31-8. Force on a Moving Charge or on a Current in a Magnetic Field. From Eq. (1) the force F on a charge q moving in a magnetic field is

$$F = Bqv \sin \theta \tag{13}$$

The force is mutually perpendicular to B and to the component $v \sin \theta$ of the velocity of the charge normal to the field. If the fingers of the right hand are curled in the direction the vector $v \sin \theta$ must be rotated toward the vector B, the thumb will point in the direction of the force on a positive charge.

If a charge moves at right angles to a uniform field, its path is circular, since the force is constant in magnitude and always perpendicular to the motion. The magnetic force is the centripetal force.

$$Bqv = \frac{mv^2}{r} \tag{14}$$

When the charges are moving along a conductor in a magnetic field the force dF on any element dl of the conductor is, from Eq. (2)

$$dF = BI \, dl \sin \theta \tag{15}$$

where θ is the angle between the conductor and the flux. The resultant force on the conductor is the vector sum of the contributions of the elements. For a straight conductor of length l in a uniform field the sum becomes

$$F = BIl \sin \theta \tag{16}$$

In Fig. 9, a magnetic field of flux density

B is shown directed horizontally toward the right. A current I is directed vertically downward in this field. From the rule given above the force F on this conductor must be normal to the page and directed out from the paper.

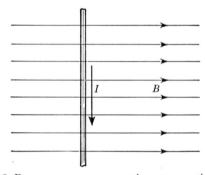

FIG. 9. Force on a current normal to a magnetic flux.

Viewed from above, the conductor and field of Fig. 9 appear as in Fig. 10. Conventionally the symbol ⊙ is used to represent a current toward the reader while a current away from the reader is indicated ⊕. Above the conductor in Fig. 10, the clockwise magnetic field due to the electric current is in the same direction as the externally applied field. The magnetic field above the wire is therefore strengthened. Below the wire, the field due to the current is opposite in direction to the external field. The field below the wire is therefore weakened. It is found by experiment that a current in a magnetic field experiences a force directed from the strong part of the field toward the weak part of the field. It is seen that the result is a force downward on the wire. The force is at right angles both to the current and to the field.

In any situation involving an electric current in a magnetic field, the direction of the side push on the conductor may be predicted by analyzing the fields, as has been done for the case shown in Fig. 10.

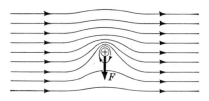

FIG. 10. Force on a current in a magnetic flux.

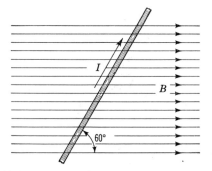

FIG. 11. Force on a straight current not at a right angle with a uniform flux density.

It should be emphasized that the B in Eqs. (15) and (16) represents the flux density of the field in which the current is immersed and not the field near the conductor due to the current. In other words, Eq. (16) gives a measure of the force which a current experiences when placed in a magnetic field set up by some other means.

It will be noted that the force is a maximum when the current is normal to the field and zero when the current is parallel to the field.

Example: In Fig. 11 is shown a current of 25 amp in a wire 30 cm long and at an angle of 60° to a magnetic field of flux density 8.0×10^{-4} weber/m². What is the magnitude and direction of the force on this wire?

$$F = BIl \sin \theta = (8.0 \times 10^{-4} \text{ weber/m}^2)$$
$$\times 25 \text{ amp} \times 0.30 \text{ m} \times 0.87$$
$$= 5.2 \times 10^{-3} \text{ newton}$$

The direction of the force can most safely be determined by visualizing the resultant field caused by the field due to the current and the field in which the wire is placed. Because of the field due to the current, the field above the wire will be strengthened while that below the wire will be weakened. Hence the conductor is pushed away from the observer, from the stronger and toward the weaker field.

31-9. Torque on a Current-carrying Coil in a Magnetic Field. A current-carrying coil in a magnetic field will experience a torque tending to rotate the coil when the plane of the coil has a component that is parallel to the direction of the field (Fig. 12a). From a consideration of the resultant field that is produced (Fig. 12b), it will be observed that the wire GH is urged upward while wire CD is forced downward. These forces, equal in magnitude but opposite in direction, give rise to a couple, the net torque being the product of one of the forces and the

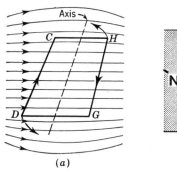

(a)

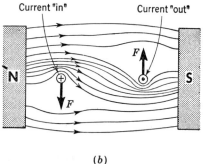

(b)

FIG. 12. A current-carrying coil placed in a magnetic flux experiences a torque.

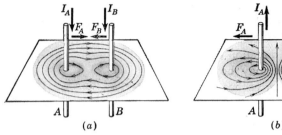

FIG. 13. Resultant fields and forces between parallel current-carrying conductors.

perpendicular distance between their lines of action. By Eq. (16), the force is

$$F = BI(GH) \sin 90° = BI(GH)$$

and hence the torque is

$$L = BI(GH)(GD)$$

But $(GH)(GD)$ is the *area* A of the coil and hence

$$L = BIA \qquad (17)$$

When the plane of the coil makes an angle α with the field, the torque is

$$L = BIA \cos \alpha \qquad (18)$$

In general, a coil will tend to rotate in a field until its plane is normal to the field. This is the position where the coil links the maximum flux. It may therefore be stated that a coil freely suspended in a magnetic field will align itself so as to include a maximum number of lines of induction through the cross section of the coil. Equation (18) is a basic equation for electric motors. If the coil has more than one turn, the torque will be increased in proportion to the number of turns N. The general equation is

$$L = BNIA \cos \alpha \qquad (19)$$

The torque is expressed in meter-newtons when B is in newtons per ampere-meter (webers/m²), I is in amperes, and A is in square meters. Although Eq. (19) has been derived for the case of a rectangular coil, it can be shown that the same equation applies to a coil of any shape.

Example: A rectangular coil 30 cm long and 10 cm wide is mounted in a uniform field of flux density 8.0×10^{-4} newton/amp-m. There is a current of 20 amp in the coil, which has 15 turns.

When the plane of the coil makes an angle of 40° with the direction of the field, what is the torque tending to rotate the coil?

$$L = BNIA \cos \alpha = 8.0 \times 10^{-4} \frac{\text{newton}}{\text{amp-m}} \times 15$$
$$\times 20 \text{ amp} \times (0.30 \times 0.10)\text{m}^2 \times 0.77$$
$$= 0.011 \text{ m-newton}$$

31-10. Forces between Currents. When parallel current-carrying conductors are adjacent, each exerts a force on the other. We may think of one of the currents with its accompanying field as being situated in the field caused by the other current. By Eq. (16) this will result in a force between the current-carrying conductors. The two circular fields combine in the manner shown in Fig. 13. In terms of the flux picture, we visualize the effects as if they were caused by the lines acting like stretched rubber bands with tension in the direction of their lengths. Hence currents in the same direction, as in Fig. 13a, produce an attractive force. We may visualize this in another manner by noting that the field between the wires is much weaker than the field outside the wires and hence they tend to move away from the strong field and toward the weaker one. Unlike the rubber-band analogy the lines are visualized as having a repulsive force in a direction perpendicular to their lengths. This assists us in seeing why currents in opposite directions, as in Fig. 13b, produce a force of repulsion. Since the two currents in this case combine to produce a strong field between the wires and weak fields outside the wires, it follows that the wires are repelled from each other, since they tend to move from the stronger toward the weaker fields.

A measure of the forces between parallel current-carrying conductors may be obtained from Eq. (16) and the expression for the field near a long straight conductor. From Eq. (8) the field of current I_A in wire A is given by

$$B = \mu_0 \frac{I_A}{2\pi s}$$

From Eq. (16), the force on current I_B in wire B is therefore

$$F = BIl = \mu_0 \frac{I_A}{2\pi s} \times I_B l = \mu_0 \frac{I_A I_B l}{2\pi s} \quad (20)$$

where s is the distance from A to B and l is the length of wire B.

The relation expressed by Eq. (20) may be used to define the mks unit of current: the *ampere* is a current that, when it is maintained in two infinitely long conductors, parallel to each other and one meter apart in a vacuum, will cause a force on each conductor of exactly 2×10^{-7} newton per meter length. The numbers chosen in this definition are such as to make the unit thus defined essentially the same as the ampere defined by other methods.

Example: Two straight parallel wires each 90 cm long are 1.0 mm apart. There are currents of 5.0 amp in opposite directions in the wires. What is the magnitude and sense of the force between these currents?

$$F = \mu_0 \frac{I_A I_B l}{2\pi s} = \frac{(4\pi \times 10^{-7} \text{ weber/amp-m})}{2\pi \times 0.0010 \text{ m}}$$
$$\times 5.0 \text{ amp} \times 5.0 \text{ amp} \times 0.90 \text{ m}$$
$$= 4.5 \times 10^{-4} \text{ newton}$$

SUMMARY

The forces between magnets are believed to be caused by the forces that moving electric charges in atoms exert on each other.

A *magnetic field* is a region in which there is a force on a moving charge in addition to the Coulomb forces.

Magnetic induction is defined from the force on the moving charge by the equation

$$B = \frac{F}{qv \sin \theta}$$

It is a vector quantity whose direction is the direction of motion of the charge for which the force is zero.

The magnetic induction, the normal velocity $v \sin \theta$, and the force are mutually perpendicular.

Magnetic induction is represented by *lines of induction*, parallel to B, called *magnetic flux* Φ, chosen so that the number of lines of induction per unit area of a surface perpendicular to B is equal to B. When B is in newtons per ampere-meter and the area is in square meters the flux is in *webers*.

The magnetic induction is also called *flux density* since it is the flux per unit area

$$B = \frac{\Phi}{A} \quad \text{or} \quad \Phi = BA$$

Flux density is measured in webers per square meter.

Magnetic fields are observed in the neighborhood of currents and near magnetized materials.

Each element of a current contributes to the flux density at all points about the conductor by an amount

$$dB = K \frac{I \sin \theta \, dl}{s^2}$$

In the mks system

$$K = \frac{\mu_0}{4\pi} = 10^{-7} \frac{\text{weber}}{\text{amp-m}}$$

where μ_0 is called the *permeability* of empty space.

The flux density in empty space near a conductor may be found by summing up the contributions of all the elements of the current. For several arrangements these sums are:

Center of a circular coil

$$B = \mu_0 \frac{NI}{2r}$$

Near a long straight current

$$B = \mu_0 \frac{I}{2\pi s}$$

On the axis of a coil

$$B = \mu_0 \frac{NIr^2}{2(r^2 + x^2)^{3/2}}$$

On the axis of a solenoid

$$B = \mu_0 \frac{NI}{2l} (\cos \phi_1 - \cos \phi_2)$$

At the center of a long solenoid

$$B = \mu_0 n I$$

The force upon a conductor in a magnetic field is given by

$$dF = BI \, dl \sin \theta$$

For a straight conductor in a uniform magnetic field

$$F = BIl \sin \theta$$

The torque on a coil in a magnetic field is given by

$$L = BNIA \cos \alpha$$

The force of a current I_A on a parallel current I_B is given by

$$F = \mu_0 \frac{I_A I_B l}{2 \pi s}$$

The *ampere* is a current that, when it is maintained in two infinitely long conductors, parallel to each other and one meter apart in a vacuum, will cause a force on each conductor of 2×10^{-7} newton per meter length.

QUESTIONS   **1.** A cable carrying a direct current is buried in a wall that stands in a north-south plane. On the west side of the wall a horizontal compass needle points south instead of north. What is (a) the position of the cable and (b) the direction of the current in the cable?

2. A wire in the north-south direction has maintained in it a current directed north. Describe what happens to a compass needle, of the conventional type, mounted on vertical bearings, as the needle is placed (a) above the wire, (b) below the wire, and (c) at the right side of the wire.

3. A coil in the plane of the paper is connected to a battery. The current in the coil is clockwise. (a) What is the direction of the flux density near the center of the coil? (b) What will be the relative change in flux density if the radius of the coil were doubled? (c) if the number of turns were doubled also?

4. The small circle in Fig. 14 represents a current-carrying conductor, per-

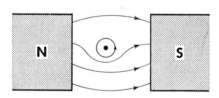

FIG. 14.

pendicular to the page. The curved lines represent the flux between poles of an electromagnet. What is the direction of the current in the conductor?

5. A circular loop of wire hangs by a thread in a vertical plane. An electric current is maintained in the loop in a counterclockwise direction as seen from the front face, A. To what direction (N, S, E, or W) will the front face of the coil turn when it is free to rotate in the earth's magnetic field?

6. A "tangent galvanometer" consists of a flat, circular coil of a few turns N and radius r. The coil is placed with its plane parallel to the horizontal component of the earth's magnetic field, of flux density B. A small compass needle mounted at the center of the coil is deflected through an angle ϕ when there is a current I in the coil. Derive the equation for this angle in terms of I and B and the constants of the coil.

7. Sketch a curve to show how the magnetic flux density near a long, straight current varies with the distance away from the current.

8. A stream of electrons is projected horizontally toward the right. A magnet brought near the electron beam produces a field directed downward. Explain what happens.

9. What sort of path will electrically charged particles follow if they are initially moving at right angles to a uniform flux density, in a vacuum? Will such particles experience an energy change during this motion? Explain briefly.

10. Why are magnetic fields used in many machines designed to accelerate charged particles to high energy?

11. An electron of charge e and mass m moves with a velocity v normal to a uniform magnetic field of induction B. Because of the force on the electron at right angles to B and v, it will be accelerated and move with uniform speed in a circle of radius r. Derive the equation which gives r in terms of B, e, m, and v. Solve the equation for e/m and discuss the significance of this ratio.

12. Plot a curve to show the variation of the torque on a coil in a magnetic field as the plane of the coil is rotated with respect to the field.

13. "Helmholtz coils" consist of two large, flat, circular coils mounted with a common axis and at a distance apart equal to their common radius. (a) Show that this arrangement produces a uniform flux density over a small space midway between the coils. (b) Derive an equation for this flux density when the coils have the same current in the directions to produce additive effects.

14. Two long, straight, insulated wires are suspended vertically. The wires are connected in series and a heavy current from a battery is maintained in them. What happens to these wires? The battery is replaced by an a-c source. Explain what happens in this case.

15. Explain what would happen to the configuration of a loosely wound loop of flexible wire when a current is maintained in the loop.

16. Two current-carrying coils are placed at a distance from each other, with their centers on a straight line. This line is perpendicular to one of the coils. What must be the position of the second coil and the relative direction of the currents in order that the coils may attract each other? In what position will there be no force?

17. A loosely wound helix made of stiff wire is mounted vertically with the lower end just touching a dish of mercury. When a current from a battery is started in the coil, the wire executes an oscillatory motion with the lower end jumping out of and into the mercury. Explain the reasons for this behavior. Would the apparatus behave similarly if an a-c source were used instead of the battery?

PROBLEMS   1. Find the current in conductor *CDEFG* (Fig. 15) when the magnetic flux

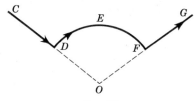

Fig. 15.

density at O is 1.0×10^{-7} w/m² if the radius OD is 3.0 cm and the length of the arc *DEF* is 8.0 cm. What is the direction of the magnetic flux at O?

2. What is the magnetic induction at the center of a flat circular coil of 100 turns of wire and 152 mm radius that carries a current of 6.28 amp? Show by a sketch the direction of this field.   *Ans.* 2.60×10^{-3} w/m²

3. There is a current of 1.00 amp in a wire 1.00 ft long, bent into a circular arc of 1.00-ft radius. What is the flux density at the center of this arc?

4. A current of 18 amp in a circular segment of wire (such as *DEF* in Fig. 15) produces a flux density at the center of the arc of 4.48×10^{-4} w/m². The wire makes an angle of 3.0 radians at the center *O*. What is its radius of curvature? *Ans.* 1.2 cm

5. What current would have to be maintained in a circular coil of wire of 50 turns and 254 mm radius in order to just cancel the effect of the earth's magnetic field at a place where the horizontal component of the earth's field has an induction of 1.86×10^{-5} w/m². How must the coil be set up?

6. Two concentric circular loops of wire having radii of 9.42 cm and 6.28 cm, lie in the same plane and are connected in series. What flux density is produced at the center of the coils when there is a current of 30.0 amp (*a*) in the same direction? (*b*) in opposite directions?

Ans. 5.00×10^{-4} w/m²; 1.00×10^{-4} w/m²

7. A flat circular coil has 30 turns wound closely on a radius of 18.5 cm. A small compass needle is mounted on a vertical axis at the center of the coil. The coil is adjusted until its plane is parallel to the earth's magnetic field, which at that place has a flux density whose horizontal component is 2.08×10^{-5} w/m². There is a current of 0.358 amp in the coil. Through what an ge will the compass needle be deflected?

8. A flat, circular coil of 30 turns and 6.0-cm radius is connected in series with a second coil of 25 turns and 15-cm radius. The two coils are concentric, but their planes are normal. What is the flux density at the center when there is a current of 8.0 amp in the coils? *Ans.* 2.63×10^{-3} w/m²

9. A very long, straight wire of radius *a* carries a current producing a magnetic flux density of 1.0×10^{-5} w/m² at the surface of the wire. What is the value of the flux density at (*a*) a point 2*a* from the center of the wire? (*b*) a point *a*/2 from the center of the wire? (*c*) the center of the wire?

10. Two long, parallel wires carry currents perpendicular to the plane of the paper through points *A* and *B*. The currents are each 10 amp, in the same direction. Consider an equilateral triangle *ABC*, 20 cm on a side. Determine the flux density at point *C*. *Ans.* 1.7×10^{-5} w/m²

11. Two long, straight parallel wires in which there are currents of 2.0 and 3.0 amp in the same direction are 10 cm apart. Find the magnitude and the direction of the flux density at a point halfway between them.

12. Find the magnitude of the magnetic induction at a point midway between two long straight parallel wires 20.0 cm apart. One wire carries a current of 15.0 amp and the other a current 25.0 amp in the same direction. Show the direction of the field by a diagram. *Ans.* 2.0×10^{-5} w/m²

13. An upward current of 7.2 amp is maintained in a long, straight wire in a place where the horizontal component of the earth's magnetic flux density is 2.38×10^{-5} w/m². Calculate the resultant magnetic flux density at a point 8.0 cm from the wire (*a*) north of the wire and (*b*) west of the wire.

14. A long, straight wire *A* carries a current of 5.25 amp. Another wire *B* parallel to it 15.0 cm away carries 10.0 amp in the opposite sense. What is the magnetic induction at a point *P* 10.0 cm from *A* and 25.0 cm from *B*? Show clearly its direction by a sketch. *Ans.* 2.5×10^{-6} w/m²

15. A toroid has a closely wound coil with 30 turns per inch of length. What is the magnetic induction in the coil for a current of 5.25 amp? Show the direction of this field.

16. A solenoid 524 mm long is wound with 4000 turns of wire. What is the magnetic induction at the center of the solenoid when there is a current of 2.84 amp in the winding? Indicate by a sketch the direction of the field.

Ans. 2.73 $\times$ 10^{-2} w/m^2

17. A long solenoid has 35 turns per centimeter of length and there is a current of 8.00 amp maintained in it. A short, closely wound coil of 25 turns and 6.0-cm radius is wound over the center of the solenoid. A current of 12 amp in this coil is in the opposite sense to that in the solenoid. What is the flux density at the center of the system?

18. A solenoid 100 cm long is wound with 350 turns of wire. Another layer of 200 turns is wound over the central 50 cm of the first solenoid. There is a current of 15 amp in the longer solenoid. In the shorter solenoid there is a current of 25 amp in a sense opposite to that of the current in the longer solenoid. What is the flux density at the center of these solenoids?   *Ans.* 6.0 $\times$ 10^{-3} w/m^2

19. Find the flux density produced by a 5.0-amp current in each of the following cases: (*a*) 2.0 cm from a long, straight wire, (*b*) at the center of a 40-turn coil of 2.0-cm diameter, and (*c*) anywhere inside an infinitely long solenoid of 2.0-cm diameter and with 50 turns per centimeter.

20. Two long, straight wires 750 mm apart deliver a steady current of 50.0 amp to a motor. (*a*) Find the flux density produced at one wire by the current in the other wire. (*b*) Find the force exerted on a 300-cm length of the second wire.   *Ans.* 1.33 $\times$ 10^{-5} w/m^2; 2.00 $\times$ 10^{-3} newton

21. Two parallel wires carry equal currents in opposite directions. (*a*) If the force on one of these wires is 2.50 $\times$ 10^{-3} newton for each meter of length and the wires are 150 mm apart, calculate the current in one of the wires. (*b*) Will the currents attract or repel each other? Explain.

22. A cable 14.0 ft in length runs along the top of a railway car, 4.5 ft below the trolley wire. When there is a current of 800 amp in the trolley wire and 90 amp in the cable, what is the force between them?   *Ans.* 0.045 newton

23. In Fig. 16, *A*, *B*, and *C* are long thin wires arranged so that their centers lie at the corners of an isosceles triangle. Wire *A* carries a current of 9.0 amp into the plane of the paper, wire *B* carries 9.0 amp out of the paper, and wire *C*

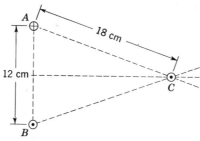

Fig. 16.

carries 3.0 amp out of the paper. Find the magnitude and direction of the force, per unit length, exerted on wire *C* due to the currents in wires *A* and *B*. The wires maintain their relative positions.

24. A conductor 500 mm long makes an angle of 60° with a uniform magnetic field of induction 5.00 $\times$ 10^{-4} w/m^2. What force is exerted on the conductor when it carries a current of 18.0 amp? Make a sketch to show the direction of the force.   *Ans.* 3.88 $\times$ 10^{-3} newton

25. A wire 125 cm long and carrying a current of 30 amp is placed at an angle of 30° with a uniform magnetic field of induction 4.0 $\times$ 10^{-4} w/m^2. What force is exerted by the field on the current? By the aid of a figure show the directions of the field, current, and force.

26. The plane of a rectangular loop of wire 50.0 by 80.0 mm is parallel to a uniform magnetic field whose induction is 1.50×10^{-2} w/m². (*a*) If the loop carries a current of 10.0 amp what torque acts on it? (*b*) What is the torque if the dimensions of the loop are 40.0 by 100 mm? Show the sense of the torque by the use of a figure.   *Ans.* 6.00×10^{-4} newton-m

27. The plane of a rectangular loop of wire 5.26 by 8.14 cm makes an angle of 30° with a uniform magnetic field whose flux density is 1.58×10^{-3} w/m². (*a*) What torque acts on the coil when the current is 5.12 amp? Make a sketch to show the sense of this torque. (*b*) How could this length of wire be arranged to give a maximum torque in this field?

28. A 25-turn rectangular coil 12 by 15 cm is placed with its plane parallel to a flux density of 0.0040 w/m². For a current of 400 ma in the coil, what is the torque when the 12-cm side is (*a*) parallel and (*b*) perpendicular, to the flux density?   *Ans.* 7.2×10^{-4} m-newton

29. A flat, circular coil of 10 turns lies horizontally where the horizontal component of the earth's magnetic field has a flux density of 2.0×10^{-5} w/m². What torque acts on the coil if it has a diameter of 20 cm and carries a current of 0.50 amp?

30. A 50-turn rectangular coil of wire, *ABCD*, 4.0 cm by 5.0 cm, is suspended in a vertical plane. A horizontal uniform flux density of 2.0 w/m² is maintained in the plane of the coil. (*a*) Compute the torque experienced by the coil when there is in it a current of 0.30 amp. (*b*) In a diagram show the direction of the current, flux, and torque.   *Ans.* 0.060 m-newton

31. In Fig. 17, the solenoid consists of 1200 turns and measures 35 cm in length by 2.3 cm in diameter. It carries a current of 1.5 amp in the sense indicated. The windings are separated so that a straight wire carrying a current of 18

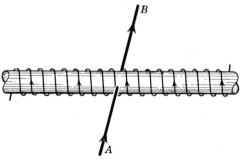

Fig. 17.

amp from *A* to *B* is inserted, to pass through the center of the solenoid, at right angles to its axis. Find the force on the portion of straight wire which is inside the solenoid.

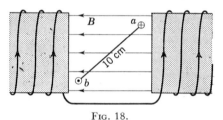

Fig. 18.

32. The one-turn rectangular coil of Fig. 18 carries a current of 10 amp in the sense shown, "in" at a. The width ab of the coil is 10 cm, the length 20 cm. Its plane makes an angle $\phi = 30°$ with the magnetic flux density $B = 0.25$ w/m². (a) Find the force on the conductor a, of length 20 cm. (b) Find the torque required to hold the coil in the position shown.

Ans. 0.50 newton; 0.043 m-newton

33. A single square loop of wire carrying a current i and having edges of length a is suspended by a torsionless fiber attached to the mid-point of one edge. The plane of the loop is perpendicular to the flux density B at equilibrium. If the loop is rotated a small angle α about the axis and then released, what is the frequency of the resultant simple harmonic motion? The moment of inertia of the loop about the axis of rotation is I.

34. A rectangular loop of wire in which there is a current of 5.00 amp is placed in a uniform field of induction 2.14×10^{-3} w/m². The coil is 30.0 cm long and 15.0 cm wide. (a) How much torque must be applied to keep the coil from rotating? (b) How much torque would be required if the loop were circular and its area were 450 cm²? *Ans.* 4.81×10^{-4} newton-m

35. Calculate the period of rotation of a free electron moving in a plane perpendicular to the magnetic flux of the earth, where $B = 0.60 \times 10^{-4}$ w/m².

36. A circuit in the form of an equilateral triangle with sides 10 cm and with a 4.0-volt battery at the center of the base is suspended from its upper vertex by a nonconducting fiber with a torsion constant 1.0×10^{-6} m-newton. If a homogeneous magnetic flux of 0.010 w/m² is set up parallel to the original plane of the triangle, the triangle comes to rest after turning 0.010 radian. Considering the angle to be small, what is the resistance in the circuit?

Ans. 1.70×10^4 ohms

37. A particle of mass 0.020 gm travels in a straight horizontal line between two horizontal charged plates between which there is an electric field of 2.0 volts/cm, upward. A magnetic flux density of 2.0 w/m² is directed at right angles to the electric field ("into the paper"). If the particle bears a charge of 1.0×10^{-6} coulomb, what is its speed?

32. *Electric Instruments*

Practically all electrical measurements involve either the measurement or detection of electric current. The measurement of electric current can be accomplished by means of any one of the three principal effects of current: heating effect, chemical effect, or magnetic effect. For the sake of accuracy and convenience the magnetic effect is utilized almost universally in electric measuring instruments.

32-1. Galvanometers. The basic electric instrument is the galvanometer, a device with which very small electric currents can be detected and measured. The d'Arsonval, or permanent-magnet, moving-coil type of galvanometer, is shown in Figs. 1 and 2. In Fig. 1*a* the coil *C* is suspended between the poles *N* and *S* of a U-shaped magnet by means of a light metallic ribbon. Connections are made to the coil at the terminals marked *t*. The cylinder of soft iron *B* and the pole faces *N* and *S* are skillfully shaped so as to produce a *radial* magnetic field in the air gap. This has the virtue of giving a field that is constant in magnitude and always parallel to the plane of the coil as the coil rotates. These conditions are necessary if the instrument is to have a scale with uniform graduations. The mirror *M* is used to indicate the position of the coil, either by reflecting a beam of light onto a scale or by producing an image of a scale to be viewed through a low-power telescope.

When a current is set up in a coil which is between the poles of a magnet, the coil is acted upon by a torque, which tends to turn

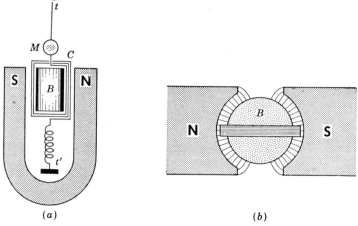

(*a*)   (*b*)

Fig. 1. Permanent-magnet, moving-coil type of galvanometer.

it until its plane is perpendicular to the line joining the poles. If a current is set up in the coil (as viewed from above) in Fig. 1b, the coil will turn toward a position at right angles to the position shown. In turning, however, it must twist the metallic ribbon that supports it; hence it turns to the position in which the torque exerted on it by the magnet is just neutralized by the reaction of the twisted ribbon.

The torque exerted on the coil by the magnet is proportional to the current in the coil, and the torque of reaction of the ribbon is proportional to the angle through which it is twisted. Since these torques are equal in magnitude and opposite in sense when the coil reaches the equilibrium position, the angle through which the coil turns is proportional to the current in it; that is $\theta \propto I$, where θ is the angular deflection of the coil. This condition is realized only in well-designed instruments, in which case the galvanometer scale is properly made with equally spaced divisions. In practice, readings are made on a linear scale, since the deflection s read on the scale is proportional to the angle of deflection θ (when θ is small).

32-2. Damping. If the current in a galvanometer circuit is interrupted, the coil will ordinarily swing back beyond the zero position and then vibrate with progressively decreasing amplitude through the zero point. This reduction of motion is called *damping*. Similarly, if a current is suddenly established in a galvanometer, the coil will ordinarily swing beyond its final equilibrium position and vibrate several times back and forth through this position before finally coming to rest. Since it is tedious to wait for this gradual dying away of the motion of the coil, artificial means are usually provided to bring the suspended system quickly to its final position.

The most common method of producing rapid damping consists of having the coil develop induced currents because of its motion in the magnetic field. Such induced currents tend to oppose the motion of the coil in the field (Chap. 35). In one of the most commonly used laboratory wall-type galvanometers, these induced currents are developed in a rectangular loop of fairly heavy copper wire which is attached side by side with the movable coil. Since the resistance of this single turn of wire is low, the induced current caused by the motion of the coil is comparatively high, and hence there is a suitable countertorque which tends to reduce the swinging of the coil about its equilibrium position.

In many ammeters and voltmeters, damping is accomplished by winding the movable coil on a light frame of aluminum. The currents induced in this frame are quite effective in producing satisfactory damping. By skillful design the pointer is caused to reach its equilibrium position very quickly with no noticeable oscillation.

For some purposes an external damping resistor is placed either in series or in parallel with the galvanometer coil. This resistance is adjusted to a critical value for a given galvanometer and circuit so as to produce a very slight underdamping. If the resistance is such as to cause an overdamping, the coil creeps to its final position with annoying slowness.

32-3. Galvanometer Sensitivity. The deflection caused by a given current depends upon the design of the instrument. This characteristic is known as the sensitivity of the galvanometer. There are numerous ways of expressing galvanometer sensitivity, each involving a statement of the electrical conditions necessary to produce a standard deflection. This standard deflection in galvanometers having attached scales is assumed to be one scale division. In galvanometers not equipped with scales (for example, galvanometers read with auxiliary telescope and scale) *the standard deflection is assumed to be* 1 *mm on a scale at a distance of* 1 *m.* Some of the most frequently used methods of expressing galvanometer sensitivity follow.

32-4. Current Sensitivity. As previously stated the galvanometer deflection s is proportional to the current I

$$s \propto I \quad \text{or} \quad I = ks$$

$$k = \frac{I}{s} \tag{1}$$

where k, the current per standard unit deflection, is called the *current sensitivity* of the galvanometer.

For sensitive galvanometers of the type shown in Fig. 2, which are read with telescope and scale, the current sensitivity k is expressed in microamperes per millimeter deflection on a scale 1 m from the mirror. The current sensitivity is numerically equal to the current in *microamperes* (millionths of an ampere and commonly abbreviated μa) required to cause a 1-mm deflection of the image on a scale 1 m distant. For the highly sensitive types of d'Arsonval galvanometers, k is about 0.00001 μa/mm, or 10^{-11} amp/mm. Other expressions of galvanometer sensitivity are derived from the current sensitivity. It should be carefully noted that the term *sensitivity* is a technical word meaning the reciprocal of sensitiveness. A sensitive galvanometer has a low sensitivity k.

32-5. Voltage Sensitivity. The voltage sensitivity is based upon the potential difference that must be impressed on the galvanometer terminals (including any external damping resistor) in order to produce the standard

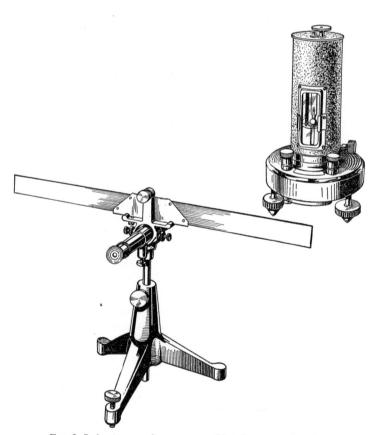

Fig. 2. Laboratory galvanometer with telescope and scale.

deflection. It is the PD per standard unit deflection and is equal to the product of the resistance of the galvanometer and the current sensitivity

$$\text{Voltage sensitivity} = kR_g \qquad (2)$$

where k is the current sensitivity and R_g the galvanometer resistance (including any damping resistance). When k is in microamperes per millimeter and R_g is in ohms, the voltage sensitivity is expressed in microvolts per millimeter.

32-6. Megohm Sensitivity. The *megohm sensitivity* of a galvanometer is the number of megohms (meg = million) resistance which must be put in series with the galvanometer in order to give the standard deflection for a potential difference of 1 volt across galvanometer and resistor. Consideration of Ohm's law shows that when the resistance of the galvanometer coil is negligible the megohm sensitivity of the galvanometer is numerically equal to the reciprocal of the current (in microamperes) required to produce the standard deflection.

32-7. Other Galvanometer Characteristics. The choice of a galvanometer is not made on the basis of sensitivity alone. Much depends on the purpose for which it is to be used. The period of the swing and the quickness with which the coil comes to rest are important. Also the resistance of the galvanometer should have the proper relation to the resistance of the circuit with which it is connected.

Portability, ruggedness, and convenience of operation are obtained in the d'Arsonval galvanometer by mounting the moving coil on jeweled pivots, attaching a pointer to the coil, and replacing the metallic ribbon suspension by two spiral springs as shown in Fig. 3. The springs, besides balancing the magnetic torque exerted on the coil, provide its external electrical connections. The current sensitivity of an instrument of this type may be expressed in microamperes per division of the scale over which the pointer moves.

Example: A galvanometer of the type shown in Fig. 2 has a current sensitivity of 0.002 μa/mm. What current is necessary to produce a deflection of 20 cm on a scale 1 m distant?

$I = ks$, where s is in millimeters (on a scale 1 m away), so that

$$I = (0.002 \ \mu a/mm)(200 \ mm) = 0.4 \ \mu a$$

On a scale twice as far away, the deflection would be twice as great.

Example: If the moving coil of the galvanometer of the example above has a resistance of 25 ohms, what is the potential difference across its terminals when the deflection is 20 cm?

$$V = IR = (0.4 \ \mu a)(25 \ ohms) = 10 \ \mu v$$

Example: A current of 2.0×10^{-4} amp causes a deflection of 10 divisions on the scale of a port-

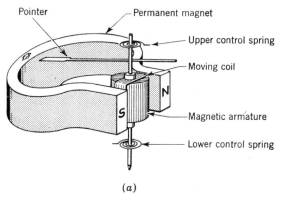

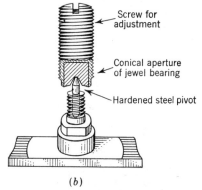

(a)   (b)

Fig. 3. (a) Diagrammatic representation of a portable-type galvanometer; (b) bearing detail.

able-type galvanometer. What is its current sensitivity?

$$k = \frac{I}{s} = \frac{0.00020 \text{ amp}}{10 \text{ divisions}} = \frac{2\bar{0}0 \mu a}{10 \text{ divisions}}$$
$$= 20 \mu a/\text{division}$$

Example: What current will cause a full-scale deflection (100 divisions) of a portable galvanometer for which $k = 20$ $\mu a/\text{division}$?

$$I = ks = (20 \mu a/\text{division})(100 \text{ divisions})$$
$$= 2\bar{0}00 \mu a = 0.0020 \text{ amp}$$

Example: Calculate (a) the voltage sensitivity and (b) the megohm sensitivity of the galvanometer in the preceding example if its resistance is 5.0 ohms.

(a) Voltage sensitivity $= kR_g$

$$= \left(20 \frac{\mu a}{\text{division}}\right)(5.0 \text{ ohms}) = 1\bar{0}0 \frac{\mu v}{\text{division}}$$

(b) Megohm sensitivity $= \frac{V}{I} = \frac{1.0 \text{ volt}}{20 \mu a}$
$$= 0.050 \text{ megohm}$$

A galvanometer is often used merely to indicate the presence and direction of a current or its absence. In fact the most common use of a galvanometer is as a null-indicating instrument, that is, as an instrument which indicates when a current is reduced to zero (Chap. 30). For this purpose the galvanometer scale need not be calibrated in terms of current.

32-8. Ballistic Galvanometer. For some purposes (such as measuring *quantity* of electricity, rather than *current*) galvanometers are designed with the moving coil having a large moment of inertia and a long period. This enables a small quantity of electricity to be discharged through the galvanometer in a time that is small in comparison with the period of the galvanometer. Under these circumstances a deflection is obtained that is proportional to the charge. This follows from the fact that the angular momentum $I\omega$ (Chap. 11) imparted to the coil is given by

$$\int I \, d\omega = \int L \, dt = K \int i \, dt$$
whence $\quad I\omega = KQ$

where I is the moment of inertia of the coil, ω is the angular speed imparted to it, L is the torque produced by the current i, K is a constant, and Q is the total charge sent through the coil. As a result of its angular momentum the coil deflects until its kinetic energy of rotation is transferred into the potential energy of the twisted suspension. The deflection s thus produced is therefore proportional to the charge, or

$$Q = k_b s$$

The constant k_b is known as the *ballistic constant* of the galvanometer. Ballistic galvanometers are useful for the comparison of capacitors (Chap. 37).

32-9. Voltmeters. The voltage across the usual galvanometer is comparatively low. If higher voltages are to be measured, it is necessary to insert a resistor of high resistance *in series* with the moving coil of the instrument. Most of the potential drop will then occur across the multiplying resistor. By properly choosing this resistance any desired voltage may be measured.

Consider, for instance, the galvanometer mentioned in the last two examples above. The voltage that is required to produce full-scale deflection is 10 mv. In order to use this galvanometer as a voltmeter registering to 10 volts, it is necessary only to increase the resistance until a potential difference of 10 volts is just sufficient to produce in the galvanometer and resistor a current of 0.0020 amp, or enough for a full-scale deflection. Hence

$$R = \frac{V}{I} = \frac{10 \text{ volts}}{0.0020 \text{ amp}} = 5\bar{0}00 \text{ ohms}$$

so that the resistance of the meter (5.0 ohms) must be increased by the addition of a series resistance R_m of 4995 ohms; as in the diagram of Fig. 4. The scale of the instrument should be labeled 0–10 volts, so that each division represents 0.1 volt. If a potential difference of 5 volts is applied to the terminals of this

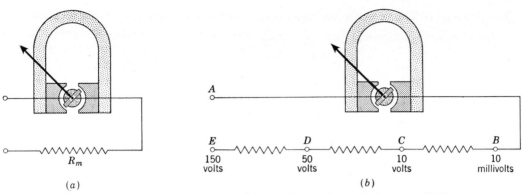

FIG. 4. Use of resistors for voltmeter multipliers. In (*a*) the voltmeter has a single range; (*b*) illustrates a multi-range instrument. Connections at *A* and *B* give a 10-mv range; *A* and *C* a 10-volt range; *A* and *D* a 50-volt range; and *A* and *E* a range of 150 volts.

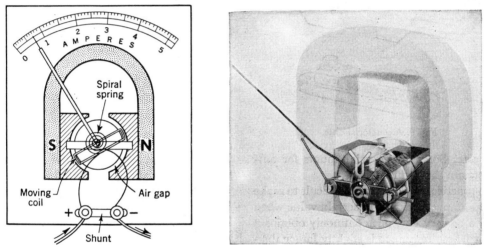

FIG. 5. The coil of an ammeter is shunted by a low resistance. The photograph shows details of the construction of a typical ammeter.

instrument, the current is

$$I = \frac{V}{R} = \frac{5 \text{ volts}}{5000 \text{ ohms}} = 0.001 \text{ amp}$$

Since 0.002 amp is the full-scale current, the deflection will be just half scale, or 50 divisions, indicating 5 volts on the 0–10 volt scale. It should be noticed that the resistance of the voltmeter is $R = R_m + R_g$, where R_m is the series resistance and R_g is that of the galvanometer.

Example: What series resistance should be used with the galvanometer just discussed in order to employ it as a voltmeter of range 0 to 200 volts?

$$R = \frac{V}{I} = \frac{200 \text{ volts}}{0.002 \text{ amp}} = 100,000 \text{ ohms}$$

total resistance, obtained by making $R_m = 99,995$ ohms. Each division on this instrument will represent 2 volts, and its scale will be labeled 0–200 volts.

32-10. Ammeters. In order to convert the galvanometer described above into an ammeter for measurements up to 5.0 amp, it is necessary to connect a low resistance, called a shunt, across its terminals, as in Fig. 5. In order to be deflected full scale, the galvanometer must carry just 0.0020 amp; hence the shunt *S* must carry the remainder of the 5.0-amp current, or 4.998 amp.

The potential difference across the meter is

$$V = IR = (0.0020 \text{ amp})(5.0 \text{ ohms})$$
$$= 0.010 \text{ volt}$$

which must be the same as that across S, thus

$$R_s = \frac{V}{I_s} = \frac{0.010 \text{ volt}}{4.998 \text{ amp}} = 0.0020 \text{ ohm}$$

This resistance is so small that a short piece of heavy strip or wire might be used for S in

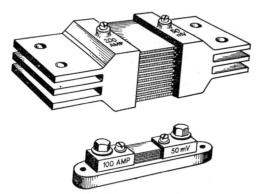

FIG. 6. Ammeter shunts.

this case. Some commercial shunts for ammeters are shown in Fig. 6.

In practice, since it is very difficult to make the resistance R_s exactly a certain value when it is to be very low, one commonly obtains a shunt whose resistance is slightly larger than is needed, inserts a comparatively large resistance r in series with the coil (Fig. 7a), and then adjusts the value of the resistance r to make the meter operate as desired.

A galvanometer may be converted into an ammeter of several different ranges through the use of a number of removable shunts, or the shunts may be self-contained by the use of a circuit such as that shown in Fig. 7b. Connection is made to the + terminal and to one of the three terminals marked high, medium, and low, respectively. The advantage of this circuit is that the shunt connections are permanently made, eliminating the error due to the variation of contact resistance when a removable shunt is used. A typical commercial d-c ammeter is illustrated in Fig. 8.

32-11. Effects of Meters in the Circuit. When an ammeter is inserted into a circuit, the current to be measured is changed by the introduction of the ammeter. It is essential that the change in current thus caused shall be a very small fraction of the current itself, that is, the resistance of the ammeter must be a small fraction of the total resistance of the circuit.

Similarly, when a voltmeter is connected between points whose potential difference is to be measured, the potential difference is changed by the presence of the voltmeter. When the voltmeter is placed in parallel with a portion of the circuit, the resistance is reduced; hence the potential difference across that part of the circuit is decreased and the total current is increased. The voltmeter introduces two errors: changing the current in the circuit and reducing the potential differ-

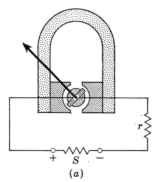

(a)

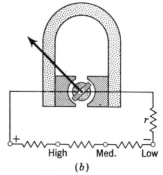

(b)

FIG. 7. Ammeter circuits.

FIG. 8. Commerical type of ammeter.

ence that is to be measured. In order that these errors shall be small, it is essential that the resistance of the voltmeter shall be very large in comparison with the resistance across which it is connected. This will ensure also that the current in the voltmeter will be small in comparison with that in the main circuit.

SUMMARY

The *galvanometer* is the basic instrument for the detection or measurement of currents and related quantities. The d'Arsonval galvanometer consists of a permanent magnet, a movable coil, and an indicating device.

Damping is the progressive dying away of a motion until the equilibrium position is reached. Electromagnetic damping is used in most electric meters.

The *current sensitivity* of a galvanometer is the current per unit deflection

$$k = \frac{I}{s}$$

The *voltage sensitivity* of a galvanometer is the voltage required per unit deflection

$$\text{Voltage sensitivity} = kR_g$$

The *megohm sensitivity* of a galvanometer is the number of megohms resistance that must be placed in series with the galvanometer in order for the galvanometer to give the standard deflection when there is a PD of one volt impressed.

A *ballistic galvanometer* gives deflections that are proportional to quantity of electricity

$$Q = k_b s$$

A galvanometer may be converted into a voltmeter by the use of a series resistance multiplier.

A galvanometer may be converted into an ammeter by the use of a low-resistance shunt in parallel with the meter.

The range of a voltmeter may be increased by the use of suitable series resistors or multipliers.

The range of an ammeter may be increased by placing low-resistance shunts in parallel with the ammeter.

QUESTIONS   1. In what respects are the actions of a galvanometer and a motor similar?

2. Describe the way in which a radial magnetic field is approximated in d-c instruments. Why is this type of field important?

3. Suppose a perfect galvanometer could be built in which the angular deflection would be directly proportional to the current. If such an instrument

were used with a lamp and straight scale, plot a rough curve to show how the scale readings would vary with the current.

4. State some ways in which a galvanometer may be made more sensitive. Describe the limitations of each of these methods, that is, why may not the instrument be made infinitely sensitive by each change?

5. Does the use of an external damping resistor change the current sensitivity of a galvanometer? the voltage sensitivity? Why is the use of such a resistor a convenience?

6. A tap key is often placed in parallel with a galvanometer and manipulated to bring the coil quickly to rest when the current is interrupted. Describe the technique used, and show why this happens. Is such a circuit underdamped, overdamped, or critically damped?

7. Explain why voltaic and thermoelectric effects are objectionable in galvanometer circuits. How may they be minimized?

8. State some of the reasons why it is a disadvantage to use a galvanometer which has too high a sensitivity for the purpose in question.

9. Give the logical reasoning to show why the deflections of a well-designed d-c voltmeter are directly proportional to the voltage at the terminals of the instrument.

10. Explain why the difference in potential indicated by a voltmeter may not be the PD between the points before the voltmeter is connected.

11. Derive a formula that gives the resistance of the multiplier necessary to increase N-fold the range of a voltmeter.

12. An ammeter and a voltmeter of suitable ranges are to be used to measure the current and voltage of an electric lamp. If a mistake were made and the meters interchanged, what would happen?

13. Some types of fuses used to protect electric meters have resistances of several ohms. Is this objectionable (*a*) in voltmeter circuits and (*b*) in ammeter circuits? Why?

14. Most ammeter binding posts are made of heavy, bare metal while voltmeter terminals are usually much lighter and well insulated. Explain why this is desirable.

15. Derive a formula that gives the resistance of the shunt necessary to increase N-fold the range of an ammeter.

16. Some electric instruments are properly called volt-ammeters. Explain why these instruments are convenient. Can such an instrument be used to measure voltage and current simultaneously? Make a conventional wiring diagram to show the essential parts of a meter that can be used either as a (*a*) galvanometer, (*b*) multirange ammeter, or (*c*) multirange voltmeter.

17. What essential differences are there between the common types of galvanometers and ammeters? between ammeters and voltmeters? Is it desirable for an ammeter to have a high resistance or a low one? Should a voltmeter have a high resistance or a low one? Why?

18. Make wiring diagrams to show two ways in which the meters could be connected in the ammeter-voltmeter method widely used for the measurement of resistance. Explain when each arrangement should be used.

PROBLEMS   **1.** A portable galvanometer has a zero-center scale and 20 divisions on each side of zero. A pointer attached to the coil deflects 15 divisions for a current of 38 μa. What is the current sensitivity of this instrument?

2. What is the current sensitivity of a galvanometer that is deflected 20.0 cm on a scale 250 cm distant by a current of 3.00×10^{-5} amp?

Ans. 0.375 $\mu a/mm$

3. The galvanometer of Prob. 2 has a resistance of 150 ohms. What is the voltage sensitivity?

4. What is the megohm sensitivity of the galvanometer of Prob. 2?

Ans. 2.67 megohms

5. A portable galvanometer is given a full-scale deflection by a current of 1.00 ma. If the resistance of the meter is 7.0 ohms, what series resistance must be used with it to measure voltages up to 50 volts?

6. A medium-sensitive galvanometer has a sensitivity of 1230 megohms and a resistance of 24.5 ohms. What is (*a*) its current sensitivity? (*b*) its voltage sensitivity? *Ans.* 8.13×10^{-4} $\mu a/mm$; 1.99×10^{-2} $\mu v/mm$

7. In an experiment to measure the sensitivity of a galvanometer a 1.50-volt cell was connected to a 2500-ohm resistor. The galvanometer was attached to taps on the resistor, with a resistance of 0.70 ohm between the taps. A deflection of 24.0 cm was noted on the galvanometer scale. The galvanometer scale was 53.6 cm from the mirror and the resistance of the galvanometer was 125 ohms. From these data calculate the current, voltage, and megohm sensitivities of this instrument.

8. A certain 3.00-volt voltmeter requires a current of 10.0 ma to produce full-scale deflection. How may it be converted into an instrument with a range of 150 volts? *Ans.* 14,$\overline{7}$00 ohms

9. Voltmeter X has a resistance of 3000 ohms, and its maximum scale reading is 30 volts. Voltmeter Y has a resistance of 5000 ohms, and its maximum scale reading is 50 volts. What is the reading of each meter if they are connected in series with each other across a potential difference of 75 volts?

10. A voltmeter of range 120 volts and resistance 96$\overline{0}$0 ohms is placed in series with another voltmeter of range 150 volts and resistance 15$\overline{0}$0 ohms. What will each meter read when they are connected to a 125-volt battery?

Ans. 108 volts; 17 volts

11. A voltmeter reads full scale when connected to terminals whose difference of potential is maintained at 5.00 volts. When a resistance of 500 ohms is placed in series with the meter, it indicates half of full-scale deflection. What is the resistance of the meter?

12. A dry cell, an adjustable calibrated resistor, and a voltmeter are connected in series. With the resistor set at zero resistance, the voltmeter reads 1.48 volts. When the resistor is adjusted to 150 ohms, the voltmeter reads 0.74 volt. What is the resistance of the voltmeter? *Ans.* 150 ohms

13. An ammeter with a range of 5.0 amp has a voltage drop across it at full-scale deflection of 50 mv. How could it be converted into a 20-amp meter?

14. It is desired to employ the galvanometer of Prob. 5 as a milliammeter of range 0 to 50 ma. What is the resistance of the shunt which should be placed across it? *Ans.* 0.14 ohm

15. If the lowest shunt resistors available in Prob. 14 are four times as large as desired, what can be done to achieve the desired result?

16. An ammeter has a resistance of 0.0090 ohm and reads up to 10 amp. What resistance shunt is needed to make full-scale deflection of the meter correspond to 100 amp? *Ans.* 0.0010 ohm

17. The total resistance of an ammeter is 0.50 ohm. Full-scale deflection is produced by a current of 2.5 amp in the instrument. (*a*) In order to use the ammeter for measuring currents up to 25 amp, what should be the resistance of the shunt used on the instrument? (*b*) In constructing this shunt an error is made and the shunt resistance is 5% too large. What effect does this have on the readings of the ammeter after the shunt is attached?

18. What part of the total current will there be in an instrument of resistance 0.60 ohm when a 0.20-ohm shunt is connected across its terminals?   *Ans.* 25%

19. An ammeter reads full scale when placed in a circuit in which a current of 10.0 amp is maintained. When á 0.050-ohm shunt is connected in parallel with the meter, its reading falls to half its original value. What is the resistance of the ammeter?

20. A certain meter gives a full-scale deflection for a potential difference of 50.0 mv across its terminals. The resistance of the instrument is 0.400 ohm. (*a*) How could it be converted into an ammeter with a range of 25 amp? (*b*) How could it be converted into a voltmeter with a range of 125 volts?

Ans. 0.00201 ohm; 999.6 ohms

21. A d'Arsonval-type electric meter has a resistance of 125 ohms. Full-scale deflection is produced by a current of 75 ma. In order to use this meter as a voltmeter for measuring up to 250 volts, what resistance should be connected in series with it?

22. A millivoltmeter with a resistance of 0.800 ohm has a range of 24 mv. How could it be converted into (*a*) an ammeter with a range of 30 amp? (*b*) a voltmeter with a range of 12 volts?   *Ans.* 800 microhms; 399 ohms

23. A moving-coil galvanometer has a resistance of 2.5 ohms, and gives full-scale deflection for a potential difference of 50 mv. If the galvanometer is converted into an ammeter with full-scale deflection at 5.0 amp, what is the current in the coil when the ammeter reads 4.0 amp?

24. A milliammeter has a resistance of 5.00 ohms, and shows a full-scale deflection when there is a current of 10.0 ma. (*a*) What resistor should be connected in series with the milliammeter in order that a full-scale deflection may correspond to 150 volts? (*b*) What is the resistance of a shunt that can be connected across the terminals of the milliammeter in order that a full-scale deflection may correspond to 10 amp?   *Ans.* 1.50×10^4 ohms; 0.00500 ohm

25. The moving coil in a portable galvanometer has a resistance of 6.0 ohms. A current of 2.0 ma produces full-scale deflection of the galvanometer. (*a*) What minimum potential difference must be applied to the coil to produce full-scale deflection? (*b*) What should be the resistance of a shunt to convert the galvanometer to a milliammeter with a full-scale deflection of 25 ma? (*c*) What should be the resistance of a resistor to convert the galvanometer into a voltmeter of 15-volt range?

26. A 50-mv meter has a resistance of 6.50 ohms. A resistance box having coils ranging from a minimum of 0.100 ohm to a total of 9999 ohms is available. What is the maximum range of a voltmeter and an ammeter that can be constructed by the use of the meter and the resistance box? (Allow for a total additional resistance of 0.002 ohm for contacts and lead wires when the resistance box is connected to the galvanometer.)   *Ans.* 0.500 amp; 77 volts

27. Two rheostats are connected in series to a 120-volt power line. One rheostat has a resistance of 90 ohms; the other has 470 ohms. (*a*) What is the voltage across the 90-ohm resistor? (*b*) What would this voltage be after a 2500-ohm voltmeter is connected in parallel with the 90-ohm rheostat? (*c*) What fact **is** illustrated by the answers to (*a*) and (*b*)?

28. An ammeter of range 1.50 amp and resistance 0.033 ohm is connected in series with an ammeter of range 1.00 amp and resistance 0.050 ohm. How much will the current change when both of these meters are inserted into a circuit of resistance 2.500 ohms? How will the reading of the meters compare?   *Ans.* 3.3%

29. In a simple series circuit a battery is connected through an ammeter to an electric lamp. A voltmeter is connected in parallel with the lamp. The ammeter indicates 0.75 amp and the voltmeter 50 volts. What is the resistance of the lamp, neglecting the fact that the voltmeter carries a small part of the current?

30. If the current in the voltmeter of Prob. 29 is 0.0010 amp for each volt indicated by it, what is the actual current in the lamp and the corrected value of its resistance?   *Ans.* 0.70 amp; 71 ohms

31. In Prob. 29 the current is increased to 1.00 amp. What will now be the reading of the voltmeter?

32. What is the resistance of the voltmeter of Probs. 29 and 30?

Ans. $10\bar{0}0$ ohms

33. An unknown resistor is to be measured by the "voltmeter-ammeter method." A 3000-ohm voltmeter is connected in parallel with the unknown resistor and a 0.250-ohm ammeter is placed in series with this combination. The ammeter reads 0.0350 amp and the voltmeter reads 8.50 volts. Calculate the value of the unknown resistance. (Do not neglect the errors introduced by the use of the meters.)

34. Some vacuum-tube voltmeters have been designed that have resistances of 1 megohm per volt of range. What current is there in such an instrument when it is giving full-scale deflection? What is the great advantage of this instrument?   *Ans.* 1 μa per volt of range

33. *Magnetic Properties; The Magnetic Circuit*

The designer of electric and magnetic machinery, such as generators, motors, transformers, and magnets, must make careful and detailed calculations of the magnetic quantities involved in these devices. The numerous electromagnetic devices consist of electric circuits linked with magnetic circuits. Hence a clear understanding of the basic principles of magnetic circuits is essential to a study of electric machinery.

Various substances differ widely in their magnetic characteristics. The metallurgist is now able to prepare many magnetic materials to specification. Scientists are continually on the hunt for new substances that can be utilized for magnetic phenomena. However, some of the basic reasons for the magnetic behavior of matter are still relatively obscure.

We have considered the magnetic fields of induction produced by currents in various typical cases. In each example the discussion was restricted to the case of the field when the medium around the current was free space (vacuum). In actual practice with electric machinery there is almost always some medium, such as iron, around the current. Experience leads to the fact that the magnetic flux in such cases is greatly different

from the flux when the medium is air. This chapter is concerned with the magnetic properties of the matter that is usually associated with magnetic circuits.

33-1. Magnetic Field Strength (Intensity). It is desirable to define a new magnetic vector H, known as magnetic field strength (also called intensity). We will define *magnetic field strength* as the ratio of the magnetic flux per unit area B_0 in empty space to the permeability μ_0 of the space

$$H = \frac{B_0}{\mu_0} \tag{1}$$

The mks unit of B_0 (given in Chap. 31) is the weber per square meter, $\mu_0 = 4\pi \times 10^{-7}$ weber/amp-m and H is in amperes per meter. When the magnetic field is produced by a current it is customary to express H in ampere-turns per meter. (See example below.)

An inspection of the equations for the flux density B near various arrangements of current-bearing conductors, as given in Chap. 31, will show that equations for H can be written for each of these cases by dividing the equation for B by μ_0, the permeability of free space. In all cases the value of H is found to be a proportionality constant times NI/l.

Example: There is a current of 6.0 amp in a closely wound solenoid of 200 turns and axial length 50 cm. What is the magnetic field strength at the center of the solenoid?

$$H = \frac{NI}{l} = \frac{200 \text{ turns} \times 6.0 \text{ amp}}{0.50 \text{ m}}$$

$$= \frac{2400 \text{ amp-turns}}{\text{m}}$$

33-2. Magnetic Permeability. In Chap. 31 the magnetic flux density in a solenoid with an air core was considered. When this air core is replaced by a bar of iron or other magnetic material the flux density is found to increase greatly (Fig. 1). The property of the magnetic material that causes this increased flux density is called its *permeability* μ. Magnetic permeability is defined by the relation

$$\text{Permeability} = \frac{\text{magnetic flux density}}{\text{magnetic field strength}}$$

$$\mu = \frac{B}{H} \tag{2}$$

The mks unit of permeability is the same as that for μ_0, the permeability of a vacuum, namely, the weber per ampere-turn-meter. From the definition of the weber the unit of μ may also be expressed in newtons per (ampere)².

33-3. Relative Permeability. It is frequently convenient to compare the permeability μ of a substance with the permeability μ_0 of empty space. This ratio is called *relative permeability* and it is defined by the equation

$$\mu_r = \frac{\mu}{\mu_0} \tag{3}$$

Since both μ and μ_0 have the same unit the relative permeability of a substance is a pure number. For air and the nonmagnetic materials, μ_r is practically equal to 1.

33-4. Types of Magnetic Substances. Materials are classified as magnetic or nonmagnetic on the basis of whether or not a force acts on the substance owing to the presence of a magnetic field. If an experiment were performed in which all available substances were brought in turn into a magnetic field, we would find, first, that all *matter is magnetic* in the sense that it experiences a force in a magnetic field, and, second, that there are two fundamentally different types of magnetic behavior.

Certain substances are repelled by magnets. A rod of such material when placed in the nonuniform field between the poles of a strong magnet will align itself at right angles to the field. Such substances are called *diamagnetic* and exhibit the property of *diamagnetism*. Bismuth, sodium chloride, lead, gold, copper, antimony, flint glass, and mercury are examples of diamagnetic substances. Dia-

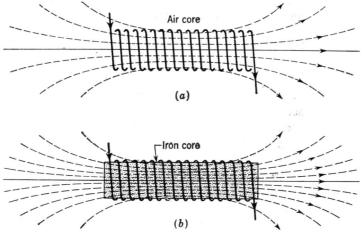

FIG. 1. Solenoid with iron core (*b*) has much greater flux than solenoid with air core (*a*).

magnetism is associated with relative permeabilities less than unity. Bismuth, a strongly diamagnetic substance, has a relative permeability $\mu_r = 0.9998$.

Just as a current in a small loop produces a magnetic field, an electron revolving in its orbit has associated with it a magnetic field. When the atom is placed in an external magnetic field, that field will change the speed of revolution of the electron in its orbit and

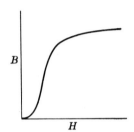

Fig. 2. Magnetization curve.

hence the magnetic qualities of the atom in a way to oppose the field (see Lenz's law, Chap. 35). If this were the only effect involved, all materials would be diamagnetic.

The second type of magnetic behavior is known as *paramagnetism*. Paramagnetic materials are attracted by magnets and have permeabilities greater than unity. A rod of paramagnetic material aligns itself parallel to the magnetic field. Aluminum ($\mu_r = 1.000022$), platinum, oxygen, copper sulfate, ferric chloride, and many metallic salts are paramagnetic.

In addition to revolving in its orbit, an electron may spin about an axis through its center. There is a magnetic quality associated with each motion. Some atoms possess permanent magnetic characteristics (dipoles) owing to unbalanced electron orbits or spins. These atoms act like tiny magnets that are oriented by an external field. Substances are paramagnetic if this effect is greater than the diamagnetic tendency common to all atoms.

A third class of elements, iron, nickel, cobalt, and certain alloys show extremely strong magnetic effects. Strongly attracted toward

magnets, they have relative permeabilities ranging to several thousand. They differ from paramagnetic materials not only in the magnitude of their permeabilities but also in that their permeabilities are variable as H changes. These *ferromagnetic substances* owe their conspicuous magnetic properties to the alignment of all the unbalanced internal electron spins in the same direction within microscopic crystal domains, causing such domains

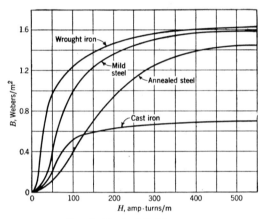

Fig. 3. Typical *B-H* curves.

to behave as tiny magnets readily aligned by an external field.

The words "magnetic substance" in practice refer to ferromagnetic materials. Since the magnetic effects of paramagnetic and diamagnetic materials are usually negligibly small, we call them "nonmagnetic."

33-5. Magnetization Curves. The effect of introducing a core of soft iron into a current-carrying solenoid is to alter greatly the magnetic characteristics of the region within the helix. That is, the flux density is greatly different in magnitude from the magnetic field strength ($B = \mu H$). The field strength H is also called the *magnetizing force*.

When a given sample of initially unmagnetized iron is subjected to a uniformly increasing magnetizing force, the resulting flux density B changes at a variable rate, as shown in Fig. 2. The magnetizing process may be considered in three stages. At first for low values of H, the flux density increases slowly. Next the flux density rises rapidly with large changes for small increments of H, and finally further increase is slow even for large increments of the magnetizing force. For small magnetizing force, few of the crystal domains are aligned by the field and B remains small. At larger values of H, the domains are rapidly lined up causing a rapid increase in B. When

that the curve does not retrace itself. In fact the value of B is found consistently to lag behind the corresponding value of H. This *lagging of the magnetization behind the magnetizing force is called hysteresis.* In Fig. 5 the curve Oa is the magnetization curve for an initially unmagnetized specimen of iron. When H is reduced to zero, the values of B follow the curve ab, so that there is a *residual magnetism* or *remanence* represented by the ordinate Ob. The

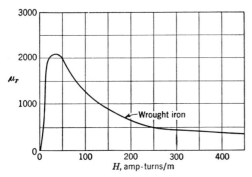

FIG. 4. Permeability as a function of field strength.

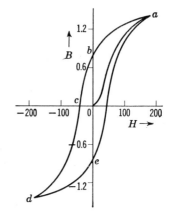

FIG. 5. Hysteresis loop.

nearly all the domains are aligned, a further increase in H produces little increase in B. At this stage the iron is described as approaching *magnetic saturation.* It is not usually profitable to magnetize the material beyond the "knee" of the saturation curve. Typical B-H or magnetization curves for various types of ferromagnetic materials are shown in Fig. 3. Such curves are of great importance for industrial work. The designer uses these curves in selecting suitable materials for specific purposes.

The curves of Fig. 3 indicate the fact that the permeability of a given ferromagnetic material is not constant in magnitude but varies greatly as the substance becomes magnetized. A typical μ-H curve is shown in Fig. 4.

33-6. Magnetic Hysteresis. Figure 2 shows the appearance of a B-H curve for an initially unmagnetized substance as the magnetizing field is increased to and beyond saturation. If the field is now reduced, it will be noted

magnetism may be reduced to zero by a magnetic field represented by the abscissa Oc. This quantity is referred to as the *coercive force.* If the field is made even more negative, the iron approaches saturation in the opposite sense, as shown by the cd portion of the curve. When the field H is again reduced to zero, the curve de indicates that there is a residual Oe in the negative sense, as compared with Ob. If the field is again increased positively, the iron again becomes saturated at a. When the field is now reduced to zero, then reversed and again increased positively the curve $abcdea$ repeats itself as this cycle is indefinitely continued. Such a cyclic curve is called a *hysteresis loop.*

It can be shown that the area within the hysteresis loop represents a measure of the energy per unit volume dissipated (as heat) in carrying the material through a cycle of magnetization.

Because of the hysteresis loss, the magnitude of the area of the hysteresis loop is a factor of great importance in the design of electric machinery, particularly for a-c use. In a-c circuits the iron is continuously being carried through complete cycles of magnetization at the rate, commonly, of 60 per second. The

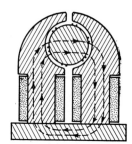

FIG. 6. A magnetic circuit.

loss of energy by hysteresis is expensive and arrangements have to be made to dissipate the heat evolved.

Soft iron is used in many parts of electric machinery because it has a relatively low hysteresis loss, together with a high permeability. For permanent magnets, a material is desired which has a high residual magnetism; here the large hysteresis loop is immaterial. In transformers certain steels are used which have large hysteresis loops, the designer being willing to accept a comparatively high iron loss in order to obtain the maximum values of flux density possible with these materials.

33-7. Magnetic Properties of Alloys. The most familiar ferromagnetic substances are iron and steel. Nickel and cobalt are also ferromagnetic, though to a much less extent than the ferrous materials. But when these elements (or a few other materials) are alloyed with iron some extraordinary ferromagnetic alloys are obtained. Many of these special metals are given trade names and are highly useful for particular types of work. For example, *permalloy* (Ni 0.79, Fe 0.21) has exceedingly high permeabilities at low field strengths and hence is of great use in certain devices such as telephone cables. Very strong permanent magnets are made of cobalt steel

(Fe 0.55, Co 0.36, Cr 0.05, Mn 0.03, C 0.01). A magnet of alnico (Al, Ni, and Co) will support a weight 1000 times the weight of the magnet.

33-8. The Magnetic Circuit. In any device every line of magnetic flux forms a closed path. Some of the flux may pass through an air portion of the circuit, other parts of the flux may go through iron or other materials. For example, in a dynamo (Fig. 6), the flux passes through the pole pieces, the air gaps near the rotor, then through the rotor, and back through the frame to the pole piece. Frequently the flux is divided, a part going through one portion of the device and other parts through the different materials of the apparatus.

The flux in a magnetic circuit can frequently be calculated under ideal conditions. For example, consider the case of a toroid (Fig. 8, Chap. 31). The use of the defining equation for Φ, with some rearrangement of terms, gives

$$\Phi = BA = \mu HA = \mu A \frac{NI}{l} \qquad (4)$$

whence $\quad \Phi = \dfrac{NI}{l/\mu A} = \dfrac{NI}{\Re} \qquad (5)$

It will be observed that this equation is somewhat analogous to Ohm's law for a metallic circuit. Hence the product NI is called the *magnetomotive force* (mmf) and the $l/\mu A$ term is called the *reluctance* of the magnetic circuit. The symbol $\Re$ is usually used for magnetic reluctance, in order that it will not be confused with R for resistance. The mks unit of mmf is the ampere-turn. The unit for $\Re$ is the ampere-turn per weber.

Example: A circular ring of iron (toroid) has a cross-sectional area of 5.00 cm², an average diameter of 30.0 cm, and is wound with a coil of 1000 turns. A current of 3.00 amp in the coil magnetizes the iron so that its relative permeability is 250. What is the flux?

$$l = \pi D = \pi \times 0.300 \text{ m} = 0.942 \text{ m}$$
$$\mu = \mu_r \mu_0 = 250 \times 4\pi \times 10^{-7}$$
$$= \pi \times 10^{-4} \text{ weber/amp-turn-m}$$

$$\Phi = \frac{NI}{l/\mu A}$$

$$= \frac{1000 \text{ turns} \times 3.00 \text{ amp}}{0.942 \text{ m}/[\pi \times 10^{-4} \text{ (weber/amp-turn-m)} \times 5.00 \times 10^{-4} \text{ m}^2]}$$

$$= 5.00 \times 10^{-4} \text{ weber}$$

33-9. Reluctances in Series and in Parallel.

In electric circuits, resistances may be connected either in series or in parallel or in series-parallel combinations. In magnetic circuits, reluctances may be connected in similar ways. Two pieces of iron joined end to end constitute two reluctances in series. If these pieces were placed so that the flux could divide between them, they would constitute a case of reluctances in parallel. For the series case the total reluctance is given by

$$\mathcal{R}_t = \mathcal{R}_1 + \mathcal{R}_2 + \mathcal{R}_3 + \cdots \qquad (6)$$

The joint reluctance of a parallel circuit is given by

$$\frac{1}{\mathcal{R}_t} = \frac{1}{\mathcal{R}_1} + \frac{1}{\mathcal{R}_2} + \frac{1}{\mathcal{R}_3} + \cdots \qquad (7)$$

Example: If an air gap 1.00 mm wide were cut across the iron ring in the preceding example, what number of ampere-turns would be necessary to maintain the same flux?

Here we have a case of two reluctances in series. Hence

$$\mathcal{R}_t = \mathcal{R}_1 + \mathcal{R}_2 = \frac{l_1}{\mu_1 A_1} + \frac{l_2}{\mu_2 A_2}$$

$$= \frac{0.941 \text{ amp-turns}}{\pi \times 10^{-4} \times 5.00 \times 10^{-4} \text{ weber}}$$

$$+ \frac{1.00 \times 10^{-3} \text{ amp-turns}}{4\pi \times 10^{-7} \times 5.00 \times 10^{-4} \text{ weber}}$$

$$= 7.75 \times 10^6 \text{ amp-turns/weber}$$

$$NI = \Phi \times \mathcal{R}_t = 5.00 \times 10^{-4} \text{ weber} \times 7.75 \times 10^6 \text{ amp-turns/weber}$$

$$= 38\overline{7}0 \text{ amp-turns}$$

As compared with the 3000 amp-turns in the preceding example, it will be noted that the addition of even a very short air gap greatly increases the mmf necessary to maintain a given flux.

33-10. Magnetic Flux Leakage.

It is very easy to prevent electrical leakage by the use of insulators. But there is no equally good magnetic insulator. Hence there is a certain amount of magnetic flux "leakage" in all magnetic circuits. Any air gap greatly increases this leakage. The derivation of Eq. (6) for a ring solenoid assumed that there was no flux leakage. This equation must, therefore, be applied only to magnetic circuits in which the flux leakage is negligible. This is one of the reasons why computations of problems in magnetic circuits are more difficult than is the case in electric circuits.

33-11. The Domain Theory of Magnetism.

Some very successful early theories of magnetism in ferromagnetic materials postulated the existence of molecular magnets that possessed many of the properties of tiny bar magnets. When a piece of iron, for example, is placed in a magnetic field, these elementary magnets align themselves more or less regularly with their like "poles" in the same direction. Ampère extended this theory by suggesting that each of the elementary magnets was a result of small closed current loops ("Ampèrian currents"). The magnetic effects of these currents were supposed to be responsible for the observed magnetism of the substance. It is now known that these tiny current loops are actually electrons spinning around their own axes, or revolving in orbits around the atomic nuclei.

More recent research has now established the theory that a ferromagnetic material contains small regions or "domains" in which the molecular magnets are quite well aligned parallel to each other. These domains are very small (say 10^{-4} cm^3) but even so they contain a large number (perhaps 10^{18}) of elementary magnets. In the unmagnetized state of a substance the polarity of the various domains has a random orientation. When a weak external magnetic field is applied, those domains that are already oriented in the direction of the field increase in volume. There may also be some rotation of the domain toward the direction of the external field. But when a strong field is applied, many entire domains move quickly into alignment with the field. These latter changes are not as reversible as the former and account for

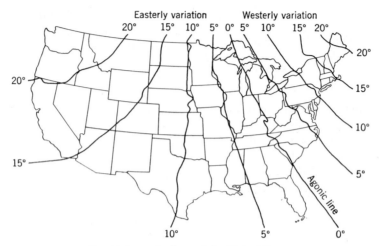

FIG. 7. Isogonic chart of the United States.

the retentivity of a substance after the external field is reduced to zero.

33-12. Terrestrial Magnetism. Many centuries ago it was observed that a compass needle aligns itself in a north-south position. About 1600, William Gilbert, physician to Queen Elizabeth, published results of his experiments which indicated that the earth acts as a great magnet and gave the first satisfactory evidence for the existence of terrestrial magnetism. The observed magnetism of the earth can be roughly portrayed as if it were due to a huge bar magnet within the earth with its axis displaced about 17° from the earth's axis and considerably shorter than the earth's diameter. The two magnetic poles of the earth are located in northern Canada and in Antarctica, both at considerable distances from the geographical poles.

On his first voyage to America, Columbus observed that a compass needle does not point directly north and that it does not everywhere point in the same direction. This variation of the compass from the true north is called *magnetic declination*. Lines drawn on a map through places that have the same declination are called *isogonic* lines. On the map in Fig. 7 is shown a series of isogonic lines. The line drawn through places that have zero declination is known as an *agonic* line. In the

United States places east of the agonic line have *west declination* and those west of this line have *east declination*. The navigator who uses a magnetic compass must continually make allowance for this *variation* of the compass.

The actual direction of the magnetic field of the earth at most places is not horizontal and only the horizontal component of the field is effective in the indications of the ordinary compass. If a magnetized needle is mounted on a horizontal axis through its center of gravity, the needle will dip from the horizontal. In the vicinity of New York City the needle would come to rest dipping at an angle of about 72° below the horizontal. Such a needle, as shown in Fig. 8, is known as a *dip needle*.

The horizontal component B_h of the earth's magnetic induction B, the vertical component B_v, and the angle of dip θ are shown diagrammatically in Fig. 9. At the earth's magnetic equator the dip is zero. At the magnetic poles it is 90°.

The strength and direction of the earth's magnetic field not only vary from place to place but also vary in time. There is a very small and periodic daily variation, an even smaller annual variation, but a very material, though erratic, secular variation, or long-time change. For example, at London, England, the declination in 1580 was 11°E, in 1655 it was zero, in 1810 it became 24°W, and in 1940 was about 8°W. Large and very erratic variations occur at certain times. These are known as magnetic "storms." They do not necessarily occur simultaneously with meteorological storms, but are probably related to variations in electric currents in the earth's atmosphere. There is correlation in time between magnetic storms and the occurrence of sunspots and it is generally agreed that the two are intimately related.

FIG. 8. Dip needle.

The facts of terrestrial magnetism are so complex and the observed data are comparatively so meager and contradictory that theories as to the origin and nature of the earth's magnetism are not at present on a firm basis.

SUMMARY

Magnetic field strength (intensity) is the ratio of the magnetic flux density in free space to the permeability of the space

$$H = \frac{B}{\mu_0}$$

The mks unit of H is the ampere-turn per meter.

Magnetic permeability μ is defined by

$$\text{Permeability} = \frac{\text{magnetic flux density}}{\text{magnetic field strength}}$$

$$\mu = \frac{B}{H}$$

Relative permeability is the ratio of the permeability of a substance to the permeability of empty space

$$\mu_r = \frac{\mu}{\mu_0}$$

Relative permeability is a pure number. Its value for air and many "nonmagnetic" substances is practically equal to 1.

Substances are classified according to their relative permeabilities as follows: diamagnetic, μ_r less than 1; paramagnetic, μ_r greater

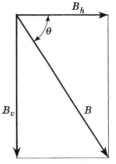

FIG. 9. Horizontal and vertical components of the earth's induction B.

than 1; and ferromagnetic, μ_r much greater than 1 and dependent upon H.

An iron core introduced into a solenoid greatly increases the magnetic flux. As the magnetizing force is increased the flux increases but not in direct proportion. The iron finally becomes *saturated*.

Hysteresis is the lagging of the magnetization of a magnetic material behind the magnetizing force. The area within a hysteresis loop is a measure of the energy per unit volume lost during a cycle of magnetization.

Certain alloys have ferromagnetic qualities much more pronounced than those of the constituent metals.

Magnetomotive force in magnetic circuits is analogous to emf in electric circuits

$$\text{mmf} = NI$$

The mks unit of mmf is the ampere-turn.

Magnetic *reluctance* is the ratio of mmf to

magnetic flux

$$\mathcal{R} = \frac{\text{mmf}}{\Phi}$$

The mks unit of $\mathcal{R}$ is the ampere-turn per weber.

The reluctance of a magnetic path is given by

$$\mathcal{R} = \sum \frac{l}{\mu A}$$

The law of the magnetic circuit is

$$\Phi = \frac{\text{mmf}}{\mathcal{R}}$$

The laws of reluctances in series and in parallel correspond closely with those for resistances in series and in parallel.

In series

$$\mathcal{R}_t = \mathcal{R}_1 + \mathcal{R}_2 + \mathcal{R}_3 + \cdots$$

In parallel

$$\frac{1}{\mathcal{R}_t} = \frac{1}{\mathcal{R}_1} + \frac{1}{\mathcal{R}_2} + \frac{1}{\mathcal{R}_3} + \cdots$$

Magnetic *flux leakage* is the failure of all of the flux to follow the prescribed magnetic circuit.

The *domain theory of magnetism* postulates small regions in ferromagnetic materials in which the molecular magnets are lined up in one direction. When an external field is applied the domains may grow or shift directions, sometimes in sudden jumps.

The earth acts as a great magnet. A magnetic compass indicates the direction of the magnetic north; this differs from the geographic north by an angle known as the *declination* (or variation). A *dip needle* shows the angle between the horizontal and the direction of the earth's magnetic field.

QUESTIONS
1. Explain why an iron core is pulled into a current-carrying solenoid.

2. A circular iron ring (toroid) may be magnetized in various ways. What would be the nature of the magnetic field external to the ring in each case?

3. Explain how one could magnetically "insulate" a body by placing it within a soft-iron shield.

4. Describe a simple demonstration by which one might illustrate roughly the molecular theory of magnetism.

5. Why are soft-iron pole pieces ("keepers") placed over the ends of horseshoe magnets during storage?

6. Describe and explain what happens when a bar magnet is repeatedly broken into smaller pieces and the pieces rolled in iron filings.

7. Describe an experiment to demonstrate the difference between diamagnetism, paramagnetism, and ferromagnetism.

8. On the basis of modern theory as to the electrical nature of atoms, suggest a possible explanation for the magnetic nature of certain materials. Why are other materials nonmagnetic?

9. Plot a curve to show the variation of H with I in a solenoid. If an iron core were inserted in the solenoid, how would the curve be altered? What would the B *vs.* I curve look like?

10. After a piece of wrought iron has been magnetized until it approaches magnetic saturation, the field strength is doubled. What happens to the induction?

11. An alternating sine-wave emf is impressed upon a coil wrapped on an iron core. Will the flux density follow a sine curve? Why?

12. An unmagnetized steel rod and an exactly similar magnetized bar are available, but no other apparatus is to be used. How could one show which of the bars is the permanent magnet?

13. Explain clearly why the nature and size of the hysteresis loop is so im-

portant to the designer of a-c machinery. Describe the loops for various types of commonly used ferromagnetic materials.

14. How might one expect the power loss due to hysteresis to vary with the following: the frequency of the a-c magnetizing current? the volume of the specimen? the maximum flux density to which the specimen is subjected?

15. One method of demagnetizing a watch is to place it in a coil carrying an alternating current and then gradually reduce the current to zero. Explain.

16. Is magnetomotive force a *force?* Does it have the same dimensions as work? Compare its dimensions with those of electric current.

17. Show that magnetic field strength is equal to the space gradient of mmf, that is, $H = \text{mmf}/l$.

18. Sketch the magnetic circuits in a four-pole dynamo.

19. Compare the similarities and dissimilarities of magnetic permeability and electric resistivity in the equations

$$\mathcal{R} = \frac{l}{\mu A} \qquad \text{and} \qquad R = \rho \frac{l}{A}$$

20. By multiplying the units of the two coordinates in the hysteresis loop shown in Fig. 5, show that the product BH does give the units of energy/volume.

21. Why are gyrocompasses and radio compasses now so commonly used in navigation, especially in the polar regions, instead of the magnetic compass?

PROBLEMS   **1.** What is the permeability of a certain steel in which a magnetic field strength of 543 amp-turns/m produces an induction of 1.13 newtons/amp-m?

2. A specimen of annealed iron has a permeability of 6.75×10^{-3} newton/amp^2 when it is in a magnetic field of strength 152 amp-turns/m. What is the magnetic induction in this iron?   *Ans.* 1.02 newtons/amp-m

3. A cylindrical iron bar 150 cm long and diameter 6.48 cm is placed with its long axis parallel to a uniform magnetic field of strength 18.2 amp-turns/m. The permeability of the iron under these circumstances is 4.75×10^{-4} newton/amp^2. What is the magnetic flux in the iron?

4. In a dynamo the magnetic lines of force pass normally from the poles into an iron armature (see Fig. 6). Assume that a certain armature is in the form of a uniform cylinder 25 cm long with a radius of 7.0 cm. The magnetic field in the air gap has a strength, constant in magnitude, of $11\bar{9}0$ amp-turns/m. How many lines of force enter the armature?   *Ans.* 8.2×10^{-5} weber

5. What is the relative permeability of a piece of annealed iron that has a permeability of 6.0×10^{-3} weber/amp-m?

6. The iron core of an electromagnet in a field of 150 amp-turns/m has a flux density of 1.07 webers/m^2. What is its relative permeability?   *Ans.* $56\bar{7}0$

7. A coil of 600 turns is wound uniformly on an iron ring whose mean diameter is 15.0 cm and whose cross section is 5.0 cm^2. The relative permeability of the iron is 500. Calculate the magnetic flux and the flux density within the ring when a current of 15 amp is maintained in the coil.

8. A toroid is 100 cm long and has a cross-sectional area of 30.0 cm^2. It is wound with a coil of 800 turns of wire and there is a current of 2.50 amp in it. The iron core has a relative permeability under the given conditions of 300. Calculate the magnetic field strength in the coil, the total flux, and the flux density.   *Ans.* $20\bar{0}0$ amp-turns/m; 2.25×10^{-3} weber; 0.753 w/m^2

9. A toroid 50.0 cm long is wrapped with 2000 turns of wire. An iron core within the toroid has an area of 100 cm² and a relative permeability of 1000. When there is a current of 3.00 amp in the coil, what is the magnetic field strength at the center of the toroid? the flux density? the flux?

10. A circular ring of iron has a cross section of 6.0 cm² and a mean radius of 8.0 cm. The ring is wound with 400 turns of wire. Find the total magnetic flux in the ring when there is a current of 10 amp in the coil and the relative permeability of the iron is 300.   *Ans.* 1.8 × 10⁻³ weber

11. There is a current of 500 ma in a solenoid 100 cm long, 10.0 cm² in cross section, and having 600 turns. Calculate the field strength at the center of the solenoid, the mmf of the solenoid, the reluctance of the region within the solenoid, and the flux.

12. A toroid has a mean diameter of 20 cm, a sectional area of 5.0 cm², and is wound with 400 turns of wire. (1) When there is a current of 5.0 amp in the toroid, compute (*a*) the ampere-turns, (*b*) the strength of the field inside the coil, (*c*) the flux density, and (*d*) the flux. (2) What would the flux be if the coil were filled with an iron core of relative permeability 200?

Ans. 2̄000 amp-turns; 3̄200 amp-turns/m; 4.0 × 10⁻³ w/m²; 2.0 × 10⁻⁶ weber; 4.0 × 10⁻⁴ weber

13. A toroidal iron ring with a mean radius of 10 cm and cross section of 10 cm² is magnetized by a coil of 100 turns in which there is a 5.0-amp current. Find the mmf and the magnetic flux in the ring if the relative permeability for the iron under these conditions is 1000.

14. A circular iron ring has a mean diameter of 20.0 cm and a sectional area of 30.0 cm². It is wound with a coil of 1000 turns. The ring contains an air gap 1.00 mm long. If the iron has a relative permeability of 200, what current should there be in the coil to produce a flux of 1.00 × 10⁻³ weber?

Ans. 1.10 amp

15. A circular iron ring has an average diameter of 40 cm and a sectional area of 120 cm². One semicircular half of the iron has a relative permeability of 200, and the other semicircular half has a relative permeability of 1000. A small transverse cut, 1.00 mm wide, is made in one portion of the ring. If the ring is wound uniformly with a coil of 2000 turns, what current would have to be maintained in the coil to produce a flux of 1.00 × 10⁻³ weber?

16. A magnetic circuit of three parts, in series, consists of a wrought-iron portion 50 cm long and 120 cm² area, relative permeability 1000; a cast-iron portion 40 cm long and 220 cm² in sectional area, relative permeability 200; and an air gap 1.5 mm long and 300 cm² in sectional area. Allowing 10% for magnetic leakage, determine how many ampere-turns are required to produce a flux of 1.6 × 10⁻² weber in the circuit.   *Ans.* 2̄600 amp-turns

17. The series magnetic circuit of a dynamo consists of a wrought-iron portion 50.1 cm long, with a sectional area of 20.0 cm², relative permeability 1000; a cast-iron portion 40.0 cm long and 200-cm² sectional area, relative permeability 200; and an air gap 5.00 mm long with a sectional area of 300 cm². Allowing 20% for magnetic leakage, determine the ampere-turns necessary to produce a flux of 1.60 × 10⁻² weber.

18. A circular iron ring of relative permeability 400 has an average diameter of 30.0 cm and a sectional area of 120 cm². A transverse cut, 1.00 mm long, is made at one place in the iron. If the ring is wound uniformly with a solenoid of 250 turns, what current must there be in order to produce a flux of 1.00 × 10⁻² weber in the core?   *Ans.* 8.9 amp

19. The core of a transformer is circular, with a central crossarm, made somewhat in the shape of the Greek letter θ. The diameter of the circular outside member is 50 cm. The circular cross-sectional area of each member is 30 cm². The relative permeability of the central arm is 400, while that of the other parts is 600. The central arm is wrapped with a coil of 1000 turns. What is the flux density in each member when there is a current of 3.0 amp in the coil?

20. A magnetic circuit is made in the form of a rectangle with a vertical bar connecting the mid-points of the horizontal pieces. The central bar is 40 cm long and 200 cm² in cross section. The outer rectangle is 100 cm wide, 40 cm high, and 100 cm² in cross section. The relative permeability of the iron is 300. A coil of 400 turns is wound on the central bar. What is the flux density in the central bar when the current in the coil is 20 amp? *Ans.* 1.7 w/m²

21. If a gap 1.5 mm wide is cut transversely in the central vertical bar of Prob. 20, what would be the flux density in the gap for a current of 20 amp?

22. An electromagnet is constructed of iron, relative permeability 500, in the form of a rectangle. The vertical members are each 30 cm long and 64 cm² in cross section. The horizontal members are each 50 cm long and 90 cm² in cross section. There is an air gap of 2.0 cm in the upper horizontal piece. On each upright there is a coil of 1500 turns. What current is required to produce a flux density of 2.5 w/m² in the gap if the effective area of the gap is 10% greater than that of the pole pieces? *Ans.* 16 amp

23. If the pole pieces of the magnet of Prob. 22 were separated to a distance of 4.0 cm, what would be the flux density in the gap? Assume that the effective area of the gap is 25% greater than that of the poles.

24. A magnet is made of iron in the shape of a toroid of mean radius 30 cm, area of cross section 80 cm², and relative permeability 400. A bar 50 cm long, of cross section 160 cm², and relative permeability 200, is connected across the circle along a diameter. What mmf produced by a coil on the cross bar is required to produce a flux density of 1.2 w/m² in the straight bar?
Ans. 4.62×10^3 amp-turns

25. If a gap 2.0 cm wide is cut in the straight bar of problem 24, what will be the flux density in the gap for a mmf of 1200 amp-turns?

26. The core of an electromagnet is toroidal with a 44-cm bar along the diameter in which there is an air gap of 4.0 cm. The iron has a relative permeability of 400 and a cross section of 120 cm². The mean diameter of the toroid is 50 cm. What mmf produced by coils on the cross bar is necessary to produce a flux density of 0.50 w/m² in the gap? *Ans.* 1.67×10^4 amp-turns

27. At a certain point the horizontal component of the earth's magnetic field has a strength of 2.8 amp-turns/m and the vertical component a strength of 4.0 amp-turns/m. (*a*) What is the angle of dip at this point? (*b*) Calculate the total strength of the earth's field at this place.

28. At a point in central Pennsylvania the earth has a field strength of 6.5 amp-turns/m and the angle of dip is 70°. What are the horizontal and vertical components of the field strength at this place?
Ans. 2.1 and 6.1 amp-turns/m

29. The earth's magnetic field in a laboratory is 6.0 amp-turns/m and the angle of dip is 60°. Find the magnetic flux passing through (*a*) the floor, (*b*) an east-west wall, and (*c*) a north-south wall, each of which has an area of 108 ft².

34. Electric Energy and Power

In order to maintain an electric current in a circuit, energy must be supplied from some source, such as a battery or generator. The rate at which this energy is expended is the power required to maintain the current. The cost of this electric energy is a major factor in the design and utilization of many devices. The concepts of electric energy and power are intimately associated with the corresponding ones considered in basic mechanics. The conversions between mechanical and electric energy furnish one of the essential topics to be considered in the study of electricity.

The flow of electricity in a wire or other conductor always produces heat. Electric soldering, electric welding, electric heating, and electric lighting provided by arcs or incandescent lamps are among the important processes that utilize the heating effect of an electric current. With suitable devices the energy of an electric current may be utilized to produce mechanical work, chemical change, or radiation.

34-1. Electric Energy. The definition of the potential difference between two points in an electric circuit is the work per unit charge expended in transporting the electricity from the one point to the other. In equation form

$$\text{Potential difference} = \frac{\text{work}}{\text{charge}} \qquad v = \frac{dw}{dq} \quad (1)$$

Equation (1) may be written in the form

$$dw = v \, dq = vi \, dt \qquad (2)$$

The lower-case letters are conventionally used to represent *instantaneous* values. When v and i are constant, the energy equation may be written in the form

$$W = VIt \qquad (3)$$

In the mks system V is in volts, I in amperes, t in seconds, and W is in joules. Equations (1) to (3) are applicable to all cases in which there are conversions of electric energy. These equations are valid for both sources and sinks, provided the V term includes all the potential differences in the arrangement being considered. If we consider the case of a resistor and write $V = IR$, the energy equation can be written in the form

$$W = I^2Rt \qquad (4)$$

Example: A 60-ohm electric lamp is left connected to a 240-volt line for 3.00 min. How much energy is taken from the line?

$$I = \frac{V}{R} = \frac{240 \text{ volts}}{60 \text{ ohms}} = 4.0 \text{ amp}$$

$$W = I^2Rt = (4.0 \text{ amp})^2 \times 60 \text{ ohms} \times 180 \text{ sec}$$
$$= 17{,}200 \text{ joules}$$

34-2. Heating Effect of Electric Current. It is a fact of everyday experience that a conductor in which there is an electric current is thereby heated. In some cases, such as the electric iron and toaster, this heating is desirable. In many other cases, particularly in electric machinery such as dynamos and transformers, the heating is most undesirable.

384

Not only does this heat represent an expensive loss of energy, but it necessitates careful design of the apparatus to get rid of the heat.

In the heating devices the wire in which the useful heat is produced is called the heating element. It is often embedded in a refractory material, which keeps it in place and retards its oxidation. If the heating element is exposed to air, it should be made of metal that does not oxidize readily. Nickel-chromium alloys (such as Nichrome) have been developed for this purpose.

34-3. Mechanical Equivalent of Heat. From the principle of the conservation of energy it follows that whenever electric energy is expended and heat is evolved, the quantity of heat produced is always strictly proportional to the energy expended. This statement is a form of the first law of thermodynamics (Chap. 22).

Energy is expressed in Eq. (4) in terms of the joule, which is basically a mechanical unit. Energy in the form of heat is often measured in terms of the calorie. Experiments are necessary to establish the relation between the joule and the calorie or between any unit of mechanical energy and heat. These experiments have demonstrated the fact that there is a direct proportion between the expenditure of mechanical energy W and the heat Q developed. This important law of nature is represented by the equation

$$W = JQ \qquad (5)$$

where J (after Joule) is the proportionality factor called the *mechanical equivalent of heat.* Relationships for the conversion of heat to mechanical energy as given in Chap. 22 include: 1 cal = 4.19 joules.

34-4. Joule's Law. By combining Eqs. (4) and (5) a useful form of the equation for heat developed in an electric circuit is obtained, namely,

$$Q = \frac{W}{J} = \frac{I^2Rt}{J} \qquad (6)$$

It should be noted that if one wishes to change calories to joules, he multiplies the number of calories by 4.19 joules/cal and if he wishes to change joules to calories, he divides the number of joules by 4.19 joules/cal.

Example: How many calories are developed in 1.0 min in an electric heater which draws 5.0 amp when connected to a 110-volt line?

From Eq. (6)

$$Q = \frac{I^2Rt}{J} = \frac{VIt}{J} = \frac{(110 \text{ volts})(5.0 \text{ amp})(60 \text{ sec})}{4.19 \text{ joules/cal}}$$
$$= 7.9 \times 10^3 \text{ cal}$$

The facts represented by Eq. (6) are sometimes referred to as Joule's law for the heating effect of the electric current. From this equation it is evident that the heat developed in an electric conductor varies directly with:

1. The square of the current (if R and t are constant)
2. The resistance of the conductor (if I and t are constant)
3. The time (if I and R are constant)

One method of measuring the mechanical equivalent of heat makes use of the electric

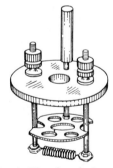

Fig. 1. Electric calorimeter.

calorimeter (Fig. 1). This consists of a double-walled calorimeter containing water, into which are inserted a thermometer and a coil of wire. An ammeter is connected in series with the coil, and a voltmeter is connected in parallel with it. By means of a variable resistor the current in the coil is kept at a constant value I for a time t. If, in addition, either the resistance R of the coil is known or the potential difference V between its ends is read on the voltmeter, the electric energy supplied can be calculated. From the rise in temperature and the mass of water and calorimeter, the heat developed can be determined. If these values are substituted in Eq. (6), the mechanical equivalent of heat can be obtained.

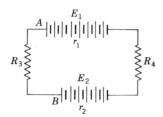

FIG. 2. Sources and sinks of electric energy.

Example: In a typical experiment performed to measure the mechanical (electrical) equivalent of heat the following data were obtained: resistance of the coil, 55 ohms; applied voltage, 110 volts; mass of water, 153 gm; mass of calorimeter, 60 gm; specific heat of calorimeter, 0.10 cal/gm C°; time of run, 1.25 min; initial temperature of water 10.0°C; final temperature, 35.0°C. Find the value of J.

$$I = \frac{V}{R} = 110 \text{ volts}/55.0 \text{ ohms} = 2.00 \text{ amp}$$

From Eq. (6)

$$J = \frac{I^2Rt}{Q} = \frac{I^2Rt}{(M_wS_w + M_cS_c)(t_f - t_i)}$$
$$= \frac{(2.00 \text{ amp})^2(55.0 \text{ ohms})(75 \text{ sec})}{(153 \text{ gm} \times 1.00 \text{ cal/gm C}° + 60 \text{ gm}}$$
$$\times 0.10 \text{ cal/gm C}°)(35.0°C - 10.0°C)$$
$$= 4.15 \text{ joules/cal}$$

34-5. Applications of the Heating Effect. The incandescent lamp is a familiar application of the heating effect of an electric current. A tungsten (wolfram) filament, protected from oxidation by being placed in an inert gas, is heated by the current to a temperature of about 3000°C, converting a small part of the electric energy into light.

Home lighting circuits and other electrical installations are commonly protected by fuses.

These are links of readily fusible metal, usually an alloy of lead and tin. When the current increases above a predetermined safe value, the fuse melts ("burns out") before more valuable equipment is damaged.

Electric furnaces play an important role in industry. In resistance furnaces, heating is produced by maintaining the current in metallic conductors or silicon carbide rods which surround the material to be heated, or in some furnaces by using the material itself to conduct the current. Temperatures up to 2500°C are so attained. In arc furnaces material is heated, perhaps to 3000°C, by concentrating on it the heat from one or more electric arcs. Both types of furnaces are used to produce steel, silicon carbide (carborundum, a valuable abrasive), and calcium carbide.

34-6. Transformations of Energy. The relations between work and energy are the same whether we are dealing with electricity, heat, or mechanics. The production and use of electric energy involve a series of transformations of energy. Radiation from the sun plays a part in providing potential energy for a hydroelectric plant or the coal for a steam-generating plant. In the latter the chemical energy of coal is converted into heat in the furnace, from heat to work by the steam engine, and from work to electric energy by the generator driven by the steam engine. The energy of the electric current may be converted into work by an electric motor, into heat by an electric range, into light by a lamp. It may be used to effect chemical change in charging a storage battery or in electroplating. The expression $W = VIt$ (as applied to d-c circuits) represents the electric energy used in any of these cases.

Consider the circuit shown in Fig. 2. Energy is supplied to the circuit by the battery A. It converts chemical energy into electric energy in an amount

$$W_1 = IE_1t$$

where E_1 is the emf of the battery A. Because of internal drop, the terminal voltage V_1 of battery A will be less than E_1, and there will be a loss of energy $I^2 r_1 t$ because of heating within the battery itself. Hence the energy W_2 delivered to the external circuit is

$$W_2 = IV_1 t = I(E_1 - Ir_1)t = IE_1 t - I^2 r_1 t$$

Battery B is inserted into the circuit in such manner as to oppose the emf of battery A. Therefore battery B takes energy out of the circuit. Any device that introduces a counter emf in a circuit, for example, a storage battery being charged or an electric motor, receives energy from the circuit.

The energy supplied to battery B in this circuit is

$$W_3 = IV_2 t = I(E_2 + Ir_2)t = IE_2 t + I^2 r_2 t$$

Note that V_2, the terminal PD of battery B, is greater than E_2, since there is a reverse current in this battery. Of the energy supplied to battery B, a portion, $I^2 r_2 t$, is expended as heat within the battery because of its internal resistance. The remainder, $IE_2 t$, is converted into chemical energy in charging the battery.

The product of the current, counter emf, and time in any device represents the energy that can be taken from the circuit by that device for purposes other than heating. Since no such machine is 100 per cent efficient, the actual conversion of energy is less than this maximum.

In this circuit the battery A transforms chemical energy into electric energy in amount $IE_1 t$. Of this energy, $IE_2 t$ is available for reconversion into chemical energy at battery B. Energy $I^2 r_1 t + I^2 r_2 t$ is converted into heat inside the batteries, and $I^2 R_3 t + I^2 R_4 t$ is converted into heat by the external resistors.

Example: In the circuit of Fig. 2, $E_1 = 27$ volts; $E_2 = 6.0$ volts; $r_1 = 0.60$ ohm; $r_2 = 0.40$ ohm; $R_3 = 2.0$ ohms; and $R_4 = 4.0$ ohms. Calculate the following: the total energy W_1 supplied to the circuit, the energy W_2 delivered to the external circuit, the energy W_3 supplied to battery B, the energy W_4 converted by B into chemical energy,

the energy W_5 which is converted into heat in the circuit; each in 3.5 min.

$$E = E_1 - E_2 = 27 \text{ volts} - 6.0 \text{ volts} = 21 \text{ volts}$$
$$R = r_1 + r_2 + R_3 + R_4$$
$$= (0.60 + 0.40 + 2.0 + 4.0) \text{ ohms} = 7.0 \text{ ohms}$$
$$I = \frac{E}{R} = \frac{21 \text{ volts}}{7.0 \text{ ohms}} = 3.0 \text{ amp}$$
$$t = 3.5 \text{ min} = 210 \text{ sec}$$
$$W_1 = IE_1 t = 3.0 \text{ amp} \times 27 \text{ volts} \times 210 \text{ sec}$$
$$= 1\bar{7},000 \text{ joules}$$
$$W_2 = IE_1 t - I^2 r_1 t = 1\bar{7},000 \text{ joules} - (3.0 \text{ amp})^2$$
$$\times 0.60 \text{ ohm} \times 210 \text{ sec} = 1\bar{6},000 \text{ joules}$$
$$W_3 = IE_2 t + I^2 r_2 t = 3.0 \text{ amp} \times 6.0 \text{ volts}$$
$$\times 210 \text{ sec} + (3.0 \text{ amp})^2 \times 0.40 \text{ ohm} \times 210 \text{ sec}$$
$$= 4\bar{6}00 \text{ joules}$$
$$W_4 = IE_2 t = 3.0 \text{ amp} \times 6.0 \text{ volts} \times 210 \text{ sec}$$
$$= 3\bar{8}00 \text{ joules}$$
$$W_5 = I^2 R t = (3.0 \text{ amp})^2 \times 7.0 \text{ ohms} \times 210 \text{ sec}$$
$$= 1\bar{3},000 \text{ joules}$$

34-7. Power and Energy. Since power P is the rate of doing work or the rate of use of energy, it may always be obtained by dividing the energy W by the time t which is taken to use or to generate the energy. Symbolically (for d-c circuits)

$$\bar{P} = \frac{W}{t} = \frac{VIt}{t} = VI \qquad (7)$$

In mks units, $\bar{P}$ is the average power in joules per second, that is, in watts, if V is given in volts and I in amperes. Thus the power in watts used by any electric device, such as a calorimeter, is found by multiplying the ammeter reading by the voltmeter reading. If the electric power is entirely used in producing heat in a resistor R, then, from Eq. (4),

$$\bar{P} = \frac{W}{t} = \frac{I^2 R t}{t} = I^2 R \qquad (8)$$

(Note that the symbol W in these equations represents *energy*, in joules. It does not stand for watt, which is a unit of power.)

Example: An electric furnace, operating at 120 volts, requires 3.0 hp. Calculate the current and the resistance.

$$P = 3.0 \text{ hp} \times 746 \frac{\text{watts}}{\text{hp}} = 2\bar{2}00 \text{ watts}$$

$$P = VI$$

$$2200 \text{ watts} = 120 \text{ volts} \times I$$

$$I = 18 \text{ amp}$$

$$R = \frac{V}{I} = \frac{120 \text{ volts}}{18 \text{ amp}} = 6.7 \text{ ohms}$$

If the power is not constant, its instantaneous value p is the derivative of the electric energy with respect to time, or $p = dw/dt$. In this case Eqs. (7) and (8) can be rewritten in the forms

$$p = \frac{dw}{dt} = vi = i^2R = \frac{v^2}{R} \qquad (8a)$$

where the lower-case letters are used to indicate *instantaneous* values.

34-8. Units and Cost of Electric Energy. A very practical aspect of the use of any electric device is the cost of its operation. It should be noted that the thing for which the consumer pays the utility company is *energy and not power.*

$$\text{Energy} = \text{power} \times \text{time}$$

A power of 1 watt used for 1 sec requires 1 joule of energy. This is a rather small unit for general use. The most common unit is the *kilowatt-hour* (kw-hr), which is the energy consumed when a kilowatt of power is used for 1 hr. One kilowatt-hour is equal to 3.6×10^6 joules.

The cost of electric energy is given by the equation

$$\text{Cost} = P \times t \times (\text{unit cost})$$
$$= \frac{VIt \times (\text{cost per kw-hr})}{1000 \text{ watts/kw}}$$

when V is expressed in volts, I in amperes, and t in hours.

Example: What is the cost of operating for 24 hr a lamp requiring 1.0 amp on a 100-volt line if the cost of electric energy is \$0.050/kw-hr?

$$\text{Cost} = \frac{(100 \text{ volts})(1.0 \text{ amp})(24 \text{ hr})(\$0.05/\text{kw-hr})}{1000 \text{ watts/kw}}$$
$$= \$0.12$$

34-9. Measurement of Power by Voltmeter-ammeter Method. A simple and widely used method for measuring power (in d-c circuits) is to measure the current in the circuit by an ammeter and the voltage with a voltmeter. The power is simply the product of these two readings. (For precise measurements certain corrections must be made owing to the effect one instrument has on the reading of the other.)

34-10. The Wattmeter. The wattmeter, as the name suggests, is an instrument for measuring power. It consists essentially of two coils at right angles, one fixed and one movable. The fixed coil is made of heavy wire of low resistance and is connected in series with the load. The movable coil is made of small wire and is connected in series with a *multiplier* of high resistance; this coil is connected in parallel with the load. By analogy with the methods of connecting ammeters and voltmeters, these two coils are called the *current* and *voltage* coils, respectively. The torque acting on the movable coil is proportional to both the current in the fixed coil and the voltage across the potential coil. Hence the resultant indication of the meter is proportional to the product of the current and the voltage, that is, to the power (for direct current). A typical wattmeter is illustrated in Fig. 3.

34-11. The Watt-hour Meter. The watt-hour meter is a device for the measurement of electric energy. This is the type of meter which is so commonly found in houses for indicating the amount of energy which has been furnished by the electrical utility company. The electrodynamometer type of meter (Fig. 4) is basically a special type of motor. It is designed so that the armature A of the motor revolves at a speed that is proportional to the power used. This is accomplished by having the field coils F and F' of the motor connected in *series* with the load, thus producing a magnetic field that is proportional to the *current* in the load. The armature is connected in parallel with the load, through a multiplying resistor R. Hence its magnetic

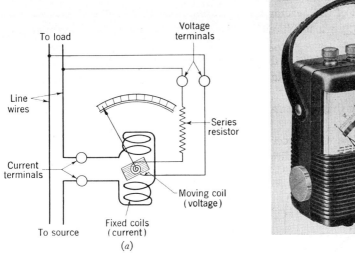

FIG. 3. (*a*) Idealized diagram of a wattmeter; (*b*) portable wattmeter.

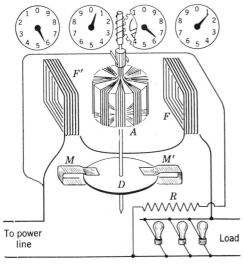

FIG. 4. A watt-hour meter.

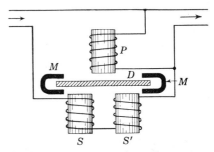

FIG. 5. Induction type of watt-hour meter.

and *M'*. The induced eddy currents thereby generated (see Chap. 35) act as a brake on the armature and provide a mechanism for adjusting the rate of the rotation when the magnets are moved toward or away from the disk in servicing the device.

34-12. The Induction Type of Watt-hour Meter. The electrodynamometer type of watt-hour meter is usually used on d-c circuits. For a-c use, the instrument is modified, in accordance with the schematic diagram of Fig. 5. This device is essentially a single-phase induction motor. The coil *P* is the voltage coil, in parallel with the load. The current coils *S* and *S'* are in series with the load. The rotor is an aluminum disk *D* that is caused to turn by the rotating magnetic field established by the combination of the currents in

field is proportional to the voltage of the load. The resultant torque, being separately proportional to each of these fields, is therefore dependent upon their product and hence to the product of current and voltage, or the power. Suitable pointers, geared to turn with the armature, indicate on their respective dials the number of watt-hours (more often kilowatt-hours) used in the load. The aluminum disk *D* connected to the armature spindle rotates in the field of the magnets *M* the voltage and current windings. The disk revolves between the poles of the permanent magnets *MM*, thus providing a mechanical load for the motor action of the rotor. The rotor shaft is geared to a set of indicating dials, as in the electrodynamometer type previously described.

It must be emphasized that *all watt-hour meters measure energy*, not power.

34-13. Thermoelectricity. Under certain conditions, heat can be transformed directly

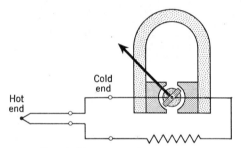

Fig. 6. Thermocouple pyrometer.

into electric energy. If a circuit is formed of two (or more) dissimilar metals the junctions of which are kept at different temperatures, an emf is generated, which produces an electric current in the circuit. The energy associated with the current is derived from the heat required to keep one junction at a higher temperature than the other. The industrial importance of such a circuit is that it provides an accurate and convenient means of measuring temperatures with electric instruments.

In an arrangement called a *thermocouple pyrometer* (Fig. 6) two wires of dissimilar metals are welded together at one end, the other ends being connected to a millivolt-meter. If the cool end (reference junction) of the thermocouple is maintained at a constant and known temperature (often that of an ice bath, 0°C), there will be an increase of emf as the temperature of the warm end of the thermocouple is increased. It is possible to calibrate this system to make it a temperature-measuring device.

Certain alloys are more suitable than the pure metals for thermocouple use, since they produce relatively large emf's and resist contamination. Practical temperature measurements can be made with such thermocouples over the range from −200 to 1600°C.

Thermocouples are often connected in series with alternate junctions exposed to the source of heat. Such an arrangement, called a *thermopile*, can be made extremely sensitive—sufficiently so to measure the heat received from a star, or, in a direction finder, to detect the heat from an airplane motor.

SUMMARY

Energy is required to maintain a current in a circuit.

Electric energy may be converted into heat, mechanical work, chemical energy, or radiant energy.

Electric energy is expressed by

$$dw = v\,dq \qquad \text{or} \qquad w = \int v\,dq = \int vi\,dt$$

For constant voltage and current

$$W = VIt$$

In the case of energy supplied to a resistor, *Joule's law* states that

$$W = I^2Rt$$

The *mechanical equivalent of heat* is defined by

$$J = \frac{W}{Q}$$

One calorie = 4.19 joules.

The heat developed by an electric current is given by

$$Q = \frac{W}{J} = \frac{I^2Rt}{J}$$

Electric energy supplied by a source of emf is EIt; that which is expended as heat is I^2Rt; and that going into useful mechanical work or chemical energy is $E'It$, where E' is the counter emf.

Electric *power* is given by

$$\bar{P} = \frac{W}{t} = VI$$

When the power is not constant

$$p = \frac{dw}{dt} = vi$$

For a resistor

$$P = I^2R = \frac{V^2}{R}$$

The power is in watts when the current is in amperes, the PD in volts, and the resistance is in ohms; 1 hp = 746 watts.

Electric energy is often measured in kilowatt-hours. One *kilowatt-hour* is the energy consumed when a power of one kilowatt is used steadily for one hour.

The cost of electric energy is given by

Cost = $P \times t \times$ (unit cost)

$$= \frac{VIt \times \text{(cost per kw-hr)}}{1000 \text{ watts/kw}}$$

Electric power may be measured by a voltmeter-ammeter method (in d-c circuits only) or by a wattmeter.

A watt-hour meter is used for the measurement of electric energy. It is a motor whose speed depends upon the power utilized, and its indications integrate power × time = energy.

A *thermocouple* transforms heat into electric energy. A *thermopile* is a group of thermocouples in series. Thermoelectric devices are extensively used to measure and control temperature.

QUESTIONS   **1.** Classify and trace the various sources of energy which are transformed into electric energy, and show that ultimately all of them came from the sun.

2. Of what is the horsepower-hour a unit? Derive the relation between the horsepower-hour and the joule.

3. Some fuse links are made with a constricted part in the center. Explain why this is a desirable type of construction.

4. Describe a way in which a frozen water line could be thawed out by electricity. Is this feasible for a long, underground pipe? Explain.

5. Modern electric lamps are filled with nitrogen under a pressure of approximately 1 atm. Why are such lamps more efficient than the former type in which all possible gas was removed?

6. Mention a number of ways in which various kinds of energy may be converted into the energy of an electric current.

7. Show that the rate of heating of a conductor with a constant voltage impressed on it varies directly with the cross section of the conductor.

8. Two current-carrying wires A and B have the same length and are made of the same material, but the diameter of A is twice that of B. How many times greater is the heating effect in A compared to the heating in B when (*a*) the wires are connected in parallel and (*b*) the wires are connected in series?

9. An electric circuit includes the following: a rheostat, a storage battery being charged, a generator, an electroplating cell, and a switch. Explain which device is (*a*) a source, (*b*) a sink, and (*c*) neither a source nor a sink of energy.

10. Arrange the following energy units in order of increasing magnitude: kilowatt-hour, foot-pound, erg, and joule.

11. Which process has the greater efficiency: the conversion of chemical energy of coal into electric energy in a power plant, or the conversion of electric energy into radiant energy in the coils of a d-c electric stove?

12. In a lightning flash is there a large voltage? current? power? energy? Explain.

13. Arrange the following household devices in the order of increasing power consumption: (*a*) electric fan, medium size, (*b*) electric lamp, medium size, (*c*) electric iron, (*d*) refrigerator, (*e*) radiant heater, and (*f*) electric oven. (Indicate typical values for each device.)

14. What is it that is dangerous to the human body: current, voltage, or some combination of these and other factors?

15. Show why the watt per second, kilowatt per hour, and similar units do not represent quantities that are ordinarily used.

16. Can two identical 110-volt 60-watt lamps be satisfactorily used on a 220-volt circuit? Could two 220-volt lamps be used on a 110-volt circuit? Could a 60-watt 110-volt lamp and a 100-watt 110-volt lamp be satisfactorily used together on a 220-volt circuit? Explain.

17. A 115-volt 25-watt lamp and a 115-volt 150-watt lamp are connected in parallel to a 115-volt source of power. What is the effect on the brightness of each lamp if the connections are changed so that the lamps are now connected in series? Assume that the resistances of the lamps remain constant.

18. Show that a cell of emf E and internal resistance r connected to an external resistor R delivers a maximum power to R when $R = r$.

19. Justify the fact that the cell in Question 18 furnishes a maximum power in R equal to $E^2/4R$.

20. In the voltmeter-ammeter method for the measurement of power the voltmeter may be connected either in parallel with the device studied or in parallel with the device plus the ammeter. Draw the wiring diagram for these two arrangements. Discuss the relative errors introduced by the current in the voltmeter in the first case and the PD across the ammeter in the second case.

21. If the terminals were not marked, could one tell by inspection which binding posts on a wattmeter are intended for the voltage and which are designed for the current terminals? Show why these binding posts should have different physical characteristics.

22. A wattmeter is connected to the following arrangements of lamps inserted in a 120-volt power circuit: (*a*) one 60-watt lamp, (*b*) two of these lamps in parallel, (*c*) two of these lamps in series, and (*d*) a pair of lamps in parallel joined in series to another pair in parallel. What will the reading of the wattmeter be in each case?

23. Describe some ways by which dishonest persons attempt to influence the readings of their household watt-hour meters. One of the methods used by the utility meter man for adjusting the speed of a watt-hour meter is to move the magnets closer together or farther apart. Explain how this influences the readings of the meter.

24. State some of the relative advantages and disadvantages of thermoelectric pyrometers as compared with the usual mercury thermometer.

PROBLEMS   **1.** A current of 2.00 amp is maintained in a resistor. Each minute 3600 joules of energy are required to move the charge through the resistor. What is the PD across the resistor?

2. A storage battery of emf 6.50 volts and internal resistance 0.36 ohm is charged for 12 hr with a current of 15.0 amp. (*a*) How much energy is supplied to the battery? (*b*) What energy is lost because of the heat developed in the battery?   *Ans.* 7.68×10^6 joules; 3.48×10^6 joules

3. A current of 0.70 amp is maintained in an electroplating cell. If the potential difference across the terminals of the cell is 5.0 volts, how many joules of energy are furnished to it by the electric current during 20 min?

4. If increasing the difference of potential across the cell of Prob. 3 to 10 volts causes the current to rise to 1.25 amp, what is the resistance of the cell under these conditions? (HINT: Do not neglect the voltaic emf of the cell.)

Ans. 9.1 ohms

5. How much energy is used each minute by a d-c motor in which there is a current of 12 amp at 110 volts?

6. How much heat would be generated in 10 min by a uniform current of 12 amp in a rheostat of resistance 20 ohms?   *Ans.* 4.18 × 10⁵ cal

7. A current of 4.0 amp is maintained for 3.0 min in a wire of resistance 5.0 ohms, submerged in 600 gm of water in a calorimeter equivalent to 6.0 gm of water. Compute the rise in temperature of the water.

8. A coil of wire having 5.0 ohms resistance is lowered into a liter of water at 10°C and connected to a 110-volt circuit. How long will it take for the water to come to the boiling point? Neglect the heat required to change the temperature of the wire and the vessel.   *Ans.* 155 sec

9. Some large electromagnets used with cyclotrons have coils made of copper tubing with water forced through the tubing to dissipate the heat generated by the heavy currents in the coils. One such coil has a resistance of 0.65 ohm and carries a current of 350 amp. A stream of water at the rate of 1.25 ft³/min flows through the tubes. Calculate the rise in temperature of the water.

10. When a vessel containing 1500 gm of hot water is allowed to cool, its temperature when it passes 90°C is falling at the rate of 12.0° per min. A wire of 6.00 ohms resistance is submerged in the water. What must the current in the wire be to keep the temperature of the water at 90°C?   *Ans.* 14.4 amp

11. In a student experiment performed to measure the mechanical equivalent of heat by the electric calorimeter method, the following data were observed: resistance of coil, 55 ohms; line voltage, 110 volts; mass of water, 156 gm; mass of calorimeter, 60 gm; specific heat of calorimeter, 0.10 cal/gm C°; time of run, 1.25 min; initial temperature of water, 10.0°C; final temperature of water, 35.0°C. Determine the percentage difference between the student's observed value of J and the standard value.

12. A storage battery of emf 35 volts and internal resistance 0.045 ohm is connected to a generator that develops an emf of 115 volts and has an internal resistance of 0.125 ohm. The wires between the generator and battery have a resistance of 0.33 ohm. A rheostat is inserted in the line to reduce the current to 20 amp. What heat is developed in the line wires in 30 minutes?

Ans. 5̄7,000 cal

13. A 40-volt storage battery of 4.0 ohms internal resistance is to be charged from a 110-volt d-c line. (*a*) What is the resistance of the rheostat which must be placed in series with the battery if the charging rate is to be 5.0 amp? (*b*) What is the total energy supplied to the battery in 6.0 hr? (*c*) What is the heat loss in the battery in this time?

14. If the coils of a resistance box are (each) capable of dissipating energy at a rate of 4.0 watts, what is the highest voltage one could safely apply across a 2.0-ohm coil? a 200-ohm coil? What is the current in each case?

Ans. 2.8 volts; 28 volts; 1.4 amp; 0.14 amp

15. The following resistors are connected in parallel to a power line, kept at a constant PD: resistor *A*, 10 ohms; resistor *B*, 40 ohms; resistor *C*, 10 ohms and resistor *D*, 20 ohms, *connected in series*. Show the relative amounts of power used in the resistors: P_A/P_B; P_C/P_D; P_A/P_C; P_D/P_B.

16. A 220-volt motor is supplied by a 10.0-ohm line. The motor is operating at 85 per cent efficiency and is developing 2.00 hp at the pulley. Find the power lost in the line.   *Ans.* 637 watts

17. What is the efficiency of an electric motor that delivers 3.0 hp (useful) when taking a current of 65 amp from a 115-volt line?

18. A certain motor has the name plate stamped "3.00 amp, 110 volts." At what speed could it raise vertically a 50.0-kg man if the entire system had an efficiency of $33\frac{1}{3}\%$?   *Ans.* 22.4 cm/sec

19. A Prony brake is used to measure the mechanical output from a small motor. It is found that the brake exerts a force of 5.3 lb on the brake arm, which is 6.0 in. long. The motor takes a current of 6.2 amp from the 120-volt line when it is running at 1600 rpm. What is the efficiency of the motor?

20. Find the cost at 1.00 cent per kilowatt-hour of running an electric furnace for 10.0 hr if it takes 10,000 amp at 100 volts.   *Ans.* $100

21. A bank of 48 incandescent lamps (in parallel), each having a (hot) resistance of 220 ohms, is connected to a 110-volt circuit. Find (*a*) the power and (*b*) the cost of operating the lamps for 24 hr at 5.0 cents per kilowatt-hour.

22. When electric energy costs 6.0 cents per kilowatt-hour, how much will it cost to heat 4.5 kg of water from 20°C to the boiling point, if no energy is wasted?
                                                                          Ans. 2.5 cents

23. An electric heating coil uses 2200 watts when connected to a 110-volt line. Find (*a*) its resistance and (*b*) the cost of operating it for 5.0 hr at 3.0 cents per kilowatt-hour.

24. A generator with a brush potential (terminal PD) of 117.5 volts delivers current to two rheostats of resistances 55.0 ohms and 220 ohms, connected in parallel, through a line having a resistance of 3.00 ohms. Calculate (*a*) the horsepower used in the 55.0-ohm resistor, (*b*) the cost of operating the 220-ohm resistor for 30.0 min at 10.0 cents per kilowatt-hour, and (*c*) the heat generated in the 3.00-ohm resistor in 10.0 min. (Assume all the apparatus to be in use at all times.)   *Ans.* 0.295 hp; 0.275 cents; 2690 calories

25. Four 110-volt, 55-watt electric lights are joined in parallel. This arrangement is connected in series with a toaster that has a resistance of 55 ohms. The whole is connected to a 220-volt generator. What current is in the group of lights? What will it cost to operate the toaster (only) under these conditions for 5.0 hours at 10 cents per kilowatt-hour?

26. A motor operates at 100 volts and is supplied with 2.00 hp from a generator 23.8 ft away. The diameter of the two wires connecting the motor and generator is 0.0500 in. and the resistivity is 10.5 ohm-circular mils/ft. (*a*) What is the cost of the energy used in the line resistance during an 8-hr day at the rate of 5.0 cents per kilowatt-hour? (*b*) What heat would be developed in the line wire in this time?   *Ans.* 1.8 cents; 3.1×10^5 cal

27. It is desired to determine accurately the power taken by a coil R of approximate resistance 20 ohms by connecting it in a circuit with an ammeter and voltmeter. The voltmeter has a range of 150 volts and a resistance of 15,000 ohms. The ammeter has a range of 1.5 amp and resistance of 0.033 ohm. Should the meters be connected so that (*a*) the voltmeter measures the PD across both R and the ammeter, or (*b*) so that the ammeter measures the total current in R and the voltmeter? What per cent error is introduced in each case by the effect of one instrument on the readings of the other?

28. In a test on an electric hot plate, the temperature of a 1200-gm copper calorimeter (specific heat, 0.093 cal/gm C°) containing 3.00 kg of water rose from 30.0 to 43.6°C in 4.00 min. The wattmeter connected to the hot plate read 875 watts. Find the efficiency of the hot plate.   *Ans.* 84.3%

29. A two-wire power line 10 mi long delivers 100 kw at 3300 volts to a factory. If the resistance of each wire is 2.0 ohms/mi, what is the voltage supplied to the line at the power plant?

30. A certain electric oven has a resistance of 10 ohms and is supplied with a current of 10 amp. What power is used by the oven? At what rate is heat developed? What is the cost of operating the oven for 12 hr if energy costs 3.0 cents per kilowatt-hour?   *Ans.* 1.0 kw; 2$\overline{4}$0 cal/sec; 36 cents

31. A new Nichrome wire heating element is to be put into a 660-watt, 110-volt electric heater. What length of wire is necessary if the resistance of the wire when hot is 0.40 ohm per foot?

32. A coil of resistance wire 500 cm long is connected to a 110-volt power main and is observed to raise the temperature of a liter of water 5.0 C° in 75 sec. What is the resistance of the wire? If the wire had the same cross section but was twice as long, what would have been the rise in temperature in the same time?
                                Ans. 43 ohms; 2.5 C°

33. A 75-watt lamp designed for use on 25 volts is to be used on a 120-volt source. (*a*) What is the resistance of the lamp under its normal operating conditions? (*b*) How much resistance must be connected in series with the lamp in order that it may operate normally when connected to the 120-volt source?

34. Connected in parallel to the same 110-volt line are five 60-watt lamps and an 880-watt heater. Find (*a*) the total current, (*b*) the energy used in 10 hours, and (*c*) the cost of operating the group for 10 hr if energy costs 3.0 cents per kilowatt-hour.   *Ans.* 10.8 amp; 11.8 kw-hr; 35 cents

35. If a 32-volt, 50-watt tungsten filament lamp is operated from a 110-volt source, what resistance must be connected in series with the lamp in order that it may operate at normal brightness?

36. The heating element of an electric heater consists of 200 cm of Nichrome wire 0.50 mm in diameter. The resistivity of Nichrome is 100 microhm-cm. Find the resistance of the element, the energy in calories developed in the coil in 5.0 min when connected to a 110-volt circuit, and the cost of operating the element for 20 hr if energy costs 5.0 cents per kilowatt-hour.
                                Ans. 10.2 ohms; 8.5 $\times$ 10^4 cal; $1.19

37. Two wires having resistances of 3.0 and 12.0 ohms are placed in parallel across the terminals of a 6.0-volt storage battery. What is the ratio of the heat generated in the low-resistance wire to that in the high-resistance one?

38. An electric iron which has a resistance of 10.0 ohms when in use is connected in parallel with lamps having a resistance of 15.0 ohms. If both are connected to a constant potential difference of 120 volts, what is the minimum rating of fuse that could be used at the source of power without breaking the circuit?
                                Ans. 20 amp

39. The resistance of a power transmission line is 15 ohms. The power consumed at the end of the transmission system is 1200 kw. What is the ratio of the power lost in transmission when the load *PD* is 3300 volts to the power lost when the load *PD* is 550 volts?

40. A 15.0-hp d-c motor requiring 21.0 amp is to run a water pump located 1000 ft from a generating station where power is available at 550 volts. The generator and motor are connected by copper wire of resistivity 10.4 ohm-circular mils/ft. What size wire is needed?   *Ans.* 160 mils diameter

41. A coil of 7.00 ohms resistance is permanently connected across the terminals of a battery whose emf is 8.70 volts and internal resistance is 0.30 ohm. An unknown resistor is then connected in parallel with the 7.00-ohm coil and the potential difference at the battery terminals becomes 7.90 volts. What power is being developed in the unknown resistor?

42. What current is taken by an electric hoist operating at 250 volts if it is raising a 2500-lb load at a uniform speed of 200 ft/min and its over-all efficiency is 25%? What would it cost to operate this device for 3.00 min at 5.0 cents per kilowatt-hour? *Ans.* 181 amp; 11 cents

43. A battery of emf 16.7 volts and internal resistance 6.75 ohms is connected to a rheostat of resistance R. For what value of R is there a maximum power in the rheostat? What is the amount of this power?

44. A subway train uses an energy of 12 kw-hr for each mile when traveling at a uniform speed of 30 mi/hr on level track. Calculate the force opposing its motion. *Ans.* 6000 lb

35. *Induced Emf's*

The electric energy available from thermo-couples or chemical sources is relatively coslty and small in amount. Present-day large-scale production and distribution of electric energy were made economically feasible by the discoveries of Michael Faraday and

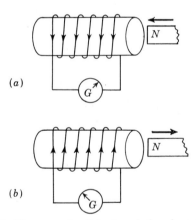

(a)

(b)

FIG. 1. Magnet and coil to show induced currents.

Joseph Henry who, independently and at about the same time (1831), discovered the principles of induced emf's on which is based the design of generators, transformers, and motors.

35-1. Induced EMF's and Currents. Figure 1 represents a coil of wire connected to a sensitive galvanometer *G*. If the *N* pole of a bar magnet is thrust into the coil, the galvanometer will deflect, indicating a momentary current in the coil in the direction specified

by arrows (*a*). This current is called an *induced current,* and the process of generating the emf is known as *electromagnetic induction.* As long as the bar magnet remains at rest within the coil, no current is induced. If, however, the magnet is suddenly removed from the coil,

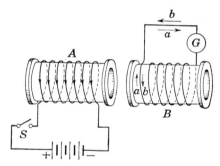

FIG. 2. Current induced by the interaction of two circuits.

the galvanometer will indicate a current in the direction (arrows, *b*) opposite to that at first observed. Faraday found that *an emf is induced in a conductor when there is any change of magnetic flux linked by the conductor.*

A voltage may also be induced in a coil by the change in the magnetic field associated with a change in current in a nearby circuit. For example, in Fig. 2 is shown a coil *A* connected to a battery through switch *S*. A second coil *B* connected to a galvanometer is nearby. When the key *S* is closed, producing a current in the coil *A* in the direction shown, a

397

momentary current is induced in coil B in a direction (arrow a) opposite to that in A. If S is now opened a momentary current will appear in B, having the direction of arrow b. In each case there is a current in B only while the current in A is *changing*. A steady current in A accompanied by a motion of A relative to B is also found to induce a current in B.

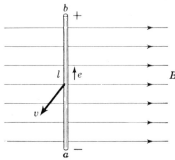

FIG. 3. Flux density B, motion v, and induced emf e when a conductor moves in a uniform field.

We observe that in all cases in which a current is induced in B, the magnetic flux through B is also changing.

35-2. Faraday's Law of Induced EMF. The value of the emf induced in a circuit is found to depend only upon the number of turns in the circuit and the time rate of change of the magnetic flux Φ linked with the circuit. The average emf $\bar{E}$ is given by

$$\bar{E} = -N\frac{\Delta\Phi}{\Delta t} \qquad (1)$$

The instantaneous value of the emf is given by

$$e = -N\frac{d\Phi}{dt} \qquad (2)$$

where N is the number of turns. When $d\Phi/dt$ is expressed in webers per second, the emf e is given in volts. If $d\Phi/dt$ is expressed in maxwells per second, Eqs. (1) and (2) must have a factor 10^{-8} on the right-hand side to give the emf in volts.

The negative sign is often introduced in Eqs. (1) and (2) to express the fact that the induced emf is in such a direction as to oppose

(by its magnetic field) the change which produced it, as explained below.

Example: A coil of 600 turns is threaded by a flux of 8.0×10^{-5} weber. If the flux is reduced to 3.0×10^{-5} weber in 0.015 sec, what is the average induced emf?

From Eq. (1)

$$\bar{E} = -N\frac{\Delta\Phi}{\Delta t} = -600\,\frac{(8.0 - 3.0)10^{-5}\ \text{weber}}{0.015\ \text{sec}}$$
$$= -2.0\ \text{volts}$$

35-3. EMF Induced by Motion. Whenever a charge q moves in a magnetic field it experiences a force F [Eq. (13), Chap. 31] given by

$$F = qvB \sin\theta \qquad (3)$$

A moving charge constitutes a current. The force on a charge in motion is that on the equivalent conventional current (Chap. 31). The vectors representing v, B, and F are mutually perpendicular. If the charge is free to respond to this force, it will move in the direction of F.

An electric conductor, such as a copper wire, has free electrons in it. Consider a wire moving across a magnetic field (Fig. 3). *Positive* charges in the wire would experience a force directed toward b; *electrons* experience a force in the opposite direction and the free electrons accumulate at a leaving a deficiency of electrons at b. Equation (3) gives $F/q = vB \sin\theta$. This is the same as if an electric field had been set up in the conductor directed from a toward b, with a magnitude $\mathcal{E} = F/q = vB \sin\theta$. Hence the emf $e(= w/q)$ in the wire of length l is

$$e = lvB \sin\theta \qquad (4)$$

When B is expressed in webers per square meter, l in meters, and v in meters per second, the emf is in joules per coulomb, or volts.

This emf exists whether or not there is a complete circuit for current. If the moving conductor slides along stationary conducting rails (Fig. 4), a current will be established in the sense shown.

Example: The flux density B in a region between the pole faces of an electromagnet is 0.76 weber/m², horizontally toward the right. Find the emf induced in a straight conductor 10 cm

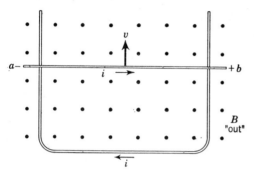

Fig. 4. Current resulting from the emf induced in conductor ab moving across a uniform flux density B (out of page).

long, perpendicular to B ($\theta = 90°$), when it moves downward at an angle α of 60° with respect to B with a speed of 1.0 m/sec.

$$\text{Induced emf } e = lvB \sin \theta \sin \alpha$$
$$e = (0.75 \text{ weber/m}^2)(0.10 \text{ m})(1.0 \text{ m/sec}) \sin 90°$$
$$\times \sin 60°$$
$$e = 0.066 \text{ volt} = 66 \text{ mv}$$

35-4. Lenz's Law. *Lenz's law* states that whenever an emf is induced, the induced current is in such a direction as to oppose (by its magnetic action) the change inducing the current.

Lenz's law is a particular example of the conservation of energy principle. An induced current can produce heat or do chemical or mechanical work. The energy must come from the work done in inducing the current. When induction is due to the motion of a magnet or a coil, work is done; therefore the motion must be resisted by a force. This opposing force comes from the action of the magnetic field of the induced current. When a change in current in a primary coil induces an emf in a neighboring secondary coil, the current in the secondary will be in such a direction as to require the expenditure of addi-

tional energy in the primary to maintain the current.

Example: A horizontal circular coil of wire is lowered toward a bar magnet held vertically with its N pole uppermost (Fig. 5). What is the direction of emf induced in the coil?

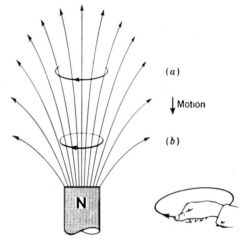

Fig. 5. Emf induced in a coil moving from a to b in a nonuniform flux density.

As the coil is lowered from position a to position b, the upward flux through it increases. By Lenz's law, the flux due to the induced emf must be downward. The right-hand rule predicts that the induced current will be clockwise, as viewed from above.

Whenever a straight wire, such as ab in Fig. 4, is drawn across a magnetic field, an emf is induced in the conductor. There will be an induced current in the wire if it is made a part of a closed circuit as indicated in the figure. In accordance with Lenz's law, the direction of the induced emf is such as to oppose the motion of the conductor.

Therefore the direction of the induced current is such as to add to the field ahead of the current and weaken the field behind the current, since from Ampère's law (Chap. 31) the force on the current is directed from the strong part of the field to the weaker portion of the field. Hence the direction of the induced current depends upon the direction of the field and that of the motion. These three directions are mutually at right angles to each other.

Example: A horizontal straight wire 10 m long extending east and west is falling with a speed of 5.0 m/sec, at right angles to the horizontal component of the earth's magnetic field, 0.30×10^{-4} weber/m². (a) What is the instantaneous value of the emf induced in the wire? (b) What is the direction of the emf? (c) Which end of the wire is at the higher electrical potential?

(a) From $e = lvB \sin \theta$
$$e = (10 \text{ m})(5.0 \text{ m/sec})(0.30 \times 10^{-4} \text{ weber/m}^2)$$
$$= 0.0015 \text{ volt}$$

(b) From Lenz's law, the magnetic force on the wire must be upward. But the force on a conductor is from the region of strong magnetic field toward weak. To produce a strong field under the wire, the field due to the induced current should be in the same direction as the earth's field, north. The right-hand rule predicts an emf (or current) from W to E to produce such a magnetic field.

(c) Under the action of an emf directed from W to E, positive charge will migrate toward E; E will be at the higher potential. (If an external circuit were connected to this generator, the positive current in the external circuit would be from E to W, or from high potential to low.)

SUMMARY

Most commercial sources of electric energy involve the generation of an emf by *electromagnetic induction*.

An emf is induced whenever there is a change of magnetic flux linking an electric circuit, or motion of a conductor through a magnetic field

$$e = -N \frac{d\Phi}{dt}$$

The emf induced in a straight wire moving through a uniform magnetic field of induction B with a velocity v at an angle θ with the field is given by
$$e = lvB \sin \theta$$

Lenz's law states that the induced emf is always in such a direction as to oppose the change which gives rise to it. The direction of a current induced in a moving conductor is such as to build up the magnetic field ahead of the conductor and weaken the field behind the conductor.

QUESTIONS   **1.** Two identical hoops, one of copper, the other of aluminum, are similarly rotated in a magnetic field. Explain reasons for the different torques required.

2. A bar magnet falls with uniform speed through a coil of wire with its plane horizontal. The long axis of the magnet is normal to the plane of the coil. As the N pole of the magnet approaches the coil, in what sense is the emf induced? What is the direction of the force which acts upon the wire? Describe the way in which the induced emf in the coil varies with time, as the magnet drops through the coil.

3. The coils wound on the spools of resistance boxes are often made of bifilar wires, that is, a wire doubled back upon itself. Make a sketch of such a resistance spool. Explain why this arrangement gives coils which are practically noninductive.

4. Derive the general equation for induced emf, beginning with Ampère's law for the force on a current-carrying conductor in a magnetic field.

5. In an experiment on electromagnetic induction, the flux in a coil is changed by a constant amount in various measured times. Plot a curve to show the variation of the induced emf as a function of time.

6. Explain clearly why Lenz's law must follow from the principle of conservation of energy.

7. Sometimes students believe that Ohm's law does not apply to an inductive circuit. Show that the law is applicable when it is properly interpreted.

8. Explain what happens to the electrons in a straight wire when the wire is moved through a magnetic field. Give an example to show the direction of the induced emf and the induced current. Indicate the end of the conductor which has the highest potential.

PROBLEMS   **1.** The N pole of a magnet is brought down toward a flat coil of 20 turns lying on a table. (a) If the flux through the coil changes from 10×10^{-5} to 50×10^{-5} weber in 0.30 sec, what is the average magnitude of the induced emf? (b) Is it clockwise or counterclockwise as you look down on the coil?

2. A wire "cuts" a flux of 0.030 weber in 0.020 sec. What average emf is induced in the wire?   *Ans.* 1.5 volts

3. A coil of wire of 10 turns, each enclosing an area of 900 cm², is in a plane perpendicular to a magnetic field of flux density 5.0×10^{-5} w/m². The coil is turned to a position parallel to the field in 0.50 sec. Find the average emf induced.

4. In one of the coils of a generator armature 100 wires pass across a pole near which there is a magnetic flux density of 1.5 w/m². The pole face has an area of 1000 cm². If the armature moves across the pole in $\frac{1}{20}$ min, what is the average emf induced in the coil by the "cutting" of this flux?   *Ans.* 30 volts

5. A flat rectangular coil 10.0 cm by 5.0 cm of 500 turns of wire rotates at 60 rev/sec in a uniform field of 4.0×10^{-5} w/m² (Fig. 6). Find (a) the induced

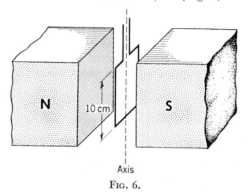

Axis

Fig. 6.

emf at any instant t, (b) the maximum emf, and (c) the average emf during a quarter cycle.

6. A copper disk of radius 10.0 cm rotates 5.0 rev/sec with its axis parallel to a magnetic field of 0.50 w/m². The rotation is clockwise, as viewed in the direction of the field. (a) Determine the difference in potential developed between the center and the edge of the disk. (b) Which is at the higher potential?

Ans. 0.079 volt; edge

7. A magnetic field of uniform flux density B is established in a horizontal direction above a certain horizontal line ab. Below the line, $B = 0$. If a square wire frame (Fig. 7) of side L, mass m, and resistance R is placed part inside and

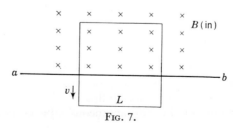

Fig. 7.

part outside the field with the sides perpendicular to the field, at what velocity of fall will there be no acceleration?

8. A Ferris wheel is 100 ft in diameter. Its axis of rotation is on a north-south line. (*a*) If the horizontal component of the earth's flux density is 2.0×10^{-5} w/m² and the wheel is rotating at 2.0 rev/min, what is the potential difference existing between the axle and the end of one spoke? (*b*) Which is at the higher potential? *Ans.* 490 μv

9. A wire 200 cm long moves at right angles to a magnetic field of flux density 1.0 w/m² with a velocity of 30 cm/sec. The wire is connected to a circuit whose resistance is 12.0 ohms. (*a*) What is the induced emf? (*b*) What is the force on the wire? (*c*) At what rate is mechanical work being done?

10. A flat, circular coil has 150 turns, a radius of 12.0 cm and a resistance of 0.85 ohm. The coil is placed with its plane normal to the earth's magnetic field, where *B* is 7.5×10^{-5} w/m². When the coil is rotated through 90° in ⅛ sec, what charge circulates in the coil? *Ans.* 6.0×10^{-4} coulomb

11. In an experiment to determine the flux density of the region between the pole pieces of a magnet, a 30-turn coil of 50 ohms resistance and area 2.0 cm² is placed with its plane perpendicular to the field; it is then withdrawn quickly from the field. The charge flowing in the operation is found to be 5.0×10^{-4} coulomb. Determine the flux density.

12. A toroid (ring) of circumference 10 m and cross section 0.0010 m² is magnetized by a coil of 1000 turns carrying a current of 1.0 amp. The ring is broken and its ends separated by a distance of 1.0 mm. A second coil with 100 turns is wound around the gap as shown in Fig. 8 and connected in a ballistic

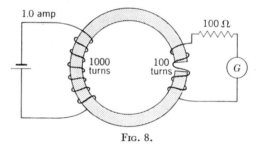

1.0 amp

100 Ω

1000 turns

100 turns

G

FIG. 8.

galvanometer circuit of total resistance 100 ohms. If the permeability of the ring is assumed to remain constant and equal to 7.43×10^{-3} weber/(amp-turn-m) how much charge passes through the galvanometer when the ring is suddenly pushed together, closing the gap? Neglect the emf induced in the galvanometer coil as well as any fringing of the magnetic field. *Ans.* 2.76×10^{-4} coulomb

13. A train is traveling north with a speed of 20 m/sec. The distance between the rails is 2.0 m and the vertical component of the earth's flux density is 4.0×10^{-5} w/m². (*a*) Find the potential difference between the rails. (*b*) If the leakage resistance between the rails is 100 ohms, what is the retarding force on the train?

14. An east-west wire falls to the ground with a speed of 25 cm/sec. If the horizontal component of the earth's magnetic flux density is 2.0×10^{-5} w/m², find the emf induced in 100 m of the wire. *Ans.* 0.50 mv

15. A rectangular loop of wire 30 cm long and 20 cm wide rotates about an axis normal to a uniform flux density of 5.0×10^{-3} w/m². The coil makes 360 rev/min. Find the instantaneous value of the induced emf when the plane of the coil is parallel to the field. What is the average emf induced as the coil turns through the next 90°?

16. A closed rectangular coil of wire 20 cm by 50 cm rotates at a uniform speed of 5.0 rev/sec about an axis perpendicular to a uniform magnetic field of 0.080 w/m². The loop has a resistance of 0.20 ohm. (a) What is the maximum magnetic flux included by the rotating coil? (b) What is the maximum emf developed in the coil? (c) What is the average current in the coil during one-half revolution from the position of maximum flux?

Ans. 0.0080 weber; 0.25 volt; 0.80 amp

17. A flat, circular coil is constructed from a wire 600 cm long, having a resistance of 75 milliohms. The coil has 25 turns and its ends are connected to form a closed circuit. A magnet is moved near the coil, causing the flux to change by 5.0×10^{-5} weber in 0.085 sec. Calculate the average induced emf and the charge which circulates in the coil.

18. In an experiment to determine the flux density of the region between the pole pieces of a magnet a 50-turn coil of 30 ohms resistance and area 2.0 cm² is placed with its plane perpendicular to the field and then quickly withdrawn from the field. The charge flowing in the operation is found to be 5.0×10^{-4} coulomb. Determine the flux density.   *Ans.* 1.5 w/m²

19. A coil having 250 turns of wire has an area of 32 cm² and is rotated in a uniform magnetic field of flux density 5.0×10^{-6} weber/m² at a rate of 600 rev/min. The resistance of the coil is 2.0 ohms. Calculate (a) the average emf developed in a half turn from the instant the coil is perpendicular to the field, (b) the average emf developed in a whole turn, (c) the average current under condition a, and (d) the quantity of electricity displaced under condition a.

20. (a) What emf is induced in a straight wire 50 cm long, perpendicular to a flux density of 0.20 w/m², when the wire is moved with a speed of 5.00 m/sec at right angles to the field? Make a sketch to show clearly the directions of the field, motion, and emf. (b) What emf would be generated if the velocity made an angle of 30° with the field?   *Ans.* 0.50 volt; 0.25 volt

21. A rectangular loop of wire 30 cm long and 20 cm wide rotates about an axis normal to a uniform flux density of 5.0×10^{-3} w/m². The coil makes 360 rpm. Find the instantaneous value of the induced emf when the plane of the coil is parallel to the field. What is the average emf induced as the coil turns through the next 90°?

22. A closed rectangular coil of wire 20 cm by 50 cm rotates at a uniform speed of 5.0 rps about an axis perpendicular to a uniform flux density of 8.0×10^{-2} w/m². The loop has a resistance of 0.20 ohm. (a) What is the maximum magnetic flux included by the rotating coil? (b) What is the maximum emf developed in the coil? (c) What is the average current in the coil during 1 rev?

Ans. 8.0×10^{-3} weber; 0.25 volt; zero

23. A metal spoke in a wheel is 80 cm long. If the wheel makes 30 rev/min in a plane perpendicular to the earth's magnetic field where the flux density is 5.0×10^{-5} w/m², find the difference in potential between the axle and the rim of the wheel. Which part is at the higher potential when the wheel rotates clockwise as seen by one looking in the positive direction of the field?

24. The wire spoke of an automobile wheel is 45 cm long. The wheel turns through 90° in 0.050 sec. If this motion is perpendicular to a magnetic flux density of 3.5×10^{-5} w/m², what average emf is induced in the wire?

Ans. $1\bar{1}0 \ \mu v$

36. *Electromagnetic Induction*

A device for converting mechanical energy into electric energy is called a *generator*. A *motor* transforms electric energy into mechanical energy. The distribution of electric energy from the generating plant to industrial and household users is greatly facilitated by the use of *transformers*, devices for changing the voltage in a-c circuits. The principles of induced emf's (Chap. 35) are basic to the design of each of these devices for converting energy, and to the design of circuits for communication, in telephony, radio, television, and radar.

36-1. The Transformer. It was previously shown that a change in the current in one of two neighboring coils causes an emf to be generated in the other coil. The induced emf and, therefore, the induced current can be greatly increased by winding the two coils on a closed, laminated iron core, as in Fig. 1. This combination of two coils and an iron core is one type of transformer. Suppose that an alternating current is maintained in the primary coil of the transformer. This current is constantly changing; hence the magnetic flux in the iron core also varies periodically, thereby producing an alternating emf in the secondary coil.

Since the rate of change of flux is nearly the same in the primary and secondary coils it follows that the induced emf's in the coils are directly proportional to the respective numbers of turns in the coils. Symbolically

$$\frac{E_p}{N_p} = \frac{E_s}{N_s} \qquad (1)$$

where E is used for induced emf and N for the number of turns. In practice the voltage impressed on the primary from the outside source is somewhat greater than E_p, the in-

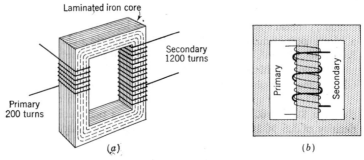

Laminated iron core

Secondary 1200 turns

Primary 200 turns

Primary

Secondary

(*a*)

(*b*)

Fɪɢ. 1. Transformers: (*a*) core type, (*b*) shell type. Transformer (*a*) is a step-up and (*b*) is a step-down transformer.

404

duced emf in the primary, and the secondary voltage at the terminals is slightly less than E_s, the emf induced in the secondary.

The efficiency of a commercial transformer operating under favorable conditions is very high, only a few per cent less than ideal. Hence the power input to the primary is nearly equal to the power output from the secondary.

$$V_p I_p = V_s I_s \quad \text{(approximately)}$$

or $\quad \dfrac{I_p}{I_s} = \dfrac{V_s}{V_p} \quad \text{(approximately)} \quad (2)$

The currents are thus seen to be inversely proportional to the respective voltages (approximately).

36-2. Distribution of Electric Energy. Whenever electric energy is to be used at any considerable distance from the generator, an a-c system is used because the energy can then be distributed without excessive loss; whereas, if a d-c system were used, the losses in transmission would be very great.

In an a-c system the voltage may be increased or decreased by means of transformers. The terminal voltage at the generator may be, for example, 12,000 volts. By means of a transformer the voltage may be increased to 66,000 volts or more in the transmission line. At the other end of the line "step-down" transformers reduce the voltage to a value that can safely be used. In a d-c system these changes in voltage cannot readily be made.

One might ask why all this increase and decrease in voltage is needed. Why not use a generator that will produce just the needed voltage, say, 115 volts? The answer lies in the amount of energy lost in transmission. In d-c circuits, and in the ideal case in a-c transmission lines, the power delivered is $P = VI$, where V is the (effective) voltage and I the current. (It will be shown later that in a-c circuits $P = VI$ only in special cases.) If a transformer is used to increase the available voltage, the current will be decreased.

Suppose that a 10-kw generator is to supply energy through a transmission line whose resistance is 10 ohms. If the generator furnishes 20 amp at 500 volts,

$$P = VI = (500 \text{ volts})(20 \text{ amp})$$
$$= 10,000 \text{ watts}$$

The heating loss in the line is

$$I^2R = (20 \text{ amp})^2(10 \text{ ohms}) = 4000 \text{ watts}$$

or 40 per cent of the original power. If a transformer is used to step up the voltage to 5000 volts, the current will be only 2 amp, and the loss

$$I^2R = (2 \text{ amp})^2(10 \text{ ohms}) = 40 \text{ watts}$$

or 0.4 per cent of the original power.

A second transformer can be used to reduce the voltage at the other end of the line to whatever value is desired. With 2 or 3 per cent loss in each of the transformers, the over-all efficiency of the system may be increased from 60 to 95 per cent by the use of transformers. Thus alternating current, through the use of transformers producing very high voltages, makes it possible to furnish electric power over transmission lines many miles in length.

Example: A step-down transformer at the end of a transmission line reduces the voltage from 2400 volts to 120 volts. The power output is 9.0 kw and the over-all efficiency of the transformer is 92 per cent. The primary ("high tension") winding has 4000 turns. How many turns has the secondary or "low tension" coil? What is the power input? What is the current in each of the two coils?

$$P_s = 9.0 \text{ kw} = 9\bar{0}00 \text{ watts}$$

$$\frac{E_p}{E_s} = \frac{N_p}{N_s}$$

In Eq. (1), the emf's are the induced emf's. If the efficiency is high, the error introduced by using the terminal voltages is not excessive. Then

$$\frac{2400 \text{ volts}}{120 \text{ volts}} = \frac{4000 \text{ turns}}{N_s}$$

Hence $\quad N_s = 200 \text{ turns}$

$$\text{Eff.} = \frac{P_s}{P_p}$$

$$0.92 = \frac{9\bar{0}00 \text{ watts}}{P_p}$$

Therefore $P_p = 9800$ watts

$$I_p = \frac{9800 \text{ watts}}{2400 \text{ volts}} = 4.1 \text{ amp}$$

$$I_s = \frac{9000 \text{ watts}}{120 \text{ volts}} = 75 \text{ amp}$$

To assist in insulating the coils and to dissipate the heat in a power transformer, the core and coils are submerged in oil contained in a metal housing. Sometimes in the larger

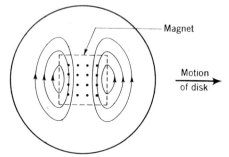

FIG. 2. Eddy currents in a disk moving in front of a magnet.

sizes this oil is circulated through the transformer and cooled by various means.

The losses in a transformer are of two types. The *copper losses* are caused by the heat developed from the I^2R power consumption on account of the resistance of the wire in the coils. In practice these losses are minimized by the use of wire of large size, although there is an obvious economic limit to the size of wire that should be used. Other losses are due to the hysteresis and eddy current losses in the iron core. These are known as *iron losses*.

36-3. Eddy Currents. When a large block of a conducting substance is moved through a nonuniform magnetic field or when in any manner there is a change in the magnetic flux through the conductor, induced currents will exist in eddies through the solid mass. These are referred to as *eddy currents*. This effect was discovered by the physicist Foucault (1819–1868) and the currents are sometimes referred to as Foucault currents. In Fig. 2 is shown a metal disk that is being moved to the right across a nonuniform mag-

netic field assumed to be from an N pole placed behind the disk. The right-hand rule shows the direction of the currents in the eddies in the disk. These currents tend to set up magnetic fields, which, reacting with the field which gave rise to them, will oppose the motion of the disk through the field. The disk acts as though it were imbedded in a very viscous medium. Eddy currents produce heat

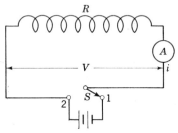

FIG. 3. An inductive circuit. Switch S can be used (1) to apply a potential V or (2) to "short" the coil ($V = 0$).

and hence consume energy. They are frequently a source of considerable difficulty to the electrical designer.

Eddy currents may be minimized by *laminating* the block of metal, that is, by making it up out of many very thin sheets or laminations. The planes of these laminations must be arranged parallel to the magnetic flux. Many a-c machines, such as transformers and dynamos, have their magnetic parts made up of laminated sections.

36-4. Growth and Decay of Current. When a switch is closed connecting a battery to a coil of wire (position 1 of Fig. 3), the current does not instantaneously reach its steady value given by $I = V/R$ but starts at zero and rises gradually to that value. During the time the current is building up, the relation $I = V/R$ does not tell the whole story. In fact it can be shown that $I = V/R$ only when the current is not changing. In general, therefore, we cannot use the relation $V = IR$ in connection with inductive circuits.

While the current in a coil is increasing, the magnetic field around it is being built up; hence energy is being supplied from the battery to create the magnetic field. The electricity that passes through the coil thus does work in two ways: (1) in passing through the electric resistance of the coil and (2) in doing its share to build up the magnetic field around the coil. At every instant the potential difference across the coil can be divided into two

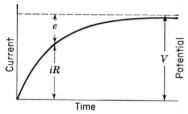

FIG. 4. Rise of current and change of potential after a steady PD is applied to an inductive circuit.

parts, so that $V = iR + e$, where i is the instantaneous current and e is the induced emf. Here iR is equal to the work per unit charge done against the electric resistance of the coil, whereas e is equal to the work per unit charge done in changing the magnetic field. The work per unit charge done by the battery on the electricity passing through it is V. The equation can be rewritten $e = V - iR$, showing that, as the current i becomes larger, e becomes smaller. When the current is no longer increasing, e is zero, and $V = IR$, since no energy is being used in creating a magnetic field.

The current in a circuit rises as shown in Fig. 4, rapidly at first and then more and more slowly, until any change in it can no longer be detected. It is then said to have reached its maximum, or steady value, for which $V = IR$. The time taken for this to happen is usually a small fraction of a second. When the circuit contains a coil with a closed iron core, the rise may require as much as several tenths of a second. It is instructive to note that the iR drop due to the resistance may be laid off proportional to the ordinate on the current-time curve (Fig. 4), and the induced emf e is the corresponding distance from this ordinate to the line representing the sum of iR and e, namely, the applied voltage V.

For the current in a coil to decrease, the energy given to the magnetic field must be taken back into the circuit; hence electricity passing through the coil receives energy per unit charge e from the decreasing of the magnetic field. At the same time, it does work per unit charge iR against electric resistance.

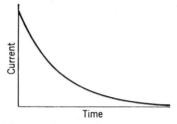

FIG. 5. Decay of current in an inductive circuit.

When the coil is short-circuited (position 2 of Fig. 3), the total work done per unit charge is thus

$$V = 0 = iR - e \qquad (3)$$

while the current is decreasing. A typical curve showing the decay of current in an inductive circuit is shown in Fig. 5.

36-5. Back EMF and Forward EMF. When the magnetic flux is increasing in a

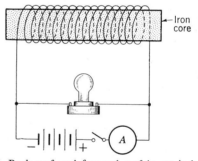

FIG. 6. Back emf and forward emf in an inductive circuit.

circuit, the induced emf is, by Lenz's law, in such a direction as to oppose this growth. Such an emf is called a "back emf." If the flux is decreasing in a circuit, the induced emf has a direction such as to oppose this decay, that is, to prevent the flux from decreasing. This emf is referred to as a "forward emf." In Fig. 6 is shown a highly inductive coil connected to a battery through a switch and an ammeter. (The lamp will temporarily be ignored.) When the switch is closed, it will be noticed that the ammeter only gradually rises to its final steady value. This is caused by the fact that there is initially a back emf in the coil. The voltages in the circuit are expressed by the equation

$$V = iR + e \qquad (4)$$

where V represents the work per unit charge supplied by the source battery, iR is the work per unit charge lost in heating the resistor, and e is the induced emf, or the energy per unit charge stored up in the magnetic field. As the magnetic flux in the coil builds up to its final maximum value, its rate of change decreases, finally becoming zero. Since e varies directly with the rate of change of flux, its value decreases when the current increases until finally when $e = 0$ the current becomes the ordinary Ohm's-law value V/R.

Now consider the lamp which is in parallel with the coil. Imagine the lamp to be designed for 115 volts and the battery to have a voltage of 50 volts. With the switch closed, the lamp is noticed to glow only dimly. When the switch is quickly opened, however, the lamp temporarily shines very brilliantly. The current in the lamp is supplied by the induced emf in the coil. The high temporary current indicates that the forward emf induced as the flux dies away is quite large, on account of the large rate at which the flux changes at the instant after the switch is opened.

Example: An inductive coil having a resistance of 3.0 ohms is connected to a battery having a terminal PD of 60 volts. What is the induced emf in the coil at an instant when the current has risen to one-fourth of its steady value?

The steady current is given by

$$I = \frac{V}{R} = \frac{60 \text{ volts}}{3.0 \text{ ohms}} = 20 \text{ amp}$$

The instantaneous current, which is one-fourth of the steady current, is $^{20}\!/_{4}$ or 5.0 amp. Since

$$V = iR + e$$
$$e = V - iR$$
$$= 60 \text{ volts} - (5.0 \text{ amp} \times 3.0 \text{ ohms}) = 45 \text{ volts}$$

36-6. Self-inductance. An emf e induced in a coil because of the change in current in that coil is called the *emf of self-inductance.*

This emf of self-induction can be accounted for in terms of the ideas presented in connection with induced currents in general, namely, an emf is induced in a coil when there is any change in the magnetic field threading it, whether that change is caused by the motion of a bar magnet, a change in the current in a neighboring coil, or by a change in the current in the coil itself. Since a magnetic field is associated with the current in a coil, any change in that current changes the magnetic field around it; hence an emf opposing the change in the current is induced in the coil.

The *self-inductance* of a coil is defined as its emf of self-induction divided by the rate at which the current in it is changing. The emf of self-induction is given by the equation

$$e = -L\frac{di}{dt} \qquad (5)$$

where L is the self-inductance, e is the induced emf, and di/dt is the rate of change of current. This equation is actually the defining equation for self-inductance. The negative sign shows conventionally that the induced emf is one of opposition to the change of current.

The unit of self-inductance, called the *henry,* is the self-inductance of a coil in which an emf of 1 volt is induced when the current in it is changing at the rate of 1 amp/sec.

We may think of the self-inductance of a circuit as that property of the circuit which causes it to oppose any change in the current in the circuit. The role of inductance is therefore analogous to that of inertia in mechanics, since inertia is the property of matter which causes it to oppose any change in its velocity.

Example: A circuit in which there is a current of 5 amp is changed so that the current falls to zero in 0.1 sec. If an average emf of 200 volts is induced, what is the self-inductance of the circuit?

$$\bar{E} = L\frac{\Delta i}{\Delta t}$$

$$200 \text{ volts} = L\frac{5 \text{ amp}}{0.1 \text{ sec}}$$

$$L = 4 \text{ henrys}$$

36-7. Mutual Inductance. When the current changes in one of two adjacent circuits, some of the change in flux associated with the first or primary circuit A links the nearby or secondary circuit B, Fig. 7. Hence an emf is induced in the secondary circuit. This phenomenon is called *mutual induction*. Mutual inductance is the property of a pair of circuits by virtue of which any change of current in one of the circuits induces an emf in the other circuit. It is evident that the value of this emf will depend upon the rate of change of the current in the primary coil and the geometrical constants of the two circuits. *Mutual inductance* M may therefore be defined as the ratio of the emf induced in the secondary to the time rate of change of current in the primary

$$e_s = -M\frac{di_p}{dt} \quad \text{or} \quad M = \frac{-e_s}{di_p/dt} \quad (6)$$

The negative sign is used to indicate the fact that the induced emf is in such a direction as to oppose the change of current.

The mutual inductance is expressed in henrys when e_s is in volts and di_p/dt is in amperes per second. The unit of mutual inductance, the henry, is the mutual inductance of that pair of circuits in which a rate of change of current of 1 amp/sec in the primary causes an induced emf of 1 volt in the secondary. Mutual inductance is of importance to the electrical designer in calculations involving transformer coils, dynamo apparatus, and other electric machinery.

Example: A pair of adjacent coils has a mutual inductance of 1.5 henrys. If the current in the primary changes from 0 to 20 amp in 0.050 sec, what is the average induced emf in the secondary?

If the secondary has 800 turns, what is the change of flux in it?

$$\bar{E}_s = M\frac{\Delta i_p}{\Delta t} = 1.5 \text{ henrys}\frac{20 \text{ amp}}{0.050 \text{ sec}}$$
$$= 6\overline{0}0 \text{ volts}$$

$$\bar{E}_s = N_s\frac{\Delta\Phi}{\Delta t}$$

$$6\overline{0}0 \text{ volts} = 800\frac{\Delta\Phi}{0.050 \text{ sec}}$$

$$\Delta\Phi = 0.038 \text{ weber}$$

36-8. Energy in Inductive Circuits. When the current is established in an inductive circuit, energy must be expended against

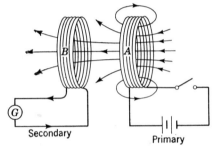

FIG. 7. An emf is induced in the secondary when the current changes in the primary.

the emf of self-induction in creating a magnetic field in the circuit. This energy is given by

$$W = \int_0^t ei \, dt$$

By substitution of $e = L \, di/dt$, the equation becomes

$$W = \int_0^t L\frac{di}{dt}i \, dt = \int_0^I Li \, di$$
$$= \left[\frac{1}{2}Li^2\right]_0^I = \frac{1}{2}LI^2 \quad (7)$$

This storage of energy in a magnetic circuit is of importance in such electrical apparatus as transformers, radio circuits, and induction coils. In the case of a single circuit, the energy is referred to as the magnetic energy of self-induction. The energy is given by Eq. (7) in joules when the self-inductance is in henrys and the current is in amperes.

36-9. The Simple Generator. The simplest possible generator is a single coil of wire turning in a uniform magnetic field as in Fig. 8. The magnetic field is parallel to the plane of the paper and both the axis of rotation and the plane of the coil are perpendicular to the plane of the paper. The plane represented by *GH* is perpendicular to the magnetic field.

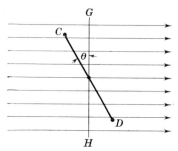

FIG. 8. Coil rotating in a uniform magnetic field.

At a certain instant the plane of the coil, represented by *CD*, makes an angle θ with *GH*. At that instant the flux threading the coil is $BA \cos \theta$, where *B* is the flux density of the magnetic field and *A* is the area of the coil. If the coil is rotating, say counterclockwise, at the instant considered the emf *e* generated in the coil is

$$e = -N\frac{d\Phi}{dt} = -NBA\frac{d \cos \theta}{dt}$$

$$= NBA \sin \theta \frac{d\theta}{dt} \quad (8)$$

$$e = NBA\omega \sin \theta \quad (9)$$

where ω is the angular speed of rotation of the coil. Equation (9) represents the instantaneous emf at each position θ of the coil as it rotates. The emf varies sinusoidally, reaching its maximum value when $\theta = 90°$ (coil horizontal) and zero value for $\theta = 0°$ or $180°$ (coil vertical) as shown in Fig. 9. The emf *alternates*, reversing direction twice in each rotation of the coil.

One complete rotation of the coil produces one *cycle* of the emf, causing one cycle of current in any circuit connected across the terminals. The number of cycles per second is called the *frequency*.

As we see from Eq. (9) the maximum value of the emf of the simple generator depends upon the number of turns of the coil, the area of the coil, the flux density of the field, and the angular speed of rotation

$$e_m = NBA\omega \quad (10)$$

If *B* is in webers per square meter, *A* is in

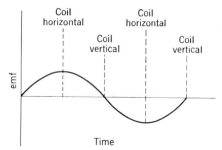

FIG. 9. Variation of emf with time in a single coil turning in a uniform magnetic field.

square meters, and ω is in radians per second, the emf is in volts

$$e = e_m \sin \theta \quad (11)$$

36-10. The A-C Generator. A simple generator is an a-c generator. The coil in which the emf is induced is called the *armature*. A high voltage may be obtained in an a-c generator by having the coil wound on an iron core, thus increasing the flux linked by

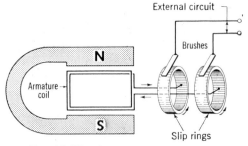

FIG. 10. Slip rings on an a-c generator.

the coil, and also by having a large number of turns in series for each coil. Where the coil rotates, the ends of the coils are connected to circular rings called *collecting rings* or *slip rings*. Carbon (graphite) brushes bearing on these rings make connection to the outside circuit (Fig. 10). The basic elements of an a-c generator are (1) a *field magnet*, (2) the *armature*, and (3) the *slip rings and brushes*. In many a-c generators the armature is made stationary and the field magnet is caused to rotate.

36-11. The D-C Generator. An ideal generator can never have a one-directional

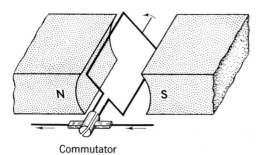

Fᴵɢ. 11. A simple generator with a commutator produces a one-directional current in the external line.

current in the coil itself but it is possible to have a one-directional current in the outside circuit by reversing the connections to the outside circuit at the same instant the emf changes direction in the coil. The change in connections is accomplished by means of a *commutator* (Fig. 11). This device is simply a split ring, each side being connected to the respective end of the coil. Brushes, usually of graphite, bear against the commutator as it turns with the coil. The position of the brushes is so adjusted that they slip from one commutator segment to the other at the instant the emf changes direction in the rotating coil. In the external line there is a one-directional voltage, which varies as shown in Fig. 12. The curve is similar to that of Fig. 9, with the second half inverted. To produce a steady,

one-directional current, many armature coils are used rather than a single coil. These are usually wound in slots distributed evenly around a laminated, soft-iron cylinder. With this arrangement of the coils there must be many commutator segments as well as many

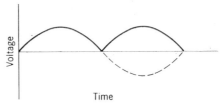

Fᴵɢ. 12. Variation of voltage with time in the external line of a simple generator with a commutator.

coils. The connections are so arranged that emf's add at any instant. The average of the instantaneous emf's during a revolution is the emf E of the generator.

36-12. The Magnetic Field. The magnetic field of the generator may be produced by means of a permanent magnet or by an electromagnet. If a permanent magnet is used, the machine is commonly called a *magneto*. When the field is supplied by an electromagnet, several connections are possible. Four common possibilities are illustrated in Fig. 13. Assuming that the speed of the generator remains constant, the emf of the separately excited generator will remain constant as the load increases, while the terminal potential difference decreases by the amount of the $I_a R_a$ drop in the armature. In the shunt generator, the TPD decreases more rapidly as the load increases, since the lowered TPD decreases the field and thus the emf. In the

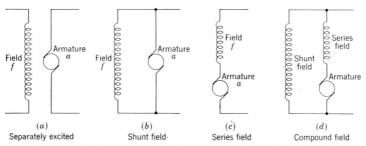

| (a) | (b) | (c) | (d) |
| Separately excited | Shunt field | Series field | Compound field |

Fᴵɢ. 13. Diagrams of the connections of field and armature in d-c generators.

series generator, an increase in load increases the field and hence the emf. By use of a compound field it is possible to keep the TPD almost constant as the load increases.

Whenever there is a shunt field, there are three currents involved in the generator: the

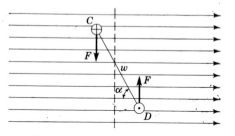

FIG. 14. The motor effect: the forces acting on the two conductors perpendicular to the field produce a torque.

armature current I_a, the field current I_f, and the line current I_l. In this generator, the source of current is the armature and hence

$$I_a = I_f + I_l \qquad (12)$$

The field coils act as a resistor for steady currents, while the armature must be treated as a part of a circuit that has a source of energy. For the field

$$V = I_f R_f$$

For the armature

$$V = E - I_a R_a \qquad (13)$$

The power $I_a E$ converted from mechanical to electric power in the armature supplies the power $I_a^2 R_a$ used in heating the armature, the power $I_f^2 R_f$ supplied to the field windings, and the power $I_l V$ delivered to the line.

$$I_a E = I_a^2 R_a + I_f^2 R_f + I_l V \qquad (14)$$

Example: A shunt generator has a terminal potential difference of 120 volts when it delivers 1.80 kw to the line. The resistance of the field coils is 240 ohms and that of the armature is 0.400 ohm. Find the emf of the generator and the efficiency.

$$P = I_l V$$

$$I_l = \frac{P}{V} = \frac{1800 \text{ watts}}{120 \text{ volts}} = 15.0 \text{ amp}$$

$$I_f = \frac{V}{R_f} = \frac{120 \text{ volts}}{240 \text{ ohms}} = 0.500 \text{ amp}$$

$$I_a = I_f + I_l = 0.50 \text{ amp} + 15.0 \text{ amp}$$
$$= 15.5 \text{ amp}$$

$$V = E - I_a R_a$$
$$E = V + I_a R_a = 120 \text{ volts} + 15.5 \text{ amp}$$
$$\times 0.400 \text{ ohm} = 126 \text{ volts}$$

Input:

$$P_i = I_a E = 15.5 \text{ amp} \times 126 \text{ volts} = 1950 \text{ watts}$$

Output:

$$P_o = I_l V = 1800 \text{ watts}$$

$$\text{Eff.} = \frac{P_o}{P_i} = \frac{1800 \text{ watts}}{1950 \text{ watts}} = 0.923 = 92.3\%$$

36-13. The Motor Effect. As described in Chap. 31, when a current-bearing conductor is placed in a magnetic field, the field is distorted and the conductor experiences a force directed from the strong part of the field toward the weaker part. This effect is illustrated in Fig. 14. The plane of the coil is perpendicular to the magnetic field. The current is directed outward in D and inward in C. The result is a force F on each conductor given by Ampère's law

$$F = BIl \qquad (15)$$

since the current is perpendicular to the flux and l is the length of the conductor in that direction. The forces are equal in magnitude but opposite in direction. Thus a couple acts to rotate the coil, and the torque is equal to the product of the force and the perpendicular distance between the forces. If w is the width of the coil,

$$\text{Torque} = Fw = BIlw \cos \alpha \qquad (16)$$

If B is expressed in webers per square meter, I in amperes, and l and w in meters, the force is in newtons and the torque is in meter-newtons. For a coil of N turns

$$\text{Torque} = NBIA \cos \alpha \qquad (17)$$

where A is the area of the coil and α is the angle between the plane of the coil and the magnetic flux.

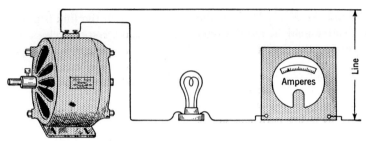

Fig. 15. Circuit to show the back emf of a motor.

When the coil has turned until its plane is perpendicular to the field, the torque becomes zero. If the coil turns beyond this point, there will be a torque to return it to this position unless the direction of the current is changed. In order for the coil to continue to rotate, there must be a commutator to reverse the direction of the current at the proper instant.

Example: An armature coil of 25 turns is 60 cm long and 20 cm wide. The armature current is 100 amp and the effective flux density in the air gap is 0.30 weber/m². What is the torque when the plane of the coil is parallel to the field?

$$A = (0.60 \text{ m})(0.20 \text{ m}) = 0.12 \text{ m}^2$$

Torque $= NBIA \cos \alpha = 25$
$\times$ 0.30 weber/m² $\times$ 100 amp
$\times$ 0.12 m² $\times$ 1.0 = 90 m-newtons

36-14. D-C Motors. The side push that a current-bearing conductor experiences in a magnetic field is the basis for the operation of the common d-c motor. In construction the motor is similar to the generator having a magnetic field, a commutator, and an armature. When a current is maintained in the armature coils, the force on the conductors produces a torque tending to rotate the armature. The amount of this torque depends upon the current, the flux density, the diameter of the coil, and the number and length of the active conductors on the armature. The commutator is used to reverse the current in each coil at the proper instant to produce a continuous torque.

36-15. Back EMF in a Motor. Consider an experiment in which an ammeter and an incandescent lamp are connected in series with a small motor (Fig. 15). If the armature is held stationary as the current is turned on, the lamp will glow with full brilliancy, but when the armature is allowed to turn, the lamp grows dim and the ammeter reading decreases.

This shows that the current in a motor is smaller when the motor is running freely than when the rotation of its armature is retarded. The current is diminished by the development of a *back emf*, which acts against the driving voltage. That is, every motor is at the same time a generator. The direction of the induced emf will always be opposite to that of the voltage impressed on the motor, and it will be proportional to the speed of the armature. When the motor armature revolves faster, the back emf is greater and the difference between the impressed voltage and the back emf is therefore smaller. This difference determines the current in the armature, so that there is a larger current in a motor when it is running slowly than when it is running fast. The current is much larger when the motor is starting than when it is operating at normal speed. For this reason adjustable starting resistors in series with the motor are frequently used to minimize the danger of excessive current while starting.

Since the emf E induced in the armature of the motor opposes the impressed voltage V, we may apply to the armature the equation previously used for a part of a circuit that includes a sink of energy

$$V = E + I_a R_a \qquad (18)$$

For a series motor, the relationship of Eq. (18)

applies to the motor as a whole. For the motor that has a shunt field, it applies only to the branch including the armature.

Example: A d-c series motor operates at 120 volts and has a resistance of 0.300 ohm. When the motor is running at rated speed the armature current is 12.0 amp. What is the back emf in the armature?

$$V = E + IR$$
$$E = V - IR = 120 \text{ volts} - 12.0 \text{ amp}$$
$$\times 0.300 \text{ ohm}$$
$$= 116 \text{ volts}$$

The increase in current with decrease in speed makes a motor somewhat self-regulating. An increase in load causes the motor to slow down, thus causing an increase in current. Since the torque is proportional to the current, an automatic increase in torque accompanies an increase in load.

The power supplied to a motor is the product of the line current and the impressed voltage $(I_l V)$. A part of this power $I_f{}^2 R_f$ is used to heat the field coils, a part $I_a{}^2 R_a$ is used to heat the armature, and the remainder $I_a E$ is available for operating the motor and thus represents the useful power

$$I_l V = I_f{}^2 R_f + I_a{}^2 R_a + I_a E \qquad (19)$$

SUMMARY

The basic equations for an ideal transformer are

$$\frac{E_p}{E_s} = \frac{N_p}{N_s}$$
$$\frac{I_s}{I_p} = \frac{N_p}{N_s} \qquad \text{(approximately)}$$

Electric energy is transmitted long distances at high voltage and low current in order to minimize the $I^2 R$ heating loss in the line.

Eddy (Foucault) currents are the currents induced in relatively large bodies of conducting material when they are linked with variable magnetic fluxes.

A *back emf* or a *forward emf* is generated in a circuit when the flux is growing or when it is decreasing, respectively.

Self-inductance is that property of an electric circuit which causes it to oppose any change of current in the circuit. It is defined by

$$L = \frac{-e}{di/dt}$$

Mutual inductance is the property of a pair of circuits whereby a change of current in one circuit causes an induced emf in the other circuit. It is defined by

$$M = \frac{-e_s}{di_p/dt}$$

The energy stored in an inductive circuit is given by

$$W = \tfrac{1}{2} L I^2$$

Generators transform mechanical energy into electric energy, while *motors* transform electric energy into mechanical energy.

An elementary generator consists of a coil of wire rotating in a uniform magnetic field. The emf induced in an ideal generator is alternating in character. It is given by

$$e = e_m \sin \theta$$
$$e_m = NBA\omega$$

A d-c generator differs from an a-c generator in that the d-c generator has a *commutator* to make it deliver a unidirectional current to the external circuit.

The terminal potential difference of a d-c generator is given by

$$V = E - I_a R_a$$

Of the *power* generated, part is used in heating the field coils and armature of a d-c generator and the remainder is delivered to the line

$$I_a E = I_a{}^2 R_a + I_f{}^2 R_f + I_l V$$

The *torque* on an armature coil of a motor is given by

$$\text{Torque} = NBIA \cos \alpha$$

The *back emf* generated in a d-c motor armature nearly equals the voltage impressed upon it. This back emf reduces the current which there would otherwise be in the armature, in accordance with the equation

$$V = E + I_a R_a$$

The power delivered to a d-c motor is $I_l V$. The power available to operate the motor after the heating losses in the armature and field coils is $I_a E$.

$$I_l V = I_f^2 R_f + I_a^2 R_a + I_a E$$

QUESTIONS

1. When the primary winding of a step-up transformer is connected to the supply mains and no current is drawn from the secondary winding, what limits the energy taken by the transformer to a small value? Show how the primary current is automatically adjusted as the secondary load is changed.

2. The coils of a well-designed transformer are wound very tightly on the iron core. Why is this design more satisfactory than one in which the coils are loosely wound on the iron core? Explain carefully the distinction between the voltage impressed upon the primary and the emf induced in it; also the difference between the emf induced in the secondary and the terminal PD of the secondary when it is under load.

3. Since there is no electrical connection between the primary and secondary of a transformer, what is the mechanism for the transfer of energy between these circuits? Even a well-designed transformer becomes warm in use. State reasons why this is true.

4. A certain amount of power is to be transmitted over a long distance. If the voltage is stepped up 10 times, how much is the line loss reduced? How much could the size of the wire be reduced in order for the line loss to be kept the same as for transmission at the original low voltage?

5. What happens to the motion of a copper pendulum bob when it swings between the poles of a strong electromagnet? What becomes of the kinetic energy of the pendulum? Describe some devices in which eddy currents are of value. Mention some in which such currents are objectionable. State reasons in each case.

6. A flat aluminum disk is rotated between the poles of a U-shaped magnet, with the axis of rotation parallel to the magnetic field. Assign letters A, B, C, D to the edges of the disk at points 90° apart and letter O to the center of the disk. Between which two lettered points is the induced emf a maximum? Make a sketch to show the paths of the induced currents.

7. The self-inductance of an air-core coil is independent of the value of the current in the coil. This is not true of an iron-core coil. Explain.

8. Compare the growth of currents in inductive and noninductive circuits. Sketch a curve of current *vs.* time for a circuit of high inductance; for one of low inductance.

9. What will be the effect on the self- and mutual inductance of solenoids when iron cores are inserted? State reasons. Mention some of the factors upon which the mutual inductance of a pair of adjacent coils depends, indicating the manner in which the mutual inductance varies with such factors.

10. Is an electric generator a "generator of electricity"? Where is the electricity before it is "generated"? What does such a machine "generate"?

11. A glance at a dynamo will indicate whether it has slip rings or a commutator. How will this information enable one to know whether the machine is an a-c or a d-c dynamo?

12. Why are there many commutator segments, rather than just two, on the common d-c generator?

13. Is the terminal potential difference of a shunt generator when there is no external load equal to the emf of the generator? Explain.

14. Draw a curve showing the variation of the terminal potential difference of a separately excited generator as the load increases.

15. Draw a curve showing the variation of the terminal potential difference of a shunt generator as the load current is increased.

16. Draw a curve showing the variation of the terminal potential difference of a series generator as the load current is increased.

17. A railway electric locomotive uses its d-c motor as a generator for braking purposes on long down grades. Show how this may be done and what happens to the energy.

18. Usually an automobile has a generator and a starting motor as separate units. How do they differ and why? Would it be possible to make one machine that would serve both purposes?

19. A d-c shunt motor rotates in a clockwise direction when power is supplied to it with the current in a certain direction. How must it be rotated as a generator so that the current will be in the same direction?

20. How can one reverse the direction of rotation of a d-c motor?

21. Explain fully and clearly the reason for using a "starting box" with a motor. Describe the action of this device.

22. Describe an experiment that one might make to measure the input and output power of a d-c motor.

23. Describe an experiment that might be performed to measure the over-all efficiency of a motor-generator set used to convert a-c power to d-c power.

24. From a consideration of the connections shown in Fig. 13, suggest characteristics of the way that the torque produced by a motor of each kind would change as the load is increased.

PROBLEMS   **1.** A transformer is designed to operate at 15 kw and $2200/122$ volts. Neglecting all losses, what is the turn ratio? the primary and secondary currents?

2. A 110-volt PD is applied to the primary of a step-up transformer that delivers 2.0 amp from its secondary. There are 25 times as many turns in one winding as in the other. Find (*a*) the voltage of the secondary and (*b*) the current in the primary. Assume no losses in the transformer.   *Ans.* 2.8 kv; 50 amp

3. A step-up transformer operates on a primary voltage of 220 volts. The ratio of primary to secondary turns is 1 to 50. The primary current is 200 amp. Assuming ideal conditions, what is (*a*) the secondary voltage, (*b*) the secondary current, and (*c*) the power output?

4. The primary and secondary coils of a transformer have 500 and 2500 turns, respectively. (*a*) If the primary is connected to a 110-volt a-c line, what will be the voltage across the secondary? (*b*) If the secondary were connected to the 110-volt line, what voltage would be developed in the smaller coil? (Assume ideal conditions.)   *Ans.* 550 volts; 22.0 volts

5. A step-down transformer operates on a primary voltage of 2200 volts. The ratio of primary to secondary turns is 1 to 50. The primary current is 2.00 amp. Assuming ideal conditions, what are (*a*) the secondary voltage, (*b*) the secondary current, and (*c*) the power output?

6. A transformer has a primary of 500 turns and a resistance of 0.200 ohm. The secondary has 2500 turns and a resistance of 3.00 ohms. The iron losses in the transformer for a secondary output of 10.0 kw at 1200 volts are 200 watts.

Calculate (*a*) the secondary current, (*b*) the copper loss in secondary, (*c*) the copper loss in primary, and (*d*) the efficiency of the transformer.

Ans. 8.33 amp; 208 watts; 365 watts; 93%

7. A radio transformer has 690 turns of wire in the primary coil, which is connected to a 120-volt a-c source. The secondary coil supplies 6.3 volts to the tube filaments. How many secondary turns are required, allowing 5% more for losses?

8. The hysteresis loss of an iron core used in a small transformer on 60-cycle circuits is found to be 10 watts. Assume that the magnetizing field and magnetic induction remain constant over a wide range of frequencies. Determine the hysteresis loss at 400 cycles/sec. *Ans.* 67 watts

9. A certain transformer has 1100 turns of wire in the primary coil. It is operated in a 330-volt a-c circuit. A number of 60-watt lamps are operated at 110 volts from the secondary of the transformer. Assuming ideal conditions, (*a*) what is the approximate number of turns of wire in the secondary coil? (*b*) What is the current in the secondary winding when 20 lamps are operated? (*c*) If the loss of energy in the transformer and connecting wires is 10% of the input, what is the current in the primary winding when 30 lamps are operated in the secondary circuit?

10. A certain amount of power is to be sent over each of two transmission lines to a distant point. The first line operates at 220 volts, the second at 11,000 volts. What must be the relative diameters of the line wires if the line loss is to be identical in the two cases? (Carefully justify the reasons for the answer.)

Ans. $50/_1$

11. Find the power loss in a transmission line whose resistance is 1.5 ohms, if 50 kw are delivered by the line (*a*) at $5\bar{0},000$ volts and (*b*) at $5\bar{0}00$ volts.

12. An inductive coil has a resistance of 9.50 ohms. A battery of 115 volts is suddenly connected to the coil. After the current has risen to 10.0 amp, it is changing at a rate of 160 amp/sec. What is the self-inductance of the coil?

Ans. 125 mh

13. A cylindrical coil of wire 35 cm long and 5.0 cm in diameter consists of 800 turns of wire carrying a current. (*a*) Find the flux density in the center of the coil if the current is 4.5 amp. (*b*) If the current decreases at the rate of 2.0 amp/sec, what emf will be induced in the coil? (*c*) What is the self-inductance of the coil?

14. A coil of wire has a self-inductance of 0.0020 henry in air, and carries a current of 0.10 amp. What is the change in the magnetic energy associated with the coil when it is immersed in liquid oxygen, and still carries a current of 0.10 amp? For air $(\mu_r - 1) = 3.6 \times 10^{-7}$; for liquid oxygen $(\mu_r - 1) = 4.0 \times 10^{-3}$. *Ans.* 4.0×10^{-8} joule

15. Show that the self-inductance of a coil will vary with the square of the number of turns in the coil.

16. An impressed emf of 50 volts at the instant of closing the circuit causes the current in coil *A* to increase at the rate of 20 amp/sec. Find the self-inductance of the coil. At the same instant the changing flux from *A* through a nearby coil *B* induces an emf of 100 volts in *B*. What is the mutual inductance of the coils? *Ans.* 2.5 henrys; 5.0 henrys

17. A toroid, Fig. 16, made of a paramagnetic substance, is wound uniformly with N_1 turns of wire carrying a current *i*. The mean circumferential length of the ring is *L*; its cross section is *A*. When the magnetizing current is cut off, a charge q is sent through the galvanometer connected to a secondary of N_2 turns. The resistance of the galvanometer is R. In terms of i, N_1, N_2, q, L, and A, calculate (a) the relative permeability of the substance and (b) the self-inductance of the toroid.

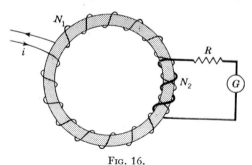

FIG. 16.

18. Two coils A and C are placed near each other. A current change of 6.00 amp in A produces a flux change of 12 webers in C, which has 2000 turns. What is the mutual inductance of the system?   *Ans.* 400 mh

19. An inductive circuit has a self-inductance of 250 mh and a resistance of 18.0 ohms. A battery of emf 120 volts is connected to the circuit and the current rises until it is changing at the rate of 192 amp/sec. How much energy is stored in the magnetic field at this instant?

20. A coil of 20.0 ohms resistance is connected to a 100-volt d-c line. At the instant when the current has grown to 3.00 amp, it is increasing at the rate of 80.0 amp/sec. What is the inductance of the coil? What energy is stored in it when the induced emf becomes zero?   *Ans.* 500 mh; 6.25 joules

21. A pure inductance L is connected in series with a resistance R and a switch S across a battery of voltage V. At time $t = 0$, switch S is closed. (a) Calculate the energy stored in the magnetic field of the coil at any subsequent time t, and make a rough plot of energy *vs.* time; indicate pertinent quantities such as asymptotic values. (b) Calculate the total energy dissipated in the resistor up to time t and sketch a graph as in part (a). (c) Calculate the voltage across the inductor as a function of t, and sketch a graph as in part (a).

22. A simple a-c generator develops a voltage that has a maximum value of 160 volts. What is the instantaneous value of the voltage when the plane of the coil makes an angle of 50° with the flux?   *Ans.* 102 volts

23. When the armature of a generator cuts a flux of 600 webers, an emf of 120 volts is induced. How much would the flux have to be for the generator to have a terminal voltage of 115 volts, when delivering a current of 20.0 amp? The armature resistance is 1.80 ohms.

24. The flux of a generator field is held at 400 webers. When the armature speed is 1800 rpm, the terminal potential difference at no load is 150 volts. What will be the TPD when the machine is running at a speed of 2400 rpm with a load current of 25.0 amp? The resistance of the generator is 1.20 ohms.
    Ans. 170 volts

25. A d-c series generator has a no-load voltage of 115 volts. At full load, the terminal potential difference is 110 volts, and the power output is 2.20 kw. What is the armature resistance?

26. A d-c series generator has an armature resistance of 0.120 ohm. At no load the terminal voltage is 124 volts, and at full load it is 115 volts. Assuming the generated emf to remain constant, how much power does the generator deliver at full load?   *Ans.* 8.62 kw

27. A shunt generator has a field resistance of 360 ohms and an armature resistance of 0.800 ohm. The generator delivers 4.00 kw to the external line at 120 volts. Find the emf and the efficiency of the generator.

28. A shunt generator has a field resistance of 240 ohms and an armature resistance of 1.50 ohms. The generator delivers 3.00 kw to the external line at 120 volts. Find the emf of the generator and its efficiency.   *Ans.* 158 volts; 74.2%

29. A shunt generator has a field resistance of 52.0 ohms and an armature resistance of 0.300 ohm. The machine will overheat if the armature current is greater than 50.0 amp. What must be the emf at this maximum current so that the terminal voltage will be 300 volts? What is the maximum power delivered? What is the efficiency at maximum load?

30. A certain shunt generator has a field resistance of 240 ohms and an armature resistance of 0.600 ohm. The machine will overheat if the armature loss is greater than 240 watts. What is the maximum armature current? If the emf under these conditions is 150 volts, what is the power output? What is the efficiency?   *Ans.* 20.0 amp; 2.68 kw; 89.4%

31. The armature of a series motor has a resistance of 0.240 ohm. When running on a 110-volt circuit, it takes 5.00 amp. What is the back emf?

32. The voltage impressed across the armature of a series motor is 115.0 volts, the back emf is 112.4 volts, and the current is 20.0 amp. What is the armature resistance?   *Ans.* 0.13 ohm

33. A series motor connected across a 110-volt line has an armature current of 20 amp and develops a back emf of 104 volts when running at normal speed. What current would there be in the armature at the instant the switch were closed if no starting box were used?

34. What is the back emf in a shunt motor which has an armature resistance of 2.00 ohms and in which an impressed voltage of 110 volts produces an armature current of 10.0 amp? If the speed were reduced one-half and the field current remained the same, what current would there be in the armature?
                              Ans. 90 volts; 32.5 amp

35. The voltage impressed on a series motor is 115.0 volts; the back emf is 112.0 volts; the current is 6.00 amp. What current would there be if the motor were stopped altogether?

36. A series motor has a back emf of 115 volts when the current is 10.0 amp and the applied voltage is 120 volts. What will be the current in this motor at the instant that the switch is closed?   *Ans.* 240 amp

37. A 1.00-hp motor having an efficiency of 85.0% is connected to a 220-volt line. What is the current in the motor?

38. What current is taken from 110-volt mains by a motor which is 80% efficient and which is delivering 10 hp?   *Ans.* 85 amp

39. A shunt-wound d-c motor has an armature resistance of 1.00 ohm and a field resistance of 200 ohms. When connected to a 110-volt line, there is developed a back emf of 105 volts. Find (*a*) the power delivered to the motor, (*b*) the power available for operating the motor, and (*c*) the efficiency of the motor.

40. A shunt motor has a field resistance of 240 ohms and an armature resistance of 1.50 ohms. When it is connected to a 110-volt line, an ammeter in the line reads 5.00 amp. Find the back emf, the power delivered, and the efficiency of the motor.   *Ans.* 103 volts; 468 watts; 85%

37. Capacitance

A device in which electricity may temporarily be stored is called a *capacitor*. (The term *condenser* is also frequently used.) Almost any insulated body possesses to some extent the ability to retain for a time an electric charge and hence such a body might be called a capacitor. However, the most effective capacitors are made of metallic "plates," which

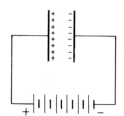

FIG. 1. A simple capacitor.

are insulated from each other and surrounding objects. Such devices have the ability to store a considerable quantity of electricity that may temporarily be held bound for later use (though often this later time may be a matter of a millionth of a second). Capacitors are used in such devices as radio sets, all sorts of electronic apparatus, telephone and telegraph equipment, and automobile ignition systems.

37-1. Simple Capacitors. A simple electric capacitor is formed by placing two metal plates near each other, with a sheet of paper, mica, or other insulating material between (Fig. 1). If a battery is connected to these plates, though there is essentially no flow of electrons through the insulating medium, electrons do leave one of the plates and enter the positive terminal of the battery, while the same number leave the negative terminal of the battery and enter the other plate. As this happens, the first plate becomes positive, the second negative, and this continues until the potential difference between the plates is equal to the emf of the battery. Thereafter there is no more current and the capacitor is said to be charged. Note that electricity does not flow *through* the capacitor, but only into and out of the plates that compose it.

37-2. Capacitance. The *capacitance* of a capacitor is the ratio of the amount of electricity transferred, from one of its plates to the other, to the potential difference produced between the plates. In the form of an equation

$$\text{Capacitance} = \frac{\text{charge}}{\text{potential difference}}$$

$$C = \frac{Q}{V} \qquad C = \frac{dq}{dv} \qquad (1)$$

It is important to note the fact that the charge which a particular capacitor can be given is not limited by the capacitance. More and more charge can be given to the capacitor by increasing the PD between the plates. The ratio of the charge to the PD is a constant for a given capacitor. This ratio is the capacitance.

37-3. Units of Capacitance.

The unit of capacitance in the mks system is the farad, so named in honor of Faraday. A farad is the capacitance of a capacitor which acquires a PD of 1 volt when it receives a charge of 1 coulomb. The farad is so large a unit that it would take a capacitor of unheard-of-proportions to have a capacitance of 1 farad; hence, the microfarad (μf, one-millionth of a farad) is the unit most frequently used. In some cases the micromicrofarad ($\mu\mu f$) is a convenient unit.

The defining equation for capacitance, Eq. (1), may be written in the form

$$Q = CV \tag{1a}$$

which states that the electricity which can be stored upon the plates of a capacitor is directly proportional to the voltage between the plates.

Example: A capacitor having a capacitance of 3.0 μf is connected to a 50-volt battery. What charge will there be in the capacitor?

$$Q = CV = 3.0\mu f \times 50 \text{ volts} = 150 \text{ }\mu\text{coulombs}$$

37-4. Permittivity.

Air is used as a medium between the plates of many types of capacitors, especially those used in high-frequency circuits, such as radar. But other capacitors utilize solid or liquid dielectrics, such as mica, paraffined paper, or oil. When such dielectrics are in the electric field of the charged plates the charges in the dielectrics are displaced and the molecules are said to be *polarized*. In effect one surface of the dielectric acquires a positive charge and the other side becomes negative. The electric field inside the dielectric caused by these polarized charges is opposite in sense to the applied field. Thus the resultant field within the insulator is less intense than was the case when there was only empty space between the plates. This property of the dielectric is called its permittivity ϵ. The defining equation for ϵ is Coulomb's law

$$F = \frac{1}{4\pi\epsilon} \frac{QQ'}{s^2} \tag{2}$$

For empty space the permittivity is designated by the symbol ϵ_0. The value of $1/4\pi\epsilon_0$ is approximately 9×10^9 newton-m²/coulomb² and ϵ_0 is 8.87×10^{-12} coulomb²/newton-m².

The *relative permittivity*, $\epsilon_r = \epsilon/\epsilon_0$, of a dielectric is a pure number, ranging from 1 to 10 for many widely used insulators. A list of the relative permittivities of a few common insulators is given in Table 1.

TABLE 1. RELATIVE PERMITTIVITY

Solids	
Glass...................	6 –10
Mica....................	5.6– 6.6
Paraffined paper.........	2.1– 2.3
Porcelain...............	6 – 7

Liquids	
Alcohol................	25
Oil....................	2 – 2.2
Turpentine.............	2.2– 2.3
Water..................	80 –83

Gases	
Carbon dioxide..........	1.00097
Air....................	1.00060
Hydrogen..............	1.00026
Water vapor...........	1.007

37-5. Capacitance of a Parallel-plate Capacitor.

We shall first derive the expression for the total number of lines of force ψ which emerge from a charge Q. This may be done as follows: consider the charge to be enclosed by a sphere of radius r. The electric field intensity at the surface of the sphere is given by

$$\mathcal{E} = \frac{Q}{4\pi\epsilon r^2}$$

It has been agreed conventionally to represent the intensity of an electric field by the number of lines of force per unit area (in a vacuum) or by this number divided by the permittivity ϵ of the medium if the charge is surrounded by some substance other than a vacuum. Hence

$$\mathcal{E} = \frac{\psi}{\epsilon A}$$

Remembering that the area A of a sphere is $4\pi r^2$ and equating the two expressions for $\mathcal{E}$, we obtain

$$\frac{\psi}{4\pi r^2 \epsilon} = \frac{Q}{4\pi \epsilon r^2}$$

From which $\psi = Q$. This indicates the fact that the total number of lines of force extending from a charged body is just equal to the

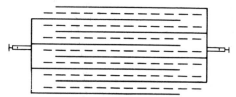

FIG. 2. A multiplate capacitor.

charge on the body, that is, one line of force extends from each coulomb of charge. In the electrostatic family of units $\psi = 4\pi Q$, so that 4π lines of force extend from each statcoulomb of charge.

Consider next a pair of charged plates, separated by a dielectric, as shown in Fig. 1. If the plates are large and their separation small, the electric field intensity between them is everywhere uniform. This field is given by

$$\mathcal{E} = \frac{\psi}{\epsilon A} = \frac{Q}{\epsilon A}$$

From this equation and the definitions of electric field intensity ($\mathcal{E} = F/q$), potential ($V = W/q$), and work ($W = F \times s$), it follows that

$$V = \frac{W}{q} = \frac{F}{q}s = \mathcal{E}s = \frac{Q}{\epsilon A}s$$

If we make use of the defining equation for capacitance and substitute the value of V from the equation above, we obtain

$$C = \frac{Q}{V} = \frac{Q}{Qs/\epsilon A}$$

Hence

$$C = \frac{\epsilon A}{s} = \frac{\epsilon_r \epsilon_0 A}{s} \tag{3}$$

The capacitance is in farads when A is in meters^2, s is in meters, and $\epsilon(= \epsilon_r \epsilon_0)$ is in coulomb^2 per newton-meter^2.

37-6. Commercial Capacitors. In order to increase the capacitance of capacitors so that they will hold sufficiently large quantities of electricity for commercial purposes, use is made of a large number of plates, each of large area. An idealized diagram of a multiplate capacitor is shown in Fig. 2. In high-grade capacitors mica is used as a dielectric. Inexpensive capacitors of capacitance up to 10 μf are usually made of alternate layers of tin or aluminum foil and waxed paper. These are frequently wound into rolls under pressure and sealed into moisture-resisting metal containers. *Electrolytic capacitors* of large capacitance, up to 50 μf, are made by using an insulating layer formed by chemical action directly on the metal plates of the capacitor. The slight space between the layers is filled with an electrolyte in liquid or paste form, this constituting one of the plates. A variable-capacitance *air capacitor* is shown in Fig. 3. This type of capacitor is widely used in radio circuits and electronic devices.

For a multiple capacitor, such as those shown in Figs. 2 and 3, the capacitance given by Eq. (3) must be increased by the factor $(N - 1)$, where N is the total number of plates. It will be seen that this is logical since N plates must be used to make up $N - 1$ individual capacitors.

It will be observed that in order to have a capacitor of large capacitance it is desirable to use an insulator of high permittivity, plates of large area, and a small separation of the plates.

Example: A parallel-plate capacitor is made of 350 plates, separated by paraffined paper 0.0010 cm thick ($\epsilon_r = 2.5$). The effective size of each plate is 15 cm $\times$ 30 cm. What is the capacitance of this capacitor?

Fig. 3. An air capacitor.

$\epsilon = \epsilon_r \epsilon_0 = 2.5 \times 8.87$
$\qquad\qquad \times 10^{-12} \text{ coulomb}^2/\text{newton-m}^2$

$s = 1.0 \times 10^{-5}$ m

$A = 0.15 \text{ m} \times 0.30 \text{ m} = 0.045 \text{ m}^2$

$C = \dfrac{\epsilon A}{s}(N - 1)$

$\quad = \dfrac{2.5 \times 8.87 \times 10^{-12} \text{ coulomb}^2/\text{newton-m}^2}{1.0 \times 10^{-5} \text{ m}} \times$
$\qquad\qquad\qquad 0.0045 \text{ m}^2 \times (350 - 1)$

$C = 35 \times 10^{-6} \text{ farad} = 35 \mu f$

37-7. Dielectric Strength.
Dielectric strength refers to the potential gradient (voltage per unit thickness) which must be applied to cause a disruptive discharge through the

TABLE 2. DIELECTRIC STRENGTH
Average values

Substance	kv/cm to puncture
Air	30
Transformer oil	75
Turpentine	110
Paraffin oil	160
Kerosene	160
Paraffin, solid	250– 450
Paraffined paper	300– 500
Mica	300– 700
Ebonite	300–1000
Glass	300–1600

insulator. This factor is a measure of the insulating quality of the material. Capacitors are rated to be able safely to stand the given voltages and should not be used at higher potentials. Approximate values of the dielectric strengths of some commonly used insulators are given in Table 2.

37-8. Combinations of Capacitors.
In Fig. 4 are shown three capacitors of separate

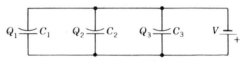

Fig. 4. Capacitors in parallel.

capacitances, C_1, C_2, and C_3, connected in parallel and joined to a cell of terminal voltage V. Obviously, all the capacitors are charged to the same potential, since they are all connected directly to the cell. By definition of capacitance, the charge on each capacitor is, respectively,

$$Q_1 = C_1 V \qquad Q_2 = C_2 V \qquad Q_3 = C_3 V$$

the PD over each being the same. The total charge Q is equal to the sum of the separate charges

$$Q = Q_1 + Q_2 + Q_3$$

If C represents the joint capacitance, $Q = CV$, and therefore by substitution for Q, Q_1, Q_2, and Q_3, we get

$$CV = C_1V + C_2V + C_3V$$

By dividing both sides of the equation by V, we obtain

$$C = C_1 + C_2 + C_3 \qquad (4)$$

That is, *for capacitors connected in parallel, the joint capacitance is the sum of the several capacitances.*

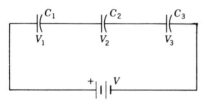

FIG. 5. Capacitors in series.

In Fig. 5, the capacitors are shown connected in series. Each of these capacitors holds the same quantity of electricity. This follows from the fact that if the capacitors are initially uncharged a charge upon one plate always attracts upon the other plate a charge equal in magnitude and opposite in sign. Let V_1, V_2, and V_3 represent the voltages over the several capacitors and V the voltage over the whole. For the series connection, it follows that

$$V = V_1 + V_2 + V_3$$

If we substitute in this equation the various values

$$V = \frac{Q}{C} \qquad V_1 = \frac{Q}{C_1} \qquad V_2 = \frac{Q}{C_2} \qquad V_3 = \frac{Q}{C_3}$$

we have

$$\frac{Q}{C} = \frac{Q}{C_1} + \frac{Q}{C_2} + \frac{Q}{C_3}$$

By dividing both sides of the equation by Q, we obtain

$$\frac{1}{C} = \frac{1}{C_1} + \frac{1}{C_2} + \frac{1}{C_3} \qquad (5)$$

That is, for capacitors connected in *series*, the *reciprocal* of the joint capacitance is equal to

the sum of the *reciprocals* of the several capacitances.

Example: Three capacitors have capacitances 0.50, 0.30, and 0.20 μf. What is their joint capacitance when arranged to give (*a*) a minimum capacitance and (*b*) a maximum capacitance?

In series

$$\frac{1}{C} = \frac{1}{0.50\ \mu f} + \frac{1}{0.30\ \mu f} + \frac{1}{0.20\ \mu f}$$
$$C = 0.097\ \mu f$$

In parallel

$$C = C_1 + C_2 + C_3 = (0.50 + 0.30 + 0.20)\mu f$$
$$= 1.00\ \mu f$$

37-9. Reasons for Connecting Capacitors in Series or in Parallel. A series connection of capacitors is used when it is desired to divide a high voltage among several capacitors, any one of which could not sustain the entire voltage. The voltage per capacitor in such a series connection is *inversely* proportional to the capacitance of the capacitor, that is, the capacitor of least capacitance has the largest voltage across it. Capacitors are connected in parallel when a large capacitance is desired at a moderate or low potential. Such a combination of capacitors will hold a large charge. An interesting example of capacitors in series is the "strain type" of insulators used on high-voltage transmission lines. Such insulators, shown in Fig. 6, are essentially capacitors connected in series, thus dividing the total voltage between the several units.

37-10. Growth and Decay of Charge in a Capacitor. When a steady voltage is introduced into a circuit containing only capacitance and resistance, the charge flows into the capacitor rapidly at first. As the PD between the plates rises, the growth of charge is reduced until the transfer of electricity stops entirely when the voltage of the capacitor becomes equal to the emf of the charging battery or generator. The rate at which the charge grows is an exponential, or logarithmic, function of time. The charge q in the capacitor at any time t after the applied voltage V is introduced is given by

$$q = CV(1 - e^{-t/RC}) \qquad (6)$$

The curve of growth of charge is the rising curve in Fig. 7. It may be seen that after a

FIG. 6. Strain-type insulators.

comparatively long time the last term in Eq. (6) becomes zero and $q = CV = Q$, the final steady value of the charge.

When a charged capacitor is discharged through a circuit of comparatively high resistance, the decay of the charge also proceeds according to an exponential function of time, in accordance with the equation

$$q = Qe^{-t/RC} \qquad (7)$$

The decay of charge is shown in the descending curve of Fig. 7, this curve being the complement of the growth curve. The growth or decay of charge proceeds more slowly the greater the value of the capacitance and the greater the resistance in series with the capacitor. The product RC is known as the *time constant* of the circuit; it is roughly the time required for the growth of charge to proceed to two-thirds of its final value. In most cases this time is a fraction of a second; the time is much longer when a capacitor is charged or discharged through a circuit of

very high resistance (of the order of megohms). It should be emphasized that the charge and discharge curves are similar to those in Fig. 7 only for the case of a high resistance. When the resistance is low, the nature of the discharge may be quite different.

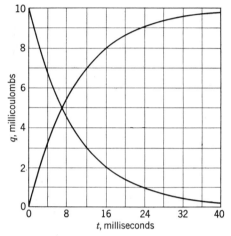

FIG. 7. Growth and decay of charge in a capacitor.

37-11. Dielectric Absorption. Residual Charge. When a PD is impressed upon a capacitor having a solid dielectric between the plates, there will be a rush of electricity into the plates, as shown in Fig. 7. However, this may be followed by a small and decreasing flow, so that there may be a slight delay in the establishment of a stable electrical state. Also, immediately after a capacitor is discharged, if the plates are left insulated for a short time, they will acquire a PD of the same sign as before. A second and smaller discharge may then be obtained. This process may be repeated several times, with decreasing effects. The charges remaining after the first discharge are called *residual charges*. The process in a capacitor which produces these effects is known as *dielectric absorption*. Gases show no such effects.

When a capacitor is carried through cycles of charge and discharge, as is always the case in a-c circuits, there are electromechanical effects produced which result from physical distortions of the molecular structure of the insulator between the plates. These effects are called *dielectric hysteresis.* They are quite similar to the magnetic hysteresis discussed in Chap. 33. They result in power losses within the dielectric which cause heating and other effects that are often quite serious. Occasionally this heating effect is put to use, as, for example, in the bonding of laminated wooden and plastic materials.

37-12. Energy Stored in a Charged Capacitor. When a charge is moved from one plate of a capacitor to another, work must be done. From the definition of PD this work is given by

$$dW = v \, dq$$

where v is the PD across the plates when the charge is q. Since $v = q/C$, the total energy expended in charging the capacitor may be obtained from

$$\int dW = \frac{1}{C} \int_0^Q q \, dq = \frac{1}{2C} \left[q^2 \right]_0^Q$$

Hence $$W = \frac{1}{2} \frac{Q^2}{C} \qquad (8)$$

Since $Q = CV$, this energy may be given as

$$W = \frac{1}{2}CV^2 = \frac{1}{2}QV \qquad (9)$$

When C is in farads, V in volts, and Q in coulombs, the energy is in joules.

Example: A 0.250-μf capacitor is connected to a 300-volt battery. What energy does the capacitor have after it is charged to the potential of the battery?

$$W = \frac{1}{2}CV^2 = \frac{1}{2}(0.250 \times 10^{-6} \text{farad})(300 \text{ volts})^2$$
$$= 1.12 \times 10^{-2} \text{ joule}$$

SUMMARY

A *capacitor* is a device in which electricity temporarily may be stored.

The *capacitance* of a capacitor is defined by

$$\text{Capacitance} = \frac{\text{charge}}{\text{potential}}$$

$$C = \frac{Q}{V} \qquad C = \frac{dq}{dv}$$

The *farad* is the capacitance of a capacitor that acquires a charge of 1 coulomb when the voltage between its plates is 1 volt (1 μf = 10^{-6} farad; 1 $\mu\mu$f = 10^{-12} farad).

The *permittivity* ϵ of a dielectric is defined from Coulomb's law for the force between charges. For empty space

$$\epsilon_0 = 8.87 \times 10^{-12} \text{ coulomb}^2/\text{newton-m}^2$$

The *relative permittivity* ϵ_r is the ratio ϵ/ϵ_0 and is dimensionless.

A *parallel-plate capacitor* has a capacitance given by

$$C = \frac{\epsilon A}{s} = \frac{\epsilon_r \epsilon_0 A}{s}$$

The *dielectric strength* of a material is the minimum potential gradient that will cause a disruptive discharge.

When capacitors are connected in *parallel*

$$V = V_1 = V_2 = V_3 = \cdots$$
$$Q = Q_1 + Q_2 + Q_3 + \cdots$$
$$C = C_1 + C_2 + C_3 + \cdots$$

For capacitors in *series*

$$V = V_1 + V_2 + V_3 + \cdots$$
$$Q = Q_1 = Q_2 = Q_3 = \cdots$$
$$\frac{1}{C} = \frac{1}{C_1} + \frac{1}{C_2} + \frac{1}{C_3} + \cdots$$

A charged capacitor contains energy as indicated by

$$W = \frac{1}{2}QV = \frac{1}{2}CV^2 = \frac{1}{2}\frac{Q^2}{C}$$

QUESTIONS   1. Explain why in the design of capacitors the binding posts and surface insulators are made of materials which have exceedingly high resistivities. Is this equally true of resistance boxes?

2. A fairly good analogy to a capacitor is an automobile tire into which air is pumped. Show how the phenomena in these two cases are analogous.

3. An air capacitor having parallel plates is charged to a certain PD. The capacitor is then immersed in transformer oil. What happens to the capacitance of the system? to the charge? to the PD?

4. A gold-leaf electroscope is fitted with a pair of plates instead of the usual knob. The plates are separated by a thin insulator. A 90-volt battery is connected to the plates. What happens to the gold leaf? With the battery still connected the plates are separated to a considerable distance. Explain what happens to the gold leaf. Explain what would happen if the battery were disconnected before the plates are separated.

5. In automobile ignition circuits a capacitor is placed in parallel with the breaker points. Show how this greatly reduces the sparking at these points. What is the cause of the sparking?

6. The PD across a given capacitor is varied and the charge is noted for each value of the PD. (*a*) Plot a curve of the charge as a function of the PD. (*b*) Plot a curve of capacitance as a function of the PD.

7. The relative permittivity of distilled water is very high, about 80. Why is such water never used for the dielectric in capacitors? Why is mica used so widely in capacitors?

8. The relative permittivity of a material is frequently measured in the laboratory by measuring the capacitance of a parallel-plate capacitor with the material as a dielectric and measuring the capacitance with the same plates separated by the same thickness of air and then dividing the first capacitance by the second. Show why this procedure is justified.

9. Suggest some differences in design which might be found in a 1-μf 120-volt capacitor and a 1-μf 600-volt capacitor of equal quality. Also between an inexpensive capacitor and a high-grade type of the same electrical characteristics.

10. Two unlike capacitors of different potentials and charges are placed in parallel. What happens to their PD's? How are their charges redistributed?

11. What is the capacitance of a short-circuited capacitor?

12. Four similar capacitors are connected in series and joined to a 36-volt battery. The mid-point of the capacitor group is grounded. What is the potential (*a*) of this point? (*b*) of each end of the group of capacitors?

13. Two identical capacitors are to be charged by connecting them to a battery. Compare quantitatively the relative total charges taken from the battery for the following cases: (*a*) only one capacitor used, (*b*) each capacitor separately charged, (*c*) capacitors connected in series, and (*d*) capacitors connected in parallel.

14. Three capacitors rated at 100 volts and 1, 2, and 3 μf are connected in series. If the group is joined to a 300-volt circuit, which capacitor is likely to puncture first? Answer the same question for a parallel connection of these capacitors. Explain.

15. Plot rough graphs to show the growth and decay of *current* in the charge and discharge of capacitors.

16. In the curve of the growth of charge in a capacitive circuit (Fig. 7), show that the ordinates are proportional to the voltages across the capacitor and that the remaining vertical distances to the asymptotic maximum are proportional to the iR drops in the circuit.

17. The dielectric properties of many insulators used in capacitors are greatly affected by temperature. Explain why capacitors designed for d-c or low-frequency circuits cannot be used in high-frequency circuits. Would this be true of air capacitors?

18. Discuss the following characteristics of dielectrics in their relationships to use in capacitors: permittivity, dielectric strength, dielectric loss (electric hysteresis), insulation resistance, temperature coefficients, tensile and compressive properties.

19. What type of energy is stored up in a capacitor? in a storage cell? in an inductive circuit? Why are capacitors not used in place of secondary batteries?

20. Derive Eq. (6) for the growth of charge in a capacitor and Eq. (7) for the decay of charge.

21. (*a*) Derive the equation for the current in a circuit containing resistance and capacitance to which a steady PD is applied. (*b*) Derive the equation for the current in this circuit when the applied PD is suddenly removed and the circuit is simultaneously closed.

22. A capacitor is separately charged to a series of voltages, and the energy thus stored is determined for each value of the voltage. Sketch the energy *vs.* voltage curve which would be obtained from such an experiment.

PROBLEMS   **1.** What charge is there in a 3.45-μf capacitor when the PD between the plates is 125 volts?

2. A certain capacitor having a capacitance of 2.00 μf is charged to a difference of potential of 100 volts. What is the charge on this capacitor?

Ans. 200 μcoulombs

3. A 2150 μμf capacitor acquires a charge of 0.750 μcoulomb. What is the voltage across the capacitor?

4. Calculate the area in square miles of a parallel-plate air capacitor having a capacitance of 1.0 farad when the plates are separated by 1.0 mm.

Ans. 43 mi²

5. A parallel-plate capacitor has plates 30 by 30 cm, separated by a mica dielectric 0.10 mm thick ($\epsilon_r = 6.0$). What is the PD between the capacitor plates when there is a charge of 7.00 μcoulombs on the plates?

6. A capacitor is made up of 21 plates alternately connected in parallel and separated by sheets of mica 0.400 mm thick, the area of each plate being 150 cm² and ϵ_r for mica being 6.00. Calculate the capacitance.   *Ans.* 0.0398 μf

7. An air capacitor has a capacitance of 135 μμf. What would be its capacitance if the air were replaced by mica, $\epsilon_r = 6.42$?

8. A 0.500-μf capacitor is placed in parallel with a 0.750-μf capacitor and the group is joined to a 110-volt d-c source. What charge is taken from the source? What are the charges on each capacitor?

Ans. 137 μcoulombs; 55.0 μcoulombs; 82.0 μcoulombs

9. A capacitor of capacitance 5.00 μf and potential 250 volts is placed in parallel with another capacitor of 10.00-μf capacitance and potential 375 volts. The capacitors are connected positive to positive and negative to negative. What is the resultant potential of the parallel group?

10. Three capacitors of capacitance 2.0 μf, 3.0 μf, and 4.0 μf are connected in series across a 1300-volt line. What is the drop in potential across each capacitor?

Ans. 6̄00 volts; 4̄00 volts; 3̄00 volts

11. A capacitor of capacitance 5.50 μf is placed in series with a capacitor of unknown capacitance. The charge on the unknown is 4.35 millicoulombs. The voltage of the system is 1000 volts. Calculate the capacitance of the unknown capacitor.

12. Six ½-μf capacitors are connected first in series and then in parallel. What are the respective joint capacitances of the combinations? What charge appears on each capacitor in each case when the group is connected to a $6\bar{0}0$-volt battery?   *Ans.* 83 mμf; 3.0 μf; 50 μcoulombs; $3\bar{0}0$ μcoulombs

13. A parallel-plate capacitor which has 11 circular plates, 40 cm in diameter and separated by mica ($\epsilon_r = 5.4$) 0.10 mm thick, is connected in series with a 1.0-μf capacitor across a 500-volt line. Find the potential difference across each capacitor.

14. Two capacitors of capacitance 2.0 μf and 4.0 μf are connected in parallel. This group is connected in series with a 3.0-μf capacitor across an 800-volt line. Find the PD across each capacitor.   *Ans.* $2\bar{7}0$ volts; $5\bar{3}0$ volts

15. Show how one might connect a group of 1-μf capacitors so as to obtain the following capacitances: 0.5, 1, 1.5, 2 and 2.25 μf, respectively.

16. Three capacitors of capacitance 0.100, 0.200, and 0.500 μf are connected in parallel, and the group is then connected in series with another group of 0.100, 0.200, and 0.500 μf connected in series. Calculate the total capacitance.
          Ans. 54.7 mμf

17. Six 1.00-μf capacitors are so arranged that their joint capacitance is 0.750 μf. If a PD of 600 volts is applied to the combination, what charge will appear on each capacitor?

18. A capacitor of capacitance 3.00 μf is charged to a potential of 150 volts. If the voltage were changed to 500 volts in 5.25 millisec, what average current would there be?   *Ans.* 0.20 amp

19. A 20-μf capacitor is to be charged from a 90-volt storage battery. The charging circuit includes a rheostat of 3000 ohms resistance. What is the current (*a*) when the circuit is first closed? (*b*) when the charge on the capacitor is two-thirds the maximum value?

20. A 5.0-μf capacitor is charged to a potential difference of 800 volts and discharged through a conductor. How much energy is given to the conductor during the discharge?   *Ans.* 1.6 joules

21. A capacitor is charged during a time of 25 μsec. During this interval there is an average current of 1.75 amp. The PD produced across the capacitor is 45 volts. Calculate the energy stored in the capacitor.

22. Three capacitors of capacitances 2.0, 3.0, and 6.0 μf are charged by a 60-volt battery. Find the energy of the stored charge when the capacitors are connected (*a*) in parallel and (*b*) in series.   *Ans.* 0.020 joule; 0.0018 joule

23. Three capacitors of capacitance 0.300, 0.400, and 0.600 μf are connected in parallel. The group is then connected in series with another group of 0.100, 0.200, and 0.500 μf connected in series. A voltage of 300 volts is applied to the combination. (*a*) What is the charge on the 0.400-μf capacitor? (*b*) What is the energy in the 0.200-μf capacitor?

24. Three 1.00-μf capacitors are charged to potentials of 100, 200, and 300 volts. The capacitors are then connected in series and joined to a 450-volt battery. What is the total energy of the system before and after the series connection is made? How do you account for the difference?
          Ans. 0.0700 joule; 0.0437 joule

25. Three 1.00-μf capacitors are charged to potentials of 100, 200, and 300 volts. The capacitors are then connected in parallel, positive terminals to positive terminals. What is the resultant potential difference? What is the total energy before and after this connection?

26. A 10-μf capacitor charged to a potential difference of 1200 volts is connected terminal to terminal to an uncharged 20-μf capacitor. What is the resulting potential difference?   *Ans.* $4\bar{0}0$ volts

27. How can several 0.0010-μf capacitor units be connected to give a total capacitance of 6.7 $\times$ 10^{-4} μf?

28. A 2.0-μf capacitor is connected in series with a resistor of 5000 ohms across a 1500-volt line. What is the current at the instant the switch is closed? If the current remained at this value, how long would it take to charge the capacitor fully? *Ans.* 0.30 amp; 1.0 $\times$ 10^{-2} sec

29. Two capacitors of 1.0-μf and 2.0-μf capacitance are separately charged to potentials of 100 volts and 200 volts, respectively. The two positive terminals and the two negative terminals are then connected. Find the resulting potential and the energy stored in the system.

30. A 10-μf capacitor A is charged to a potential difference of 500 volts. A 15-μf capacitor B is charged to a potential difference of 1000 volts. The positive terminal of A is now connected to the negative terminal of B and the negative terminal of A to the positive terminal of B. What is the resulting potential difference? *Ans.* 400 volts

31. Two capacitors of capacitance 2.0 μf and 4.0 μf are connected in parallel and charged to a potential of 1200 volts. When they are discharged through a conductor, how much heat is developed in the conductor?

32. A 4.0-μf capacitor is connected in series with a 2500-ohm resistor across a 500-volt line. What is the current in the resistor at the instant (*a*) the switch is closed? (*b*) the capacitor is half charged? (*c*) the capacitor is fully charged? *Ans.* 0.20 amp; 0.10 amp; zero

33. A 0.0050-μf 1000-volt capacitor is needed. There are available only a number of 0.0025-μf 500-volt units. How should they be connected to make the required capacitance?

34. Two capacitors of 3.0 and 5.0 μf are connected in series and a 110-volt difference in potential is applied to the combination. What is the potential difference across the 3.0-μf capacitor? What is the energy in the 5.0-μf capacitor? *Ans.* 69 volts; 4.2 $\times$ 10^{-3} joule

35. A 25-μf capacitor is connected in series with a half-megohm resistor and a 120-volt storage battery. What is the charge and PD in the capacitor 6.0 sec after the circuit is closed? What is the current at this instant?

36. (*a*) Show that the unit of RC is the second. (*b*) What is the simplest unit of $\sqrt{LC}$?

37. A 12.5-μf capacitor, a megohm resistor, and a 100-volt d-c source are connected in series. Calculate the data and plot a charge-time curve for times of 0, 5, 10, 25, 50, and 100 sec.

38. After the capacitor in Prob. 37 is fully charged the applied voltage is removed and the circuit is closed. Calculate the data and plot the charge-time curve for times of 0, 5, 10, 25, 50, and 100 sec.

38. *Alternating-current Series Circuits*

The use of electric machinery makes possible the transmission of energy from the place at which it is easily produced to the point at which it is to be used. The electric energy can there be converted into any other form of energy that best suits the needs of the consumer.

In the early generation of electricity the energy was consumed not far from the generator, and d-c systems were almost universally used. As it became desirable to transmit electric energy over greater distances, power losses in the lines became excessive and in order to reduce these losses a-c systems were set up. At the present time a-c systems are used almost exclusively in power lines. Where the application requires that direct current be employed, a local rectifying system or motor-generator set is installed.

Radio and a host of modern electronic devices are fundamentally applications of principles of high-frequency alternating currents. Many of the laws of a-c circuits are like those for d-c circuits but there are many significant differences. Some of these differences become quite pronounced in the region of ultrahigh frequencies, such as those used in radar devices.

38-1. Nomenclature in A-C Circuits. In Chap. 36, the form of emf curve generated in an ideal alternator was described. The instantaneous values of the emf e are related to the maximum values e_m as shown by curve a of Fig. 1 and given by the equation

$$e = e_m \sin \theta \qquad (1)$$

where θ is the angle between the given position of the coil and its position when the generated emf is zero. The instantaneous values of the current in an a-c circuit similarly may follow a sine curve, as shown by curve b of Fig. 1, so that the instantaneous current i in terms of the maximum current i_m is given by

$$i = i_m \sin \theta \qquad (2)$$

Example: The voltage in an a-c circuit varies harmonically with time with a maximum of 170 volts. What is the instantaneous voltage when it has reached 45° in its cycle?

$$e = e_m \sin \theta = 170 \text{ volts} \times 0.71 = 120 \text{ volts}$$

In the common 60-cycle a-c circuit, there are 60 complete cycles each second, that is, the time interval of 1 *cycle* is $\frac{1}{60}$ sec. It should be noted that this corresponds to a reversal of the *direction* of the current every $\frac{1}{120}$ sec (since the direction reverses twice during each cycle).

Radio broadcast frequencies are of the order of one million cycles per second. A few

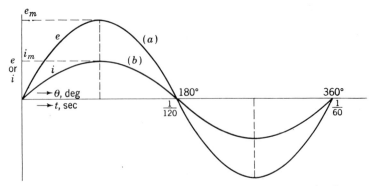

FIG. 1. Instantaneous values of voltages and currents in a-c circuits.

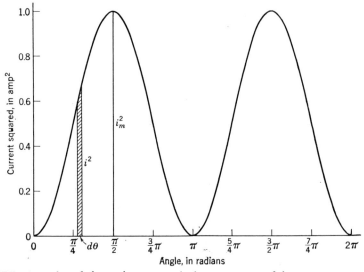

FIG. 2. Effective value of alternating current is the square root of the mean square current. .

modern ultrahigh-frequency devices use frequencies of the order of 3×10^{10} cycles per second.

38-2. Effective Values of Current and Voltage. Suppose that in a rheostat of resistance R there is an alternating current whose maximum value is 1.0 amp. Certainly the rate at which heat is developed in the resistor is not so great as if a steady direct current of 1.0 amp were maintained in it.

Remembering that the rate at which heat is developed by a current is proportional to the square of its value ($P = I^2R$), one can see that the average rate of production of heat by a varying current is proportional to the average value of the square of the current. The square root of this quantity is called the effective, or root-mean-square (rms), current. The effective value of a current is equal to the magnitude of a steady direct current that would produce the same heating effect. The value ordinarily given for an alternating current is its effective, or rms, value.

A curve of current squared for one cycle of a sinusoidal current is shown in Fig. 2. The value of the average of the square of the current can be obtained by calculating the area of one lobe of this curve and dividing this area by the width of the lobe. In order to compute the lobe area, we sum up all the infinitesimal areas $i^2 d\theta$, such as that shown in the shaded rectangle, and obtain

$$\int_0^\pi i^2 d\theta = \int_0^\pi i_m^2 \sin^2 \theta \, d\theta$$

$$= i_m^2 \left[\frac{\theta}{2} - \frac{\sin 2\theta}{4} \right]_0^\pi = \frac{\pi}{2} i_m^2$$

The average ordinate is obtained by dividing this lobe area by π, the width of the lobe; thus the average ordinate is $\frac{1}{2}i_m^2$. Hence the square of the steady current I which would produce the same heating effect as the alternating current is given by

$$I^2 = \frac{1}{2}i_m^2$$

The square root of this value is the root-mean-square or effective current, namely,

$$I = \frac{i_m}{\sqrt{2}} = 0.707 i_m \qquad (3)$$

Similarly, the effective value V of an alternating voltage is defined as its rms value. If the voltage varies sinusoidally

$$V = 0.707 v_m \qquad (4)$$

Example: What is the maximum value of a 6.0-amp alternating current?

$$I = 0.707 i_m = 6.0 \text{ amp}$$

so that $\quad i_m = \dfrac{6.0}{0.707} \text{ amp} = 8.5 \text{ amp}$

It is standard practice to use capital letters, such as I and V, for effective values in a-c circuits. The lower-case letters, such as i and v, are used to indicate instantaneous values. Unless otherwise clearly stated, effective values are understood when a-c quantities are mentioned. For example, a "voltage of 25 volts" refers to an effective value of 25 volts. These are the values indicated by ordinary meters.

38-3. Phase Relations of Current and Voltage in A-C Circuits. In an a-c circuit containing only pure resistance (that is, no inductance or capacitance) the instantaneous values of current and voltage are always *in phase*. This means that they both are zero at

the same instant, both pass through their maximum values at the same instant and always have similar time relationships. This is illustrated in Fig. 1 and is as demanded by Eqs. (1) and (2).

It is rare for a circuit to include only pure resistance. Most circuits also contain inductance and frequently capacitance. In such circuits there is a time interval, or *phase difference*, between the maximum value of the applied voltage and the maximum value of the current. This phase difference is usually given in terms of an angle ϕ and is expressed in degrees.

Consider a circuit which contains only pure inductance, that is, no resistance or capacitance. The induced emf e_L in such a circuit is given by

$$e_L = -L \frac{di}{dt} \qquad (5)$$

where L is the inductance and di/dt is the time rate of change of current. The negative sign is used to show conventionally that the induced emf is in such a direction as to oppose the change of current. Therefore, to maintain the flow, there must be an impressed voltage $v_L = - e_L = L di/dt$. From Eq. (2)

$$i = i_m \sin \theta = i_m \sin 2\pi f t$$

and hence

$$v_L = L \frac{di}{dt} = 2\pi f L i_m \cos \theta \qquad (6)$$

From Eq. (6) we see that the inductive voltage is represented by a cosine curve when the current is represented by a sine curve (Fig. 3). Therefore the inductive voltage v_L is 90° ahead of the current in phase.

It is impossible to have an inductor with only pure inductance, since the windings must contain some resistance. In such cases the angle of lag is less than 90°. Hence the phase angle for circuits containing resistance and inductance may vary from 0° for a circuit with resistance only to 90° for a circuit with inductance only. An example of an angle of lag of 30° is shown in Fig. 4.

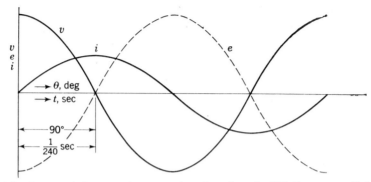

FIG. 3. In a circuit having pure inductance the current lags the voltage by 90°. Curve v, applied voltage; curve i, current; curve e, induced voltage.

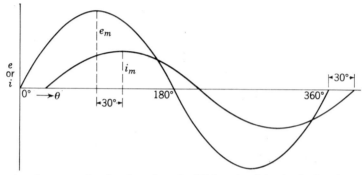

FIG. 4. Curves showing the current lagging the voltage by 30° in a circuit having both resistance and inductance.

When an alternating voltage is impressed upon a capacitor, there are surges of charge into and out of the plates of the capacitor. This results in an alternating current in the circuit outside the capacitor, even though the plates of the capacitor are separated by a perfect insulator. From the defining equation for capacitance it follows that

$$v_C = \frac{q}{C} = \frac{\int_0^t i\,dt}{C} = \frac{1}{C}\int_0^t i_m \sin 2\pi ft\,dt \quad (7)$$

$$v_C = -\frac{i_m}{2\pi fC}\cos 2\pi ft = -\frac{i_m}{2\pi fC}\cos \theta \quad (8)$$

The cosine factor of Eq. (8) indicates that the capacitive voltage is 90° out of phase with the current and the negative sign shows that it is behind the current in phase. In circuits containing both capacitance and resistance the phase angle may vary from $-90°$ for a pure capacitance to 0° for a circuit containing resistance only.

The most general series circuit is one containing resistance, inductance, and capacitance. These may be present in all proportions so that the current may either lag or lead the voltage by 90° or less. This phase relation is expressed by the equations

$$e = e_m \sin \theta \qquad i = i_m \sin (\theta - \phi) \quad (9)$$

The phase angle ϕ is considered positive when the current lags the voltage and negative when the current leads the voltage; hence the sign of ϕ must always be introduced properly in Eq. (9).

Example: In an a-c circuit with capacitance predominating, the current leads the voltage by 30°. The effective value of the current is 100 amp. What is the instantaneous current when the voltage passes through its zero value?

$$i_m = \frac{I}{0.707} = \frac{100 \text{ amp}}{0.707} = 141 \text{ amp}$$
$$i = i_m \sin (\theta - \phi)$$
$$= 141 \text{ amp} \times \sin [0° - (-30°)] = 70.5 \text{ amp}$$

38-4. Inductive Reactance. The *inductive reactance* X_L of an inductor is defined as the ratio of the effective value of the inductive voltage V_L to the effective value of the current I

$$X_L = \frac{V_L}{I} \tag{10}$$

It was shown in Eq. (6) that

$$v_L = 2\pi f L i_m \cos\theta$$

Hence the effective value of V_L is given by

$$V_L = \frac{v_{Lm}}{\sqrt{2}} = \frac{2\pi f L i_m}{\sqrt{2}} = 2\pi f L I$$

Since $\quad I = \dfrac{i_m}{\sqrt{2}}$

therefore $X_L = \dfrac{V_L}{I} = \dfrac{2\pi f L I}{I} = 2\pi f L \tag{11}$

This inductive reactance $X_L = 2\pi f L$ is expressed in ohms when f is in cycles per second and L is in henrys.

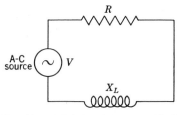

FIG. 5. Circuit containing resistance and inductance.

The portion of the applied voltage which must be used because of this induced emf is called the *reactance drop in potential*. It is equal to the product of the current and the inductive reactance and may be written as

$$V_L = IX_L$$

In our discussion of a-c circuits we shall consider series circuits only. In such circuits the current is the same in all parts. Therefore we refer phases to the common current phase. Thus the various voltages are ahead or behind the current in phase.

The conventional wiring diagram for a circuit containing resistance and inductance is shown in Fig. 5. The resistance portion is

shown diagrammatically as physically separated from the inductor; in practice this is rarely the case.

The voltage and phase relations in a circuit containing a pure resistor and a pure inductor in series are shown in Fig. 6. Such a figure is known as a *phase diagram*. The resistance drop (IR) is in phase with the current

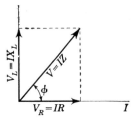

FIG. 6. Reactive and resistance components of the applied voltage in an inductive circuit.

and is laid off along the positive direction of the X axis. The reactance drop (IX_L) leads the current by 90° and is laid off along the Y axis. The impressed voltage V is the vector sum of IR and IX_L. The angle ϕ is the phase angle.

38-5. Impedance. The joint effect of resistance and reactance in an a-c circuit is known as impedance; it is designated by the symbol Z. *Impedance* is defined as the ratio of the effective voltage to the effective current. The defining equation is

$$Z = \frac{V}{I} \tag{12}$$

Impedance is measured in ohms, since V is in volts and I in amperes.

For a circuit containing only resistance and inductance it is clear from Fig. (6) that

$$Z^2 = R^2 + X_L^2 \tag{13}$$

The current in an a-c circuit containing resistance and inductance is given by

$$I = \frac{V}{Z} = \frac{V}{\sqrt{R^2 + X_L^2}} \tag{14}$$

An application of this equation offers a very direct method for measuring X_L and hence L

by Eq. (11). The current in an inductive circuit is measured when a known voltage is impressed. The resistance R is then measured and, if the frequency is known, every factor in Eqs. (11) and (14) is known except L.

Example: In an inductive circuit a coil having a resistance of 10 ohms and an inductance of 2.0 henrys is connected to a 120-volt 60-cycle a-c source. What is the current?

$$Z^2 = R^2 + X_L^2 = 10^2 + (2\pi \times 60 \times 2.0)^2$$
$$Z = 760 \text{ ohms}$$
$$I = \frac{V}{Z} = \frac{120 \text{ volts}}{760 \text{ ohms}} = 0.16 \text{ amp}$$

38-6. Capacitive Reactance. The *capacitive reactance* X_C of a capacitor is defined as

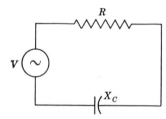

FIG. 7. Circuit containing resistor and capacitor in series.

the ratio of the effective value of the capacitive drop in potential V_C to the effective value of the current I

$$X_C = \frac{V_C}{I} \tag{15}$$

From Eq. (8) the instantaneous value of the capacitive voltage is $v_C = (-i_m/2\pi fC) \cos \theta$ and the effective value is $V_C = I/2\pi fC$. Therefore

$$X_C = \frac{V_C}{I} = \frac{I/2\pi fC}{I} = \frac{1}{2\pi fC} \tag{16}$$

This capacitive reactance $X_C = 1/2\pi fC$ is in ohms when f is in cycles per second and C is in farads.

The conventional wiring diagram for a circuit containing resistance and capacitance in series is shown in Fig. 7. The corresponding phase diagram is shown in Fig. 8. It is apparent from Fig. 8 that the impedance of a cir-

cuit containing only resistance and capacitive reactance is given by the equation

$$Z^2 = R^2 + X_C^2 \tag{17}$$

The current in a circuit containing resistance and capacitive reactance is expressed by the equation

$$I = \frac{V}{Z} = \frac{V}{\sqrt{R^2 + X_C^2}} \tag{18}$$

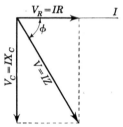

FIG. 8. Phase diagram for circuit containing resistor and capacitor in series.

Example: In the circuit of Fig. 7, the values are as follows: $C = 30 \ \mu f$, $V = 120$ volts, and $R = 25$ ohms. What is the current? What is the phase angle?

$$X_C = \frac{1}{2\pi fC} = \frac{1}{2\pi \times 60 \times 30 \times 10^{-6}} = 88 \text{ ohms}$$
$$Z = \sqrt{R^2 + X_C^2} = \sqrt{25^2 + 88^2} = 91 \text{ ohms}$$
$$I = \frac{V}{Z} = \frac{120 \text{ volts}}{91 \text{ ohms}} = 1.3 \text{ amp}$$
$$\phi = \arctan \frac{-X_C}{R} = \arctan \frac{-88 \text{ ohms}}{25 \text{ ohms}}$$
$$= -74.2°$$

38-7. Series Circuits Containing Resistance, Inductance, and Capacitance. We will first consider an ideal case of a series circuit (Fig. 9) containing pure resistance (without inductive or capacitive effects), pure inductance (without resistance or capacitive effects), and pure capacitance (without resistance or inductive effects). The voltages in this circuit are shown in the "clock" (phase) diagram of Fig. 10. In Fig. 10a, the voltage V_R across the resistor is laid off in phase with the current. The voltage V_L across the inductive coil is 90° ahead of the current. The voltage V_C across the capacitor lags the current by 90°. Hence the net reactive voltage is $V_L - V_C$ and is designated V_X in Fig. 10b. From

$$V_X = IX = IX_L - IX_C = I(X_L - X_C)$$

it follows that the net reactance X of the series

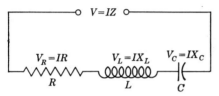

FIG. 9. A series circuit containing pure resistance, pure inductance, and pure capacitance.

circuit is $X = X_L - X_C$. The impedance Z is given by

$$Z = \sqrt{R^2 + X^2} = \sqrt{R^2 + (X_L - X_C)^2}$$
$$Z = \sqrt{R^2 + (2\pi fL - 1/2\pi fC)^2} \qquad (19)$$

Hence

$$I = \frac{V}{Z} = \frac{V}{\sqrt{R^2 + (2\pi fL - 1/2\pi fC)^2}} \qquad (20)$$

The ideal case represented by Fig. 9 never exists in practice. The resistor usually contains more or less inductance; the inductor necessarily includes some resistance; the capacitor may have sufficient losses to offer appreciable equivalent resistance. However, the phase diagram of the voltages in such a circuit may be reduced to one like that in Fig. 10, where in this case V_R represents the voltage across all the resistance in the circuit, V_L the total inductive voltage of the circuit, and V_C the total capacitive voltage. As before, V_X represents the net reactive voltage and V the voltage of the entire circuit.

38-8. The Choke Coil. A coil made up of a large number of turns of heavy copper wire has little resistance in a d-c circuit, but, because of its high inductance, it offers a large impedance in an a-c circuit. By fitting the coil with a variable iron core, the impedance may easily be varied within wide limits. Such a device is useful for many purposes instead of a rheostat, such as for dimming lights, and

possesses the important advantage over a rheostat in that the I^2R heating loss is much less. In other words, the coil acts as a "choke" without requiring a large expenditure of energy in the form of heat, as is the case of an ordinary resistor.

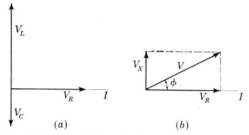

(a)   (b)

FIG. 10. Phase relations of voltages in a series circuit having resistance, inductance, and capacitance. In this circuit the inductive reactance is shown predominant over the capacitive reactance.

38-9. Power in A-C Circuits. In d-c circuits the power is given by $P = VI$. In such circuits both the current and voltage are assumed to be steady and in phase. In a-c circuits this is not the case. During half of the cycle, energy is supplied to the reactive component of the circuit, but this energy is returned to the source during the other half of the cycle. Hence no power is required to maintain the current in the part of the circuit which is purely reactive. All the power is used in the resistance portion of the circuit. From Fig. 10, $P = IV_R$. But $V_R = V \cos \phi$ and therefore

$$P = VI \cos \phi \qquad (21)$$

where P is the average power in watts when V is the effective value of the voltage and I is the effective value of the current. The angle ϕ is the angle of lag of the current behind the voltage. The quantity $\cos \phi$ is called the *power factor* of the circuit. Note that the power factor can vary anywhere from zero for a purely reactive circuit to unity for a pure resistance.

This expression for P can also be obtained by noting that the instantaneous power is the product of the instantaneous voltage and current, $p = vi$. The average power for a cycle can then be derived by integration, following the same procedure as that used in determining the rms value of current. This leads to Eq. (21).

From Eq. (21) and Fig. 10b it may be seen that

$$\cos \phi = \frac{IR}{IZ} = \frac{R}{Z} \qquad (22)$$

Example: (a) Find the current in a circuit consisting of a coil and capacitor in series, if the applied voltage is 110 volts, 60 cycles/sec; the inductance of the coil is 0.80 henry; the resistance of the coil is 50.0 ohms; and the capacitance of the capacitor is 8.0 μf. (b) Find the power used in the circuit.

$$X_L = 2\pi f L = 2\pi(60)(0.80) \text{ ohms} = 3\overline{0}0 \text{ ohms}$$

$$X_C = \frac{1}{2\pi f C} = \frac{1}{2\pi(60)(8.0)(10^{-6})} \text{ ohms}$$
$$= 3\overline{3}0 \text{ ohms}$$

$$Z = \sqrt{R^2 + (X_L - X_C)^2}$$
$$= \sqrt{(50)^2 + (300 - 330)^2} \text{ ohms}$$
$$= \sqrt{50^2 + (-30)^2} \text{ ohms} = 58 \text{ ohms}$$

$$I = \frac{V}{Z} = \frac{110 \text{ volts}}{58 \text{ ohms}} = 1.9 \text{ amp}$$

$$\cos \phi = \frac{R}{Z} = \frac{50 \text{ ohms}}{58 \text{ ohms}} = 0.86$$

$$P = VI \cos \phi = 110 \text{ volts} \times 1.9 \text{ amp} \times 0.86$$
$$= 1\overline{8}0 \text{ watts}$$

Note also that

$$P = I^2R = (1.9 \text{ amp})^2 \times 50 \text{ ohms} = 1\overline{8}0 \text{ watts}$$

There are power losses in inductors other than the usual I^2R copper losses. Such losses are due to eddy currents and hysteresis in the core of the inductor, especially if the coil is wound on an iron core. Hence the equivalent resistance of such a coil may be considerably larger than the ordinary ("ohmic") resistance as measured by the use of direct current. The equivalent resistance of an inductor may be obtained from the relation

$$R_{\text{equiv}} = \frac{P}{I^2} \qquad (23)$$

where P is the power loss and I is the current in the coil.

There may be losses in a capacitor because of inadequate insulation and dielectric hysteresis. In such cases the capacitor losses may be considered as equal to those in an equivalent resistance given by Eq. (23). In using this equation, it must be remembered that the equivalent resistance does not include any other series resistance that may be in the circuit.

38-10. Electric Oscillations. In the study of mechanical vibration (Chap. 13), it was found that oscillations can be set up in a body if certain conditions are present. The body must have inertia, a distortion must produce a restoring force, and the friction must not be too great. A massive object suspended in air by a spring meets these conditions.

In an electric circuit, analogous conditions are necessary for electric oscillations. Just as inertia opposes change in mechanical motion, inductance opposes change in the flow of electrons. The building up of charge on the plates of a capacitor causes a restoring force on the electrons in the circuit. Resistance causes electric energy to be changed into heat, just as friction changes mechanical energy to heat. To produce electric oscillations, it is necessary to have inductance, capacitance, and not too much resistance. As the frequency of mechanical vibrations depends upon the inertia (mass) and the restoring force (force constant), so the frequency of electric oscillations depends upon inductance and capacitance.

In the circuit of Fig. 11 a capacitor of capacitance C and a coil of inductance L are connected in series with a sphere gap G. The sphere gap has a high resistance until a spark jumps across but low resistance after the spark jumps. If the voltage across G is gradually increased, the charge on the capacitor will increase. When the voltage across G becomes high enough, a spark will jump and the capacitor will then discharge. The current does not cease at zero when the capacitor is completely discharged but continues, charging the capacitor in the opposite direction. It then discharges again, the current reversing in the circuit. The current oscillates until all the energy stored in the capacitor has been converted into heat by the resistance of the circuit. However, if the resistance is high, all the energy is used in the first surge and hence there are no oscillations.

The frequency f of the oscillation is determined by the values of L and C and is the frequency for which the impedance of the circuit is the least, that is, the frequency for

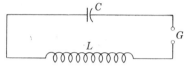

FIG. 11. Circuit for production of electric oscillations.

which the net reactance is zero. From the relation

$$X = 2\pi f L - \frac{1}{2\pi f C} = 0$$

it follows that

$$f = \frac{1}{2\pi \sqrt{LC}} \tag{24}$$

where L is the inductance in henrys and C is the capacitance in farads.

38-11. Resonance. If an alternating voltage is applied to a series circuit in which there are both capacitance and inductance, an oscillation is set up the amplitude of which depends upon the frequency. If the frequency of the impressed voltage is the same as the natural frequency of the circuit, as given by Eq. (24), the current will be much larger than for other frequencies. The circuit is then said to be in *resonance*. Figure 12 shows how the current varies with the frequency in such a circuit. For a very small range of frequencies, the current is rather large, but outside this region the current is small. This response over a very limited range of frequencies makes possible the tuning of a radio circuit. The incoming wave has a fixed frequency, and the circuit is tuned so that its natural frequency is the same as that of the

incoming wave. The tuning is usually done by adjusting the value of the capacitance.

The value of the current in a resonant circuit depends also upon the resistance of the circuit (Fig. 12). If the resistance is small, the current curve has a higher and more distinct peak; such a circuit may be more sharply tuned. For a larger circuit resistance, the currents are smaller and the resonant value is not so sharply marked.

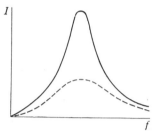

FIG. 12. Resonance in a series circuit: small resistance, solid line; larger resistance, dashed line.

It may be noted from Eq. (20) that for resonance when $X_L = X_C$

$$I = \frac{V}{R}$$

just as if the circuit contained only resistance, with no inductance or capacitance present.

In a series circuit at resonance the voltage across the inductor and that of the capacitor may each be very large, with only a moderate applied voltage. The inductive voltage is equal in magnitude and opposite in sense to the capacitive voltage. Under these circumstances the current and the applied voltage are in phase with each other.

SUMMARY

Alternating currents are used very much more than direct currents because of the economy of transmission made possible by the ease with which a-c voltages may be stepped up or stepped down.

The effective or rms value of a sinusoidal current is

$$I = 0.707 \times i_m$$

In a-c circuits the current and voltage are:

1. In phase for noninductive resistors
2. 90° out of phase for pure inductances or pure capacitances

The current *lags* the voltage in *inductive* circuits by angles ranging from zero to 90°, depending upon the relative values of the resistance and inductive reactance.

The current *leads* the voltage in *capacitive* circuits by angles ranging from zero to 90°, depending upon the relative values of the resistance and capacitive reactance.

In circuits containing resistance, inductance, and capacitance, the phase relation between current and voltage is given by

$$e = e_m \sin \theta \qquad i = i_m \sin (\theta - \phi)$$

Inductive reactance is defined by the ratio

$$X_L = \frac{V_L}{I}$$

$$X_L = 2\pi f L$$

Capacitive reactance is defined by the ratio

$$X_C = \frac{V_C}{I}$$

$$X_C = \frac{1}{2\pi f C}$$

Impedance is defined by the ratio

$$Z = \frac{V}{I}$$

$$Z = \sqrt{R^2 + X^2}$$

The impedance of a series circuit containing R, L, and C is given by

$$Z = \sqrt{R^2 + \left(2\pi f L - \frac{1}{2\pi f C}\right)^2}$$

The power in an a-c circuit is

$$P = VI \cos \phi$$

Power factor is the cosine of the angle by which the current is out of phase with the voltage, $\cos \phi = R/Z$.

The equivalent resistance due to losses in a capacitor or inductor is given by

$$R_{\text{equiv.}} = \frac{P}{I^2}$$

When $X_L = X_C$, the circuit is said to be in *electrical resonance*, and the current is a maximum for a given voltage and resistance.

The frequency of the oscillations in a resonant circuit is determined by L and C

$$f = \frac{1}{2\pi \sqrt{LC}}$$

QUESTIONS   1. In some a-c ammeters the deflections are nearly proportional to the square of the current. What are some of the desirable and undesirable features of such instrument scales? Plot a curve to show the deflection *vs.* current relations in such an instrument.

2. In considering the voltage in an a-c circuit required to puncture a capacitor, should one be concerned with the effective, maximum, or average values? Explain.

3. A long section of wire is available. Compare the inductive reactance of the wire under the following conditions: (*a*) long, straight wire, (*b*) wire doubled back upon itself at the center, (*c*) wire wound as a long solenoid of small radius, (*d*) wire wound as a short coil of large radius, and (*e*) iron core inserted in coil (*c*).

4. An iron-core inductor and a good-quality capacitor are connected in series in a 60-cycle a-c circuit. (*a*) Compare their equivalent resistances. (*b*) Compare their equivalent resistances in a 500-cycle circuit. (*c*) How would the equivalent resistances compare in the 60-cycle circuit if the capacitor were of a poor quality (that is, had appreciable losses).

5. A circuit contains a fixed resistor in series with a variable capacitor. Plot a curve to show the variation of the impedance with the capacitive reactance as the capacitance is varied from zero to an infinitely large value.

6. An air-cored solenoid of negligible resistance is connected to an a-c generator having a constant emf but whose frequency can be varied. Plot a curve of current as a function of frequency for this case. Plot a similar curve for the case in which the generator is connected to a good-quality capacitor.

7. How would one expect the equivalent resistance of a high-quality 500-volt 1-μf mica capacitor to compare with a cheap 500-volt 1-μf paper capacitor?

8. A noninductive resistor, an iron-cored solenoid, and a good-quality capacitor are in series in an a-c circuit. The current in the circuit and the voltage across each part are measured by a-c meters. The applied voltage is then raised and the readings repeated. The process is continued for several increasing voltages. Explain what values would be expected for the V/I ratios for each part of the circuit.

9. A choke coil placed in series with an electric lamp in an a-c circuit causes the lamp to become dimmed. Why is this? A variable capacitor added in series in this circuit may be adjusted until the lamp glows with normal brilliance. Explain why this is possible.

10. Compare the power in watts with the apparent power in volt-amperes for the following apparatus in an a-c circuit: (*a*) electric lamp, (*b*) choke coil, and (*c*) capacitor.

11. Show clearly how it is much more nearly possible to have "wattless" current in a-c capacitor circuits than it is in a-c circuits containing choke coils.

12. Explain clearly how an a-c wattmeter is designed to indicate the true power not merely the volt-amperes.

13. It is desired to measure the power factor in an a-c circuit, but no power-factor meter is available. A supply of various other meters is at hand. Explain how one might make the desired measurement.

14. Show why the kilovolt-ampere rating of a generator is more significant than the power rating in expressing the characteristics of the dynamo. When are these ratings identical?

15. A resistor, capacitor, and inductor are connected in series to a 120-volt a-c generator. Sketch a curve to show how the current in the circuit varies with the frequency of the generator, the voltage being kept constant.

16. What average power is expended in a resistor in a quarter of a cycle? (State the answer symbolically.)

17. A familiar type of a-c motor has three similar coils wound on an iron frame so that the coils make an angle of 120° with each other. Each of these coils is energized from one of the phases in a three-phase supply line, the voltages of which differ in phase by 120°. Show trigonometrically why these coils produce a rotating magnetic field.

18. Derive by a process of integration the equation for average power in an a-c circuit, namely, $P = VI \cos \phi$, beginning with the expression for instantaneous power $p = vi$. Show why the average power is zero in inductors and capacitors without resistance.

19. (*a*) Plot a curve of instantaneous power against time in an a-c circuit of unity power factor. (*b*) Repeat for the case of power factor less than unity. (*c*) Explain the significance of the negative parts of the curves.

PROBLEMS   *In each of the following problems in which it is appropriate draw a phase diagram, roughly to scale, to represent the voltages involved.*

1. A capacitor has a maximum rating of 550 (peak) volts. What is the highest a-c voltage (effective) across which it can safely be connected?

2. A 60-cycle a-c circuit has a voltage of 120 volts and a current of 6.00 amp (effective values). (*a*) What are the maximum values of these quantities? (*b*) What is the instantaneous value of the voltage $\frac{1}{720}$ sec after the voltage has zero value?   *Ans.* 170 volts; 8.50 amp; 85.0 volts

3. A capacitor is frequently placed across a 110-volt line to reduce the noise in radios. What is the smallest voltage rating such a capacitor should have?

4. An alternating emf has an effective value of 125 volts. What is the instantaneous value at the instant when θ is 75°?   *Ans.* 170 volts

5. Two generators are connected in series. One develops an emf of 225 volts, the other an emf of 120 volts. If the first generator is 90° in phase ahead of the second, what is the emf of the two generators in series?

6. A solenoid has an average d-c emf of 43.8 volts induced when the current is changed by 12.5 amp in 0.100 sec. What is the inductive reactance of this solenoid in a 60-cycle circuit?   *Ans.* 132 ohms

7. A coil of inductance 0.525 henry is connected to a 120-volt d-c source and a current of 0.450 amp is noted. What current would be observed if the coil were connected to an a-c source of 60 cps, 120 volts?

8. An inductor has a resistance of 15.00 ohms. On a 120-volt 60-cycle line this inductor takes a current of 2.50 amp. What is the self-inductance of the coil?
                    Ans. 121 mh

9. What is the impedance of a circuit in which there is a 60-ohm rheostat in series with a coil of inductive reactance 50 ohms?

10. A choke coil has a resistance of 4.00 ohms and a self-inductance of 2390 μh. It is connected to a source of 500-cycle 110-volt alternating emf. Calculate the reactance, impedance, and current of the circuit.
                    Ans. 7.50 ohms; 8.50 ohms; 12.9 amp

11. What is the reactance of a 0.60-henry coil on a 60-cycle line? What is the current if the applied voltage is 110 volts and the coil resistance is 100 ohms?

12. A coil has an inductance of 478 μh. (*a*) What is its reactance in a 1000-cycle a-c circuit? (*b*) If connected in series with a resistor of 4.00 ohms, what current would there be in a 1000-cycle 110-volt line?   *Ans.* 3.00 ohms; 22.0 amp

13. A coil which takes 10 amp from a 20-volt d-c circuit takes 3.0 amp from a 120 volt 60-cycle line. What is the resistance, inductive reactance, and inductance of the coil?

14. A coil of wire has a resistance of 30 ohms and an inductance of 0.10 henry. (*a*) What is its inductive reactance X_L in a 60-cycle circuit? (*b*) its impedance Z? (*c*) What current will there be if the coil is connected to a d-c source of 120 volts? (*d*) to a 60-cycle a-c source of 120 volts?
                    Ans. 38 ohms; 48 ohms; 4.0 amp; 2.5 amp

15. A current of 2.50 amp is observed in a 120-volt 60-cycle circuit which consists of a "pure" resistor and a "pure" inductor in series. The voltages across the resistor and the inductor are found to be identical. Calculate the value of the resistance and the inductance.

16. A "pure" inductor and a "pure" resistor are connected in series in an a-c circuit. A voltmeter reads 30 volts when connected across the inductor and 40 volts when connected across the resistor. What will it read when connected across both?   *Ans.* 50 volts

17. A 200-ohm resistor and a coil having a resistance of 125 ohms and an inductance of 0.250 henry are connected in series. What is the voltage across each when there is a 60-cycle 240-volt PD impressed?

18. What is the reactance of a 2.00-μf capacitor on a 110-volt 60-cycle line? What is the current?   *Ans.* 13$\overline{2}$0 ohms; 0.0833 amp

19. A variable capacitor of negligible resistance is placed across an a-c source whose effective voltage remains constant. The current in the capacitor is 12 ma. If the capacitance is doubled and the frequency is made three times as large, what will be the new current?

20. (a) What is the reactance of a 3.00-μf capacitor in a 60.0-cycle a-c circuit? (b) What is the impedance of this capacitor in series with a resistance of 300 ohms? (c) What current would there be if this capacitor and resistor were connected to a 1200-volt line?   *Ans.* 883 ohms; 933 ohms; 1.29 amp

21. A series circuit includes a 120-volt 60-cycle source, a resistor of 50.0 ohms, a pure inductance of 100 ohms reactance, and a capacitor of 60.0 ohms reactance. Compare the current in this circuit with the current which would be obtained from a 120-volt 25-cycle source.

22. A 120-ohm rheostat and a good-quality 15.2-μf capacitor are connected in series and joined to a 60-cycle 600-volt line. What is the voltage across each?
                                          Ans. 341 volts; 495 volts

23. A 25.0-μf capacitor having an equivalent resistance of 3.00 ohms is connected in series with a 50.0-ohm resistor. When a 500-cycle 300-volt PD is impressed on the circuit, what is the voltage across the capacitor? across the resistor?

24. A resistor of 4.00 ohms, an inductive coil of negligible resistance and inductance 2.39 mh, and a good-quality 30.0-μf capacitor are connected in series to a source of 500-cycle 110-volt alternating emf. Calculate the reactance of each part of the circuit and the current in the line.
                              Ans. 7.50 ohms; 10.6 ohms; 21.8 amp

25. Circuit elements having pure resistance, inductance, and capacitance are connected in series to an a-c source. A voltmeter reads 40 volts when connected across the resistor, 50 volts across the inductor, and 20 volts across the capacitor. What should the voltmeter read when connected across all three at once?

26. A choke coil takes a current of 5.00 amp from a 120-volt a-c source. A wattmeter connected to the coil reads 450 watts. What is the (a) apparent power, (b) real power, and (c) power factor?
                              Ans. 600 volt-amp; 450 watts; 0.75

27. A fluorescent lamp unit connected to a 110-volt a-c line takes 1.20 amp and requires 110 watts power. What is the power factor?

28. A coil is connected across 220-volt 60-cycle mains. The current in the coil is 4.0 amp and the power delivered is 324 watts. Find the resistance and the inductance of the coil.   *Ans.* 20.3 ohms; 136 mh

29. A coil takes 3.0 amp and 108 watts from a 120-volt 60-cycle line. What is its resistance and inductance?

30. A 250-μf capacitor has an equivalent resistance of 12.5 ohms. What power does it take from a 60-cycle 120-volt line? What is the power factor?
                                          Ans. 670 watts; 0.765

31. A lamp bank operates at a current of 12 amp and a voltage of 120 volts. What power is taken from (a) d-c mains and (b) a-c mains?

32. A 0.10-henry coil (resistance, 100 ohms) and a 10-μf capacitor are connected in series across a 110-volt a-c line. Find the current and the power if the frequency is (a) 60 cycles/sec and (b) 25 cycles/sec.
                          Ans. 0.44 amp; 20 watts; 0.18 amp; 3.2 watts

33. A rheostat and a choke coil of appreciable resistance are connected in series and joined to a 60-cycle 70.0-volt line. The voltage across the rheostat is 25.0 volts and that across the coil is 60.0 volts. Calculate the power factor of the circuit. (HINT: Use the law of cosines.)

34. There is a current of 0.600 amp in a 60-cycle a-c circuit, which consists of a 40.0-ohm lamp, a choke coil of 50.0 ohms resistance, and a capacitor having a negligible resistance, connected in series. The voltage across the coil is 50.0 volts and that across the capacitor is 170 volts. Find the total voltage of the circuit, the power, and the power factor.   *Ans.* 141 volts; 32.4 watts; 0.383

35. A 40.0-volt 500-cycle a-c source is connected to a series circuit containing a 5.00-ohm resistor, a capacitive reactance of 4.00 ohms, and a coil which has a resistance of 1.25 ohms and 12.0 ohms inductive reactance. Calculate the power and the power factor.

36. A capacitor and a coil are connected in series across a 520-volt 60-cycle line. The capacitor has a capacitive reactance of 240 ohms. The coil has a resistance of 60.0 ohms and an inductive reactance of 320 ohms. Find (*a*) the current in the circuit, (*b*) the power factor, (*c*) the power delivered, and (*d*) the capacitance of the capacitor. Is the current lagging or leading?

Ans. 5.20 amp; 0.600; 1620 watts; 11.1 μf

37. A 10.0-ohm resistor and a 0.20-henry inductor of negligible resistance are connected in series with a high-quality capacitor across a 60-cycle main. A voltmeter, an ammeter, and a wattmeter are connected in the circuit. The voltmeter reads 110 volts, the ammeter 5.0 amp, and the wattmeter 250 watts. What is the capacitance of the capacitor? Assume the current is ahead of the voltage in phase.

38. Given a 60-cycle sinusoidal emf of 142 volts (maximum) applied to a circuit having an inductance of 1.0 henry, a capacitance of 0.50 μf, and a resistance of 200 ohms, calculate (*a*) the effective voltage, (*b*) the impedance, (*c*) the effective current, and (*d*) the power factor. Is the current leading or lagging?

Ans. 100 volts; 4900 ohms; 20 ma; 0.041

39. A noninductive resistor of 20 ohms, a coil of negligible resistance and of inductance 300 mh, and a 105-μf capacitor are connected in series across 110-volt 60-cycle mains. Find the current, the power delivered, the power factor, and the potential difference between the terminals of each of the three members.

40. A capacitor and coil are connected in series across a 390-volt 60-cycle a-c line. The capacitor has a capacitive reactance of 480 ohms. The coil has a resistance of 50.0 ohms and an inductive reactance of 360 ohms. Find (*a*) the current in the circuit, (*b*) the power factor, and (*c*) the power delivered. Is the current lagging or leading?   *Ans.* 3.00 amp; 0.384; 450 watts

41. A 10.0-ohm resistor, a 10-mh inductor, and a 250-μf capacitor are connected in series across a 110-volt a-c line. For what frequency will the current be greatest? What is the value of that current?

42. A coil of negligible resistance and inductance 80 mh, a 7.0-ohm resistor, and a 25-μf capacitor are connected in series across 110-volt a-c supply mains of variable frequency. For what frequency is the current a maximum? What is that maximum value? When the current has this value what is the voltage across the inductor? across the resistor? across the capacitor?

Ans. 113 cycles/sec; 16 amp; 890 volts; 110 volts; 890 volts

43. An alternating voltage of 115 volts and frequency 60 cycles/sec is impressed upon a circuit consisting of an electric lamp of 12 ohms resistance, a pure inductance of 2.50 henrys, and a pure capacitance, all connected in series. What must be the value of the capacitance for the circuit to be in resonance? What is the value of the current under these circumstances?

39. Conduction in Gases; Electronics

In the modern development of physics one of the important ideas is that of the electron. The existence of an elementary quantity of electricity was suggested by the experiments on electrolysis conducted by Faraday, which indicated that each ion taking part in electrolysis has a fixed charge, the smallest being that on the monovalent ion. Stoney (1874) attempted to determine the magnitude of this charge by using the measured mass of silver deposited by a coulomb and Avogadro's number N, the number of atoms in a gram atom. From these data he computed the charge per atom. To this unit of charge he gave the name "electron." The value obtained by Stoney was inaccurate because his value of N was in error.

In 1870, Sir William Crookes discovered the phenomenon of cathode rays and later (1879) suggested that the rays consist of streams of negatively charged particles. J. J. Thomson confirmed this hypothesis, showed that all these particles are alike, and named the particles *electrons*.

The subject of *electronics* properly includes all phenomena in which electrons are involved, even though the term is often restricted to the much smaller branch of physics and engineering dealing with vacuum tubes and vacuum-tube circuits. In our discussion we shall adopt the broader definition of the field.

39-1. Conduction of Electricity in Solids and in Liquids. In Chap. 28 conduction of electricity in solids and in liquids was discussed. There it was stated that solid conduction consists of the drift of electrons that have been temporarily detached from the parent atoms. On the other hand, conduction in liquid electrolytes is ionic in nature. Ions, produced by dissociation of molecules, drift through the solution when a potential difference is maintained. Whereas in solid conduction a single kind of charged particle, the negative electron, moves in the process, in electrolytic conduction both positively and negatively charged particles take part in the motion, the positive particles moving in one direction while the negative move in the opposite. Moreover, the particles moving in electrolytic conduction are of atomic or molecular mass, consisting of charged atoms or groups of atoms, while in solids the moving particles have the mass of the electron, much smaller than that of the smallest atom.

39-2. Conduction of Electricity in Gases at Atmospheric Pressure. A third type of conduction occurs in gases. This type of con-

445

duction is similar to liquid conduction in that both positive and negative ions move in the process, but it differs in the very important respect that very few of the ions exist before the beginning of the conduction process. Most of the ions are produced as a result of collisions between moving particles and molecules of the gas. Also the ions are of both atomic and electronic nature.

Under normal conditions a gas is a very poor conductor of electricity. There are very few ions present to take part in the conduction. If a low voltage is applied to the specimen of gas, each ion moves toward the appropriate terminal. In this motion the ions collide frequently with molecules of the gas. In these collisions further ionization rarely takes place, because the ion colliding with a molecule seldom has enough energy to remove an electron from the molecule. As the potential difference applied to the gas is increased, each ion will acquire more energy, on the average, between collisions. When the voltage is great enough that an ion acquires between collisions sufficient energy to ionize the atom or molecule that it strikes, two or more new ions are produced, one being the electron knocked off the atom and the other being the atom less its electron. Thus the number of ions builds up very rapidly and a disruptive discharge, or spark, occurs. This process of cumulative ionization is called *ionization by collision*.

Ionization by collision is dependent upon the interaction of individual ions and atoms or molecules. Whether or not an atom is ionized will depend upon the energy acquired by the ion and also upon the energy necessary to ionize the atom struck. Thus the potential required to produce a disruptive discharge will depend upon the kind of gas, since the energy necessary to ionize the molecules varies from gas to gas. The potential V through which an electron must fall in order to have enough energy to ionize the atom that it hits is called the *ionizing potential* of that atom and is characteristic of the atom. The

energy acquired is Ve, where e is the charge of the electron.

The potential necessary to produce a disruptive discharge is also dependent upon the distance between the atoms or molecules, since that distance must be great enough that

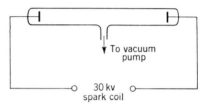

FIG. 1. A low-pressure electric discharge tube.

the fall in potential is equal to the ionization potential of the gas. That is, the potential required for the disruptive discharge depends upon the pressure. When the pressure is high, the ions will move only small distances between collisions since the molecules are close together. A very high potential gradient is then required to produce the discharge. The voltage gradient necessary to produce a spark between fairly large terminals in air at atmospheric pressure is about 30,000 volts per centimeter. If the pressure is reduced, the average distance between molecules is greater and hence, on the average, the ion moves farther between collisions. Hence a smaller potential gradient is required for the ion to acquire sufficient energy between collisions in order to ionize the molecule that it strikes.

39-3. Discharge of Electricity through Gases at Low Pressure. An interesting experiment on phenomena of electric discharges through gases at reduced pressures may be performed by the use of the apparatus shown in Fig. 1. A glass tube about 3 ft long is connected to a vacuum pump. Cylindrical aluminum electrodes sealed into the ends of the tube are attached to the terminals of a source of high voltage, such as an induction coil. When the gas in the tube is at atmospheric pressure, the sparks will pass across the short air gap between the terminals of the induction coil. As the gas pressure in the tube is continuously reduced, the discharge begins to

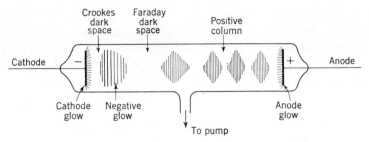

FIG. 2. Discharge of electricity through a gas at reduced pressure.

pass through the long tube, in preference to the shorter path between the terminals of the coil in air at atmospheric pressure. The gas in the tube emits light of a color characteristic of the particular gas used. When air is used, the first discharge to appear consists of long sparklike streamers emitting bluish-violet light. As the pressure is reduced further a glow appears on the cathode, or negative terminal. At still lower pressure, this glow moves away from the cathode and a pinkish glow appears throughout most of the tube. The appearance of the tube at a pressure of a few tenths of a millimeter of mercury is shown schematically in Fig. 2. Each of the electrodes is covered by a velvety glow, known, respectively, as the cathode and anode glow. A comparatively dark space near the cathode is called the *Crookes dark space*. Near it is a short region of light known as the *negative glow*, this being followed by another darker portion designated the *Faraday dark space*. The major portion of the tube is filled with a striated series of bright and dark regions called the *positive column*.

If the pressure of the gas in the tube is lowered below the optimum value for the type of discharge just described, it will be observed that the Crookes dark space becomes larger, finally filling the whole tube. At this stage most of the ions traverse the whole length of the tube without colliding with a molecule of the gas. Consequently, there are few ions produced, and the discharge current decreases. The voltage required to maintain the discharge rises rapidly until finally, at very high vacuum, the discharge becomes nearly impossible.

39-4. Cathode Rays. At intermediate pressure, about 0.001 mm of mercury, many of the positive ions will traverse nearly the whole length of the tube without collision and strike the cathode with enough energy to cause it to emit a considerable number of

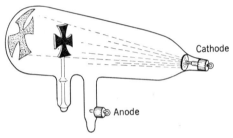

FIG. 3. Cathode rays travel in straight lines.

electrons. These electrons stream away from the negatively charged cathode in directions at right angles to the surface. Such electrons are called *cathode rays*. Historically the study of their properties has yielded very rich dividends.

Some of the properties of cathode rays can be demonstrated rather easily. A few of these properties are listed below.

Cathode rays travel in straight lines perpendicular to the surface of the cathode. If a discharge tube contains a metal obstruction in the path of the cathode rays, the shadow cast by the obstruction is sharp, indicating that the rays travel in straight lines (Fig. 3). If the surface of the cathode is made concave, the rays are focused at the center of curvature of the cathode (Fig. 4), which shows that they travel at right angles to the surface.

Cathode rays have kinetic energy. When an intense beam of cathode rays is allowed to fall on a target, the target is heated by the impact of the rays (Fig. 4). Also, if the target is movable, it can be set into motion by the impact of the particles.

Cathode rays can produce fluorescence. If a beam of cathode rays is allowed to fall on a suitable material, light is emitted. The color is characteristic of the fluorescing material. If the

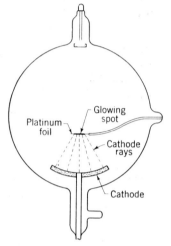

FIG. 4. Heating effect of cathode rays.

walls of the tube are ordinary soft glass, they will fluoresce with an apple-green color. Some materials will continue to emit light for a short time after the beam has been discontinued.

Cathode rays can be deflected by a magnetic field. If cathode rays are confined in a small beam and a magnet is brought near, the pencil of rays is deflected in the direction that moving negative charges would be deflected.

Cathode rays are deflected by an electrostatic field. If the narrow pencil of rays is passed between two plates, one of which is positive and the other negative, the electrons will be deflected toward the positive plate.

Cathode rays can produce x rays. If the energy of the cathode rays is sufficiently high, very penetrating radiation is emitted when they strike a target. These penetrating rays are called x rays. Their properties will be discussed in a later chapter.

39-5. Electrons. J. J. Thomson gave the name *electron* to the particles that make up the streams of cathode rays and studied their properties by use of the deflection in electric and magnetic fields. In Fig. 5 is shown a diagram of apparatus similar to that used by Thomson. The cathode rays are accelerated as they move toward the anode. Some of them pass through the opening in the anode and a narrow pencil proceeds into the region beyond the anode. There the particles pass between two plates spaced a distance s apart and differing in potential by V. Each particle will experience a force as it moves between the plates and it will be deflected downward:

$$F = \mathcal{E}e \qquad (1)$$

where $\mathcal{E}$ is the strength of the electric field and e is the charge of the particle. But $\mathcal{E} = -\Delta V/\Delta s$. If the field between the plates is uniform, the magnitude of the field strength will be $\mathcal{E} = V/s$ and

$$F = \frac{V}{s} e \qquad (2)$$

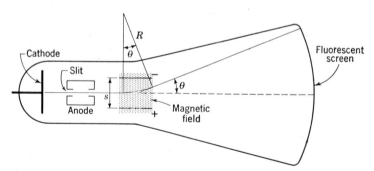

FIG. 5. Diagram of apparatus used to measure e/m for the electron.

If V is in volts, s in meters, and e in coulombs, Eq. (2) gives the force in newtons. Since the force is constant and perpendicular to the initial path, the path of the particle between the plates is parabolic like that of a projectile.

If in place of the electric field a magnetic field is used, directed out of the paper toward the reader, the particles again experience a force, this time perpendicular to the direction of motion of the particles and the particles will move in a circular path while in the field. The force on a current is

$$F_1 = BIl$$

If in the stream of electrons there are n electrons per unit length, each moving with a speed v, the current is $I = nev$, and

$$F_1 = Bnevl$$

But there are nl electrons in the field. Thus the centripetal force F on a single electron is $F = F_1/nl$ and

$$F = Bev = \frac{mv^2}{R} \qquad (3)$$

$$v = \frac{BeR}{m} \qquad (4)$$

If both electric and magnetic fields are present at the same time, the magnetic field deflects the particles upward, while the electric field deflects them downward. Thus one can adjust the fields so that the resultant force is zero and there will be no deflection of the beam as shown by no change in position of the spot on the fluorescent screen. Then, from Eqs. (2) and (3),

$$\frac{V}{s} e = Bev \qquad (5)$$

When we substitute for v from Eq. (4) we obtain

$$\frac{V}{s} e = Be \frac{BeR}{m} \qquad (6)$$

$$\frac{e}{m} = \frac{V}{sB^2R} \qquad (7)$$

Thus from measurements of V and B Thomson was able to determine the ratio of charge to mass for the electron and found it to be much greater than the corresponding ratio for the hydrogen ion. Later, more accurate measurements showed its value to be about 1837 times that of the hydrogen ion. The present most probable value of e/m for the electron is 1.75890×10^{11} coulombs/kg.

39-6. Charge of the Electron. Thomson's experiment enabled him to determine e/m but not to determine independently either e or m for the electron. Townsend, Thomson, and Millikan carried out experiments designed to measure the charge e. Townsend and Thomson worked with clouds of water droplets which when charged were supported by electric fields between two parallel horizontal plates. These experiments were not very accurate, partly because of evaporation of the water droplets. Millikan, in his famous oil-drop experiment, modified and improved the procedure, minimizing evaporation by the use of oil and observing individual small droplets for comparatively long times. His apparatus is shown schematically in Fig. 6. The size of the droplets could be determined from the rate of fall when the plates were

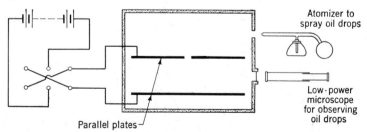

FIG. 6. Apparatus for an oil-drop experiment. Ionization between the plates may be produced by radioactive material or an x-ray tube not shown.

uncharged. By adjusting the potential difference between the plates, the droplet could be held stationary or caused to rise or fall in the field of view. When the droplet is stationary, its weight is balanced by the force of the field

$$\frac{V}{s} q = mg \qquad (8)$$

where V is the potential difference of the plates, q ($= ne$) is the charge on the droplet, s is the distance between the plates, and m is the mass of the droplet. Using many droplets of different sizes and various charges it was found that all charges were whole-number multiples of a smallest charge e. At present the most probable value for e, which may be determined by various methods, is $e = 1.60206 \times 10^{-19}$ coulomb. The electronic charge e is a natural unit of electric charge.

From the values of e and e/m, one can compute the mass of the electron

$$m = \frac{e}{e/m} = \frac{1.60206 \times 10^{-19} \text{ coulomb}}{1.75890 \times 10^{11} \text{ coulombs/kg}}$$
$$= 9.1083 \times 10^{-31} \text{ kg}$$

39-7. Conduction of Electricity in a Vacuum. In all conduction of electricity there is a transfer of some kind of charged particle. Hence in a perfect vacuum there can be no conduction at all. At high vacuum, the number of ionic carriers is so small that the current is negligible even at high voltages. Few ions are produced by collision because of the rarity of such occurrences. Hence if there is to be appreciable conduction in a region of high vacuum, ions must be introduced by some process. The most common of the processes is *thermionic emission*.

39-8. Thermionic Emission. In any substance, gas, liquid, or solid, the particles of the medium are in constant motion if the temperature is above the absolute zero. The temperature is a measure of the average kinetic energy of the particles. If a liquid is in an open container, it will evaporate because some of the molecules have sufficient energy

to escape from the surface. As the temperature of the liquid is raised, more and more of the molecules acquire the necessary energy, and hence the evaporation becomes more rapid. This process occurs also in solids though it is usually slower at ordinary temperatures since greater energies are required to break through the surface.

It has already been noted that in metallic conductors there are always present free electrons in addition to the molecules of the conductor. Both molecules and electrons take part in the thermal agitation, but the electrons, being of much smaller mass, have higher average speeds than the molecules. If the temperature is raised sufficiently, many of the electrons will attain speeds sufficient for them to leave the metal. The temperature at which this process begins depends upon the kind of metal and the condition of its surface. As electrons are emitted by a heated wire, the wire becomes positively charged, while the electrons collect in a "cloud" around it. This charge around the filament is called a *space charge*. Other electrons, as they tend to leave the filament, are attracted by the wire and repelled by the space charge. These effects combine to stop the emission unless the filament is connected into a circuit so that it is supplied with electrons and the space charge is largely removed.

39-9. The Diode. If a filament and a plate are sealed into an evacuated tube, a two-element electron tube, or *diode* (Fig. 7), is formed. When the filament is heated by an electric current, electrons are emitted. If the plate is made positive with respect to the filament, electrons will be attracted to the plate and there will be a current in the tube. If, however, the plate is made negative with respect to the filament, the electrons will be repelled and there will be no current. The diode thus acts as a *valve*, permitting flow in one direction but not in the other. If it is connected in an a-c line, the diode acts as a rectifier; there is a current during the half cycle in which the plate is positive.

If the plate is positive with respect to the filament, electrons will flow across, but not all the electrons that come out of the filament reach the plate, because of the space charge. Figure 8 shows a graph of potential against distance across the tube. Because of the space

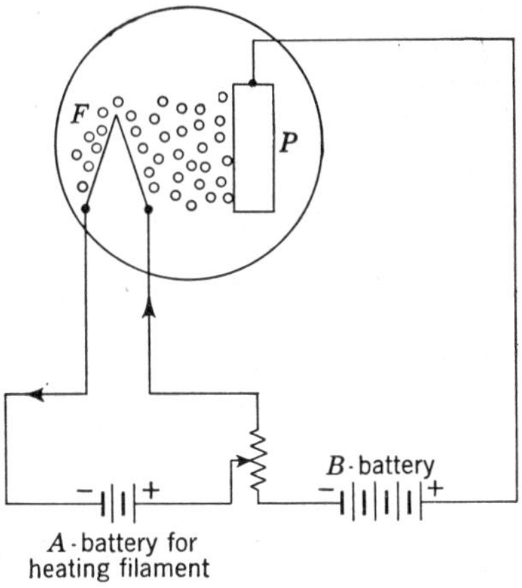

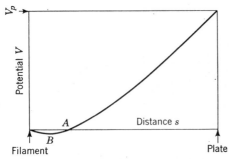

FIG. 7. A diode.

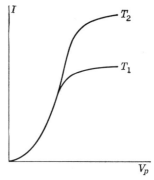

FIG. 9. Plate current as a function of plate potential.

FIG. 8. Variation of potential between filament and plate.

reach the plate. Further increase of V_p produces no change. *Saturation* has been reached. At a higher temperature T_2 more electrons are emitted; hence the saturation current is higher.

If the plate potential is kept constant while the filament temperature is increased, the current increases at first but reaches saturation because of the increase in the electron cloud around the filament.

39-10. The Triode. If a third element, the *grid*, is inserted into the tube near the filament, it can be used as a control for the tube current. Such a tube is called a *triode*, or three-element tube. The grid usually consists of a helix, or spiral, of fine wire so that the electrons may freely pass through it. Small variations of the grid potential will cause large changes in the plate current, much larger than those caused by similar changes in the plate potential. If the grid is kept negative with respect to the filament, electrons will not be attracted to the grid itself, and there will be no grid current. A typical variation of plate current with grid potential V_g is shown in Fig. 10. A part of the curve is practically a straight line. If the grid voltage varies about a value in this region, the fluctuations of the plate current will have the same shape as the variations of grid voltage. The tube will *amplify* the disturbance without distorting it.

The triode also acts as a *detector* or partial rectifier if the grid voltage is adjusted to the

charge, the potentials at points out to A are below the potential of the filament. An electron will reach the plate only if it has sufficient speed as it leaves the filament to reach B, the point of lowest potential, before it is stopped. If the difference of potential V_p between filament and plate is increased, the potential at B rises, and more electrons will be able to reach the plate. The current depends upon V_p, as is shown in the graph of Fig. 9. At a temperature T_1 the current increases as the potential is raised until nearly all the electrons emitted by the filament

bend of the curve. With this adjustment an increase in grid voltage above the average produces considerable increase in plate current, but a decrease in grid voltage causes little change in plate current. The plate current fluctuates in response to the grid signal,

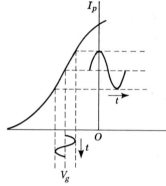

Fig. 10. Operating characteristics of a vacuum-tube amplifier.

but the fluctuations are largely on one side of the steady current.

In Fig. 11 is shown a simple receiving circuit. When the waves strike the antenna, they set up oscillations in the circuit, which is tuned to the frequency of the waves. This

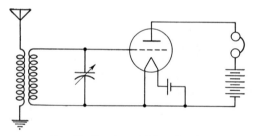

Fig. 11. Simple receiving circuit.

causes the potential of the grid to vary, and the tube acting as a detector produces a variation in current according to the amplitude of the signal. This causes the earphones to emit sound.

In radio circuits, triode electron tubes are used to produce high-frequency oscillations, to act as detectors or rectifiers, and to act as amplifiers. Tubes of different characteristics are used for each of these purposes.

In many tubes the filament merely acts as a heater of a sleeve that covers it and is insulated from it. The sleeve, or *cathode*, is the element that emits electrons.

For many purposes tubes are constructed with more than three active elements. They

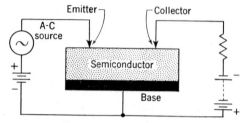

Fig. 12. Transistor circuit.

are named from the number of active elements, as *tetrode*, *pentode*, etc.

39-11. Transistor. One outgrowth of years of research on semiconductors and rectifiers is a device called a *transistor* that may be used in place of an electron tube.

An example of the semiconductor is germanium. Pure germanium has few electrons available for conduction (Chap. 51) and hence is a poor conductor. When minute traces of an impurity, for example, antimony, which is capable of supplying conduction electrons, are added to the germanium the conduction is slightly increased. With this type of impurity the negative conduction electrons are free to migrate within the crystal and hence this is called n-type germanium. If, instead, a different impurity is added, for example, gallium, which is able to borrow electrons from the germanium, gaps or "holes" appear in the structure that are electron deficiencies and therefore equivalent to positive charges. The holes may migrate through the crystal and furnish the equivalent of a moving positive charge. This is called p-type germanium. Both types of germanium are used in making transistors. Other semiconductors are also used.

In one form, the point-contact type, the transistor consists of a small block of semiconducting material, if germanium usually n-type, with three electrodes properly placed

(Fig. 12). One electrode, the base, makes close contact with the semiconductor; the other two are fine points that make light contact. One point contact is called the emitter, the other the collector. The emitter is connected to the base through a low-voltage

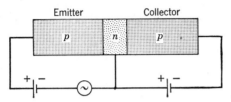

FIG. 13. Circuit for junction-type transistor.

battery in such a manner that the emitter is positive. The collector is connected to the base by a higher voltage battery so that the collector is negative. For the proper values of emitter and collector currents a small change in emitter current causes a large change in collector current. The transistor acts primarily as a current amplifier whereas the electron tube is primarily a voltage amplifier.

A second kind of transistor is the junction type, Fig. 13. It consists of three sections, the two end sections of the same type, n or p, and the central section of the other, p or n. They would be labeled n-p-n or p-n-p. Suitable connections are shown in Fig. 13 for a p-n-p type. For the n-p-n type the emitter and collector voltages are negative and positive respectively. Junction transistors are more stable as amplifiers than point-contact transistors, give higher power gain and less noise.

Certain advantages of the transistor over an electron tube are quite apparent. The transistor is much smaller than the tube and

thus the circuit can be more compact. No energy is necessary to heat a filament; thus there is a saving in space and weight by elimination of the heater source. The elimination of the filament also tends to increase stability in the circuit and to permit longer life.

39-12. Cathode-ray Tubes. The fact that cathode rays are really electrons traveling at high speed away from the cathode is made use of in instruments such as television tubes and cathode-ray oscilloscopes. The oscilloscope tube was first developed by the physicist Braun in 1897. The essentials of a modern tube are shown in Fig. 14. Cathode rays from the thermionic cathode C pass through a small hole in a control grid and are accelerated by the voltage applied to the anode A. The electrons then pass between two pairs of parallel plates to which various test voltages may be applied. One pair of plates V is horizontal, the other H is vertical. The electric fields of these plates therefore cause deflections, either vertically or horizontally in proportion to the values of the test voltages applied. The spot of light on the fluorescent screen S at the large end of the tube can travel around with extraordinary rapidity, because of the very small mass of the electrons and their high speeds. Hence these tubes can be used to follow transient variations of voltage, which are of entirely too high frequency for any mechanical device to follow.

39-13. Positive Rays; Mass Spectrograph. The atomic masses of elements historically have been measured by conventional chemical methods, using comparatively large

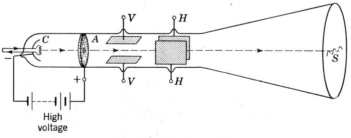

FIG. 14. Cathode-ray tube.

amounts of the material under test. Developments in electronics have provided scientists with apparatus far more precise and capable of making measurements on individual atoms and ions. One such device is known as the *mass spectrograph*, a well-chosen designation,

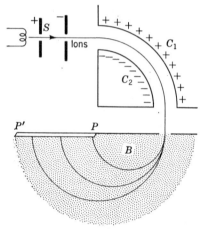

FIG. 15. A Dempster-type mass spectrograph.

since it enables measurements to be made of atomic masses and to separate a mixture of ions into a veritable spectrum of atoms having different masses.

A form of mass spectrograph designed by Dempster (1936) is shown schematically in Fig. 15. This apparatus is based upon the fact that a beam of ions moving through electric and magnetic fields suffers a deflection that depends upon the charges and masses of the ions. Hence ions of various masses are deflected differently. A source of positive ions near the slit S is made to pass through a radial electric field set up by the cylindrical capacitor plates C_1 and C_2. The ions are thereby bent into paths that are arcs of circles. Those

that emerge from the slit have a common velocity and enter a magnetic field that is at right angles to the electric field. The magnetic field causes the ions of different masses to be separated so that they fall at different places on the photographic plate PP'. The blackening of the plate gives clear indication of the masses of the respective ions. A typical mass spectrogram is shown in Fig. 16.

39-14. Isotopes. Studies of positive rays first showed that not all atoms of a given element have identical atomic masses. Although the various atoms of a given element have exactly the same chemical properties, it was shown by mass spectrographic studies that such atoms frequently have different atomic masses. Elements which have the same chemical properties (atomic number, or position in the periodic table) but different masses are known as *isotopes*. Chlorine, atomic mass 35.46, is a mixture of isotopes of masses 35 and 37. The case of hydrogen is an extreme example. Its atomic mass is 1.00813 and it is a mixture of ordinary hydrogen of mass 1 and "heavy hydrogen" of mass 2. This isotope (unlike other cases) has been given the special name of *deuterium*. A third isotope of mass 3 has also been identified. It has been named *tritium*. Various elements are composed of quite different numbers of isotopes, ranging from 1 for many elements to 10 for tin.

39-15. The Photoelectric Effect. The action of electromagnetic radiation (light) in causing the emission of electrons is called the *photoelectric effect*. Light of suitable frequency incident upon certain metallic surfaces causes the emission of electrons from these materials. A photoelectric tube (Fig. 17) consists of a

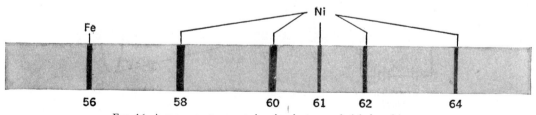

FIG. 16. A mass spectrogram showing isotopes of nickel and iron.

cathode having a photosensitive surface and an anode suitably arranged in a glass bulb, which is either evacuated or filled with an inert gas at low pressure. Common light-sensitive surfaces are potassium, cesium, sodium, barium, rubidium, and certain

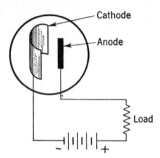

FIG. 17. A photoelectric tube.

oxides. The anode is frequently a wire parallel to the axis of the cathode, connected to the positive terminal of a battery through a sensitive meter.

The number of photoelectrons emitted per second by the cathode as a result of the radiation falling upon it is directly proportional to the intensity of the incident radiation. The current in the meter therefore faithfully measures the intensity of the radiation.

39-16. Photovoltaic Cells. A photovoltaic device is one in which the energy of the incident light produces an emission of photoelectrons creating a potential difference that may be used to maintain an electric current, without the use of an auxiliary battery. The most common type in use today is exemplified by the Weston photronic cell (Fig. 18). This cell has a thin film of selenium formed on an iron plate. Light incident upon the selenium surface produces a photovoltaic effect resulting in the iron becoming a positive terminal and the selenium a negative terminal of the cell. A sensitive meter connected across these two surfaces will indicate a current. This current is proportional to the intensity of the light and the meter may therefore be calibrated directly in suitable units, for example as an exposure meter.

39-17. Applications of Photoelectric Cells. The motion-picture industry depends on photoelectric devices for the recording and reproduction of sound. These cells also are used extensively in control devices in industry. By sending a beam of light across the

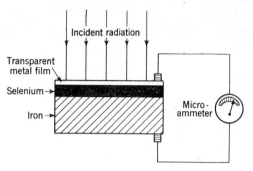

FIG. 18. A Weston photronic cell.

path of a succession of moving objects and into a photoelectric cell it is possible to count the number of objects, to detect inferior ones, and to actuate automatic control devices. These cells are used to actuate burglar alarms, to turn lights off or on at suitable times, to open doors as one approaches, to count vehicular traffic, to control power devices, and to furnish television signals.

SUMMARY

All electrical conduction consists of motion of some charged particles. In metals the carriers are electrons; in electrolytes they are positive and negative ions formed by dissociation; in gases they are positive and negative ions produced by collisions between ions and molecules of the gas.

Gases under standard conditions are very poor conductors but become rather good conductors at reduced pressure.

Cathode rays are streams of electrons. They emerge normally from the surface of the cathode, travel in straight lines, may be easily deflected by magnetic or electric fields, cause fluorescence when they strike many minerals, and produce heating, chemical, and physiological effects upon matter.

Electrons are basic particles of electricity. All charges are multiples of the electronic charge. The ratio of charge to mass of the electron can be determined by means of deflection in magnetic and electric fields. The charge was first accurately determined by the Millikan oil-drop experiment.

In order to have conduction in a vacuum charges must be introduced. This is most conveniently done by *thermionic emission*, the emission of electrons by a conductor when it is heated to a sufficiently high temperature.

Two-element tubes, or *diodes*, act as rectifiers in a-c circuits.

Three-element tubes, or *triodes*, may be used as amplifiers, oscillators, or detectors.

Transistors are devices for using the rectifying and amplifying properties of semiconductors. They can replace electron tubes for many uses.

Cathode-ray oscilloscopes are used to study rapidly varying voltages and other transient or cyclic phenomena. As such they are useful in radar and television.

Positive rays are streams of positive ions. They are used in the mass spectrograph for the identification and measurement of atomic masses and the study of isotopes.

The *photoelectric effect* is the liberation of electrons in a material by means of radiation. In many photoelectric cells the photoelectric current is proportional to the intensity of the radiation.

Photovoltaic cells are those in which light produces an emf used to maintain an electric current.

QUESTIONS   **1.** Would a spark discharge begin at the same potential difference for all gases at a given pressure?

2. Lightning is a huge spark between charged clouds. How might the voltage required to produce lightning vary from clouds near the earth as compared with those very high in the atmosphere?

3. Could there ever be a disruptive discharge of electricity between the earth and the moon? Why?

4. Electrodes are set at the two ends of a tube in which the pressure of air can be varied. Sketch a curve of pressure *vs.* potential difference necessary to produce a discharge.

5. State and describe briefly the three main functions that are performed by thermionic vacuum tubes in modern radio receivers.

6. Describe a number of practical uses of an electron tube.

7. In using a three-element tube as an amplifier, it is desirable to arrange the circuit so that the linear portion of the characteristic curve is used. Show why this is desirable and what happens when other portions of the curve are used.

8. How can one determine the portion of the characteristic curve that is used when a three-element tube is operating?

9. Why is it true that a thermionic tube should produce a louder radio signal than a crystal detector?

10. Explain why it is expected that the wireless transmission of power over long distances is commercially impractical. Why then is it possible to utilize receiving sets at great distances from the transmitter?

11. Radio reception is frequently very seriously interfered with when an electric shaver is being used near the radio receiver. Show why this is to be expected. How may this be minimized?

12. Show clearly why the mass spectrograph gives data on the atomic masses of individual ions while conventional chemical methods yield results only on average atomic masses.

13. A circuit consists of a battery, a rheostat, and a photoelectric cell, connected in series. The voltage across the rheostat is found to change with the illumination on the photoelectric cell. Explain why this is true.

14. Make a list of some of the services that can be performed by the aid of relays actuated by photovoltaic cells.

PROBLEMS   *Whenever needed in the following problems, take the electronic charge to be* 1.60×10^{-19} *coulomb, the electronic mass* 9.108×10^{-31} *kg, and the mass of an atom of unit atomic mass* 1.66×10^{-27} *kg. An alpha particle has a mass of four atomic mass units and a positive charge of two electronic units.*

1. An electron volt is a unit of energy. Express this unit in joules. What is the speed of an electron accelerated by a potential difference of 1.00 volt?

2. An electron is accelerated by a potential difference of 12 volts. Find the energy acquired by the electron and its speed.

Ans. 1.9×10^{-18} joule; 2.0×10^{6} m/sec

3. What energy is acquired by an electron in falling through a potential difference of 50.0 volts? What is its speed after this acceleration if it starts from rest?

4. The PD between the filament and the plate of diode is 120 volts. What speed does an electron acquire in moving from the cathode to the anode of this tube?   *Ans.* 6.50×10^{6} m/sec

5. A cathode-ray tube has plates that are separated by 6.25 mm. There is a a PD of 3.16 kv applied to the plates. What is the average acceleration of a cathode-ray electron caused by the electric field between these plates?

6. A stream of electrons from the cathode of a triode equivalent to a current of 1.36 ma strikes a thin metallic grid with a speed of 8.64×10^{6} m/sec. The grid reduces the speed of the electrons to one-third of the original value. At what rate is heat developed in the grid?   *Ans.* 6.12×10^{-2} cal/sec $= 0.256$ joule/sec

7. A stream of electrons, accelerated by a potential difference of 100 volts, passes midway between two plates 2.00 cm apart and 5.00 cm long. The beam continues to a screen 20.0 cm beyond the plates. What is the deflection of the beam on the screen when a potential difference of 20.0 volts is maintained between the plates?

8. A stream of particles of atomic mass 4.0 and double electronic charge is accelerated by a potential difference of 100 volts and projected midway between two parallel plates 1.00 cm apart and 3.00 cm long. What is the deflection of the beam on a screen 15.0 cm beyond the plates when a potential difference of 20.0 volts is maintained between the plates?   *Ans.* 5.0 cm

9. What speed must an electron have for its path to be a circle of radius 1.00 cm if it is projected normal to a magnetic field where $B = 0.0020$ w/m²?

10. A beam of electrons moving with a uniform speed of 4.00×10^{7} m/sec is projected normal to a uniform magnetic field where $B = 0.0010$ w/m². What is the path of the beam in the magnetic field?   *Ans.* Circle of radius 22.7 cm

11. Calculate the period of revolution of a free electron moving in a plane perpendicular to the magnetic field of the earth with a speed of 2.65×10^{6} m/sec at a place where the magnetic induction is 0.76×10^{-4} w/m².

12. An alpha particle is constrained to move in a circular path of radius 354 mm by a uniform magnetic field of induction of 0.085 w/m². (*a*) What is the speed of the particle? (*b*) What work is done by the field on the particle?

Ans. 1.45×10^{6} m/sec; zero

13. A proton is projected at right angles into a uniform magnetic field of induction of 8.62 w/m². The speed of the proton is 2.43×10^{5} m/sec. Calculate the acceleration of the proton.

14. An electron is projected at right angles into a uniform electric field of intensity 7.85×10^3 newtons/coulomb that causes the electron to be deflected 2.54 mm from its path. Show how a magnetic field must be arranged and calculate its flux density in order to keep the electron from being deflected if the initial speed of the electron is 3.75×10^6 m/sec.   *Ans.* 2.09×10^{-3} w/m^2

15. A proton moving with a speed of 1.15×10^5 m/sec enters at an angle of $40°$ a uniform magnetic field of induction 0.283 w/m^2. Calculate the acceleration of the proton.

16. The electron in a hydrogen atom revolves in an approximately circular orbit of radius 5.28×10^{-9} cm. (*a*) If a hydrogen atom is situated in a uniform magnetic field of induction 11.2 w/m^2 perpendicular to the orbit, what is the centripetal magnetic force? (*b*) Compare this force with the electrostatic force of attraction by the nucleus.   *Ans.* 3.91×10^{-12} newton; $1/(2.1 \times 10^4)$

17. A stream of electrons is accelerated by a potential difference of 50 volts and proceeds into a uniform magnetic field where $B = 0.0080$ w/m^2. What is the radius of the path in the magnetic field?

18. A stream of positive ions is accelerated by a potential difference of 120 volts and then passes into a uniform magnetic field ($B = 0.0378$ w/m^2) where they move in a circular path of radius 20.0 cm. Each ion carries one electronic unit of charge. What is the atomic mass of the ions?   *Ans.* 23

19. A charged particle travels in a straight line between two horizontal charged plates between which there is an electric field of 2.0 volts/cm upward. A magnetic flux density of 2.0 w/m^2 is directed at right angles to the electric field "into the paper". If the particle has a positive charge of 1.0×10^{-6} coulomb, what is the magnitude and direction of its velocity?

20. Calculate the nature and magnitude of the path described by an alpha particle which is projected with a speed of 4.25×10^2 m/sec at right angles to a uniform magnetic field of induction 0.382 w/m^2.   *Ans.* $r = 23 \times 10^{-6}$ m

21. What electric field would just support a water droplet 1.0×10^{-4} cm in diameter, carrying one electronic charge?

22. An oil droplet whose mass is 2.5×10^{-11} gm and which carries two electronic charges is between two horizontal plates 2.0 cm apart. Assume that the droplet is entirely supported by electric forces. What must be the potential difference between the plates to support the droplet?   *Ans.* 15,000 volts

23. Two isotopes of copper have mass numbers of 63 and 65. If the positive ions are accelerated by a potential difference of 25 volts and deflected $180°$ by a magnetic field ($B = 0.0200$ w/m^2), what will be the separation of the lines on the photographic plate? Assume each ion carries a single electronic charge.

24. Positive ions each carrying a single electronic charge are accelerated in a Dempster-type mass spectrograph by a potential difference of 30 volts. They leave the slit moving normal to a magnetic field in which $B = 0.018$ w/m^2. They are deflected $180°$ in the field and strike a photographic plate. One group of ions is known to be sodium, atomic mass 23; the others are unknown. On the plate the second and third lines are, respectively, 1.0 and 1.8 cm beyond the sodium line. Find the atomic mass of each of the unknowns.   *Ans.* 24; 25

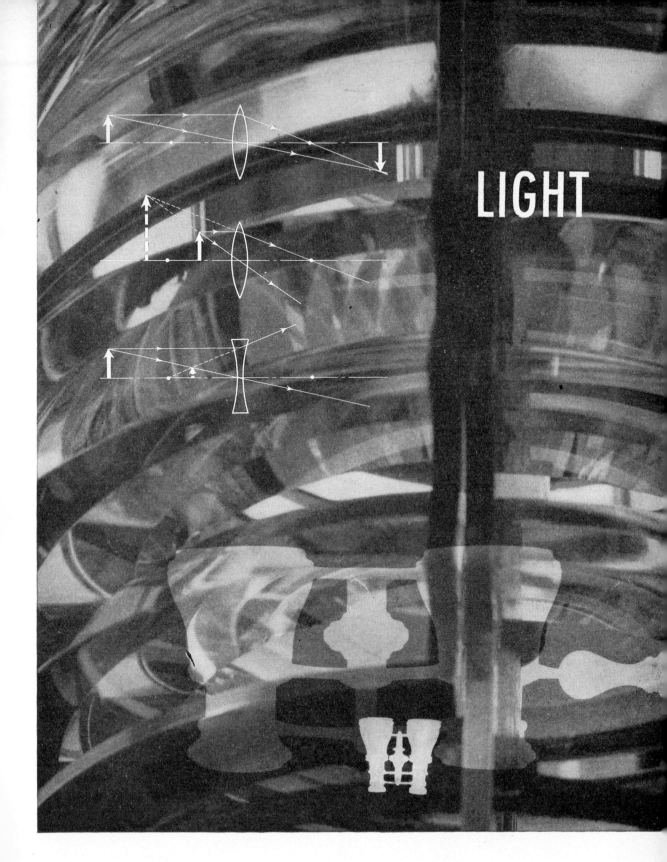

LIGHT

40. *Light and Illumination*

Optics is the field of science which treats of light, its sources, its propagation, and the effects which it suffers and produces. Much of the everyday usefulness of light can be understood from a study of *geometrical* optics, the branch which treats light propagation in terms of rays, which are straight lines in homogeneous mediums. In *physical* optics, light is treated as an electromagnetic wave phenomenon and its propagation is studied by means of wave fronts. *Physiological* optics embraces the geometrical and physical optics of the eye and its parts, together with the physiology (and much of the psychology) of the visual process. *Quantum* optics originated when the quantum theory of radiation was applied to explain the exchange of energy between light and electrons in the photoelectric effect (Chaps. 28, 39, 49), and to explain the regularities in the frequencies of light radiated by atoms (Chap. 49).

Much is known about radiant energy but sufficient mystery remains to suggest that the continued study of radiation may lead to exciting discoveries.

40-1. Nature of Light. Early investigators of light tried to answer the question: Is luminous energy transmitted by emission of particles or by emission of waves? This question could be answered satisfactorily only by observing the behavior of light.

In Chap. 23 we have listed five characteristics of wave motions, common to all waves:

1. Straight-line propagation within a uniform medium
2. Reflection at the boundary of a medium
3. Refraction where there is a change of speed
4. Interference
5. Diffraction

But particles travel in straight lines when no net force acts on them; particles may be reflected at a suitable boundary; and the direction of motion of particles may be changed when their speed changes. However, particles cannot show interference or diffraction effects.

At the time of Newton and Huygens (late seventeenth century) only linear propagation, reflection, and refraction had been observed for light. In the absence of evidence of interference and diffraction, Newton favored the theory that light had a particle nature. In contrast, and in spite of failure to observe interference and diffraction, Huygens believed in the wave nature of light. Observation of interference and diffraction (early nineteenth century) upheld Huygens' belief. During most of the nineteenth century the wave nature of light was generally accepted.

Energy in transit in the form of radiant energy can be detected and studied only when it is intercepted by matter and converted into thermal, electric, chemical, or mechanical energy. The energy and wavelength of radiant energy can thus be measured by purely physical means. Other aspects of radiant energy depend upon the presence and response of an observer. *Light* is the aspect of radiant energy of which a human observer

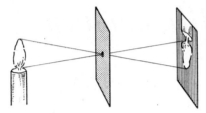

FIG. 1. Formation of an image in a pinhole camera by the straight-line propagation of light.

is aware through the visual sensations which arise from the stimulation of the retina of the eye.

The wavelength of radiant energy capable of visual detection varies from about 3.9 to 7.6 ten-thousandths of a millimeter. Light wavelengths are usually expressed in angstrom units (A) or in microns (μ). One angstrom unit is 10^{-8} cm. One micron (a millionth of a meter) is 10^{-4} cm. The range of visible radiation is 390 to 760 mμ (millimicrons) or 3900 to 7600 A. Because of the very short wavelength, there is little spreading of light around and behind obstacles as is observed with water waves and sound waves. Except for such diffraction effects, to be discussed later, light travels in straight lines in a homogeneous medium. The rectilinear propagation of light is made use of in sighting with a plumb line, in aiming a gun, or in forming a photographic image in a pinhole camera (Fig. 1).

Radiation similar to light and having wavelengths between 390 and 100 mμ constitutes *ultraviolet* radiation and is detected by photographic means. That in the wavelength range from 760 mμ to 1 mm is called *infrared* radiation. The longer wavelengths of infrared radiation are most readily detected by their thermal effects. According to the electromag-

netic theory of light, originated by Maxwell, all these waves are the same in kind as those which constitute the electromagnetic oscillations of radio waves.

Study of the interaction between matter and energy has added to our ideas about light an important assumption which is the basis of the *quantum theory*. According to this theory

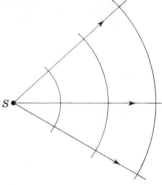

FIG. 2. Light waves and rays. The concentric arcs represent sections of wave fronts. The straight lines represent rays.

energy transfers between light and matter occur only in discrete amounts of energy (quanta), which are proportional to the frequency as given by

$$W = hf \qquad (1)$$

If f is the frequency in vibrations per second and h is Planck's constant, whose value is determined experimentally to be 6.61×10^{-34} joule-sec, the energy W is in joules (Chap. 49).

40-2. Waves and Rays. The representation of a wave motion was discussed in Chap. 23. Figure 2 shows spherical waves spreading from a small source and also the radial lines, called *rays*, drawn to show the direction in which the waves are moving. The rays are merely convenient construction lines that often enable us to discuss the travel of light more simply than by drawing the waves.

40-3. Shadows. In Fig. 3a, light from a small source encounters an obstacle placed between the source and a screen. The ob-

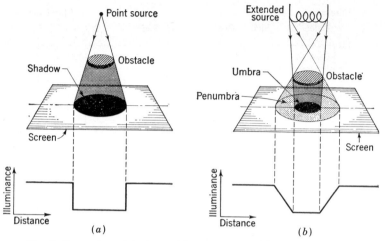

FIG. 3. Formation of shadows: (*a*) point source; (*b*) extended source.

stacle casts a shadow, that is, all parts of the screen are illuminated except the area within the curve determined by drawing rays from the source that just touch the edge of the obstacle at each point. A graph of the illumination measured along the axis of the screen is represented in the lower part of Fig. 3*a* and shows the sudden drop of illumination within the shadow.

If the source is not small (Fig. 3*b*) or if there is more than one source, the shadow will consist of two parts: a completely dark one, where no light arrives at the screen, and a gray shadow, which is illuminated from part of the source only.

During a total eclipse of the sun, the moon comes directly between the earth and the sun. Within the central cone of rays, no light is received from any part of the sun's disk. A person located within the central cone experiences a total eclipse and does not see the sun at all. But a person located anywhere in the penumbra region (Fig. 3*b*) sees a crescent-shaped part of the sun—a partial eclipse.

40-4. Sources of Light. Our most important source of light and life-sustaining radiation is the sun. Most artificial sources of light are hot bodies which radiate light but which also emit much infrared radiation. Hence as producers of visible radiation they have a low efficiency. Generally the efficiency of such light sources improves as the operating temperature is increased. The early carbon-filament electric lamp, which supplanted the open-flame gas light, employed an electrically heated filament as the source of radiation. The filament was mounted in an evacuated glass envelope to prevent its oxidation. In a modern electric lamp the use of a tungsten spiral filament in a bulb containing inert gas permits operation at a higher temperature (3000°C) without excessive evaporation of the filament.

The carbon arc also uses the heating effect of an electric current. Most of the light originates at the crater of the positive carbon which attains a temperature of 3700°C. The brilliant white light of a carbon arc is frequently used for searchlights and commercial motion-picture projectors. High-temperature light sources approach sunlight in the whiteness of their radiation. But no artificial sources of light operate at temperatures as high as the 6000°C measured for the sun's photosphere, the layer of ionized gases in which sunlight originates.

Most light sources in common use produce light from an incandescent solid. Such light contains all visible wavelengths, though in varying intensities. Light obtained by main-

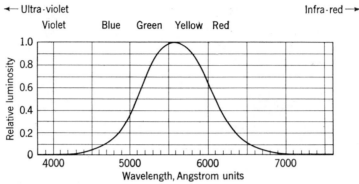

FIG. 4. Standard luminosity curve.

taining electric current in a gas at low pressure has its intensity concentrated in one or several narrow wavelength bands. A low-pressure mercury-arc lamp has a characteristic bluish light and also emits ultraviolet radiation. Such lamps are used for photographic work, some kinds of industrial illumination, germicidal purposes, and advertising signs, but they are not suited for general indoor illumination. By operating the discharge in a tiny quartz tube containing mercury vapor at high pressure, 50 to 100 atm, the quality of the light is improved, all wavelengths now being present although some are still emphasized.

A fluorescent lamp consists of a thin-walled glass tube in which an electric current is maintained in mercury vapor at low pressure. The ultraviolet radiation from the glow discharge is absorbed by fluorescent substances affixed to the inner wall. These reemit the radiant energy with a shift of wavelength into the visible range. The color of the light can be adjusted by the choice of fluorescent powders: calcium tungstate for blue, zinc silicate for green, cadmium borate for pink, or mixtures for white.

40-5. Luminous Flux. Practical measurements of light, called photometry, are concerned with three aspects: the luminous intensity of the source, the luminous flux or flow of light from the source, and illuminance of a surface.

The energy radiated by a luminous source is distributed among many wavelengths. Only radiant energy in the wavelength interval from 390 to 760 mμ produces a visual sensation, and in that interval the radiant energy is not all equally effective in stimulating visual sensation. The standard luminosity (visibility) curve of Fig. 4 represents the ratio of the power at the wavelength of the eye's greatest sensitivity to produce a given brightness sensation to the power at the chosen wavelength necessary to produce the same brightness sensation. The maximum ordinate is thus arbitrarily assigned a value of 1. The curve represents the average response of many individuals and is assumed to be the normal response.

We define luminous flux in terms of the curve of Fig. 4. We may divide the visible region into many wavelength intervals so short that the response of the eye can be considered the same over any one such interval. For each interval we multiply the radiant energy per unit time in the interval by the corresponding ordinate of the curve and add the products so obtained. This sum is called the *luminous flux.* It represents the part of the total radiant energy per unit time that is effective in producing the sensation of sight. The other photometric quantities are defined in terms of luminous flux. Since the process here described is difficult to carry out, the unit of luminous flux is not defined directly from this procedure but in terms of the flux from a standard source.

40-6. Luminous Intensity of a Point Source. While no actual source of light is ever confined to a point, many are so small in comparison with the other dimensions considered that they may be regarded as point sources. From such a source light travels out in straight lines. If we consider a solid angle ω with the source at the apex, the luminous flux included in the angle remains the same at all distances from the source. The *luminous intensity of a point source is defined as the luminous flux per unit solid angle* subtended at the source

$$I = \frac{F}{\omega} \tag{2}$$

where F is the flux in the solid angle ω.

If a sphere of radius s is described about the apex as center (Fig. 5) the solid angle intercepts an area A on the surface of the sphere. The ratio of the intercepted area to the square of the radius is the measure of the solid angle ω in steradians

$$\omega = \frac{A}{s^2} \tag{3}$$

In building a set of photometric units, it is convenient to start with luminous intensity rather than the more fundamental luminous flux. The common unit of luminous intensity is the candle. The *candle* was originally defined as the luminous intensity *in a horizontal direction* of the flame of a standard spermaceti candle of specified dimensions burning wax at the rate of 120 grains per hour. Since the flame of a candle is a rather unsatisfactory source this primary standard has been replaced by others measured in comparison with it. Standardized electric lamps are most commonly used as secondary sources. However, in 1948 a *new international candle* was adopted, defined as one-sixtieth of the luminous intensity of a square centimeter of blackbody radiator (Fig. 6) operated at the temperature of freezing platinum, 2046°K. The new unit is about 1.9 per cent smaller than the former international candle, a differ-

ence which does not affect significantly most photometric ratings.

Most light sources have different luminous intensities in different directions. The average luminous intensity of a source measured in all directions is called its *mean spherical luminous intensity*. The total flux emitted by the source

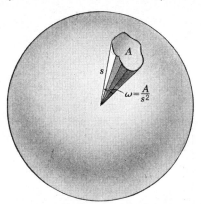

FIG. 5. Flux from a point source.

is 4π times the mean spherical luminous intensity since there are 4π steradians about a point.

The unit of luminous flux is defined from the candle. A *lumen* is the luminous flux in a unit solid angle from a point source of *one candle*.

Example: An automobile headlight equipped with a 32-candle bulb concentrates the beam on a vertical area of 125 ft² at a distance of 100 ft. What is the luminous intensity of the headlight?

The purpose of the reflector and lens is to concentrate the beam into a small solid angle. The total flux emitted by the bulb is given by

$$F = 4\pi I = 4\pi \times 32 \text{ candles} = 4\bar{0}0 \text{ lumens}$$

For the beam, the solid angle is

$$\omega = \frac{125 \text{ ft}^2}{(100 \text{ ft})^2} = 0.0125 \text{ steradian}$$

$$I = \frac{F}{\omega} = \frac{4\bar{0}0 \text{ lumens}}{0.0125 \text{ steradian}} = 3\bar{2},000 \text{ candles}$$

40-7. Illuminance. When visible radiation comes to a surface, we say that the surface is illuminated. The measure of the illumination is called illuminance. The *illumi-*

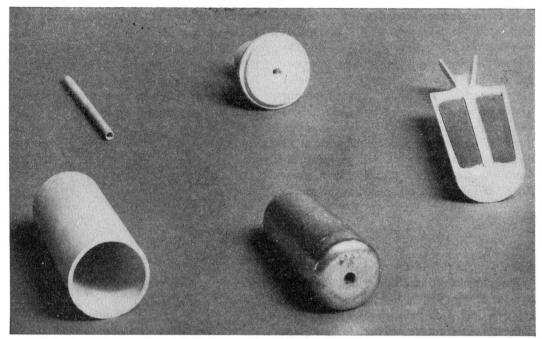

FIG. 6. The national primary standard of light. The incandescent cavity in an ingot of platinum at 2046°K provides 60 *candles* per square centimeter.

nance of a surface is the *luminous flux per unit area that reaches the surface*

$$E = \frac{F}{A} \qquad (4)$$

At any point on a surface, the illuminance may be expressed by

$$E = \frac{dF}{dA} \qquad (4a)$$

The flux F may come from one or many sources; it may come to the area from any direction. The flux used in Eq. (4) is the sum total of the flux from all the sources that irradiate the surface being considered. Among the units of illuminance are the *lumen per square foot* (foot-candle) and the *lumen per square meter* (lux).

For *point sources* there is a simple relationship between illuminance E and luminous intensity I. By definition

$$I = \frac{F}{\omega}$$

or $\qquad\qquad F = I\omega \qquad\qquad (5)$

When luminous flux from the point source P (Fig. 7) falls on the surface around O, the normal to the surface at O makes an angle θ with the direction PO of the flux. The solid angle ω subtended at P by a small area A of the surface is

$$\omega = \frac{A}{s^2} \cos \theta$$

where s is the distance PO from the source to the screen. From Eq. (5)

$$F = I\omega = \frac{IA \cos \theta}{s^2}$$

From Eq. (4)

$$E = \frac{F}{A} = \frac{IA \cos \theta}{s^2 A}$$

$$E = \frac{I}{s^2} \cos \theta \qquad (6)$$

For light from a point source the illuminance of a surface varies inversely with the square of the distance from the source and directly with the cosine of the angle between the direction of flow and the normal to the surface. When the surface is perpendicular to the light beam, the angle θ becomes zero and $\cos \theta = 1$. For this special case, Eq. (6) reduces to

$$E = \frac{I}{s^2} \qquad (7)$$

For a uniform point source whose luminous intensity is 1 candle, the luminous flux sent out is 4π lumens. If this source is taken as the center of a sphere 1 ft in radius, the flux through the area of the sphere (4π ft^2) is 4π lumens. The illuminance of this surface is 1 lumen/ft^2. This unit is also called the *foot-candle* since it is the illuminance of a surface 1 ft from a point source of one candle. Similarly, the lumen per square meter is also called the *meter-candle*.

Example: A small unshaded electric lamp of luminous intensity 32 candles is 4.0 ft above the top of a table. Find the illuminance of the table (*a*) at a point directly below the lamp and (*b*) at a point 3.0 ft from the point directly below the lamp.

Directly below the lamp the light falls normally on the surface. From Eq. (7)

$$E = \frac{I}{s^2} = \frac{32 \text{ candles}}{(4.0 \text{ ft})^2} = 2.0 \frac{\text{lumens}}{\text{ft}^2}$$
$$= 2.0 \text{ ft-candles}$$

At the second point

$$s = \sqrt{(4.0 \text{ ft})^2 + (3.0 \text{ ft})^2} = 5.0 \text{ ft}$$

and

$$\cos \theta = \frac{4.0 \text{ ft}}{5.0 \text{ ft}} = 0.80$$

From Eq. (6)

$$E = \frac{I}{s^2} \cos \theta = \frac{32 \text{ candles}}{(5.0 \text{ ft})^2} \times 0.80 = 1.0 \frac{\text{lumens}}{\text{ft}^2}$$
$$= 1.0 \text{ ft-candle}$$

Example: A small unshaded electric lamp hangs 6.0 ft directly above a table. To what distance should it be lowered to increase the illuminance to 2.25 times its former value?

$$E_2 = 2.25 E_1$$

From Eq. (7)

$$\frac{I}{s_2^2} = 2.25 \frac{I}{s_1^2}$$
$$s_2^2 = \frac{s_1^2}{2.25} = \frac{(6.0 \text{ ft})^2}{2.25}$$
$$s_2 = 4.0 \text{ ft}$$

40-8. Lighting. In planning the artificial lighting of a room, the type of work to be

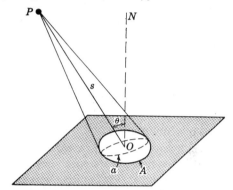

FIG. 7. Illuminance produced by a point source.

done there or the use to which the room is to be put is the determining factor. Experience has shown that certain illuminances are desirable for given purposes. Some figures are given in Table 1.

TABLE 1. LEVELS OF ILLUMINATION—
GOOD PRESENT-DAY PRACTICE

Place	Illuminance, foot-candles
Baseball outfield, major league.........	100
Home:	
Living room, general illumination....	5
Supplementary illumination, reading..	20
Kitchen work counters.............	50
Library:	
Reading and stack rooms..........	30
Research study areas.............	50
Machine shop:	
Rough bench and machine work.....	20
Jewelry and watch manufacturing....	300
Schools:	
Auditorium......................	10
Corridors.......................	5
Classrooms......................	30
Show windows....................	100–200
Intense interior illuminance to minimize daylight reflections in window glass........................	1000

The values listed refer to illuminance that should be maintained in service. The initial illuminance observed for a new installation generally declines, because of deterioration of the source and reflecting surfaces. Dull daylight supplies an illuminance of about 100 ft-candles, while direct sunlight when the sun is at the zenith gives about 9600 ft-candles.

In addition to having the proper illuminance it is essential to avoid *glare*, or uncomfortable local brightness such as that caused by a bare electric lamp or by a bright spot of reflected light in the field of vision. Glare may be reduced by equipping lamps with shades or diffusing globes and by avoiding polished surfaces or glossy paper.

40-9. Photometers. A *photometer* is an instrument for comparing the luminous intensities of light sources. A familiar laboratory form of such an instrument usually consists of a long graduated bar with the two lamps to be compared mounted at or near the ends. A movable dull-surfaced white screen is placed somewhere between the lamps and moved back and forth until both sides of the screen appear to be equally illuminated. When this condition is attained

$$E_1 = E_2$$

From Eq. (7)

$$\frac{I_1}{s_1^2} = \frac{I_2}{s_2^2} \tag{8}$$

where I_1 and I_2 are the luminous intensities of the two sources and s_1 and s_2 are their respective distances from the screen. If one source is a standard lamp of known luminous intensity, that of the other may be found by comparison using Eq. (8).

Example: A standard 48-candle lamp placed 36 in. from the screen of a photometer produces the same illumination there as a lamp of unknown intensity located 45 in. away. What is the luminous intensity of the latter lamp?

Substitution in Eq. (8) gives

$$\frac{I_1}{48 \text{ candles}} = \left(\frac{45 \text{ in.}}{36 \text{ in.}}\right)^2$$

$$I_1 = 75 \text{ candles}$$

Notice that the distances may be expressed in any unit when substituting in the equation, so long as they are both in the same unit.

In ordinary lighting the value of total flux from a lamp is more significant than is the luminous intensity in a particular direction. Total flux is most simply measured by use of an integrating sphere. The lamp is placed in a large sphere with a white diffusing interior wall. The flux emerging from a small hole in the wall is measured by means of a photometer set at the hole. The flux emerging from the hole is proportional to the total flux emitted by the source within the sphere. In practice, a source of known output is placed in the sphere and a reading made to calibrate the comparison source.

40-10. Foot-candle Meter. In planning a practical lighting installation for a room, one should take into account not only the direct illumination from all light sources but also the light that is diffused or reflected by the walls and surrounding objects. For this reason it is often very difficult to compute the total illuminance at a given point, but this quantity can be measured by the use of instruments known as *foot-candle meters*. The most commonly used type of this instrument makes use of the photoelectric effect (Chap. 39). The light falling on the sensitive surface causes an electric current whose value is proportional to the radiant flux and hence to the illuminance. This current operates an electric meter whose scale is marked directly in foot-candles (Fig. 8).

This instrument gives objective readings but it has the disadvantage that the sensitivity curve for the photoelectric cell is not the same as that for the human eye. However, the two curves are somewhat similar, and if close similarity is desired it can be obtained by the use of a special filter over the photoelectric cell.

40-11. Luminance of Extended Sources. Since the introduction of diffusing shades, fluorescent lamps, and indirect lighting fixtures, many light sources must be treated as extended sources rather than points. The *luminance B_θ* of a surface element A (Fig. 9) **in any direction** θ is defined as the luminous flux per unit solid angle (I_θ) per unit area of source projected on a plane perpendicular to that direction

$$B_\theta = \frac{I_\theta}{A \cos \theta} \qquad (9)$$

or *luminance is the source intensity per unit projected area of emitting surface.*

Fig. 8. Photoelectric foot-candle meter.

A perfectly diffusing surface is one for which luminance is independent of direction of observation. The intensity (lumens per unit solid angle, or candles) of a perfectly diffusing plane source is therefore proportional to the cosine of the angle between the perpendicular to the surface of the source and the direction of observation.

Luminance can be expressed in candles per square centimeter (of projected area), or in candles per square foot. A special unit of luminance, the *lambert*, is defined as $1/\pi$ candle per square centimeter.

The new international candle mentioned above is actually a unit of luminance rather than of luminous intensity. That is, the luminance of a complete (blackbody) radiator at 2046°K is defined as 60 new candles/cm².

TABLE 2. TYPICAL VALUES OF LUMINANCE

Source	Luminance, candles/m²
Surface of sun	2×10^9
Tungsten-lamp filament at 2700°K	10^7
Standard source (blackbody at 2046°K)	600,000
White paper in sunlight	25,000
Fluorescent lamp	6,000
Clear sky	3,200
White paper in moonlight	0.03

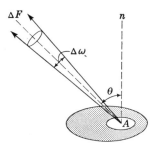

Fig. 9. The intensity of the surface element A in direction θ is $I_\theta = \Delta F/\Delta\omega$.

40-12. Efficiency of Light Sources. The term *efficiency* as applied to light sources has the same meaning as it does when applied to machines, namely, the ratio of output to input power. The useful output of a light source is that part of the radiant flux to which the eye is sensitive, that is, the *luminous* flux. The input power is usually supplied electrically and is measured in watts. Thus the efficiency of a lamp is stated in *lumens per watt*, in contrast to the dimensionless ratio or percentage used in giving the efficiency of a machine.

The efficiencies of practical light sources are small. Not all the electric power is converted into radiant flux; some is lost as heat. Of the radiant flux produced, only a small fraction lies in the region 390 mμ to 760 mμ which causes a visual sensation. The efficiency of incandescent sources increases with increase in temperature (Table 3). A blackbody would have its greatest luminous efficiency at a temperature of 6500°K, which is roughly the temperature of the sun's surface. It is a challenge to engineers to develop cool sources of

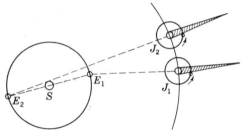

FIG. 10. Römer's method of measuring the speed of light.

light which may use phenomena such as fluorescence to channel more of the electrical input into luminous flux and thus achieve luminous efficiencies greater than that of a thermal (blackbody) radiator.

TABLE 3. LUMINOUS EFFICIENCIES

Source	Flux, lumens	Efficiency, lumens/watt
14-watt 15-in. fluorescent lamp..	490	35
24-watt tungsten lamp (vacuum)	260	10
30-watt 36-in. fluorescent lamp..	1500	50
40-watt tungsten lamp (gas-filled, coiled-coil filament).........	465	12
60-watt tungsten lamp (similar).	835	14
100-watt tungsten lamp (similar)	1630	16
100-watt 60-in. fluorescent lamp.	4400	44
500-watt tungsten lamp........	9950	20

40-13. Speed of Light. The speed with which light, and in fact all radiant energy, travels through space is one of the most precisely measured quantities in the physical sciences. This speed, moreover, is one of the most important constants in physical theory. Galileo was one of the first to suggest that light takes a finite time to travel between two points and to attempt to measure this time. The immense speed of light calls for the measurement of its passage over great distances or the precise determination of small time intervals, or both.

Römer in 1675 made a measurement of the speed of light over an astronomical distance. He noticed that when the earth was closest to Jupiter (Fig. 10) the eclipses of one of the moons of Jupiter occurred about 500 sec ahead of the time predicted on the basis of yearly averages and that they were late by the same amount when the earth was farthest from Jupiter. He concluded that the difference of 1000 sec was the time required for light to traverse the diameter of the earth's orbit (186,000,000 mi).

Since the time of Römer several investigators have devised methods for measuring the speed of light. Michelson in 1926–1929 measured the speed of light over an accurately measured terrestrial distance, the 22 mi between Mt. Wilson and Mt. San Antonio, using an ingenious method of timing. An octagonal mirror M (Fig. 11) is mounted on the shaft of a variable speed motor. Light from a source S falls on the mirror M, at an angle of

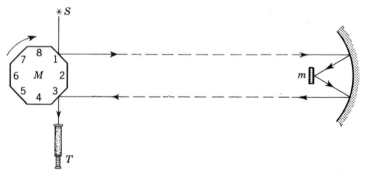

FIG. 11. Michelson's method of measuring the speed of light.

45°, and is reflected to a distant mirror m, which returns it. With M stationary the reflected ray strikes M_3 at an angle of 45° and is reflected into the telescope T. When mirror M is set in rotation, light returning to it from mirror m will generally strike M_3 at an angle different from 45°, and hence light will not enter the telescope. When, however, the speed of M is sufficient so that section 2 of the octagonal mirror M is brought into the position formerly occupied by section 3 in the time required for light to go from M_1 to m and back to M_2, light will again enter the telescope. The experiment consists of varying the speed of the motor until light reappears in the telescope. This speed is accurately measured by stroboscopic comparison with a signal of standard frequency. The time for the light to travel a distance of $2\overline{Mm}$ is then one-eighth of the time required for one revolution of M. In these experiments the speed of the motor was about 500 rps and the final adjustment was made by noticing the displacement of the beam from the cross hair of the telescope. The currently accepted value for the speed of light is

$$c = 2.997929 \times 10^8 \text{ m/sec}$$

or about $186,\overline{0}00$ mi/sec. Thus it takes light 8.3 min to travel the $9\overline{3},000,000$ mi from the sun to the earth.

40-14. Speed of Light in Different Materials. The speed of light is different in each material, being less in any material medium than in a vacuum. Foucault (1850) and Michelson each measured the speed of light in water by placing tubes of water in the path of the light. In this way the speed of light in water was found to be about three-fourths of its speed in air. This was a decisive experiment, for it eliminated temporarily one of two rival theories of light.

Newton (1666) had suggested that light might consist of particles or corpuscles shot from a body. He showed that ordinary laws of mechanics could account for the observed characteristics of light, provided light traveled faster in a dense material (water) than in air. The wave theory developed by Huygens (1678) competed with the corpuscular theory for a hundred years by offering an equally logical explanation of reflection and refraction and a simpler explanation of diffraction. The wave theory predicted that light must travel slower in a dense medium (water) than in air. Foucault's direct measurement of the speed of light in water decided the controversy in favor of the wave theory. The corpuscular theory became dormant.

Recently studies of the interaction of light and matter, notably the photoelectric effect, have shown that light behaves as if it were comprised of energy particles (quanta). While we have not returned to Newton's concept of light as made up of mass particles, current theory is forced to view light as having both wave and particle characteristics.

SUMMARY

Radiant energy within certain limits of wavelength (3900–7600 A) is visible as *light*. Neighboring ranges of wavelengths comprise the ultraviolet and infrared radiations.

Light is transmitted in waves, which can pass not only through some ("transparent") materials, such as glass, but also through empty space (vacuum).

Lines drawn in the direction of travel of light waves are called *rays*. In a homogeneous substance the rays are straight lines.

Most sources of light are hot bodies, which simultaneously emit invisible radiations.

Measurement of the luminous intensity of a light source takes account only of the portion of the emission that evokes *visual sensation*.

The *luminous intensity* of a point source is evaluated in terms of the power that arouses the brightness sensation experienced from a standard candle and is expressed in *candles*.

The *candle* is now defined in terms of the blackbody radiation emitted at the temperature of melting platinum.

Luminous flux is the quantity of visible radiation passing per unit time. The unit of luminous flux is the *lumen*, which is the flux emitted by a point source of 1 candle through a solid angle of 1 steradian.

$$I = \frac{F}{\omega}$$

The total luminous flux emitted by a point source is

$$F = 4\pi I$$

The *illuminance* of a surface is the luminous flux per unit area that reaches the surface

$$E = \frac{F}{A}$$

Illuminance is expressed in lumens per square foot (foot-candles) or lumens per square meter (luxes).

For light from a point source, the illuminance on a surface is given by the inverse square law

$$E = \frac{I}{s^2} \cos \theta$$

A *photometer* is an instrument for comparing the luminous intensities of two point sources.

A *foot-candle meter* is an instrument that measures a constant fraction (whose value depends upon spectral distribution) of the radiant flux, and is calibrated in units of illuminance.

Luminance is the luminous intensity per unit projected area emitted by an extended source. It is measured in candles per square foot or in candles per square meter

$$B_\theta = \frac{I_\theta}{A \cos \theta}$$

In a vacuum, the speed of light is about 3.00×10^8 m/sec. In any substance the speed is always less than this.

QUESTIONS   1. Describe a theoretical and an experimental verification of the inverse square law of illumination. Does the photometer experiment *verify* the inverse square law? Explain.

2. Does the inverse square law apply even approximately to the beam from an automobile headlight? to illumination from a fluorescent lamp? to illumination under a skylighted ceiling? to light from a bonfire? Explain.

3. How would you determine experimentally the effective luminous intensity of a searchlight?

4. Light from a student lamp falls on a paper on the floor. Mention the factors on which the illuminance of the paper depends.

5. With the aid of a diagram, show that an illuminance of 1 ft-candle is the same as 1 lumen/ft².

6. Sketch a shadow photometer with which you could compare the intensity of a light source with that of a lamp of known luminous intensity using only meter sticks and a white wall. What measurements would be made?

7. When a diffusing globe is placed over a bare electric lamp of high intensity, the total amount of light in the room is decreased slightly, yet eyestrain may be considerably lessened. Explain.

8. What are some advantages and disadvantages of the indirect system of lighting?

9. Compare the advantages of black and light-colored walls in a photographic dark room.

10. Show that the illuminance on a given surface distant s from a line source of light (fluorescent lamp) is given by

$$E = \frac{2I}{Ls}$$

where I/L is the intensity per unit length of the lamp in candles per foot. HINT: Consider a cylinder of radius s and length L concentric with the lamp. Calculate the illuminance on the cylinder produced by light proceeding radially from the lamp.

11. Derive an equation for calculating the speed of light from the quantities measured in the Michelson method.

12. A member of a radio studio audience in New York is seated 150 ft from the performer while a radio listener hears him in Cedar Rapids, 1000 mi away. Which auditor hears the performer first?

PROBLEMS   *Assume point sources of light, unless otherwise stated.*

1. Sunlight enters a darkened room through a tiny aperture in the roof when the sun is directly overhead. What will be the size of the sun's image on the floor 12 ft below the aperture? The sun is 93 million miles away and its diameter is 865,000 miles.

2. What is the effect on the illumination of a work table if a lamp hanging 4.5 ft directly above it is lowered 1.0 ft? *Ans.* Increased 65%

3. What is the illuminance on the surface 10 ft from a 100-candle lamp in a room with black walls? Would it be different if the walls were white? Explain.

4. It is desired to have an illuminance of 25 ft-candles on a drafting table. What incandescent lamp should be used if it is to be located 6.0 ft directly above the table and if two-thirds of the light received on the table is reflected from the walls and ceiling? *Ans.* $\overline{3}00$ candles

5. An engraver wishes to double the illuminance he is now getting from a lamp 55 in. away. Where should the lamp be placed in order to do this?

6. If a lamp that provides an illuminance of 8.0 ft-candles on a book is moved 1.5 times as far away, will the illumination then be sufficient for comfortable reading? *Ans.* No, 3.6 ft-candles

7. At what distance from a source of effective intensity 100 candles would a book receive the same illumination that it would receive from a 25-candle source 5.0 ft distant?

8. What is the illuminance on the pavement at a point directly under a street lamp of 800 candles hanging at a height of 20 ft? *Ans.* 2.0 ft-candles

9. Find the luminous intensity of a lamp that gives an illuminance on a surface placed 3.0 ft away equal to that of dull daylight.

10. What is the total illuminance produced by two 60-candle lamps each 4.0 ft from a surface and one 45-candle lamp 3.0 ft from this surface if all the light falls on the surface normally? *Ans.* 12.5 ft-candles

11. At what angle must a surface be inclined in order that the light falling on it from a 100-candle lamp at a distance of 50 cm will give an illuminance of 0.030 lumen/cm²?

12. A pool table measuring 4.0×8.0 ft is illuminated by three light bulbs. There are identical bulbs 4.0 ft directly above the mid-point of each end of the table and a bulb rated at 1965 lumens 3.0 ft above the center of the table. To maintain a high degree of sportsmanship, it is agreed that the illuminance on the table at the side pockets shall be no less than 50 ft-candles. Find (*a*) the luminous intensity of the bulbs over the ends of the table and (*b*) the illuminance on the table at the corner pocket. *Ans.* $\overline{1}100$ candles; 84 ft-candles

13. What is the illuminance in foot-candles on a screen 6.0 ft from a 72-candle lamp? How far from the screen and on the same side as the first lamp must an additional 40-candle lamp be placed in order that the illuminance on the screen will be doubled?

14. What illuminance will be given on a desk by a 36-candle fluorescent lamp 1.0 ft long placed 18 in. above the surface? (For an extended line source, the illumination decreases as the inverse first power of the distance, $E = 2I/Ls$. See Question 10.)   *Ans.* 48 ft-candles

15. What illuminance will be produced on a table by a fluorescent lamp (line source) of 40 candles/ft hung horizontally 24 in. above the table?

16. A 16-candle lamp is placed 10 in. from a screen. How far from the screen and on the same side as the first lamp must a 100-candle lamp be placed so that the total illuminance on the screen becomes three times its former value?

Ans. 1.5 ft

17. If the light of the full moon is found to produce the same illuminance as a 1.0-candle source does at a distance of 4.0 ft, what is the effective luminous intensity of the moon? (The mean distance to the moon is $23\overline{9},000$ mi.)

18. A table 7.0 ft long is illuminated by two lamps. A 200-candle lamp is 4.0 ft above the left-hand end and a 150-candle lamp is 3.0 ft above the right-hand end. Find the illuminance of the table 3.0 ft from the left-hand end.

Ans. 10 ft-candles

19. A room 15 ft by 20 ft with black walls and ceiling is illuminated by three 50-candle lamps arranged at the ceiling 8.0 ft above the floor, in a line parallel with the longer wall of the room, 5.0, 10.0, and 15.0 ft from one end and in the middle laterally. Find the illuminance of the floor directly below one of the end lights.

20. A searchlight has a source of 80.0 candles. The reflector and lens concentrate the light on an area 50.0 ft in diameter at a distance of 200 yards. Calculate the effective source intensity of the searchlight.   *Ans.* 1.85×10^5 candles

21. A 16-candle point source is placed at the focus of a parabolic mirror so that the reflected rays are parallel. The mirror is cut so that it has an opening 6.0 in. in diameter, and the focus is in the plane of the opening. Find the illuminance due to direct and reflected light on a screen 3.0 ft from the source at a point within the reflected beam.

22. A photometer has a standard 30-candle lamp at one end and a lamp of unknown intensity at the other. The two sides of the screen are equally illuminated when the screen is 3.0 ft from the standard lamp and 5.0 ft from the unknown. What is the luminous intensity of the latter?   *Ans.* 83 candles

23. At what position on a photometer scale, which is 4.0 ft long, should a screen be placed for equal illumination by a 20-candle lamp and a 45-candle lamp placed at the two ends of the scale?

24. A sample 60-watt lamp produces on a screen 2.00 m away the same illuminance as produced by a 16-candle standard lamp 1.00 m from the screen. What is the efficiency of the sample lamp?   *Ans.* 13.4 lumens/watt

25. A 160-candle lamp is 125 cm from a photometric screen, producing on it the same illuminance as an unknown lamp at 175 cm distance. If the unknown lamp takes 0.85 amp at 110 volts, what is its efficiency?

26. If a photographic print can be made in 14 sec when the printing frame is held 2.0 ft from a lamp, what is the correct exposure time when it is held 3.0 ft away?   *Ans.* 31 sec

27. A 20-candle standard lamp is placed at one end of a 3.0-m photometer bar. At the other end is a 2.0-cm flat circular window having uniform luminance such that the photometer is balanced with the screen 1.0 m from this window. What is the luminance of the window?

28. A 150-candle lamp is suspended 8.0 ft above a sheet of white blotting paper which reflects 75% of the light incident upon it. Calculate (a) the illuminance of the paper and (b) its luminance. *Ans.* 2.3 ft-candles; 1.7 candles/ft²

29. A point source of luminous intensity I is located a distance D above the center of a thin ground glass disk of radius R. The disk transmits one-half of the light incident on it and each element of the disk may be considered a diffuse light source. (a) What is the illuminance on a small surface a distance D below the disk, on the axis of the disk, and perpendicular to that axis? (b) If the point light source has a luminous flux of 10 lumens, if $D = 1.0$ m, and $R = 2.0$ m, what is the numerical value of the illuminance (part a) in foot-candles?

30. A point source is placed at the center of an optically translucent spherical shell of inner radius a and outer radius b. Show that the luminance of the light emerging from the outer surface is given by

$$B = B_0 \frac{a_2}{b_2} e^{-\alpha(b-a)}$$

where B_0 is the incident luminance at the inner surface and α is the absorption coefficient. HINT: The amount of light absorbed through a thin shell of thickness dr is $dB = -\alpha B\, dr$.

31. What minimum speed of rotation is necessary for an eight-sided mirror used in a Michelson experiment for measuring the speed of light if the distance from the rotating mirror to the fixed reflector is 22 mi?

32. The speed of light is to be measured by means of a revolving mirror. If the distance between the rotating mirror and the fixed mirror is 5.00 mi, how fast must the mirror rotate in order that the angle between the incident beam and the reflected beam shall be 3.00°? *Ans.* 77.5 rev/sec

33. The nearest star, Alpha Centauri, is 4.3 light-years distant from the earth. How far is this in miles? (A light-year is the distance light travels in one year.)

34. The speed of light has been measured by means of a toothed wheel rotating at high speed. Assume such a wheel to have 480 teeth that are just as wide as the spaces between them. A beam of light perpendicular to the wheel passes between two teeth and falls normally upon a stationary mirror 500 m away. Compute the minimum speed of rotation which will cause a tooth to intercept the reflected beam. *Ans.* 312 rev/sec

41. *Reflection of Light*

An object is seen by the light that comes to the eye from the object. If the object is not self-luminous, it is seen only by the light it reflects. The reflection of light makes a room with white walls much lighter than a similar room with black walls. The "high lights" produced by reflection on polished doorknobs and car fenders are so characteristic of convex

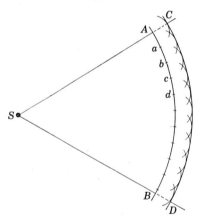

Fig. 1. Huygens' construction.

surfaces that an artist uses them to suggest curved surfaces in a painting. Reflection at the concave surface behind a head lamp sends light where it is needed to make other objects visible, by reflected light.

When light reaches a boundary of the medium in which it is traveling, one or more of three things can happen. Usually some of the light is reflected back into the first

medium and part is transmitted into the second. The part that enters the second medium may be all absorbed, if the medium is opaque, or partly absorbed and partly transmitted if the medium is transparent. For example, if light comes normally (perpendicularly) from air to a surface of ordinary glass, about 4 per cent of the light is reflected. Of the 96 per cent that enters the glass some is absorbed; the remainder proceeds to the second glass surface where again about 4 per cent is reflected at normal incidence. If the incidence is not normal at either surface, a higher portion is reflected at that surface.

41-1. Huygens' Principle. Suppose waves originate at a point source S (Fig. 1) and travel through a uniform medium. The waves will arrive simultaneously at all parts of a surface such as AB that are equidistant from S. Thus the waves at AB are all in the same phase and hence that surface represents a part of a *wave front*. Christian Huygens (1629–1695) devised a method of construction for finding new wave fronts. His principle states that each point on a wave front may be considered as a new source of disturbance sending out wavelets. In Fig. 1, wavelets from A, a, b, c, d, etc., are shown. The new wave front is the surface CD tangent to all the wavelets. Huygens' principle, published in 1690, was fruitful in explaining and predicting many properties of light.

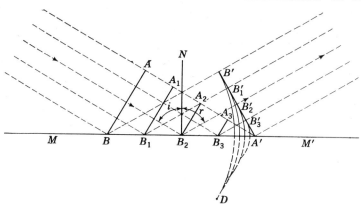

FIG. 2. Reflection of light by Huygens' principle.

The propagation of light can be represented in a diagram by drawing successive wave fronts, located by applying Huygens' principle. However, the construction of a fairly accurate wave-front diagram is usually a tedious task. It is easier and often quite as satisfactory to draw a few *rays* representing the direction of propagation of the light wave. In an isotropic medium (a material whose physical properties are the same in all directions) the rays will be straight lines perpendicular to the wave fronts. In Fig. 1, the lines SAC and SBD are rays.

41-2. Laws of Reflection. It is found by experience that when light, or any wave motion, is reflected from a surface, the reflected ray at any point makes the same angle with the perpendicular, or normal, to the surface as does the incident ray. The angle between the incident ray and the normal to the surface is called the *angle of incidence i;* the angle between the reflected ray and the normal is called the angle of reflection r (Fig. 2). The laws of reflection may then be stated:

1. *The angle of incidence is equal to the angle of reflection.*
2. *The incident ray, the reflected ray, and the normal to the surface lie in the same plane.*

These laws hold for any incident ray and the corresponding reflected ray.

In Fig. 2 a parallel beam of light is incident on the mirror surface MM'. A wave front in the incident beam is represented by AB at the instant one edge of this front reaches the mirror. At later times this wave front reaches positions A_1B_1, A_2B_2, A_3B_3, and A' successively. At this latter instant the wave front would be at $A'D$ if the mirror were not present. The presence of the reflecting surface starts a Huygens' wavelet upward from B, which spreads outward to B' in the time it takes for the upper part of the wave front AB to travel to the mirror at A'. When the wave front reaches B_1, B_2, etc., wavelets start upward also and will reach B_1', B_2', etc., at the instant the upper edge of the incident wave front reaches A'. The line $A'B'$ tangent to the arcs drawn from B, B_1, etc., indicates the position of the wave front immediately after reflection. The reflection has inverted the wave front.

In the right triangles BAA' and $A'B'B$ of Fig. 2, the sides AA' and BB' were drawn equal. Thus the triangles are similar. Since angle $B'BA'$ is equal to angle $AA'B$, it follows that their complements are equal. Therefore angle i equals angle r.

41-3. Kinds of Reflection. Sunlight falling on a mirror surface, such as still water or polished glass or metal, is reflected regularly, that is, the angle of reflection equals the angle of incidence. If an observer is to see the light, his eye must be placed within the reflected beam. When sunlight falls on a piece of white blotting paper, the

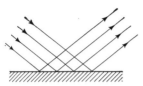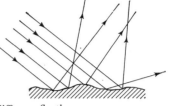

FIG. 3. Regular and diffuse reflection.

light is scattered in all directions and the observer may see it from any position near it. These are examples of regular and diffuse reflection. A smooth, plane surface reflects parallel rays falling on it all in the same direction, while a rough surface reflects them

which the light comes or appears to come. If the light, after reflection, actually passes through the points where the image is located, the image is called a *real* image; if the light only appears to come from the points where the image is located, the image is called

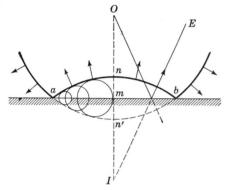

FIG. 4. Reflection in a plane mirror, wave-front diagram.

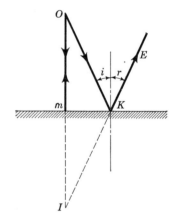

FIG. 5. Reflection in a plane mirror, ray diagram.

diffusely in many directions (Fig. 3). At each point on the rough surface the angle of incidence is equal to the angle of reflection, but the normals have many directions.

An observer sees an object only if light comes to his eye from that object. In this process the observer assumes that the light has traveled in straight lines from the source to his eye. If the light has been reflected diffusely by a surface, it comes to the eye in the same manner as it would from a self-luminous surface and one reports that he sees that surface. If, however, the surface reflects regularly, the light comes, or appears to come, to the eye from some point in front of or behind the reflecting surface. In this case one does not see the reflecting surface but rather he sees an *image* located at the point from

a *virtual* image. The eye sees a virtual image as well as it sees a real image. However, a real image will appear on a screen placed at its position while a virtual image will not.

41-4. Plane Mirrors. When light from a point source, proceeding in spherical wave fronts, falls on a plane mirror, the wave fronts are reflected with their curvatures reversed. In Fig. 4, there is a point source of light above a plane mirror. At the instant considered, points a and b on the wave front have just reached the mirror, while the central part of the wave has been reflected upward a distance mn equal to the distance mn', which it would have progressed below the line amb in the absence of the mirror. The center of curvature of the reflected wave front *anb* is at point *I*, whose distance *mI* below the mirror is equal to the distance *mO* at which the source *O* lies above the mirror. The reflected wave front proceeds toward an observer at *E* as if it came from *I*. Point *I* is the virtual image of the real source at *O*. This image lies below the mirror the same distance the object lies above it. The image is virtual

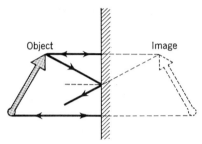

FIG. 6. Image of an extended object (arrow) formed by a plane mirror.

because the light does not actually pass through it.

The position of an image formed by a mirror can be located even more readily in a ray diagram. In Fig. 5, a ray *OK* from the source *O* reaching the mirror at *K* is reflected along *KE*, making angle *r* equal angle *i*. A ray reaching the mirror along the normal *Om* makes zero angle of incidence and is reflected back on itself. Lines *Om* and *EK*, when extended below the mirror, intersect at *I*. Rays from *O* after reflection at the plane mirror travel as if they originated at *I*. The point *I* is the virtual image of the source *O*. The triangles *OmK* and *ImK* are similar, and the image distance *mI* is equal to the object distance *Om*.

The image of an extended source or object in a plane mirror is found by taking one point after another and locating its image. The familiar result is that the complete image is the same size as the object and is placed symmetrically with respect to the mirror (Fig. 6).

41-5. Optical Lever. In many physical and technological instruments, small displacements must be indicated or recorded.

One way of magnifying such effects to make them readily measurable is by the use of a ray of light reflected by a small mirror mounted on the moving system, the ray forming a sort of "inertialess" pointer. This arrangement is called an *optical lever* and is used in such pieces of apparatus as indicating and recording galvanometers, pyrometers, elastometers, and

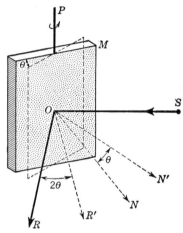

FIG. 7. The optical lever.

sextants. In Fig. 7, *SO* represents a ray or narrow beam of light striking the mirror *M* mounted on a body, for example, the coil of a galvanometer, which is to rotate about the axis *P*. When the mirror is turned through any angle θ, the reflected beam turns through an angle twice as great. As the mirror turns through the angle θ, the normal also turns through the same angle, decreasing the angle of incidence by θ. The angle between the incident and reflected rays is always twice the angle of incidence. Thus the angle that the reflected ray makes with the incident ray is reduced by 2θ. The position of the reflected beam may be observed on a screen some distance away and from the change in its position the angle of turn may be computed.

Example: A small beam of parallel light falls on the plane mirror of a galvanometer making an angle of 30° with the normal. The mirror is then turned through 5°. Through what angle is the reflected beam turned?

In the first position of the mirror (Fig. 7), angle *SON* is 30° and the angle of reflection *NOR* is 30°. The angle of rotation $\theta = 5°$. The new angle of incidence *SON'* and the new angle of reflection *N'OR'* are both 25°. Hence the reflected beam has been rotated 10° from *OR* to *OR'*.

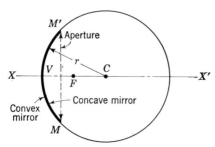

FIG. 8. Spherical mirrors.

41-6. Spherical Mirrors. If the reflecting surface is curved rather than plane, the same law of reflection holds but the size and position of the image formed are quite different from those of an image formed by a plane mirror.

Curved mirrors are commonly made as portions of spherical surfaces. Spherical mirrors are classified as *concave* or *convex* when the reflecting surface is on the inside or outside, respectively, of the spherical shell (Fig. 8). The *center of curvature C* of the mirror is the center of the sphere. The *radius of curvature r* of the mirror is the radius of the sphere. The radius is conventionally taken as positive for concave mirrors, negative for convex mirrors. A line connecting the middle point or vertex *V* of the mirror and the center of curvature is

called the *principal axis* of the mirror; it is marked *XX'*. The diameter *MM'* of the circular outline of the mirror is called the *aperture* of the mirror. Most spherical mirrors used for optical purposes have apertures small compared with their radii of curvature.

Figure 9 shows a concave and a convex mirror with the beam of light directed on each made up of rays parallel to the principal axis. By applying the law of reflection to each ray, it is seen that the bundle of rays parallel to the principal axis will converge through a common point *F* after reflection from a concave mirror, or will diverge after reflection from a convex mirror as though they originated from a common point *F* behind the mirror. The point *F* to which rays parallel to the principal axis converge (or from which they diverge) is called the *principal focus* of the mirror. The distance *f* of the principal focus from the mirror is called the *focal length*.

The concentration of rays at the principal focus of a concave mirror can be shown experimentally by allowing sunlight to fall on the mirror along *XX'* and moving a bit of paper or a match along the axis to find the point *F* where it will ignite. The principal focus of a convex mirror is a *virtual* focus because the rays do not actually pass through it but merely appear to do so.

When the aperture of the mirror is small, the principal focus of a spherical mirror lies on the principal axis halfway between the mirror and its center of curvature. This rela-

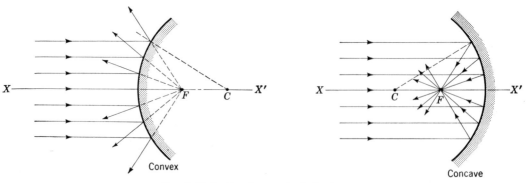

FIG. 9. Reflection from spherical mirrors.

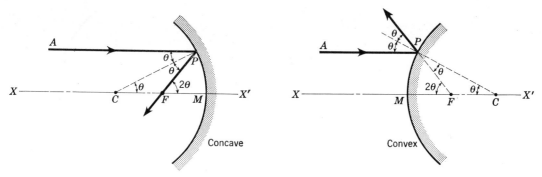

Fig. 10. Location of the principal focus of a spherical mirror.

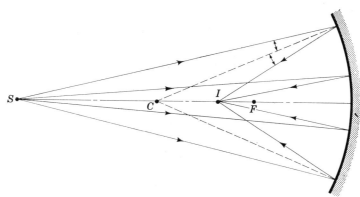

Fig. 11. The points S and I are conjugate foci.

tion can be proved from the law of reflection for either of the mirrors of Fig. 10. A ray AP parallel to the principal axis strikes the mirror at P and is reflected along PF. At P the angle of reflection is equal to the angle of incidence, θ. The angle between the reflected ray and the principal axis at F is 2θ, since it is an exterior angle of the triangle PCF. For mirrors whose aperture is small compared to the radius of curvature, the angles θ are small and the arc PM may be considered a line perpendicular to the axis XX'. Hence

$$\frac{PM}{CM} = \tan\theta \quad \text{and} \quad \frac{PM}{FM} = \tan 2\theta \quad (1)$$

For small angles we can set the angles (in radians) equal to their tangents, so that

$$\frac{PM}{CM} = \theta = \frac{1}{2}\frac{PM}{FM} \quad (2)$$

or $\quad CM = 2FM$

showing that the principal focus F lies halfway between the center of curvature and the middle of the mirror surface M, when the aperture is small. When the aperture of the mirror is not small, the approximation made here is not valid and the rays parallel to the principal axis do not all come to a single point.

41-7. Images Formed by Spherical Mirrors. Concave mirrors have wide application because of their ability to make rays of light converge to a *focus*. If rays coming from a point S (Fig. 11) strike the concave spherical mirror, the reflected rays may be constructed by applying the law of reflection at each point of reflection, the direction of the normal being that of the radius in each case. All rays from S will be found to pass after reflection very nearly through the single point I, which is the real image of the source S. If the object

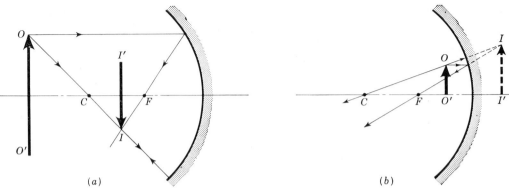

FIG. 12. Location of the image formed by a concave mirror.

is placed at I, the image will be formed at S, for the direction of each ray will merely be reversed from that shown in the figure. Any two points so situated that light from one is concentrated at the other are *conjugate foci*.

Since the image is formed by converging rays that actually pass through it, the image

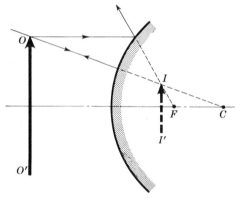

FIG. 13. Location of the image formed by a convex mirror.

is real. This real image can be formed on a screen and viewed in that way.

The problem of locating the image of an extended source or object can be solved graphically by drawing rays to locate a few pairs of conjugate foci. The graphic method is indicated in Fig. 12. From any point O on the object, two rays are drawn to the mirror and their directions after reflection indicated. The point of intersection of these rays after reflection will be the image I (conjugate focus) of the point O on the object from which

they originated. Two rays whose directions can be predicted readily are: first, the ray from O parallel to the principal axis which after reflection passes through F; and second, the ray from O in the direction OC along a radius of the mirror which after reflection returns along the same line. The intersection of these rays at I locates the image of the head of the arrow. All other rays from O pass through I after reflection. Another pair of rays could be drawn from O' to locate I'.

In Fig. 12a, the image is seen to be real, inverted, and diminished in size, as it will be whenever the object lies at a distance greater than the radius in front of a concave mirror. If the object were between C and F, the image would be real, inverted, and magnified. When the object is placed nearer to the concave mirror than the principal focus (Fig. 12b), the rays from O diverge after reflection as if from the point I. The image is virtual; it cannot be formed on the screen but can be observed by looking into the mirror. The rays do not pass through the virtual image but arrive at the eye *as if* they had originated at the virtual image. The image is virtual, erect, and magnified. The image of any real object formed by a convex mirror (Fig. 13) is always virtual, erect, and diminished.

41-8. The Mirror Equation. There is a simple relation between the distance p of the object from the mirror, the distance q of the image from the mirror, and the focal length f. To derive this relationship, consider Fig. 14 in which three rays have been drawn from point O on the object to locate the corresponding point I on the image. From one pair of similar triangles (shown shaded), taking $PM = OO'$, we have

$$\frac{II'}{PM} = \frac{I'F}{FM} = \frac{q - f}{f} = \frac{q}{f} - 1 \qquad (3)$$

From another pair of similar triangles, $OO'M$, and $II'M$, it follows that

$$\frac{II'}{OO'} = \frac{I'M}{O'M} = \frac{q}{p} \qquad (4)$$

Since $PM = OO'$, the left-hand members of Eqs. (3) and (4) are equal and

$$\frac{q}{p} = \frac{q}{f} - 1$$

If we divide by q, we have

$$\frac{1}{p} + \frac{1}{q} = \frac{1}{f} \qquad (5)$$

Since the focal distance f equals $r/2$, the mirror equation may be written

$$\frac{1}{p} + \frac{1}{q} = \frac{2}{r} \qquad (6)$$

If any two of the quantities of Eq. (5) or Eq. (6) are known, the third can be calculated. Equations (5) and (6) apply to both concave and convex mirrors when the proper convention regarding signs is followed. The focal length f (or the radius of curvature r) is taken

as *positive* for a *concave* (converging) mirror, *negative* for a *convex* (diverging) mirror. The object distance p and the image distance q are taken as *positive* for *real* objects and images, *negative* for *virtual* objects and images, formed behind the mirror.

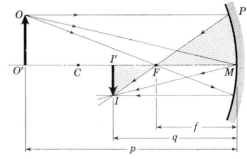

Fig. 14. Diagram for the derivation of the mirror equation.

The mirror equation is always written with positive signs when expressed in algebraic symbols, as in Eqs. (5) and (6). Negative signs are introduced only with the numerical values that are substituted for these symbols, as required by the sign conventions just stated.

The methods of physical optics may also be used to find the relation between image distance, object distance, and focal length in any mirror problem. As an illustration of this method, consider a parallel beam of light Sd impinging upon a convex mirror amb in Fig. 15. If the mirror were not present, the wave

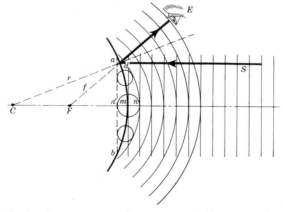

Fig. 15. Reflection from a convex mirror, represented by a wave-front diagram.

front could continue its motion undisturbed to the dotted position $an'b$. But when the center of the wave front meets the mirror at m, it is turned back, and by Huygens' principle the reflected wavelet reaches n in the same time in which it would have reached n' if there were no mirror. By constructing the wavelets from other points on the mirror one obtains the reflected wave front anb whose center is at F. The light that enters the eye appears to originate at point F behind the mirror. Hence F is the principal focus of the mirror, since the waves were proceeding in a direction parallel to the principal axis before reflection. In general, a mirror changes the curvature of a wave by $1/f$ and the curvature of the reflected wave $1/q$ differs from that of the incident wave $1/p$ by an amount $1/f$. In the case just considered, the curvature of the incident wave is zero, and the curvature of the reflected wave is $1/f$.

Example: A candle is held 3.0 in. from a concave mirror whose radius is 24 in. Where is the image of the candle?

Figure 12b illustrates the conditions of the problem. From the general mirror equation

$$\frac{1}{p} + \frac{1}{q} = \frac{1}{f} = \frac{2}{r}$$

we have

$$\frac{1}{3.0 \text{ in.}} + \frac{1}{q} = \frac{1}{12 \text{ in.}}$$

$$\frac{1}{q} = \frac{1 - 4}{12 \text{ in.}} = -\frac{3}{12 \text{ in.}}$$

$$q = -4.0 \text{ in.}$$

The negative sign for q indicates that the image lies behind the mirror and is a virtual image.

41-9. Magnification. The linear magnification produced by a mirror is the ratio of image size to object size. From the similar triangles, $OO'M$ and $II'M$, in Fig. 14, it is apparent that the size of the image II' is to the size of the object OO' as the image distance q is to the object distance p. This will be true for any spherical mirror, neglecting signs.

$$\text{Magnification} = \frac{\text{image height}}{\text{object height}}$$

$$M = \frac{q}{p} \tag{7}$$

Example: A man has a concave shaving mirror whose focal length is 20 in. How far should the mirror be held from his face in order to give an image of twofold magnification?

An erect, virtual, magnified image is desired. Figure 12b illustrates the conditions of the problem. The equation

$$M = \frac{q}{p} = 2$$

gives a relation between p and q without regard to sign. But since the image is virtual, p and q have opposite signs or

$$q = -2p$$

Substitution in the general mirror equation gives

$$\frac{1}{p} + \frac{1}{-2p} = \frac{1}{20 \text{ in.}}$$

$$\frac{2 - 1}{2p} = \frac{1}{20 \text{ in.}}$$

$$p = 10 \text{ in.}$$

41-10. Spherical Aberration. The foregoing discussion of spherical mirrors applies only to mirrors whose apertures are small compared with their radii of curvature and for objects on or near the principal axis. Under other conditions the images formed are blurred and imperfect. For example, the extreme rays reflected from a mirror of large aperture (Fig. 16) cross the axis closer to the mirror than do the rays which are reflected nearer the center of the mirror surface and pass through the focal point F. This imperfection is called *spherical aberration*. The image is drawn out into a surface formed by the intersecting rays; the trace of this surface in the plane of the paper is a curved line called the *caustic* of the mirror. A caustic curve can be observed on the surface of liquid in a glass tumbler when the inner surface of the glass is illuminated obliquely.

It is possible to design the reflecting surface of a mirror of such shape that all rays reaching it from a definite object point will be brought to a common focus. For an object point at a great distance (incident rays

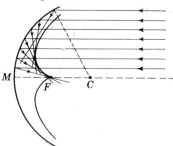

FIG. 16. Spherical aberration.

parallel) the mirror should be a paraboloid. The most common use is in the mirror of the automobile headlight. When the filament is placed at the focus of the mirror, the rays sent out form a parallel beam (Fig. 17). A very slight shift in the position of the filament causes a marked displacement of the beam. The searchlight mirror and the big reflectors of astronomical telescopes are other applications of the parabolic mirror.

SUMMARY

Huygens' principle states that light progresses as a wave, that every point on a wave front acts as a secondary source sending ahead wavelets, and that at any instant the new wave front is the surface tangent to all these wavelets.

When light is regularly reflected, the angle of reflection is equal to the angle of incidence. The reflected ray, the incident ray, and the normal to the surface are in the same plane. These are the *laws of reflection.*

The *image* formed by a plane mirror is the same size as the object, is erect, and is located as far behind the mirror as the object is in front of it.

When a plane reflector is rotated through a given angle, the reflected ray is deviated through twice as large an angle. This is the principle of the optical lever.

The *principal focus* of a spherical mirror is the convergence point for rays parallel to and close to the principal axis of the mirror. It is located halfway between the mirror and its center of curvature.

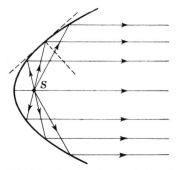

FIG. 17. Reflection from a parabolic mirror.

The *mirror equation* is

$$\frac{1}{p} + \frac{1}{q} = \frac{2}{r} = \frac{1}{f}$$

The mirror equation applies to both concave and convex mirrors. The radius of curvature r and focal length f are taken as positive for concave (converging) mirrors and negative for convex (diverging) mirrors. The object distance p and the image distance q are taken as positive for real objects or images and negative for virtual objects or images.

The *linear magnification* is defined by the equation

$$\text{Magnification} = \frac{\text{image size}}{\text{object size}}$$

For spherical mirrors

$$M = \frac{q}{p}$$

The equation holds for both concave and convex mirrors, where the right-hand term stands for the absolute value of q/p, without regard to sign.

Not all rays parallel to the principal axis of a spherical mirror are reflected to a single focus. The rays farther from the axis are reflected to cross the axis nearer to the mirror than those close to the axis. This imperfection is called *spherical aberration.*

1. A plane wave strikes a plane mirror at an angle of incidence of 30°. By the use of Huygens' wavelets construct the reflected wave front.

2. A carpenter who wishes to saw through a straight board at an angle of 45° places his saw at the correct angle by noting when the reflection of the edge of the board in the saw seems to be exactly perpendicular to the edge itself. Explain by the use of a diagram.

3. Compare the reflection of light from white blotting paper with that from a plane mirror. Which is more readily seen at a distance? Why? Why should one sit with his back to a window for most comfortable reading?

4. How can a real image be distinguished from a virtual image? Can each type of image be projected on a screen. Why?

5. Using Fig. 5, prove geometrically that the image point I is the same distance from the mirror as the object point O.

6. Show that for a plane mirror the image moves away from the object twice as fast as the mirror moves from the object.

7. Identical twins stand at equal distances on opposite sides of an opaque wall. What is the minimum size of window which must be cut in the wall so that they can obtain a full view of each other? How must the window be placed? What would the answers to these questions be as the twins move farther away from the wall? (Compare with Probs. 1 and 2.)

8. If light waves are to converge to a point after reflection in a plane mirror, what must be their form before reflection?

9. Two plane mirrors are placed at an angle of 90°. A ray of light falls on one mirror. What is the direction of the ray after two reflections? How is this principle used in reflectors on highway signs?

10. Prove the fact that when a plane mirror is rotated a beam of light reflected from it will rotate twice as fast as the mirror. Suggest some practical applications of this fact.

11. What types of mirrors might possibly be used to make a "burning glass"?

12. Two concave spherical mirrors have equal focal lengths but different apertures. Which mirror will form the hotter image of the sun? Why? Answer the same question for two mirrors of equal aperture but different focal lengths.

13. A luminous object has its image formed by a concave mirror. Can the radiant energy concentrated on unit area in the image ever exceed the energy emitted per unit area of the source?

14. Where must an object be placed in front of a concave mirror in order that the image be erect and of the same size as the object? Illustrate by a ray diagram.

15. Does a convex mirror ever form an inverted image? Why? Illustrate by ray diagrams.

16. Draw appropriate ray diagrams to locate the approximate position and size of the image formed by a concave spherical mirror (Fig. 12) when the object lies (*a*) beyond *C*, (*b*) at *C*, (*c*) between *C* and *F*, and (*d*) inside *F*. Identify the nature of each image, real or virtual.

17. Construct a graph showing the image distance (ordinates) against object distance (abscissas) for a concave mirror as the object distance is varied from plus infinity to minus infinity. Construct a similar graph for the case of a convex mirror.

18. A distant object is brought toward a concave spherical mirror. Describe the changes in the size of the image as the object distance varies from infinity to zero.

19. Two spherical mirrors of the same size and having focal lengths 1 ft and $\frac{1}{2}$ ft are placed in the path of the parallel rays from a searchlight. Compare the sharpness of the images formed by the two mirrors.

20. A searchlight comprises a light source and a reflecting mirror of radius R. What should be the distance between the source of illumination and the mirror if as much light as possible is to be concentrated into a beam that neither converges nor diverges? What form of mirror is needed for this purpose? What characteristics should the luminous source have?

PROBLEMS   *Sketch a ray diagram for each of the following problems involving spherical mirrors.*

1. A man 5 ft 10 in. tall stands 4.0 ft from a large vertical plane mirror. (*a*) What is the size of the image of the man formed by the mirror? (*b*) How far from the man is his image? (*c*) What is the shortest length of mirror in which the man can see himself full length? (*d*) What length of mirror would suffice if he were 10.0 ft away?

2. It is desired to mount a plane mirror so that a lady can see a full-length image of herself. How short a mirror will serve this purpose for a person 5 ft 8 in. tall? How should it be mounted?   *Ans.* 34 in.

3. A man 6.0 ft tall stands 15 ft away from a large, vertical plane mirror. What is the angle subtended at his eye by his image in the mirror?

4. Two vertical, plane mirrors face each other 8.0 m apart. A candle is set 1.5 m from one mirror. An observer in the middle of the room looks into the other mirror and sees two distinct images of the candle. How far are these images from the observer?   *Ans.* 10.5 m; 13.5 m

5. An electric lamp with a concentrated filament of 300 candles intensity is placed 2.5 ft in front of a plane mirror. What is the illuminance 9.0 ft in front of the lamp? Neglect the radiation from the walls of the room.

6. An observer walks toward a plane mirror at a speed of 12 ft/sec. With what speed does he approach his image?   *Ans.* 24 ft/sec

7. The distance of comfortable, distinct vision is about 25 cm for the average person. Where should a person hold a plane mirror in order to see himself conveniently?

8. A narrow beam of light reflected from the mirror of a galvanometer falls on a scale 2.0 m away placed perpendicular to the reflected rays. If the spot of light moves laterally a distance of 40 cm when a current is maintained in the instrument, through what angle does the mirror turn?   *Ans.* 5.7°

9. A concave mirror has a radius of curvature of 10 cm. Locate the image when an object is (*a*) 20 cm from the mirror and (*b*) 5.0 cm from the mirror.

10. An object is placed 20 cm in front of a concave mirror of radius 60 cm. Where is the image?   *Ans.* −60 cm

11. An object is located 2.0 ft in front of a polished metal ball 1.0 ft in diameter. Locate the image.

12. An object is located on the principal axis of a convex mirror 20 in. in front of the mirror. The image is 6.7 in. behind the mirror. What is the radius of curvature of the mirror?   *Ans.* −20 in.

13. The straight filament of a showcase lamp is placed with its center 18 in. from a concave mirror of focal length 9.0 in., and on the principal axis. The filament makes an angle of 30° with the principal axis. Locate the position of the image of the lamp filament.

14. In a solar heater, water flows through a glass pipe located above and parallel to a semicylindrical concave reflecting surface. If the reflector has a diameter of 3.0 ft how far above the reflector should the center of the pipe be located? Should the axis of the cylinder be located in an east-west or north-south direction? Is it desirable to rotate the mirror during the day?   *Ans.* 9.0 in.

15. A candle 2.0 in. high is placed 18 in. from a concave mirror of 12-in. radius, on the principal axis. Determine the size of the image.

16. The moon is approximately 2160 mi in diameter. What is the size of the image of the moon formed by a concave mirror of 3.0 m radius when the moon is at its nearest distance from the earth, 221,000 mi?   *Ans.* 15 mm

17. A dentist holds a concave mirror of radius of curvature 6.0 cm at a distance 2.0 cm from a filling in a tooth. What is the magnification of the image of the filling?

18. What is the focal length of a shaving mirror that gives a twofold magnification of the face placed 1 ft in front of it?   *Ans.* 2 ft

19. How far must one stand from a concave mirror having a focal length of 2.0 ft. in order that he may see an erect image of his face twice its natural size?

20. A convex mirror whose focal length is 15 cm has an object 10 cm tall and 60 cm away. Find the position, nature, and size of the image.
    Ans. −12 cm; 2.0 cm

21. A concave mirror has an object 10 cm tall and 60 cm from the mirror. The radius of curvature is 30 cm. Find the position, nature, and height of the image.

22. A concave mirror has a radius of curvature of 24 cm. A small lamp bulb is held on the axis 18 cm from the mirror. Find the position and nature of the image and its magnification.   *Ans.* 36 cm; 2.0

23. A spherical concave mirror has a focal length of 10 cm. An object 1.5 cm tall is 20 cm from the mirror. How tall is the image?

24. A concave mirror has a radius of curvature of 20 cm. Locate the image and determine its size when an object 4.0 cm high is 5.0 cm in front of the mirror.
    Ans. −10 cm; 8.0 cm

25. A convex mirror gives an image one-third the size of the object when the object is 30 cm in front of the mirror. What is the radius of curvature of the mirror?

26. When an object is placed 30 cm from a convex mirror the image formed is one-fifth the size of the object. What is the radius of curvature of the mirror?
    Ans. −15 cm

27. A concave mirror has a radius of curvature of 3.0 ft. Locate the image and determine its size when an object 6.0 in. high is 1.0 ft in front of the mirror.

28. Find the position, nature, and size of the image of an object 4.0 cm long formed by a concave spherical mirror, if the object is 100 cm from the mirror and the radius of curvature is 40 cm.   *Ans.* 25 cm; 1.0 cm

29. An ornamental silvered sphere has a diameter of 2.0 ft. When a 6.0-in. pencil is held 15 in. from the mirror, where is its image formed? What is the height of that image?

30. The sun has a diameter of 864,100 mi and is distant, on the average, 92,900,000 mi from the earth. What will be the size of its image formed by a concave mirror of 6.0 ft radius?   *Ans.* 0.33 in.

31. How far from a concave spherical mirror of 12-cm focal length must a small object be placed on the axis of the mirror to form an inverted image twice the height of the object?

32. An object is 5.0 cm high. It is desired to form a real image 2.0 cm high,

100 cm from the object. What type of mirror is needed and of what focal length should it be?   *Ans.* 48 cm

33. A concave and a convex mirror, each of radius 40 cm, face each other at a distance of 60 cm. An object 5.0 mm high is placed midway between the mirrors. Find the position and size of the image formed by successive reflections from the two mirrors (*a*) if the first reflection is at the concave mirror and (*b*) if the first reflection is at the convex mirror.

34. A concave mirror has a radius of curvature of 50 cm. Find two positions at which an object may be placed in order to give an image four times as large. What is the position and character of the image in each case?

Ans. 31 cm; 19 cm; 125 cm; −75 cm

42. *Refraction of Light*

We have previously noted the fact that light travels in straight lines in homogeneous mediums. When light is incident on a boundary surface, some of the light is reflected. Some of the light is also absorbed. But in many transparent substances a large portion of the light penetrates the material and emerges at the other side, as, for example, in the case of a glass plate.

A light wave (or ray) that enters another medium obliquely will undergo an abrupt change in direction if the speed of the wave in the second medium is different from that in the first. This bending of the light path is called *refraction* (Sec. 23-9).

A pencil dipped obliquely through the surface of water appears to be bent sharply where it enters the water. A coin so placed on the bottom of a cup as to be hidden by the sides of the cup may become visible when the cup is filled with water. Objects appear enlarged and distorted when viewed through the curved surface of a bottle. These are examples of the refraction of light as it passes from one material to another. The simple laws of refraction make possible the construction of the lenses for spectacles, magnifiers, cameras, telescopes, and microscopes, which extend the usefulness of our eyes.

42-1. Refraction. Consider the simplest case of refraction, that of a plane wave meet-

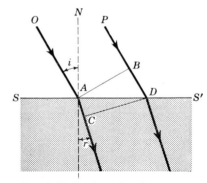

Fig. 1. Refraction of a plane wave.

ing a plane surface. In Fig. 1, *AB* represents an advancing plane wave, *OA* and *PB* are rays normal to the wave front, and *NA* is the normal to the surface of the medium at *A*. The direction of the incident ray *OA* is defined by the angle of incidence *i*, which it makes with the normal *NA*. The plane containing the incident ray and the normal to the surface is called the plane of incidence. The angle *r* between the refracted ray *AC* and the normal is called the angle of refraction.

The incident ray, the refracted ray, and the normal to the surface lie in the same plane.

Refraction may be explained on the basis of the wave theory quite simply. Let SS' in Fig. 2 represent the boundary surface between two optical materials and AB a plane wave front in the first medium at the instant one edge of the beam enters the second medium. A Huygens' wavelet starting from A will move a distance AC in the second medium in the same time that the wave moves from B to D in the first medium. As the original wave front AB moves on, secondary wavelets will be started from successive points, such as A' and A'', on the surface SS' to the right of A. When the point B of the original wave front has reached D, all the secondary waves will have spread into the second medium. There will be a new wave front CD in the second medium which is the envelope of all the secondary wavelets. Because the wave travels

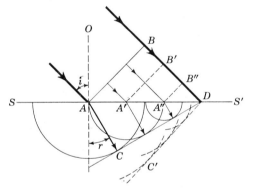

FIG. 2. Refraction represented by a Huygens' wave diagram.

more slowly in the second medium than in the first, the new wave front CD is not parallel to the original wave front AB. The light has been refracted. The dotted construction lines of Fig. 2 show that the wave would have reached the position $C'D$ in the time considered if it had continued at its original speed.

From this consideration of Fig. 2 we note that when a ray of light passes from one material into another in which its speed is less than in the first, the ray is bent toward the normal. If the light travels from the medium of less speed into that of greater

speed, the ray will be bent away from the normal. This would represent a condition in which the direction of propagation of the light in Fig. 2 is reversed.

42-2. Index of Refraction. Since the change in direction of light as it goes from one medium to another depends upon the speeds of light in the two mediums we may use the ratio of the two speeds in expressing relationships in refraction. The *index of refraction* of a substance relative to the surrounding medium may be defined as the ratio of the speed v_1 in the first medium to the speed v_2 in the second medium

$$\frac{v_1}{v_2} = n_r \tag{1}$$

If the first medium is empty space, v_1 becomes the speed c of light in empty space. The special index of refraction for this case is called the *absolute* index of refraction and we will represent it by n without the subscript. Thus

$$\frac{c}{v} = n \tag{2}$$

The relative index is related to the absolute indices of the two mediums since $v_1 = c/n_1$ and $v_2 = c/n_2$. Then

$$n_r = \frac{v_1}{v_2} = \frac{c/n_1}{c/n_2} = \frac{n_2}{n_1} \tag{3}$$

The relationship between the angle of incidence i and the angle of refraction r may be expressed in terms of the indices of refraction. In Fig. 1 light travels from B to D in the first medium in the same time t that it travels from A to C in the second medium. Thus

$$BD = v_1 t \quad \text{and} \quad AC = v_2 t$$

Since DA is perpendicular to AN and BA is perpendicular to AO, $\angle DAB = \angle i$. Likewise $\angle ADC = \angle r$.

$$\frac{BD}{AD} = \sin i$$

$$\frac{AC}{AD} = \sin r$$

By dividing we obtain

$$\frac{BD}{AC} = \frac{\sin i}{\sin r}$$

or

$$\frac{v_1 t}{v_2 t} = \frac{v_1}{v_2} = \frac{\sin i}{\sin r} = \frac{n_2}{n_1} = n_r \quad (4)$$

and

$$n_1 \sin i = n_2 \sin r \quad (5)$$

Equation (4) expresses the fact that, for a given wavelength and a given pair of substances, the ratio of the sine of the angle of

TABLE 1. INDICES OF REFRACTION
(for wavelength 5893 A)
Solids

Crown glass	1.517
Barium flint glass	1.568
Barium crown glass	1.574
Light flint glass	1.580
Dense flint glass	1.655
Fluorite	1.434
Calcite (ordinary ray)	1.658
(extraordinary ray)	1.486
Canada balsam	1.530
Diamond	2.419
Quartz, fused	1.4585
Ice at $-8°C$	1.31

Liquids (n relative to air)

Benzene at 20°C	1.501
Carbon disulfide at 20°	1.643
Carbon tetrachloride at 20°	1.461
Ethyl alcohol at 20°	1.354
Water at 0°C	1.334
20°	1.333
40°	1.331
80°	1.323

Gases and vapors at 0°C and 760 mm Hg

Dry air	1.000292
Carbon dioxide	1.00045
Ethyl ether	1.00152
Water vapor	1.000250

incidence to the sine of the angle of refraction is a constant, independent of the angle of incidence. This statement was developed by Snell and is known as *Snell's law*.

The numerical value of an index of refraction is characteristic of the two mediums, but it depends also on the wavelength of the

light. Hence an index of refraction is specified definitely only when the wavelength of the light is stated. Unless otherwise mentioned, an index is usually given for yellow light. The absolute index of refraction for air under standard conditions is 1.0002918 for light having the wavelength of the D line of sodium (5893 A). Since the absolute index n for air is so near to unity, it follows that for a solid or a liquid the absolute index and the index relative to air differ only slightly and it is usually not necessary to distinguish between them.

Example: Light passes at an angle of incidence of 30° from glass into the air. What is the angle of refraction if the index of refraction of this glass is 1.50?

The relative index of refraction for light that goes from glass into air is $1/1.50 = 0.667$.

Hence, since

$$n_r = \frac{\sin i}{\sin r}$$

$$\sin r = \frac{\sin i}{n_r} = \frac{\sin 30°}{0.667} = 0.750$$

$$r = 49°$$

Example: A ray of light in water ($n_w = \frac{4}{3}$) is incident upon a plate of crown glass ($n_g = 1.517$) at an angle of 45°. What is the angle of refraction for the ray in the glass?

By Snell's law

$$\frac{\sin 45°}{\sin r} = \frac{1.517}{1.333} = 1.137$$

$$\sin r = \frac{0.707}{1.137} = 0.624$$

$$r = 49°$$

42-3. The Shallowing Effect of Refraction. When a spherical wave front passes from one material to another through a plane surface, the form of the wave front is changed and it is in general no longer spherical. A particular case of interest, represented by Fig. 3, is that of waves from a point source O in some optically dense medium emerging into air.

When the wave front from O has reached A, the secondary wavelet from P will have reached Q where $PQ = \frac{4}{3}(OA - OP)$, since light has a speed in air four-thirds of that in

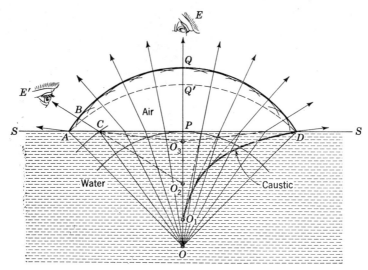

FIG. 3. The apparent depth of an object under water is less than its depth below the surface.

water. The secondary wavelet from C will have spread to a radius $CB = \frac{4}{3}(OA - OC)$. By drawing similar secondary wavelets from successive points along APD, one can locate the new position of the advancing wave front AQD and show that this wave front is no longer spherical. For an observer at E looking vertically down, the wave front arrives with a radius of curvature O_1P and the source appears to be at O_1 at a depth three-fourths of the actual depth of the object O below the surface of the water. To an observer at E' the object seems to be at O_2 still closer to the surface. If the normals to the emergent wave front are extended downward, they are found to be tangent to the caustic curve O_1D. For any position of viewing, the object appears to lie along the line OP, at a depth that lies between O_1 and O_3.

For any medium when viewed from a direction normal to the surface of separation, the ratio of the real depth to the apparent depth is equal to the relative index of refraction of the medium.

$$\frac{\text{Real depth}}{\text{Apparent depth}} = n_r \qquad (6)$$

Example: A plate of glass 1.00 in. thick is placed over a dot on a sheet of paper. The dot appears 0.640 in. below the upper surface of the

glass when viewed from above through a microscope. What is the index of refraction of the glass plate?

From Eq. (6)

$$n_r = \frac{1.00 \text{ in.}}{0.640 \text{ in.}}$$

$$n_r = 1.57$$

42-4. Mirages, Atmospheric Refraction. On still, sunny days there may be a layer of

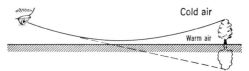

FIG. 4. A mirage is formed by atmospheric refraction upward.

hot expanded air in contact with the heated ground. Light travels faster in the rarer hot air than in the denser cool air above it. Hence light rays entering the warm air obliquely from above will be refracted upward. One may see inverted images of distant objects (Fig. 4) suggestive of the reflections in a smooth pool of water. Mirages on a small scale are often observed over concrete highways on still, hot days.

A mirage of another sort called *looming* may occur when atmospheric conditions are re-

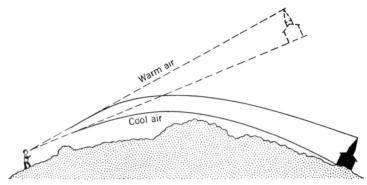

FIG. 5. Looming is caused by atmospheric refraction downward.

versed and the lower strata of air are cooler than the upper strata, as would be the case over a snow field or a body of cold water. Rays of light from a distant object are then deviated downward. One may see an image of a ship above the ship itself, or the curvature

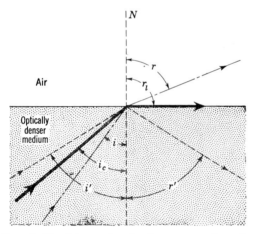

FIG. 6. Total internal reflection occurs when the angle of incidence exceeds the critical angle.

of the light rays may bring into view objects normally below the horizon (Fig. 5).

The change of the refractive index of air with changing temperature is easily observed in a turbulent stream of hot air rising from a stove or radiator, since there is an apparent wavering of objects seen through the non-homogeneous air. A ray of light entering the earth's atmosphere obliquely is bent toward the normal. Hence we see light from the sun while it is slightly below the horizon; and the

sun is flattened in appearance at sunrise and sunset. The positions of the sun and stars always appear to be higher than their actual positions, except when they are directly overhead.

42-5. Total Internal Reflection. In speaking of optical materials, it is customary to refer to relative speeds of light in terms of "optical density." A material of lesser speed is called optically more dense.

If we consider the passage of light from an optically denser medium out into air, as in Fig. 6, we observe that as the angle of incidence i is increased the angle of refraction r increases and approaches the limiting value $r_l = 90°$, beyond which of course, there could be no light refracted into the air. The limiting angle of incidence in the denser medium, which makes the angle of refraction 90°, is called the *critical angle* of incidence i_c. From the law of refraction $n_1 \sin i = n_2 \sin 90°$

$$\sin i_c = \frac{n_2}{n_1} = \frac{1}{n_r} \qquad (7)$$

where n_r is the index of refraction of the optically denser medium relative to the other.

When the angle of incidence is increased beyond its critical value i_c, we find that the light is totally reflected, making the angle of reflection r' equal to the angle of incidence i'. Total reflection can take place only when the light in the optically denser medium is incident on the surface separating it from the optically less dense medium.

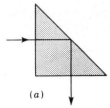 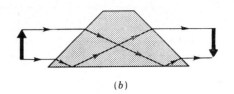

(a)   (b)

FIG. 7. Totally reflecting prisms.

Example: What is the critical angle between carbon disulfide and air?

$$\sin i_c = \frac{1}{n_r}$$

where n_r is the index of refraction of carbon disulfide relative to air.

$$\sin i_c = \frac{1}{1.643} = 0.608$$
$$i_c = 37°27'$$

Total reflection is utilized in various optical instruments. A beam of light may be turned through 90° by a 45° right-angle prism of glass having polished faces (Fig. 7a). Total reflection in the prism of Fig. 7b inverts the image and such an inverting prism may be used in binoculars or in a projection lantern to give an upright image of an object that otherwise would appear inverted.

42-6. Refraction through Plane-parallel Plates. When a ray of light passes through a

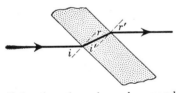

FIG. 8. Refraction through a plane-parallel glass plate.

layer of transparent material that has plane parallel surfaces and emerges again into the first medium, the emergent ray is parallel to its original direction but is displaced laterally. This may be seen by applying the laws of refraction at each of the surfaces represented in Fig. 8.

42-7. Refraction by a Prism. When light passes from air through a glass prism, it is bent toward the thicker part of the prism. In

Fig. 9, A is the refracting angle and δ is the angle of deviation, measured between the original direction of the incident ray and the direction of the refracted ray. The deviation is found to depend on the prism angle, the index of refraction of the prism material, and the angle of incidence i. Minimum deviation D occurs when the ray passes through the prism symmetrically making i equal to i'.

From Fig. 9, the deviation δ is the sum of that $(i - r)$ taking place at the first surface and that $(i' - r')$ at the second:

$$\delta = i - r + i' - r' = (i + i') - (r + r')$$

But $r + r' = A$; for minimum deviation $i = i'$, and hence $r = r'$.

Therefore for minimum deviation

$$D = 2i - A \quad \text{or} \quad i = \frac{1}{2}(A + D)$$

and

$$r = \frac{A}{2}$$

If we substitute these values in Snell's law, $n_1 \sin i_1 = n_2 \sin r_2$, we have

$$\frac{n_2}{n_1} = n_r = \frac{\sin \frac{1}{2}(A + D)}{\sin \frac{1}{2}A} \tag{8}$$

A precise method for measuring the index of refraction of a prism is based on this equation.

Example: Light from a sodium lamp when passed through a 60°00′ prism has a minimum angle of deviation of 51°20′. What is the index of refraction of the glass?

$$n = \frac{\sin \frac{1}{2}(60°00' + 51°20')}{\sin \frac{1}{2}(60°00')} = \frac{\sin 55°40'}{\sin 30°00'}$$

$$n = \frac{0.8257}{0.5000} = 1.651$$

Equation (8) can be used only when the prism is so adjusted that the ray passes

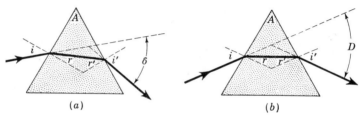

FIG. 9. Refraction by a prism. The deviation δ in (a) is greater than the minimum deviation D in (b). For minimum deviation, $i = i'$.

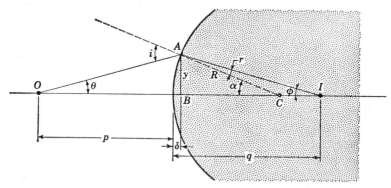

FIG. 10. Refraction at a spherical surface.

through the prism perpendicular to the bisector of the angle of the prism. For any other angle of incidence, it is possible to compute the deviation (now greater than the minimum) by following the ray through the prism, calculating the angles of incidence and refraction at each surface.

42-8. Refraction at a Spherical Surface. When light is refracted at a spherical surface the refraction at each point is consistent with the general law of refraction. If the rays from an object point O (Fig. 10) make small angles with the axis (line through the center of curvature), the rays meet at an image point I. From the law of refraction

$$\frac{\sin i}{\sin r} = \frac{v_1}{v_2} = \frac{n_2}{n_1} \qquad (9)$$

where n_1 and n_2 are the indices of refraction of the first and second mediums respectively, or

$$n_1 \sin i = n_2 \sin r \qquad (10)$$

From the geometry of triangle COA of Fig. 10

$$i = \theta + \alpha$$

And from CAI

$$\alpha = r + \phi \qquad \text{or} \qquad r = \alpha - \phi$$

$$\tan \theta = \frac{y}{p + \delta} \qquad \tan \phi = \frac{y}{q - \delta} \qquad \sin \alpha = \frac{y}{R}$$

If the angles are small, the angle, its sine, and its tangent are equal and δ is negligible. To this degree of approximation

$$\sin i = i = \frac{y}{p} + \frac{y}{R}$$

and

$$\sin r = r = \frac{y}{R} - \frac{y}{q}$$

Then from Eq. (10)

$$\frac{n_1 y}{p} + \frac{n_1 y}{R} = \frac{n_2 y}{R} - \frac{n_2 y}{q}$$

$$\frac{n_1}{p} + \frac{n_2}{q} = \frac{(n_2 - n_1)}{R} \qquad (11)$$

Equation (11) is valid only if the angles are small. If the rays diverge from the axis more than allowed by this approximation, the rays do not all pass through a single image point.

Conventions of sign must be used in Eq. (11). We may use the same convention for the signs of p and q as that used for mirrors (Sec. 41-8). It is convenient to call R positive when it is measured from the surface to the center in the direction of the light leaving the surface, negative if in the opposite direction. This convention is consistent with that used for the radii of spherical mirrors in Sec. 41-8. It follows from this convention that a refracting surface that is convex to the incident light has a positive R while one that is concave has a negative R.

Example: A water tank has a small window that is a section of a sphere of 6.0-in. radius. The convex side of the window is on the outside of the tank. A small light is placed 30.0 in. from the window (a) on the outside, and (b) on the inside of the tank. Find the position of the image in each case.

$$(a) \quad \frac{n_1}{p} + \frac{n_2}{q} = \frac{n_2 - n_1}{R}$$

$$\frac{1.00}{30.0 \text{ in.}} + \frac{1.33}{q} = \frac{1.33 - 1.00}{6.0 \text{ in.}}$$

$$q = 61 \text{ in.}$$

The image is real and inside the water.

$$(b) \quad \frac{1.33}{30.0 \text{ in.}} + \frac{1.00}{q} = \frac{1.00 - 1.33}{-6.0 \text{ in.}} = \frac{0.33}{6.0 \text{ in.}}$$

$$q = 94 \text{ in.}$$

The image is real and outside the water.

SUMMARY

Refraction is the change in direction of a light ray because of change in speed.

The *index of refraction* of a substance relative to the surrounding medium is the ratio of the speed v_1 of light in the first medium to the speed v_2 in the second medium.

$$\frac{v_1}{v_2} = n_r$$

The *absolute* index of refraction is the ratio of the speed of light in empty space to the speed in the medium.

$$\frac{c}{v} = n$$

Snell's law states that

$$\frac{\sin i}{\sin r} = \frac{n_2}{n_1} = n_r$$

A transparent body appears to be less thick than it really is because of the refraction at its surface. The amount of this shallowing effect depends upon the angle at which it is viewed.

Mirages result from atmospheric refraction.

Total internal reflection may occur when light passes from a medium of less speed to one of greater speed. As the light proceeds in this direction, it is bent away from the normal. The angle of incidence in the denser material for which the angle of refraction is 90° is called the *critical angle*. If the angle of incidence in the denser material is greater than the critical angle, total reflection occurs.

When light passes through a body whose surfaces are plane and parallel, the rays are displaced but not deviated.

When light passes from air through a glass prism, it is bent toward the thicker part of the prism. The amount of deviation depends upon the angle of the prism, the angle of incidence, and the index of refraction of the prism. Minimum deviation occurs when the ray passes through the prism symmetrically, making $i = i'$. For minimum deviation D

$$n_r = \frac{\sin \frac{1}{2}(A + D)}{\sin \frac{1}{2}A}$$

For refraction at a spherical surface, radius R

$$\frac{n_1}{p} + \frac{n_2}{q} = \frac{n_2 - n_1}{R}$$

QUESTIONS   **1.** How could one show experimentally that light travels faster in air than in water?

2. A bundle of rays parallel to the principal axis is reflected by a convex mirror in air. If the mirror is placed in water, will the divergence of the rays from the mirror be the same? Illustrate by sketches.

3. When carbon disulfide is diluted with xylol, an index of refraction of unity, relative to glass, may be obtained. A glass plate immersed in this mixture is nearly invisible. Why? How does the fact that white light is a mixture of various wavelengths affect the appearance of the plate?

4. Show how the "shallowing effect" in water appears to a fisherman as he moves away from the shore of a lake.

5. When a piece of thick plate glass is placed in a beam of convergent light, what happens to the point of convergence? Explain by the use of a diagram.

6. A coin is placed at the bottom of a metal pail in such a position that it is just barely hidden from sight. Show by the aid of a diagram why the coin becomes visible when water is poured into the vessel.

7. If a stick standing slantwise in a pond is viewed obliquely from above, the part under water appears to be bent upward. Explain by the aid of a sketch.

8. If a hunter desired to shoot a fish whose image could be seen in clear water, should he aim above or below the fish? Explain by the aid of a sketch.

9. Describe, with a diagram, the sort of view a fish might see on looking up from a small, circular pool.

10. Explain the causes of the twinkling of stars.

11. Explain the waviness frequently observed over a hot surface. Is this effect similar to the "wet" mirage often seen by a motorist ascending a hill on a hot dry day?

12. Explain the effect refraction has on the duration of daylight. How would this effect differ in a clear atmosphere as compared with one with considerable smog?

13. If the air is warmer near the ground than it is at the level of a target, will a marksman aiming a rifle at the bull's-eye tend to hit the target above or below the bull's-eye?

14. If there were no air surrounding the earth, how would the appearance of the sky be affected?

15. Describe the effect of the variation of density with altitude of the earth's atmosphere on the direction of a beam of light from a star. Would you expect this effect to be significant? Explain.

16. It is impossible for light falling upon a pane of glass in an ordinary window to be totally reflected. Explain why this must be true.

17. Show by the use of a diagram how light can be "piped" through a curved quartz rod with little loss in intensity. What is a practical application of this effect?

18. From a consideration of the critical angle, explain why a diamond examined in a beam of light sparkles more brilliantly than a piece of glass of the same shape.

19. Why is a right-angle prism a better reflector than a plane silvered mirror? Would the reflection be improved by covering with a metallic coating the polished surface at which the reflection takes place?

20. When one looks down into a glass of water, he cannot see the table through the walls of the tumbler although the fingers where they are in contact with the glass walls may be seen. Explain by the aid of a ray diagram.

21. How is the deviation of a beam of light by a prism affected by placing the prism under water? What would happen to the deviation if the prism were of air, for example, if the prism were hollow with plane glass sides?

22. Trace a beam of light through a crown-glass prism that is immersed in (*a*) air, (*b*) water, and (*c*) carbon disulfide.

23. Compare the angle of minimum deviation for yellow light for a 60° diamond prism with that for a 60° prism made of ice.

PROBLEMS

1. Yellow sodium light has a wavelength in air of 589.3 mμ. What is the frequency? What is the wavelength in water, $n = 1.33$?

2. When a ray of light is incident on the surface of a certain liquid at an angle of incidence of 48° the angle of refraction within the liquid is 35°. What is the relative index of refraction of the liquid? *Ans.* 1.30

3. For a certain transparent material the angle of refraction is 25° when the angle of incidence is 35°. What is the speed of light in this medium?

4. A beam of light is incident on a surface of water at an angle of 30° with the normal to the surface. The angle of refraction in the water is 22°. What is the speed of the light in the water? *Ans.* 2.25×10^8 m/sec

5. A layer of water overlies a layer of carbon tetrachloride. If the angle of incidence at the air surface of the water is 40°, what is the angle of refraction in the carbon tetrachloride?

6. A layer of ice ($n = 1.33$) lies on a glass ($n = 1.50$) plate. A ray of light makes an angle of incidence of 60° on the surface of the ice. Find the angle between this ray and the normal in the glass. *Ans.* 35°

7. A beam of yellow light enters a dense flint-glass plate at an angle of 40° with the normal. The flint glass lies on top of a plate of crown glass. What is the angle of refraction in the crown glass?

8. A tank of benzine is 4.00 ft deep. How deep does it appear when looking vertically downward? *Ans.* 2.66 ft

9. A tank 308 cm deep is filled with ethyl alcohol ($n = 1.35$). (*a*) How deep will it appear to an observer who looks directly downward? (*b*) A plane mirror is suspended with its face horizontal at a depth of 154 cm. An object is suspended 254 mm above the mirror. Find the apparent depth of the image formed by the mirror.

10. A telescope is pointed at a angle of 40° to the vertical over the edge of a tank full of water so that the edge of the tank limits the field of vision. How high must the tank be to make a small body at the bottom, 25.4 cm from the side nearest the telescope, just visible in the telescope? *Ans.* 46.0 cm

11. A rod stands obliquely in water, making an angle of 45° with the normal to the surface. An observer places a second rod near the surface so that it appears to be in line with the immersed portion of the first. What angle will the second rod make with the first?

12. A point source of light is located 275 cm below the surface of a lake. Calculate the area of the surface that transmits all the light that emerges from the surface. *Ans.* 30.4 m²

13. What is the critical angle at the interface between water and carbon tetrachloride? Which direction must the light be going to have total reflection?

14. What is the critical angle for total internal reflection for dense flint glass that is immersed in water? How would the critical angle be affected if the glass were immersed in carbon disulfide? *Ans.* 53.7°

15. A point source of light is located 12.5 cm below the surface in an aquarium. Make a drawing to show all the reflected and refracted rays for angles of incidence of 15°, 30°, 45°, 60°, and 75°. Show also the rays for the critical angle of incidence.

16. What is the largest possible angle of refraction for yellow light incident upon a surface of fused quartz? *Ans.* 43.3°

17. A Nicol prism is made by cementing together with Canada balsam ($n = 1.530$) two pieces of calcite ($n = 1.658$). Determine the critical angle.

18. At what angle of incidence should a ray of light approach the surface of diamond ($n = 2.42$) from within, in order that the emerging ray shall just graze the surface?   *Ans.* 24.4°

19. A ray of yellow light is incident at an angle of 40° on a piece of barium crown glass whose faces are parallel and 24.0 mm apart. What is the angle of emergence? How much is the ray displaced?

20. An aquarium 3.0 ft long is filled with water. A beam of light is incident upon one end of the aquarium at an angle of 25°. Neglecting the effect of the glass walls of the aquarium, calculate the lateral displacement of the emergent beam.   *Ans.* 4.3 in.

21. A ray of light is incident upon a piece of optical glass at such an angle that the angle between the reflected and refracted beams is 90°. Prove that $n_r = \tan i$ for this case.

22. Show that a light wave that passes through a plate of optical glass with parallel sides of thickness s suffers a sidewise displacement x given by

$$x = \frac{s \times \sin(i - r)}{\cos r}$$

23. A prism of diamond has angles of 60°. The angle of incidence of yellow light on one face is 60°. At which face does it emerge? What is the angle of emergence?

24. A glass ($n = 1.50$) cube is 4.0 cm on a side. A ray of light is incident on one face 1.0 cm from the edge at an angle of incidence of 60° and directed toward the near side. Where and at what angle will the ray emerge from the cube?
                                        Ans. At face opposite incident face, 1.8 cm from edge; 60°

25. A flint-glass prism ($n = 1.624$) has a refracting angle (vertex) accurately ground to 60°. A beam of light is incident on this prism at an angle of 50°. Calculate the angle of deviation (not minimum).

26. A beam of light strikes normally one of the faces of a 60° dense flint-glass prism. Trace the path through the prism and determine the angle of deviation of the beam.   *Ans.* 60°

27. Compare the angle of minimum deviation for yellow light of a 40° diamond prism with that of a 40° prism made of ice.

28. A fused-quartz rod is 30.0 mm in diameter. One end is in the form of a hemisphere. A small source of light is placed on the axis of the rod 45 cm from the hemispherical end. Find the position of the image.   *Ans.* 51 mm

29. The left end of a glass rod ($n = 1.58$) is ground and polished to a convex hemispherical surface of radius 51.6 mm. An object is located on the axis 205 mm to the left of the vertex of the convex surface. Find the position of the image.

30. The glass rod of Prob. 29 is immersed in water and the object is placed on the axis 205 mm from the surface. Find the position of the image.
                                                                          Ans. −957 mm

31. A tank of ethyl alcohol has a small window that is a section of a sphere of radius 90 cm. The concave surface is on the outside. Find the position of the image of a source that is placed 80 cm from the window (*a*) outside the tank and (*b*) inside the tank.

32. An 8.0-in. glass ($n = 1.50$) sphere has half its surface silvered. Sunlight falls on the unsilvered half. Where is the image of the sun formed by the emergent light?   *Ans.* 2.0 in. outside the silvered surface

43. *Thin Lenses*

When light passes through an object made of a transparent material it is, in general, deviated both at entrance and at emergence. Just how much resultant deviation there will be depends upon the shape of the refracting body as well as upon the relative index of refraction.

We have observed that a ray of light is bent toward the thicker part of an optically dense prism. Consider the double prism of Fig. 1a. Two rays parallel to the common base pass through one of the prisms, and each is bent around the base. They emerge parallel to each other, since the prism has not changed the curvature of the wave front. If a second pair of rays parallel to the first (Fig. 1b) passes through the other prism, they will also

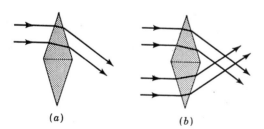

(a)   (b)

Fig. 1. Refraction by a double prism.

be deviated and each will cross the first pair. However, the four rays do not reach any

common point. Such a pair of prisms does not focus a set of rays.

If, however, we change the shape of the transparent body, we can arrange it so that each of the parallel rays is bent by a different amount and all will intersect at a common point. Such a body with its curved surfaces changes the shape of the wave front. A transparent body with regular curved surfaces that produce changes in the shape of the wave front is called a *lens*.

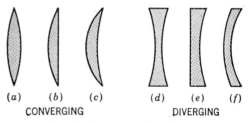

(a)   (b)   (c)   (d)   (e)   (f)
CONVERGING   DIVERGING

Fig. 2. Lenses of various forms.

43-1. Lenses. The curved surfaces of lenses may be of any regular shape, such as spherical, cylindrical, parabolic, or even curves that deviate from these regular surfaces. The most common forms of lenses are those in which the surfaces are parts of spheres or one spherical and the other plane. Spherical surfaces are used because they are easiest to make. The line joining the centers of the two spheres is called the *principal axis* of the lens. Typical forms of spherical lenses are shown in Fig. 2. The lenses are named from the two surfaces as double convex (*a*), double concave (*d*), plano-concave (*e*), etc.

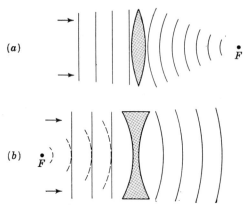

FIG. 3. Refraction of a plane wave by a lens.

A lens produces a change in the curvature of a wave front passing through it. If the lens is made of optically dense material, as is usual, the speed of light in the lens is less than in air, and a thin-edged lens retards light passing through the center more than light passing near the edge. Hence a plane wave (Fig. 3*a*) will have its central part retarded on passing through a thin-edged lens and will converge toward a point *F* after emerging.

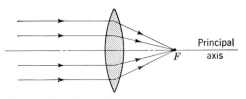

FIG. 4. Focusing of light by a converging lens.

Conversely, a thick-edged lens will render a plane wave divergent (Fig. 3*b*).

The propagation of light through lenses and the formation of images may be represented in wave-front diagrams based on Huygens' principle. It is easier, however, to use ray diagrams. Consider a glass lens such as *a* of Fig. 2 on which is incident a set of rays from a very distant source on the axis of the lens. These rays will be parallel to the axis. Each ray is bent around the thicker part of the glass. As they leave the lens, they converge toward a point *F* (Fig. 4). Any lens that will cause a set of parallel rays to converge is called a *converging* lens. The point *F* to which the *rays parallel to the principal*

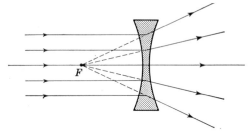

FIG. 5. The principal focus (virtual) of a diverging lens.

axis are brought to a focus is called the *principal focus*. The distance from the center of the lens to the principal focus is called the *focal length* of the lens. A thin lens has two principal foci, one on each side of the lens and equally distant from it.

If a lens such as *d* of Fig. 2 is used in the same manner, the rays will again be bent around the thicker part and in this case will diverge as they leave the lens (Fig. 5). Any lens that is optically more dense than its surroundings and thicker at the edge than at the middle will cause a set of rays parallel to the axis to diverge as they leave the lens and is called a *diverging* lens. The point *F* from which the rays diverge on leaving the lens is the principal focus. Since the light is not actually focused at this point, it is known as a *virtual* focus.

If the source is not very distant from the lens, the rays incident upon the lens are not parallel but diverge as shown in Fig. 6. The behavior of the rays leaving a converging lens depends upon the position of the source. If the source is farther from the lens than the principal focus, the rays converge as they leave the lens as shown in Fig. 6*a*; if the source is exactly at the principal focus, the emerging rays will be parallel to the principal axis as shown in Fig. 6*b*. If the source is between the lens and the principal focus, the divergence of the rays is so great that the lens is unable to cause them to converge but merely reduces the divergence. To an observer beyond the lens, the rays appear to come from a point Q rather than from P, as

lens, they pass through the points occupied by the image. The image can be formed on a screen and viewed there. Such an image is called a *real* image. If the rays diverge on leaving the lens, they do not pass through the points occupied by the image and the image

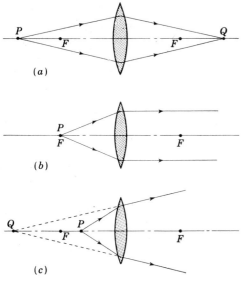

FIG. 6. Effect of a converging lens on light originating (a) beyond the principal focus, (b) at the principal focus, and (c) between the lens and the principal focus.

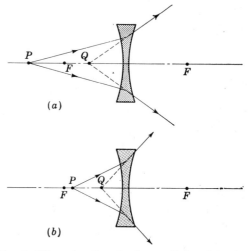

FIG. 7. Effect of a diverging lens on light originating (a) beyond the principal focus and (b) closer than the principal focus.

shown in Fig. 6c. The point Q is a virtual focus.

A diverging lens causes the rays emerging from the lens to diverge more than those which enter. No matter what the position of the real source, the emergent rays diverge from a virtual focus as shown in Fig. 7.

43-2. Image Formation by Lenses. When the rays converge after passing through the

cannot be formed on a screen. The image can be seen by looking through the lens. This type of image is called a *virtual* image. Its position is the place from which the diverging rays appear to come. Thus Figs. 4 and 6a represent the formation of real images, while Figs. 5, 6c, and 7 represent virtual images. Note that a diverging lens produces only virtual images of real objects while a converging lens may produce either real or virtual images, depending upon the location of the real object.

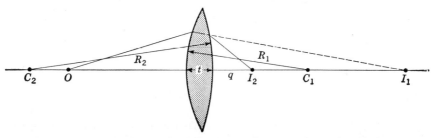

FIG. 8. Formation of image by refraction at the two surfaces of a thin lens.

43-3. The Thin-lens Equation. The relationship between object distance, image distance, and focal length of a lens may be found by considering the refraction at each surface. If an object is at O, Fig. 8, the first surface of the lens forms an image I_1. The position of this image is found by use of Eq. (11), Chap. 42:

$$\frac{n_1}{p} + \frac{n_2}{q_1} = \frac{n_2 - n_1}{R_1} \qquad (1)$$

The image formed by the first surface becomes the object for the second surface. In Fig. 8 the light leaving the first surface would reach I_1 if the second surface did not intervene and hence I_1 is a real image for the first surface. If the second surface does intervene, the light does not reach I_1 and hence I_1 becomes a *virtual* object for the second surface. The object distance for the second surface is therefore negative and is given by $-(q_1 - t)$, where t is the thickness of the lens. For the second surface

$$\frac{n_2}{-(q_1 - t)} + \frac{n_1}{q} = \frac{n_1 - n_2}{R_2} \qquad (2)$$

If the lens is *thin*, that is, its thickness is small compared to the other dimensions involved, t can be neglected and Eq. (2) reduces to

$$\frac{n_2}{-q_1} + \frac{n_1}{q} = \frac{n_1 - n_2}{R_2} \qquad (3)$$

By adding Eqs. (1) and (3) we obtain

$$\frac{n_1}{p} + \frac{n_1}{q} = (n_2 - n_1)\left(\frac{1}{R_1} - \frac{1}{R_2}\right) \qquad (4)$$

or

$$\frac{1}{p} + \frac{1}{q} = \left(\frac{n_2}{n_1} - 1\right)\left(\frac{1}{R_1} - \frac{1}{R_2}\right) \qquad (5)$$

If the object is at infinity, $1/p = 0$, the image is at the principal focus, and $q = f$. Thus

$$\frac{1}{f} = \left(\frac{n_2}{n_1} - 1\right)\left(\frac{1}{R_1} - \frac{1}{R_2}\right) \qquad (6)$$

Hence, for *thin* lenses

$$\frac{1}{p} + \frac{1}{q} = \frac{1}{f} \qquad (7)$$

Equations (1) and (2) may be applied to any spherical lens to find object and image distances, subject to the restriction that the rays must not make large angles with the axis. This restriction is inherent in Eq. (11), Chap. 42. The rest of these equations apply to thin lenses. Since the lens is thin, the measurement of p, q, and f is to the lens; its thickness is negligible. If the lens is turned around, R_1 and R_2 are interchanged in Eq. (6) and the sign of each is reversed. Thus there is no change in f. For a thin lens the focal length is independent of the order of the surfaces.

In using Eqs. (1) to (7) we must follow a consistent set of conventions of sign. Such a set is listed in Secs. 41-7 and 42-8. These conventions are:

1. Object and image distances are taken positive for real objects and images, negative for virtual objects and images.

2. The radius of curvature R is positive when it is measured from the surface to the center in the direction of the light leaving the surface and negative if in the opposite direction. It follows from this convention and Eq. (6) that, for any thin lens that is thicker in the middle than at the edges, f is positive if the relative index of refraction n_2/n_1 is greater than 1 and negative if n_2/n_1 is less than 1. The third convention then follows.

3. The focal length f is positive for a converging lens and negative for a diverging lens.

Example: A plano-convex lens (Fig. 2*b*) of focal length 12 cm in air is to be made of glass of refractive index 1.50. What should be the radius of curvature of the curved surface?

From Eq. (6)

$$\frac{1}{12 \text{ cm}} = \left(\frac{1.50}{1.00} - 1\right)\left(\frac{1}{R_1} - \frac{1}{\infty}\right)$$
$$R_1 = 6.0 \text{ cm}$$

Example: A converging lens made of glass ($n = 1.66$) has a focal length f_a of 5.0 in. in air. What is the focal length f_w when it is placed in water ($n = 1.33$)?

From Eq. (6)

$$\frac{1}{f_w} = \left(\frac{1.66}{1.33} - 1\right)\left(\frac{1}{R_1} - \frac{1}{R_2}\right)$$
$$\frac{1}{f_a} = \left(\frac{1.66}{1.00} - 1\right)\left(\frac{1}{R_1} - \frac{1}{R_2}\right)$$

If we divide the second of these equations by the first we obtain

$$\frac{f_w}{f_a} = \frac{0.66}{0.25}$$

and

$$f_w = \frac{0.66}{0.25} \, 5.0 \text{ in.} = 13 \text{ in.}$$

Example: When an object is placed 20 in. from a certain lens, its virtual image is formed 10 in. from the lens. Determine the focal length and character of the lens.

From Eq. (7)

$$\frac{1}{20 \text{ in.}} + \frac{1}{-10 \text{ in.}} = \frac{1}{f}$$
$$f = -20 \text{ in.}$$

The negative sign shows that the lens is diverging.

43-4. Image Determination by Means of Rays. When an object is placed before a lens, it is possible to determine the position of

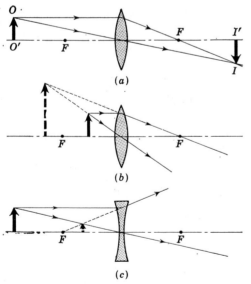

Fig. 9. Image formation traced by means of ray diagrams.

the image graphically. By drawing at least two rays whose complete paths we know, the

image point corresponding to a given object point may be located. Suppose we have as in Fig. 9a a converging lens with an object, represented by the arrow OO' placed some distance in front of the lens. Let F represent the principal foci on the two sides of the lens. A point on the object, such as the tip of the arrow O, may be considered to be the source of any number of rays. Consider the ray which proceeds toward the center of the lens. Since the surface at the point of entrance of this ray is parallel to the surface at the point of emergence, there is no deviation of this ray. We are here treating only *thin* lenses, and hence the displacement of the ray is negligible. Thus for thin lenses the ray through the optical center of the lens is a straight line.

A "thin" lens may be considered as one whose thickness is negligible in comparison with the radii of curvature of its surfaces.

Now consider another ray from the tip of the arrow—one that travels parallel to the principal axis. We saw from Fig. 4 that all rays parallel to the principal axis which strike a converging lens pass through the principal focus after emerging. Thus the ray we have drawn from the tip of the arrow will, after refraction by the lens, pass through F. If this line is continued, it will cut the ray through the center of the lens at a point I. This is the image point corresponding to the tip of the arrow. The other image points, corresponding to additional points of the arrow, will fall in the plane through I perpendicular to the lens axis. In particular, the image of the foot of the arrow will be on the axis if the foot of the arrow itself is so placed. An inverted real image of the arrow will actually be seen if a card is held in the plane II'. Inversion takes place also in the sidewise direction so that if the object has any extent in a direction normal to the plane of the figure, right and left will be reversed.

Figure 9b shows how to locate the image when an object is placed closer to a converging lens than the focal length. We have already seen from Fig. 6c that this results in a virtual image. The reason, from the point of view of the ray construction, is that the ray through the lens center and the ray passing through F do not intersect on the right-hand side of the lens, but diverge instead. However, the rays *appear* to have come from some point located by projecting them back to the left until they cross. This point is the *virtual image* of the tip of the arrow. The entire virtual image is represented by the dotted arrow. It cannot be formed on a screen but may be viewed by looking into the lens from the right. It is customary to represent real rays in the ray diagram by solid lines and their extensions backward (virtual rays) by dotted lines as in Fig. 9.

In a similar way, the formation of a virtual image by a diverging lens is shown in Fig. 9c.

43-5. Magnification. In every example of image formation described, we may see from the graphical construction that

$$\frac{\text{Size of image}}{\text{Size of object}} = \frac{\text{distance of image from lens}}{\text{distance of object from lens}}$$

The first ratio is called the *linear magnification*, or simply the magnification. Hence, in symbols,

$$M = \frac{q}{p} \tag{8}$$

where p is the distance of the object from the lens and q is that of the image.

Example: The lens system of a certain portrait camera may be considered equivalent to a thin converging lens of focal length 10.0 in. How far behind the lens should the plate be located to receive the image of a person seated 50.0 in. from the lens? How large will the image be in comparison with the object?

Substitution in Eq. (7) gives

$$\frac{1}{50.0 \text{ in.}} + \frac{1}{q} = \frac{1}{10.0 \text{ in.}}, \quad \text{or} \quad q = 12.5 \text{ in.}$$

From Eq. (8)

$$M = \frac{12.5 \text{ in.}}{50.0 \text{ in.}} = 0.250$$

The image will be one-fourth as large as the object.

Example: Determine the location and character of the image formed when an object is placed 9.0 in. from the lens of the previous example.

Substitution in Eq. (7) gives

$$\frac{1}{9.0 \text{ in.}} + \frac{1}{q} = \frac{1}{10.0 \text{ in.}}$$
$$q = -90 \text{ in.}$$

The negative sign shows that the image lies to the left of the lens and is therefore virtual. It is larger than the object in the ratio

$$M = \frac{90 \text{ in.}}{9.0 \text{ in.}} = 10$$

43-6. Power of a Lens—Diopter. The power of a lens is the amount by which it can change the curvature of a wave. Thus the power D of a lens is the reciprocal of its focal length

$$D = \frac{1}{f} \tag{9}$$

Hence the shorter the focal length of a lens, the greater is its power. Opticians express the power of a lens in terms of a unit called the *diopter*, the power of a lens that has a focal length of one meter. In using Eq. (9), the focal length must be expressed in meters to give the power in diopters.

Example: What is the power (diopters) of a diverging lens whose focal length is -20 cm?

$$f = -20 \text{ cm} = -0.20 \text{ m}$$
$$\text{Power} = \frac{1}{-0.20 \text{ m}} = -5.0 \text{ diopters}$$

43-7. Lens Combinations. Two or more lenses are used in combination in most optical instruments. The location, size, and nature of the final image can be determined by the use of the lens equation or by use of a ray diagram. By either method we find first the image formed by the first lens, use that image as the object of the second lens, and locate the image formed by the second lens. If there

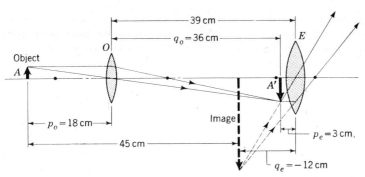

Fɪɢ. 10. An enlarged, virtual image formed by successive refractions by two lenses.

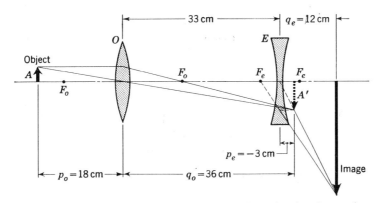

Fɪɢ. 11. An enlarged, real image formed by successive refractions by two lenses.

are more than two lenses, we continue this process; the object of each lens is the image formed by the preceding lens.

When we have combinations of lenses, we frequently have *virtual objects* for the second and succeeding lenses. For real objects, the rays diverge from each point on the object. Thus the rays entering a lens from a real object are always diverging. When the object of one lens of a combination is the image formed by the preceding lens, the rays entering the second lens may be converging toward a position beyond the lens. The object then is said to be *virtual*. Such a situation is shown in Fig. 11. For a virtual object, the object distance is negative.

When lenses are used in combination, each magnifies the image from the preceding lens. Hence the total magnification produced by the combination is the product of the magnifications of the individual lenses.

Example: Two converging lenses O and E having focal lengths 12 cm and 4 cm, respectively, are placed 39 cm apart on a common principal axis. A small object is placed 18 cm in front of lens O. Find the position, nature, and magnification of the image formed by the combination of lenses.

A conventional ray diagram (Fig. 10) is drawn to scale to locate the image A' of object A formed by lens O. Image A' is found to be real. It serves as a real object for lens E. Starting from A', a ray diagram is drawn through lens E showing that the final image is virtual, enlarged, and inverted (compared with the object A).

The lens equation applied to lens O gives

$$\frac{1}{18 \text{ cm}} + \frac{1}{q_o} = \frac{1}{12 \text{ cm}}$$
$$q_o = 36 \text{ cm}$$

Magnification $M_o = \dfrac{q_o}{p_o} = \dfrac{36 \text{ cm}}{18 \text{ cm}} = 2.0$

Since the image formed by lens O lies 36 cm

from O, the object distance for lens E is 39 cm − 36 cm = 3 cm = p_e.

If we apply Eq. (7) to lens E, we have

$$\frac{1}{3 \text{ cm}} + \frac{1}{q_e} = \frac{1}{4 \text{ cm}}$$

$$q_e = -12 \text{ cm}$$

Magnification $M_e = \dfrac{q_e}{p_e} = \dfrac{12 \text{ cm}}{3 \text{ cm}} = 4$

Total magnification $M = M_o \times M_e = 2 \times 4 = 8$

The final image is formed 45 cm from the object; it is virtual, inverted, and magnified eight times.

Example: A converging lens O of focal length 12 cm and a diverging lens E of focal length −4.0 cm are placed 33 cm apart on a common principal axis. A small object is placed 18 cm in front of lens O. Find the position, nature, and magnification of the image formed by the combination of lenses (Fig. 11).

For the first lens

$$\frac{1}{18 \text{ cm}} + \frac{1}{q_o} = \frac{1}{12 \text{ cm}}$$

$$q_o = 36 \text{ cm}$$

$$M_o = \frac{36 \text{ cm}}{18 \text{ cm}} = 2$$

The image formed by lens O lies behind lens E and is therefore a virtual object for that lens.

For the second lens

$$-\frac{1}{3 \text{ cm}} + \frac{1}{q_e} = -\frac{1}{4.0 \text{ cm}}$$

$$q_e = 12 \text{ cm}$$

$$M_e = \frac{12 \text{ cm}}{3 \text{ cm}} = 4$$

Total magnification = $M_o M_e = 2 \times 4 = 8$

The final image is formed 63 cm from the object; it is real, inverted, and magnified eight times.

In the ray diagram for this problem (Fig. 11) the real image A', which would be formed by lens O alone, falls behind lens E. It is treated as the virtual object for lens E and the final image is found by drawing a conventional ray diagram for lens E. This is merely a convenient device. It does not, of course, imply that rays return through lens E. Furthermore, the rays that are drawn from the intermediate image A' do not represent continu-

ations of the rays from A. A dotted line is projected back from the head of A' parallel to the axis. This would represent the continuation of a ray that entered the lens from the left parallel to the axis. This ray leaves the lens as though it had come from the principal focus.

43-8. Thin Lenses in Contact. When two or more thin lenses are in contact, they may be treated as a single lens by finding the focal length of a single lens that would produce the same refraction as the combination. One method of finding the equivalent focal length is to treat the image of the first lens as the object of the second lens as with other lens combinations. A somewhat simpler method uses the powers of the lenses. Each lens changes the curvature of the wave by the amount of its power D. The total change in curvature is the sum of the two changes. That is,

$$D = D_1 + D_2 \qquad (10)$$

or

$$\frac{1}{f} = \frac{1}{f_1} + \frac{1}{f_2} \qquad (11)$$

where f is the focal length of the combination and f_1 and f_2 are the focal lengths of the individual lenses.

43-9. Spherical Aberration. In the derivation of the equations for refraction at spherical surfaces the treatment was limited to rays that make small angles with the axis. Unless the aperture of a lens is very small there are rays that make angles larger than justified by this approximation. Thus the rays that enter the lens near its edge are brought to a focus closer to the lens than are the central rays. This characteristic of a spherical lens is called *spherical aberration* (see also Sec. 41-9). Its effect may be minimized by using a diaphragm in front of the lens to decrease its effective aperture, a sharper image being then produced with consequent loss of light.

43-10. Coma. Another form of spherical aberration occurs for object points that are laterally displaced from the principal axis. Rays from such points may intersect in the

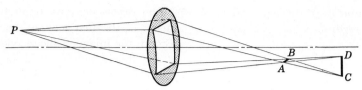

Fig. 12. Astigmatism.

focal plane, not as a sharp focus, but in a comet-shaped figure (hence the term "coma"). This effect can be minimized by using a compound lens having several surfaces, or more simply by an aperture stop that eliminates rays which are not near the principal axis.

43-11. Astigmatism. Astigmatism is the lens defect whereby horizontal and vertical

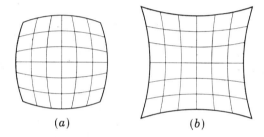

(a)   (b)

Fig. 13. "Barrel" and "pincushion" distortion of square-mesh object.

lines in an object are brought to a focus in different planes, as the two lines AB and CD in Fig. 12. Astigmatism arises from the lack of symmetry of a lens or a lens system about the line from the center of the lens to an object. In the eye this occurs when the curvature of the cornea is different in different axial planes. But astigmatism occurs even for a perfectly spherical lens whenever the source P is not on the optical axis of the lens. It is corrected, along with other defects, by a combination of lenses.

43-12. Distortion. Another aberration, known as *distortion*, is caused by the fact that the magnification of an image varies at different parts of the image. The central part of the image may be accurate, but the outer parts are not faithful images of the object. When a diaphragm is used to reduce spherical aberration and is inserted between the lens and the object, the image is distorted so that a square-mesh object appears as the barrel-shaped image shown in Fig. 13a. If the diaphragm is placed on the opposite side of the lens from the object, the square-mesh object gives an image of pincushion shape, as shown in Fig. 13b. The effects of distortion may be minimized by using two lenses and placing a diaphragm between them.

A lens that is corrected for such defects as spherical aberration, astigmatism, distortion, and chromatic aberration (Chap. 45) is called an *anastigmatic* lens.

SUMMARY

When rays of light pass through a lens, they are bent toward the thicker part of the lens if the lens has an index of refraction greater than that of the surrounding medium. Rays parallel to the principal axis of the lens pass through a point called the *principal focus*. The distance of the principal focus from the lens is called the *focal length*.

A *real image* is formed if the rays actually pass through the image after refraction. A *virtual image* is formed if the rays only appear to come from the image after refraction.

A *converging lens* makes a set of parallel rays converge after refraction. A *diverging lens* renders a set of parallel rays divergent after refraction.

A converging lens forms *real images* when the real object is farther from the lens than the principal focus, but *virtual images* when the real object is between the lens and the principal focus. A diverging lens forms a virtual image of any real object.

The focal length f of a lens is given in terms of its radii of curvature R_1 and R_2 and the indices of refraction n_2 of the lens and n_1 of the surrounding medium.

$$\frac{1}{f} = \left(\frac{n_2}{n_1} - 1\right)\left(\frac{1}{R_1} - \frac{1}{R_2}\right)$$

The position, size, and nature of an image can be determined by means of a *ray diagram* or by use of the *lens equation*

$$\frac{1}{b} + \frac{1}{q} = \frac{1}{f}$$

Conventionally, f is to be taken as positive for a converging lens and negative for a diverging lens; p and q are positive for real objects and images, negative for virtual objects and images.

The *linear magnification M* is the ratio of the size of the image to the size of the object. It is related to the object and image distances by the equation

$$M = \frac{q}{p}$$

The power of a lens is the amount by which it can change the curvature of a wave. It is the reciprocal of the focal length. When the focal length is expressed in meters, the power is in *diopters*.

Lens combinations are treated by using the image of the first lens as the object of the second, the image of the second as the object of the third, and so on through the whole combination. When the image of one lens is located beyond the next lens, it serves as a *virtual object* for the second lens and the object distance for that lens is negative.

Spherical aberration is the defect of a lens by which rays entering near the edge of the lens are brought to a focus nearer the lens than the rays that enter near the center.

Coma is a form of lateral spherical aberration whereby rays from object points not on the principal axis are focused in a comet-shaped image.

Distortion is caused by variations in the magnification of the outermost portions of an image, resulting in barrel-shaped or pin-cushion-shaped images of a square-mesh object.

Astigmatism is the defect whereby horizontal and vertical lines are brought to a focus at different distances.

Both spherical aberration and astigmatism can be reduced by decreasing the aperture of the lens.

QUESTIONS   1. How large does a lens have to be in order to give a complete image of a distant object? Compare this case with the corresponding one for the plane mirror.

2. What effect is produced on the curvature of a plane wave by a plane mirror? by a convex mirror? by a concave lens? Illustrate by diagrams.

3. Trace the paths of a beam of parallel rays which are incident upon a hollow-glass sphere immersed in water.

4. Trace a beam of rays parallel to the principal axis of a crown-glass convex lens when the lens is in (a) air, (b) water, and (c) carbon disulfide. Describe the path of these rays if an "air" lens were used in each of these materials.

5. Draw appropriate ray diagrams to locate the approximate position and size of the image formed by a converging lens of focal length f when the object lies at a distance (a) greater than $2f$, (b) $2f$, (c) between $2f$ and f, and (d) less than f. Identify the nature of each image: real or virtual; larger or smaller than the object.

6. Describe and illustrate with ray diagrams three different laboratory methods of finding the focal length of a concave lens.

7. Show that the thin-lens equation $1/p + 1/q = 1/f$ is that of an equilateral hyperbola. Note the fact that the asymptotes of the curve are the lines $p = f$ and $q = f$.

8. Draw a set of rectangular coordinates (four quadrants). Plotting object distance p along the horizontal axis and image distance q along the vertical,

draw a graph showing corresponding object and image points (conjugate points) for a converging lens of focal length 12 in. Consider the object distances as varying from plus to minus infinity.

9. Draw an object-distance *vs.* image-distance graph for a diverging lens of focal length 12 in. for object distances varying from plus to minus infinity.

10. Does the column of mercury in a clinical thermometer look broader or narrower than it really is? Explain.

11. Check the results of the examples in Sec. 43-5 by drawing ray diagrams to scale on squared paper. Verify the magnification as well as the position of the image in each case.

12. Two identical convex lenses of focal lengths f are placed a distance $3f$ apart. Indicate whether the combination produces a real or a virtual image when a lamp is placed, relative to the first lens, (*a*) between infinity and $2f$, (*b*) between $2f$ and f, (*c*) at f, and (*d*) between the principal focus and the lens.

13. Which of the following statements are true? If a converging beam of light is incident upon a double-convex lens the image (*a*) is always real, (*b*) is always virtual, and (*c*) may be real or virtual, depending upon the convergence of the beam and the power of the lens.

14. What are the two factors that determine whether a lens is converging or diverging?

15. Under what conditions does a double-convex lens become a diverging lens?

16. Describe some cases in which it is convenient to use a combination of lenses, rather than a single lens.

17. What type of lens is a tumbler filled with water? Would one expect such a lens to have a large or a small amount of spherical aberration?

PROBLEMS **1.** A converging lens of fused quartz has a concave surface of radius of curvature 24 cm and a convex surface of radius 40 cm. What is the focal length of the lens?

2. A double-convex lens, both surfaces of which have radii of 20 cm, is made of glass whose index of refraction is 1.50. Find the focal length of the lens.
Ans. 20 cm

3. A 12.5-diopter converging lens is to be made from glass of index of refraction 1.500. If each surface is to have the same curvature, what should be the common radius of curvature?

4. A certain converging lens made of glass of index of refraction 1.52 has a focal length of 10.0 cm. What is the focal length of this lens in water?
Ans. 37 cm

5. What is the focal length of the lens of Prob. 2 if it is immersed in carbon disulfide of index of refraction 1.643?

6. A lens is constructed by cementing together the edges of two watch glasses, each of radius of curvature 25.0 cm. The resulting lens is immersed in ethyl alcohol. What is the focal length of this air lens? Is it converging or diverging?
Ans. −47.8 cm

7. A lens is made by cementing together two watch glasses with their concave faces toward each other. The radius of curvature of each surface is 20.0 cm. Find the focal length of the lens when (*a*) it contains air and is immersed in water, (*b*) it contains carbon disulfide and is in air, and (*c*) it contains carbon disulfide and is immersed in water.

8. A lens is made by cementing a watch glass of 20.0 cm radius of curvature to a flat glass plate. Find the focal length of the lens when (*a*) it contains air and is immersed in water, (b) it contains water and is immersed in carbon disulfide, and (c) it contains carbon disulfide and is immersed in water.

Ans. −80.7 cm; −106 cm; 85.7 cm

9. A fused quartz lens of index of refraction 1.458 has one convex and one concave surface whose radii are 246 and 408 mm, respectively. An object 15 mm high is placed 165 cm from the lens. Where is the image and how high is it?

10. A glass lens (n = 1.50) has a concave surface of radius 206 mm and a convex surface of radius 618 mm. A candle flame 12.5 mm high is 126 mm from the lens. Where is the image and how high is it?   *Ans.* −105 mm; 10.4 mm

11. A thick lens has a convex surface of radius of curvature 81.6 cm and a plane surface. The distance between the two surfaces is 52.4 mm. The index of refraction of the glass is 1.60. Find the principal focal point on the side of the plane surface.

12. An object 40.6 mm high is placed 52.4 cm from a converging lens. An image is formed 25.8 cm from the lens. (a) How large is the image? (b) Is the image real or virtual? (c) What is the focal length of the lens?

Ans. 20.0 mm; real; 17.4 cm

13. A lens has a focal length of −250 mm. Locate the image and find its size when an object 18 mm high is placed (a) 500 mm from the lens, and (b) 125 mm from the lens.

14. An object 20.4 mm high placed 10.0 cm from a converging lens produces an erect image 40.8 mm high. (a) Where is the image? (b) Is it real or virtual? (c) What is the focal length of the lens?   *Ans.* −20.0 cm; 20.0 cm

15. A piece of a meter stick 15.6 mm long stands vertically at the left of a lens and 125 cm from the lens. An observer at the right of the lens sees the image of the stick at a distance of 11.8 cm on the left of the lens. What is the focal length of the lens and what is the length of the image?

16. At what distance from a converging lens of focal length 5.24 cm must an object be placed in order that a real image may be formed twice the size of the object?   *Ans.* 7.86 cm

17. A certain lens when placed 254 mm from an object forms a virtual image four times as large as the object. What kind of lens is used and what is its focal length?

18. A plano-convex lens (R = 12.0 cm, n = 1.50) is cemented over an opening in the side of a water tank. A small light source is placed outside the tank 30.0 cm from the opening. Where is the image if (a) the curved surface is outside and (b) if the plane surface is outside?   *Ans.* 158 cm; −70 cm

19. What minimum distance can there be between an object and its image formed by a converging lens if the image is (a) real or (b) virtual?

20. A converging lens has a focal length of 3.33 cm. What lens must be combined in contact with it in order to produce a lens of focal length 9.00 cm?

Ans. f = −5.28 cm

21. Two thin lenses of focal lengths 8.0 cm and −3.0 cm are placed in contact. What is the focal length of the combination?

22. The focal lengths of two lenses are 10 cm and 20 cm. What is the focal length of the combined lenses when they are placed in contact?   *Ans.* 6.7 cm

23. A thin lens has a focal length of −30 cm. What is the nature and power of this lens?

24. What is the focal length of a 2.5-diopter spectacle lens?   *Ans.* 40 cm

25. The glass of a 0.50-diopter lens has an index of refraction of 1.60. If the lens faces are of equal curvature, what is the radius of curvature of each?

26. A diverging lens of -30.0 cm focal length is placed 10.0 cm from an object. A converging lens of focal length 40.0 cm is placed 12.5 cm beyond the first lens. Find: (*a*) the position of the resultant image, (*b*) the magnification. (*c*) Is the final image real or is it virtual?   *Ans.* -40.0 cm; 1.5

27. A diverging lens B of 20 cm focal length is placed 45 cm to the right of a converging lens A of 30 cm focal length. A small object is placed 50 cm to the left of A. Find: (*a*) the position of the final image, (*b*) the linear magnification. (*c*) Is the image real or virtual? (*d*) Is it erect or inverted?

28. A lens of $+20$ cm focal length forms an inverted image 60 cm to the right of the lens. A second lens of focal length -30 cm is placed 20 cm to the right of the first lens. (*a*) Where is the first object? (*b*) Locate and describe the final image.   *Ans.* 30 cm; -120 cm

29. An object is placed at the 0.0-cm mark on an optical bench and a convex lens is placed at the 50.0-cm mark. A real image is formed at the 70.0-cm mark. Without moving the object or the convex lens, a diverging lens is placed at the 60.0-cm mark and a new real image is formed at the 80.0-cm mark. Find the focal length of each lens.

30. A beam of sunlight falls on a diverging lens of focal length 10 cm, and 15 cm beyond this is placed a converging lens of 15-cm focal length. Find where a screen should be placed to receive the final image of the sun.

Ans. 38 cm beyond converging lens

44. *The Eye and Optical Instruments*

In the lowest animals, the eye may be merely a collection of pigmented cells capable of distinguishing between light and darkness. In more highly developed forms the eye includes

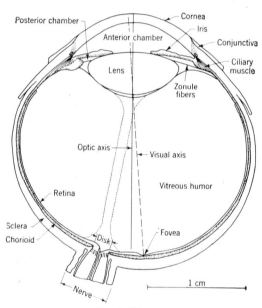

Fig. 1. The eye.

a lens which forms real images and a fine-grained mosaic of receptors which records the pattern of intensities and wavelengths in the image and submits that pattern to the brain for interpretation. The response of the visual system to different intensities and wavelengths of illumination, its ability to dis-

tinguish size and position, and the common errors of vision are of such practical importance as to have received extensive study. Spectacle lenses compensate for faults of vision, but physiological remedial measures are as yet little understood. Many optical instruments are designed to extend the usefulness of the human eye by exploiting its advantageous characteristics, or by compensating for its shortcomings. Most of them serve to increase the size of the image; but the effect of looking through them may be to change the apparent distance of objects (as does a telescope) rather than to change apparent size (as does a magnifier or a microscope).

44-1. The Human Eye. The eye (Fig. 1) contains a lens, a variable diaphragm (the iris), and a sensitive screen (the retina) on which the cornea and lens form a real, inverted image of objects within the field of vision. The eye is a nearly spherical structure held in a bony cavity of the skull in which it can be rotated to a certain extent in any direction by the complex action of six muscles. The eye has a tough fibrous coat of which about one-sixth, the *cornea*, is transparent, admitting light. Within the eyeball behind the cornea is the opaque, muscular *iris*, which has a central opening, the pupil. This contracts and dilates to control the amount of light admitted. The lens is a trans-

FIG. 2. Locating the "blind spot" of the eye.

parent biconvex body composed of myriads of microscopic, glassy fibers, which readily slide on one another so that the lens can change its shape. The lens is held just behind the iris by a system of spokelike ligaments (zonule fibers) that are relaxed or tensed by the action of a muscle (the ciliary), producing changes in the curvature of the lens. These changes in the focusing ability of the lens accomplish *accommodation*, the adjustment of the distance of the image for the exact distance of the retina, in accordance with the external distance to the object of regard.

Lining the wall of the eyeball is the *retina*, a sensitive membrane whose stimulation results in the visual sensation. The spaces between the cornea and the zonule (anterior and posterior chambers) are occupied by a salt solution, the aqueous humor, and the interior region between lens and retina is filled by a jellylike vitreous humor. The humors have about the same index of refraction (little higher than that of water). The principal refraction occurs as light enters the curved outer surface of the cornea, and lesser refractions take place as it enters and leaves the lens, whose index is considerably higher than that of the humors.

Many millions of light receptors, the *rods* and *cones*, form one layer of the retina. These are connected to a smaller number of intermediary nerve cells which in turn are connected to a still smaller number of optic nerve fibers. From all over the inner surface of the retina these converge at one spot where they pass out through the eyeball wall, forming the optic nerve, which connects the retina and the brain. Here at the head of the optic nerve ("disk"), is an insensitive region or "blind spot," since there are no rods or cones there. The existence of the blind spot can easily be verified by closing the left eye and looking intently at the **x** in Fig. 2. As the book is moved toward the eye, the square disappears when the page is about 10 in. from the eye. On moving the page closer the black dot may also be made to disappear. Still closer, the square and dot will reappear in turn. More centrally located than the blind spot there is a pit in the retina, the *fovea*, which contains only cones. Here, vision is most acute. It is this portion of the retina, embracing about 1 degree of the visual field, which is always used when we look directly at an object. Evidently the eyes will have to turn toward each other, so that their axes converge, in order to bring an image of a nearby object into position on the fovea in each eye.

44-2. Refractive Errors. An optically normal eye, when the ciliary muscle is entirely relaxed, forms an image of a distant object on the retina (Fig. 3a). If the object approaches closer than about 20 ft, the image recedes behind the retina unless a sufficient degree of accommodation is exercised.

Figure 3b represents a nearsighted (myopic) eye that is relaxed. The rays from a very distant point focus in front of the retina, usually because the eyeball is too long. Such an eye cannot focus a distant object, but will see very close objects distinctly. To correct this nearsighted vision, a diverging lens is needed to diminish the refraction. The opposite condition, that of a farsighted (hyperopic) eye which is too short, is shown in Fig. 3c. A converging lens is needed to overcome farsightedness.

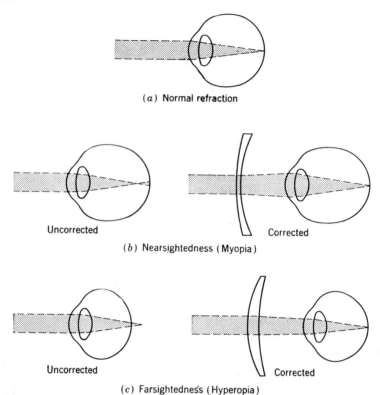

(a) Normal refraction

Uncorrected   Corrected

(b) Nearsightedness (Myopia)

Uncorrected   Corrected

(c) Farsightedness (Hyperopia)

Fig. 3. Correction of nearsightedness and farsightedness by spectacle lenses.

Example: A certain farsighted person has a minimum distance of distinct vision of 150 cm. He wishes to read type at a distance of 25 cm. What focal length glasses should he use?

Since the person cannot see clearly objects closer than 150 cm, the lens must form a virtual image at that distance.

$$p = 25 \text{ cm}$$
$$q = -150 \text{ cm}$$
$$\frac{1}{p} + \frac{1}{q} = \frac{1}{f}$$
$$\frac{1}{25 \text{ cm}} + \frac{1}{-150 \text{ cm}} = \frac{1}{f}$$
$$f = 30 \text{ cm}$$

Astigmatism, a common defect in human eyes, is a failure to focus all lines of an object-plane in a single image-plane, but it arises from a cause different from that of the astigmatism which is one of the aberrations of spherical lenses or mirrors. Ocular astig-matism is generally due to unequal curvature of the front surface of the cornea, the surface being distorted by a certain amount of cylindrical curvature. A person with this defect will see radial lines (Fig. 4) parallel to the axis of the cylindrical curvature of his eye less sharply than other lines. To correct the astigmatism a cylindrical lens is so arranged that the convergence produced by the eye and spectacle lens together is the same in all meridians. Astigmatism often occurs in com-bination with nearsightedness or farsighted-ness, both being neutralized by a single lens incorporating both spherical and cylindrical corrections.

There is a normal dwindling of the power of accommodation so that by the age of about forty-five positive lenses are needed for read-ing. Eyes originally myopic, and formerly corrected by diverging lenses, may in fortu-nate cases be perfectly adjusted for reading by removing the spectacles. More often a special reading correction, less divergent than the old spectacle (and perhaps even positive), is needed. Bifocal glasses, for myopics, have the upper area negative for distant viewing, the lower area less strongly negative, or even

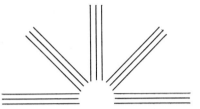

Fig. 4. Astigmatic dial for locating the meridians of ocular astigmatism.

somewhat positive, for reading. For hyperopic eyes bifocal glasses always have both areas positive, the lower one of greater power (by about two diopters).

44-3. Sensitivity of the Eye. The eye can detect extremely small amounts of luminous energy. A dark-adapted eye can detect light equivalent to that received from a single candle distant 15 to 20 mi, in which case the retina is receiving only a few quanta of light (Chap. 40). The sensitivity of the eye varies greatly for different wavelengths (Fig. 4, Chap. 40).

44-4. Persistence of Vision. The visual system lags a bit in its response to a stimulus, and the sensation lasts an even greater fraction of a second after the stimulus ceases. This retention of the mental image, referred to as the persistence of vision, prevents the appearance of any "flicker" when a motion-picture film is projected on a screen at the rate of at least 16 screen-illuminations/sec (24 frames/sec or 72 screen-illuminations/sec are used in commercial motion pictures) even though the screen is completely dark while the film is in motion in the projector. The illusion of movement in a motion picture is due to a fortunate propensity of the visual system to "fill in" the positions of a moving object intermediate between those imaged discretely and successively upon the retina.

44-5. Stereoscopic Vision. The importance of binocular vision in judging position and relative distance may be appreciated by closing one eye and trying to bring two pencil points together when the pencils are held in the hands at arm's length and moved

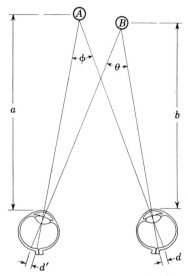

Fig. 5. Binocular vision: arrangement for the measurement of stereoscopic visual acuity. If A and B are just discriminable, $\theta - \phi$ is the stereo threshold in angular terms and $d' - d$ is the corresponding retinal disparity. The values of $\theta - \phi$ and $d' - d$ are independent of the absolute values of a and b.

at right angles to the line of sight. When a single nearby object is viewed with both eyes, the axes of the eyes are turned toward each other. Distance is estimated by solution of the triangle whose base is the distance between the two pupils, averaging 64 mm. The amount of convergence enables us to make a crude estimate of the distance of the object; but its size (when known) tells us most about its distance. Far better is our ability to say which of two objects is the nearer. This depends upon the fact that the interpupillary distance subtends a different angle (called the binocular parallax) at each of the objects. The difference in the binocular parallaxes needs only to be a few seconds of arc for the difference in distance to be detectable (Fig. 5).

For distances greater than about 700 ft,

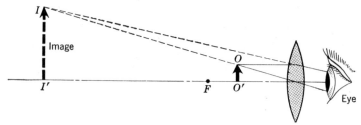

Fig. 6. A simple magnifier.

the inclination of the optic axes is so slight that both eyes see practically the same view, and distances are judged by the apparent sizes of familiar objects rather than by stereoscopic vision. Prism binoculars (Fig. 10) and range finders in effect increase the interpupillary distance, and with an extended base line of known length, permit distances to be calculated by the solution of a triangle in which the base and two angles are known.

44-6. Limitations of Vision. The visibility of an object depends on size, contrast, intensity, time, and the adaptation of the eye. A deficiency in one of these factors, within certain limits, may be compensated for by an increase in one or more of the other factors. Thus close machine work or the inspection of small parts may be facilitated by increased illumination and contrasting colors. Illuminations recommended for various visual tasks are listed in Table 1, Chap. 40.

In the retinal mosaic of rods and cones the most sensitive part, the fovea, is about a millimeter in diameter and its central part, 0.2 mm in diameter, contains only cones. The angular field of most distinct vision is about 1°, which is subtended by a circle of 4.4 mm at a distance 25 cm from the eye. Two fairly wide lines can just be distinguished by the eye when their angular separation is about 1 min of arc, in which case the centers of the image lines are only a few thousandths of a millimeter apart on the retina. When the smallness or distance of an object exceeds the limitations for direct visibility, the eye requires optical aids, some of which will be briefly described.

44-7. Magnifier. A simple magnifier is a converging lens placed so that the object to be examined is a little nearer to the lens than its principal focus (Fig. 6). An enlarged, erect, virtual image of the object is then seen. The image should be at the distance of most distinct vision, which is about 25 cm from the eye, the magnifier being adjusted so that the image falls at this distance.

The *linear magnification* is the ratio of the image size to the object size; that is,

$$\text{Magnification} = M = \frac{II'}{OO'} = \frac{q}{p} \quad (1)$$

The thin-lens equation

$$\frac{1}{p} + \frac{1}{q} = \frac{1}{f}$$

gives

$$\frac{q}{p} = \frac{q}{f} - 1$$

and if $q = -25$ cm

$$M = \frac{25 \text{ cm}}{f} + 1 \quad (2)$$

where f is in cm.

The magnifier in effect enables one to bring the object close to the eye and yet observe it comfortably. When the object is thus brought closer, it subtends a larger angle at the eye than it would at a greater distance.

Example: A converging lens of 5.0-cm focal length is used as a simple magnifier, producing a virtual image 25 cm from the eye. How far from the lens should the object be placed? What is the magnification?

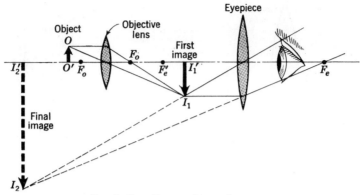

FIG. 7. Ray diagram for a microscope.

From the lens equation

$$p = \frac{fq}{q - f} = \frac{5.0(-25)}{-25 - 5.0} = 4.2 \text{ cm}$$

$$M = \frac{25}{4.2} = 5.9$$

A magnifier is frequently used as an eyepiece or ocular in an optical instrument in combination with other image-forming lenses.

44-8. The Microscope. Whenever high magnification is desired, the *microscope* is used. It consists of two converging lenses (in practice, lens systems), a so-called *objective* lens of very short focal length and an *eyepiece* of moderate focal length. The objective forms within the tube of the instrument a somewhat enlarged, real image of the object. This image is then magnified by the eyepiece. The final image seen by the eye is virtual and very much enlarged.

Figure 7 shows the ray construction for determining the position and size of the image. The object is placed just beyond the principal focus of the objective lens, and a real image is formed at II'. This image is, of course, not caught on a screen but is merely formed in space. It consists, as does any real image, of the points of intersection of rays coming from the object. This image is examined by means of the eyepiece, which serves here as a simple magnifier. The position of the eyepiece, then, should be such that the real image I_1I_1' lies just within the principal focus F_e'. Hence the final image I_2I_2' is

virtual and enlarged, and it is inverted with respect to the object.

The magnification produced by a microscope is the product of the magnification M_e produced by the eyepiece and the magnification M_o produced by the objective lens. Hence, for a final image at the distance of most distinct vision (25 cm)

$$M = M_o M_e = \frac{q_o}{p_o}\left(\frac{25 \text{ cm}}{f_e} + 1\right) \quad (3)$$

where p_o and q_o are the distances of object and first image, respectively, from the objective, and f_e is the focal length of the eyepiece, all distances measured in centimeters. In practice the largest magnification employed is usually about 1500.

Example: A microscope has an objective lens of 10.0-mm focal length and an eyepiece of 25-mm focal length. What is the distance between the lenses, and what is the magnification if the object is in sharp focus when it is 10.5 mm from the objective?

Consider the objective alone

$$\frac{1}{10.5 \text{ mm}} + \frac{1}{q} = \frac{1}{10.0 \text{ mm}}$$
$$q = 210 \text{ mm}$$

Consider the eyepiece alone, with the virtual image at the distance of most distinct vision (250 mm)

$$\frac{1}{p'} + \frac{1}{-250 \text{ mm}} = \frac{1}{25.0 \text{ mm}}$$
$$p' = 22.7 \text{ mm}$$

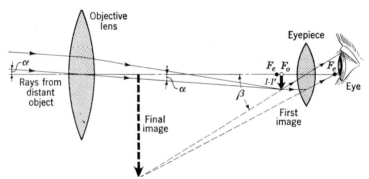

FIG. 8. Ray diagram for a refracting telescope.

Distance between lenses $= q + p' = 210$ mm $+ 22.7$ mm $= 233$ mm $= 23.3$ cm

Magnification by objective: $M_o = \dfrac{210 \text{ mm}}{10.5 \text{ mm}} = 20.0$

Magnification by eyepiece: $M_e = \dfrac{250 \text{ mm}}{22.7 \text{ mm}} = 11.0$

Total magnification

$$M = M_e M_o = 11.0 \times 20.0 = 220$$

As a check, Eq. (3) gives

$$M = \frac{q_o}{p_o}\left(\frac{25 \text{ cm}}{f_e} + 1\right) = \frac{21.0 \text{ cm}}{1.05 \text{ cm}}\left(\frac{25 \text{ cm}}{2.5 \text{ cm}} + 1\right)$$
$$= 2\bar{2}0$$

44-9. Refracting Telescopes. The astronomical refracting telescope, like the compound microscope, consists of an objective lens system and an eyepiece. The instruments differ, however, in that the objective of the telescope has a long focal length. Light from the distant object enters the objective, and a real image is formed within the tube (Fig. 8). The eyepiece, used again as a simple magnifier, leaves the final image inverted.

It should be noted that, whereas the *same* rays might have been traced through both lenses, in Fig. 8 two *different* pairs of rays are traced. The first is perhaps the better representation of the physical action of the lenses, but the second procedure is the more practical. In it, the first pair of rays traced through the objective is used to locate the first (real) image. Then from a convenient point on this image two more rays are drawn, one passing through the center of the eyepiece (undevi-

ated), the other entering the eyepiece parallel to its principal axis and refracted to pass through the principal focus F_e. By this artifice the final (virtual) image is located.

Angular magnification is defined as the ratio of the angle β subtended at the eye by the image to the angle α which the object subtends at the lens or eye. The angular magnification can be computed from the geometry of Fig. 8. Neglecting the length of the telescope, the first image subtends the same angle α at the center of the objective lens as the object does at the observer's naked eye, and similarly the first and second images subtend the same angle β at the optical center of the eyepiece. Hence

Angular magnification $= \dfrac{\beta}{\alpha} \doteq \dfrac{II'/f_e}{II'/f_o}$

$$= \frac{f_o}{f_e} \quad (4)$$

Owing to the approximations made, Eq. (4) applies only for distant objects. This formula shows that apparently unlimited values of M may be obtained by making f_o very large and f_e very small. Other factors, however, limit the values employed in practice, so that magnifications greater than about 2000 are rarely used in astronomy.

Which of the features of the telescope make it valuable depends upon whether it is to be used in conjunction with an eye or with a photographic plate. All the cones of light leaving the eyepiece pass through the image (exit pupil) it forms of the objective aperture.

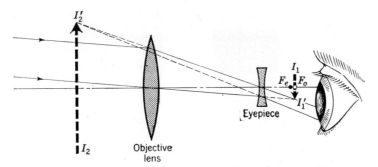

Fig. 9. A diagram of a Galilean telescope.

So long as the exit pupil of the instrument (objective diameter/magnification) agrees in size with the pupil of the eye, differences in magnification cannot affect the amount of light per unit area (illuminance) of the retinal image. Any improvement in the visibility of a faint star is then directly attributable to the enlargement of the retinal image. But when photography is employed, the light-gathering ability of the objective lens (or of the mirror of a reflecting telescope such as the giant 200-in. Mt. Palomar instrument) becomes of the greatest importance. The amount of light collected by the objective is directly proportional to its area. A lens of 800 mm aperture will gather in $(800/8)^2 = 10,000$ times as much light as will the pupil of the eye at night (when it is 8 mm in diameter). Huge telescope lenses and mirrors make possible the photography of invisible stars within reasonable exposure time. The eye, on the contrary, can take only snapshots, no time exposures. But a "night glass" can increase the brightness of a faint star, which is invisible through a field glass of equal power designed for daytime use, only by reason of the fact that the exit pupil of the day glass is too small to fill the eye pupil and that of the night glass is as large as the nighttime pupil or even larger.

Example: A reading telescope comprising an objective of 30.0-cm focal length and an eyepiece of 3.0-cm focal length is focused on a scale 2.0 m away. What is the length of the telescope (distance between lenses)? What magnification is produced?

Consider the objective

$$\frac{1}{200 \text{ cm}} + \frac{1}{q} = \frac{1}{30.0 \text{ cm}}$$
$$q = 35.3 \text{ cm}$$

For the eyepiece

$$\frac{1}{p'} + \frac{1}{-25 \text{ cm}} = \frac{1}{3.0 \text{ cm}}$$
$$p' = 2.7 \text{ cm}$$

Telescope length $= 35.3 \text{ cm} + 2.7 \text{ cm} = 38.0 \text{ cm}$

Magnification by objective

$$M_o = \frac{35.3 \text{ cm}}{200 \text{ cm}} = 0.176$$

Magnification by eyepiece

$$M_e = \frac{25 \text{ cm}}{2.7 \text{ cm}} = 9.4$$

Total magnification

$$M = M_e M_o = (9.4)(0.176) = 1.6$$

Note that Eq. (4) is not applicable to a telescope focused on a nearby object, and would lead to an erroneous result if applied here.

A Galilean telescope (Fig. 9) consists of a converging objective lens, which alone would form a real inverted image $I_1 I_1'$ of a distant object practically at the principal focus, and a diverging eyepiece lens. In passing through the concave lens, rays that are converging as they enter are made to diverge as they leave. To an observer the rays appear to come from $I_2 I_2'$, the enlarged virtual image. With this design of telescope an erect image is secured.

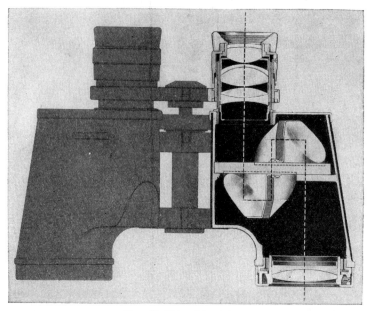

Fig. 10. Prism binocular.

For a distant object the angular magnification is

$$M = \frac{f_o}{f_e} \qquad (5)$$

Two Galilean telescopes are mounted together in opera glasses. Such glasses are no longer used in military operations, for their field is small and they are limited, in practice, to a magnification of not more than four. Modern military field glasses are prism binoculars, which have several advantages.

44-10. The Prism Binocular. The prism binocular (Fig. 10) consists of two astronomical telescopes in each of which two totally reflecting right-angle prisms are used to erect the image and shorten the over-all length. The two prisms are set with half of the hypotenuse face of one in contact with half of the hypotenuse face of the other, and with the long dimensions of these faces at right angles to each other. The combination inverts the image and exchanges left and right sides. The image formed by the objective lenses and prisms is therefore real but has the same orientation as the object itself, and so too does the final virtual image formed by the

eyepiece. With this construction, advantage is taken of the fact that the distance between the objectives can readily be made greater than the distance between the eyes, thus enhancing the stereoscopic effect as an aid to the perception of distances.

44-11. The Photographic Camera. A camera consists of a converging lens at one end of a lightproof enclosure and a light-sensitive film or plate at the other end of the enclosure where it receives the real inverted image formed by the lens. The amount of light that reaches the film depends on the effective area of the lens (usually regulated by an iris diaphragm) and the time of exposure. The lens aperture or diameter of the effective opening is usually given as a fraction of the focal length. Thus an $f/11$ lens means that the diameter of the aperture is one-eleventh of the focal length. This notation is convenient for expressing the "speed" of the lens (the relative exposure time required), since the amount of light per unit area reaching the film is proportional to the square of the diameter of the lens opening and inversely proportional to the square of the focal length of the lens.

Example: Under certain conditions the correct film exposure time is $\frac{1}{20}$ sec with a lens "speed" of $f/4.5$. What is the correct exposure time when the lens is diaphragmed to $f/6.3$?

The apertures are $A_1 = f/4.5$, $A_2 = f/6.3$

$$\frac{t_1}{t_2} = \left(\frac{A_2}{A_1}\right)^2 = \left(\frac{4.5}{6.3}\right)^2$$

$$t_1 = \frac{1}{20} \text{ sec}$$

$$t_2 = \left(\frac{6.3}{4.5}\right)^2 \left(\frac{1}{20} \text{ sec}\right) = \frac{1}{10} \text{ sec}$$

When a lens is focused for a certain distance, object points at that distance only are imaged with maximum sharpness. Points at other distances from the lens are imaged as blurred circles termed *circles of confusion*. The farther a point is from the plane focused on, the greater is the size of the circle of confusion. If the circle of confusion is below a certain size, it appears to the eye as a point and the image appears sharp. The range of distances on the near and far sides of the plane focused upon, within which the details are imaged with acceptable sharpness, is called the *depth of field* and is of particular importance in photography.

Depth of field depends on the relative aperture and the focal length of the lens, the distance focused upon, and the size of the circle of confusion which is acceptable. For a given lens, the smaller the aperture, the greater is the depth of field. For the same object distance, the depth of field increases for decreasing focal length, one of the advantages of a miniature camera with short focal-length lens. The depth of field decreases rapidly as the object focused upon approaches the camera. It is, therefore, important to determine the distances more carefully for near objects than for distant objects. The greatest range of depth is that obtained when the lens is focused for the *hyperfocal distance*, or the shortest distance for which the far limit extends to infinity.

For the most critical definition of sharpness, the circle of confusion should not subtend more than 2 min of arc at the eye. If a photographic print is to be viewed at the distance for normal vision, the circle of confusion in the negative should not exceed approximately $\frac{1}{2000}$ of the focal length of the camera lens. Many cameras are provided with a depth of focus table based upon this criterion.

SUMMARY

The eye contains a lens, a variable diaphragm (iris), and a sensitive screen (retina) on which the lens forms a real, inverted image of objects within the field of vision.

Accommodation, the adjustment of the eye for seeing at different distances, is accomplished by changes in the curvature of the lens.

The conventional distance of most distinct vision is 10 in. or 25 cm.

Nearsightedness is compensated by a diverging (concave) spectacle lens, farsightedness by a converging (convex) spectacle lens.

The magnification produced by a lens used as a simple magnifier is $M = 25 \text{ cm}/f + 1$, where f is the focal length in centimeters and the lens is adjusted so the image falls at the distance of most distinct vision, 25 cm.

The microscope consists of a short-focus objective and a longer focus eyepiece. The magnification is given by

$$M = \frac{q_o}{p_o}\left(\frac{25 \text{ cm}}{f_e} + 1\right)$$

The astronomical telescope consists of a long-focus objective and an eyepiece. The magnification is given by

$$M = \frac{q_o \, q_e}{p_o \, p_e}$$

Angular magnification is the ratio of the angle subtended at the eye by the image to the angle subtended by the object.

The Galilean telescope consists of a long-focus objective and a negative eyepiece.

The f-number of a camera lens is the quotient of its focal length and its aperture.

The depth of field of a lens is the range of distances on the near and far sides of the plane focused upon, within which the object structure is imaged with acceptable sharpness.

QUESTIONS   **1.** Name three common eye defects, and state the type of spectacle lens that is used to compensate for each.

2. Compare and contrast the optical arrangements of the human eye and those of a photographic camera.

3. Why does not the "blind spot" in the eye impair one's vision?

4. Explain the optical illusion frequently observed in motion pictures when the wheels of a forward-moving vehicle appear to be stationary, or even to be turning backward.

5. Why does a young person who wears glasses not need bifocals?

6. What determines the magnification produced by a simple magnifier? by a microscope?

7. Consider that in Fig. 6 the object subtends an angle α at the lens or eye and its image subtends a larger angle β. The magnifying power depends on this gain in angle, β/α, subtended at the eye. On this basis, derive an equation for the magnification of a simple magnifier.

8. How does increasing the focal length of the objective affect the magnification observed with a microscope? a telescope? Explain the difference.

9. If a person were looking through a telescope at the full moon how would the appearance of the moon be changed by covering half of the objective lens?

10. If telescopes do not magnify the images of the very distant fixed stars, how do they enable us to see stars invisible to the unaided eye?

11. How does a terrestrial telescope differ, in general, from an astronomical telescope?

12. Should one use a lens of long or short focal length for a simple magnifier? for a microscope objective? for a telescope objective?

13. How will changing the aperture of a camera lens from $f/2$ to $f/8$ affect (a) the size of the image, (b) the illuminance of the image, (c) the exposure time, (d) the sharpness of the image, and (e) the depth of field?

14. Is the image of a lantern slide projected on a screen erect or inverted? Explain with the aid of a diagram.

15. Show that the depth of focus of a camera increases as the f-number of the stop increases. HINT: Show that for a given lens the diameter of the circle of confusion is directly proportional to the diameter of the aperture, and hence inversely proportional to the f-number of the stop used.

16. Show that in a camera it is desirable to use a lens of short focal length and a small film size in order to reduce the size of the circle of confusion relative to the picture area, and still be able to use low f-numbers for high speed.

PROBLEMS   **1.** (a) Spectacles of what diopter power are required for reading purposes by a person whose near point is at 200 cm? (b) If the far point of a myopic eye is at 30 cm, what spectacles are required for distant vision?

2. Light entering the eye is refracted chiefly at the cornea. Assuming the eye to be 25 mm from cornea to retina and to be filled with a homogeneous medium of refractive index 1.336, calculate (a) the radius of curvature of the cornea and (b) the length of the retinal image of an object 10 cm long placed 1.0 m from the eye. (Use wave-front diagram and calculate curvature.)

Ans. 6.2 mm; 2.5 mm

3. A certain farsighted person cannot see distinctly objects closer than 50 cm to the eye. Find the power in diopters of the spectacle lenses that will enable this person to see objects 25 cm away.

4. A person has a minimum distance of direct vision of 8.0 ft. What kind of lenses and of what focal length are required for spectacles to enable him to read a book at a distance of 18 in.?   *Ans.* Converging; 22 in.

5. A person whose near point is 15 cm uses a 5.0-cm focal length lens to magnify a small object. (*a*) What is the distance of the object when in focus? (*b*) What magnification results?

6. A certain farsighted person can read fairly clearly without spectacles at a distance of 80.0 cm. His glasses have a power of 2.5 diopters. What is his reading distance when wearing glasses?   *Ans.* 27 cm

7. The distance from the retina to the eye lens in a particular eye is 2.5 cm. The eye can see well when looking at very distant objects, and can accommodate sufficiently to change the focal length by 0.10 cm. What is the closest distance at which the eye can see?

8. A nearsighted man cannot see clearly objects more than 5.0 m away. Because of an error by his oculist, he receives spectacles intended for a near-sighted man who cannot see clearly objects more than 10.0 m away. When wearing these spectacles, what is the greatest distance at which he can focus clearly?   *Ans.* 10 m

9. A farsighted man needs a lens with a power of +1.50 diopters. The inner face of the lens is to fit against an eyeball having radius of curvature of 1.20 cm. Glass is available with an index of refraction 1.63. What must be the curvature for the outer face of the lens? The index of refraction of the cornea is 1.33.

10. A "10× magnifier" is one that produces a magnification of 10 times. According to Eq. (2), what is its focal length? How large an image of a flash-light lamp 0.25 in. in diameter will this lens be able to produce on a card held 5 in. away from the lens?   *Ans.* 1.1 in.; 0.9 in.

11. A reading glass produces an image 5.0 in. from the lens when the object is 45 in. on the other side of the lens. What magnification does this lens give when used as a simple magnifier with the image at the normal distance of most distinct vision?

12. A magnifying glass of focal length 6.0 cm is used to view an object by a person whose smallest distance of distinct vision is 25 cm. If he holds the glass close to the eye, what is the best position of the object?   *Ans.* 4.8 cm

13. A linen tester is a simple magnifier for use in counting the number of threads per linear inch in fabrics. The tester shown in Fig. 11 consists of a lens

Fig. 11.

of 13-mm focal length mounted in a folding frame, the lower arm of which is cut out to cover an area of fabric 0.50 in. square. What is the approximate mag-nification when the image is formed at the distance of most distinct vision?

14. A crude microscope is constructed of two spectacle lenses of focal lengths 5.0 cm and 1.0 cm, spaced 20 cm apart. (*a*) Where must the object be placed to enable the observer to see a distinct image at a distance of 25 cm from the eyepiece? (*b*) What is the linear magnification?   *Ans.* $p_o = 1.07$ cm; 89×

15. A microscope is provided with objectives of focal lengths 16 mm, 4.0 mm, and 1.6 mm, each of which forms an image 160 mm beyond its focal point. The oculars have magnifying powers of 5× and 10×. What is (a) the largest and (b) the least linear magnification obtainable with the microscope?

16. A microscope has an objective lens of focal length 0.90 cm placed 13.0 cm from an eyepiece of 5.00-cm focal length. A bug 0.050 cm long is placed 1.0 cm from the objective. Locate, describe, and find the size of the final image.

Ans. $q_e = -20$ cm; size = 2.3 cm

17. A microscope has an eyepiece of focal length 2.50 cm and an objective of focal length 1.6 cm. If the distance between objective and eyepiece is 22.1 cm, determine the magnification produced when the final image is an infinite distance away.

18. A certain biological specimen being examined under a microscope cannot be subjected to illumination greater than 10,000 lumens/ft² without injury. If the apparent illumination in the image must be at least 1 lumen/ft² for satisfactory viewing, what is the maximum useful magnification?   *Ans.* 100

19. A microscope has an objective lens of focal length 5.0 mm and an eyepiece of 8.0-cm focal length. The microscope is adjusted to give a magnification of 500 when the final image is at infinity. If the illuminance at the object is $5\bar{0},000$ lumens/ft², what is the maximum apparent brightness at the final image?

20. The Yerkes refracting telescope has an objective of diameter 40 in. and a focal length of 65 ft. (a) What magnifying power should be used to give an exit pupil of 2.0 mm, matching the entrance pupil of the eye? (b) What focal length eyepiece is needed for this magnifying power? (c) Show that if some other magnifying power is used, there is no gain in the total light in the retinal image.   *Ans.* 509×; 1.5 in.

21. The illuminance from direct sunlight on a certain day is 7500 lumens/ft². If the Yerkes telescope (Prob. 20) were used to view the sun, which subtends an angle of about 0.5°, what would be the illuminance of the sun's disk in the focal plane of the objective?

22. What would be the magnifying power of the Yerkes telescope (Prob. 20) when used with an eyepiece of 1.0-in. focal length to produce a final image at infinity?   *Ans.* $7\bar{8}0$

23. A telescope with an angular magnification of 10× is sighted at the sun and focused to give an image at infinity. How far and in what direction must the eyepiece be moved to project a sharp image of the sun on a screen 31 cm back of the eyepiece? The focal length of the objective is 50.0 cm.

24. What magnification is produced by a telescope having an objective of 30 cm and an eyepiece of 5.0-cm focal length (a) when sighted on a distant object, and (b) when used to read a scale 5.0 m distant?   *Ans.* 6.0; 0.26

25. A simple telescope is used in the laboratory to view a scale 4.5 m from the objective of the telescope. The focal length of the objective lens is 45 cm. (a) What must be the focal length of the eyepiece so that, when placed 5.0 cm from the image formed by the objective, it will form the final image in the plane of the original scale? (b) What is the magnification produced by the telescope?

26. A simple telescope consists of two converging lenses of focal lengths 2.0 in. and 10.0 in. What is (a) their distance apart, and (b) the magnification, if the telescope is used to view a scale 10.0 ft from the objective, the final image being in the plane of the object?   *Ans.* 12.9 in.; 6.0

27. A telescope has a thin objective of focal length 20.0 cm and aperture 5.0

cm, and an eyepiece of 4.0-cm focal length and 2.0-cm aperture. Locate the position and size of exit pupil and the size of the field of view.

28. A large refracting telescope has an objective of focal length 62 ft. If atmospheric conditions do not warrant the use of magnification higher than 1500, what focal length should the eyepiece have?   *Ans.* 0.50 in.

29. Certain binoculars have objectives of aperture 5.0 cm and focal length 20.0 cm, and eyepieces of aperture 1.0 cm and focal length 2.5 cm. Determine the diameter of the exit pupil.

30. A pair of opera glasses has objective lenses of focal length 5.33 in. (*a*) If the magnifying power of the glasses is 4×, what is the focal length of the eyepieces? (*b*) What is the approximate length of the glasses?
                                   Ans. −1.33 in.; 4.0 in.

31. Draw to scale a ray diagram for a telescope having an objective of 40 cm and an eyepiece of 5.0-cm focal length, and another ray diagram for a Galilean telescope having an objective of 40 cm and an eyepiece of −5.0-cm focal length, when both telescopes are adjusted for viewing a distant object. Mention advantages and disadvantages of each type of telescope.

32. A reconnaissance plane is equipped with a camera having a lens of 24-in. focal length. An observer photographs the ground with the camera properly focused when the plane is 18,000 ft above a river. (*a*) What is the distance between the film and the optical center of the lens? (*b*) If the image of the river on the developed negative is 1.5 in. wide, what is the actual width of the river?
                                   Ans. 24 in.; 1$\overline{1}$00 ft

33. A photographer wishes to take his own portrait, using a plane mirror and a camera of focal length 10 in. If he stands beside his camera at a distance of 3.0 ft from the mirror, how far should the lens be set from the plate?

34. A miniature camera whose lens has a focal length of 2.0 in. can take a picture 1.0 in. high. How far from a building 120 ft high should the camera be placed to receive the entire image?   *Ans.* 2$\overline{4}$0 ft

35. A camera has a lens of focal length 5.0 cm. If the tolerable circle of confusion has a diameter of 0.005 cm, determine the maximum depth of field at an aperture of *f*/2.5 for an object distance of 4.0 m.

36. A certain camera lens has a focal length of 5.0 in. A second converging lens of focal length 10.0 in. can be mounted immediately in front of this lens to serve as a portrait attachment. Calculate the position of the image formed of an object 20 in. in front of the camera.   *Ans.* 4.0 in.

37. A camera having an *f*/4 lens is used to copy black-and-white line drawings at a distance of 4.0 ft with a magnification of ⅓. Find the maximum illuminance on the film (in foot-candles) if the surface brightness of the white areas is 0.10 lumen/cm² and there is a 20% loss in the lens.

38. If a correct camera exposure for a certain scene is ¹⁄₁₀₀ sec when the diaphragm is set at *f*/3.5, what exposure time is required at *f*/12.5?
                                   Ans. 0.13 sec

39. In a copying camera, the image should be of the same size as the object. Prove that this is the case when both object and image are at a distance 2*f* from the lens.

40. Two camera lenses have focal lengths of 7.0 in. and 5.0 in., respectively. The first has a free diameter of 0.50 in. What diameter must the other have in order that they may both have the same exposure time?   *Ans.* 0.36 in.

41. In a motion-picture camera that takes pictures at 8, 16, 24, or 32 frames per second, the exposure time is inversely proportional to the frames per second. If the aperture setting of $f/8$ is correct at 8 frames per second, what are the correct apertures at the other speeds?

42. In a photographic enlarger light passes through the negative and the lens and then falls onto the sensitive paper. Using an enlarging lens of focal length 5.0 in., the lens and the paper support are adjusted until a negative 2.0 in. long is enlarged to a length of 16 in. (*a*) What is the distance p from negative to lens? (*b*) What is the distance q from lens to paper? (*c*) If the illuminance on a clear part of the negative is 25 ft-candles and if all the light passes through the lens, what is the illuminance on the corresponding part of the enlarging paper?

Ans. 5.6 in.; 45 in.; 0.39 ft-candles

43. In a photographic enlarger, a lens of focal length 4.0 in. projects an image of the negative on the printing paper. When using a 2.0 × 2.5-in. negative placed 5.0 in. from the lens, what should be the distance from lens to printing paper? What size will the image be?

44. An enlarging camera is so placed that the lens is 30 in. from the screen on which an image five times the size of the object is to be projected. (*a*) How far is the object from the lens? (*b*) What is the focal length of the lens?

Ans. 6.0 in.; 5.0 in.

45. A lantern slide 3.0 in. wide is to be projected onto a screen 30 ft away by means of a lens whose focal length is 8.0 in. How wide should the screen be to receive the whole picture?

46. A projection lantern is to produce a magnification of 50 diameters at a distance of 40 ft from the objective. Find the distance of the lens from the lantern slide, and the equivalent focal length of the objective lens.

Ans. 9.6 in.; 9.4 in.

47. A lantern slide 3.0 in. wide is to be projected on a screen at a distance of 20 ft by means of a lens of 6.0-in. focal length. How wide a screen will be needed to receive the whole picture?

48. If we wish to project a motion picture on a screen 10.0 ft distant from the film and the projected picture is to be 60 times the size of the picture on the film, what must be the focal length of the lens?   *Ans.* 2.0 in.

49. A stereopticon must be placed 40 ft from the screen on which it projects a picture. The lantern slide is $3\frac{1}{4}$ by $4\frac{1}{2}$ in., and the focal length of the lens is 12 in. How large should the screen be to receive the full image?

45. Dispersion; Spectra

Newton (1666) discovered that a narrow beam of sunlight on passing through a prism is spread out into a spectrum. This experimental evidence indicates that there are many components in sunlight and that not all travel with the same speed in a single medium. The phenomenon of dispersion can be used to analyze light from other sources also, and often provides an important means of identifying materials and of studying atomic and molecular structure.

45-1. Dispersion by a Prism. Measurements on the refraction of light as it passes from air into glass show that the amount of refraction depends upon the wavelength (Fig. 1). Light of all wavelengths is reduced in speed in glass, but blue-producing light which is refracted the greatest amount travels slower than red-producing light which is refracted least. The variation of the index of refraction n with the wavelength of light is called the *optical dispersion* $(dn/d\lambda)$ of a substance. By measuring values for n for a series of known wavelengths one can determine the dispersion curve characteristic of a given substance.

The dispersion curves of all transparent substances are of the same general form (Fig. 2), the larger values of n being associated with shorter wavelengths, but there are marked differences in the total variation of n throughout the visible spectrum. Substances showing a rapid change in n with wavelength in this region are said to have a high dispersion and usually have also a high index of refraction.

If a substance absorbs light strongly in a narrow-wavelength region, the values of n there change rapidly with wavelength.

The amount of dispersion produced by a prism is expressed quantitatively by the angular separation of particular parts of the spectrum. When a ray of white light is incident upon a prism (Fig. 3) the light is broken into its components and each component is deviated by a different angle, for example, δ_r for red-producing light and δ_v for violet-producing light. The angular disper-

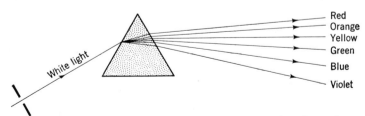

Fig. 1. Spectrum formed by the passage of light through a glass prism.

sion ψ between the violet and red regions is the difference between the deviations

$$\psi = \delta_v - \delta_r \qquad (1a)$$

This angular dispersion depends upon the angle of incidence as well as upon the indices of refraction. If the angle of incidence is such as to produce minimum deviation for an intermediate ray, say yellow, the two deviations will each be near minimum and we may

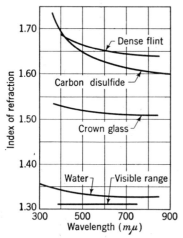

Fig. 2. Dispersion curves.

use as approximations the relationships for that condition. Then

$$\psi = D_v - D_r \qquad (1)$$

The minimum deviation D of a ray produced by a prism is related to the prism angle A and the index of refraction n by Eq. (5), Chap. 42,

$$n = \frac{\sin \frac{1}{2}(D + A)}{\sin \frac{1}{2}A} \qquad (2)$$

When the prism angle is small, the sines of the angles may be placed equal to the angles (in radians), giving

$$n = \frac{\frac{1}{2}(D + A)}{\frac{1}{2}A} \qquad (3)$$

from which the deviation is

$$D = A(n - 1) \qquad (4)$$

Equation (4) may be used as an approximate

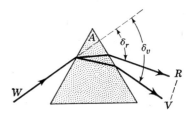

Fig. 3. Dispersion of light by a prism.

relation for small angles A (with less than 5 per cent error up to 30°), and for deviations D near minimum deviation. Definite values of deviation or dispersion are specified with reference to particular lines or wavelengths in the desired regions of the spectrum.

Example: Find the dispersion from the F line (blue) to the C line (red) in the spectrum produced by a crown-glass prism of refracting angle 15° (0.262 radian).

$$\psi = D_F - D_C = A(n_F - 1) - A(n_C - 1)$$
$$= A(n_F - n_C)$$

From the values of the index of refraction in Table 1,

$$\psi = 0.262(1.5233 - 1.5146) = 0.00228 \text{ radian}$$
$$= 7.8'$$

TABLE 1. VARIATION OF THE INDEX OF REFRACTION OF GLASSES WITH WAVELENGTH

Color	Solar spectrum line	Wavelength, A	Ordinary crown	Borosilicate crown	Medium flint	Dense flint
Violet.............	H	3969	1.5325	1.5388	1.6625	1.6940
Blue..............	F	4861	1.5233	1.5297	1.6385	1.6691
Yellow...........	D	5893	1.5171	1.5243	1.6272	1.6555
Red..............	C	6563	1.5146	1.5219	1.6224	1.6500

OPTICAL SPECTRA

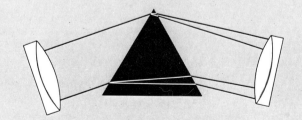

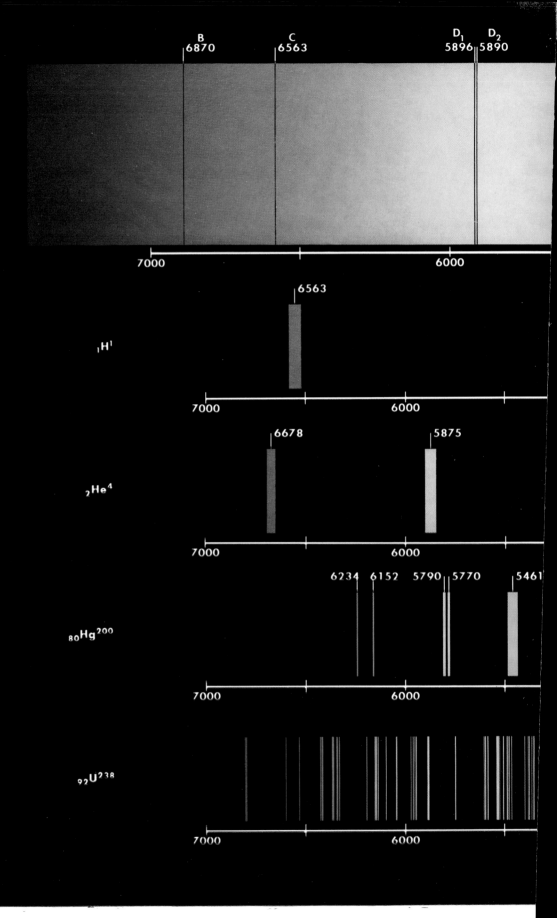

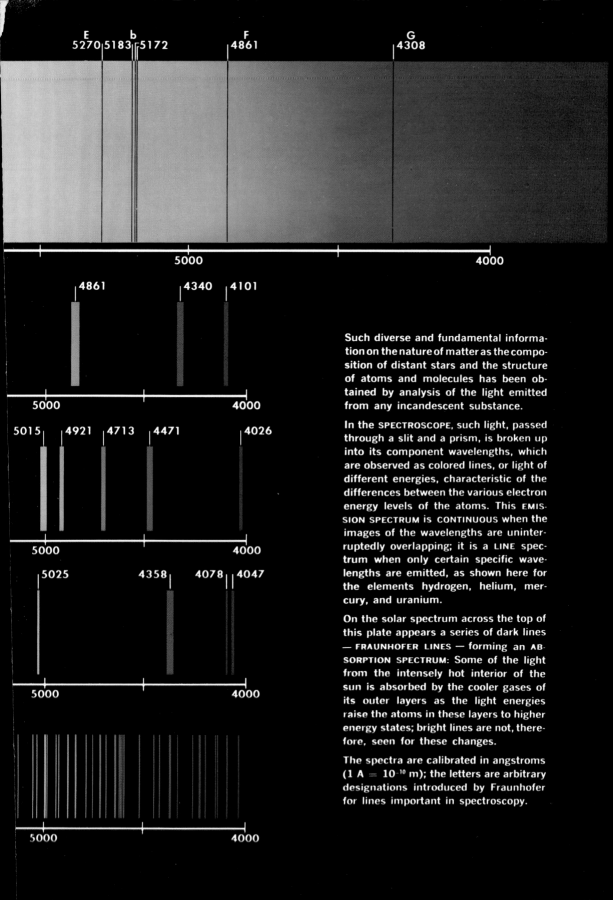

Such diverse and fundamental information on the nature of matter as the composition of distant stars and the structure of atoms and molecules has been obtained by analysis of the light emitted from any incandescent substance.

In the SPECTROSCOPE, such light, passed through a slit and a prism, is broken up into its component wavelengths, which are observed as colored lines, or light of different energies, characteristic of the differences between the various electron energy levels of the atoms. This EMISSION SPECTRUM is CONTINUOUS when the images of the wavelengths are uninterruptedly overlapping; it is a LINE spectrum when only certain specific wavelengths are emitted, as shown here for the elements hydrogen, helium, mercury, and uranium.

On the solar spectrum across the top of this plate appears a series of dark lines — FRAUNHOFER LINES — forming an ABSORPTION SPECTRUM: Some of the light from the intensely hot interior of the sun is absorbed by the cooler gases of its outer layers as the light energies raise the atoms in these layers to higher energy states; bright lines are not, therefore, seen for these changes.

The spectra are calibrated in angstroms (1 A = 10^{-10} m); the letters are arbitrary designations introduced by Fraunhofer for lines important in spectroscopy.

45-2. Achromatic Prism. Glasses of different dispersion characteristics can be used together to obtain deviation of light without dispersion, a condition that is commonly required in optical instruments. An *achromatic prism* is constructed of two prisms placed so as to deviate the light in opposite directions. The prism materials and prism angles are chosen so that one prism annuls the dispersion of the other while only partly canceling the deviation.

Example: It is desired to combine a 15° crown-glass prism with a flint-glass prism so that the achromatic combination will produce deviation without dispersion for the F (blue) and C (red) lines. (*a*) What should be the angle of the flint-glass prism? (*b*) What deviation will the compound prism produce for the middle of the spectrum, the D (yellow) line?

For no dispersion, $\psi = \psi'$, and the refracting angles are placed opposite as in Fig. 4.

$$\psi = D_F - D_C = A(n_F - 1) - A(n_C - 1)$$
$$= A(n_F - n_C)$$

Similarly

$$\psi' = A'(n'_F - n'_C)$$
$$A(n_F - n_C) = A'(n'_F - n'_C)$$
$$15°(1.5233 - 1.5146) = A'(1.6385 - 1.6224)$$
$$A' = 15° \left(\frac{0.0087}{0.0161}\right) = 8.1° \text{ for the flint-glass prism}$$

Deviation $= D_D - D'_D = A(n_D - 1)$
$$- A'(n'_D - 1)$$
$$= 15°(0.5171) - 8.1°(0.6272) = 2.7°$$

45-3. Achromatic Lens. When light passes through a lens, it is bent around the thicker part of the lens. The short wavelengths are refracted more than the long wavelengths.

Thus violet rays are focused closer to a converging lens than are red rays (Fig. 5). This property of a lens to converge to different foci the rays of light of different wavelengths coming from a single point is called *chromatic aberration*. Its presence in a simple magnifier

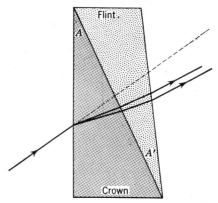

Fig. 4. An achromatic prism combination.

can be seen by the fringes of color which surround each image. Chromatic aberration would be objectionable in most optical instruments. This type of aberration is eliminated in an *achromatic lens* by combining a positive lens and a negative lens of different glass in such a way that one lens annuls the dispersion of the other while only partly canceling its focusing power (Fig. 6). Strictly, an achromatic lens of two components can be designed to bring to the same focus only two particular wavelengths.

45-4. Prism Spectroscope. A spectroscope (Fig. 7) is a combination of a prism and achromatic lenses used to segregate the various wavelengths in a beam of light and thus to permit examination of its spectrum. Light

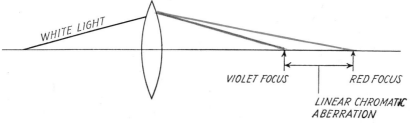

Fig. 5. Chromatic aberration in a lens.

from the source to be examined falls on an adjustable narrow slit S' placed at the principal focus of a convex lens L_1. The rays emerging from the lens are thus collimated, that is, made parallel. This beam falls on a prism in which it is deviated toward the base and dispersed into rays of different wavelengths.

FIG. 6. An achromatic lens combination.

These rays are viewed through a telescope whose objective lens L_2 forms a real image of the slit S' for each wavelength of light present. These images are side by side, with some overlap, and form a continuous or discontinuous band. This spectrum is magnified by an eyepiece, in which cross hairs or other reference marks may be located. With a narrow slit, a monochromatic image of the slit is formed by every discrete wavelength present. Each image of the slit is called a *spectrum line*.

The collimator and telescope are usually in horizontal tubes arranged to rotate about a common axis perpendicular to the prism table. If an instrument of this sort is provided with a graduated circle and verniers on the telescope and prism table, so that angles of deviation can be measured, it is called a *spectrometer*. In a *spectrograph*, a camera is substituted for the telescope so that permanent photographic records can be made. Since photographic plates can be sensitized for wavelengths beyond either end of the visible spectrum, the spectral range of the spectrograph is greater than that of the spectroscope. Since glass is not a good transmitter of

radiant energy in the infrared or ultraviolet regions, rock salt or potassium bromide prisms are used in infrared spectrometers and quartz or fluorite prisms are used in ultraviolet spectrometers to give a lower practical limit of about 1000 A. In addition the entire optical path may be evacuated to reduce the effects of atmospheric absorption of radiation.

A prism spectrometer is not useful in making primary determinations of wavelengths. Once certain wavelengths have been measured by some other method (grating spectrometer or interferometer), these standards can be used to calibrate a prism spectrometer. The line spectrum from an iron arc is frequently used as a reference, since it comprises many lines conveniently spaced throughout the spectrum.

45-5. Types of Spectra. When light produced by an incandescent solid, liquid, or gas falls directly on the slit of a spectroscope, an image of the slit is formed for each frequency emitted by the source. Such a spectrum is called an *emission* spectrum. If all the visible frequencies are emitted by the source, the images overlap and the spectrum shades continuously from one color to the next as in Fig. 5, Chap. 46. This type of spectrum is called a *continuous* spectrum. Incandescent solids, liquids, or gases under high pressure are sources of continuous spectra. In the continuous spectrum all wavelengths are present but the amount of energy radiated at each wavelength depends primarily upon the temperature of the incandescent material and to some extent upon its nature.

When light from a luminous gas or vapor under moderate or low pressure is examined by means of a spectroscope, the spectrum is

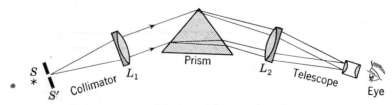

FIG. 7. Arrangement of the essential parts of a prism spectroscope.

found to be made up of definitely placed *bright lines*. Each *line* is a monochromatic image of the slit through which the light passes. Every gas emits certain definite frequencies that are characteristic of that particular gas. The bright-line spectrum of each provides a convenient and sensitive means of identifying even minute quantities of the substance. In the bright-line spectrum the wavelengths of the lines depend primarily upon the chemical nature of the material and the number and intensities of the lines depend upon the method by which energy is supplied to the atoms to "excite" them.

A third type of emission spectrum is the type that exhibits a fluted band structure which on sufficiently high dispersion is found to consist of closely spaced lines arranged in an orderly manner. *Band* spectra are characteristic of molecules while line spectra are associated with uncombined atoms.

If the light in traveling from the source to the slit of the spectroscope passes through an absorbing medium, some of the frequencies emitted by the source are absorbed in transmission. The resultant spectrum lacks these frequencies. Such a spectrum is called an *absorption* spectrum. If the absorbing medium is a gas or vapor, it absorbs those frequencies that it would itself emit if it were luminous. The intense white light from a carbon arc may be directed through sodium vapor produced by heating metallic sodium in a bunsen flame, whereupon the continuous spectrum will have dark lines corresponding to the two closely spaced yellow lines of the sodium emission spectrum.

The solar spectrum on casual inspection seems continuous, but more critical examination shows it to contain many dark lines. It is apparently an absorption spectrum formed when the white light from the intensely hot sun passes through the cooler gases surrounding the sun and there gives up energy of those frequencies which can be absorbed by atoms in the solar atmosphere. Much information about the composition of the sun has been obtained by comparing its absorption lines, called *Fraunhofer lines*, with the spectra of known elements in the laboratory. In making such identifications, allowance is made for absorption in the earth's atmosphere. Helium was identified on the earth only after that element had been discovered in the sun.

If the absorbing medium is a liquid or a solid, whole bands of frequencies are absorbed and a *band absorption* spectrum is produced. The colors of fabrics, glasses, and liquids are produced in this way.

45-6. Distribution of Energy in the Spectrum. The distribution of energy in a spectrum can be measured by allowing each narrow wavelength region in turn to fall on the blackened surface of a thermopile. The resulting deflection of a galvanometer is a measure of the energy in a particular region.

A solid is caused to radiate increasing amounts of energy as its temperature is raised. At comparatively low temperatures most of this energy is in the infrared. As the temperature of the source is raised, more energy is radiated at each wavelength, and the maximum in the distribution is shifted toward shorter wavelengths (Fig. 8). This change in energy distribution is responsible for the familiar change in the color of a body as it is heated to incandescence and for the indications of high temperature implied by the terms "red hot" and "white hot."

There is a definite proportionality between absorption and emission at the same temperature for any wavelength. This is Kirchhoff's law. Thus a good absorber is also a good radiator. A blackbody, which absorbs all radiant energy incident on it, is also the perfect radiator. The total energy radiated at all wavelengths is proportional to the area under the distribution curve, and this was shown by Stefan to vary as the fourth power of the absolute temperature for a perfect radiator (Chap. 21).

45-7. Fluorescence and Phosphorescence. Fluorescence is a process in which a substance absorbs radiant energy and then

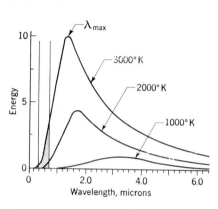
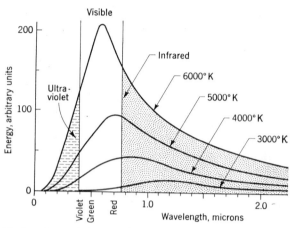

Fɪɢ. 8. Distribution of radiant energy from an ideal radiator (blackbody). 1 micron (μ) = 10^{-6} m = 10^4 angstroms (A).

immediately reemits an appreciable part of it with its wavelengths longer than those absorbed. Often the term refers to the changing of ultraviolet light to visible light. In the commercial fluorescent lamp a low-pressure mercury-vapor arc emits much of its radiant energy in an ultraviolet line (2537 A) of the mercury spectrum. The inner surface of the tubular bulb is coated with fluorescent materials, called phosphors, which absorb the invisible ultraviolet and emit visible light.

In some materials the molecules disturbed by the absorption of light do not immediately return to their original state and their emission of light continues after the exciting radiation is removed. This delayed fluorescence is called *phosphorescence*. Sulfides of barium and calcium exhibit this effect. Luminous paints which are excited by daylight may glow for several hours in the dark.

45-8. Color of the Sky. The molecules of the atmosphere, and other particles in it, that are smaller than the longest wavelengths of visible light are more effective in scattering light of short wavelengths than light of longer wavelengths. The amount of scattering is inversely proportional to the fourth power of the wavelength (Rayleigh effect). The light beam from a projection lantern has a bluish color when viewed from the side by scattered light. Light from the sun near the horizon passes through a greater distance in the earth's atmosphere than does the light received when the sun is overhead. The correspondingly greater scattering of short wavelengths accounts for the reddish appearance of the sun at rising and at setting. When looking at the sky in a direction away from the sun, we receive scattered sunlight in which short wavelengths predominate, giving the sky its characteristic bluish color.

SUMMARY

The variation of the index of refraction with the wavelength of light is called the *optical dispersion* of a substance.

The minimum deviation D produced by a prism depends on the prism angle A and the index of refraction n.

$$n = \frac{\sin \frac{1}{2}(D + A)}{\sin \frac{1}{2}A}$$

The *angular dispersion* ψ of two particular wavelengths produced by a prism is the angular separation between their deviated rays.

$$\psi = D_v - D_r$$

For a prism of small angle

$$D = A(n - 1)$$

An *achromatic* prism (or lens) is a double

prism (or lens) that produces deviation without dispersion.

When light rays of different wavelengths coming from the same point are brought to different foci by a lens, the lens is said to exhibit *chromatic aberration*.

A *prism spectroscope* is a combination of a prism and achromatic lenses for the purpose of separating the various wavelengths in a beam of light into its spectrum.

A *spectrum line* is the monochromatic image of the slit through which the light is received in a spectroscope.

Spectra are classified as *continuous*, *band*, or *line* according to their appearance.

The radiation process is reversible, giving rise to both *emission* and *absorption* spectra.

Fluorescence is a process in which a substance absorbs radiant energy and reemits it in wavelengths different from those absorbed. If the process continues after the exciting radiation is removed, it is called *phosphorescence*.

QUESTIONS

1. What evidence can you suggest to show that all frequencies of light have the same speed in a vacuum but different speeds in other mediums?

2. What is the physical explanation of the formation of a spectrum by a glass prism?

3. If the shape of a prism, the angle of incidence, and the index of refraction are known, show how the path of a ray through the prism can be traced.

4. If the angle of incidence is not near that required for minimum deviation, how would a continuous spectrum be changed from that when the deviation is near minimum?

5. An achromatic prism produces deviation without dispersion. Could one set up a system of prisms that would produce dispersion without deviation of a central ray? Explain.

6. What evidence have we that there is calcium in the sun?

7. Light from a carbon arc passes through dense mercury vapor and then enters a spectroscope. Describe the appearance of the spectrum.

8. Show how the Doppler effect (Chap. 24) might be used to study the motions of the stars.

9. What sort of spectrum is given by moonlight? (The moon has no atmosphere.)

10. What sort of spectrum is obtained from a fluorescent mercury arc lamp?

11. Account for the colors observed in a cut diamond.

12. Account for the gorgeous colors of sunrise and sunset.

PROBLEMS

1. What is the speed of yellow light (5893 A) in water? in dense flint glass?

2. A certain yellow light has a wavelength of 0.000060 cm in air. (*a*) Express this wavelength in microns, millimicrons, and angstrom units. (*b*) What is the frequency of the radiation in kilocycles per second?

Ans. 0.60 μ; 600 mμ; 6000 A; 50 $\times$ 10^{10} kc/sec

3. The wavelength of yellow light from a sodium lamp is 0.00005893 cm. (*a*) How many waves are there in 1.00 cm? (*b*) What is the frequency? (*c*) If the speed of sodium light in water is three-fourths of its speed in air, what is the wavelength of sodium light in water?

4. Red light (6563 A) enters a medium flint glass. (*a*) What is the frequency of the waves in this glass? (*b*) the speed? (*c*) the wavelength?

Ans. 4.57 $\times$ 10^{14}/sec; 1.85 $\times$ 10^{10} cm/sec; 405 mμ

5. (*a*) Compute the ratio of the speed of yellow light in dense flint glass to its speed in crown glass. (*b*) What is this ratio for violet light?

6. A beam of white light falls on a plate of medium flint glass making an angle of incidence of 30°0′. What is the angle of dispersion between the **violet** and the red rays refracted in the glass?   *Ans.* 27′

7. A beam of white light is incident at an angle of 60.0° upon a piece of dense flint glass. Calculate the angular dispersion of the red (6563 A) and violet (3969 A) rays in this glass.

8. Find the angular dispersion of the violet (3969 A) and the yellow (5893 A) rays for a 20° dense flint-glass prism.   *Ans.* 0.77°

9. A 60°0′ dense flint-glass prism is adjusted in a spectrometer to give minimum deviation of the yellow (589 mμ) light. What is the angular dispersion between red (656 mμ) and blue (486 mμ) rays emerging from the prism?

10. A prism is made of medium flint glass and has a refracting angle of 60°0′. The prism is adjusted in a spectrometer to give minimum deviation for the yellow wavelengths from a sodium lamp. What deviation will it produce for the violet (397 mμ) light from a calcium source?   *Ans.* 52°32′

11. A crown-glass prism has a refracting angle of 70.0°. A ray of light from a sodium flame is sent through the prism, and the angle of minimum deviation is found to be 50.0°. What is the index of refraction of the prism for this light?

12. A flint-glass prism has a refracting angle of 60.0° and an index of refraction of 1.640 for light of wavelength 456 mμ. What is the angle of minimum deviation?   *Ans.* 50°10′

13. A 20.0° crown-glass prism is combined with a medium-flint glass prism to make a compound prism achromatic for blue (486 mμ) and red (656 mμ) rays. What minimum deviation is produced for yellow (589 mμ) rays?

14. An 18° crown-glass prism is to be combined with a dense flint-glass prism so that the combination will be achromatic, producing deviation without dispersion for the violet (3969 A) and yellow (5893 A) rays. What should be the refracting angle of the flint-glass prism?   *Ans.* 7.2°

15. A hollow prism of 60.0° refracting angle, made of thin glass plates, is filled with carbon disulfide whose index of refraction is 1.6182, 1.6276, and 1.6523 for the red, yellow, and blue wavelengths, respectively. (*a*) What is the angle of minimum deviation for yellow rays? (*b*) What is the angular dispersion between red and blue rays?

16. (*a*) What angle should a medium flint-glass prism have so that when it is combined with a 10° ordinary crown-glass prism, as in Fig. 4, yellow light is not bent at all? (*b*) What will then be the angular dispersion of red and blue rays?
                              Ans. 8.2°; 0.045°

17. A converging crown-glass lens has a focal length of 25 cm for the violet (3969 A) rays. Find its focal length for red (6563 A) rays.

18. A converging lens of flint glass has an index of refraction of 1.650 for yellow light and a focal length of 1.250 ft for this light. For a certain red light the focal length is found to be 1.275 ft. What is the index of refraction of the lens for this red light?   *Ans.* 1.637

19. A double-convex crown-glass lens has a focal length of 25.0 cm for blue (486 mμ) light and an index of refraction of 1.524 for this light. Find the focal length for red light (656 mμ) for which the index of refraction is 1.514.

20. A pencil of rays of white light parallel to the principal axis falls upon a double-convex lens of dense flint glass. The lens has radii of curvature each 40.0 cm. Calculate the separation of the focal points for red (656 mμ) and blue (486 mμ) rays.   *Ans.* 9 mm

21. The curved surface of a plano-convex lens has a radius of curvature of

20.0 cm. The index of refraction of the glass is 1.580 for red light and 1.620 for violet light. Find the separation of the red and violet focal points.

22. A crown-glass plano-convex lens has a radius of curvature of 5.00 in. What radius of curvature has the medium flint-glass plano-concave lens, which with the first lens makes an achromatic pair for blue and red light rays?

Ans. 9.3 in.

23. A convex crown-glass lens has a focal length of 10.0 cm for yellow light. What is the focal length of the dense-flint lens that will make an achromatic doublet for blue and red light?

24. Compare the power needed to maintain a carbon filament at 1500°C to that required for its operation at 1200°C, assuming that all power is radiated in blackbody radiation.

Ans. 2.1/1

46. *Color*

The phenomena of color constitute some of the most striking and pleasing aspects of light. Psychologically, color is a sensation. But it can be related to physical stimuli. A given color sensation, however, can be produced by more than one type of stimulus. The

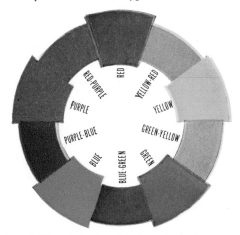

Fig. 1. Hue circle showing the principal hues.

science of *colorimetry* seeks to relate the average person's perception of color to the physical light stimulus in such a way as to provide practical graphical and numerical specifications of color.

46-1. Color Classification. In the study of spectra we have observed that light from the sun or other source after passing through a narrow slit is dispersed by a prism into a spectrum, each part of which gives a different color sensation. Each part of the spectrum may be named as a *hue*, such as red, orange, yellow, green, blue, and violet. Not all hues are observed in the spectrum of sunlight. The purples are notably absent.

The evolution of a graphic method of color classification has been suggested by Deane B. Judd somewhat as follows: Suppose that we have a trunk full of colored papers and that we attempt to classify the colors. After separating them, we note that there are some that lack the quality of hue. Some are white, some are grays, and some are black. Each of these will reflect equally all parts of the sunlight that falls upon it. A white would reflect nearly all, a black none, and the various grays an intermediate amount.

We first separate the papers into two classes: the *grays* (achromatic colors) that lack hue and the *chromatic colors* that have hue. We next group the chromatic colors by hue as red, yellow, etc. We further notice that intermediate groups can be found that form a continuous circle, ranging from red through orange and on through green to blue. Purple completes the circle back to red (Fig. 1). This is classification by hue.

The grays are now placed in a series from white through grays of decreasing lightness to black. Among the colors of one hue some of the samples are darker or lighter than others. We find that we can match the lightness of

538

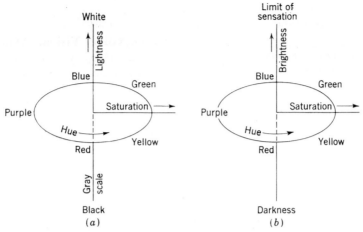

FIG. 2. Dimensions of the psychological color solid, (*a*) for surface colors, with illuminance constant throughout the solid, and (*b*) for unattached colors, with brightness considered as an aspect of the color itself.

each to one of the grays of the achromatic series. By finding the equivalent gray we classify a color by lightness. *Lightness* is the impression of the relative amount of incident light that a surface reflects, irrespective of hue.

We now notice still a third characteristic, *saturation*, which is the degree of difference from a gray of the same lightness. We use such adjectives as vivid or strong to describe high saturation; weak is used to describe low saturation. For the grays, the saturation is zero. For a two-part mixture composed of a chromatic color and a gray, the saturation is increased by increasing the amount of the chromatic color.

These three aspects of color can be represented on a color solid (Fig. 2*a*). Hue changes around the circle, as in Fig. 1, lightness increases upward, and saturation increases outward from the axis. Many such color solids have been devised.

A single point in the color solid of Fig. 2*a* represents one surface color differing from all others in at least one of the three attributes: hue, saturation, or lightness. The color solid can be used to set up an "atlas" system of standard colored surfaces. A page from one such system, the Munsell, is shown in Fig. 3. In using such an atlas, the unknown sample is matched visually under standard illumina-

tion to one specimen of the atlas and is specified by the designation of that specimen. Such atlas systems have limitations. They are useless for the specification of colored light

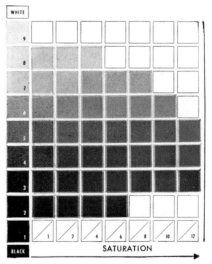

FIG. 3. Sample page of a Munsell color atlas (with designation of coordinates changed).

sources and are applicable only with considerable difficulty to transparent materials. However, in its field the Munsell system has been accepted by the American Standards Association.

The color solid (Fig. 2*b*) referring to colors of *self-luminous* areas has the dimensions of hue, saturation, and brightness. *Brightness* is the subjective impression of the rate at which light is being emitted from unit area toward the observer and ranges from very dim to very bright or dazzling. It is the intensive aspect of the visual sensation.

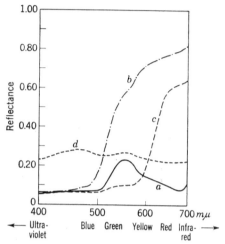

FIG. 4. Spectrophotometer curves of familiar objects: (*a*) leaf (Boston ivy), (*b*) lemon, (*c*) tomato, and (*d*) gray cloth.

46-2. Colorimetry. We examine colored objects by light transmitted through them or reflected from their surfaces. The color observed depends not only on the characteristics of the object but also on the color of the light illuminating it. Daylight, or a light source approximating daylight, is the usual standard for the illumination of colored surfaces.

The physical basis of the hue and saturation of a sample (called its *chromaticity*) may be completely described by stating the fraction of the incident energy from a standard illuminant that the colored object transmits or reflects at each wavelength. An instrument for measuring this fraction is called a *spectrophotometer*. The instrument draws curves representing the spectral distribution similar to those in Fig. 4. The spectrophotometric curve could be used as a specification of color stimulus. However, we cannot accurately imagine the appearance of an object from the shape of the curve. Moreover, two objects of

the same color may have quite different spectrophotometer curves.

46-3. Color Vision. Many theories of color vision have been proposed. None is completely satisfactory. In one, the Young-Helmholtz, or *three-component theory*, it is assumed that in the eye there are three types of retinal cones. All three types are sensitive to nearly the whole of the visible spectrum, but each has a region of maximum sensitivity, one in the red, one in the green, and one in the blue (Fig. 5). If one type of receiver alone could be stimulated, the sensation produced would be completely saturated red or green or blue. Actually any stimulus affects all three and the three effects are integrated in the proportions that each is aroused by the stimulating light. Thus a single sensation is produced. The hue aroused by any wavelength is determined by the curve that is uppermost at that wavelength, with some influence from the relative height of the next uppermost. Blue-green and yellow are positioned in the spectrum by the crossings of two upper curves. Saturation is largely determined by the relative height of the lowest curve, since it determines an amount of desaturating whiteness present in the sensation from even a monochromatic light.

The three-component theory has led to a workable system of color specification and matching. Colors may be synthesized by mixtures of two or more wavelengths. The result can be predicted from Fig. 5. If two or more wavelengths reach the retina at the same time, they will produce a *single hue* at some *particular saturation*. Only by chance will the saturation be the same as that of the same hue when it is aroused by a single wavelength.

True purples do not appear in the spectrum. They are not aroused by a single wavelength, but require mixtures of short- and long-wavelength light.

The sensation of white requires *equal* excitation of each of the three sensation-producing factors. There is equal excitation, for example, when the exciting source is daylight, since the

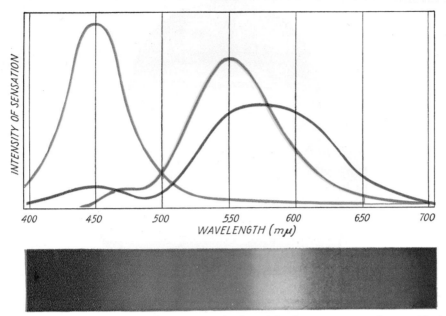

Fig. 5. Sensation curves of the normal color-vision mechanism of the three-component theory, with the appearance of the solar spectrum (to which the curves pertain) suggested beneath.

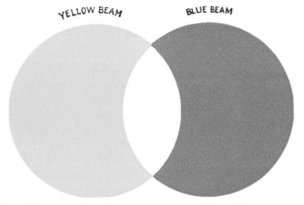

Fig. 6. Additive mixture of complementary patches of light on a screen.

areas under the three curves of Fig. 5 are all the same. The daylight spectrum is thus an "equal-energy" spectrum. The sensation of white can also be produced by less than the whole spectrum if the combination is such as to give the required equal excitation. Any two pairs of wavelength regions that satisfy this condition and thus produce white are called *complementary* colors. Thus blue and yellow are complementaries (Fig. 6). Any wavelength toward one end of the spectrum

has a complementary wavelength somewhere in the other end. In Fig. 1, complementaries are nearly directly across the color circle.

A mid-spectral wavelength and one from either end of the spectrum can be mixed in various proportions to produce all the hues in the corresponding half of the spectrum. With a mid-spectral wavelength and two terminal wavelengths, called three *primary colors*, additive mixtures can be made that will produce any hue of the spectrum or any of the purples.

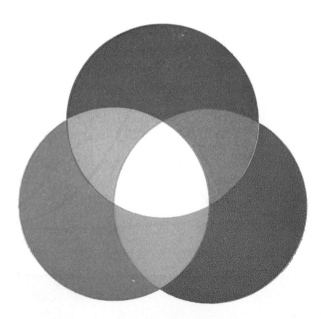

FIG. 7. Additive mixture of three primary lights in projected patches allowed to overlap on a screen.

Figure 7 represents patches of primary lights falling on a screen and so adjusted in intensity that in the region where the three patches overlap there is equal excitation of the three sensation-producing factors, giving white. Any other mixture of these lights on the screen will produce some hue in some degree of saturation.

46-4. Color by Absorption, Addition, and Subtraction. From the foregoing, we see that we cannot tell by inspection of a colored light or object what the exact physical basis of its color is. A source will ordinarily arouse the sensation of hue if it is confined to a small part of the spectrum. A source may arouse the same hue if it emits a band of wavelengths of considerable width, or several bands, so long as these do not cancel each other's effects by complementation, or even if the source emits energy of all the wavelengths in the spectrum if the energy distribution is substantially different from that of an equal-energy spectrum.

Any appreciable disturbance of the energy distribution in an equal-energy spectrum will create hue and hence chromatic color. If an object is illuminated with daylight and ab-

sorbs selectively, it will reflect or transmit an altered spectral distribution of energy and hence will be perceived as colored.

No object reflects only a single wavelength (absorbing the rest), or even a very narrow band of wavelengths. More commonly, a colored object owes its color to a minor subtraction from the daylight falling on it. For example, a yellow pencil can be thought of as a "minus-blue" object. It reflects not merely the yellow but the whole of the spectrum except for the short-wave blue-violet region. The red- and green-producing wavelengths reaching the retina arouse a yellow sensation "additively" in the visual system. This yellowness is added to that aroused by the yellow-producing wavelengths. The pencil is consequently lighter than it could be if it reflected only the yellow-producing energy.

When daylight falls on colored-glass filters, selective absorption "subtracts" some parts of the spectrum and thus affords opportunity for unabsorbed parts to have simple additive effects, resulting in color (Fig. 8).

The color of a pigment can be thought of as due to the fact that the pigment subtracts (absorbs) from the light reaching it that light

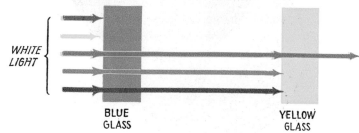

FIG. 8. Subtractive effects of colored glass upon white light.

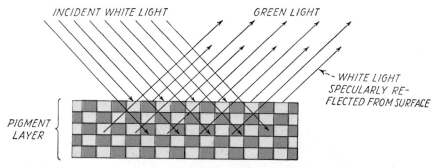

FIG. 9. Subtractive production of green by a mixture of blue and yellow pigments.

which is supplementary to the light which the pigment reflects. A mixture of yellow and blue *paints* is green, although yellow and blue *lights* are complementary and produce white light when added (Fig. 6). The yellow paint (which reflects red, yellow, and green) absorbs blue and violet light; and the blue paint (which reflects violet, blue, and green) absorbs yellow and red. Nothing but green light remains to be reflected by a mixture of the paints (Fig. 9; compare with Fig. 8). What is "additive" or "subtractive" is not the color experience, but the method of production of the spectral distribution of energy in the light reaching the eye.

46-5. Color Specification. Colors created by either reflected or transmitted light can be specified in terms of a mixture of lights producing a visual match for the sample. A device (Fig. 11) in which a given color is matched by the addition of three primaries is called a *tricolorimeter*. One finds experimentally that by using any three primaries in A, B, and C, in suitable proportions, many colors in S can be matched. But there is *no* set of three primaries that can be added in this way so as to match *all* colors in S. For some, one of the primary beams represented in Fig. 11 must be shifted to illuminate the left side of the field, "subtracting" this primary

RED FILTER

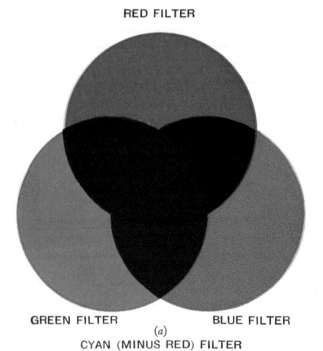

GREEN FILTER   BLUE FILTER
(a)

CYAN (MINUS RED) FILTER

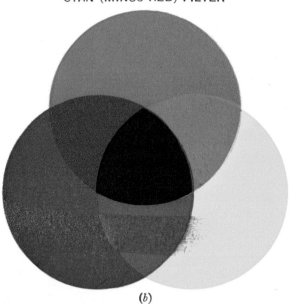

(b)

MAGENTA (MINUS GREEN) FILTER   YELLOW (MINUS BLUE) FILTER

FIG. 10. Subtractive production of colors by the overlapping of filters in the white-light beam from a single projector. In (a) the primaries are the same as those of Fig. 7. In (b) the primaries are the complementaries of the primaries of (a). (This picture should be viewed in strong white light.)

from the right side. If our process is understood to include subtraction, that is, if negative amounts of the primaries may be used, then it is found that any color can be matched by some mixture in proper proportions of any three primaries whatever.

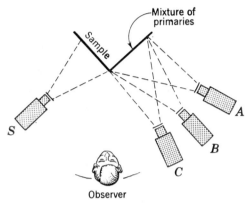

Fig. 11. Colorimetry: color matching by the additive mixture of three primaries.

As an example, let the three primaries be spectrum lights of wavelengths 450 mμ, 550 mμ, and 620 mμ. Illuminate the left side of the field by spectrally homogeneous light of constant radiant flux whose wavelength is successively varied throughout the spectrum, and gage the relative amounts of the three primaries needed to secure color match with S at each wavelength. The results are given in Fig. 12, in which ordinates of curves A, B, and C, at each wavelength, indicate the amounts of the three primaries needed to match a spectrum light of that wavelength. Thus the tristimulus values for light of wavelength 500 mμ are

$$A = 12 \qquad B = 55 \qquad C = -30 \quad (1)$$

The system of color specification adopted by the Commision Internationale de l'Eclairage (CIE) expresses color-mixture data in terms of three primaries so chosen that the curves corresponding to A, B, and C in Fig. 12 lie everywhere above the axis. This avoids the use of negative values in computations. It

requires the use of primaries which lie outside the realm of real colors, but this is not a disadvantage. A color may be specified by the relative amounts of the international primaries (Fig. 13) required in a matching mixture. These are called the *tristimulus values*

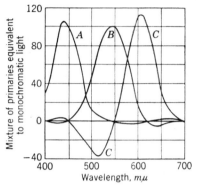

Fig. 12. Color mixture data for monochromatic primaries of wavelengths (A) 450 mμ, (B) 550 mμ, and (C) 620 mμ. (*Adapted from A. C. Hardy and F. H. Perrin, "The Principles of Optics," McGraw-Hill Book Company, Inc., 1932.*)

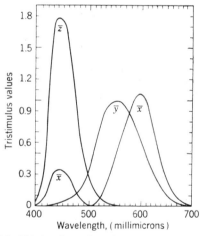

Fig. 13. Tristimulus values for the spectrum colors. The values of $\bar{x}$, $\bar{y}$, and $\bar{z}$ are the amounts of the three CIE primaries required to color match a unit amount of energy having the indicated wavelength. (*Adapted from A. C. Hardy, "Handbook of Colorimetry," M.I.T., 1936.*)

of the color and are designated X, Y, and Z. The tristimulus specifications for a small portion of the spectrum are designated $\bar{x}_\lambda$, $\bar{y}_\lambda$, and $\bar{z}_\lambda$. Thus the CIE tristimulus values for light of wavelength 500 mμ are

$$\bar{x}_{500} = 0.00492$$
$$\bar{y}_{500} = 0.32300 \qquad (2)$$
$$\bar{z}_{500} = 0.27201$$

46-6. Chromaticity Diagram. *Spectrum Colors.* A three-dimensional diagram would be necessary to specify a color if the three tristimulus values were plotted directly. This

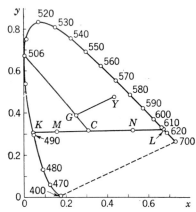

FIG. 14. Chromaticity diagram. The curved line is the spectrum locus. The green (*G*) may be regarded as a mixture of Illuminant *C* and a spectrum color having a wavelength of 506 mμ. (*Adapted from A. C. Hardy, "Handbook of Colorimetry," M.I.T., 1936.*)

inconvenience is avoided by introduction of three related quantities, *x*, *y*, and *z*, known as the *chromaticity coordinates*, defined as follows:

$$x = \frac{X}{X + Y + Z}$$
$$y = \frac{Y}{X + Y + Z} \qquad (3)$$
$$z = \frac{Z}{X + Y + Z}$$

Since $x + y + z = 1$, the values of any two of these coordinates are sufficient to determine completely the chromaticity. The quantities *x* and *y* are usually chosen, and the *y* values of all possible colors plotted against the *x* values of those same colors comprise the CIE *chromaticity diagram* (Fig. 14).

Again considering light of wavelength 500 mμ, and using values from Eq. (2), we

find for the chromaticity coordinates

$$x = \frac{0.00492}{0.59993} = 0.00820$$
$$y = \frac{0.32300}{0.59993} = 0.53839 \qquad (4)$$
$$z = \frac{0.27201}{0.59993} = 0.45341$$

Hence this color may be represented in the chromaticity diagram by a point whose coordinates are $x = 0.00820$ and $y = 0.53839$. When this procedure is carried out for each wavelength in the visible spectrum, the curve called the *spectrum locus* (Fig. 14) is obtained.

Light Beams. The tristimulus value *Y* of a light beam of given spectral distribution is found by multiplying the ordinate of the $\bar{y}$ curve (Fig. 13) at each wavelength by the radiant flux of the light beam at that wavelength, and summing over the visible spectrum. This integration is usually performed graphically, or by an approximate mathematical method. When one has found the *X* and *Z* values by a like process, he may calculate the chromaticity coordinates *x*, *y*, and *z*, from Eq. (3).

Surface Colors. The color sensation produced by light reflected from an opaque object depends both on the composition of the incident light and on the reflectivity of the object at each wavelength. The CIE has recommended three standard light sources, produced by incandescent lamps and filters. Illuminant *C* corresponds closely to average daylight. The chromaticity coordinates of Illuminant *C* (plotted in Fig. 14) are $x = 0.3101, y = 0.3163$.

Consider now the computation of the chromaticity coordinates of a green paint whose percentage reflection is given as *R* in Fig. 15, when illuminated by Illuminant *C*, whose spectral composition is given by curve *C*. The product (*P*) of the relative flux of the original beam at a particular wavelength (ordinate of curve *C*) and the reflection factor of the paint at that wavelength (ordinate of curve *R*) gives the relative flux of the light reflected from the paint at that wavelength.

The procedure for obtaining the tristimulus values from curve P is now the same as that for computing the tristimulus values for any light beam of known flux distribution. One finds

$$X = 15.5 \qquad Y = 24.2 \qquad Z = 22.6 \quad (5)$$

The corresponding values of the chromaticity coordinates are

$$x = 0.25 \qquad y = 0.39 \qquad (6)$$

This point, shown plotted as G in Fig. 14, represents the chromaticity of the green paint.

46-7. Dominant Wavelength, Purity, and Luminance. All colors that may be produced by the additive mixture of any two given colors will be represented by points on the straight line joining the given colors on the chromaticity diagram. Thus all colors obtainable by the additive mixture of the two colors G and Y (Fig. 14) are represented on the segment GY.

Since complementary colors are those which when added produce white, spectral colors complementary to one another lie at the intersection with the spectrum locus of straight lines passing through the "white point" C. Thus K and L are complementary. Colors M and N, K and N, or M and L are also complementary.

It is evident that all real colors must lie within the area enclosed by the spectrum locus and the dotted line, since every real color can be considered to be a mixture of its spectral components. Furthermore, any color can be considered to be a mixture of Illuminant C and spectrum light of a certain wavelength, called the *dominant wavelength* of that color. The fractional distance at which the given color lies along the line joining the white point and the dominant wavelength is called the *purity* of the color. Thus the green paint has a dominant wavelength of 506 mμ and a purity of 20 per cent.

Before the CIE system and its chromaticity diagram were devised, dominant wavelength and purity were determined directly with "monochromatic colorimeters," in which a sample was matched by a wavelength and intensity of monochromatic light (mixed with white light) found by trial and error. The specification of a color in terms of dominant wavelength and purity permits the appearance of the color to be visualized more readily than would its specification in terms of

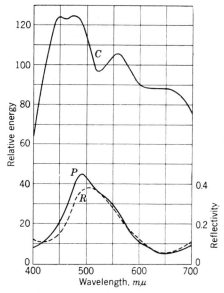

FIG. 15. (R) Reflectivity (percentage reflection) curve of a green paint. (C) Distribution of energy radiated per unit time by Illuminant C. (P) Distribution of energy reflected per unit time from the green paint. (*Adapted from A. C. Hardy, "Handbook of Colorimetry,"* M.I.T., 1936.)

chromaticity coordinates, and is often preferred for this reason. The treatment of purples is "special" in all except atlas systems of color specification, and is omitted from this chapter.

The luminance (photometric brightness) of a sample is found by evaluating the spectral distribution of the light reflected from it, weighted by the standard luminosity curve of Fig. 4, Chap. 40. The luminance at any wavelength is the radiance of the reflected light at that wavelength multiplied by the corresponding ordinate of the luminosity curve. Integration of this product over the entire spectrum gives the luminance of the sample. The necessity of making this integration separately is avoided because the Y curve of the international primaries was deliberately made to have the same shape as the luminosity curve, by proper choice of the primaries. The same integration which gives the Y tristimulus value therefore also gives the luminance. Thus the green paint for which Y was 24.2 has a luminance of 24.2 per cent of that of the standard magnesium oxide. The green paint is then specified by

$$\text{Luminous reflectance} = \frac{24.2}{\text{per cent}} \quad \left.\right\} \quad \text{or} \quad \left\{ \begin{array}{l} \text{Photometric} \\ \text{brightness} = \\ 24.2 \text{ (relative} \\ \text{to 100 for a} \\ \text{perfect white} \\ \text{paint)} \end{array} \right.$$

$$\left. \begin{array}{l} x = 0.25 \\ y = 0.39 \end{array} \right\} \quad \text{or} \quad \left\{ \begin{array}{l} \text{Dominant} \\ \text{wavelength} = 506 \text{ m}\mu \\ \text{Purity} = 20 \text{ per cent} \end{array} \right.$$

SUMMARY

A color sensation is described by *hue, saturation*, and *brightness* (self-luminous area) or *lightness* (non-self-luminous object). These attributes of color depend upon the physical quantities *wavelength, purity*, and *energy*.

Color aspect	Physical determinant
Hue.........	Assortment of wavelengths and their intensities
Saturation....	Colorimetric purity: percentage of monochromatic light in a mixture of monochromatic and white light required to match the sample

Color aspect	Physical determinant
Brightness....	Proportional, at each wavelength, to the logarithm of the radiant energy per unit time
Lightness.....	Ratio of the luminance (luminous flux per unit area per unit solid angle) of the object to the luminance of its surroundings, or, in most cases, luminous reflectance

The wavelengths in the visible spectrum extend from about 380 to 760 mμ. The chief spectral hues, in order, are violet, blue, green, yellow, orange, and red.

Complementary beams are monochromatic (or polychromatic) pairs which when mixed in the proper proportions produce the sensation of white.

Colors are commonly formed by the *addition* of lights or by the *subtraction* of certain wavelengths from the light source.

Any three beams having wavelengths near the two extremes and the middle of the spectrum are called *primaries* and when added in proper proportions produce the sensation of white, or when combined in other proportions (sometimes negative) can match any color.

Chromaticity coordinates specify a color quantitatively in terms of the relative amounts of three artificial (CIE) primaries necessary to produce a visual equivalent of that color.

A color may be specified also by stating its *dominant wavelength* and its *purity*. These may be obtained graphically from the chromaticity diagram or directly by the use of a monochromatic colorimeter.

QUESTIONS   1. What determines the color of an opaque object?

2. Why does a dark-blue suit appear black by candlelight?

3. What is responsible for the color of a nonluminous body? What effect has the character of the illuminant?

4. Explain why a block of ice is transparent whereas snow is opaque and white.

5. Explain the ghastly appearance of a person in the light of a mercury-arc lamp.

6. A lamp has a colored lens which transmits chiefly light of wavelengths near 6300 A. What wavelength would this light have under water? What color would the lamp appear to a submerged swimmer? Explain.

7. The manufacture, packaging, and processing of panchromatic photo-

graphic film is carried out under the faint illumination of green safelights. Why is this color chosen? Why are red safelights used in handling orthochromatic film?

8. Why is it dangerous to view an arc-welding operation without glasses? What protection do glasses provide?

9. Why is red light used as a danger signal?

10. Compare the mixing of colored lights with the mixing of pigments.

11. Why does mixing blue and yellow light in proper amounts give white light, whereas mixing blue and yellow pigments or paints gives green?

12. What are complementary colors? Explain their production through retinal fatigue. (Look intently at a brightly lighted red object, and then immediately look at a white paper.)

13. Interpret the definition of color recommended by the Committee on Colorimetry of the Optical Society of America: "Color consists of the characteristics of light other than spatial and temporal inhomogeneities; light being that aspect of radiant energy of which a human observer is aware through the visual sensations which arise from the stimulation of the retina of the eye."

14. In what different ways is the work of the colorimetrist important?

15. Mention some of the precautions and limitations in specifying colors by reference to a color atlas of standard samples.

16. Is lightness largely independent of brightness, or closely related to it? Consider, for example, that a patch of snow in a dim place looks white, and a pile of coal out in the sunlight looks black, even though the luminance of the coal may be greater than that of the snow.

PROBLEMS   **1.** What is the wavelength of monochromatic light complementary to (*a*) the sodium yellow line at 589 mμ? (*b*) the mercury blue line at 436 mμ?

2. By consideration of the chromaticity diagram, what three monochromatic primaries would probably produce the largest possible range of natural object colors when additively mixed?   *Ans.* 700 mμ; 520 mμ; 400 mμ

3. Three colored glasses *R*, *G*, and *B* produce light having *x* and *y* trichromatic coordinates as follows: (*R*) 0.56, 0.34; (*G*) 0.30, 0.63; and (*B*) 0.20, 0.20. (*a*) On a tracing of the chromaticity diagram, locate these colors. (*b*) Show the location of all colors that can be matched by mixtures of *R* and *G*; *R* and *B*; and *G* and *B*. (*c*) Where are the colors which if mixed with *R* can be matched by a mixture of *G* and *B*?

4. From the chromaticity diagram, compute the dominant wavelength and purity of the *R*, *G*, and *B* colors of Prob. 3.

Ans. (*R*) 608 mμ, 72%; (*G*) 550 mμ, 81%; (*B*) 477 mμ, 55%

5. The tristimulus values of two pigmented surfaces under Illuminant *C* are

$$X_1 = 16 \qquad Y_1 = 24 \qquad Z_1 = 22$$
$$X_2 = 10 \qquad Y_2 = 20 \qquad Z_2 = 15$$

How do the two surfaces differ with respect to (*a*) dominant wavelength? (*b*) purity? (*c*) average reflectance?

47. *Interference and Diffraction*

Thus far we have considered the linear propagation of light, reflection at a boundary between two media, and refraction where the speed of light changes. All these phenomena are explainable on the basis of a wave theory of light. However, if light is to be considered as having a wave nature, interference and diffraction effects must be expected. Among the early experimenters in phenomena of light were Newton and Huygens. These two scientists reached directly opposite conclusions regarding the nature of light from similar observations. Because he failed to observe interference effects, Newton held that light must be particle in nature. Conversely, Huygens believed the wave theory explained reflection and refraction more satisfactorily and hence upheld that theory in spite of the lack of knowledge of interference phenomena. It was not until nearly a hundred years later that Thomas Young in 1801 performed his famous experiment showing interference in light. The fact that light exhibits interference effects is the best evidence that luminous energy travels in a manner that may be represented by a wave motion. Optical apparatus designed to utilize interference effects permits the measurement of wavelengths or distances with a greater precision than that attainable in almost any other type of physical measurement.

47-1. Young's Double-slit Experiment.
As pointed out in Chap. 23, whenever two wave trains pass through the same region of a medium, each continues through the medium as though the other were not present. However, at every point in that region the resultant disturbance is the sum of the disturbances created by the individual waves, that is, the waves interfere.

An arrangement similar to that used by Young to produce an interference pattern is shown in Fig. 1. Here S is a narrow slit with a source of monochromatic light behind it, and A and B are two narrow slits parallel to S. Light progresses from S to A and B. A series of wave fronts are shown; the solid arcs represent maxima, the broken arcs minima. In accordance with Huygens' principle, each of the slits A and B may be considered as a new source of disturbance with wavelets traveling out from each. The wavelets leave A and B in phase with each other and in the region to the right they reinforce each other at certain places, producing brightness, and annul each other at other places, leaving darkness. Reinforcement occurs where the two waves arrive in phase with each other, for example, where two maxima arrive together as at the points marked P_1 or where two minima arrive together as at points marked P_2. For such points the distances traveled by the wavelets from A and B are either equal or differ by a whole number of wavelengths. Such points lie on the heavy solid lines of Fig. 1.

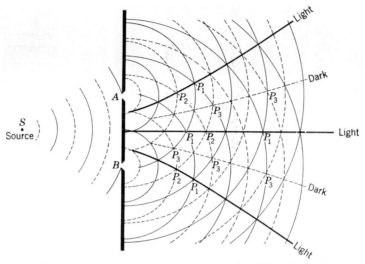

FIG. 1. Interference of light from two identical slits. Wave-front diagram.

Annulment occurs where the wavelets from A and B arrive out of phase with each other by a half wavelength, for example, where a maximum and a minimum arrive together as at the points marked P_3. For such points the distances traveled by the wavelets from A and B differ by an odd number of half wavelengths. Some such points lie on the dotted lines (marked "dark") of Fig. 1.

Within this region of overlapping wavelets we can predict the reinforcement (constructive interference) or annulment (destructive interference) in terms of the path difference from the two slits. There will be constructive interference at every point for which the path difference is any whole number of wavelengths ($N\lambda$). There will be destructive interference if the path difference is any *odd* number of half wavelengths $[(2N - 1)\lambda/2]$.

Consider a screen that is placed perpendicular to the bisector of AB as shown in Fig. 2. The point P_0 is equidistant from A and B and hence the wavelets reaching P_0 will be in phase, producing constructive interference and a central bright fringe. Moving out from P_0, one reaches a point P_1 that is one half wavelength farther from A than from B. That is,

$$AP_1 = BP_1 + \tfrac{1}{2}\lambda$$

The wavelets reaching P_1 are out of phase by a half wavelength, producing destructive interference and a dark fringe. Farther out from the central fringe is another point P_2

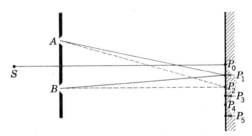

FIG. 2. Interference of light from two slits. Ray diagram.

that is one whole wavelength farther from A than from B, so that

$$AP_2 = BP_2 + \lambda$$

Here there is again constructive interference since the wavelets are in phase. At P_3, the path difference is $\tfrac{3}{2}\lambda$; at P_4, 2λ; at P_5, $\tfrac{5}{2}\lambda$, etc. We observe that there will be alternate bright and dark fringes on either side of the central bright fringe. The general conditions stated above must apply to these fringes. Whenever the path difference is any whole number of wavelengths, including zero, there is constructive interference and a bright

FIG. 3. Interference fringes produced by light from two identical slits. (*Courtesy Jenkins and White*, "*Fundamentals of Optics*," McGraw-Hill Book Company, Inc., 3d ed., 1957.)

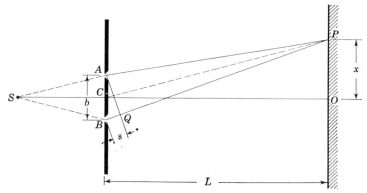

FIG. 4. Spacing of fringes formed by light from two slits.

fringe. Whenever the path difference is an odd number of half wavelengths there is destructive interference and a dark fringe.

Bright fringe:

$$\text{Path difference} = N\lambda$$
$$N = 0,1,2,3, \ldots$$

Dark fringe:

$$\text{Path difference} = (2N - 1)\frac{\lambda}{2}$$
$$N = 1,2,3, \ldots$$

In Fig. 3, there is shown a picture of interference fringes formed as described here.

The spacing between fringes may be examined with the aid of Fig. 4, in which vertical dimensions are exaggerated for clarity. The line SO is drawn perpendicular to the plane containing the slits, and a screen is set perpendicular to SO. Lines AP and BP represent rays from each of the slits reaching the screen at P, distant x from O. By drawing

AQ so that AP equals QP the path difference for the two rays may be expressed as $s = BQ$. The dotted line from P to C is perpendicular to AQ and hence angles BAQ and OCP are equal. Since these angles are small,

$$\sin BAQ = \tan OCP \quad \text{(approximately)}$$

giving
$$\frac{s}{b} = \frac{x}{L} \tag{1}$$

The relations which show that the path difference

$$s = N\lambda \qquad \text{for reinforcement} \quad (2)$$

and

$$s = (2N - 1)\frac{\lambda}{2} \qquad \text{for annulment} \quad (3)$$

may be combined with Eq. (1) to give for the distance of the fringe from the central bright band

$$x = N\lambda \frac{L}{b} \qquad \text{for bright fringes} \quad (4)$$

and

$$x' = (2N - 1) \frac{\lambda}{2} \frac{L}{b} \qquad \text{for dark fringes} \qquad (5)$$

Since the distance of a bright fringe from the central bright fringe is proportional to the number N of the fringe, the fringes must be equally spaced. At the same time the distance is directly proportional to the wavelength and hence the spacing is greater for long wavelengths (red) than it is for shorter wavelengths (blue).

When white light is used as a source, each wavelength produces its own interference fringes. The fringe pattern will then be colored, the color at each point depending on which wavelengths are reinforced by interference. Such colored designs may be observed by looking at a distant source of white light through a piece of silk or a fine-mesh screen.

If the slits A and B are illuminated by two different sources, no interference fringes will be observed, for the waves progressing from the slits will be continually and rapidly changing in phase. Interference patterns can be produced when light from a single source travels by different paths to the observer or screen.

Example: Yellow light from a sodium-vapor lamp ($\lambda = 5893$ A) is directed upon two narrow slits 0.100 cm apart. Find the positions of the first dark and first bright fringes on a screen 100 cm away.

$$x' = \frac{(2N - 1)(\lambda/2)L}{b}$$
$$= \frac{(2 \times 1 - 1)(5893 \times 10^{-8} \text{ cm}/2)(100 \text{ cm})}{0.100 \text{ cm}}$$
$$= 0.0295 \text{ cm} \qquad \text{(dark)}$$
$$x = \frac{N\lambda L}{b} = \frac{(1)(5893 \times 10^{-8} \text{ cm})(100 \text{ cm})}{0.100 \text{ cm}}$$
$$= 0.0589 \text{ cm} \qquad \text{(bright)}$$

Thus the first dark fringe is 0.0295 cm from O (Fig. 4) and the first bright fringe is 0.0589 cm from O. The second dark fringe would be 0.0884 cm from the center, etc., the separation of adjacent dark (or bright) fringes being 0.0589 cm.

47-2. Interference in Thin Films. Thin transparent films, such as soap bubbles or oil on water, show streaks that may be accounted for by the principles of interference. In Fig. 5, E represents the eye focused on a thin film of thickness t from which is reflected light from a monochromatic source. A ray of light AB incident on the film at angle i will be partly

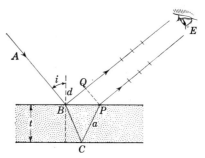

Fig. 5. Interference in a thin transparent film.

reflected from the front surface along BE and partly refracted into the film along BC. The latter ray will be partly reflected from the back surface of the film to emerge along CPE so that PE is parallel to BE. If these two rays enter the eye, an interference effect can be expected, since they have traveled by different paths to the eye.

To determine the kind of interference produced, we must find the number of waves or fractions of waves by which the paths differ. By drawing PQ perpendicular to the reflected rays, it is evident that the ray reflected within the film travels farther than the ray reflected at the surface by an amount $2a - d$, where a represents the distance BC or CP. Since light travels slower in the film than in air, there are more waves per unit length in the film than in air. Hence the distance $2a$ in the film is equivalent in waves to a distance $2na$ in air, where n is the index of refraction of the material of the film. For normal incidence, $i = 0$ and $a = t$.

It might be expected that an extremely thin film whose thickness was only a small fraction of the wavelength of any visible light would appear bright, since the path difference would be too small to produce destructive interference. Actually such a film appears black, that is, there is complete destructive interference. This may be observed in a soap film. As it thins just before it breaks, it appears black by reflection. This and other evidence indicate that a phase difference of $\frac{1}{2}\lambda$ or 180° is introduced by the fact that one of

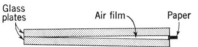

Glass plates   Air film   Paper

FIG. 6. Two glass plates separated by a wedge of air.

the two interfering rays is reflected in air, the other in an optically denser medium. Consequently, the total retardation of ray $BCPE$ with respect to ray BQE is $2na + \lambda/2$. For the special case of normal incidence where $a = t$

$$\text{Retardation} = 2nt + \frac{\lambda}{2} \qquad (6)$$

Constructive interference and brightness will occur when the retardation is a whole number of wavelengths; destructive interference and darkness will occur when the retardation is an odd number of half wavelengths.

Example: Two rectangular pieces of plate glass are held in contact along one pair of edges while the opposite edges are separated by a thin sheet of paper (Fig. 6). When the plates are viewed by the light from a sodium lamp reflected normally they are seen to be crossed by 17 dark interference fringes. For sodium light $\lambda = 5893$ A. What is the thickness of the paper?

Since the fringes are dark, the retardation must be an odd number of half wavelengths

$$\text{Retardation} = (2N - 1)\frac{\lambda}{2} = 2t + \frac{\lambda}{2}$$
$$t = \frac{(N - 1)\lambda}{2}$$
$$\lambda = 0.00005893 \text{ cm}$$

For the seventeenth dark fringe

$$N = 17$$
$$t = \frac{(17 - 1)(0.00005893 \text{ cm})}{2} = 0.00047 \text{ cm}$$

The interference fringes formed by the film between two surfaces are similar to the contour lines on a topographic map and they indicate the variations in thickness of the air film separating the two optical parts. The interference patterns (Fig. 7) are very useful in routine inspection of the polishing of fine lenses and in the preparation of very flat test plates of glass or metal. By repeated inspection and polishing, these plates may be made optically flat within a tenth of a wavelength of mercury light, or to about 0.000005 cm.

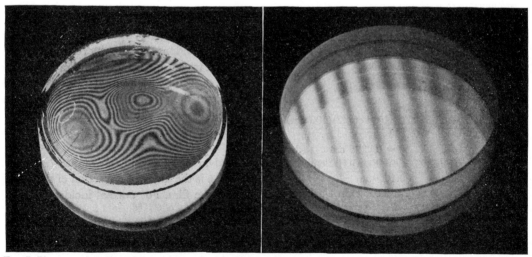

FIG. 7. Photographs of interference fringes in thin films between two glass plates. Parallel fringes indicate that the surfaces are optically plane. Irregular fringes indicate that the surfaces are not plane.

Thin-film interference can be observed when light is reflected from front and back surfaces of any transparent thin film. One of the most common observations is the color of oil films on water or that in bubbles. When the illumination is by monochromatic light, we see light and dark areas dependent upon the thickness of the film. If white light is used, colored areas are observed. The retardation depends upon wavelength. A given thickness will produce destructive interference for one wavelength band, leaving the complementary color. A film of varying thickness will thus show many colors.

One example of thin-film interference is that produced in the air film between a convex lens of large radius of curvature and an optically flat plate placed in contact with the lens. When viewed by reflected monochromatic light, there will be destructive interference at the point of contact because of the $\frac{1}{2}\lambda$ change in phase of the ray reflected in the air film at the glass surface. Since the film increases in thickness as the distance from the point of contact increases, the central dark circle is surrounded by alternate bright and dark circular bands. The retardation depends upon the thickness of the film as given in Eq. (6). These interference rings are called *Newton's rings*.

Newton's rings will also be produced by the film between lens and plate when viewed by transmitted light. In this case the central spot is bright because the waves that interfere are those that are transmitted without reflection and those that are twice reflected. Thus the change of phase is a whole wavelength.

47-3. The Michelson Interferometer. The interferometer is an instrument that uses interference in the measurement of wavelengths of light in terms of a standard of length or in the measurement of distances in terms of known wavelengths of light. The essential parts of the interferometer devised by Michelson are two plane mirrors M and M' and two glass plates A and B arranged as shown in Fig. 8. The plate A is lightly

silvered on the back so that of the light that falls on that surface half is reflected and half is transmitted.

A beam of monochromatic light from source S falls on the plate A where it is divided into two beams. These advance to the mirrors M' and M, return to the plate A, and then proceed to the eye at E. If the mirrors

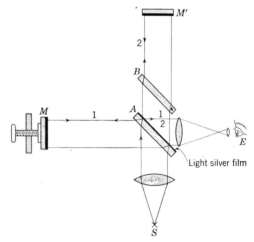

FIG. 8. Michelson interferometer.

are equidistant from A, the two beams will travel optically similar paths, the plate B serving only to introduce the same retardation in beam 2 as is introduced in beam 1 by its two passages through A.

If the optical paths happen to be equal, the beams 1 and 2 will arrive at E in phase and produce a bright field by constructive interference. If the distance AM is increased $\frac{1}{4}\lambda$ by moving mirror M, the optical path for ray 1 will be lengthened $\frac{1}{2}\lambda$ and the destructive interference of rays 1 and 2 at E will give a dark field. Usually mirrors M and M' are made nearly but not quite perpendicular to give a field crossed by alternate bright and dark interference fringes, which may be counted as they move past a reference mark as M is moved. For each fringe that passes the index, the optical path has been changed by one wavelength, that is, M has moved a half wavelength.

If N successive dark fringes are counted as

the mirror is moved a distance D, then

$$N\frac{\lambda}{2} = D \qquad \text{or} \qquad \lambda = \frac{2D}{N} \qquad (7)$$

Michelson measured wavelengths in terms of the standard meter bar. From such measurements a wavelength can be set up as a standard of length that can be reproduced accurately. The standard now proposed is the

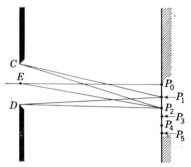

FIG. 9. Spacing of fringes in a single-slit diffraction pattern.

orange line of the spectrum of krypton 86. In terms of this wavelength

$$1\text{ m} = 1,650,763.73\lambda_{\text{Kr}}$$

All other wavelengths can be compared with this standard and from it the standard meter could be reproduced.

Example: An interferometer illuminated with red light from cadmium ($\lambda = 6438$ A) is used to measure the distance between two points. Calculate this distance if 239 fringes pass the reference mark as the mirror is moved from one of the points to the other.

From Eq. (7)

$$D = N\frac{\lambda}{2} = \frac{239(6.438 \times 10^{-5}\text{ cm})}{2} = 0.00769\text{ cm}$$

47-4. Diffraction. Light travels in straight lines in a uniform medium, but commonly changes direction where there is a change of medium or a change of properties of a single medium. Thus we observe reflection and refraction. Careful observation shows that there is also a slight bending around obstacles. The spreading of light into the region

behind an obstacle is called *diffraction*. Diffraction occurs in accordance with Huygens' principle and is an interference phenomenon.

Any obstacle introduced into the light beam from a point source will produce diffraction effects under proper conditions. A slit, a wire, a hole, or a straight edge are examples of such obstacles. A straight edge illuminated by a beam of monochromatic light from a point source casts a shadow that is not geometrically sharp. A small amount of light is bent around the edge into the geometrical shadow and the shadow is bordered by many alternate light and dark bands.

47-5. Diffraction by a Single Slit. If the obstacle in the light beam is a single narrow slit, a pattern of fringes will be formed on a screen placed behind the slit. Such an arrangement is shown in Fig. 9. If the slit CD is parallel to the wave front, each point in the slit can be considered as a source of Huygens' wavelets, all starting in phase. At every point on the screen these wavelets combine in some manner to produce the effect at that point. At P_0, on the perpendicular bisector of the slit, wavelets from C and D arrive in phase since these points are equidistant from P_0. Similarly pairs of points in the upper and lower halves of the slit will combine to contribute to the light at P_0. Thus P_0 is bright. At points off the perpendicular bisector, the path lengths from the two edges of the slit are no longer equal. Let P_1 be a point such that $CP_1 = DP_1 + \lambda/2$. The wavelets from C and D will arrive at P_1 a half wave out of phase and hence will annul each other. However, wavelets from all other points in the slit are not annulled by other wavelets, and hence P_1 is still within the bright central band. If P_2 is located so that $CP_2 = DP_2 + 2\lambda/2$, wavelets from C and from D will arrive in phase, but $EP_2 = DP_2 + \lambda/2$ and $CP_2 = EP_2 + \lambda/2$. Thus a wavelet from E will annul a wavelet from D, a wavelet from a point just above E will annul a wavelet from a point just above D, and so on across the two halves of the slit. The wavelets from the upper half of the slit annul those from the lower half, producing darkness at P_2. We may think of the slit as divided into zones whose edges are successively $\frac{1}{2}\lambda$ farther from the point considered. Thus, for the point P_1, the slit makes up only one zone, and P_1 is bright. For P_2, the slit has two zones, and the wavelets from the two zones annul each other. At another point P_3 for which $CP_3 = DP_3 + \frac{3}{2}\lambda$, the slit has three zones. Two of these zones annul, leaving the light from the third, and P_3 is bright but less bright than P_1. Similarly, for P_4, there are four zones and darkness; for P_5, five zones and brightness but again less bright than P_3. The variation of intensity in such a pattern is shown in Fig. 10. Here there is a bright and wide central band with narrower and less intense side fringes. The zones are called Fresnel zones after the man who originated this method of analysis. Figure 11 is a picture of a single-slit diffraction pattern. The picture represents a pattern obtained when the screen is far enough from the slit so that the rays can be considered parallel. Such diffraction is called *Fraunhofer* diffraction.

The conditions that a point shall be bright or dark can be written in terms of the path difference of the wavelets from the two edges of the single slit. We have found that where the path difference is a whole number of wavelengths there is darkness.

Path difference: $s = N\lambda$ for darkness
$N = 1,2,3, \ldots$

Where the path difference from the two edges

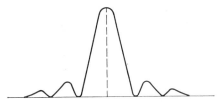

Fig. 10. Intensity distribution in a single-slit diffraction pattern.

of the slit is an odd number of half wavelengths, there is brightness. We may write this condition

Path difference:

$$s = (2N + 1)\frac{\lambda}{2}   \text{for brightness}$$
$$N = 1,2,3, \ldots$$

The spacing of the fringes can be computed by reference to Fig. 12 in terms of the path

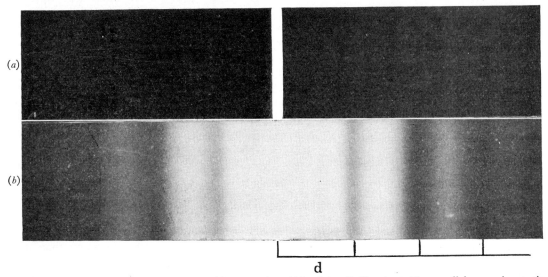

(a)

(b)

d

Fig. 11. A single-slit diffraction pattern. (a) Shows the width of the slit illuminated by parallel monochromatic light; (b) an actual photograph of the diffraction pattern. (*Courtesy Jenkins and White, "Fundamentals of Optics," McGraw-Hill Book Company, Inc., 3d ed., 1957.*)

difference s, the slit width b, and the distance L from the slit to the screen.

$$\sin \theta = \frac{s}{b} \quad \text{(approximately)}$$

$$\tan \theta = \frac{x}{L}$$

Since the angles are small, the sine and tangent are approximately equal and

$$\frac{s}{b} = \frac{x}{L} \tag{8}$$

To find the distance from the middle of the

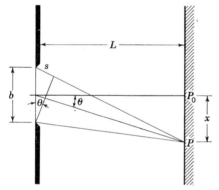

FIG. 12. Ray diagram for diffraction from a single slit.

central bright band to any given fringe, one must insert the appropriate value of the path difference s. When this substitution is made and the equation solved for x, λ appears in the numerator and b in the denominator. Thus the separation of the fringes is greater for longer wavelengths and increases as the width of the slit decreases.

Example: A plane wave of monochromatic light of wavelength 5893 A passes through a slit 0.500 mm wide and forms a diffraction pattern on a screen 1.00 m away from the slit and parallel to it. Compute the separation of the first dark bands on either side of the central bright band, that is, the width of the central bright band.

From Eq. (8)

$$\frac{x}{L} = \frac{s}{b}$$

For the first dark band

$$s = 1 \times \lambda = \lambda$$

$$x = \frac{\lambda L}{b} = \frac{(0.00005893 \text{ cm})(100 \text{ cm})}{0.0500 \text{ cm}} = 0.118 \text{ cm}$$

where x is the distance of the first dark band from the middle of the central bright band. The separation of the two first-order dark bands is

$$2x = 2(0.118 \text{ cm}) = 0.236 \text{ cm} = 2.36 \text{ mm}$$

For obstacles of different shape, a similar treatment can be set up. The zones may be different in shape for various obstacles.

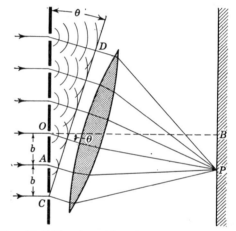

FIG. 13. Diffraction of light by an optical grating.

47-6. Resolving Power of a Lens. If a circular opening is illuminated by light from a point source, the diffraction pattern will be a set of circular fringes. If a lens is used to form an image, the image of each point is not a point but a small diffraction disk. The size of the disk depends upon the aperture (diameter) of the lens and the wavelength of the light used. A larger aperture decreases the size of the disk while a longer wavelength increases it. In the image formed by a lens, two points will appear as separate if their diffraction disks do not overlap by more than the radius of the disk. The *resolving power* of a lens is its ability to separate the images of two points that are close together. The resolving power is directly proportional to the aperture of the lens and inversely proportional to the wavelength of the light. Thus increasing the aperture of a lens increases its resolving power since it decreases the diameter of the diffraction disk and thus two images can be closer together without overlapping by as much as the radius of the disk.

47-7. The Diffraction Grating. The principles of diffraction and interference find important application in the measurement of wavelength with the optical diffraction grating. A grating for use with transmitted light is a glass plate upon which is ruled a large number of equally spaced opaque lines, usually several thousand per centimeter.

A parallel beam of monochromatic light falling on the grating (Fig. 13) sends waves in all forward directions from each slit. Along certain definite directions waves from adjacent slits are in phase and reinforce each other. Consider the parallel rays making an angle θ with OB, the normal to the grating, which are brought to focus on the screen at P by an achromatic lens. If the ray AP travels a distance λ farther than ray CP, then waves from A and C will interfere constructively at P. So also will waves from all the slits for they will differ in phase by a whole number of wavelengths. The wave front CD makes an angle θ with the grating. From the smallest right triangle, the path difference λ is seen to be $CA \sin \theta$. Calling the grating space $CA = b$, the condition for reinforcement in the direction θ may be written

$$b \sin \theta = \lambda \quad \text{(first order)} \quad (9)$$

In general, there will be other directions on each side of OB for which waves from adjacent slits differ in phase by 2λ, 3λ, etc., and for which the corresponding bright images P_2, P_3 . . . are called the *second-order*, *third-order*, etc., images. The grating equation can be written in the more general form

$$b \sin \theta_N = N\lambda \quad (10)$$

where b is the grating space and N is the order of the spectrum.

With white light each diffracted image is dispersed into its component colors and continuous spectra are produced at P_1, P_2, etc. The dispersion is greater in the higher order spectra. In each order the colors appear in the sequence violet to red with increasing deviation. There is overlapping of the spectra; for example, the red and orange in the second-order spectrum overlap the violet of the third order, since 2λ for the long wavelengths is greater than 3λ for the short wavelengths.

Example: The deviation of the second-order diffracted image formed by an optical grating having $5\overline{0}00$ lines/cm is 32°. Calculate the wavelength of the light used.

$$b \sin \theta_N = N\lambda$$
$$b = \tfrac{1}{5000} \text{ cm} = 0.00020 \text{ cm}$$
$$\lambda = \frac{b \sin \theta_N}{N} = \frac{0.00020 \text{ cm} \times 0.53}{2}$$
$$= 0.000053 \text{ cm} = 5\overline{3}00 \text{ A}$$

SUMMARY

In common with other forms of wave motion, light exhibits the phenomena of *interference*.

In order to observe interference effects with light, the light from a single source is made to traverse different optical paths to introduce a phase difference, and then the beams are reunited. *Constructive* interference occurs whenever the optical path difference $s = N\lambda$; *destructive* interference occurs whenever the path difference $s = (2N - 1)\lambda/2$.

When light is reflected at the boundary of an optically denser medium, it undergoes a phase change of $\tfrac{1}{2}\lambda$ or 180°.

Newton's rings are the interference fringes formed in the air films between optical surfaces. By their spacing they provide a sensitive means of measuring the curvatures of those surfaces.

The Michelson *interferometer* utilizes the interference of two light beams traveling different paths as the fundamental method of measuring wavelength. If N successive fringes are counted as the mirror is moved a distance D,

$$\lambda = \frac{2D}{N}$$

The spreading of light into the region behind an obstacle is due to *diffraction*. Diffraction occurs in accordance with Huygens' principle and is an interference phenomenon.

The *resolving power* of a lens is the smallest angular distance at which the images of two point sources can be recognized as separate.

Owing to diffraction, this minimum angle of resolution varies directly with the wavelength of the light and inversely with the aperture of the lens.

A diffraction grating utilizes the diffraction of light from many closely spaced parallel slits to disperse light into its component wavelengths. Light of wavelength λ deviated through angle θ_N forms a bright image when

$$b \sin \theta_N = N\lambda$$

QUESTIONS

1. In double-slit interference how does the spacing of the slits affect the separation of the fringes?

2. If light is bent around obstacles, why can we not see around a house?

3. Why are optical interference tests among the most accurate known to science?

4. Why is interference of the light waves from two different lamps never observed?

5. When two light waves interfere at some point to produce darkness, what becomes of the energy?

6. Derive, in terms of the wavelength, the separation of the slits, and the distance from the slits, an expression for the distance between two adjacent bright fringes in a double-slit interference pattern.

7. How does the origin of the colors observed in a soap bubble in sunlight differ from that of the colors observed when sunlight passes through a glass prism?

8. Why are interference colors not observed in a very thick film—in a piece of glass, for example?

9. Why are Newton's rings circular?

10. In the construction of a Michelson interferometer what parts must be made with great accuracy?

11. The characteristic yellow light from sodium comprises two lines of wavelengths 5890 and 5896 A, and is thus not a monochromatic source. How could a Michelson interferometer be used to measure very precisely the wavelength separation of the two sodium yellow lines?

12. If a screen with a small circular opening is placed between a point source of monochromatic light and another screen, a diffraction pattern will be formed on the second screen. For points on the axis of the opening, what will be the shape of the Fresnel zones? Will the number of zones be the same for all points on the axis? How would the intensity of the central spot change as the distance to the second screen increases?

13. Will the angular separation of orders be greater for a grating with many lines per inch or for a grating with fewer lines?

14. Will the angular separation between red and blue rays be greater in the first-order or in the second-order spectrum?

15. Will the image of the slit be more sharply defined in the first-order spectrum or in the third-order spectrum?

16. Contrast the formation of a spectrum by a diffraction grating with the production of the spectrum of the same light source by a glass prism.

17. Imagine a light made up of wavelengths spaced at 100-A intervals. Make a rough sketch of the appearance of the spectrum viewed in a prism spectroscope and in a grating spectroscope.

18. What factors govern the choice between a prism and a diffraction grating for use in a spectrograph?

PROBLEMS   **1.** Monochromatic light from a narrow slit illuminates two parallel slits 0.15 mm apart. On a screen 80 cm away bright interference bands are observed 3.0 mm apart. Find the wavelength of the light.

2. Light from a narrow slit passes through two parallel slits 0.20 mm apart. The two central dark interference bands on a screen 100 cm away are 2.95 mm apart. What is the wavelength of the light?   *Ans.* 5900 A

3. If the two parallel slits in Young's interference experiment are 0.300 mm apart, how far is the first dark band from the central image on a screen 100 cm away when light of 7500 A is used?

4. Two slits 0.125 mm apart are illuminated by light of wavelength 4500 A. What is the separation of the second bright bands on either side of the central bright band when the screen is 60.0 cm from the plane of the slits?
Ans. 0.865 cm

5. A line source of monochromatic light, wavelength 4900 A, is placed 0.200 cm in front of the plane of a mirror. A screen is placed perpendicular to the plane of the mirror, 200 cm from the source. What is the separation of the fringes produced?

6. Light from a single slit passing through a double prism of very small angle proceeds as though it had come from two sources (Fresnel biprism). With such an arrangement, light of wavelength 5460 A produces fringes whose separation is 0.200 mm at a distance of 120 cm. What is the distance between the two apparent sources?   *Ans.* 3.28 mm

7. Two slits are illuminated by light that consists of two wavelengths. One wavelength is known to be 6000 A. On a screen the fourth dark fringe of the pattern for the known wavelength coincides with the fifth light fringe for the other wavelength. What is the unknown wavelength?

8. Two slits 0.125 mm apart are illuminated by light composed of two wavelengths 6000 A and 5000 A. A screen is 120 cm from the slits. At what distance from the central bright band will a light fringe of one pattern coincide with a light fringe of the other?   *Ans.* 2.9 cm

9. A quartz fiber is placed between the edges of two flat glass plates which are in contact at the other end. The wedge-shaped air film between the plates is viewed by reflected monochromatic light of wavelength 5890 A and is found to be crossed by 35 dark interference bands. Calculate the diameter of the quartz fiber.

10. Two optically flat disks lie one on the other. A sheet of paper 0.0500 mm thick is inserted between the two disks at one edge. How many dark interference fringes will appear by reflected light if the disks are illuminated by light of wavelength 5890 A? What will be the shape of the fringes?   *Ans.* 171

11. When the movable mirror of a Michelson interferometer is moved 0.100 mm, how many dark fringes pass the reference mark if light of wavelength 5800 A is used?

12. An interferometer illuminated with monochromatic light of wavelength 6438 A is used to measure the distance between two points. Compute the distance if 311 interference fringes pass the reference mark while the interferometer mirror moves from one point to the other.   *Ans.* 0.0100 cm

13. A single slit 0.110 mm wide is illuminated with monochromatic light. Diffraction bands are observed on a screen 80.0 cm beyond the slit. The second dark band is 5.87 mm from the central bright band. Compute the wavelength of the light used.

14. A slit 0.500 mm wide causes a diffraction pattern on a screen 300 cm away when illuminated with sodium light (wavelength 5890 A). Find the distance from the central image to the first dark band.   *Ans.* 3.53 mm

15. A slit 0.0520 mm wide is illuminated by light of wavelength 5460 A. Find the width of the central bright diffraction band on a screen 120 cm away. Find the distance between the two third-order bright fringes.

16. A slit 0.0845 mm wide is illuminated by monochromatic light. On a screen 80.0 cm from the slit the second-order bright fringes are separated by 3.03 cm. What is the wavelength of the light?   *Ans.* 6̄400 A

17. A student places a small sodium lamp just in front of a blackboard. Standing 20.0 ft away he views the light at right angles to the blackboard while holding in front of his eye a transmission grating ruled with 14,500 lines/in. He has his assistant mark on the board the positions of the first-order diffracted images on each side of the lamp. The distance between these marks is found to be 14 ft 2 in. Compute the wavelength of the light.

18. A monochromatic beam of light of wavelength 6000 A falling on a grating at normal incidence gives a first-order image at an angle of 30°0′. Find the grating constant.   *Ans.* 83̄30 lines/cm

19. The deviation of the second-order diffracted image formed by an optical grating of 6000 lines/cm is 30°. Calculate the wavelength of the light used.

20. A yellow line and a blue line of the mercury-arc spectrum have wavelengths of 5791 and 4358 A, respectively. In the spectrum formed by a grating that has 5000 lines/in., compute the separation of the two lines in the first-order spectrum and in the third-order spectrum. Compare the angle of diffraction for the yellow line in the third order with that for the blue line in the fourth order.   *Ans.* 1.63°; 5.1°

48. *Polarized Light*

Interference and diffraction effects have given us perhaps our best evidence that light has wave characteristics. But these phenomena leave unanswered the questions of what it is that vibrates and how. Indeed, with a suitable change of scale, our discussion of reflection, refraction, wavelength, interference, and diffraction is just as true for sound as for light. The fact that light can be polarized, however, its vibrations being confined to a single plane, shows conclusively that its wave properties are transverse, in contrast to the longitudinal waves associated with sound.

48-1. Polarization. Experiments with transverse waves in a rope (Fig. 1) show that a slot *P* can be used to confine the vibrations to one plane, after which they can be transmitted or obstructed by a second slot *A*, depending on whether it is placed parallel or perpendicular to the first slot. The slotted frame *P* is called a *polarizer*. The waves emerging from the polarizer are confined to one plane and the wave is said to be *plane-polarized*. The slotted frame *A* is the *analyzer* of the plane-polarized wave. The plane that contains the wave form is called the *plane of polarization*. Polarizability is characteristic of *transverse* waves. If the rope were replaced by a coiled spring, compressional (longitudinal) waves in it would pass through slots regardless of their orientation.

According to the electromagnetic theory of light, a light wave consists of an electric vibration accompanied by a magnetic vibration at right angles to it. In the following discussion the light vibrations refer to the vi-

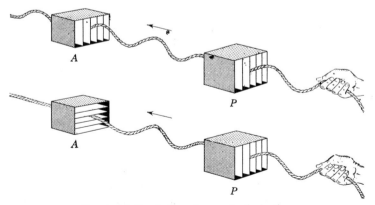

Fig. 1. Mechanical analogue of polarization.

563

brating electric field. A light wave traveling through space can be represented at any point at any instant by a line whose direction and length represent the direction and displacement of the vibrating electric field. Such a line is purely diagrammatic and is called a *light vector*.

The light from ordinary sources is unpolarized. By suitable interaction with matter, light can be made plane-polarized. This

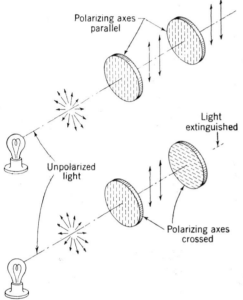

Fig. 2. Production and detection of polarized light by a polarizer and an analyzer.

interaction may be one of reflection from a transparent surface, refraction through a crystal, selective absorption in certain crystals, or scattering by small particles.

Except in the rarest of special conditions, and only momentarily, the unaided eye cannot detect any difference between polarized and unpolarized light. Hence an analyzer must be used to detect the state and plane of polarization of a light beam, as indicated in Fig. 2.

48-2. Polarization by Reflection. When a beam of light strikes a piece of glass, it is in part reflected and in part transmitted. When the incident beam is ordinary, unpolarized

light it is found that the reflected and refracted rays are each partly plane-polarized. It is observed that, in the reflected beam, the polarized part has vibrations perpendicular to the plane of incidence (parallel to the reflecting surface), while in the refracted beam the polarized part has vibrations parallel to the plane of incidence.

The fact that light may be polarized by reflection can be shown by allowing the light

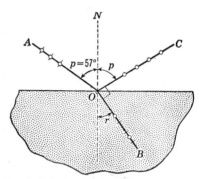

Fig. 3. Polarization by reflection of light.

reflected from the glass to fall on a second piece of glass. When the two glass plates have their surfaces parallel, the polarized light reflected from the first glass will be reflected also by the second glass. When, however, the second glass is rotated 90° about the reflected ray as an axis, there will be little or no reflection of the polarized part from the second glass plate. Thus the second glass plate can be used as an analyzer to test the polarization of light.

The degree of polarization of light reflected from a glass plate, or other nonconducting surface, depends upon the angle of incidence. The polarization of the reflected beam is found to be complete when the reflected ray is perpendicular to the refracted ray (Fig. 3). The vibrations in the incident ray AO are in all planes. These can be represented by their components perpendicular and parallel to the plane of incidence. These components are shown in Fig. 3 by small circles and by short lines, respectively. The angle of incidence p, called the *polarizing angle*, for which the

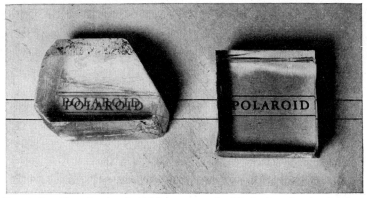

FIG. 4. Double refraction in calcite compared with single refraction in glass.

polarization of the reflected beam is complete, is related simply to the index of refraction of the reflecting material. In Fig. 3 the angle COB is 90°; therefore $p + r = 90°$. Thus $\sin r = \cos p$. Hence

$$n = \frac{\sin i}{\sin r} = \frac{\sin p}{\cos p} = \tan p \qquad (1)$$

This relation between the index of refraction and the polarizing angle is known as *Brewster's law*.

At the polarizing angle (about 57° for glass) none of the vibrations that lie in the plane of incidence is reflected. The reflected beam is then plane-polarized, but of relatively low intensity, since only about 8 per cent of the incident beam is reflected at the polarizing angle. A pile of 6 to 12 plates is often used to attain sufficient intensity by combining reflected rays from all the surfaces.

The transmitted beam is not completely plane-polarized at the polarizing angle. When a pile of plates is used, the successive reflections remove more and more of the vibration perpendicular to the plane of incidence from the transmitted beam. If many plates are used, the transmitted beam is also practically plane-polarized in a plane perpendicular to that of the reflected beam.

48-3. Intensity in Polarized Light. Consider a beam of light passing through a polarizer and an analyzer (Fig. 2) and that the analyzer has been rotated by an angle θ

from its position of maximum transmission. The amplitude A of the plane-polarized light incident on the analyzer may be resolved into the component $A \cos \theta$ which is transmitted and the component $A \sin \theta$ which is reflected or absorbed. Since the intensity is proportional to the square of the amplitude

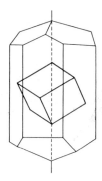

FIG. 5. The crystal form of calcite.

(Chap. 23), the intensity I of the beam transmitted by the analyzer when set at angle θ is given in terms of the maximum intensity I_0 by

$$I = I_0 \cos^2 \theta \qquad (2)$$

48-4. Double Refraction. If a crystal of Iceland spar (calcite, $CaCO_3$) is laid on a printed page, one observes through it two refracted images of the type (Fig. 4). This phenomenon was observed as early as 1669 by Bartholinus who realized that he had come upon a fundamental question in refraction. It was later observed by Huygens

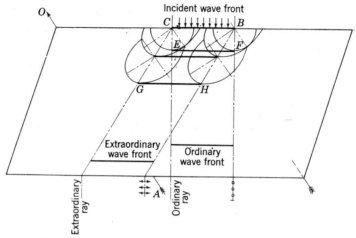

FIG. 6. Huygens wave fronts in a doubly refracting crystal.

(1690) that the rays which produced the two images were plane-polarized, in mutually perpendicular planes.

The common form of calcite crystal is shown in Fig. 5. It has a tendency when struck to cleave obliquely in three definite planes forming rhomboidal fragments. The external symmetry of the crystal is an indication of a corresponding symmetry in the lattice work of atoms comprising the crystal. This suggests that light energy may be transmitted with different speeds in such a crystal, depending on the orientation of its vibrations with respect to the planes of atoms which make up the crystal. Double refraction is unusual only in the sense that our ordinary experience in optics is with isotropic materials such as air, glass, and water, which do not exhibit this effect.

The line joining the two blunt corners of the equilateral rhombohedron in Fig. 5 coincides with the principal crystallographic axis of the calcite. The direction of this line, not the line itself, is called the *optic axis*. In this particular direction light travels with the same speed regardless of the plane of its vibration. Hence in this direction there is no double refraction. Any plane passing through the principal axis is called a *principal section*.

When a parallel beam falls obliquely on a surface of a calcite rhombohedron, the light is split into two parts. Both are refracted. Measurement of the angles of incidence and refraction shows that for every angle of incidence the index of refraction for one ray (the ordinary ray) is 1.658 (for sodium yellow light of 5893 A). But for the other ray (the extraordinary ray) the refractive index alters with the angle of incidence, varying between 1.486 and 1.658. The one ray is called *ordinary* because its index of refraction is constant, while the other ray is called *extraordinary* because its index of refraction varies with angle of incidence. This shows that the speed of the ordinary ray is less than that of the extraordinary ray except in the special direction along the optic axis when both travel with the same speed.

If a pencil dot is viewed through a calcite crystal, the image formed by the ordinary ray will appear closer than that formed by the extraordinary ray. If the obtuse corners of the crystal are ground off and polished to form surfaces perpendicular to the optic axis, a ray entering along the optic axis is neither refracted nor polarized.

Huygens applied his wave construction to explain the ordinary and extraordinary rays. Around points B and C (Fig. 6) are drawn spheres representing the ordinary wave fronts

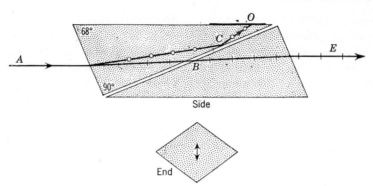

Fig. 7. A Nicol prism.

and spheroids representing the extraordinary wave fronts. Each spheroid has its axis of revolution parallel to the optic axis, so that the two surfaces touch at the points that lie in the direction of the crystal axis. The envelope of the spheres is the plane EF which determines the ordinary wave front, while the plane GH is the envelope of the spheroids which locates the extraordinary wave front. It should be noted that the extraordinary ray is not perpendicular to the wave front.

48-5. The Nicol Prism. The two rays inside a calcite crystal are completely plane-polarized in directions at right angles to each other. Nicol (1832) used an artifice to separate these rays to give a single beam of plane-polarized light. A calcite rhombohedron (Fig. 7) has the ends polished down so that the acute angle between them and the sides is 68° (instead of the 71° obtained by cleavage). The length is so chosen that the crystal can be sawed in a diagonal plane perpendicular to these two new faces and to the optic axis. The sawed surfaces are polished, and are then cemented together with a layer of Canada balsam. The index of refraction of the balsam (1.530) is intermediate between the two indices for calcite, $n_O = 1.658$ and $n_E = 1.486$.

With the crystal angles properly chosen, the extraordinary ray travels through the Nicol prism in the direction ABE. The ordinary ray, however, strikes the cement layer at C at an angle exceeding its critical angle

and is internally reflected toward the side of the crystal where it may be absorbed in black paint.

The intensity of the polarized light from a Nicol prism or any other polarizing device is always less than half the intensity of the incident beam. One polarized component is removed, and the light also loses intensity by

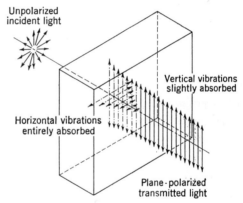

Fig. 8. Production of polarized light by a dichroic crystal.

reflection at boundary surfaces and by absorption.

48-6. Polarization by Selective Absorption. Certain crystals, known as *dichroic*, produce two internal beams polarized at right angles to each other, and in addition strongly absorb the one beam, while transmitting the other (Fig. 8). Tourmaline has this property. Unfortunately the plane-polarized light transmitted is colored. In 1852, Herapath, an English physician, discovered that dichroic crystals of quinine iodosulfate (herapathite) transmit a beam as plane-polarized light with transmission close to the ideal 50 per cent for all wavelengths of visible light (Fig. 9). The potential usefulness of this material led to extensive experiments culminating in the invention by Land (1929) of a practical method for embedding the tiny synthetic

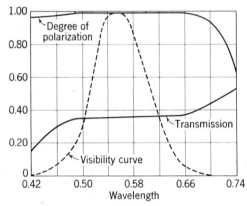

FIG. 9. The spectral distribution of the relative intensity (lower curve) and the degree of polarization (upper curve) of light transmitted by Polaroid polarizing material.

crystals (about $10^{11}/cm^2$) in a transparent cellulosic film in uniform alignment. The thin film 0.001 to 0.004 in. thick thus acts like a single huge crystal. This Polaroid sheet, sometimes bonded between glass plates, has the advantage of large size, low cost, and a polarizing effectiveness approaching that of a Nicol prism except at the extremities of the spectrum.

More recently Polaroid materials have been prepared by aligning molecules rather than the tiny crystals. They consist of aligned molecules of polymeric iodine in a sheet of polivinyl alcohol (in H sheet) or aligned molecules of polyvinylene (in K sheet). These molecular polarizers are superior in several respects, such as greater stability and freedom from scattered light.

48-7. Polarization by Scattering. When a strong beam of light is passed through a region containing no fine particles, it is not visible from the side. If, however, the beam is intercepted by fine particles, such as smoke, dust, or colloidal suspensions, the beam is partly scattered and becomes visible. In this *Tyndall effect*, the color and the intensity of the scattered light depend on the size of the particles. Very small particles scatter chiefly blue light, as in the case of cigar smoke or the "blue" sky (Sec. 45-7). As the particles are made larger, the longer wavelengths also are scattered until the scattered light appears white.

Scattered light is partly plane-polarized. The vibrations are perpendicular to the plane determined by the direction of the incident light and the line of sight (Fig. 10).

48-8. Optical Rotation. When two Polaroid light polarizers or two Nicol prisms are held in the line of vision in the crossed position, no light gets through and the field of view is dark. If now a crystal of quartz or a tube of sugar solution is placed between the crossed polarizer and analyzer, the light reappears. Monochromatic light can be extinguished by rotation of the analyzer. Materials that have the property of rotating

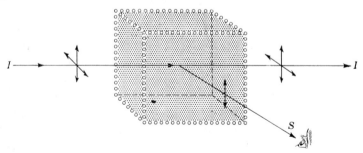

FIG. 10. Polarization by scattering.

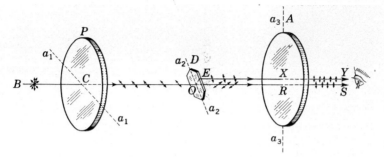

FIG. 11. Production of color by interference effects in polarized light.

the plane of polarization while transmitting polarized light are called *optically active* substances. The rotation is proportional to the amount of optically active substance in the path, and it provides an accurate way of determining the concentration of, say, sugar in an inactive solvent. *Polarimeters* are instruments for measuring optical rotation.

48-9. Interference Effects. When light travels through a birefringent material such as calcite, the crystal plate produces a difference in phase between the ordinary and extraordinary rays, because of the difference in the speeds of the two rays. By choosing a suitable thickness of crystal it is possible to retard one ray a half wavelength relative to the other. Nevertheless, interference bands or rings are never observed. One concludes that two rays of light polarized at right angles to each other do not interfere. They can cross one another without disturbance.

To the conditions for interference mentioned in Chap. 47 we must now add that the vibrations in the interfering rays must be in the same plane. An arrangement for producing such interference is shown in Fig. 11. A ray of unpolarized white light BC becomes plane-polarized white light after passage through polarizer P. It is then allowed to strike a doubly refracting crystal D whose optic axis a_2 is inclined at about 45° to the plane of vibration a_1. In the crystal D the ray is resolved into an ordinary ray OR vibrating perpendicularly to a_2a_2 and an extraordinary ray EX vibrating parallel to a_2a_2. There will be a

phase difference between the rays emerging from crystal D, but they will not interfere since their vibrations are in mutually perpendicular planes. Finally the analyzer A passes only the vertical components of these vibrations, giving two emergent rays RS and XY whose vibrations are in the same plane.

These rays are now capable of interference. If the relative retardation is an odd number of half wavelengths, the corresponding color is annulled by interference and its complementary color is transmitted.

The arrangement described is useful in the examination of crystals and thin rock sections, for differentiating isotropic and anisotropic materials, for detecting characteristics of structure not otherwise noticed, and for mineral identification.

48-10. Applications of Polarized Light. For several centuries polarized light gave valuable evidence as to the nature of light, but its production by inconvenient or expensive devices limited its usefulness to the laboratory. The production of polarizing materials in thin sheets, such as the various Polaroid light polarizers, opens new possibilities for utilizing polarized light.

Perhaps the simplest application of Polaroid sheets is the control of the intensity of light. Such an arrangement is suggested by Fig. 12. An outer polarizing sheet is fixed in position and an inner one may be rotated to adjust the amount of light transmitted from maximum when the planes are parallel to zero when they are perpendicular.

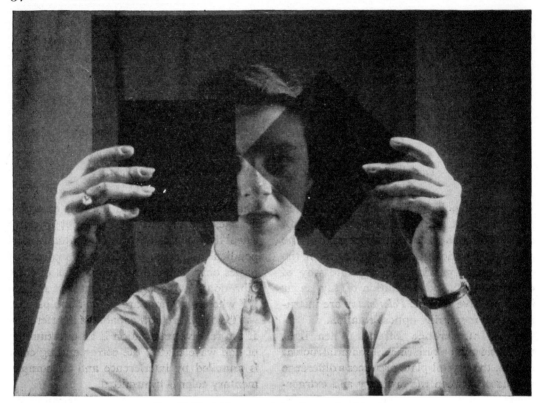

Fig. 12. Variable transmission by a polaroid pair.

The use of Polaroid glasses for eliminating glare from reflected light makes use of the fact that the polarized component has vibrations parallel to the reflecting surface. The glasses are set so that they will not transmit this component.

In photography it is often desirable to enhance the effect of sky and clouds by eliminating some of the actinic rays from the sky. Since light from the sky is partly polarized by scattering, a suitably oriented polarizing disk in front of the camera lens will serve as a "sky filter," with obvious advantages over the common yellow filter when color film is used.

Three-dimensional pictures may be projected with the two components polarized in directions at right angles to each other. If these double pictures are viewed through Polaroid glasses oriented to allow the right eye to see one picture but the left eye the other, the impression of three dimensions is attained. Similarly aerial pictures may be taken from slightly different angles and when viewed in a manner similar to that of the three-dimensional pictures will give a better perception of depth.

48-11. Photoelasticity. Certain materials such as glass or transparent bakelite become doubly refracting under mechanical strain. When the material is placed between crossed polarizer and analyzer, patterns of interference fringes can be observed. These patterns are used in detecting strains in glassware, as in the examination of glass-to-metal seals in electron tubes.

Complex engineering structures may be analyzed by photoelastic studies of transparent models. The regions of greatest strain are those of the closest spacing of fringes (Fig. 13). Quantitative measurements often can be obtained from the photoelastic constants of the material and the observed spacing of

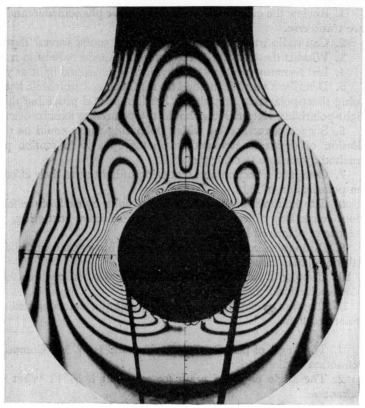

FIG. 13. Strain pattern in an eyebar connecting rod.

fringes. The strains in gears or other moving parts are sometimes studied by chilling the photoelastic model and thus freezing the strains in the sample, which may then be studied at rest.

SUMMARY

Polarization is the process by which the vibrations of a wave motion are confined to a definite pattern.

Polarizability is a characteristic of *transverse* waves.

Light may be plane-polarized by reflection by nonconducting surfaces, by refraction, by transmission through crystals showing double refraction, or by scattering from small particles.

The *angle of polarization p* is that angle at which light reflected from a substance is almost completely plane-polarized. By Brewster's law, $n = \tan p$.

The intensity I of a beam transmitted by a polarizing device upon which plane-polarized light is incident is given by

$$I = I_0 \cos^2 \theta$$

where I_0 is the maximum intensity transmitted and θ is the angle through which the device has been rotated from its position of maximum transmission.

When plane-polarized light passes through an *optically active* material, the plane of polarization is rotated through an angle that depends on the material, the length of the path traversed, and the wavelength of the light.

Certain materials such as glass or transparent bakelite become doubly refracting under strain. The science of photoelasticity relates these changes in optical properties to the strains producing them and furnishes a method of measuring strains.

QUESTIONS   1. Review the evidence that light is a wave phenomenon and that the waves are transverse.

2. Can radio waves be polarized? x rays? sound waves? Explain.

3. What is the function of the layer of Canada balsam in a Nicol prism?

4. List as many practical applications of polarized light as you can.

5. Describe a possible method for minimizing automobile headlight glare by using sheet-polarizing material in headlamps and providing the driver with a light-polarizing viewer. How should the polarizing axes be oriented?

6. Suggest a method by which polarizing filters could be used to give the illusion of depth in stereoscopic photographs or in motion pictures. Is the method applicable to color pictures?

7. Compare reflection and scattering of light as to their effects on color and on polarization of light.

8. Cite examples of the production of color by each of the following: reflection, refraction, diffraction, interference, selective scattering, and the interference of polarized light.

9. Distinguish between the influence of thin crystals and that of thick crystals on a beam of polarized light.

10. How could you distinguish experimentally between unpolarized light and plane-polarized light?

11. Diagram an experimental arrangement for detecting strains by the use of polarized light.

PROBLEMS   1. The angle of polarization for diamond is 67°34′. Compute the index of refraction of diamond.

2. The angle of polarization for rock salt is 57°4′. What is the index of refraction?   *Ans.* 1.544

3. A certain glass has an index of refraction of 1.65. At what angle of incidence is the light reflected from this glass plane-polarized?

4. Water has an index of refraction of 1.33. At what angle must a light beam be incident on the water surface in order that the reflected beam be plane-polarized?   *Ans.* 53°4′

5. For sodium yellow light determine the polarizing angles for ordinary crown glass, medium flint glass, and dense flint glass.

6. Calculate the speed of the ordinary ray and also the highest speed of the extraordinary ray in a calcite crystal for the yellow light from a sodium lamp.
                    Ans. 1.81×10^{10} cm/sec; 2.02×10^{10} cm/sec

7. A beam of light of wavelength 5893 A falls on a slab of calcite in a direction normal to the optic axis. Calculate the wavelengths of the ordinary light wave and the extraordinary light wave.

8. Photometric measurements show that when light falls on a glass plate at the angle, of polarization, 16% of the light that has its vibrations perpendicular to the plane of incidence is reflected. From the back surface of the same plate, 16% of the remaining light vibrating in that plane is reflected. What is the intensity ratio of vibrations in and at right angle to the plane of incidence in the beam transmitted through two plates?   *Ans.* 2/1

9. Sodium yellow light is incident normally on a face of a calcite crystal cut parallel to its optic axis. Compute the ratio of the major to the minor axis of the E wavelets (Fig. 6). Find the number of E and O waves contained in a crystal of thickness 0.100 mm.

10. Compute the critical angle for total reflection of the ordinary ray at the layer of Canada balsam in a Nicol prism for $\lambda = 589$ mμ. *Ans.* $67.3°$

11. Two Nicol prisms are set for maximum transmission. One prism is rotated through $60°$. What is the per cent reduction in the light transmitted?

12. Two Nicol prisms have their planes parallel to each other. One of the Nicol prisms is then turned so that its principal plane makes an angle of $40°$ with the principal plane of the other prism. What per cent of the light originally transmitted by the second Nicol prism is now transmitted by it?

Ans. 77% amplitude or 59% intensity

13. The sensitivity of a photographic plate is to be determined by exposing successive portions to light from a standard lamp transmitted through two Nicol prisms. Designating as 1.00 the illuminance on the plate when the prisms are parallel, through what angles should the analyzer Nicol prism be rotated to produce illuminances 0.80, 0.60, 0.40, 0.20, and 0?

14. The two indices of refraction for yellow light in quartz are 1.544 and 1.553. For what thickness of quartz will the two beams differ in phase by a half wavelength when they emerge? *Ans.* 0.0033 cm

15. The two indices of refraction of quartz for yellow light are 1.544 and 1.553. For what thickness will the two rays emerge one and one quarter wavelengths out of phase?

16. A thin plate of calcite is cut with the optic axis parallel to the plane of the plate. What is the minimum thickness needed to produce destructive interference for sodium light when the plate is placed between crossed Nicol prisms?

Ans. 3.4×10^{-4} cm

17. What minimum thickness of calcite crystal is needed to introduce a phase difference of (*a*) $45°$, (*b*) $90°$, and (*c*) $180°$, between the emergent O and E rays when plane-polarized light is incident normally upon it?

18. A beam of plane-polarized light is incident on a calcite crystal with its vibrations making an angle θ with the principal section of the crystal. (*a*) Show that the relative amplitudes of O and E beams is given by $A_O/A_E = \tan \theta$. (*b*) If $\theta = 30°$, find the relative amplitudes and intensities of the two beams.

Ans. 0.577; 0.333

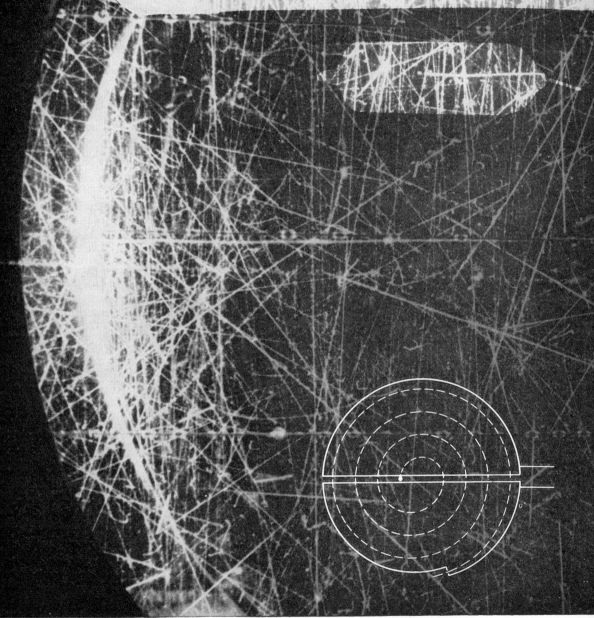

MODERN PHYSICS

49. Relativity and Quantum Theory

Relativity and quantum mechanics are the two great theories of twentieth century physics. They are regarded as fundamental in the understanding of atomic and nuclear phenomena. Hence, although both theories are mathematically complex and cannot be developed here in detail, we shall examine the observations which inspired the development of these theories and some of the important consequences of each.

The "special" theory of relativity predicts that the mechanics of particles with speeds approaching the speed of light is somewhat different from Newton's mechanics. The concepts of space and time are shown to be interrelated. A particle speed greater than the speed of light in empty space is shown to be impossible. Mass and energy are shown to be interconvertible. (The "general" theory of relativity is Einstein's theory of gravitation and will not be discussed here).

49-1. The "Ether." The wave properties of light demonstrated during the first part of the nineteenth century were explained in Maxwell's brilliant electromagnetic theory of radiation. It was difficult for scientists of the nineteenth century, as for us, to conceive of a wave motion apart from a material medium to transmit its vibrations. So they invented a medium called the *ether* for the propagation of light. This suggested two consequences worthy of experimental check:

1. Light waves should travel with a definite speed ($c = 3 \times 10^8$ m/sec in free space) with respect to ether itself. Then the apparent speed of light relative to a body moving through the "ether" should differ from c and should depend on the speed of the body.

2. By measurements on light waves, it should be possible to determine an "absolute velocity" of the earth or any other body.

An experiment to detect motion of the earth relative to the "ether" would require very sensitive apparatus. The speed of the earth in its orbit is about 3×10^4 m/sec, or only about 10^{-4} times the speed of the light signals that would be used in the experiment.

49-2. Michelson's Interferometer. With the problem in mind of measuring the earth's speed through the "ether," Michelson devised an interferometer, an instrument in which interference patterns produced by a divided light beam are used to reveal differences in the optical paths (see Sec. 47-3).

When the optical paths (Fig. 1) happen to be equal, beams 1 and 2 will arrive at E in phase and produce a bright field by constructive interference. As distance AM is increased $\lambda/4$ by moving mirror M, the optical path for ray 1 is lengthened by $\lambda/2$ and destructive interference of rays 1 and 2 at E gives a dark field. Mirrors M and M' are made nearly but not quite perpendicular to produce a field crossed by alternate bright

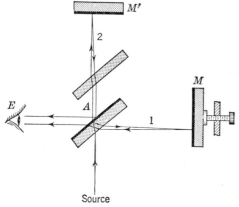

FIG. 1. Michelson's interferometer.

and dark interference fringes (Fig. 2). These may be counted as they move past a reference mark R. For each fringe that passes the mark, the optical path has changed by one wavelength. This change might be produced by moving M a half wavelength. However, the change could also be produced by a change in

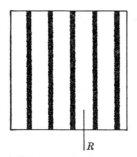

FIG. 2. Fringes and reference mark.

the speed of light in beam 1 (on the substitution, for example, of a gas of different index of refraction for the air in that one beam).

49-3. The Michelson-Morley Experiment. Assume that the earth travels through stationary "ether" with a speed v and that light has a speed c in the "ether." Consider a Michelson interferometer arranged so that

one of its two equal arms is parallel to the earth's velocity v, Fig. 3. Then the times required for the light beams to travel the distances AMA and $AM'A$ will be unequal. The speed of a beam traveling from A to M is $c - v$ relative to the interferometer. On

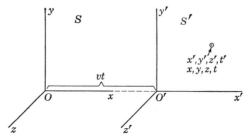

FIG. 3. Reference system S' moves with constant velocity v in x direction relative to reference system S.

the return from M to A, the speed of the beam relative to the interferometer is $c + v$. The time for the round trip AMA is thus

$$t_1 = \frac{s}{c - v} + \frac{s}{c + v} = \frac{2sc}{c^2 - v^2} \quad (1)$$

Since v is small compared with c, we may use the binomial theorem to obtain the approximation

$$t_1 = \frac{2s/c}{1 - v^2/c^2} = \frac{2s}{c}\left(1 + \frac{v^2}{c^2} + \ldots\right) \quad (2)$$

A wave front leaving A toward mirror M' will be returned, according to Huygen's principle, but only after A has moved to a new position A' (Fig. 3). The component of the velocity of the light in the direction perpendicular to the motion of the interferometer is $\sqrt{c^2 - v^2}$. The time for the round trip $AM'A$ is

$$t_2 = \frac{2s}{\sqrt{c^2 - v^2}} = \frac{2s/c}{\sqrt{1 - v^2/c^2}}$$
$$= \frac{2s}{c}\left(1 + \frac{1}{2}\frac{v^2}{c^2} + \ldots\right) \quad (3)$$

Waves which are in phase when they reach A from the monochromatic source will differ in phase when they return to A after reflection because of the time difference

$$\Delta t = t_1 - t_2 = \frac{sv^2}{c^3} \qquad (4)$$

If the interferometer is rotated 90°, paths 1 and 2 will have their roles interchanged and the total retardation will be $2sv^2/c^3$. The number of fringes passing the reference mark should be

$$N = \frac{\text{path difference}}{\text{wavelength}} = \frac{c \, \Delta t}{\lambda}$$
$$= \frac{c2sv^2}{\lambda c^3} = \frac{2sv^2}{c^2\lambda} \qquad (5)$$

To estimate the magnitude of fringe shift to be expected, we may assume that the earth's velocity through the "ether" is the same as its orbital velocity, about 30 km/sec. By using multiple reflections, Michelson and Morley attained an effective path s of about 10 m. For light of wavelength 5000 A we should then estimate a maximum fringe shift of

$$N = \frac{2 \times 10 \text{ m}(3 \times 10^4 \text{ m/sec})^2}{(3 \times 10^8 \text{ m/sec})^2(5.0 \times 10^{-7} \text{ m})}$$
$$= 0.4 \text{ fringe} \qquad (6)$$

A fringe shift of this amount is readily detectable with the apparatus. It should then be possible to measure the fringe shift and from it compute the velocity of the earth relative to the "ether," that is, the absolute velocity of the earth.

Surprisingly, Michelson and Morley found *no* fringe shift when the interferometer was rotated in a pool of mercury. Measurements were made during day and night, at various locations in Europe and America and at various seasons of the year, to assure that at least some measurements would be made when the earth had a large velocity relative to the "ether." Always null results were obtained, as if the interferometer were at rest $(v = 0)$ relative to the medium in which light is transmitted. It appeared that optical experiments cannot detect motion of the earth relative to the "ether."

Michelson and Morley reported their results in 1887. No subsequent experimental evidence contradicts them. Some lingering doubts were laid to rest in a review article published in the *Reviews of Modern Physics* (pages 167–178) in 1955.

Several attempted explanations for the apparent impossibility of measuring the earth's absolute motion failed to gain acceptance when they either did violence to established theory, disagreed with known astronomical data, or introduced too many special hypotheses.

49-4. Postulates of the Special Theory of Relativity. The negative result of the Michelson-Morley experiment was interpreted by Einstein as indicating that only relative velocities can be measured. Consequently the general laws of physics must be independent of the velocity of the particular reference system of coordinates used to state them, otherwise it would be possible to ascribe some absolute meaning to different velocities.

The special or restricted relativity theory of 1905 dealt with reference systems moving at a constant velocity with respect to each other (Fig. 3). Einstein based his theory on two postulates:

1. The laws of physical phenomena are the same when stated in terms of either of two reference systems moving at constant velocity relative to each other (and can involve no reference to motion relative to an "ether").

2. The velocity of light in empty space is the same for all observers and is independent of the velocity of the light source relative to the observer.

These two postulates require us to give up our intuitive conception of time which Newton described as "absolute, true, and mathematical time (which) of itself and by its own nature, flows uniformly on, without regard to anything external." Indeed, we now find that if two events take place at different locations, it is not always possible to say which of the two precedes the other, or that they occur simultaneously.

49-5. Relativistic Transformations of Coordinates.

The two postulates of the special relativity theory require that the transformations of coordinates which classical (Newtonian) physics would use in Fig. 3 be replaced by those in the second column of Table 1. Here v is the speed of axis S' relative to axis S.

TABLE 1. TRANSFORMATIONS OF
COORDINATES APPLICABLE TO FIG. 3

Classical	Relativistic	
$x' = x - vt$	$x' = \dfrac{x - vt}{\sqrt{1 - v^2/c^2}}$	(7)
$y' = y$	$y' = y$	(8)
$z' = z$	$z' = z$	(9)
$t' = t$	$t' = \dfrac{t - vx/c^2}{\sqrt{1 - v^2/c^2}}$	(10)

Events which happen at the same place at different times, as measured in one reference system, may be seen from another system to happen at different places as well. Also, a difference in spatial position with respect to one system may correspond to a difference in both space and time with respect to another. In the four dimensions of "space-time," space differences can be converted partly into time differences, and vice versa.

Example: Show that relativistic Eqs. (7)–(10) predict that the speed of light will be the same in each coordinate system of Fig. 3.

Suppose that a light signal starts from origin O of Fig. 3 at time $t = 0$ and moves in the x direction. It will arrive at a point $x = X$ at the time $t = X/c$, since its speed through the laboratory is c. A second observer moving with the reference frame S' will say that the light signal arrives at the point

$$x' = \frac{X - v\dfrac{X}{c}}{\sqrt{1 - \dfrac{v^2}{c^2}}}$$

at the time $\qquad t' = \dfrac{\dfrac{X}{c} - \dfrac{v}{c^2} X}{\sqrt{1 - v^2/c^2}}$

He will compute its speed u' in the primed (moving) coordinate system as

$$u' = \frac{x'}{t'} = \frac{X - \dfrac{v}{c} X}{\dfrac{X}{c} - \dfrac{v}{c^2} X} = c$$

49-6. Addition of Velocities.

Consider two observers, A at rest in reference system S (Fig. 3) and B at rest in reference system S'. System S' moves with constant velocity v relative to S. Suppose an object flies past these two observers in the x direction. Observer B measures the speed of the object relative to himself as u'. To express u' in terms of the coordinates of observer A at rest in the laboratory reference system S, we have

$$u' = \frac{\Delta x'}{\Delta t'} = \frac{\Delta \left(\dfrac{x - vt}{\sqrt{1 - v^2/c^2}} \right)}{\Delta \left(\dfrac{t - vx/c^2}{\sqrt{1 - v^2/c^2}} \right)}$$

$$= \frac{\Delta x - v\,\Delta t}{\Delta t - \dfrac{v}{c^2}\,\Delta x} = \frac{u - v}{1 - \dfrac{uv}{c^2}} \quad (11)$$

where in the last step we have divided numerator and denominator by Δt and let $\Delta x/\Delta t = u$, the speed of the object in the laboratory S. Thus

$$u' = \frac{u - v}{1 - \dfrac{uv}{c^2}} \quad \text{or} \quad u = \frac{u' + v}{1 + \dfrac{vu'}{c^2}} \quad (12)$$

Example: A rocket moves above the laboratory with a speed $v = 0.90c$. A "flying saucer" passes the rocket with a speed $u' = 0.90c$. Find the speed of the flying saucer as determined at the laboratory.

Classical mechanics would predict this speed as the speed relative to the rocket plus the speed of the rocket relative to the laboratory, or $1.80c$. But the relativistic theorem for addition of velocities, Eq. (12), gives

$$u = \frac{0.90c + 0.90c}{1 + \dfrac{0.90c \times 0.90c}{c^2}} = \frac{1.80c}{1 + 0.81} = 0.994c$$

No moving body has a speed greater than c, the speed of light.

49-7. Variation of Mass. We have previously written the equation of motion for a body as $F = ma$, and also in terms of momentum as

$$F = \frac{mv_2 - mv_1}{t} = \frac{\Delta(mv)}{\Delta t} \quad (13)$$

In relativity theory, the conservation of momentum remains a basic principle of mechanics. It turns out that in order to have the total momentum of an isolated system remain constant, the momentum of a particle must be defined as

$$\text{Momentum} = mv = \frac{m_0 v}{\sqrt{1 - v^2/c^2}} \quad (14)$$

That is, it is necessary to assume that a particle which has a mass m_0 when at rest, has a mass

$$m = \frac{m_0}{\sqrt{1 - v^2/c^2}} \quad (15)$$

when it is moving with speed v. The quantity m_0 is called the *rest mass*.

Variation of mass with speed can readily be observed for small particles, such as electrons, which can be accelerated to enormously large speeds.

Example: An electron at rest has a mass of 9.11×10^{-31} kg. At what speed would the mass of the electron be doubled?

We want $m = 2m_0$. From Eq. (15)

$$1 - \frac{v^2}{c^2} = \frac{m_0^2}{m^2} = \frac{1}{4}$$

$$\frac{v^2}{c^2} = \frac{3}{4} \qquad v = 0.86c = 2.6 \times 10^8 \text{ m/sec}$$

49-8. Kinetic Energy. In classical physics, force may be defined as the time rate of change of momentum. This definition of force is retained in relativistic mechanics, but the mass must be recognized as a variable. The kinetic energy of an object can be calculated as the energy required to accelerate it from rest to its final speed v. The result is

$$KE = \frac{m_0 c^2}{\sqrt{1 - v^2/c^2}} - m_0 c^2$$

$$KE = mc^2 - m_0 c^2 \quad (16)$$

Equation (16) says that as a particle is speeded up its energy is increased and that the increase in energy $(m - m_0)c^2$ is proportional to the increase in mass. This result suggests that we identify c^2 times the relativistic mass of the particle with the total energy of the particle

$$\text{Total energy} = mc^2 = KE + m_0 c^2 \quad (17)$$

The total energy of a free particle consists of its rest energy (the energy $m_0 c^2$ it has at rest) plus its kinetic energy (the energy KE it has because of its motion).

Example: Consider an electron which has been accelerated from rest through a potential difference of 500 kv. Find (a) its kinetic energy, (b) its rest energy, (c) its total energy, (d) its mass, and (e) its speed.

(a) $KE = e \, \Delta V = 500$ kev

(b) $m_0 c^2 = (9.108 \times 10^{-31} \text{ kg})$
$$\times (2.998 \times 10^8 \text{ m/sec})^2$$
$$= 8.186 \times 10^{-14} \text{ joule} = 511 \text{ kev}$$

(c) Total energy $= (500 + 511)$ kev $= 1011$ kev

(d) Since $\dfrac{m}{m_0} = \dfrac{mc^2}{m_0 c^2} = \dfrac{\text{total energy}}{\text{rest energy}} = \dfrac{1011 \text{ kev}}{511 \text{ kev}}$

$= 1.98$, the mass of the electron is $m = 1.98 m_0 = 18.1 \times 10^{-31}$ kg

(e) From the relation

$$m = 1.98 m_0 = m_0 \left(1 - \frac{v^2}{c^2}\right)^{-\frac{1}{2}}$$

$$1 - \frac{v^2}{c^2} = \frac{1}{(1.98)^2}$$

Hence $v/c = [1 - 1/(1.98)^2]^{\frac{1}{2}} = 0.863$ and the electron speed $v = 0.863c = 2.59 \times 10^8$ m/sec.

49-9. Blackbody Radiation. Modern quantum theory, so essential in the understanding of many atomic phenomena, had its origin in the study of the "temperature" radiation from an ideal (blackbody) radiator. It was found that (as shown in the curves of Fig. 9 of Chap. 45) for a given temperature the energy emission has a maximum value at a particular wavelength which is inversely proportional to the absolute temperature (Wien's law). Also the total power emitted in all wavelengths is proportional to the fourth power of the absolute temperature (Stefan-Boltzmann law).

Prior to 1900 many attempts had been made to express in an equation the experimentally determined distribution of power in the spectrum of a blackbody. Investigators based their calculations on what appeared to be similarities between radiation and a perfect gas. In particular, an analogy was sought between the distribution of energies among the molecules of a gas and the frequencies of the molecular oscillators or dipoles which were assumed to emit the electromagnetic radiation.

49-10. Planck's Quantum. After a long series of observations and speculations failed to produce an acceptable energy-distribution law for blackbody radiation, Planck departed from the conventional lines of reasoning in classical physics. He retained the general concept of oscillators but suggested that a body emits and absorbs radiant energy only in multiples of a definite small amount, the *quantum*, the magnitude of which, $h\nu$, depends on the frequency ν.

$$E = h\nu \qquad (18)$$

The constant h, known as Planck's constant, may be thought of as having the dimensions of *energy* times *time*, or *momentum* times *distance*. Making use of Eq. (18), which can be expressed as $E = hc/\lambda$, Planck was able to derive an expression for the distribution of energy in the continuous spectrum emitted by a blackbody in full agreement with experimental data. Furthermore, the value for h computed from these data was confirmed by values for h determined when the quantum theory was used to interpret such new

phenomena as the photoelectric effect, the line spectrum of hydrogen, and the Compton scattering of x rays. The experimental value for h is

$$h = 6.62 \times 10^{-27} \text{ erg-sec}$$

49-11. The Photon. Einstein suggested (1905) that not only is radiation emitted and absorbed in whole numbers of energy quanta, as proposed by Planck, but that the electromagnetic energy is also propagated through space in definite quanta or *photons*, moving with the speed of light. This extension of the quantum theory implies a modification of the wave theory of light in favor of a particle theory.

49-12. Photoelectric Effects. Einstein used Planck's idea of interchange of energy in quanta to examine the photoelectric emission of electrons from the surface of a metal (Chap. 39). If the whole energy of a quantum is given to an electron it would be emitted from the surface provided that energy were sufficient to take the electron through the surface. If the minimum energy for escape (called the work function) is w_0, then there will be emission only if $h\nu > w_0$. Thus

$$h\nu = w_0 + \tfrac{1}{2}mv^2 \qquad (19)$$

where $\tfrac{1}{2}mv^2$ is the energy of the electron after it has emerged from the surface. This *Einstein photoelectric equation* predicts that there should be a smallest frequency for which photoelectrons will be emitted by a given surface. This prediction is in accord with observation.

49-13. The Compton Effect. An effect observed and explained by A. H. Compton in 1923 gives direct confirmation of the photon

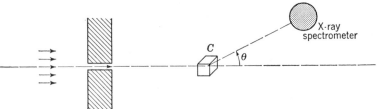

FIG. 4. Apparatus for observing Compton scattering of x rays.

hypothesis. Compton allowed a beam of monochromatic x rays (Fig. 4) to fall on a scattering material C and then examined the scattered radiation with an x-ray spectrometer. Scattered radiation having the same wavelength as the incident beam was

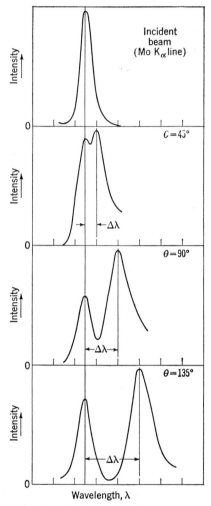

FIG. 5. Wavelength shift due to Compton scattering.

found, as expected from the electromagnetic wave theory. But in addition Compton observed a scattered wavelength λ' greater than that of the original beam (Fig. 5). The shift in wavelength, $\Delta\lambda = \lambda' - \lambda$, was found to become larger as the scattering angle θ was increased. This scattering with an increase in wavelength is called the *Compton effect* and

cannot be explained by the classical wave theory which suggests no way of introducing a frequency (or wavelength) change in scattering.

The photon picture of electromagnetic radiation provides a straightforward explanation of the Compton effect. We picture a photon as having zero rest mass; its total energy is its kinetic energy. Since the energy of a photon is $E = h\nu$, we can calculate its mass from $E = mc^2$

$$mc^2 = h\nu \qquad \text{or} \qquad m = \frac{h\nu}{c^2}$$

The momentum of a photon is

$$p = mc = \frac{h\nu}{c} \qquad (20)$$

We now interpret the Compton scattering as the elastic collision of a photon with an electron of the scattering material which is free and at rest before the collision (Fig. 6). To satisfy conservation of momentum,

X components: $\dfrac{h\nu'}{c} \cos\theta + p\cos\phi = \dfrac{h\nu}{c}$

Y components: $\dfrac{h\nu'}{c} \sin\theta - p\sin\phi = 0$

where p is the momentum of the electron after the collision and ν' is the frequency of the scattered photon. Since we assume an elastic collision, the final kinetic energy must be equal to the initial kinetic energy

$$h\nu = h\nu' + \text{KE}$$

where KE is the final kinetic energy of the electron.

If we write the momentum equations as

$$pc\cos\phi = h\nu - h\nu'\cos\theta$$
$$pc\sin\phi = h\nu'\sin\theta,$$

square, and add, we get

$$p^2c^2 = (h\nu)^2 - 2 \times h\nu \times h\nu'\cos\theta + (h\nu')^2 \qquad (21)$$

By combining two equations we get a useful relationship between the total energy

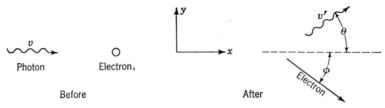

F<small>IG</small>. 6. Compton scattering of a photon.

and the momentum of a particle:

$$E = m_0c^2/\sqrt{1 - v^2/c^2}$$
$$p = m_0v/\sqrt{1 - v^2/c^2}$$
$$E^2 = p^2c^2 + m_0^2c^4 \qquad (22)$$

Hence for the recoil electron

$$p^2c^2 = (\text{KE})^2 + 2(\text{KE})m_0c^2$$

From the energy equation $\text{KE} = h\nu - h\nu'$

$$p^2c^2 = (h\nu - h\nu')^2 + 2m_0c(h\nu - h\nu') \quad (23)$$

By substitution of Eq. (23) in Eq. (21) we find

$$m_0c^2h\nu - m_0c^2h\nu' = h\nu \times h\nu'(1 - \cos\theta)$$

On dividing by h^2c^2 and substituting

$$\frac{1}{\lambda} = \frac{\nu}{c}$$

we finally obtain

$$\lambda' = \lambda + \frac{h}{m_0c}(1 - \cos\theta) \qquad (24)$$

which fits the experimentally measured wavelength shift as a function of scattering angle θ.

That part of the radiation which is scattered without wavelength change (Fig. 5) is accounted for by assuming that these photons were scattered by electrons strongly bound in atoms. The recoiling mass is that of the whole atom, the photons experience negligible loss of energy in collision with the heavy atom and hence the wavelength of these photons will be very close to that of the incident photons.

SUMMARY

The result of the Michelson-Morley experiment is interpreted as showing that only relative velocities can be measured.

Einstein's relativity theory of 1905 assumes that: (1) physical phenomena are described by the same laws in either of two reference systems moving at constant velocity relative to each other, and (2) all observers measure the same velocity for light in free space, regardless of the velocity of the light source relative to the observer.

An object moving with velocity u' relative to an axis which itself has a velocity v relative to an observer will appear to the observer to have velocity

$$u = \frac{u' + v'}{1 + \dfrac{vu'}{c^2}}$$

A particle which has mass m_0 when at rest has a mass

$$m = \frac{m_0}{\sqrt{1 - v^2/c^2}}$$

when it is moving with speed v.

The total energy of a free particle consists of its rest energy plus its kinetic energy

$$\text{Total energy} = mc^2 = m_0c^2 + \text{KE}$$

Planck's theory of radiation is based on the assumption that a body emits and absorbs radiant energy only in multiples of a *quantum*, whose magnitude is proportional to the frequency of the radiation

$$E = h\nu$$

Einstein's explanation of photoelectric emission predicts that the photoelectron shall have a kinetic energy equal to the energy $h\nu$ of the incident photon minus the energy w_0 required for escape

$$\text{KE} = \tfrac{1}{2}mv^2 = h\nu - w_0$$

Compton's interpretation of the scattering of x rays confirms Planck's quantum hypothesis, and assigns to a photon the momentum $h\nu/c$. The increase in wavelength observed in the scattered radiation is given by

$$\lambda' - \lambda = \frac{h}{m_0 c}(1 - \cos\theta)$$

REFERENCES

Lillian R. Lieber, *The Einstein Theory of Relativity*, Farrar & Rinehart, Inc., New York, 1945.

Herbert Dingle, *The Special Theory of Relativity*, Chemical Publishing Company, Inc., New York, 1941.

Albert Einstein, *The Meaning of Relativity*, 5th ed., Princeton University Press, Princeton, N. J., 1955.

Robert Bruce Lindsay and Henry Margenau, *Foundations of Physics*, chaps. 7 and 8, John Wiley & Sons, Inc., New York, 1936.

F. K. Richtmyer, E. H. Kennard, and T. Lauritsen, *Introduction to Modern Physics*, especially chaps. 3, 4, 5, and 10, McGraw-Hill Book Company, Inc., New York, 1955.

PROBLEMS 1. Show that the relativistic formula for kinetic energy, Eq. (16), reduces to $\frac{1}{2}m_0 v^2$ when v is very small compared to c. HINT: Use the binomial expansion for the square root.

2. If your space ship is flying with a speed of $0.50c$ relative to the earth and another space ship passed you with a speed of $0.50c$ relative to you, how fast is it going relative to the earth? *Ans.* $0.80c$

3. Assume that you are moving with a speed $0.80c$ past a man who picks up a watch and then sets it down. If you observe that he held the watch for 10 sec, how long does he think he held it? HINT: Use the time transformation of Eq. (10). You want to find $\Delta t = t_2 - t_1$ when you know $\Delta t' = t_2' - t_1'$.

4. Find the contraction in length of a 1.0-mi long train when travelling at 80 mi/hr. HINT: From Eq. (7) show that the contraction of a moving length is given by $l = l_0\left(1 - \dfrac{v^2}{c^2}\right)^{1/2}$. *Ans.* 4.6×10^{-10} in.

5. Show that the speed v, momentum p, and total energy E of any particle are related by the equation $\dfrac{v}{c}E = pc$

6. What are the speed and mass of an electron whose kinetic energy is (a) 5000 ev, (b) 1.0 Mev? *Ans.* (a) $0.14c$, $1.00097m_0$; (b) $0.941c$, $2.96m_0$

7. At what speed must a particle be moving to have a mass twice as great as its rest mass?

8. The mass of an electron at rest is 9.11×10^{-31} kg. What is its mass at speeds of (a) 0.100, (b) 0.90, and (c) 0.99 that of light? *Ans.* 9.15×10^{-31} kg; 2.09×10^{-30} kg; 6.45×10^{-30} kg

9. The mass of a proton at rest is 1.67×10^{-27} kg. What is the mass when it is moving with a speed 78% that of light?

10. What voltage must be used to accelerate an electron in order to give it a speed one-half that of light? By what percentage is the mass increased at this speed? *Ans.* 74 kv; 15%

11. What voltage would be necessary to give an electron a speed one-third the speed of light? By what percentage is the mass increased at this speed over the rest mass?

12. How much coal having a heat of combustion of 12,000 Btu/lb would have to be burned to produce energy equivalent to the transmutation of a pound of matter into energy? *Ans.* 1.62×10^6 tons

13. How much coal having a heat of combustion of 8000 cal/gm would have to be burned to equal energy equivalent to that released if 4.032 gm of hydrogen were converted into 4.002 gm of helium?

14. What would be the wavelength of the radiation emitted if 1.00×10^{-25} gm of matter were transmuted into a single quantum of radiant energy?

Ans. 2.2×10^{-4} A

15. What is the radius of curvature of the path of an electron whose kinetic energy is 15 Mev when moving perpendicular to a field of magnetic induction 0.10 weber/m²?

16. The burning of 1.00 gm of coal liberates about 7500 cal (or 8.75 watt-hours) of energy. What energy would be released from the conversion of the entire mass into energy?   *Ans.* $25,\overline{0}00$ megawatt-hours

17. A 10-kw radio transmitter operates at a frequency of 1.40 megacycles per second. (*a*) How many photons does it emit every second? (*b*) How many photons are received per second by a receiver tuned to this frequency and located at a place where the signal strength is 5.0×10^{-6} watt?

18. A one-candle source of yellow light ($\lambda = 5900$ A) gives a flow of luminous energy of about 0.50 erg/(cm² sec) at a distance of 1.0 m from the source. A human eye when seeing a star of sixth magnitude is receiving light equivalent to that from a 10^{-8} candle source at 1.0-m distance. If the diameter of the pupil is 3.0 mm, how many quanta enter per second?   *Ans.* $1\overline{1}00$

19. Radiation of wavelength 2536×10^{-10} m from a mercury arc is used to eject photoelectrons from silver. The potential difference needed to bring the photoelectrons to rest is 0.11 volt. What is the work function of silver?

20. The longest wavelength that will cause photoelectrons to be emitted from a sodium surface is 5830 A. What energy is necessary to take the electron through the surface? If the surface is illuminated by light of wavelength 4500 A, what is the maximum speed of the photoelectrons emitted?

Ans. 3.42×10^{-12} erg; 4.70×10^5 m/sec

21. For a certain photocell it is found that a potential difference of -1.6 volts between collector and emitter reduces the photocurrent to zero when light of wavelength 3000 A falls on the emitter. What is the threshold wavelength for the emitter surface? Photons associated with light of wavelength 12,400 A have an energy of 1.0 electron-volt.

22. The surface of a certain metal is illuminated by light of wavelength 4000 A. The photoelectrons emitted are all stopped by a negative potential of 0.80 volt. What is the maximum kinetic energy of an electron emitted? What is the longest wavelength that will cause photoelectrons to be emitted at this surface?   *Ans.* 1.28×10^{-19} joule; $53\overline{9}0$ A

23. When the surface of potassium is illuminated with yellow light (5890 A) electrons are liberated which require 0.36 volt to bring them to rest. When the surface is illuminated with ultraviolet light (2537 A) the stopping potential for the photoelectrons is 3.14 volts. Derive values for (*a*) Planck's constant h, (*b*) the work function w_0 for potassium, and (*c*) the long-wavelength limit of the photoelectric effect for potassium.

24. Radiation of wavelength 3750 A falls upon a surface whose work function is 2.0 electron volts. Compute the maximum speed of the emerging photoelectrons.   *Ans.* 6.8×10^7 cm/sec

25. An x-ray photon of wavelength 0.20 A is scattered at an angle of 90° with its original direction after colliding with an electron initially at rest. Find the Compton shift in wavelength and the wavelength of the scattered photon.

26. An x-ray beam has a wavelength of 0.20 A. Find (*a*) the mass and (*b*) the momentum of its photons.   *Ans.* 1.1×10^{-28} gm; 3.3×10^{-18} gm cm/sec

27. A 250-kev photon is scattered by a free electron (Compton effect). The kinetic energy of the recoil electron is 200 kev. What is the wavelength of the scattered photon?

50. *Atomic Physics*

During the nineteenth century, the golden age of classical physics, science advanced at a much more rapid pace than during any earlier period. The avalanche in the development of science led to specialization: physics, astronomy, chemistry, engineering, etc., became recognized as separate disciplines (Chap. 1). At the same time the greatest achievements in physics were in the correlation of apparently diverse phenomena.

During the twentieth century, physics has developed at an even more accelerated pace and entirely new fields, unsuspected in 1890, are of concern to physicists today. Also there has been a subtle change in the approach to nature. The earlier emphasis on mechanical models has given way to theories which are much more mathematical and abstract. Interest has extended to submicroscopic phenomena not directly observable. Finally, an earlier trend toward specialization may have become reversed in the joining of chemistry and physics and the gradual merging with biochemistry and biophysics. The present great interest in atomic and nuclear physics arises both from the basic nature of the problems studied and from the technical applications, which have worldwide importance.

50-1. Development of the Atomic Viewpoint. Evidence of the existence of atoms came first from the study of simple chemical reactions during the latter half of the eighteenth century. By about 1800 it had been demonstrated that:

1. A particular compound always comprises the same elements chemically united in the same proportions by mass.

2. When two elements, A and B, combine as constituents of more than one compound, the masses of B which unite with a fixed mass of A (and vice versa) are related to each other in the ratios of whole numbers, which are usually small.

A simple kinetic theory of gases, based on the atomic viewpoint, gave a convincing interpretation of the pressure exerted by a gas, as we have seen in Chap. 18. Through this theory, measurements of latent heat and surface tension gave an estimate of the diameters of molecules, of the order of 10^{-8} cm. The theory gained further credibility by predicting the relation between the viscosity and density of a gas and the coefficient of diffusion of a streaming gas. The development of kinetic theory made it evident that heat is associated with the kinetic energy of molecules. It appeared likely that the propagation of sound is also a manifestation of molecular motion. But the atomic theory so far discussed offered no explanation of the nature of electricity and magnetism or of the nature of light.

Among the many important discoveries made during the nineteenth century, some apparently gave answers to long-standing controversies; others introduced new phenomena. Interference, diffraction, and polarization phenomena of light were observed in the early years of the century and led to acceptance of the wave theory of light. The work of Faraday in electrolysis helped confirm the atomic nature of matter and supported ideas of electricity as discrete particles. Faraday and Henry (1831) discovered electromagnetic induction, providing the basis for the electrical industry. Joule (1847) demonstrated the identity of mechanical energy and heat. Maxwell, with the background of Faraday's experiments, worked out a theory of electromagnetic radiation. This theory predicted that an oscillating charge would radiate energy in waves. The prediction was confirmed by Hertz (1887) who produced and detected electromagnetic waves with an oscillating electric circuit.

By 1890, the system of "natural philosophy" looked fairly satisfactory and complete. Not all known phenomena were fully explained, but each had a background that looked promising. In fact some scientists believed that all major discoveries had been made and that future research would be mere refinement of measurement.

Suddenly physicists were confronted with a remarkable series of discoveries. During the decade between 1895 and 1905:

Röntgen discovered x rays (1895).

Becquerel discovered radioactivity (1896).

Thomson identified electrons (1897).

Planck stated the basic postulate of quantum theory (1900).

Einstein formulated the basic viewpoint of relativity (1905).

These discoveries, in focusing attention on the structure of atoms, led to the profound change of viewpoint in physics implied by the contrasting terms *classical physics* and *modern physics*.

50-2. The Discovery of X Rays. At the time of Röntgen's discovery, the most active

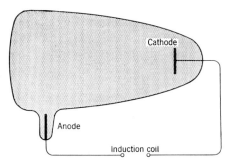

Fig. 1. Diagram of the Röntgen x-ray tube.

field of research in physics was that of electric discharge in gases at low pressure. Wilhelm Röntgen, professor of physics at Würzburg, studying the conduction of electricity in gas at low pressure covered the discharge tube with black paper. With the apparatus (Fig. 1) in a darkened room, he observed that a fluorescent screen nearby lighted up. Röntgen soon found that the agency that caused the fluorescence originated at the end of the tube where the cathode rays struck the glass wall. Röntgen recognized immediately the importance of his discovery and proceeded at once to study the properties of the new radiation that he called *x rays*.

Among the observations that were included in Röntgen's first report were the following:

1. Many substances fluoresce under the action of x rays.

2. Photographic plates are affected by x rays.

3. All substances are more or less transparent to x rays. Books and thin sheets of wood are very transparent; aluminum weakens the effect but does not destroy it. Lead glass is quite opaque but other glass of the same thickness is much more transparent. Dark shadows of the bones of the hand are apparent. The opacity of a substance is

found to depend not only on its density but also on some other property.

4. X rays travel in straight lines. Röntgen failed to find reflection or refraction of x rays because his apparatus was not sufficiently sensitive. Later both phenomena were observed.

5. X rays are not deflected by a magnetic field.

6. X rays discharge electrified bodies whether charged positively or negatively.

7. X rays are generated when cathode rays strike any solid body. Röntgen found that a heavier element such as platinum is a more efficient generator of x rays than a lighter element such as aluminum. He designed a tube using a concave cathode to concentrate the cathode rays on a platinum target set at an angle of 45°. This design became almost standard until the introduction of the high-vacuum Coolidge tube about 1913.

Within three months after the announcement of the discovery of x rays they were being used for medical purposes in the hospitals of Vienna.

50-3. Discoveries in the Field of X Rays. In the years following the discovery of x rays it was generally assumed that they are electromagnetic waves of very short wavelength. Since no means of deflecting them was known, most of the experiments depended upon absorption. It was found that when x rays fall on a particular substance, x rays are reemitted. These are fluorescent radiation. Barkla (1908), by the use of the rather crude absorption method, was able to show that some of the x rays emitted by the secondary material were scattered without change in quality but that others were characteristic of the fluorescing material and that this characteristic radiation consisted of at least two types, one more penetrating than the other. He called these K and L radiations.

In 1912, von Laue with Friedrich and Knipping succeeded in producing diffraction of x rays. A narrow pencil of x rays was passed through a zinc sulfide crystal and onto a

photographic plate. The central spot on the plate was surrounded by regularly spaced spots (Fig. 2). This was the first *direct* evidence of the wave nature of x rays. Also it showed that atoms are regularly spaced in the crystal.

Following the experiment of von Laue, W. H. and W. L. Bragg (1912), using the

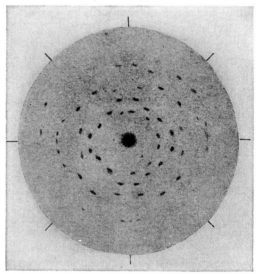

FIG. 2. Diffraction pattern formed by x rays passing through a crystal of zinc sulfide. (*This photograph is a copy of an original picture published by Friedrich, Knipping, and von Laue in 1913.*)

cleavage face of a crystal, obtained a type of reflection, really diffraction, as in the von Laue experiment. They assumed that the regularly spaced atoms of the crystal could be considered as in planes. If a set of planes is spaced a distance d apart in the crystal, the waves would be reflected in accordance with the equation

$$n\lambda = 2d \sin \theta \qquad (1)$$

The constant d could be computed from the atomic mass, the density, and Avogadro's number. By the use of the Bragg spectrometer (Fig. 3), it was first possible to measure the wavelengths of x rays. In these measurements the Braggs discovered in the x-ray beam rays that are characteristic of the material of the target. These are superimposed on a general x radiation.

Moseley (1913) studied these characteristic x rays systematically for many target elements. He identified them with Barkla's K and L radiation. He also found that there is a simple relation between the frequency of a

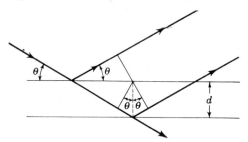

FIG. 3. Principle of the Bragg x-ray spectrometer. The parallel lines represent planes that are rich in atoms.

given line for successive elements and a *number* assigned to the elements in the order of their appearance in the periodic table

$$\sqrt{f} \propto Z$$

The number Z is called the *atomic number*.

The measurement of wavelengths of x rays made it possible to use them as tools for studying the arrangement of atoms in crystals. This use has given us extensive knowledge of such structure in crystals.

50-4. The Hydrogen Spectrum. An electric discharge in a gas at low pressure pro-

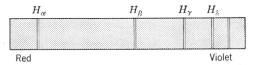

FIG. 4. Balmer series lines of hydrogen.

duces a glow of light whose wavelengths are characteristic of the particular gas (Chap. 45). It was early suspected that the light emitted by a gas is a clue to the structure of its individual atoms or molecules. Interest centered

on hydrogen, the simplest atom. By 1885 Balmer proposed an empirical formula to account for the four lines that he was able to see and measure, the so-called H_α, H_β, H_γ, and H_δ lines, Fig. 4. Balmer showed that the measured wavelengths fit the following formula:

$$\lambda = 3645.6 \, \frac{n^2}{n^2 - 4} \text{ Angstroms} \qquad (2)$$

$$n = 3, 4, 5, \cdots$$

This equation was rewritten by Rydberg in the form

$$\frac{1}{\lambda} = R \left(\frac{1}{2^2} - \frac{1}{n^2} \right) \qquad (3)$$

$$\begin{cases} n = 3,4,5, \cdots \\ R = 1.097 \times 10^{-3} \text{A}^{-1} \end{cases}$$

This Rydberg formula allows one to compute the wavelengths from differences between terms which turn out to be naturally connected with the process of radiation. The possibility of varying the constant term in Eq. (3) suggests other series. When the $1/2^2$ of Eq. (3) is replaced by $1/1^2$ the equation fits the Lyman series photographed in the ultraviolet. When $1/2^2$ is replaced by $1/3^2$ the equation fits the lines of the Paschen series in the infrared, Fig. 5.

While these formulas represented a remarkable achievement in discovering relationships among a large number of measured wavelengths, the equations were obtained by empirically fitting measured wavelength values. A derivation of the equations was not achieved until 1913, in terms of an atomic model and assumptions made by Niels Bohr.

50-5. The Nuclear Atom. Speculation as to the structure of atoms began soon afte their existence was accepted. Prout (1815)

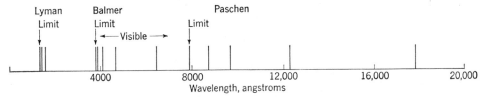

FIG. 5. Some series of spectral lines in the spectrum of hydrogen.

suggested that "all elements are made up of atoms of hydrogen." Since many of the elements were found to have atomic weights that were not exact multiples of that of hydrogen, the suggestion was not very seriously considered. After the discovery of radioactivity and the electron, interest in atomic structure became greater. The electrical nature of matter required that there be equal quantities of positive and negative electricity in the uncharged atom. J. J. Thomson suggested an atom model consisting of a sphere throughout which there is uniform distribution of positive electricity with electrons embedded within the sphere in such positions as to be stable. There was no evidence to support or to deny this model and it was retained until experimental evidence inconsistent with it was found.

Rutherford (1911) studied the scattering of α particles by gold foil. Using a thin beam of α particles he counted the flashes as they struck fluorescent material. He found that most of the α particles were scattered through small angles but that a few were deflected more than 90°. He was unable to explain these large angles of scattering on the basis of the Thomson atom model but could explain the large deflection on the assumption that *the positive charge is concentrated in a very small region, less than 10^{-12} cm in diameter*. The negative charge must therefore surround a positive *nucleus*.

50-6. The Bohr Atom Model. Niels Bohr (1913) combined several earlier developments to set up a specific picture of atomic structure. He assumed a nuclear atom with electrons moving in circular paths about the nucleus. This picture he applied to the simplest of all atoms, hydrogen.

He assumed that the atom obeys the laws of mechanics and electrostatics. He applied to the atom the quantum ideas of Planck. In applying the quantum idea, he assumed that the electrons are restricted to certain particular orbits: those for which the angular momentum of the electron is an integral multiple

of $h/2\pi$. A set of such orbits is shown in Fig. 6. He further assumed that there is no radiation as long as an electron remains in one orbit but that energy is absorbed by the atom when the electron is moved from an orbit of lower energy to one of higher energy and emitted

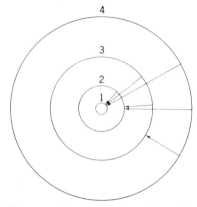

FIG. 6. Diagram of a few of the possible orbits in the Bohr atom model for hydrogen. The arrows indicate transitions that produce lines in the spectral series of hydrogen. Those ending at orbit 2 correspond to the red and blue lines of the spectrum of hydrogen produced in the ordinary Geissler tube (see Chap. 45).

when the electron moves in the reverse direction. Since there are only discrete orbits, this restriction requires that energy be absorbed or emitted in quanta.

The calculation of the frequencies of radiation emitted or absorbed may be outlined as follows. The centripetal force needed to hold the electron in its circular orbit is supplied by the electrostatic (Coulomb) force of attraction toward the nucleus

$$\frac{mv^2}{r} = \frac{Ze^2}{(4\pi\epsilon_0)r^2} \qquad \text{(for hydrogen, } Z = 1) \quad (4)$$

Since only those orbits are permitted for which

$$mvr = \frac{nh}{2\pi} \qquad (5)$$

the speed of the electron may be written

$$v = \frac{nh}{2\pi mr} \qquad (6)$$

From Eq. (4), the kinetic energy of the electron is

$$\frac{1}{2} mv^2 = \frac{Ze^2}{(4\pi\epsilon_0)2r}$$

Elimination of v from the last two equations gives for the radius of an orbit

$$r = \frac{n^2h^2(4\pi\epsilon_0)}{4\pi^2mZe^2} \qquad (7)$$

The potential energy of the electron at distance r from the nuclear charge Ze is

$$\frac{Ze}{(4\pi\epsilon_0)r}(-e) = -\frac{Ze^2}{(4\pi\epsilon_0)r} \qquad (8)$$

The total energy (sum of kinetic and potential) is

$$W = \frac{Ze^2}{(4\pi\epsilon_0)2r} + \left(-\frac{Ze^2}{(4\pi\epsilon_0)r}\right)$$
$$= -\frac{Ze^2}{(4\pi\epsilon_0)2r} = -\frac{2\pi^2mZ^2e^4}{(4\pi\epsilon_0)^2h^2} \times \frac{1}{n^2} \qquad (9)$$

The assumption that radiation is emitted only for an orbital transition and that the energy of the photon is given by

$$h\nu = W_i - W_f \qquad (10)$$

leads to an expression for the frequency of a spectrum line, when Eq. (9) is substituted for W

$$\nu = \frac{2\pi^2mZ^2e^4}{(4\pi\epsilon_0)^2h^3}\left(\frac{1}{n_f^2} - \frac{1}{n_i^2}\right)$$
$$= cR\left(\frac{1}{n_2^2} - \frac{1}{n_1^2}\right) \qquad (11)$$

To compare the predictions of the Bohr theory with the value of the Rydberg constant previously determined empirically, we may note that since $1/\lambda = \nu/c$, the constant R of Eq. (3) should be derivable from the atomic constants which appear in Eq. (11), that is

$$R = \frac{2\pi^2m(1)^2e^4}{(4\pi\epsilon_0)^2h^3c}$$

The value so calculated for R agrees fully with the empirical value. The Bohr model and assumptions predict the experimentally determined wavelengths in the various series of the spectrum of hydrogen.

Example: Calculate the wavelength of the first line in the visible (Balmer) series of the hydrogen spectrum.

$$\frac{1}{\lambda} = R\left(\frac{1}{n_2^2} - \frac{1}{n_1^2}\right) = 1.097 \times 10^{-3} \text{ A}\left(\frac{1}{2^2} - \frac{1}{3^2}\right)$$
$$= 1.52 \times 10^{-4} \text{ A}^{-1}$$
$$\lambda = 6560 \text{ A}$$

Example: Calculate the radius of the first Bohr orbit for hydrogen, and the speed of the electron in the first orbit.

$$r = n^2 \frac{h^2(4\pi\epsilon_0)}{4\pi^2me^2} =$$
$$(1)^2 \frac{(6.63 \times 10^{-34} \text{ joule-sec})^2}{4\pi^2 9.108 \times 10^{-31} \text{ kg } (1.60 \times 10^{-19} \text{ coulomb})^2}$$
$$\times \frac{1}{(8.99 \times 10^9 \text{ n-m}^2/\text{coulomb}^2)}$$
$$r = 0.53 \times 10^{-10} \text{ m}$$
$$v = \frac{1}{n}\frac{2\pi e^2}{h(4\pi\epsilon_0)} = \frac{2\pi(1.60 \times 10^{-19} \text{ coulomb})^2}{(1)6.63 \times 10^{-34} \text{ joule-sec}}$$
$$\times 8.99 \times 10^9 \frac{\text{n-m}^2}{\text{coulomb}^2} = 2.2 \times 10^6 \text{ m/sec}$$

Note that $v/c = 0.0073$ so that the relativity correction for increase in mass of the electron is slight.

From $m = \dfrac{m_0}{\sqrt{1 - \dfrac{v^2}{c^2}}}$, $m = 1.000027m_0$.

The Bohr atom model gave a basis of attack on all line spectra. It was not possible to compute completely the spectra of other more complicated atoms, but approximations were made that yielded satisfactory results. It was soon found that the picture was too simple to explain all the facts; however, certain fundamentals have remained. The nuclear atom with outside electrons is firmly established. The concrete picture of the orbits is not retained, but the concept of *energy levels* for the electrons in each atom remains. An atom is excited when an electron is moved from a lower (inner) energy level to a higher (outer) level, and a definite amount of energy is required to accomplish the change. Radiation accompanies the reverse transition. The energy is radiated in quanta whose size depends upon the energy change. All energy changes between atoms and radiation, whether absorption or emission, occur in quanta. Thus we have a sort of particle characteristic in these interchanges. The packets of energy are called *photons*. Each photon has energy $h\nu$.

50-7. Wave Mechanics. The success of the Bohr theory in the study of atomic spectra led to an examination of the relationship of particles and waves. Light has many characteristics that are essentially properties of waves. However, in those phenomena that involve transfer of energy, explanations require a type of particle nature. Thus there is a dual picture of light, part wave and part particle.

If light has a dual wave and particle nature, might not all particles also have a wave nature? Among those who considered this question was Louis de Broglie (1925). A photon has an energy $E = h\nu$. It can be assigned a mass from the relation $E = mc^2$. Equating these energies, one can express the wavelength of the photon in terms of the mass

$$mc^2 = h\nu = \frac{hc}{\lambda}$$

$$\lambda = \frac{h}{mc} \tag{12}$$

The product mc represents the momentum of the photon. Similarly, for a particle, we may assume a wavelength as h divided by the momentum

$$\lambda = \frac{h}{mv} \tag{13}$$

De Broglie carried this picture of particle waves over into the atom. The possible orbits in the atom would be those for which the circumference is a whole number of wavelengths. On this assumption de Broglie arrived at the same set of orbits for hydrogen as did Bohr.

Experimental confirmation of the wave na-ture of particles came not long after de Broglie's theoretical work. Computation showed that the wavelength of electrons accelerated by a relatively small potential would be about that of x rays. Davisson and Germer (1927) projected electrons at crystals of nickel and obtained diffraction patterns. G. P. Thomson (1927) projected beams of electrons through thin crystalline material and obtained patterns similar to those obtained by von Laue in his classical experiment with x rays. Thus the wave nature of particles was established. We now have an application of electron waves in the electron microscope.

The theoretical development of wave mechanics has provided a very powerful tool for the study of properties of matter.

SUMMARY

The discovery of *x rays* by Röntgen in 1895 opened a new era of advance in physics. X rays are of the same nature as light but of very short wavelength.

The discovery of *diffraction of x rays* by von Laue (1912) led to the Bragg crystal spectrometer, used for measurement of x-ray wavelengths, and to the use of x rays for determining crystal structure.

Experiments on the scattering of α particles at large angles led Rutherford (1911) to propose a *nuclear atom*, a positive nucleus surrounded by electrons.

Bohr (1913) applied the quantum theory to the nuclear atom to devise an atom model that was successfully used in computing wavelengths in the spectrum of hydrogen.

De Broglie (1922) proposed that particles be treated as waves. Wave properties of electrons were verified experimentally by Davisson and Germer and by G. P. Thomson.

REFERENCES

H. Geiger and E. Marsden, "The Laws of Deflexion of α Particles through Large Angles," *Phil. Mag.*, **25,** series 6: 604–623 (1913).

G. R. Harrison, R. C. Lord, and J. R.

Loofbourow, *Practical Spectroscopy*, Prentice-Hall, Inc., Englewood Cliffs, N. J., 1948.

Gerald Holton and Duane H. D. Roller, *Foundations of Modern Physical Science*, chap. 34, Addison-Wesley Publishing Company, Reading, Mass., 1958.

Otto Oldenberg, *Introduction to Atomic Physics*, chaps. 9 and 10, McGraw-Hill Book Company, Inc., New York, 1949.

Wolfgang Pauli (ed.), *Niels Bohr and the Development of Physics: Essays Dedicated to Niels Bohr on his Seventieth Birthday*, McGraw-Hill Book Company, Inc., New York, 1955.

E. Rutherford, "The Scattering of α and β Particles by Matter and the Structure of the Atom," *Phil. Mag.*, **21**, series 6: 669–688 (1911).

Harvey E. White, *Introduction to Atomic Spectra*, McGraw-Hill Book Company, Inc., New York, 1934.

QUESTIONS   **1.** When x-ray pictures of internal organs are made, one is frequently asked to drink a preparation containing heavy atoms. Why is this helpful in making the picture?

2. How do x rays ionize gases and produce chemical changes in organic substances?

3. If transfers of light energy always occur in quanta, why do we not perceive a discontinuous structure in light that comes to the eye?

4. Why are relativity changes seldom used in studying the mechanics of everyday objects?

5. State some of the observed facts that lead to the idea of the equivalence of matter and energy.

6. In a rock-salt crystal the atoms are at the corners of cubes. What various planes of atoms might be used in the reflection of x rays? How would the grating space depend upon the choice of plane?

7. How can x rays be used in determining the structure of crystals? Would they be of any use in studying a substance that has no crystalline structure?

8. Why are wave properties of particles normally observed only when we study very small particles?

9. If both matter and radiation have both particle and wave properties, how can we decide which property to use?

PROBLEMS   *In the following problems, use the electronic charge as* 1.60×10^{-19} *coulomb and the electronic mass at rest as* 9.11×10^{-31} *kg.*

1. The minimum wavelength in angstrom units of the x radiation produced when electrons are accelerated by a potential difference V is given by $\lambda = 12{,}345/V$. Justify the expression on the basis of the quantum equation.

2. What would be the wavelength of the radiation emitted if an electron that had been accelerated by a potential difference of 300 volts had all its kinetic energy transformed into a single quantum?   *Ans.* 41.3 A

3. What would be the wavelength of the quantum of radiant energy emitted if an electron were transmuted into radiation and went into one quantum?

4. If the grating space of a calcite crystal is 3.03 A, find the wavelength of x rays that are reflected at an angle of 15.0° in the first order.   *Ans.* 1.57 A

5. In crystals of rock salt the atoms are set at the corners of cubes, 2.81 A on a side. Compute the angle in the first and the second order at which x rays of wavelength 0.721 A would be reflected.

6. Compute the ratio of the gravitational attraction to the electrostatic (Coulomb) attraction between electron and proton separated by 0.53 A in a hydrogen atom. Does this justify neglect of gravitational forces in the Bohr theory?   *Ans.* 4.4×10^{-40}

7. Justify the following statement: "The observation that the lines in the spectrum of hydrogen are very sharp is evidence that all electrons have exactly the same charge, e."

8. Find the frequency of revolution f of the electron circling about a nucleus of charge Ze in terms of the quantum number n.   *Ans.* $f = 4\pi^2 m Z^2 e^4 / n^3 h^3 (4\pi\epsilon_0)^2$

9. Construct an energy-level diagram for hydrogen. (*a*) Compute the energies of the first six states, in electron volts. (*b*) Calculate the wavelengths for the first two lines and the series limit for the Lyman, Balmer, and Paschen series.

10. Assume that a free electron having kinetic energy of 2.42×10^{-13} erg unites with a H^+ atom, goes to the lowest ($n = 1$) level, and gives up its energy in radiating a single photon. Find the frequency of the radiation.

Ans. 3.65×10^{15}/sec

11. (*a*) Discuss the possibility of observing the Balmer series in absorption. (*b*) If a tube containing atomic hydrogen is irradiated by an ultraviolet source at a wavelength of 974 A, what state would be excited? What wavelengths might be emitted? (*c*) Through what potential difference would a beam of electrons have to be passed to excite this same state by collision? (*d*) At what temperature would the average energy of the hydrogen atoms correspond to the energy of this state?

12. The bright yellow line in the helium spectrum has a wavelength of 5876 A. Compute the difference in energy between the two levels responsible for this line.   *Ans.* 3.38×10^{-19} joule

13. The red and blue lines of the hydrogen spectrum have wavelengths of 6563 A and 4861 A, respectively. Compute the difference in energy between the corresponding energy levels.

14. An electron is accelerated by a potential difference of 1.25 kv. What is the wavelength associated with the moving electron? Neglect any change in mass of the electron.   *Ans.* 0.347 A

15. (*a*) What is the de Broglie wavelength of an electron with an energy of 45 ev? (*b*) of a 3.6-Mev alpha particle? (*c*) of a grain of sand of mass 1.6 milligrams blown by the wind at 25 mi/hr?

16. What would be the wavelength associated with an electron whose speed is half the speed of light?   *Ans.* 0.04 A

51. *Solid State Electronics*

We have a convincing theory, based on the nuclear atom and quantum mechanics, which tells us that under ordinary conditions of temperature and pressure the nuclei of atoms will never get very close to one another. The combination of atoms should therefore be explainable entirely through the exchange or sharing of electrons. In terms of the easily measured masses and charges of nuclei, it should be possible to describe the formation of molecules and chemical reactions. One might expect to be able to describe crystal lattices and the mechanical, thermal, and electrical properties of solids. Practically, the difficulty is the complexity of the computations. We shall summarize in this chapter some of the successes of quantum mechanics in explaining important electric and magnetic properties of solids. This comprises but one segment of solid state physics in which there is very active research.

51-1. Distribution of Electron Speeds. The best conductors of electricity are also the best conductors of heat. Wiedemann and Franz (1850) showed that for a given temperature the ratio of thermal conductivity to electric conductivity is nearly the same for all good conductors. A classical theory proposed by Drude and Lorentz, soon after the discovery of the electron, assumed, as have later theories, that some of the electrons are free to travel throughout the whole volume of a crystalline material. These electrons dart around in all directions with the high speeds of thermal agitation. But if an electric field is applied the "electron atmosphere" experiences a relatively slow drift, superposed on the random thermal motion. The electron drift is the electric current. The transfer of any increase in the energy of random motion in any direction constitutes thermal conduction. To make quantitative predictions it is necessary to make some assumptions about the distribution of electron speeds. Theories have differed in these assumptions.

The classical theory assumed that the electron speeds followed the same distribution law as Maxwell and Boltzmann had used for molecular speeds in developing a successful kinetic theory of gases. Among a large number N of electrons, the fractional number N_v having speed v is given by

$$\frac{N_v}{N} = \frac{4}{\sqrt{\pi}} \left(\frac{m}{2kT} \right)^{3/2} v^2 \epsilon^{-mv^2/2kT} \qquad (1)$$

If we plot this expression against v, the area under the curve (Fig. 1a) between v_1 and v_2 equals the fraction of all the electrons whose

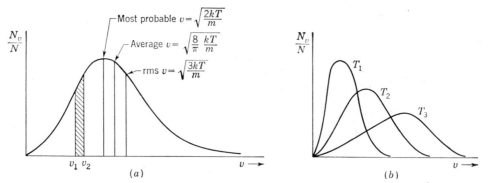

Fig. 1. (a) Graph of Maxwell-Boltzmann speed distribution function. (b) Distribution function at three different temperatures, $T_3 > T_2 > T_1$.

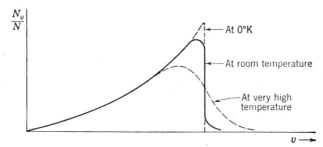

Fig. 2. Fermi distribution of speeds at various temperatures.

speeds are between v_1 and v_2. Since kinetic energy depends on the speed squared, the average kinetic energy depends on the average of the squares of the speeds. The square root of this average is called the root-mean-square (rms) speed. It is somewhat larger than the most probable speed and the average speed (Fig. 1a). It will be noted that the distribution curve becomes flatter and the maximum shifts toward higher speeds as the temperature increases (Fig. 1b).

Fermi introduced a radically different description of the free electrons in a metal. He incorporated the exclusion principle which Pauli had used to explain the periodicity of chemical properties of the elements when arranged in order of increasing atomic number. According to Pauli's principle, no two electrons in an atom can have the same quantum numbers. According to Fermi, the "free" electrons in a metal also are quantized and no two can act exactly alike. Momenta

are quantized; only two electrons (having opposite spins) can have a given momentum. As the temperature is lowered, electrons settle down by quantized steps to lower momentum values. But as a consequence of the exclusion principle some electrons will remain at momentum values considerably above zero, that is, they will have appreciable energy, even at absolute zero temperature. When the temperature rises, only the electrons of highest momentum can accept thermal energy and move to still higher momentum values.

The Fermi distribution law is expressed by

$$\frac{N_v}{N} = \frac{8\pi m^3}{h^3} \times \frac{v^2}{\epsilon^{(mv^2/2 - w_m/kT)} + 1} \qquad (2)$$

where w_m is the maximum energy an electron can have at 0°K. In Fig. 2 the progressive rounding of the curve as temperature increases represents the shift of some electrons to higher energies. The Fermi distribution curve should be compared with the Maxwell distribution, Fig. 1*b*.

51-2. Specific Heats. When thermal energy is added to a metal, the large number of free electrons sharing the energy should make a substantial contribution to the spe-

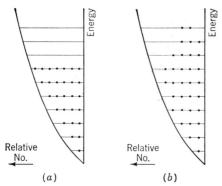

Fig. 3. Fermi distribution of energies showing (*a*) all levels filled up to a maximum, at 0°K, (*b*) some electrons promoted to higher energy levels at a high temperature.

cific heat, according to the Maxwell theory. Experimentally, however, the specific heats of most metals are close to the values attributable to the thermal agitation of the atoms themselves. The electrons absorb a negligible amount of thermal energy.

The Fermi theory successfully accounts for the slight participation of electrons in specific heats. In Fig. 3, the Fermi distribution of energy (instead of speed) is plotted, with higher energy states higher on the diagram. At 0°K all energy states are occupied up to a certain maximum (Fig. 3*a*). At a higher temperature some electrons in upper levels have been able to accept energy and move to still higher levels (Fig. 3*b*). But owing to quantum restrictions, relatively few electrons have participated in the temperature rise. The Fermi theory predicts that electrons in a conductor should contribute roughly 1 per cent of the amount predicted by the Maxwell theory, in agreement with experimental measurements of specific heats.

51-3. Conduction in Metals. The fact that all energy levels, up to a certain maximum,

are filled means that for every electron traveling to the right in a metal there is another electron traveling toward the left. Thus all electrical conduction in the metal must be due to the relatively few electrons near the top of the distribution (Fig. 3*a*) which can

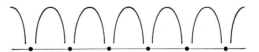

Fig. 4. Variation of potential along a one-dimensional crystal lattice.

be excited easily to an unoccupied quantum level. One concludes that electricity must be conducted by only a small fraction of all the free electrons (rather than by all, as assumed in the classical theory). In turn, this implies that an electron must be able to travel long distances without being bumped by ions in the crystal lattice. The free-electron quantum theory, like the classical theory, is unable to account for the distinction between conductors and insulators.

In the modern band theory of the electronic structure of solids, the effects of the lattice ions on the free electrons are considered to explain the occurrence of conductors, insulators, and semiconductors. The moving electrons are pictured in terms of de Broglie waves (Chap. 50) of wavelength $\lambda = h/mv$. The influence of the lattice ions arises from the variation of potential from atom to atom in the crystal, Fig. 4. The passage of the de Broglie waves is treated mathematically by methods similar to those used in investigating the passage of light waves through a similar lattice.

It turns out that the graph of electron kinetic energy against momentum instead of having the parabolic shape (Fig. 5*a*) which it would have in a conductor where there was no variation in potential, jumps discontinuously for particular values of de Broglie wavelength (Fig. 5*b*). Not all electron momenta are possible. From this point of view, the effect of the ion lattice is to pre-

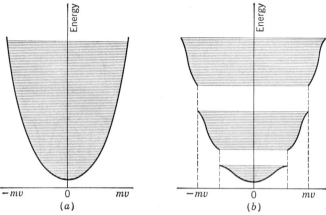

FIG. 5. Energy versus momentum, (*a*) assuming no variation of potential between atoms, and (*b*) assuming a potential variation similar to that of Fig. 4.

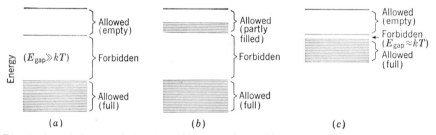

FIG. 6. Distribution of electrons in bands in (*a*) an insulator, (*b*) a conductor, and (*c*) a semiconductor.

clude certain values of electron momentum and hence to leave forbidden energy gaps at these momentum values.

The properties of conductors, insulators, and semiconductors can now be interpreted in terms of the conduction bands, Fig. 6. If the highest energy band containing electrons is full and is appreciably separated from other bands (*a*), the material is an *insulator*. To produce a current in such a material, electrons have to be advanced across an energy gap large compared to thermal energy kT. In a *conductor*, however, the highest band containing electrons is not full (*b*). Even a small external field can produce an unbalanced momentum distribution (a current) by promoting electrons to energy states of small excitation. *Semiconductors* are an intermediate case in which the highest occupied band is full (*c*), but the energy jump to the next band is comparable to kT. Increase in temperature

would be expected to lower the resistance of a semiconductor.

51-4. Thermistor. A resistance element made of a semiconducting material which has a high negative coefficient of resistivity is called a *thermistor*. One form, a bead thermistor, comprises a small bead of semiconducting material attached between two

FIG. 7. A bead thermistor.

wire leads (Fig. 7). It may be used for power measurements at microwave frequencies, for temperature measurements, and for the sensitive element in protective devices.

51-5. Transistor. A transistor (Chap. 39) consists of a semiconducting material to which contact is made by three or more electrodes and which may provide electronic rectification, or amplification, or both. A space charge layer is present at the rectifying junction between the base and the collector. By injecting, from an emitter, carriers of the opposite sign, the current carried by the junction can be varied and controlled. In practice this is accomplished in various ways.

Unlike a vacuum electron tube, a transistor requires no heater current, is small and light, and can be made mechanically strong and long-lasting. The transistor operates at relatively low voltage and relatively high current, but effects associated with the transit time of carriers limit the frequency response of the transistor. Its characteristics also are dependent on temperature.

REFERENCES

Adrianus J. Dekker, *Solid State Physics*, Prentice-Hall, Inc., Englewood Cliffs, N. J., 1957.

Charles Kittel, *Introduction to Solid State Physics*, 2d ed., John Wiley & Sons, Inc., New York, 1956.

George E. Pake, "Magnetic Resonance," *Sci. American*, **199**: 2, 58–66 (1958).

F. O. Rice and E. Teller, *Structure of Matter*, John Wiley & Sons, Inc., New York, 1949.

John C. Slater, *Introduction to Chemical Physics*, McGraw-Hill Book Company, Inc., New York, 1939.

Robert L. Sproull, *Modern Physics: A Textbook for Engineers*, John Wiley & Sons, Inc., New York, 1956.

52. *Nuclear Physics*

In one sense, nuclear physics started with the establishment of the Rutherford-Bohr picture of the atom as a nucleus surrounded by moving electrons. Experimental evidence about the nature of the nucleus started with the discovery, in 1896, of radioactivity, the spontaneous disintegration of unstable nuclei. The first artificial transmutation of one element into another was achieved by Rutherford in 1919; this was the start of the study of nuclear processes of such importance today.

52-1. The Discovery of Radioactivity. The discovery of radioactivity was a direct result of the discovery of x rays. Since cathode rays in striking a target produce x rays and also produce fluorescence on striking certain materials, the question of a connection between fluorescence and x rays was raised. In 1896, Becquerel tested this connection using a fluorescent salt of uranium. He found that even when the specimen was not irradiated it emitted a radiation that penetrated dark paper, thin foils, and other substances. Becquerel shortly discovered that this radiation was characteristic of uranium and that the physical or chemical state of the specimen did not affect the radiation. Other materials, such as thorium, were soon found to show the same properties as uranium. Pierre and Marie Curie discovered two new elements, radium and polonium, that are *radioactive*, radium being much more active than uranium.

It was discovered that the rays from these materials would affect photographic plates and ionize gases as well as produce fluorescence. As the properties were studied, evidence developed that there are three kinds of rays. One is deflected slightly in a magnetic field in the direction that a moving positive charge would be deflected and is called an α ray. A second, the β ray, is deflected in the magnetic field much more than the α ray and in the opposite direction. The third, the γ ray, is not deflected in the field.

Later experiments showed α rays to be positively charged helium atoms, β rays to be electrons, and γ rays to be electromagnetic radiation of very short wavelength.

52-2. Early Experiments in Radioactivity. The early experiments in the study of radioactivity were almost exclusively in the problems of the nature and properties of the rays themselves. We have noted that the α and β rays can be deflected by magnetic and electric fields, all affect a photographic plate or a fluorescent screen, all are more or less penetrating, and all produce ionization. These properties were further investigated and used in studying the rays.

It was found that α rays are stopped rather easily; a sheet of paper is sufficient. In air at normal atmospheric pressure, the range is a relatively few centimeters. The ranges of the α particles are quite different for the various radioactive substances.

The penetrating power of β rays is much greater than that for α rays. The range may be as great as several meters in air or more than a millimeter of aluminum.

The γ rays are much more penetrating than the β rays. They are little absorbed in air and pass through several inches of lead.

The nature of the rays was determined by a series of experiments. The β rays were shown to be negatively charged by their deflection in magnetic and electric fields. When the ratio of charge to mass was measured (Chap. 39), it was found to be the same as that for cathode rays. Thus the β rays were identified as very high-speed electrons.

The properties of α rays were also studied by deflection in magnetic and electric fields. By combining the two effects it was possible to compute the speed of the α particles and also the ratio of charge to mass. This latter quantity was found to be about twice that for an ionized hydrogen atom. Rutherford and Geiger measured the charge of the α particle by means of two experiments. The α particles from a known mass of a radioactive material fell on a metal plate for a certain time giving

it their total charge. The plate was connected to an electrometer to measure the charge. The number of particles in that time was determined by means of a "counter" (Fig. 1). A metal cylinder C has a wire W insulated from the cylinder along the axis. The

FIG. 1. Diagram of a Geiger counter.

cylinder is filled with gas at low pressure and a potential slightly less than that required for a discharge is maintained between cylinder and wire. A thin window allows α particles to enter the chamber. Each particle ionizes the gas, producing a rush of charge indicated by a throw of the electrometer E. Thus one can count the number of particles. This device is known as a *Geiger counter*. It has been greatly refined and can be used to "count" particles or radiation that enter the chamber and ionize the gas inside.

From the measurement of charge and number of particles Rutherford and Geiger determined the charge of the α particle. The value was found to be about twice that for the hydrogen atom and therefore the α particle has a mass four times that of hydrogen. This indicates a doubly charged helium atom.

The fact that α particles are charged helium atoms was confirmed by a direct experiment. The α particles were allowed to bombard a glass tube whose walls were thin enough for the particles to penetrate. An electric discharge showed no evidence of a helium spectrum in the tube before the bombardment but after considerable time there was a well-defined helium spectrum.

52-3. Ionization of Gases in Radioactivity. When a high-speed α or β particle moves through a gas, there are frequent collisions between the particles and the molecules of the gas. In these collisions ionization is produced. The number of ions produced by the particle is a measure of the energy of the particle. Thus an ionization chamber could be used for such measurements. From the ionization current in the chamber and the number of particles per second, the number of ions produced per particle can be determined. The α particle is much more efficient in ionizing than the β particle and the β particle

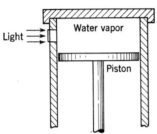

FIG. 2. Schematic diagram of a Wilson cloud chamber.

much better than the γ ray. The ionization is in the ratios of 10,000 to 100 to 1.

In 1897, C. T. R. Wilson observed that in air supersaturated with water vapor ions would serve as condensation centers, droplets forming on the ions. Later (1912), he applied this discovery to make an instrument for studying the paths of particles or rays that can ionize the gas through which they pass. In the original form (Fig. 2), the device consists of a piston above which there is a chamber in which the air is saturated with water vapor. If the piston is suddenly moved downward, the air is cooled, and hence the vapor present is more than that required for saturation. If there are condensation centers present, droplets of water will be formed. The ions formed by passage of an ionizing particle or ray can serve as the condensation centers. The ions are formed along the path of the particle or ray and hence the droplets mark the path. When brightly illuminated, these droplets can be seen or photographed. This device, known as the *Wilson cloud chamber*, has proved to be one of the most useful devices for studying the paths of particles and rays. Many important discoveries have been made possible by its use.

The paths of α and β particles were studied. The massive α particles are not easily deflected by collisions and many ions are

formed. Thus the tracks of α particles are mainly heavy and straight with an occasional fork near the end of the path where a near direct hit on an atom causes both atom and α particle to show tracks (Fig. 3).

On the other hand β particles produce much less ionization and hence lighter tracks.

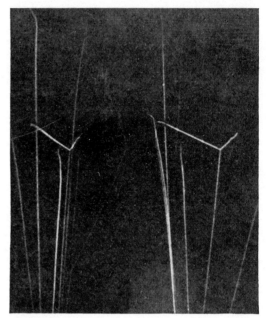

FIG. 3. Photograph of α-particle tracks in a cloud chamber. (*Courtesy of P. M. S. Blackett and Proceedings of the Royal Society.*)

Having small mass they are easily deflected and follow very crooked paths as they are deflected by one collision after another.

52-4. Radioactive Series. In the study following the discovery of radioactivity, quite a number of substances were found to show activity. Most of these are the elements of high atomic mass and high atomic number. It was found that certain of these materials were associated with each other in series, the successive members being formed by the disintegration of the preceding member.

Since α particles are helium nuclei with a double positive charge, they can come only from the nucleus, for only in the nucleus is there such mass. With the loss of an α particle, the nucleus must decrease in mass by four

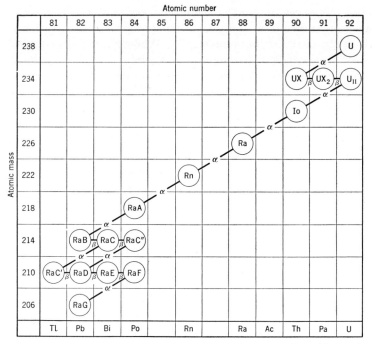

FIG. 4. Successive disintegrations in the radioactive series starting with uranium.

units (the atomic mass of helium) and decrease in charge (atomic number) by two. Since the chemical nature of the atom is associated with the atomic number, the emission of the alpha particle creates a new substance of lower atomic number. Thus uranium, atomic mass 238 and atomic number 92, emits an α particle to form a new atom, uranium X, with an atomic mass of 234 and atomic number 90. When a β particle is emitted, there is no appreciable change in atomic mass, but the charge is increased by one, and hence the atomic number is raised by one. In Fig. 4 is shown the successive transformations in the series headed by uranium. Note that in several places members of the chain are isotopes, being in the same atomic number column. The end product of the series, RaG, is lead.

52-5. Statistical Law of Radioactive Decay. The activity of a radioactive sample (the number of disintegrations per second) decreases with time. Each radioactive isotope has its own characteristic rate of decrease.

In Fig. 5 is the decay curve for a radioisotope which decreases in activity by 50 per cent every 4 hr. The curve suggests that the decay is a logarithmic function of time. If the logarithm of activity is plotted versus time, a

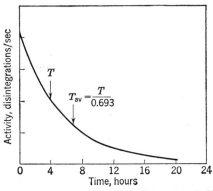

FIG. 5. Decay of a radioisotope with a 4-hr half-life.

straight line results, showing that the activity is an exponential (or logarithmic) function of time.

We can derive such an exponential decay law if we assume that: (1) disintegrations occur at random, (2) a large number of radioactive atoms are present, so that statistical methods apply, and (3) the number ΔN of atoms which disintegrate in a time Δt is proportional to the number N of atoms present. Then the decrease in the number of parent atoms is given by

$$-\Delta N = \lambda N \, \Delta t \qquad (1)$$

where λ is called the *disintegration constant*. It represents the fractional number of radioactive atoms decaying per unit time:

$$\lambda = -\Delta N / N \, \Delta t$$

One can express the number N of radioactive atoms remaining after time t in terms of the number N_0 originally present at time $t = 0$.

$$N = N_0 e^{-\lambda t} \qquad (2)$$

The time at which the number of radioactive atoms remaining is just one-half the original number is called the *half-life*, T. Its relation to the disintegration constant is apparent from

$$\frac{N}{N_0} = \frac{1}{2} = e^{-\lambda T}$$

$$T = \frac{\ln 2}{\lambda} = \frac{0.693}{\lambda} \qquad (3)$$

The *average* lifetime T_a of a single atom may be calculated by summing the lives of all the atoms and dividing by the original number of atoms. The result is

$$T_a = \frac{1}{\lambda} \qquad (4)$$

The average lifetime is the reciprocal of the disintegration constant.

The unit of activity, the *curie*, is defined as that quantity of any radioactive material which gives 3.70×10^{10} disintegrations per second. Since the curie is a relatively large unit, the *millicurie* (1 mc = 0.001 curie) and the *microcurie* (1 μc = 10^{-6} curie) are widely used. A counter near a radioactive source detects a certain fraction of the particles

emitted, and the counting rate is proportional to the activity of the source.

When the elements in a radioactive series are allowed to accumulate and to come into equilibrium, the number $N_1 \lambda_1$ of atoms of any one isotope which decay per unit time is equal to the number $N_2 \lambda_2$ of atoms of the next isotope which decay per unit time, or

$$N_1 \lambda_1 = N_2 \lambda_2 = N_3 \lambda_3 \cdots \text{(equilibrium)} \quad (5)$$

Example: The half-life of radon is 3.80 days. After how many days will only one-sixteenth of a radon sample remain?

Solution A: After 3.80 days, one-half of the original sample remains. In the next 3.80 days, one-half of this decays so that after 7.60 days one-fourth of the original amount remains. After 11.4 days, one-eighth of the original amount remains, and after four half-lives (15.2 days), one-sixteenth of the original amount remains.

Solution B:

$$\lambda = \frac{\ln 2}{T} = \frac{0.693}{3.80 \text{ days}} = 0.182/\text{day}$$

We want $N/N_0 = \frac{1}{16} = e^{-\lambda t} = e^{-0.182t}$

$$-0.182t = \ln(\frac{1}{16}) = -2.77$$

so that $\qquad t = 15.2$ days

Example: Find the activity of a 1.0-gm sample of radium ($_{88}\text{Ra}^{226}$) whose half-life is 1620 years.

The decay constant is

$$\lambda = \frac{0.693}{1620 \text{ years}} = 4.2810^{-4}/\text{yr} = 1.36 \times 10^{-11}/\text{sec}$$

One gram of Ra^{226} contains a number of atoms equal to

$$N = \frac{6.025 \times 10^{23} \text{ atoms/mole} \times 1.0 \text{ gm}}{226 \text{ gm/mole}}$$
$$= 2.7 \times 10^{21} \text{ atoms}$$

Hence
Activity = $N(1.36 \times 10^{-11}/\text{sec})(2.7 \times 10^{21} \text{ atoms})$

$$= 3.6 \times 10^{10} \frac{\text{disintegrations}}{\text{sec}}$$

$$= 0.97 \text{ curie}$$

(The activity calculated is due to the Ra^{226} isotope only. An actual sample of radium would show additional activity from the radioactive decay products of Ra^{226}.)

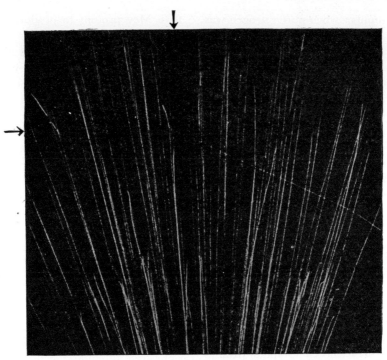

FIG. 6. Cloud-chamber photograph of the first artificial disintegration, discovered by Rutherford. The proton track slopes downward to the right and the recoil nucleus moves upward and to the left. Origin of these particles indicated by the arrows. (*After Blackett and Lees.*)

Example: It is found that 0.338 microgram of radium is in equilibrium with 1.00 gm of U^{238}. Find the half-life of U^{238}.

$$\lambda_1 N_1 = \lambda_2 N_2$$

$$\lambda_1 \times \frac{6.025 \times 10^{23}}{238}$$

$$= \frac{0.693}{1620 \text{ yr}} \frac{0.338 \times 10^{-6}}{226} 6.025 \times 10^{23}$$

$$T_1 = \frac{0.693}{\lambda_1} = \frac{226}{238} \times \frac{1620 \text{ yr}}{0.338 \times 10^{-6}}$$

$$= 4.55 \times 10^9 \text{ yr}$$

52-6. Artificial Disintegration. In natural radioactivity the rate of disintegration is independent of the physical condition of the active material. Attempts to retard or hasten the process produce no result.

In scattering experiments that led to the nuclear atom theory, the scattering atoms were all very much heavier than the α particles, so that the motion of the scattering nucleus was negligible. If light atoms are used, both α particle and scattering nucleus move after the collision in such a manner that there is conservation of energy and conservation of momentum in the collision. Such collisions cause the forked tracks occasionally seen in cloud-chamber pictures (Figs. 3 and 6). Rutherford (1918) bombarded air in a cloud chamber with α particles. He found some of the tracks produced after a collision were those of protons (hydrogen nuclei) of unusually long range. Such a track is shown in Fig. 6. The location of the collision is shown by the arrows. The track of the proton slopes downward to the right. If these protons were due to collisions with hydrogen atoms in the air, for the α particles used the range of the protons would be about 28 cm, whereas the observed range was about 40 cm. Furthermore, the protons were found to take almost any direction from the point of collision, whereas hydrogen nuclei must have forward directions only. The long-range particles were found only when nitrogen was present and increased in number when pure nitrogen was used. It was thus shown that the proton was produced when the α particle collided with a nitrogen nucleus. Furthermore, there was no evidence of a recoil α particle after the collision. Thus the α particle strikes and becomes part of the nitrogen nucleus, a proton being emitted by the resulting nucleus. We thus have the first artificial *transmutation* (change from one element to another). In this process the mass and the charge must stay essentially the same. We can write an equation to represent the transition

$$_7N^{14} + {}_2He^4 \rightarrow {}_9F^{18} \rightarrow {}_8O^{17} + {}_1H^1$$

The subscripts represent atomic number (charge) while the superscripts represent atomic mass.

52-7. Production of High-energy Particles. After the first discovery of artificial disintegration, a number of other substances were found to show the same type of disintegration upon being struck by α particles. Disintegration will occur only if the α particle enters the nucleus. Since both particle and nucleus are positive, the α particle is repelled, and hence must have high energy to reach the nucleus. The higher the charge, the more energy is required for the α particle; hence the higher atomic number elements are not readily disintegrated by natural α particles. Protons, having less charge than α particles, could penetrate nuclei more readily if given high energy. Cockcroft and Walton (1930) were the first to produce protons with energy high enough to cause disintegration. They used transformers and vacuum-tube rectifiers in series to produce a potential of 700 kv. The energy gained by the charged particle is Vq. Particle energies are frequently expressed in terms of *electron volts*, an electron volt being the energy gained by an electron in falling through a potential difference of one volt. A larger unit, a million electron volts (Mev), is commonly used as an energy unit. Particles of about 1 Mev have been produced by the method of Cockcroft and Walton. They used

0.15 Mev protons to produce disintegration of lithium.

A second method used an alternating potential of a few thousand volts to accelerate the particles successively. Several cylinders are arranged in series with gaps between

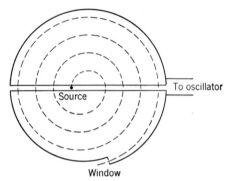

Fig. 7. Diagram of the cyclotron.

them. Alternate cylinders are connected to one side of the line. If the length of each cylinder is so made that the particles traverse it in a half cycle, the particle is accelerated at each gap and acquires high speed.

One of the most important methods for production of high-speed ions is the *cyclotron*, invented by E. O. Lawrence (1930). The cyclotron (Fig. 7) consists of a chamber in which are two semicircular, hollow metal boxes insulated from each other. The chamber is placed between the poles of a very strong electromagnet. An ion introduced near the center will travel in a semicircular path within one box. As it crosses from one box to the other, it is accelerated so that in the second box it moves in a larger circular path. The radius of the path may be obtained by equating the centripetal force mv^2/r to the centrally directed force Bqv exerted by the magnetic field B on the particle of charge q,

$$r = \frac{mv}{Bq} \qquad (6)$$

The time for the ion to travel a semicircle is

$$\frac{T}{2} = \frac{\pi r}{v} = \frac{\pi m}{Bq} \qquad (7)$$

which is independent of both the speed v of the ion and of the radius r of its path. A high-frequency alternating potential can be used to accelerate the ions each time they cross from one D-shaped chamber to another. The ions continue on a kind of spiral path, gaining kinetic energy on each crossing but remaining in phase with the alternating voltage. After many trips around the D's the high-energy ions come out a window.

By introducing various gases into the chamber to be ionized, many different kinds of particles can be produced. The most used are protons (hydrogen nuclei), deutrons (heavy hydrogen nuclei), and α particles (helium nuclei). Large cyclotrons may produce 10-Mev protons, 20-Mev deuterons, and 40-Mev α particles.

A proton with energy 4.7 Mev has a speed one-tenth that of light and experiences an appreciable relativity increase in mass. The increase of mass with speed causes higher energy ions to lag in phase with respect to the alternating voltage. This relativistic effect places a practical limit on the ion energies attainable with a conventional cyclotron.

The frequency-modulated cyclotron, or synchrocyclotron, starts with a frequency $Bq/2\pi m_0$ [see Eq. (7)] and then lowers the frequency rapidly as the ion increases in speed and in mass. This cycle is repeated hundreds of times per second to produce pulses of ions with energies as high as 500 Mev.

A source of high-speed electrons is the *betatron*. It has a chamber within a magnetic field into which electrons are introduced. The magnet is energized by alternating current and serves to accelerate the electrons during a part of a cycle and to provide an increasing field to keep them in their circular paths as the speed increases. Electrons have been accelerated to energies of the order of 350 Mev. Because of the loss of energy by radiation the practical limit is probably of the order of 1000 Mev (1 Bev). The very high energy electrons have speeds greater than 0.9999 times that of light and their mass is several hundred times the rest mass.

The *synchrotron* differs from the betatron in that the acceleration is achieved by a high-frequency field at a gap as in the cyclotron but it has the rising field of the betatron. Proton-synchrotrons provide very high energy particles, of the order of 1 to 6 Bev.

52-8. Disintegration by Accelerated Particles. By the use of accelerated particles many disintegrations can be produced. The particle energies attainable are sufficient for the particles to penetrate to the nucleus of most atoms and produce disintegration. The following equations represent examples of the many reactions that can occur.

Proton:

$$_4\text{Be}^9 + {}_1\text{H}^1 \rightarrow {}_3\text{Li}^6 + {}_2\text{He}^4$$

Deuteron:

$$_{13}\text{Al}^{27} + {}_1\text{H}^2 \rightarrow {}_{12}\text{Mg}^{25} + {}_2\text{He}^4$$

α particle:

$$_{13}\text{Al}^{27} + {}_2\text{He}^4 \rightarrow {}_{14}\text{Si}^{30} + {}_1\text{H}^1$$

Many of the products of these artificial disintegrations are radioactive. These *artificially radioactive* materials behave much as the natural radioactive materials. Each emits its characteristic particle (not always an α or β particle); each has a characteristic half-life period. The following equations represent one such change.

$$_{48}\text{Pd}^{108} + {}_2\text{He}^4 \rightarrow {}_{47}\text{Ag}^{111} + {}_1\text{H}^1$$
$$_{47}\text{Ag}^{111} \rightarrow {}_{48}\text{Cd}^{111} + {}_{-1}e^0$$
$$T = 7.5 \text{ days}$$

where T is the half-life period.

52-9. Mass-Energy Transitions. In the nuclear reactions just discussed there are many changes that involve an increase or decrease in total mass. In considering the energy relations involved in the changes, we must study the change in mass as well as the energies of the moving particles. Whenever there is a change in mass, energy $E = \Delta mc^2$

must be absorbed or emitted. Masses of the atoms are usually expressed in *atomic mass units* (amu). An amu is $\frac{1}{16}$ the mass of $_8O^{16}$ or 1 amu = 1.660×10^{-24} gm. A change of mass of 1 amu involves an energy of

$$E = \Delta mc^2 = 1.660 \times 10^{-24} \text{ gm}$$
$$\times (2.998 \times 10^{10} \text{ cm/sec})^2$$
$$= 14.94 \times 10^{-4} \text{ erg} = 14.94 \times 10^{-11} \text{ joule}$$
$$1 \text{ Mev} = 10^6 \text{ volts} \times 1.602$$
$$\times 10^{-19} \text{ coulomb} = 1.602 \times 10^{-13} \text{ joule}$$
$$1 \text{ amu} = 14.94 \times 10^{-11}/1.602 \times 10^{-13}$$
$$= 931 \text{ Mev}$$

Consider the transition involved in Rutherford's first disintegration experiment

$$_7N^{14} + _2He^4 \rightarrow _9F^{18} \rightarrow _8O^{17} + _1H^1$$

The mass of the initial α particle and nitrogen is

$$(m_N) \qquad (m_{He})$$
$$14.00753 \text{ amu} + 4.00389 \text{ amu}$$
$$= 18.01142 \text{ amu}$$

The mass of the final products, oxygen and hydrogen nucleus, is

$$(_8O^{17}) \qquad (_1H^1)$$
$$17.00450 \text{ amu} + 1.00813 \text{ amu}$$
$$= 18.01263 \text{ amu}$$

There is a gain in mass in the process of 0.00121 amu. This gain in mass must come at the expense of energy

$$E = 0.00121 \times 931 \text{ Mev} = 1.12 \text{ Mev}$$

The incident α particle must supply this energy plus the energy of the proton and recoil atom.

In other disintegrations, there may be a decrease in mass with consequent increase in energy. This energy may appear as kinetic energy of the product particles or as radiant energy (hf) in the form of γ rays. For example, the bombardment of lithium by protons may produce a γ ray

$$_3Li^7 + _1H^1 \rightarrow _4Be^8 + hf$$

52-10. The Discovery of the Neutron.

Bothe and Becker (1930), on bombarding light elements such as beryllium by α particles, found a very penetrating "radiation" that is not deflected by magnetic or electric fields. In the light of previous experience this was assumed to be γ radiation. Measurement of the energy of the ray gave a value in the neighborhood of 10 Mev, which agreed satisfactorily with the mass change in the assumed reaction

$$_4Be^9 + _2He^4 \rightarrow _6C^{13} + hf(?)$$

Curie and Joliot (1932) found that this radiation (hf) produced much more ionization if it passed through paraffin or other material containing hydrogen but that the ionization was not increased by other substances. These results indicated that the ionization was produced by protons knocked out of the paraffin. If the protons observed were produced by γ rays, the γ-ray photon would be required to have energy of the order of 50 Mev rather than the 10 Mev available from the assumed reaction. Further experiments showed recoil atoms of nitrogen that would require still higher energy for the assumed photon.

Chadwick (1932) showed that these difficulties were removed if it was assumed that the penetrating "radiation" was an uncharged particle of mass about that of the proton. This particle is called a *neutron*. The reaction would then be

$$_4Be^9 + _2He^4 \rightarrow _6C^{12} + _0n^1$$

The penetrating ability of the neutron and its failure to show tracks in a cloud chamber are explained by its lack of charge. It will have no reaction with atoms without direct collision. On the other hand, charged particles will react with nuclei when there is a close approach because of the electric forces. Thus these charged particles owe to their electric charge the ionization they produce in matter and the resistance they encounter as they pass through.

Neutrons make ideal particles for bombardment of nuclei. Since they carry no charge, they are not repelled and hence may penetrate the nucleus even when their energy is comparatively low. Examples of transformation by neutron bombardment follow.

$$_1H^1 + _0n^1 \rightarrow _1H^2 + hf$$
$$_{79}Au^{197} + _0n^1 \rightarrow _{79}Au^{198} + hf$$
$$_{79}Au^{198} \rightarrow _{80}Hg^{198} + _{-1}e^0$$
$$T = 2.7 \text{ days}$$

52-11. Characteristics of Nuclear Reactions. We may consider a general notation for a nuclear reaction in which a particle or nucleus x strikes a nucleus X and results in the emission of particle y, leaving a nucleus Y

$$x + X \rightarrow y + Y$$

The notation is often abbreviated as $X(x,y)Y$ where the first symbol stands for the struck nucleus, the symbols in parentheses stand for the incoming and outgoing particles respectively, and the symbol following the parentheses represents the residual nucleus. Thus the reaction associated with Chadwick's discovery of the neutron is written as $Be^9(\alpha,n)C^{12}$.

A reaction which is useful in the detection and counting of slow neutrons is one in which a neutron enters and an alpha particle (a readily detectable ionizing particle) leaves

$$_0n^1 + _5B^{10} \rightarrow _3Li^7 + _2He^4 \quad \text{or} \quad B^{10}(n,\alpha)Li^7$$

An important reaction initiated by photons is the photodisintegration of the deuteron into a neutron and a proton

$$hf + _1H^2 \rightarrow _1H^1 + _0n^1 \quad \text{or}$$
$$H^2(\gamma,n)H^1 \quad \text{or} \quad H^2(\gamma,p)n$$

A reaction which is useful as a source of high-energy photons is the radiative capture of protons by Li^7

$$_1H^1 + _3Li^7 \rightarrow _4Be^8 + hf \quad \text{or} \quad Li^7(p,\gamma)Be^8$$

This reaction is followed by the spontaneous disintegration of the Be^8 nucleus into two alpha particles.

In reactions in which electrons or positrons are emitted from an unstable nucleus it appears superficially that energy is not conserved. It is believed that in these reactions an additional particle, the *neutrino*, is emitted with energy sufficient to balance the energy conservation equation. The properties postulated for the neutrino (negligible mass and no charge) make its detection extremely difficult. But by 1956 the existence of the neutrino was experimentally demonstrated by detection of gamma rays produced in a sequence of events initiated by the neutrino.

In general, there is more than one possible outcome when a given particle x collides with a given nucleus X. Not enough is now known about nuclear forces and nuclear structure to predict the probability of each one of the possible reactions. A few generalizations can be made. In reactions in which nucleons and heavier particles are emitted the sum of mass plus energy remains constant. The number of nucleons (total number of protons and neutrons) also appears to remain constant. In most reactions the atomic number Z of the struck nucleus is changed by at most two units and the mass number A by at most three or four. This limitation does not apply when the bombarding particles have high energies (above 200 Mev), and it does not apply to fission reactions.

52-12. Cosmic Rays. About 1900 it was established that there is always some ionization of the air. It was assumed that this ionization is caused by radiation from the crust of the earth. Gockel (1910) as the result of observations on balloon flights found the ionization to be greater at high altitude than at the surface, indicating that the source of the ionization came from outside the earth.

Many experiments have been carried out to study the origin and nature of the *cosmic rays* that cause the ionization. Absorption methods, cloud chambers, Geiger counters, and photographic plates have all been used in the studies. The early experiments showed extremely high penetration by cosmic rays, reaching far underground and to the bottoms of deep lakes. Millikan and his collaborators, beginning in 1923, early interpreted the phenomenon as very short-wave electromagnetic radiation. Later experiments showed variation with latitude that indicated deflection of the cosmic rays in the magnetic field of the earth. This effect would be present only if there are charged particles. Identification of the particles is complicated by the fact that several kinds of secondary particles or rays are produced in the atmosphere by the primary cosmic rays. The evidence indicates that the primary rays are mainly positively charged particles, such as protons and other atomic nuclei. All other known elementary particles as well as photons appear as secondary products.

52-13. The Positron. In 1932, C. D. Anderson was studying cosmic-ray phenomena by means of a cloud chamber placed between the poles of an electromagnet. He found pairs of tracks that, from the ionization produced, were identified as those of electrons but the tracks were bent in opposite directions by the field, seeming to indicate opposite charges. To determine the direction of travel of the particles, Anderson inserted a sheet of lead across the chamber so that the track would be less curved on the initial side before the particle was slowed down by the lead. By this device he obtained tracks (Fig. 8) that were those of positively charged electrons. The curvature, ionization, and range of the particle were inconsistent with a proton track but agreed with the assumption of a positive electron or *positron*.

Positrons are not at all rare in nature, occurring in cosmic-ray phenomena near the surface of the earth almost as often as negative electrons. Also they appear frequently as products of artificial disintegration. However, they do not exist long as free positrons since they combine with negative electrons. The normal life of a free positron is a very small fraction of a second. When the electron and positron combine, they disappear and a photon is produced. Conversely, a photon often disappears while a positron-electron pair appears simultaneously. We thus have a direct conversion from particle to wave.

$$_{+1}e^0 + {}_{-1}e^0 \rightleftarrows hf$$

52-14. Mesons and Hyperons. In 1936, Anderson and Neddemeyer reported that

Fig. 8. Cloud-chamber photograph used to identify the positron. (*Courtesy of C. D. Anderson.*)

cloud-chamber pictures showed tracks in which the ionization was too small for a proton but too great for an electron. Further investigation showed the existence of a particle whose charge is the same as that of the electron (+ or −) but whose mass is intermediate between the electron and the proton. Yukawa (1935) had predicted such a particle from a theory of nuclear forces. Particles of such intermediate mass are called *mesons*. Mesons appear as secondary particles in cosmic rays; at sea level they are the most abundant component.

Mesons are unstable particles. Experiments show that they are absorbed more rapidly in air than would be expected from consideration of the absorbing mass. The decrease is accounted for by absorption and radioactive disintegration. The mean life

TABLE 1. PARTICLES OF ATOMIC PHYSICS

Name	Charge	Mass ($\times m_e$)	Mean life, sec	Character of decay
Electron......................	$-e$	1	Stable	
Proton, $_1H^1$..................	$+e$	1836	Stable	
Antiproton.....................	$-e$	1836		
Neutron, $_0n^1$..................	0	1837	15 min	
Antineutron....................	0	1837		
Positron.......................	$+e$	1	Stable	
Alpha particle, $_2He^4$..........	$+2e$	7270	Stable	
Deuteron, $_1D^2$ or $_1H^2$..........	$+e$	3630	Stable	
Photon, hf, γ..................	0	0	Stable	
Neutrino, ν....................	0	0	Stable	
Antineutrino	0	0		
Mesons				
Mu meson, $\mu^\pm$...............	$\pm e$	207	2×10^{-6}	$e^\pm + \nu + \nu$
Pi meson, $\pi^\pm$...............	$\pm e$	273	2.6×10^{-8}	$\mu^\pm + \nu$
Pi meson, π^0...............	0	264	$\sim 10^{-14}$	$\gamma + \gamma$
Tau meson, $\tau^\pm$...............	$\pm e$	965	$\sim 10^{-9}$	$\begin{cases} \pi^\pm + \pi^+ + \pi^- \\ \pi^\pm + 2\pi^0 \end{cases}$
Kappa meson, $\kappa^\pm$.............	$\pm e$	920–960	$\sim 10^{-9}$	$\mu^\pm + \nu$
Theta meson, θ^0.................	0	965	1.5×10^{-10}	$\pi^+ + \pi^-$
Theta meson, $\theta^\pm$.............	$\pm e$	955	$\sim 10^{-9}$	$\pi^\pm + \pi^0$
Hyperons				
Λ^0........................	0	2180	3.8×10^{-10}	$p + \pi^-$
Σ^+........................	$+e$	2200	$\sim 10^{-10}$	$\begin{cases} n + \pi^+ \\ p + \pi^0 \end{cases}$
Σ^-........................	$-e$		$\sim 10^{-10}$	$n + \pi^-$
Ξ^-........................	$-e$		$\sim 10^{-10}$	$\Lambda^0 + \pi^-$

period for the various types of mesons is of the order of 10^{-6} sec or less.

Several types of mesons have been observed. They may be classified by mass as light and heavy. The light mesons include the μ mesons whose mass is about 200 times the electronic mass and π mesons whose mass is about 270 times the mass of the electron. The heavy mesons have masses in the range near 1000 times the electronic mass. In their decay light mesons appear.

Hyperons are particles somewhat greater in mass than the mass of a proton. They are unstable particles and in their decay protons or neutrons and light mesons are produced.

Various known particles with some of their properties are listed in Table 1.

52-15. The Nucleus. Before 1932, only two primary particles were known, the proton and the electron. The nucleus was pictured as made up of these two particles. However, this picture was not entirely satisfactory since it would lead to some conclusions not in accord with the facts observed. With the discovery of the neutron a different picture was possible, a nucleus made up of protons and neutrons. On this basis, all atoms have nuclei that are made up of combinations of these two particles. The charge of the nucleus is the sum of the charges of the protons; the mass of the nucleus is approximately the sum of the masses of protons and neutrons. This makes a very simple explanation of isotopes since the different isotopes of a given substance differ only in the number of neutrons in the nucleus.

While the nuclear mass is approximately the sum of the masses of protons and neutrons, it is found that for any permanently stable nucleus the mass is less than this sum.

This fact is due to the conversion of some of the mass into *energy of binding*. For example, the combination of a proton and a neutron to form a deuteron results in the release of energy:

$$\Delta m = m_D - m_p - m_n = 2.014186$$
$$- 1.007593 - 1.008982 = 0.002389 \text{ amu}$$
$$= 2.225 \text{ Mev}$$

since 1 amu is equivalent to 931 Mev.

The forces that hold the particles of the nucleus together must be considered as a new type of force, *nuclear force*. Neither gravitational nor electric forces fit the observed conditions. The nuclear forces exist only over very short distances, of the order of 10^{-13} cm.

52-16. Fission. In 1934, Fermi and his collaborators attempted to produce elements beyond the normal limit at uranium. In bombardment of the lighter elements by slow neutrons the element after the capture is usually transformed by electron emission into the element of next higher atomic number. Therefore, one might expect that a similar bombardment of uranium ($Z = 92$) would produce a new element (93). This reaction has been produced with *neptunium* (93) as the resulting product. Neptunium also disintegrates by emitting a β particle to produce *plutonium* (94). Plutonium is a rather stable material having a half-life period of 30,000 years. From 1944 to 1950 four other new elements were produced in the cyclotron: americium (95), curium (96), berkelium (97), and californium (98). More recently elements einsteinium (99), fermium (100), mendelevium (101), and nobelium (102) have been reported.

In 1939, Hahn and Strassman found one of the products of neutron bombardment of uranium to be a radioactive barium $_{56}Ba^{139}$. There must then be another fragment such as $_{36}Kr$ associated with the barium fragment to make the charges equal. Neir separated the isotopes of uranium in a mass spectrograph and found that $_{92}U^{235}$ is the one that undergoes the splitting process called *fission*. Fission is a new type of radioactive process, the first

that produced particles more massive than α particles.

In the process of fission of uranium there is a decrease in total mass and therefore there is a corresponding gain in energy. Such a reaction then is a possible source of energy. This energy is controllable since the process can be started at will.

Among the products of fission one finds one to three neutrons. These neutrons are faster than the ones used to start the fission but if they strike the uranium nuclei they can cause fission. Since the fission produces the starting particles and releases energy, the reaction can perpetuate itself, provided there is enough uranium present that the neutrons produced will hit other uranium nuclei. Thus a *chain reaction* can be set up. The smallest amount of material in which such a chain reaction can be set up is called the *critical mass*. If the reaction is set up in a sample of fissionable material of greater than the critical mass, the reaction will accelerate and continue as long as the material is together. Thus, in an uncontrolled chain reaction an explosion will result. If suitable materials are introduced to absorb and slow down the neutrons produced by the fission process, a controlled reaction can be established with energy produced at a predicted rate. Such a *reactor* may be used as a source of energy, since the energy released may be converted into heat.

In the fission process there is a decrease in mass of only about one-tenth of one per cent. Proton and neutron retain their identities, the change in mass resulting from a rearrangement of these elements in the nucleus. Only in transitory particles such as the positron and the meson is there annihilation of particles with conversion of the whole mass into energy. Such a process is not a net source of energy, since at least an equivalent amount of energy is required to produce the transitory particle.

The process of fission occurs when a uranium, plutonium, or other suitable nucleus captures a neutron. The process will proceed as long as neutrons are present and will accelerate if the number of neutrons is increased. The production of an appreciable amount of nuclear energy depends upon having a mechanism that will produce a sufficiently rapid process.

52-17. Nuclear Reactor. A nuclear reactor is a device for utilizing a chain reaction for any of several purposes: to produce power, to supply neutrons, to induce nuclear reactions, to prepare radioisotopes, or to make fissionable material from certain "fertile" materials. Typical components of a reactor are: the *fissionable fuel* (U or Pu), the *moderator* (graphite or D_2O to slow down the fission-producing neutrons), the *control rods* (usually Cd strips, whose insertion captures neutrons and slows the fission rate) and the *coolant* (water, air, hydrogen, or liquid metal such as Na).

In power reactors the coolant, through a heat exchanger, may furnish steam to operate a conventional turbine and electrical generator. Breeder reactors make new nuclear fuel from fertile substances which cannot themselves sustain a chain reaction but which can be converted into fissionable material. One possible breeding reaction is represented by the following equation

$$_{92}U^{236} + _{0}n^{1} \rightarrow _{92}U^{239} \xrightarrow[23 \text{ min}]{\beta} {}_{93}Np^{239}$$

$$\xrightarrow[2.3 \text{ days}]{\beta} {}_{94}Pu^{239}$$

52-18. Fusion. Nuclear energy can also be released by fusion of small nuclei into larger nuclei if in this process there is a decrease in mass. In such a process the two positively charged nuclei must come into contact even though there are strong electrical forces of repulsion. This requires that the particles be moving with high speeds. With artificial accelerating apparatus a few nuclei are given very high speeds. Only occasionally will such a particle strike another nucleus before it has lost too much of its energy to make contact. Thus the process is extremely inefficient, and more energy must be supplied to initiate the fusion process than is realized from the reaction.

The only known way in which a fusion process can be carried out to evolve energy is by a thermonuclear reaction at extremely high temperature. The speed of the nuclei is the speed of their thermal motion. Even at the temperature of the interior of the stars, of the order of 2×10^7 degrees centigrade, the speed of the nuclei is far less than that of the particles produced in the accelerators, but in collisions they are not slowed down because all the particles are moving with the same high speeds. Hence a very small percentage of the nuclei will fuse to cause the nuclear reaction. In the sun only about one per cent of the hydrogen is thus transformed into helium in a billion years. This small change maintains the high temperature only because the radiation produced diffuses very slowly to the outside and there is a great difference in temperature between the center and the outside. On a small body such as the earth, the rate of loss of energy would be so rapid that the temperature necessary to continue such a nuclear reaction could not be maintained.

If thermonuclear reactions are initiated on the earth, they must be very rapid, because the energy is lost so quickly that slow reactions cannot continue. The reaction rate depends upon the charges of the nuclei, being greatest for small charges. Hydrogen, having the smallest charge, should have the highest rate. There are three isotopes of hydrogen, $_1H^1$, $_1H^2$, and $_1H^3$. Of these, the most abundant $_1H^1$ has a very slow rate of reaction, but the other two have a rather high rate and evolve more energy.

$$_1H^3 + {}_1H^2 \rightarrow {}_2He^4 + {}_0n^1 + 17.6 \text{ Mev}$$

Thus a hydrogen-helium reaction is possible if the proper conditions are provided. There must be an extremely high temperature and sufficiently high density of the reacting components that collisions are probable. It is possible to realize the high temperature in an explosion of uranium or plutonium. The magnitude of the hydrogen reaction depends exactly on the amount of reacting material built into the bomb. Such an explosion does not extend to the general atmosphere because of the extremely small concentration of reacting materials and the rapid loss of energy by radiation.

52-19. Controlled Fusion. The necessary condition for a thermonuclear process is the attainment of high particle energies for a time interval long enough to bring about kinetic equilibrium. Energy must be supplied initially to attain the "star temperature" needed for thermal fusion. At the same time the reactants must be confined. Ordinary walls will not suffice, for they would vaporize under bombardment of the high-energy particles and these would be quickly cooled below their fusion temperature. These problems of heating and confinement must be solved in any controlled fusion reactor.

The choice of fuel for a controlled fusion reactor is made on the basis of availability and the probability of attaining with it the necessary high temperature. One would prefer elements of low atomic number because of the low Coulomb barrier to be overcome in the fusion reaction. Possible fusion reactions of about equal probability are

$$_1H^2 + {}_1H^2 \rightarrow {}_2He^3 + {}_0n^1 \quad \text{releases 3.25 Mev}$$
$$_1H^2 + {}_1H^2 \rightarrow {}_1H^3 + {}_1H^1 \quad \text{releases 4.0 Mev}$$

Initial heating first strips the electrons from the atoms to produce a "fourth state of matter," a fully ionized gas, or *plasma*. Further heating of the plasma is done by adding electric energy, in part by using the resistance of the plasma to produce familiar ohmic heating.

The ions reacting at temperatures about 10^8 °K obviously cannot be confined by material walls. But suitably designed magnetic fields can provide a sort of "magnetic bottle." Ions gyrating in a region of varying magnetic induction B will experience a force which results in a plasma drift away from regions of strong B. In the "pinch effect" a cylindrical

current (10^6 amp) contracts because of electromagnetic forces (parallel currents attract each other). The plasma inside is thus compressed (Fig. 9) producing very high temperatures. Although the simple pinch is unstable, toroidal pinch devices with stabilizing

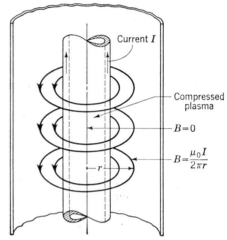

FIG. 9. The "pinch effect" in a plasma.

axial magnetic fields have produced thermonuclear temperatures with a confinement time of about one millisecond. So far, however, the power required for these devices has exceeded the useful power gained from fusion.

In the fusion process the energy released goes to both the light charged particles and to the neutrons, as kinetic energy. The neutrons carry energy to the reactor walls. But with magnetic confinement one might be able to couple the energy of the charged particles directly to exterior electric circuits. This scheme would eliminate the heat exchanger of low thermodynamic efficiency conventionally used in fission reactors.

SUMMARY

Radioactive materials emit α particles, β particles, and γ rays.

The α particles are positively charged helium nuclei, are deflected by magnetic and electric fields, show small penetration, and produce great ionization.

The β particles are electrons, are deflected

by magnetic and electric fields, show much greater penetration than α particles, and produce less ionization.

The γ rays are highly penetrating electromagnetic radiation, are not deflected by magnetic or electric fields, and produce little ionization.

The *Geiger counter* is a device that enables one to count radioactive radiations or other radiations that will ionize the gas of the counter tube.

The *Wilson cloud chamber* is used to photograph tracks of individual particles or rays.

Radioactive materials follow an exponential decay law. The *half-life period* of a radioactive material is the time required for half the atoms to disintegrate.

Artificial disintegration, discovered by Rutherford in 1919, is produced when high-speed particles enter the nucleus.

High-energy particles are produced artificially by means of high-potential accelerators. One such device is the *cyclotron*.

In artificial disintegration there may be a decrease in mass resulting in evolution of energy or an increase in mass requiring expenditure of energy.

Neutrons are uncharged particles whose mass is nearly the same as that of the proton.

Cosmic rays enter the atmosphere from outside the earth. The primary rays are positively charged particles, probably protons and other atomic nuclei.

The *positron* is a positively charged particle whose mass is that of an electron.

The *meson* is a particle whose mass is intermediate between that of the electron and that of the proton. It may carry either a positive or a negative charge, or no charge.

Hyperons are particles somewhat greater in mass than the mass of the proton.

The nucleus is believed to be composed of protons and neutrons.

Fission is the splitting of a nucleus into two or more large fragments. When this process results in a decrease in mass, it can be a source of energy.

A *chain reaction* can be set up if the reaction produces the particles that produced the reaction originally. The chain reaction cannot be maintained if the mass of fissionable material is less than a *critical mass*.

Nuclear energy can be released by the *fusion* of light nuclei into larger nuclei with consequent decrease in mass. Such reactions are the probable source of stellar radiation.

REFERENCES

Robert T. Beyer (ed.), *Foundations of Nuclear Physics*, Dover Publications, New York, 1949. Contains reprints of original papers by Chadwick, Cockcroft and Walton, Rutherford, Fermi, Yukawa, and others.

C. H. Blanchard, C. R. Burnett, R. G. Stoner, and R. L. Weber, *Introduction to Modern Physics*, Prentice-Hall, Inc., Englewood Cliffs, N. J., 1958.

Geoffrey Burbidge and Fred Hoyle, "Anti-Matter," *Sci. American*, **198**: 4, 34–39 (1958).

H. C. Corben and S. DeBenedetti, "The Ultimate Atom," *Sci. American*, **191**: 6, 88–92 (1954).

Fusion, 1958, Atomic Energy Commission.

Samuel Glasstone, *Sourcebook on Atomic Energy*, 2d ed., D. Van Nostrand Company, Inc., Princeton, N. J., 1958.

M. Goldhaber, "Speculations on Cosmogony," *Science*, **124**: 218–219 (1956). Speculations on antimatter, with references.

Otto Hahn, "The Discovery of Fission," *Sci. American*, **198**: 2, 76–84 (1958).

Irving Kaplan, *Nuclear Physics*, Addison-Wesley Publishing Company, Reading, Mass., 1955.

Ernest C. Pollard and William L. Davidson, *Applied Nuclear Physics*, 2d ed., John Wiley & Sons, Inc., New York, 1951.

Emilio Segre and Clyde E. Wiegand, "The Antiproton," *Sci. American*, **194**: 6, 37–41 (1956).

Robert R. Wilson, "Particle Accelerators," *Sci. American*, **198**: 3, 64–76 (1958).

Herman Yagoda, "The Tracks of Nuclear Particles," *Sci. American*, **194**: 1, 40–47 (1956).

QUESTIONS   1. Do α, β, and γ rays come from the same element? Show why we ordinarily find all three in many radioactive experiments.

2. Describe some of the methods for the study and measurement of radioactive rays. Discuss the relative sensitivity of these methods. How does the actual mass of these rays compare with the masses used in ordinary chemical experiments?

3. Suggest several methods by which one could estimate the age of a uranium-bearing rock. How does the age of the earth estimated in this manner (not less than 1600 million years) compare with independent estimates based on geological evidence?

4. Compare the methods and achievements of modern "atom smashers" of nuclear physics with those of the ancient alchemists. In what respects are their objectives similar and how are they unlike?

5. Why is it possible to produce higher energy α particles than protons with a given cyclotron? Is this true with other types of accelerators?

6. What limits the energy that can be given to a particle in a cyclotron?

7. Why is it more difficult to produce atomic disintegration by bombarding heavy atoms than it is for light atoms?

8. For a time the theory that all elements were made up of combinations of hydrogen atoms was accepted. What facts led to the abandonment of this hypothesis?

9. If a lithium nucleus of atomic mass 7 and atomic number 3 captures a proton and fission results in the disintegration of the nucleus into two equal parts, what is the nature of the materials thus produced?

10. When, in a nuclear change, there is an increase in mass, what is the source of the added mass?

11. When a photon disappears in producing an electron and a positron, is the energy of the photon equivalent to the mass of the particles produced? If not, what accounts for the difference?

12. What are some of the difficulties involved in the commercial utilization of nuclear energy for industrial purposes?

13. A certain reactor is designed so that there is one chance in two of a neutron leaking out; there is one chance in two of a non-escaping neutron being absorbed in nonfission capture; and the fuel gives three free neutrons per fission. Can this reactor be made to go critical?

14. In what form is the energy released in fusion reactions made available to a star?

15. What factors determine the optimum ion density in a continuously operating fusion reactor?

16. A fusion reactor loses some energy by electromagnetic radiation especially in the x-ray region when ions are suddenly decelerated in collision. To minimize this loss, what requirements should one observe in regard to ion density, purity of the gas, and atomic number Z of any impurities?

PROBLEMS   1. Express the kinetic energy of a β ray with a speed of 0.95 that of light in terms of electron volts.

2. An α particle ejected from polonium has a speed of 1.60×10^9 cm/sec. What is its energy expressed in (a) ergs and (b) electron volts?

Ans. 8.52×10^{-6} erg; 5.33 Mev

3. What uniform magnetic field would be necessary to bend the α particle

from RaC′ into a circular path of radius 30 cm? The speed of the particle is 1.92×10^9 cm/sec.

4. An α particle ejected from polonium has a speed of 1.60×10^9 cm/sec. What is the radius of curvature of its path in a uniform magnetic field of 1.20 w/m²? *Ans.* 27.6 cm

5. Radium disintegrates at the rate of approximately 0.045% per year. How many α particles are emitted per gram in one day? Would this computation be valid for a short-life substance?

6. Compute the length of the second and third cylinders of a linear accelerator if the ions are protons starting from rest, each accelerating potential is 10,000 volts, and the first cylinder is 2.00 cm long. *Ans.* 2.82 cm; 3.46 cm

7. Radium has an atomic mass of 226 and an atomic number of 88. It disintegrates with the emission of an α particle. Write the symbolic equation for this transmutation.

8. A radioactive element of atomic mass 218 and atomic number 84 disintegrates with the emission of an α particle. Find the new atomic mass and atomic number. *Ans.* 214; 82

9. In the process of the radioactive disintegration of thorium, 6 α and 4 β particles are emitted. What are the atomic mass and number of the final product of the thorium disintegration? Thorium has atomic mass 232 and atomic number 90.

10. The activity of a radioactive sample decreases from 0.010 curie to 0.003 curie in 60 days. What is the half-life of the material? *Ans.* 35 days

11. The half-life of thorium ($_{90}Th^{234}$) is 24.1 days. How many days after a sample of thorium has been purified will it take for 90 per cent to change to protoactinium ($_{91}Pa^{234}$)? *Ans.* 80 days

12. Show that if relativity effects are neglected, the kinetic energy of an ion describing an arc of radius r in the magnetic field B of a cyclotron is given by $(qBr)^2/2m$.

13. The problem of relativistic increase in ion mass (decrease in its frequency) can be met in another way than by frequency modulation. Show that it should be possible to operate a cyclotron at fixed frequency if the pole faces are shaped so that the magnetic induction varies with radius in a particular way.

14. The oscillator of a 44-in. (diameter) cyclotron operates at a wavelength of 26 m. (*a*) What magnetic field is required for resonance when using deuterons? (*b*) What is the energy of the emerging deuteron beam?

Ans. 1.50 w/m²; 17 Mev

15. Find the kinetic energy of a proton moving in a path of 25-in. radius in the uniform field of a cyclotron, where B is 1.00 w/m². *Ans.* 19 Mev

16. When carbon, atomic mass 12 and atomic number 6, is bombarded by α particles, disintegration occurs with the emission of a neutron. The element thus formed is unstable and disintegrates with the ejection of a positron. What is the final product of this transmutation and what are its atomic mass and atomic number?

17. When chlorine, atomic mass 35 and atomic number 17, is bombarded by protons, the resulting atom disintegrates, emitting an α particle. Write the equation representing the reaction.

18. When nitrogen, atomic mass 14 and atomic number 7, is bombarded with neutrons, the collisions result in disintegrations in which α particles are produced. Write the symbolic equation representing this transmutation.

19. When fluorine, atomic mass 19 and atomic number 9, is bombarded with neutrons, a new element is formed and an α particle is ejected. (*a*) What is the new element? (*b*) What are its atomic mass and atomic number?

20. When copper, atomic mass 65 and atomic number 29, is bombarded by neutrons, the resulting atom disintegrates giving a proton. Write the equation representing these transitions.

21. If a positron and an electron combine to produce a photon, what is the minimum frequency of the photon pair? Could it be greater than this minimum frequency? If so, why?

22. If the decrease in mass in a fission process is 0.10%, how much energy could be obtained from the fission of 1.0 lb of material?   *Ans.* 4.1×10^{13} joules

23. The neutron-induced fission of a U^{235} nucleus releases energy of about 200 Mev. Approximately what fraction of the rest mass is converted into energy?

24. The energy released per fission of U^{235} is 200 Mev. (*a*) How many fissions occur per second in a reactor releasing 1000 kw of fission power? (*b*) What mass of U^{235} is consumed per hour?   *Ans.* 3.1×10^{16}/sec; 40 micrograms

25. In fusion of hydrogen isotopes into helium the decrease in mass is of the order of 0.70%. How much energy could be produced by the use of 1.00 lb of hydrogen?

26. It has been suggested that after a star has converted all its hydrogen into helium, it contracts producing higher internal pressures, temperatures, and densities until it can convert helium to carbon in triple collisions, $\alpha + \alpha + \alpha \rightarrow C^{12}$. Estimate the energy released in this reaction.   *Ans.* 21 Mev

Appendix

1. SOLUTION OF PHYSICAL PROBLEMS

The ability to solve problems is a mark of an effective and efficient scientist or engineer. Through practice in the solution of problems commensurate with one's knowledge, one attains ability and confidence in independent thinking.

In problem solving, the following systematic approach is highly recommended. First, read the statement of the problem carefully, and decide exactly what is required. Then:

1. Draw a suitable diagram, and list the data given.

2. Identify the type of problem, and write physical principles which seem relevant to its solution. These may be expressed concisely as algebraic equations.

3. Determine if the data given are adequate. If not, decide what is missing and how to get it. This may involve consulting a table, making a reasonable assumption, or drawing upon your general knowledge for such information as the value of g, the acceleration due to gravity, 32 ft/sec.^{2}

4. Decide whether in the particular problem it is easier to substitute numerical values immediately or first to carry out an algebraic solution. Some quantities may cancel.

5. Substitute numerical data in the equations obtained from physical principles. Include the units for each quantity, making sure

that they are all in the same system in any one problem.

6. Compute the numerical value of the unknown, preferably with the aid of a slide rule. Determine the units in which the answer is expressed. Examine the reasonableness of the answer. Can it be obtained by an alternative method to check the result?

The student is referred to the numerous solved examples in the text for a demonstration of the form of solution recommended for physics problems.

An orderly procedure aids clear thinking, helps to avoid errors, and usually saves time. Most important, it enables a student to analyze and eventually solve those more complex problems whose solution is not immediately or intuitively apparent.

2. SIGNIFICANT FIGURES IN MEASUREMENTS AND COMPUTATIONS

Uncertainty in Measurements. The word *accuracy* has various shades of meaning depending on the circumstances under which it is used. It is commonly used to denote the reliability of the indications of a measuring instrument.

As applied to the final result of a measurement, the accuracy is expressed by stating the *uncertainty* of the numerical result, that is, the estimated maximum amount by which the result may differ from the "true" or accepted value.

Rules for Computation with Experimental Data. There is always a pronounced and persistent tendency on the part of beginners to retain too many figures in a computation. This not only involves too much arithmetic labor but, worse still, leads to a fictitiously precise result.

The following rules are recommended and will save much time that would otherwise be spent in calculation; furthermore, their careful use will result in properly indicated accuracies.

1. In recording the result of a measurement or a calculation, *one, and one only, doubtful digit is retained.*

2. In addition and subtraction, do not carry the operations beyond the first column that contains a doubtful figure.

3. In multiplication and division, carry the result to the same number of significant figures that there are in that quantity entering into the calculation which has the *least* number of significant figures.

4. In dropping figures that are not significant, the last figure retained should be unchanged if the first figure dropped is less than 5. It should be increased by 1 if the first figure dropped is greater than 5. If the first figure dropped is 5, the preceding digit should be unchanged if it is an even number but increased by 1 if it is an odd number. Examples: 3.4$\bar{5}$5 becomes 3.46; 3.4$\bar{8}$5 becomes 3.48; 6.79$\bar{0}$1 becomes 6.790.

Significant Figures. The accuracy of a physical measurement is properly indicated by the number of figures used in expressing the numerical measure. Conventionally, only those figures which are reasonably trustworthy are retained. These are called *significant figures.*

In recording certain numbers, the location of the decimal point requires zeros to be added to the significant figures. When this requirement leaves doubt as to which figures are significant, one may *overscore the last sig-*

nificant figure. This overscored figure is the first digit whose value is doubtful.

Examples:

Length of a page
    = 22.7 cm (3 significant figures)
Thickness of the page
    = 0.011 cm (2 significant figures)
Distance of the sun
    = 9$\bar{3}$,000,000 mi (2 significant figures)
Speed of light
    = 299,7$\bar{9}$0 km/sec (5 significant figures)

If each of these numbers is expressed in terms of powers of 10, there is no doubt as to the number of significant figures for only the significant figures are then retained. Thus

$$\text{Length of the page} = 2.27 \times 10^1 \text{ cm}$$
$$\text{Thickness of the page} = 1.1 \times 10^{-2} \text{ cm}$$
$$\text{Distance to the sun} = 9.3 \times 10^7 \text{ mi}$$
$$\text{Speed of light} = 2.9979 \times 10^5 \text{ km/sec}$$

There are some numbers which, by their definition, may be taken to have an unlimited number of significant figures. For example, the factors 2 and π in the relation

$$\text{Circumference} = 2\pi \text{ (radius)}$$

In calculations there is frequently need to use data that have been recorded without a clear indication of the number of significant figures. For example, a textbook problem may refer to a "2-lb weight," or in a cooperative experiment a student may announce that he has measured a certain distance as "5 ft." In such cases the values with the appropriate number of significant figures should be written from what is known or assumed about the way in which the measurements were made. If the distance referred to were measured with an ordinary tape measure, it might appropriately be written as 5.0 ft. If it were carefully measured with a steel scale to the nearest tenth of an inch, the distance might be recorded as 5.00 ft. In academic problem work a good rule to follow is to retain three figures unless there is reason to decide otherwise.

A systematic use of the rules given above relating to significant figures results in two advantages: (1) time is saved by carrying out calculations only to that number of figures which the data justify, and (2) intelligent recording of data is encouraged by noting always the least accurate of a number of measurements needed for a given determination. Attention can then be concentrated on improving the least accurate measurement or, if this is not possible, other measurements need be taken only to an accuracy commensurate with it.

3. METRIC SYSTEMS OF ELECTRIC UNITS

Historically, a cgs *electrostatic* system of units (esu) was defined from Coulomb's law, $F \propto qq'/s^2$, for the force between two point charges. The constant of proportionality was arbitrarily assigned the value unity for free space. The statcoulomb was defined as a charge of such magnitude that it would repel a like charge one centimeter distant in free space with a force of one dyne. Other electrostatic units were derived from the statcoulomb. For example, the unit of current, the statampere, is one statcoulomb per second.

In the early study of magnetism, a cgs *electromagnetic* system of units (emu) was defined on the fiction of isolated magnetic poles which obeyed a Coulomb law of force, $F \propto mm'/s^2$. The constant of proportionality was arbitrarily assigned the value unity for free space. The unit pole was defined as one of such magnitude that it would repel a like pole one centimeter distant in free space with a force of one dyne.

A *practical* system of units was based on a definition of the ampere from Faraday's laws of electrolysis. The ohm was defined as the resistance of a column of mercury of specified dimensions. The unit of potential difference, the volt, was derived from Ohm's law: $V = IR$.

The *meter-kilogram-second* (mks) system of units was devised chiefly to lessen the confusion that results from the intermingled use of the practical system and the electrostatic and electromagnetic units of the cgs system. The mks system was proposed by Professor Giovanni L. T. C. Giorgi in 1903. The International Committee on Weights and Measures adopted the mks system in 1935.

In mechanics, the mks system introduces only one new unit, the *newton*. From

$$f = ma$$

mks: 1 newton $= (1 \text{ kg})(1 \text{ m/sec}^2)$

cgs: 1 dyne $= (1 \text{ gm})(1 \text{ cm/sec}^2)$

1 newton $= (1000 \text{ gm})(100 \text{ cm/sec}^2)$
$$= 10^5 \text{ dynes}$$

TABLE 1. PERMITTIVITY AND PERMEABILITY FOR FREE SPACE

Unit system	ϵ_0 magnitude	ϵ_0 units	μ_0 magnitude	μ_0 units
mks { Unrationalized	$\dfrac{1}{9 \times 10^9}$	coulomb/volt-m or coulomb^2/newton-m^2 or	10^{-7}	weber/amp-turn-m or newton/amp^2 or
Rationalized	$\dfrac{1}{4\pi \times 9 \times 10^9}$	farad/m	$4\pi \times 10^{-7}$	henry/m
cgs { Electrostatic	1	$\dfrac{\text{statcoulomb}^2}{\text{dyne cm}^2}$	$\dfrac{1}{9 \times 10^{20}}$	$\dfrac{1}{\sqrt{\epsilon_0 \mu_0}} = c$
Electromagnetic	$\dfrac{1}{9 \times 10^{20}}$	$\dfrac{1}{\sqrt{\epsilon_0 \mu_0}} = c$	1	$\dfrac{\text{unit pole}}{\text{dyne cm}^2}$

The mks unit of work is the newton-meter which is equivalent to 10^7 dyne-cm $= 10^7$ ergs $= 1$ joule. The mks unit of power is the newton-meter per second, which is the same as the joule per second or the *watt*, the practical unit of power.

In electricity and magnetism, the mks system employs the well-known practical electrical units, such as the ampere, volt, ohm, and watt; it eliminates the powers of 10 that occur in the relations between the cgs units. The mks unit of charge, the coulomb, is one which in free space would repel an equal charge at a distance of 1 m with a force of 9×10^9 newtons. Use of this value in Coulomb's law, $F = qq'/\epsilon_0 s^2$, shows that (in unrationalized units) the permittivity of free space is not unity, but $\epsilon_0 = 1/(9 \times 10^9)$ coulomb^2/newton-m^2. Similarly, the value for the permeability μ_0 of free space in unrationalized mks units is 10^{-7} newton/amp^2.

The mks system based on Coulomb's law in the forms just described leaves an inconvenient factor 4π in the magnetic equations, and even in some electric equations factors 2π or 4π appear where their presence is not immediately suggested by any geometrical considerations. The so-called *rationalized* mks

TABLE 2. ELECTRIC AND MAGNETIC QUANTITIES IN DIFFERENT METRIC SYSTEMS

Quantity	Symbol	Rationalized mks	Unrationalized cgs electrostatic	Unrationalized cgs electromagnetic
Length..................	l	1 meter	100 cm	100 cm
Mass....................	m	1 kilogram	1000 gm	1000 gm
Time....................	t	1 second	1 sec	1 sec
Force...................	F	1 newton	10^5 dynes	10^5 dynes
Torque.................	L	1 meter-newton	10^7 cm-dynes	10^7 cm-dynes
Energy.................	W	1 joule	10^7 ergs	10^7 ergs
Power..................	P	1 watt	10^7 ergs/sec	10^7 ergs/sec
Charge.................	Q	1 coulomb	3×10^9 statcoulombs	10^{-1} abcoulomb
Current.................	I	1 ampere	3×10^9 statamperes	10^{-1} abampere
Potential difference; emf....	$V; E$	1 volt	$\frac{1}{300}$ statvolt	10^8 abvolts
Electric field intensity.....	$\mathcal{E}$	1 volt/m	$\frac{1}{3} \times 10^{-4}$ statvolt/cm	10^6 abvolts/cm
Resistance..............	R	1 ohm	$\dfrac{1}{9 \times 10^{11}}$ statohm	10^9 abohms
Resistivity..............	ρ	1 ohm-m	$\dfrac{1}{9 \times 10^9}$ statohm-cm	10^{11} abohm-cm
Permittivity, free space....	ϵ_0	$\dfrac{1}{36\pi \times 10^9}$ coulomb^2/ (newton-m^2)	$\dfrac{\text{statcoulomb}^2}{\text{dyne cm}^2}$	
Permeability, free space....	μ_0	$4\pi \times 10^{-7}$ newton/amp^2		$\dfrac{(\text{unit pole})^2}{\text{dyne cm}^2}$
Capacitance.............	C	1 farad	9×10^{11} statfarads	10^{-9} abfarad
Inductance..............	L or M	1 henry	$\dfrac{1}{9 \times 10^{11}}$ stathenry	10^9 abhenrys
Magnetic flux...........	Φ	1 weber (or volt sec)		10^8 maxwells
Magnetic flux density.....	B	1 weber/m^2		10^4 gauss
Magnetic field intensity (magnetizing force).....	H	1 amp-turn/m		$4\pi \times 10^{-3}$ oersted
Pole strength...........	m	1 weber		$\dfrac{10^9}{4\pi}$ emu

system assigns values to both ϵ_0 and to μ_0 for free space which differ from those stated above in the ratio of 4π to 1. As a consequence, expressions in which ϵ_0 and μ_0 appear have different values when stated in terms of the rationalized and the unrationalized units; the two forms of the mks system are otherwise the same. The values of ϵ_0 and μ_0 are given in the accompanying table for each of the four unit systems considered.

A comparison of expressions for capacitance in unrationalized and rationalized mks units will indicate the easier association for factors 2π and 4π with geometry in the rationalized system. In the rationalized system no π's appear in "plane" formulas, 2π appears in "cylindrical" formulas, and 4π appears in "spherical" formulas.

Capacitance of:	Unrationalized units	Rationalized units
Plane capacitor	$C = \dfrac{\epsilon A}{4\pi s}$	$C = \dfrac{\epsilon A}{s}$
Coaxial cylinders	$C = \dfrac{\epsilon L}{2 \ln (b/a)}$	$C = \dfrac{2\pi\epsilon L}{2 \ln (b/a)}$
Concentric spheres	$C = \dfrac{\epsilon ab}{b - a}$	$C = \dfrac{4\pi\epsilon ab}{b - a}$

The advantage claimed for the rationalized mks system is not that it contains fewer π's, but that they appear in the "right places."

In Table 2, some of the commonly used units of the various systems are listed with equal signs implied along any one row. Electromagnetic units for electrical quanti-ties are given the prefix *ab-* (absolute) and the name of the practical unit. Electrostatic units are indicated by the prefix *stat-* and the name of the practical unit. Nameless units are given the family designation: esu or emu.

The speed of electromagnetic radiation in free space is taken as 3×10^8 m/sec.

4. GREEK ALPHABET

Alpha (a)	A	α
Beta (b)	B	β
Gamma (g)	Γ	γ
Delta (d)	Δ	δ or ∂
Epsilon (e)	E	ϵ
Zeta (z)	Z	ζ
Eta (h)	H	η
Theta (th)	Θ	θ
Iota (i)	I	ι
Kappa (k)	K	κ
Lambda (l)	Λ	λ
Mu (n)	M	μ
Nu (n)	N	ν
Xi (x)	Ξ	ξ
Omicron (o)	O	o
Pi (p)	Π	π
Rho (r)	P	ρ
Sigma (s)	Σ	σ or ς
Tau (t)	T	τ
Upsilon (u)	Υ	υ
Phi (ph)	Φ	φ or ϕ
Chi (ch)	X	χ
Psi (ps)	Ψ	ψ
Omega (o)	Ω	ω

5. TABLES

TABLE 1. VALUES OF IMPORTANT PHYSICAL CONSTANTS*

Acceleration due to gravity (sea level, $45°$)......$g = 9.80665$ m/sec^2

Density of water, maximum...............$\rho_{H_2O} = 0.999972 \times 10^3$ kg/m^3

Density of mercury.......................$\rho_{Hg} = 13.5950 \times 10^3$ kg/m^3

Standard atmospheric pressure..............$p_0 = 760.00$ mm of mercury

$= 1013.246$ mb

Gravitational constant.....................$G = 6.670 \times 10^{-11}$ newton-m^2/kg^2

Volume of ideal gas ($0°$C, 1 atm)...........$V_0 = 22.4207$ m^3/kg-mole

Avogadro's number.......................$N_0 = 6.02486 \times 10^{26}$ per kg-mole

Ideal gas constant........................$R_0 = 8316.96$ joules/kg-mole K$°$

Boltzmann's constant......................$k = R_0/N_0$

$= 1.38042 \times 10^{-23}$ joule/K$°$

$= 8.6164$ ev/K$°$

Speed of light (free space)..................$c = 2.997930 \times 10^8$ m/sec

Electronic charge (magnitude)...............$e = 1.60206 \times 10^{-19}$ coulomb

Charge-to-mass ratio of electron............$e/m = 1.75890 \times 10^{11}$ coulomb/kg

Faraday's constant........................$F = N_0e$

$= 9.65219 \times 10^7$ coulombs/kg-mole

Planck's constant..........................$h = 6.62517 \times 10^{-34}$ joule-sec

Atomic mass unit ($\frac{1}{16}$ mass of $_8O^{16}$)......1 amu $= 1.660 \times 10^{-27}$ kg

Masses of particles at rest

Neutron:	1.008982 amu
	1.67470×10^{-27} kg
Proton:	1.007593 amu
	1.67239×10^{-27} kg
Hydrogen atom:	1.008142 amu
Electron:	5.4876×10^{-4} amu
	9.1083×10^{-31} kg
Deuterium atom:	2.014735 amu

Mass-energy conversion factors

1 amu $= 931.14$ Mev

1 gm $= 5.610 \times 10^{26}$ Mev

1 electron mass $= 0.51098$ Mev

Stefan-Boltzmann constant ....$\sigma = 5.6687 \times 10^{-8}$ joule/(m^2) (sec) ($°$K)^4

Ice point................................$T_0 = 273.16$ $°$K

* As experimental techniques improve, "best values" of the physical constants are recomputed by statistical methods. See, for example, E. R. Cohen, J. W. M. DuMond, T. W. Layton, and J. S. Rollett, "Analysis of Variance of the 1952 Data on the Atomic Constants and a New Adjustment, 1955," *Revs. Modern Phys.*, **27**: 363–380 (1955). The values listed in Table 1 (except those for G, g, and ρ) are taken from the article cited and have been expressed to an appropriate number of significant figures. Uncertainties in these constants are discussed in the original paper. The physical scale is used for all constants involving atomic masses.

TABLE 2. NATURAL SINES AND COSINES
NATURAL SINES

Angle	0.0	0.1	0.2	0.3	0.4	0.5	0.6	0.7	0.8	0.9	Complement difference
0°	0.0000	0017	0035	0052	0070	0087	0105	0122	0140	0157	0175	89°
1	0175	0192	0209	0227	0244	0262	0279	0297	0314	0332	0349	88
2	0349	0366	0384	0401	0419	0436	0454	0471	0488	0506	0523	87
3	0523	0541	0558	0576	0593	0610	0628	0645	0663	0680	0698	86
4	0698	0715	0732	0750	0767	0785	0802	0819	0837	0854	0872	85
5	0.0872	0889	0906	0924	0941	0958	0976	0993	1011	1028	1045	84
6	1045	1063	1080	1097	1115	1132	1149	1167	1184	1201	1219	83
7	1219	1236	1253	1271	1288	1305	1323	1340	1357	1374	1392	82
8	1392	1409	1426	1444	1461	1478	1495	1513	1530	1547	1564	81
9	1564	1582	1599	1616	1633	1650	1668	1685	1702	1719	1736	80
10	0.1736	1754	1771	1788	1805	1822	1840	1857	1874	1891	1908	79
11	1908	1925	1942	1959	1977	1994	2011	2028	2045	2062	2079	78
12	2079	2096	2113	2130	2147	2164	2181	2198	2215	2233	2250	77 17
13	2250	2267	2284	2300	2317	2334	2351	2368	2385	2402	2419	76
14	2419	2436	2453	2470	2487	2504	2521	2538	2554	2571	2588	75
15	0.2588	2605	2622	2639	2556	2672	2689	2706	2723	2740	2756	74
16	2756	2773	2790	2807	2823	2840	2857	2874	2890	2907	2924	73
17	2924	2940	2957	2974	2990	3007	3024	3040	3057	3074	3090	72
18	3090	3107	3123	3140	3156	3173	3190	3206	3223	3239	3256	71
19	3256	3273	3289	3305	3322	3338	3355	3371	3387	3404	3420	70
20	0.3420	3437	3453	3469	3486	3502	3518	3535	3551	3567	3584	69
21	3584	3600	3616	3633	3649	3665	3681	3697	3714	3730	3746	68
22	3746	3762	3778	3795	3811	3827	3843	3859	3875	3891	3907	67
23	3907	3923	3939	3955	3971	3987	4003	4019	4035	4051	4067	66 16
24	4067	4083	4099	4115	4131	4147	4163	4179	4195	4210	4226	65
25	0.4226	4242	4258	4274	4289	4305	4321	4337	4352	4368	4384	64
26	4384	4399	4415	4431	4446	4462	4478	4493	4509	4524	4540	63
27	4540	4555	4571	4586	4602	4617	4633	4648	4664	4679	4695	62
28	4695	4710	4726	4741	4756	4772	4787	4802	4818	4833	4848	61
29	4848	4863	4879	4894	4909	4924	4939	4955	4970	4985	5000	60
30	0.5000	5015	5030	5045	5060	5075	5090	5105	5120	5135	5150	59 15
31	5150	5165	5180	5195	5210	5225	5240	5255	5270	5284	5299	58
32	5299	5314	5329	5344	5358	5373	5388	5402	5417	5432	5446	57
33	5446	5461	5476	5490	5505	5519	5534	5548	5563	5577	5592	56
34	5592	5606	5621	5635	5650	5664	5678	5693	5707	5721	5736	55
35	0.5736	5750	5764	5779	5793	5807	5821	5835	5850	5864	5878	54
36	5878	5892	5906	5920	5934	5948	5962	5976	5990	6004	6018	53 14
37	6018	6032	6046	6060	6074	6088	6101	6115	6129	6143	6157	52
38	6157	6170	6184	6198	6211	6225	6239	6252	6266	6280	6293	51
39	6293	6307	6320	6334	6347	6361	6374	6388	6401	6414	6428	50
40	0.6428	6441	6455	6468	6481	6494	6508	6521	6534	6547	6561	49
41	6561	6574	6587	6600	6613	6626	6639	6652	6665	6678	6691	48 13
42	6691	6704	6717	6730	6743	6756	6769	6782	6794	6807	6820	47
43	6820	6833	6845	6858	6871	6884	6896	6909	6921	6934	6947	46
44°	6947	6959	6972	6984	6997	7009	7022	7034	7046	7059	7071	45°
Complement		0.9	0.8	0.7	0.6	0.5	0.4	0.3	0.2	0.1	0.0	Angle

NATURAL COSINES

TABLE 2. NATURAL SINES AND COSINES (Continued)

NATURAL SINES

Angle	0.0	0.1	0.2	0.3	0.4	0.5	0.6	0.7	0.8	0.9	Complement difference
45°	0.7071	7083	7096	7108	7120	7133	7145	7157	7169	7181	7193	44°
46	7193	7206	7218	7230	7242	7254	7266	7278	7290	7302	7314	43 12
47	7314	7325	7337	7349	7361	7373	7385	7396	7408	7420	7431	42
48	7431	7443	7455	7466	7478	7490	7501	7513	7524	7536	7547	41
49	7547	7559	7570	7581	7593	7604	7615	7627	7638	7649	7660	40
50	0.7660	7672	7683	7694	7705	7716	7727	7738	7749	7760	7771	39
51	7771	7782	7793	7804	7815	7826	7837	7848	7859	7869	7880	38 11
52	7880	7891	7902	7912	7923	7934	7944	7955	7965	7976	7986	37
53	7986	7997	8007	8018	8028	8039	8049	8059	8070	8080	8090	36
54	8090	8100	8111	8121	8131	8141	8151	8161	8171	8181	8192	35
55	0.8192	8202	8211	8221	8231	8241	8251	8261	8271	8281	8290	34 10
56	8290	8300	8310	8320	8329	8339	8348	8358	8368	8377	8387	33
57	8387	8396	8406	8415	8425	8434	8443	8453	8462	8471	8480	32
58	8480	8490	8499	8508	8517	8526	8536	8545	8554	8563	8572	31
59	8572	8281	8590	8599	8607	8616	8625	8634	8643	8652	8660	30 9
60	0.8660	8669	8678	8686	8695	8704	8712	8721	8729	8738	8746	29
61	8746	8755	8763	8771	8780	8788	8796	8805	8813	8821	8829	28
62	8829	8838	8846	8854	8862	8870	8878	8886	8894	8902	8910	27 8
63	8910	8918	8926	8934	8942	8949	8957	8965	8973	8980	8988	26
64	8988	8996	9003	9011	9018	9026	9033	9041	9048	9056	9063	25
65	0.9063	9070	9078	9085	9092	9100	9107	9114	9121	9128	9135	24
66	9135	9143	9150	9157	9164	9171	9178	9184	9191	9198	9205	23 7
67	9205	9212	9219	9225	9232	9239	9245	9252	9259	9265	9272	22
68	9272	9278	9285	9291	9298	9304	9311	9317	9323	9330	9336	21
69	9336	9342	9348	9354	9361	9367	9373	9379	9385	9391	9397	20 6
70	0.9397	9403	9409	9415	9421	9426	9432	9438	9444	9449	9455	19
71	9455	9461	9466	9472	9478	9483	9489	9494	9500	9505	9511	18
72	9511	9516	9521	9527	9532	9537	9542	9548	9553	9558	9563	17
73	9563	9568	9573	9578	9583	9588	9593	9598	9603	9608	9613	16 5
74	9613	9617	9622	9627	9632	9636	9641	9646	9650	9655	9659	15
75	0.9659	9664	9668	9673	9677	9681	9686	9690	9694	9699	9703	14
76	9703	9707	9711	9715	9720	9724	9728	9732	9736	9740	9744	13 4
77	9744	9748	9751	9755	9759	9763	9767	9770	9774	9778	9781	12
78	9781	9785	9789	9792	9796	9799	9803	9806	9810	9813	9816	11
79	9816	9820	9823	9826	9829	9833	9836	9839	9842	9845	9848	10
80	0.9848	9851	9854	9857	9860	9863	9866	9869	9871	9874	9877	9 3
81	9877	9880	9882	9885	9888	9890	9893	9895	9898	9900	9903	8
82	9903	9905	9907	9910	9912	9914	9917	9919	9921	9923	9925	7
83	9925	9928	9930	9932	9934	9936	9938	9940	9942	9943	9945	6 2
84	9945	9947	9949	9951	9952	9954	9956	9957	9959	9960	9962	5
85	0.9962	9963	9965	9966	9968	9969	9971	9972	9973	9974	9976	4
86	9976	9977	9978	9979	9980	9981	9982	9983	9984	9985	9986	3 1
87	9986	9987	9988	9989	9990	9990	9991	9992	9993	9993	9994	2
88	9994	9995	9995	9996	9996	9997	9997	9997	9998	9998	9998	1
89°	9998	9999	9999	9999	9999	1.0000	1.0000	1.0000	1.0000	1.0000	1.0000	0° 0
Complement	0.9	0.8	0.7	0.6	0.5	0.4	0.3	0.2	0.1	0.0		Angle

NATURAL COSINES

TABLE 3. NATURAL TANGENTS AND COTANGENTS

NATURAL TANGENTS

Angle	0.0	0.1	0.2	0.3	0.4	0.5	0.6	0.7	0.8	0.9	Complement difference	
0°	0.0000	0017	0035	0052	0070	0087	0105	0122	0140	0157	0175	89°
1	0175	0192	0209	0227	0244	0262	0279	0297	0314	0332	0349	88
2	0349	0367	0384	0402	0419	0437	0454	0472	0489	0507	0524	87
3	0524	0542	0559	0577	0594	0612	0629	0647	0664	0682	0699	86
4	0699	0717	0734	0752	0769	0787	0805	0822	0840	0857	0875	85
5	0.0875	0892	0910	0928	0945	0963	0981	0998	1016	1033	1051	84
6	1051	1069	1086	1104	1122	1139	1157	1175	1192	1210	1228	83
7	1228	1246	1263	1281	1299	1317	1334	1352	1370	1388	1405	82
8	1405	1423	1441	1459	1477	1495	1512	1530	1548	1566	1584	81
9	1584	1602	1620	1638	1655	1673	1691	1709	1727	1745	1763	80
10	0.1763	1781	1799	1817	1835	1853	1871	1890	1908	1926	1944	79 18
11	1944	1962	1980	1998	2016	2035	2053	2071	2089	2107	2126	78
12	2126	2144	2162	2180	2199	2217	2235	2254	2272	2290	2309	77
13	2309	2327	2345	2364	2382	2401	2419	2438	2456	2475	2493	76
14	2493	2512	2530	2549	2568	2586	2605	2623	2642	2661	2679	75
15	0.2679	2698	2717	2736	2754	2774	2792	2811	2830	2849	2867	74
16	2867	2886	2905	2924	2943	2962	2981	3000	3019	3038	3057	73 19
17	3057	3076	3096	3115	3134	3153	3172	3191	3211	3230	3249	72
18	3249	3269	3288	3307	3327	3346	3365	3385	3404	3424	3443	71
19	3443	3463	3482	3502	3522	3541	3561	3581	3600	3620	3640	70
20	0.3640	3659	3679	3699	3719	3739	3759	3779	3799	3819	3839	69
21	3839	3859	3879	3899	3919	3939	3959	3979	4000	4020	4040	68 20
22	4040	4061	4081	4101	4122	4142	4163	4183	4204	4224	4245	67
23	4245	4265	4286	4307	4327	4348	4369	4390	4411	4431	4452	66
24	4452	4473	4494	4515	4536	4557	4578	4599	4621	4642	4663	65 21
25	0.4663	4684	4706	4727	4748	4770	4791	4813	4834	4856	4877	64
26	4877	4899	4921	4942	4964	4986	5008	5029	5051	5073	5095	63
27	5095	5117	5139	5161	5184	5206	5228	5250	5272	5295	5317	62 22
28	5317	5340	5362	5384	5407	5430	5452	5475	5498	5520	5543	61
29	5543	5566	5589	5612	5635	5658	5681	5704	5727	5750	5774	60 23
30	0.5774	5797	5820	5844	5867	5890	5914	5938	5961	5985	6009	59
31	6009	6032	6056	6080	6104	6128	6152	6176	6200	6224	6249	58 24
32	6249	6273	6297	6322	6346	6371	6395	6420	6445	6469	6494	57
33	6494	6519	6544	6569	6594	6619	6644	6669	6694	6720	6745	56 25
34	6745	6771	6796	6822	6847	6873	6899	6924	6950	6976	7002	55
35	0.7002	7028	7054	7080	7107	7133	7159	7186	7212	7239	7265	54 26
36	7265	7292	7319	7346	7373	7400	7427	7454	7481	7508	7536	53 27
37	7536	7563	7590	7618	7646	7673	7701	7729	7757	7785	7813	52 28
38	7813	7841	7869	7898	7926	7954	7983	8012	8040	8069	8098	51 28
39	8098	8127	8156	8185	8214	8243	8273	8302	8332	8361	8391	50 29
40	0.8391	8421	8451	8481	8511	8541	8571	8601	8632	8662	8693	49 30
41	8693	8724	8754	8785	8816	8847	8878	8910	8941	8972	9004	48 31
42	9004	9036	9067	9099	9131	9163	9195	9228	9260	9293	9325	47 32
43	9325	9358	9391	9424	9557	9490	9523	9556	9590	9623	9567	46 33
44°	9657	9691	9725	9759	9793	9827	9861	9896	9930	9965	1.0000	45°34
Complement	0.9	0.8	0.7	0.6	0.5	0.4	0.3	0.2	0.1	0.0		Angle

NATURAL COTANGENTS

TABLE 3. NATURAL TANGENTS AND COTANGENTS (Continued)

NATURAL TANGENTS

Angle	0.0	0.1	0.2	0.3	0.4	0.5	0.6	0.7	0.8	0.9	Comp.
45°	1.0000	1.0035	1.0070	1.0105	1.0141	1.0176	1.0212	1.0247	1.0283	1.0319	44°
46	1.0355	1.0392	1.0428	1.0464	1.0501	1.0538	1.0575	1.0612	1.0649	1.0686	43
47	1.0724	1.0761	1.0799	1.0837	1.0875	1.0913	1.0951	1.0990	1.1028	1.1067	42
48	1.1106	1.1145	1.1184	1.1224	1.1263	1.1303	1.1343	1.1383	1.1423	1.1463	41
49	1.1504	1.1544	1.1585	1.1626	1.1667	1.1708	1.1750	1.1792	1.1833	1.1875	40
50	1.1918	1.1960	1.2002	1.2045	1.2088	1.2131	1.2174	1.2218	1.2261	1.2305	39
51	1.2349	1.2393	1.2437	1.2482	1.2527	1.2572	1.2617	1.2662	1.2708	1.2753	38
52	1.2799	1.2846	1.2892	1.2938	1.2985	1.3032	1.3079	1.3127	1.3175	1.3222	37
53	1.3270	1.3319	1.3367	1.3416	1.3465	1.3514	1.3564	1.3613	1.3663	1.3713	36
54	1.3764	1.3814	1.3865	1.3916	1.3968	1.4019	1.4071	1.4124	1.4176	1.4229	35
55	1.4281	1.4335	1.4388	1.4442	1.4496	1.4550	1.4605	1.4659	1.4715	1.4770	34
56	1.4826	1.4882	1.4938	1.4994	1.5051	1.5108	1.5166	1.5224	1.5282	1.5340	33
57	1.5399	1.5458	1.5517	1.5577	1.5637	1.5697	1.5757	1.5818	1.5880	1.5941	32
58	1.6003	1.6066	1.6128	1.6191	1.6255	1.6319	1.6383	1.6447	1.6512	1.6577	31
59	1.6643	1.6709	1.6775	1.6842	1.6909	1.6977	1.7045	1.7113	1.7182	1.7251	30
60	1.7321	1.7391	1.7461	1.7532	1.7603	1.7675	1.7747	1.7820	1.7893	1.7966	29
61	1.8040	1.8115	1.8190	1.8265	1.8341	1.8418	1.8495	1.8572	1.8650	1.8728	28
62	1.8807	1.8887	1.8967	1.9047	1.9128	1.9210	1.9292	1.9375	1.9458	1.9542	27
63	1.9626	1.9711	1.9797	1.9883	1.9970	2.0057	2.0145	2.0233	2.0323	2.0413	26
64	2.0503	2.0594	2.0686	2.0778	2.0872	2.0965	2.1060	2.1155	2.1251	2.1348	25
65	2.145	2.154	2.164	2.174	2.184	2.194	2.204	2.215	2.225	2.236	24
66	2.246	2.257	2.257	2.278	2.289	2.300	2.311	2.322	2.333	2.344	23
67	2.356	2.367	2.379	2.391	2.402	2.414	2.426	2.438	2.450	2.463	22
68	2.475	2.488	2.500	2.513	2.526	2.539	2.552	2.565	2.578	2.592	21
69	2.605	2.619	2.633	2.646	2.660	2.675	2.689	2.703	2.718	2.733	20
70	2.747	2.762	2.778	2.793	2.808	2.824	2.840	2.856	2.872	2.888	19
71	2.904	2.921	2.937	2.954	2.971	2.989	3.006	3.024	3.042	3.060	18
72	3.078	3.096	3.115	3.133	3.152	3.172	3.191	3.211	3.230	3.250	17
73	3.271	3.291	3.312	3.333	3.354	3.376	3.398	3.420	3.442	3.465	16
74	3.487	3.511	3.534	3.558	3.582	3.606	3.630	3.655	3.681	3.700	15
75	3.732	3.758	3.785	3.812	3.839	3.867	3.895	3.923	3.952	3.981	14
76	4.011	4.041	4.071	4.102	4.134	4.165	4.198	4.230	4.264	4.297	13
77	4.331	4.366	4.402	4.437	4.474	4.511	4.548	4.586	4.625	4.665	12
78	4.705	4.745	4.787	4.829	4.872	4.915	4.959	5.005	5.050	5.097	11
79	5.145	5.193	5.242	5.292	5.343	5.396	5.449	5.503	5.558	5.614	10
80	5.67	5.73	5.79	5.85	5.91	5.98	6.04	6.11	6.17	6.24	9
81	6.31	6.39	6.46	6.54	6.61	6.69	6.77	6.86	6.94	7.03	8
82	7.12	7.21	7.30	7.40	7.49	7.60	7.70	7.81	7.92	8.03	7
83	8.14	8.26	8.39	8.51	8.64	8.78	8.92	9.06	9.21	9.36	6
84	9.51	9.68	9.84	10.0	10.2	10.4	10.6	10.8	11.0	11.2	5
85	11.4	11.7	11.9	12.2	12.4	12.7	13.0	13.3	13.6	14.0	4
86	14.3	14.7	15.1	15.5	15.9	16.3	16.8	17.3	17.9	18.5	3
87	19.1	19.7	20.4	21.2	22.0	22.9	23.9	24.9	26.0	27.3	2
88	28.6	30.1	31.8	33.7	35.8	38.2	40.9	44.1	47.7	52.1	1
89°	57.	64.	72.	95.	115.	143.	191.	286.	286.	573.	0°
Angle	1.0	0.9	0.8	0.7	0.6	0.5	0.4	0.3	0.2	0.1	

NATURAL COTANGENTS

Index

Abampere, 624
Aberration, chromatic, 531, 534
  spherical, 484, 485, 508, 510
Absolute humidity, 212, 214
Absolute potential, 294, 299
Absolute system of units, 36
Absolute temperature scale, 197, 200, 235, 236
Absorption, coefficient of, 274
  dielectric, 425
  of light, selective, 542, 548
  of sound, 260, 261
    coefficient of, 273
      table, 274
Absorption spectra, 533, 535
A-c circuit (*see* Circuits)
Acceleration, 27, 30
  angular, 93, 99
  central, 115, 120
  due to gravity, 28
  and mass, 36
  in SHM, 134, 136, 140
  variable, 41
Accommodation, 515, 523
Accuracy, 621
Achromatic colors (grays), 538
Achromatic prism and lens, 531, 534
Acoustic resonance, 255, 261
Acoustics, 265, 274
  of rooms, 273
Action and reaction, 41, 117
Actual mechanical advantage, 65, 69
Addition of vectors, 12, 19
  method of, component, 14, 19
    parallelogram, 12, 19
    polygon, 13, 19
Additive production of colors, 542, 548
Adhesion, 177, 183
Adiabatic process, 231, 236
Agonic line, 378
Air, 166
  friction in, 157
  mass of, 166
  pressure of, 166
  resistance of, 51, 52, 157

Airfoil, 160, 162
  drag of, 158, 161
Alpha particles, 602, 616
Alternating current, 431, 439
  frequency of, 410, 431, 439
  phase of, 433, 440
Ammeter, 365, 367
Ampere, definition, 308
Ampere (unit), 353
Amperian currents, 344
Amplification of sound, 255
Amplifier, electron tube, 451
Amplitude, 247, 250
Analyzer, 563
Anastigmatic lens, 509
Angle, 92
  of attack, 161
  of contact, 180
  critical, 494, 497
  of elevation, 50
  of incidence and reflection, 477, 485
  of minimum deviation, 496, 497, 530, 534
  of polarization, 564
  of refraction, 490
  of repose, 57
Angstrom unit, 462
Angular acceleration, 93, 99
Angular harmonic motion, 138
Angular magnification, 520
Angular momentum, 107, 111
  conservation of, 107, 111
  vector properties, 108, 111
Angular motion, 92, 99
  compared with linear, 98, 99
  Newton's laws for, 96, 99
  uniformly accelerated, 98, 99
  vector properties of, 96
  (*See also* Rotary motion)
Angular speed, 92, 99, 115
Angular velocity, 92
Anode, 447
Antinode, 249, 250
Aperture, lens, 522
  mirror, 486
Arc lamp, 463
Archimedes' principle, 148, 150

Armature, 411
Artificial disintegration, 603, 607, 617
Astigmatism, 509, 510
  ocular, 516, 523
Atmosphere, pressure in, 168, 171
Atmosphere (unit), 146
Atmospheric refraction, 493, 497
Atom, structure of, 282, 588, 592
Atomic mass unit (amu), 610
Atomic number, 282, 591
Atomic spectra, 533, 535, 692
Audibility, limits of, 268

Back emf, 407, 413, 414
Ballistic galvanometer, 364, 367
Ballistics, 48, 52
Band spectra, 533, 535
Band theory of conduction, 599
Banking of curves, 119, 120
Bar, 169
Barometer, aneroid, 169
  mercury, 167
Barometric pressure, 168, 171
Barrier layer, 337
Battery, 322
  charging of, 321, 325
  storage, 321, 325
Beats, 260, 261
Bel, 269, 274
Bernoulli's theorem, 158, 162
Beta particle, 602, 616
Betatron, 609
Binaural effect, 273
Binding energy, 614, 617
Binocular, prism, 522
Binocular vision, 517
Biot-Savart law, 347, 626
Blackbody, 222, 224
Blackbody radiation, 534, 581
Blind spot, 515
Block and tackle, 71
Bohr atom model, 592
Boiling, 209, 213
Boyle's law, 169, 171, 198
Bragg diffraction of x rays, 590
Brake horsepower, 68
Breaking stress, 126

Brewster's law, 565, 571
Bridge, Wheatstone, 332, 338
Brightness, 540, 548
Brinell hardness number, 126, 128, 129
British thermal unit (Btu), 205, 213
Brownian motion, 182, 183
Bulk modulus of elasticity, 127, 129, 171
Buoyancy, 148, 166

Calorie, 205, 213
Calorimeter, 207, 213
  electric, 385
Camera, photographic, 522
Candle, 465, 469, 471
Capacitance, 420, 426
  of parallel-plate capacitor, 421, 426
  units of, 421, 426
Capacitive reactance, 436, 440
Capacitor, air, 421, 422
  charge and discharge of, 424, 426
  electrolytic, 422
  energy of, 426
  in parallel, 424, 426
  parallel-plate, 421, 426
  residual charge in, 425
  in series, 424, 426
Capillarity, 180
Carnot cycle, 233
Cathode, 447, 588
Cathode-ray oscilloscope, 453, 456
Cathode rays, 447, 453, 455
Caustic, 484
Cells, 304, 311
  dry, 304
  Edison, 305
  lead, 305
  optimum connection of, 323
  in parallel, 322, 325
  photoelectric, 455
  primary, 304
  in series, 322, 325
  storage, 305
  voltaic, 304
Center, of curvature, 480
  of gravity, 85, 87
Centigrade scale, 190, 200
Centimeter, 6
  of mercury, 146
Centipoise, 59
Central acceleration, 115, 120
Centrifugal governor, 118
Centrifugal reaction, 117, 120
Centrifuge, 118
Centripetal force, 116, 120
Cgs units, 7, 36
Chain reaction, 615, 617
Change of state, 207
Characteristic curves, 452

Charge, conservation of, 611
  electric, 281, 284, 288, 309, 311
    density of, 297, 300
    distribution of, 297, 300
    unit of, 309, 311
  of electron, 449
Charges, force between, 281, 284, 288
Charging, of battery, 321, 325
  of capacitor, 424, 426
  by conduction, 281, 284
  by induction, 282, 296
Charles's laws, 198
Chemical equivalent, 309
Choke coil, 437
Chromatic aberration, 531, 534
Chromatic colors, 538
Chromaticity, 540, 546, 548
Chromaticity coordinates, 546, 548
  diagram of, 546
Circle, of confusion, 523
  of reference, 135, 137, 140
Circuits, 316
  a-c, 431, 439
    phase relations in, 433, 440
  inductive, 435, 440
  magnetic, 376, 379
  parallel, 318
  power in, 437, 440
  resonant, 439, 440
  series, 317
Circular mil, 334, 338
Circular motion, 92, 99
  (See also Angular motion)
Cloud chamber, 604
Coefficient, of absorption, 274
  of convection, 221, 224
  of expansion, 192, 195, 200
  of friction, 56, 57, 59
  of pressure change, 196
  of restitution, 106, 111
  of rigidity, 127
  of viscosity, 59
Coercive force, 375
Cohesion, 177, 183
Collisions, 106, 107
  elastic and inelastic, 106, 111
Color, 538, 548
  by absorption, 542, 548
  by addition, 542, 548
  chromatic, 538
  classification of, 538, 548
  complementary, 541, 548
  physical correlates of, 547, 548
  primary, 541, 548
  production of, 542, 548
  of sky, 534
  specification of, 543, 548
  surface, 546
  unattached, 539
Color atlas, Munsell, 539
Color filters, 544
Color mixtures, 538, 540, 548
Color solid, 539

Color theory, Young-Helmholtz, 540
Color vision, 540
Colorimetry, 538, 540, 548
Coma, 508, 510
Commutator, 411
Compass, magnetic, 308, 378
Complementary colors, 541, 548
Complexity of sound wave, 266, 274
Component, vector, 13, 19
Component method of adding vectors, 14, 17, 19
Compressibility, 127, 129
Compressional waves, 245, 250, 253
Compton effect, 582
Computations, rules for, 622
Concave mirror, 480, 483
Concurrent forces, 16, 84
Condenser (see Capacitor)
Conductance, 335, 338
Conduction, electrical, 445, 450, 455
  of electricity through gases, 445, 455
  electrolytic, 445
  electron theories of, 597
  in solids, 599
  thermal, 218, 223
Conductivity, electrical, 335, 338
  thermal, 219, 223
Conductors, electrical, 283, 335, 599
  field inside, 298, 300
Cones, retinal, 515, 518
Conjugate foci, 481, 482
Conservation, of angular momentum, 107, 111
  of charge, 611
  of energy, 76, 77
  of mass and energy, 581, 609
  of momentum, 105, 111
Consonance, 271
Constants, physical, 626
Contact, angle of, 180
Continuous spectra, 532, 535
Convection, 218, 220, 223
  coefficient, 221, 224
Conventional current, 305, 311
Converging lens, 501, 509
Conversion of units, 8, 624
Convex mirror, 480, 483
Coordinates, relativistic, transformations of, 580
Copper loss, 406
Cornea, 514
Corona discharge, 298, 300
Corpuscular theory of light, 461, 471
Cosmic rays, 611, 617
Cost of electric energy, 388, 391
Coulomb's law in electrostatics, 284, 288
Couple, 86, 87

Critical angle, 494, 497
Critical mass, 614, 617
Critical point, 211, 213
Critical temperature, 211, 213
Crookes dark space, 447
Crystal, dichroic, 567
  doubly refracting, 565
  optic axis of, 566
Curie (unit), 606
Current, 303, 311
  alternating, 431, **439**
  conventional, 305, **311**
  direct, 411, 414
  direction of, 305
  eddy, 406, 414
  effective (rms), 432, **440**
  effects of, 307
  force on, 344, 350, 353, 354
  growth and decay of, 406, 414
  heating effect of, 384, 386, 390
  induced, 397, 400
    direction of, 399, 400
  lagging and leading, 433, 440
  magnetic field of, 308
  sources of, 303, 311
  torque on, 351, 354
  unit of, 308, 311
Current sensitivity, 362, 367
Curvature, center of, 480
  radius of, 480
Curvilinear motion, 119
Cycle, Carnot, 233
Cyclotron, 608

Damping, 248
  of galvanometer, 360, **367**
de Broglie wave, 594
Decibel, 269, 274
Decimeter, 6
Declination, magnetic, 378, 380
Density, 145, 150
  of gases, 167
Depth of field, 523
Detector, electron tube, 451
Deuterium, 454
Deuteron, 613
Deviation, minimum, angle of, 496, 497, 530, 534
Dew point, 211, 213
Dewar flask, 222
Diamagnetism, 373, 379
Diatonic scale, 271
Dichroic crystal, 567
Dielectric absorption, 425
Dielectric strength, 423, 426
Diffraction, 249, 250
  of light waves, 556, 560
    by circular aperture, 558
    at edge of shadow, 556
    Fraunhofer, 557
    by grating, 558
    by screen, 553
    by slit, 556

Diffraction pattern, **557**
Diffusion, 181, 183
Diode, 450, 456
Diopter, 506, 510
Dip needle, 378, 380
Discharge, of capacitor, 424, 426
  electric, 298, 300, 446
Disintegration, artificial, 603, 607, 617
  nuclear, 607, 609, 617
Disintegration constant, 606
Dispersion, optical, 529, 534
Displacement, 11, 247
Dissonance, 271
Distortion, 509, 510
Distribution of electric energy, 405, 414
Diverging lens, 501, 509
Domain theory, 377, 380
Dominant wavelength, 547, 548
Doppler's principle, 260, 261
Double refraction, 565
Drag of airfoil, 158, **161**
Dry cell, 304
Ductility, 128
Dyne, 36, **43**

Ear, 270, **274**
Echo, 259, 261
Eclipse, 463
Eddy currents, 406, **414**
Edison cell, 305
Effective current and voltage, 432, 440
Efficiency, 66, 69
  of heat engine, 236
  luminous, 469
Einstein mass-energy relation, 581, 609
Einstein photoelectric equation, 582, 584
Elastic collision, 106, 111
Elastic fatigue, 128
Elastic lag, 126
Elastic limit, 125, 127, 219
Elasticity, 124, 129
  coefficients of, 126
  of gases, 169, 171
  modulus of (see Modulus of elasticity)
Elasticity, of shear, 127, 129
  volume, 126, 129
Electric calorimeter, 385
Electric charge (see Charge)
Electric current, 303, 311
  in gases, 445, 455
Electric energy, 384, 390
  cost of, 388, 391
  distribution of, 405, 414
  sink of, 317, 321
Electric field, 285, 288
  inside conductor, 298, 300
  intensity of, 285

Electric field, intensity of, near a point charge, 286
Electric furnace, 386
Electric lamp, 386, 463, **471**
Electric oscillations, 438
Electric potential, 292, 299
  near isolated charge, 294
Electrical conductors, 599
Electrical resonance, 439, 440
Electricity, 5, 281
  conduction of, 283
  quantity of, 284
Electrification, 281, 288, 296
Electrochemical equivalent, 309, 311
Electrolysis, 308, 311
  Faraday's laws of, 309, 311
Electrolytic cell, 307
Electromagnet, 376
Electromagnetic induction, 397, 400, 404, 414
Electromagnetic units, 623
Electromagnetic waves, 462, 548, 561
Electromotive force (see Emf)
Electron, 282, 445, 448
  charge of, 449
  charge/mass ratio, 449
  free, 283
  mass of, 283, 284
Electron flow, 306
Electron speeds, Fermi distribution, 598
  Maxwell distribution, 597
Electron tubes, 450, 456
Electron volt, 608
Electronics, 445, 597
Electroplating, 309, **311**
Electroscope, 283
Electrostatic generator, 299, 300
Electrostatic units, 284, 288
Elevation, angle of, 50
Emf, 317, 325
  back, 407, 413, 414
  forward, 407, 414
  in generator, 409, 414
  induced, 397, 400
    direction of, 399
    in straight wire, 398
  and internal resistance, 320, 325
  measurement of, 337, 338
  and potential difference, 316
Emission spectra, 532, 535
Energy, 65, 69, 74, 77
  of charged capacitor, 426
  conservation of, 76, 77
  distribution of, in spectrum, **534**
  electric (see Electric energy)
  from fission and fusion, 615, 617
  heat, 205, 213
  kinetic (see Kinetic energy)
  potential, 65, 69, 74, 77, 125
  in rotational motion, 97, 99

Energy, transformation of, 76, 77, 307, 386, 390
   of a wave, 248, 250
Energy levels, 592
Engine, Carnot, 233
Engineering, 5
Engineering units, 8
Enthalpy, 232
Equilibrant, 17
Equilibrium, 15, 20
   condition for, first, 16, 20
     second, 82, 84, 87
   radioactive, 606
Equipotential surface, 295, 300
Equivalent resistance, 438, 440
Erg, 64
Ether, 577, 579
Evaporation, 209
Evenly tempered scale, 272
Exit pupil, 520
Expansion, coefficient of, linear, 192, 200
     volume, 195, 200
   of gases, 196, 198
   Joule-Thomson, 233
   of solids, 192, 200
   of water, 196
Expansivity, 192, 195, 200
Extraordinary ray, 564
Eye, 514, 523
   accommodation of, 515, 523
   blind spot of, 515
   refractive errors of, 515, 523
   sensitivity of, 517
Eyepiece lens, 519, 523

f-number, 522, 523
Fahrenheit scale, 190, 200
Falling bodies, 29, 30
   terminal speed, 30
Farad, 421, 426
Faraday (unit), 310, 311
Faraday dark space, 447
Faraday ice-pail experiments, 298
Faraday's law of induced emf, 398, 400
Faraday's laws of electrolysis, 309, 311
Farsightedness, 516, 523
Fathometer, 259
Fatigue, elastic, 128
Fermi distribution, 598
Ferromagnetism, 374, 379
Field (see Electric field; Magnetic field)
Field magnet, 376, 441
Figures, significant, 8, 600
Film coefficient, 221, 224
Films, interference in, 553
   surface, 178, 183
Filters, color, 542, 548
Fission, nuclear, 614, 617
Fixed point, 190, 200

Flowmeter, 160
Fluid, 145
Fluid flow, 156, 162
   through a constriction, 157
   friction in, 157, 158
   from orifice, 161
   pressure and speed in, 159, 162
   steady, 157
   streamline, 157
   tube of, 157
   turbulent, 157
Fluorescence, 533, 535
Fluorescent lamp, 464
Flux, luminous, 464, 471
   magnetic, 345
Flux density, magnetic, 345, 353
Focal length, 486, 502, 507, 509
Focus, principal, 485, 486, 502, 509
   virtual, 486, 502
Foot-candle, 466, 471
Foot-candle meter, 468, 472
Foot-pound, 64, 69
Force, 35, 43
   centripetal, 116, 120
   between charges, 281, 284, 288
   coercive, 375
   concurrent, 84
   between currents, 352, 354
   on currents, 344, 350, 353, 354
   of friction, 55
   lines of, electric, 287, 288, 295
   between molecules, 176
   moment of, 83
   nonconcurrent, 84
   nuclear, 612
   reacting, 41
Force constant, 125
Forced vibration, 139, 255, 261
Forward emf, 407, 414
Foucault current, 406, 414
Fovea, 515, 518
Fps units, 7
Fraunhofer diffraction, 557
Fraunhofer lines, 533
Free electron, 283
Freezing point, 190, 210, 213
Frequencies of vowel sounds, 270
Frequency, 135, 140, 246, 250, 410
   of alternating current, 410, 431
     resonant, 439
   of sound, 260, 266, 268
Friction, 55, 59, 117
   in air, 58
   coefficient of, 56, 57, 59
   fluid, 58, 59, 157, 159
   kinetic, 55
   limiting, 57
   rolling, 57
   sliding, 57, 59
Fundamental quantities, 6, 8
Fundamental units, 6, 8
Fundamental vibration, 254, 261
Furnace, electric, 386
Fuse, 386

Fusion, heat of, 208, 213
   nuclear, 615, 617

g (acceleration due to gravity), 28, 30, 37, 118
Gage pressure, 170, 171
Galilean telescope, 521, 523
Galvanometer, 360, 367
   ballistic, 364, 367
   damping, 360, 367
   sensitivity, 362, 367
Gamma rays, 602, 616
Gas, 166, 171
   conduction of electricity in, 445
   density of, 167
   elasticity of, 169, 171
   expansion of, 196, 198
     work by, 231, 236
   kinetic theory of, 176
   pressure of, 169, 171, 176
   specific heats of, 230, 232, 236
   and vapor, 211
Gas constant, 199
Gas laws, 198, 200
Gas thermometer, 196
Gauss (unit), 345
Geiger counter, 603
Generator, 306, 311, 409, 414
   a-c, 307, 410, 414
   compound, 411
   d-c, 411, 414
   emf in, 411
   field of, 411
   series-wound, 411
   shunt-wound, 411
   Van de Graaff, 299
Geometrical optics, 5, 461
Governor, centrifugal, 118
Gradient, temperature, 218, 223
Gram, 7, 37
Grating, diffraction, 558
Gravitation, 42, 43
Gravitational constant (G), 42, 43
Gravitational system of units, 36, 37
Gravity, 28, 30, 37, 118
   center of, 85, 87
   specific, 146, 149, 150
Greek alphabet, 625
Grid, 451
Gyration, radius of, 95, 99
Gyroscope, 110, 111

Half-life period, 606
Hardness, Brinell number, 126, 128, 129
   Rockwell number, 128
Harmonic, 254, 261
Harmonic motion, 133, 140
   angular, 138
   simple (see Simple harmonic motion)

Heat, 4, 205, 213
  exchange of, 222
  of fusion, 208, 213
  mechanical equivalent of, 229, 236, 385, 390
  specific, 206, 213, 230, 232, 236
  transfer of, 218
    by conduction, 218, 223
    by convection, 218, 220, 223
    by radiation, 218, 221, 224
    through surface films, 221, 224
  of vaporization, 207, 213
Heat engines, 233, 236
  Carnot, 233
  efficiency of, 236
Heating effect of current, 384, 390
  applications of, 386, 390
Henry (unit), 408, 414
Hooke's law, 125, 129
Horsepower, 67, 69
  human, 68
Hue, 538, 548
Humidity, absolute, 212, 214
  relative, 212, 214
  specific, 212, 214
Huygens' principle, 476, 485, 491
Hydraulic press, 150
Hydrometer, 149
Hydrostatic pressure, 147, 150
Hyperfocal distance, 523
Hyperon, 612, 613
Hyperopia, 516
Hysteresis, elastic, 126
  magnetic, 375, 379
Hysteresis loop, 375

Ideal gas laws, 198, 200
Ideal mechanical advantage, 65, 69
Ideal radiator, 222, 224
Illuminance, 465, 467, 471
Illumination, levels of, 467
Image, formation of, by lens, 503, 510
    by mirror, 481, 485
    real, 478, 485, 505
    virtual, 478, 485, 506
Impact, elastic and inelastic, 106, 111
Impedance, 435, 440
Impulse, 105, 111
  angular, 108
Inclined plane, 65, 70
Index of refraction, 491, 497, 530
  absolute, 491, 497
  measurement of, 530
Induced current and emf, 397, 400
  direction of, 399, 400
  in straight wire, 398, 400
Inductance, mutual, 409, 414
  self-, 408, 414
Induction, electrification by, 282, 296

Induction, electromagnetic, 397–400, 404, 414
  magnetic, 344, 353
  self-, 406, 409, 414
Inductive circuit, 406, 409
  energy in, 409, 414
Inductive reactance, 435, 440
Inertia, 35, 43
  moment of, 94, 95, 99
  rotational, 94, 99
Infrared radiation, 462
Insulator, electrical, 283, 600
Intensity, luminous, 465, 471
  mean spherical, 465
  of a wave, 248, 250
Intensity level (sound), 269, 274
Interfacial tension, 181
Interference, conditions for, 551, 559, 569
  constructive, 550, 559
  destructive, 550, 559
  with double slit, 532
  of light waves, 550, 559
  measurement of wavelength by, 555, 558
  Newton's rings, 555, 559
  of polarized light, 569
  with single slit, 556
  in thin films, 553
  of waves, 249, 250, 259, 261
  Young's experiment on, 550
Interference fringes, 552
Interferometer, 555, 559, 577
Internal reflection, 494, 497
Internal resistance, 320, 325
Interval, musical, 271
    diatonic, 271
    tempered, 272
Inverse square law, 466, 472
Ionization by collision, 446
Ionizing particles, 604
Ionizing potential, 446, 593
Ions, 309, 445, 604
Iris, 514
Iron loss, 406
Irreversible process, 233
Isogonic line, 378
Isothermal process, 231, 236
Isotopes, 454, 456

Jack screw, 67
Jet propulsion, 51
Joule, J. P., 229
Joule (unit), 65, 69
Joule's law, 385, 390
Joule-Thomson expansion, 233

Kelvin temperature scale, 235, 236
Kilocalorie, 206
Kilogram, 7, 37
Kilometer, 6
Kilowatt, 67, 69

Kilowatt-hour, 388, 391
Kinetic energy, 65, 69, 75, 77
  in relativity theory, 581, 584
  of rotation, 97, 99
  transformation of, 76, 77, 386, 390, 581, 584
Kinetic theory of gas, 176
Kirchhoff's law (radiation), 533

Lagging current, 433, 440
Lambert (unit), 469
Lamps, 463
  fluorescent, 464
Laue diffraction of x rays, 590, 594
Leading current, 433, 440
Length, 6, 8
Lens, 501
  aberrations of, 508, 510
    chromatic, 531, 534
    achromatic, 531, 534
    anastigmatic, 509
  circle of confusion of, 523
  combinations, 506, 510
  in contact, 508
  converging and diverging, 501, 509
  depth of field of, 523
  eyepiece, 519, 523
  f-number of, 522, 523
  focal length of, 502, 509
  magnification by, 506, 510
  microscope, 519, 523
  objective, 519, 523
  power of, 506, 510
    resolving, 558
  speed of, 522, 523
  telescope, 520, 523
Lens combinations, 506, 510
Lens equation, 504, 510
Lenz's law, 399, 400
Lever, 65, 69, 85
  optical, 479, 485
Lift, airfoil, 161
Light, 461, 471
  corpuscular theory of, 461, 471
  electromagnetic theory of, 462
  infrared, 462
  monochromatic, 532
  polarization of (see Polarization of light)
  polarized, 563
  quantum of, 462
  reflection of, 476, 485
  scattering of, 568
  selective absorption of, 542, 548
  sources of, 463, 469
  speed of, 470, 472
  ultraviolet, 462
  visible, 462, 471
  wave properties of, 461, 462, 550, 559, 563, 571
Light rays, 462
Light vector, 564

Light waves, 462, 471
 interference of, 550, 559, 569
 retardation of, 554
Lighting, 463, 464, 467, 471
Lightness, 539, 548
Limiting angle, 57
Line drop, 320
Linear and angular motion compared, 98
Linear expansion, coefficient of, 192, 200
Linear magnification, 484, 485, 506, 510, 518, 523
Lines of force, electric, 287, 288, 295
Liquid flow (see Fluid flow)
Liquid pressure, 148, 150, 159
Longitudinal wave, 244, 250, 253
Looming, 493
Loop, 249, 250
Loud-speaker, 255
Loudness, 267, 274
Lubrication, 59
Lumen, 465, 471
Luminance, 468, 472, 547
Luminosity, 464
Luminous efficiency, 469
Luminous flux, 464, 471
Luminous intensity, 465, **471**
Lux, 466, 472

Machine, 65, 69
Magnet, 344
Magnetic alloys, 376
Magnetic circuit, 376, 379
Magnetic compass, 308, 378
Magnetic declination, 378, 380
Magnetic dip needle, 378, 380
Magnetic effect of current, 308, 345, 353
Magnetic field (induction), 344, 353
 on axis of coil, 347, 353
 at center of circular loop, 346, 353
 between conductors, 352
 direction of, 344
 due to current, 308, 345, 353
 of earth, 378, 380
Magnetic flux, 345, 353, 377
Magnetic hysteresis, 375, 379
Magnetic induction, 344, 353
Magnetic permeability, 346, 353, 373, 379
Magnetic poles, 377
Magnetic properties, 372, 379
 of alloys, 376, 379
Magnetic saturation, 375, 379
Magnetic variation, 378
Magnetism, 5, 372, 379
 domain theory of, 377, 380
 terrestrial, 378, 380
Magnetization curve, 374

Magnetizing force, 374
Magnetomotive force (mmf), 376, 379
Magnification, 484, 485, 506, 510, 520
 angular, 520
 linear, 484, 485, 506, 510, 518, 523
Magnifier, 518, 523
Malleability, 128
Manometer, 170
Mass, 6, 8, 35, 43
 critical, 614, 617
 variation of, with speed, 581, 584
Mass-energy equation, 581, 609
Mass-energy transitions, 609
Mass spectrograph, 453, 456
Maxwell (unit), 345
Maxwell distribution, 597
Mean spherical luminous intensity, 465
Measurement, 5, 8, 521
Mechanical advantage, actual, 65, 69
 ideal, 66, 69
Mechanical equivalent of heat, 229, 236, 385, 390
Mechanics, 4
Mesons, 612, 617
Meter, 6
Meter-candle, 467, 472
Meter errors, 366
Method of mixture, 206
Metric system, 6, 623
Mho, 335
Michelson interferometer, 555, 559, 577
Michelson-Morley experiment, 578, 584
Microfarad, 421, 426
Micron, 462
Microphone, 272
Microscope, 519, 523
Mil, 334
Millibar, 169
Millikan oil-drop experiment, 449
Millimeter, 6
Minimum deviation by a prism, 495, 496, 530, 534
Mirage, 493, 497
Mirror equation, 482, 485
Mirrors, parabolic, 485
 plane, 487, 485
 spherical, 480, 485
Mixture, method of, 206
Mks units, 8, 623
Moderator, 615
Modern physics, 5, 577
Modulus of elasticity, 125, 129
 bulk, 127, 129, 171
 shear, 127, 129
 volume, 127, 129
 Young's, 126, 129
Molecular speeds, 176

Molecular theory of matter, **175,** 182
Molecules, 175
Moment, of force, 83
 of inertia, 94, 99
 of cylinder, 95
 of torsion, 138, 140
Moment arm, 83, 87
Momentum, 104, 111, 581
 angular, 107, 108, 111
 conservation of, 105, 111
 vector properties, 108, 111
Mosley's law, 591
Motion, 25, 35
 accelerated, uniformly, 27, 30
 angular (see Angular motion)
 curvilinear, 119
 laws of (see Newton's laws of motion)
 periodic, 133, 140
 planetary, 120
 projectile, 48, 52
 rotational (see Rotary motion)
 simple harmonic (see Simple harmonic motion)
 uniform circular, 115, 120
 wave, 243
Motor, 404, 412, 414
 back emf in, 413
 torque of, 412, 414
Munsell color atlas, 539
Musical scales, 271, 272, 274
Musical tone, 265, 274
Mutual inductance, 409, 414
Myopia, 516

Natural philosophy, **4**
Nearsightedness, 515, 523
Negative glow, 447
Network, 324
Neutrino, 592, 611, 613
Neutron, 282, 610, 613, **617**
Newton, Sir Isaac, 7, 35
Newton (unit), 37, 43
Newton-meter, 65, 69
Newton's law, of cooling, 223
 of gravitation, 42, 43
Newton's laws of motion, 35, 36, 41, 43
 angular, 96, 99
 units in, 38
Newton's rings, 555, 559
Nicol prism, 567
Node, 249, 250
Noise, 266
Nuclear fission, 614, 617
Nuclear force, 612
Nuclear fusion, 615, 617
Nuclear physics, 602
Nuclear reactions, 611
Nuclear reactor, 614, 617
Nucleus, 282, 592, 613, 617

Objective lens, 519, 523
Octave, 271
Ohm (unit), 310, 312
Ohm's law, 310, 312, 316, 325
Optic axis, 566
Optical lever, 479, 485
Optical pyrometer, 192
Optical rotation, 568, 571
Optically active substance, 569
Optics, 5, 461
　geometrical, 461, 490
　physical, 461
　physiological, 461, 514, 540
　quantum, 461
Ordinary ray, 566
Orifice, discharge from, 160, 162
　flow through, 160, 162
Oscillations, electric, 438
Oscilloscope, cathode-ray, 453
Osmosis, 182, 183
Osmotic pressure, 182, 183
Overtone, 254, 261

Parallax, 517
Parallel-axis theorem, 95
Parallel circuits, 318, 322, 325
Parallelogram method of adding vectors, 12, 19
Paramagnetism, 374, 379
Particles of atomic physics, 613
Pascal's law, 150, 151
Pelton wheel, 161
Pendulum, 77
　simple, 138, 140
　torsion, 138, 140
Pentode, 452
Penumbra, 463
Period, 135, 140
　of wave, 246, 250
Periodic motion, 133, 140
Permeability, 346, 353, 373, 379, 624
　relative, 373, 379
Permittivity, 285, 421, 426, 624
Persistence of vision, 517
Phase, in a-c circuits, 433, 440
　change of, on reflection, 554, 559
　of a wave, 246, 250
Phase angle, 434, 440
Phase diagram, 435, 440
　CO_2, 211
　water, 210
Phases of matter, 213, 228
Phosphorescence, 533, 535
Photoelastic pattern, 195
Photoelasticity, 570
Photoelectric cell, 307, 311, 455
Photoelectric effect, 454, 456, 582
Photographic camera, 522
Photometer, 468, 472
Photon, 582, 613
　disintegration by, 611
　scattering of, 582

Photovoltaic cell, 455
Photronic cell, 455
Physical constants, 626
Physical optics, 461
Physics, 4, 8
　modern, 5, 589
Physiological optics, 461, 514, 540
Piezoelectricity, 307, 311
Pitch, 266, 274
Planck's constant, 462
Plane of polarization, 563
Plane mirrors, 478
Planetary motion, 120
Plasma, 616
Poise, 59
Polarimeter, 569
Polarization, of a cell, 305
　of light, 563
　　by Nicol prism, 567
　　by reflection, 564
　　by scattering, 568
　　by selective absorption, 567
　plane of, 563
Polarized light, 563
　applications of, 569
　intensity of, 565, 571
　interference of, 569
　rotation of plane of, 568
Polarizer, 563
　Polaroid, 568
Polarizing angle, 564, 571
Polygon method of adding vectors, 13, 19
Positive column, 447
Positive rays, 453, 456
Positron, 612, 617
Potential, electric, 292
　ionizing, 445, 593
　near point charge, 294, 300
　at a point ("absolute potential"), 294, 299
Potential difference, 292, 299, 310, 311
　and emf, 316
　terminal, 321, 325
　unit, 292, 299
Potential energy, 65, 74, 77
　gravitational, 74
Potential gradient, electric, 296
Potentiometer, 337, 338
Pound, 7, 37
Poundal, 37
Power, 67, 69
　in a-c circuit, 437, 440
　electric, 387, 390
　human, 68
　of lens, 506, 510
　measurement by voltmeter and ammeter, 388
　in rotational motion, 97, 99
　units of, 67, 69
Power factor, 437, 440
Power losses, 405
Precession, 109, 111

Pressure, 146, 150
　atmospheric, 146, 166, 168
　and change of state, 209, 213
　due to gravity, 147, 150
　due to surface tension, 179, 183
　gage, 170, 171
　in gas, 169, 171, 176, 198
　hydrostatic, 147, 150
　in liquids, 148, 150, 159
　osmotic, 182, 183
　of vapor, 209
Pressure change, coefficient of, 196
Pressure gage, 170
Pressure head, 158
Prevost's theorem, 222
Primary cell, 304
Primary colors, 539, 548
Principal axis, 480, 502
Principal focus, 480, 485, 502, 509
Principal section, 566
Prism, 495, 497
　achromatic, 531
　dispersion by, 529, 534
　refraction by, 495, 497
　totally reflecting, 495
Prism binocular, 522
Prism spectroscope, 531, 535
Problems, solution of, 38, 621
Projectile, 48, 52
　and air resistance, 51, 52
　path of, 48
　range of, 50, 52
　self-propelled, 51, 52
Projectile motion, 48, 52
Proton, 282, 613
Prout's hypothesis, 591
Purity, 547
Pyrometer, 192
　thermocouple, 390

Quality, tone, 266, 274
Quantum theory, 462, 582

Radian, 92, 99
Radiation, 218, 221, 224
　blackbody, 222, 533, 581
　exchange of, 222
　infrared, 462
　ultraviolet, 462
　visible, 462
Radioactive equilibrium, 606
Radioactive series, 604
Radioactivity, 602, 616
Radius, of curvature, 480
　of gyration, 95, 99
Range, of meters, 364, 365
　of projectile, 50, 52
Rankine temperature scale, 198
Rationalized mks units, 601
Ray, 462
　ordinary and extraordinary, 566
Ray diagram, 482, 505

Reactance, 435, 436, 440
Reacting forces, 41, 117
Reaction, centrifugal, 117, 120
Reactor, nuclear, 614, 617
Reference circle, 135, 137, 140
Reflection, of light, 476, 485
    angle of, 477, 485
    diffuse and regular, 478
    internal, 494, 497
    law of, 477, 485
    phase change in, 554
    total, 494, 497
    of sound, 259
    of waves, 248
Refraction, 248, 490, 497
    atmospheric, 493, 497
    double, 565
    index of, 491, 497, 530
    through plane-parallel plate, 495, 497
    by prism, 495, 497
    shallowing effect of, 492, 497
    of sound, 258, 261
    at spherical surface, 496
Regelation, 210
Relative humidity, 212, 214
Relativity theory, 40, 42, 577, 584
    coordinates in, 580
    kinetic energy in, 581, 584
    postulates of, 579
    velocities in, 580
Reluctance, magnetic, 376, 379
Remanence, magnetic, 375
Residual charge, 425
Resistance, air, 51, 160
    electric, 310, 312
    equivalent, 438, 440
    internal, 320, 325
    specific, 334
    variation with temperature, 335, 338
Resistance box, 333
Resistance thermometer, 191, 337
Resistivity, 334, 336, 338
    variation with temperature, 335
Resistors, in parallel, 318, 325
    in series, 317, 325
Resolving power, 556
Resonance, acoustic, 255, 261
    electrical, 439, 440
    mechanical, 139, 141
Rest mass, 581, 584
Restitution, coefficient of, 106, 111
Resultant, 11, 13, 19
Retardation, 554
Retina, 515, 523
Reverberation, 273, 274
    time of, 273
Reversible process, 233, 236
Right-handed rule, 108, 111, 345, 353
Rigidity, coefficient of, 127, 129
Rocket, 52
Rockwell hardness number, 128

Rods, retinal, 515, 518
Rolling body, 98, 99
Romer, 470
Röntgen, Wilhelm K., 588
Root-mean-square (rms) current and voltage, 432, 440
Root-mean-square (rms) speed, 177
Rotary motion, 92
    acceleration in, 93, 94, 99
    compared with linear motion, 98, 99
    kinetic energy in, 97, 99
    Newton's laws for, 96, 99
    power in, 97, 99
    speed in, 92, 99
    work in, 97, 99
Rotational inertia, 94, 99
Rumford, Count (Benjamin Thompson), 228

Saturated vapor, 209, 211
Saturated water vapor, 211, 212
Saturation, color, 539, 548
    magnetic, 375, 379
Saturation current, 251
Scalar quantities, 11, 19
Scale, musical, 271, 274
    diatonic, 271
    evenly tempered, 272
Scattering, of light, 534
    polarization by, 568
    of x rays, 582, 584
Science, 3
Scientific method, 3
Screw jack, 66, 67
Second, 7
Selective absorption of light, 542, 548
Self-inductance, 408, 414
Self-induction, 406, 414
    energy of, 409, 414
Semiconductor, 336, 338, 600
Sensation curves, color, 540
Sensitivity, galvanometer, 362, 367
Shadow, 462
Shallowing effect of refraction, 492, 497
Shear modulus of elasticity, 127, 129
Shielding, electric, 298
Shunt, ammeter, 366, 367
Significant figures, 8, 621
Simple harmonic motion (SHM), 133, 140
    acceleration in, 134, 136, 140
    amplitude of, 135
    angular, 138
    circle of reference, 135
    frequency of, 135, 140
    period of, 134
    speed in, 136
Simple pendulum, 138, 140
Sink of electric energy, 317, 321

Siphon, 171
Siren, 266
Sky, color of, 534
Slide-wire potentiometer, 337, 338
Slip rings, 410
Slug, 37, 43
Snell's law, 492, 497
Solar spectrum, 533, 541
Solenoid, 348
Solid angle, 465
Solid state physics, 597
Solution of physical problems, 38, 621
Sound, 4, 253, 261
    absorption of, 260, 261, 273, 274
    amplification of, 272
    audibility of, 268
    characteristics of, 265, 274
    complexity of, 266
    detection of, 272
    frequency of, 260, 266, 268
    intensity of, 267
    intensity level of, 269, 274
    interference of, 259, 261
    location by, 273
    loudness of, 267, 274
    nature of, 253
    pitch of, 265, 266, 274
    power in, 269
    production of, 272
    quality of, 266, 274
    reflection of, 259, 261
    refraction of, 258, 261
    reproduction of, 272
    resonance in, 255, 261
    sources of, 254, 261
    speed of, 256, 261
        variation with temperature, 258, 261
    unpitched, 265, 266
    wavelength of, 254
Sound wave, 257, 261
    complexity of, 266, 274
Sounds, voice, 270
Space charge, 451
Specific gravity, 146, 149, 150
Specific heat, 206, 213
    of gas, 230, 236
    ratio of, 232
Specific humidity, 212, 214
Specific resistance, 334
Spectacle lens, 515
Spectra, absorption, 533, 535
    atomic, 533, 535, 592
    band, 533, 535
    bright-line, 533, 535
    continuous, 532, 535
    emission, 532, 535
    solar, 533
    types of, 532, 535
    visible, 462, 534
    (See also Spectrum)
Spectrograph, 532
    mass, 453

Spectrometer, 532
Spectrophotometer, 540
Spectroscope, 531, 535
Spectrum, characteristic, 532
  distribution of energy in, 533
  equal-energy, 541
  order of, 559
  solar, 533
  visible, 462, 534
  white-light, 541
  (*See also* Spectra)
Spectrum line, 533, 535, 559
  order of, 559
Spectrum locus, 546
Speed, 25, 30
  angular, 92, 99, 115
  of lens, 522, 523
  of light, 470, 472
  root-mean-square (rms), 177
  of sound, 256, 261
    variation with temperature,
    258, 261
  of wave, 245, 250
Spherical aberration, 484, 485, 508,
  510
Spherical mirrors, 480, 485
Standing waves, 249, 250
Statcoulomb, 284
States of matter, 145
  change of, 207, 228
    effect of pressure on, 209, 213
  variables of, 228
Statvolt, 292, 299
Stefan-Boltzmann law, 223, 224
Steradian, 465
Stereoscopic vision, 517
Stopping distance, 76
Storage cell, 305
  charging of, 321
Strain, 124, 126, 129
Streamlines, 157
Strength, dielectric, 423, 426
  of materials, 127
  ultimate, 127
Stress, 124, 126, 129
  thermal, 128
String, vibration of, 245, 250
Sublimation, 209
Subtractive production of colors,
  542, 548
Superconductivity, 336
Supersaturation, 212
Surface tension, 178, 183
  pressure due to, 179, 183
Synchrotron, 609
Systems of electrical units, 623,
  624

Telescope, 520, 523
Temperature, 189, 199
  absolute, 197, 200, 235, 236
  critical, 211, 213
  interval of, 191

Temperature coefficient of resist-
  ance, 335, 338
Temperature gradient, 218, 223
Temperature scales, 190, 200
  absolute, 197, 200, 235, 236
  centigrade, 190, 200
  Fahrenheit, 190, 200
  Kelvin, 197, 235, 236
  Rankine, 198
  thermodynamic, 197, 235, 236
Tensile strain and stress, 124, 126,
  129
Tension, interfacial, 181
  surface, 178, 183
Terminal speed, 30
Terminal voltage, 321, 325
Terrestrial magnetism, 378, 380
Testing procedures, 129
Tetrode, 452
Thermal capacity, 206
Thermal conductivity, 219, 223
Thermionic emission, 450, 456
Thermistor, 600
Thermocouple, 192, 306, 311, 390,
  391
Thermodynamic temperature
  scale, 197, 235, 236
Thermodynamics, first law of, 230,
  236
  second law of, 234, 236
Thermoelectricity, 306, 311, 390,
  391
Thermometer, 189
  expansion, 191
  gas, 196
  optical, 192, 193
  resistance, 191, 337, 338
  thermoelectric, 191
Thermometer scales (*see* Tempera-
  ture scales)
Thermopile, 192, 390, 391
Thermos flask, 222
Thin-lens equation, 504, 510
Thomson's e/m experiment, 448
Throttling process, 232, 236
Time, 7
Time constant, 425
Tone, musical, 265, 274
  quality of, 266, 274
Toroid, 349
Torque, 83, 87
  on coil, 351, 354
  in motor, 412, 414
  vector property of, 96
Torricelli's theorem, 161, 162
Torsion, moment of, 138, 140
Torsion pendulum, 138, 140
Total absorption, 273
Total reflection, 494, 497
Transformation of energy, 76, 77,
  386, 390
  in electric circuit, 307, 386,
  390
Transformations, relativistic, 580

Transformer, 404, 414
  losses in, 406
Transistor, 337, 338, 452, 456,
  600
Transmission line, 320, 405
Transmutation, nuclear, 608
Transverse wave, 244, 250
Triad, 271
Tricolorimeter, 543
Trigonometric functions, tables,
  627
Triode, 451, 456
Triple point, 210, 213
Triple-point diagrams, 210, 211
Tristimulus values, 545
Tritium, 454
Tube of flow, 157
Tuning of circuit, 439
Turbine, 161, 162
Turbulent flow, 59
Tyndall effect, 568

Ultimate strength, 127
Ultrasonic wave, 265
Ultraviolet radiation, 462
Uncertainty, 8, 621
Uniform circular motion, acceleration in, 115, 120
Units, British, 37
  cgs system of, 7, 8, 36, 37
  conversion of, 8, 624
  electrical, 623, 624
  electromagnetic, 623
  electrostatic, 284, 288
  fps, 7, 8
  fundamental and derived, 6, **8**
  gravitational, 37, 43
  mks, 8, 36
  for Newton's second law, table
    of, 38
Unpitched sound, 265, 266

V-2 rocket, 52
Vacuum tubes, 450
Valve, 450
Van de Graaff generator, 299
Vapor, 211
  pressure of, 212
Vaporization, 209
  heat of, 207, 213
Variation, magnetic, 378, 380
Varistor, 337, 338
Vector components, rectangular,
  13, 19
Vector diagram for a-c circuit,
  435–437
Vector properties in angular mo-
  tion, 92, 96
Vector quantities, 11, 19
Vectors, 11, 19
  addition of, 12–14, 19

Velocity, 25, 30
  angular, 92
  instantaneous, 26, 30
  in relativity theory, 600
  root-mean-square (rms), 177
Velocity ratio, 66
Venturi tube, 160
Vibration, 133, 254
  of air column, 254
  forced, 139, 255, 261
  fundamental, 254, 261
Virtual focus, 486, 502
Virtual image, 478, 485, 506
Virtual object, 504, 507
Viscosity, coefficient of, 58, 59
Visibility curve, 464
Visible spectra, 462, 534
Vision, color, 540
  distinct, distance of, 518, 523
  limitations of, 518
  persistence of, 517
  stereoscopic, 517
Voice sounds, 270
Volt, 310, 311
Voltage, 292, 310, 311
Voltage sensitivity, 362, 367
Voltair cell, 304
Voltmeter, 364, 467
Volume elasticity, 126, 129, 171
Volume expansion, coefficient of, 195, 200
Volume expansivity, 195, 200
Vowel sounds, table of, 270

Water, change of state, 207
  expansion of, 196
  vapor pressure of, 212
Water waves, 245
Watt (unit), 67, 69
Watt-hour meter, 388
Watt meter, 388, 391
Wave, 243, 250
  amplitude of, 247, 250
  complex, 266
  compressional, 245, 250, 253
  damping of, 248
  de Broglie, 594
  diffraction of, 249, 250
  in elastic medium, 246, 256
  in flexible cord, 245
  frequency of, 246, 250
  infrasonic, 265
  intensity of, 248, 250
  interference of, 249, 250, 259, 261
  longitudinal, 244, 250, 253
  period of, 246, 250
  phase, 246, 250
  polarization of, 563
  reflection of, 248, 250
  refraction of, 248, 250
  sound, 253, 256, 261
  speed of, 245, 250
  standing, 249, 250
  transverse, 244, 250
  ultrasonic, 265
  in water, 245
Wave front, 476

Wave front, diagram of, for lenses, 502
  for mirrors, 478
Wave mechanics, 594
Wave motion, 243
Wave nature of particles, 594
Wave properties of light, 461, 462, 550, 559, 563, 571
Wavelength, 247, 250
  dominant, 547
  of sound, 254, 257, 261
Weber (unit), 345
Weight, 7, 37
  acceleration due to, 28, 30
Weight-density, 145, 149, 150
Wheatstone bridge, 332, 338
Wheel and axle, 71, 97
White light, 540
Wilson cloud chamber, 604
Work, 64, 68
  by expanding gas, 231, 236
  in rotary motion, 97, 99

X-ray tube, 588
X rays, 589, 594
  diffraction of, 590, 594
  scattering of, 582, 584

Yard (British), 6
Young's double-slit experiment, 550
Young's modulus, 126, 129, 246
Young-Helmholtz color theory, 540